2019/20

THE GUIDE TO

MAJOR TRUSTS

16th edition

Ian Pembridge
& Scott Mason

Additional research by
Mairéad Bailie, Denise Lillya,
Jennifer Reynolds & Judith Turner

dsc
directory of social change

995038571 7

Published by the Directory of Social Change (Registered Charity no.
800517 in England and Wales)

Head office: Resource for London, 352 Holloway Rd, London N7 6PA

Northern office: Suite 103, 1 Old Hall Street, Liverpool L3 9HG

Tel: 020 7697 4200

Visit www.dsc.org.uk to find out more about our books, subscription
funding websites and training events. You can also sign up for e-newsletters
so that you're always the first to hear about what's new.

The publisher welcomes suggestions and comments that will help to inform
and improve future versions of this and all of our titles. Please give us your
feedback by emailing publications@dsc.org.uk.

It should be understood that this publication is intended for guidance only
and is not a substitute for professional or legal advice. No responsibility for
loss occasioned as a result of any person acting or refraining from acting
can be accepted by the authors or publisher.

First published 1986
Second edition 1989
Third edition 1991
Fourth edition 1993
Fifth edition 1995
Sixth edition 1997
Seventh edition 1999
Eighth edition 2001
Ninth edition 2003
Tenth edition 2005
Eleventh edition 2007
Twelfth edition 2010
Thirteenth edition 2012
Fourteenth edition 2014
Fifteenth edition 2016
Sixteenth edition 2018

ISBN 978 1 78482 053 4

British Library Cataloguing in Publication Data
A catalogue record for this book is available from the British Library

Cover and text design by Kate Griffith
Typeset by Marlinzo Services, Frome
Printed and bound in the UK by CPI Group (UK) Ltd, Croydon, CR0 4YY

FSC
www.fsc.org
MIX
Paper from
responsible sources
FSC® C013604

Contents

Foreword by Kath Abrahams   **iv**

About the Directory of Social Change   **iv**

Introduction   **v**

How to use this guide   **x**

Grant-makers in alphabetical order   **1**

Community foundations   **483**

Glossary of terms   **487**

Subject index   **489**

Geographical index   **525**

Foreword

The best form of fundraising is always a partnership. Whether we are seeking to persuade a member of the public to support our cause with a modest donation, or making a bespoke application to a grant-maker, the approach in each case differs but our aim should be the same – to inspire others to join us to make a difference in the world together.

An important factor in this inspiration is a clear sense of the impact potential supporters could have by joining forces with us. All too often, this can sadly get lost in the mechanics of fundraising, but it is absolutely vital that it sits at the heart of any request for support. This was reinforced to me recently at a 'Meet the Funder' conference session where the importance of demonstrating impact came through strongly as a key theme. Equally important is making sure you approach those most likely to want to partner with you – again this applies more generally but is one of the essentials in any approach to a grant-maker.

This is why I was delighted to be asked to introduce the latest edition of *The Guide to Major Trusts*. How very fortunate that in an ever-changing and increasingly uncertain funding environment, we can continue to rely on the veritable mine of up-to-date information contained in this guide. I first came across it over twenty-five years ago and it is as valuable now as it was then – providing clear, comprehensive information to help you navigate through this complex world and find the partners that will be right for your charity.

The grant-makers in this guide give a combined annual total of £5.5 billion in grants, showing just how significant these sources of funding continue to be. Accessing available grants however remains a highly competitive process, requiring us to do our research carefully. Once we understand which potential partners are most likely to support our causes, and which aspect of our aims chime particularly with theirs, we increase our chances of success immeasurably. If we combine a targeted approach with a clear sense of the impact we could have together, our chances of success increase even further. With this in mind, I recommend this guide most highly to you and wish you every success in inspiring the partners that are right for your mission.

Kath Abrahams
Director of Engagement and Fundraising, Diabetes UK

About the Directory of Social Change

The Directory of Social Change (DSC) has a vision of an independent voluntary sector at the heart of social change. The activities of independent charities, voluntary organisations and community groups are fundamental to achieve social change. We exist to help these organisations in achieving their goals.

We do this by:

- Providing practical tools that organisations and activists need, including online and printed publications, training courses, and conferences on a huge range of topics
- Acting as a 'concerned citizen' in public policy debates, often on behalf of smaller charities, voluntary organisations and community groups
- Leading campaigns and stimulating debate on key policy issues that affect those groups
- Carrying out research and providing information to influence policymakers, as well as offering bespoke research for the voluntary sector

DSC is the leading provider of information and training for the voluntary sector and publishes an extensive range of guides and handbooks covering subjects such as fundraising, management, communication, finance and law. Our subscription-based websites contain a wealth of information on funding from grant-makers, companies and government sources. We run more than 300 training courses each year, including bespoke in-house training provided at the client's location. DSC conferences and fairs, which take place throughout the year, also provide training on a wide range of topics and offer a welcome opportunity for networking.

For details of all our activities, and to order publications and book courses, go to www.dsc.org.uk, call 020 7697 4200 or email cs@dsc.org.uk.

Introduction

Welcome to the sixteenth edition of *The Guide to Major Trusts*. The purpose of the guide is to provide a comprehensive and practical funding resource that enables charity professionals, including trustees, chief executives, fundraisers and volunteers, to access the billions of pounds awarded in the UK by grant-makers each year.

Data collection

This guide contains over 1,000 of the UK's largest grant-makers taken from DSC's database, which contains details of over 4,500 charitable funders.

Over the course of our research, we looked at Charity Commission records, annual reports and accounts, websites and occasionally directly contacted the grant-makers themselves. In this edition, the majority of the accounts we used were from 2016/17 (67%) and 2016 (23%). However, some charities' accounts were not available to view on the Charity Commission's website due to them having an income of less than £25,000. In these circumstances, grant totals were estimated based on the charity's total expenditure and previous patterns of giving. Where up-to-date accounts had not been submitted, the latest available accounts were used.

Criteria for inclusion

To be included in the guide, grant-makers should have the capacity to make at least £200,000 in grants in the UK per year. Those in the guide with grant totals under this threshold may have given over this amount in previous years or are likely to have the capacity to exceed this amount in the near future. In order to make the guide as useful as possible to fundraisers, certain grant-makers have been excluded. These are mainly:

- Grant-makers that predominantly give overseas
- Grant-makers that give to a small number of beneficiaries each year
- Grant-makers that give to the same beneficiaries each year
- Grant-makers that give to individuals only

We also exclude grant-makers that have ceased to exist or are being wound up with any remaining funds fully committed. Some of the larger grant-makers that are in the process of winding up or have wound up since the last edition of this guide include:

- Tesco Charity Trust
- The HB Allen Charitable Trust
- The Audrey and Stanley Burton 1960 Charitable Trust
- The Connie and Albert Taylor Charitable Trust

In this edition, we have included over 200 grant-makers that have not been included in previous editions of the guide. These are a mixture of grant-makers that have increased their grant-making capacity, newly registered grant-makers and grant-makers not previously known to us.

Findings

The 1,004 grant-makers included in this guide awarded a combined total of £5.5 billion in grants. A further £75.5 million was distributed by the 46 UK community foundations listed in the table on page 483.

Although the vast majority of these funders are registered grant-making charities, there are also a number which are not. Some of the largest funders, such as the Big Lottery Fund, the Heritage Lottery (giving £432.6 million in grants during the 2016/17 financial year) and the arts councils (including Creative Scotland) are non-departmental public bodies. Excluding the funding given by these bodies, funding from grant-making charities amounted to £3.65 billion. If we look at the 697 grant-makers which appear in both this edition and the previous edition, there has been an overall increase in giving of £178.4 million, or 6.2%.

This guide includes a diverse range of grant-makers: from those supporting general charitable purposes (41.6% of the funders in this guide) and charities working in areas such as social welfare (59%), health (50.4%) or education (50.2%); to those specifically concentrating on so-called less popular causes, such as providing support for people suffering from substance abuse, victims of domestic violence and LGBT groups.

The top 25 funders gave a combined £1.86 billion, accounting for 33.9% of this edition's grant total. In the last edition, the contributions made by the top 25 amounted to £1.82 billion. However, The Wellcome Trust's grant total has increased by over £130 million from the last edition. The Wellcome Trust is the largest grant-maker in the guide (giving just over £930 million in 2016/17) and its annual giving can often have a significant

Top 25 grant-makers

(excluding public bodies, e.g. Big Lottery Fund, arts councils)

		Areas of work	Total grants
1 (1)	The Wellcome Trust	Biomedical research; history of medicine; biomedical ethics; public engagement with science	£931.7 million
2 (4)	British Heart Foundation (BHF)	Cardiovascular research	£111.8 million
3 (2)	The Leverhulme Trust	Academic research	£78.9 million
4 (3)	Comic Relief	Tackling poverty and social injustice; children and young people; women and girls; community development	£74.4 million
5 (6)	Oxfam (GB)	Humanitarian work; development; tackling inequality	£63.1 million
6 (8)	BBC Children in Need	Disadvantaged children and young people (aged 18 and under)	£62.8 million
7 (7)	The Garfield Weston Foundation	Arts; education; youth; health; museums and heritage; community; environment; faith; social welfare	£62.75 million
8 (10)	Esmée Fairbairn Foundation	Arts; children and young people; environment; social change; food	£40.5 million
9 (22)	The Gatsby Charitable Foundation	Plant science; neuroscience; technical education; Africa; public policy; the arts; general charitable purposes	£36.3 million
10 (5)	The Monument Trust	General charitable purposes; arts and heritage; health and community care, particularly HIV/AIDS, sexual health and hospices; social development; criminal justice, particularly rehabilitation of offenders and homelessness	£35.2 million
11 (-)	The Save the Children Fund	Children and families, with a particular focus on: overseas aid; health care and nutrition; disasters and emergencies; education; child rights, safeguarding and protection	£32.7 million
12 (-)	The Grace Trust	General charitable purposes, with a particular emphasis on: the care and Christian education of children and young people; alleviating poverty; humanitarian relief	£31 million
13 (-)	Groundwork UK	Environment; social welfare; communities	£30.4 million
14 (13)	The Wolfson Foundation	Medical and scientific research; education; health; social welfare; heritage; arts	£30.4 million
15 (16)	The British Academy for the Promotion of Historical Philosophical and Philological Studies (The British Academy)	Humanities and social sciences	£28.8 million
16 (18)	The Henry Smith Charity	Social welfare	£28.1 million
17 (-)	Achisomoch Aid Company Ltd	Orthodox Jewish causes; general charitable purposes	£23.7 million
18 (-)	The Sackler Trust	Education; art; science; medical research	£21.1 million
19 (-)	The Basil Larsen 1999 Charitable Trust	General charitable purposes	£21.05 million
20 (-)	Lloyd's Register Foundation	Engineering-related education; research; science and technology; safety	£20.6 million
21 (-)	The Vodafone Foundation	General charitable purposes, with a preference for technology, disadvantaged communities, humanitarian crises and disasters	£20.6 million
22 (-)	Paul Hamlyn Foundation	Arts; education; young people; social justice	£20.02 million
23 (21)	Arthritis Research UK	Arthritis and related musculoskeletal diseases	£20 million
24 (23)	The Sigrid Rausing Trust	Human rights and social justice	£19.9 million
25 (-)	Masonic Charitable Foundation	Social welfare; health; disability; education; young people; medical and social research; hospices	£18.75 million
			Total £1.86 billion

effect on the overall grant totals for our guides. For this edition, the cut-off figure for inclusion in the top 25 is a grant total of £18.75 million, compared with £19.8 million in the last edition. As is our usual practice, we have not included public bodies – the Big Lottery Fund, Awards for All, Heritage Lottery Fund, the arts councils and Creative Scotland – in this table, partly as it is an opportunity to celebrate the work of grant-makers that are registered charities.

There are ten new entries in the top 25 table, most of which are large, established grant-makers. Other grant-makers of note include:

▶ Groundwork UK, which manages a number of grant schemes for its business, public sector and voluntary sector partners. It awarded £30.4 million in grants in 2016/17, compared with £6.5 million in 2014/15. This sharp rise in giving is largely due to the Bags of Help grant scheme, which Groundwork administers on behalf of Tesco. The scheme funds local community projects through the sale of plastic carrier bags and accounted for £28 million of the organisation's grant total in 2016/17.

▶ The Masonic Foundation is a new charity which takes over the work of the four central masonic charities – The Freemasons' Grand Charity, the Royal Masonic Trust for Girls and Boys, the Masonic Samaritan Fund and the Royal Masonic Benevolent Institution. Grants are made to masonic and non-masonic charities, with £7.66 million awarded to the former in 2016/17.

The Sackler Trust has seen a significant increase in its grant-making in recent years, from £443,500 in 2012 to £21.1 million in 2016. Significant grants were made to a number of organisations in 2016, including the University of Sussex (£6 million), Moorfields Eye Hospital (£3 million) and the Royal College of Art (£2 million).

Innovation

During the course of our research, we found many excellent examples of innovation in grant-making, but perhaps the most interesting involves the fundraising practice of crowdfunding. The concept of crowdfunding has been around since the 1990s and today there are numerous online platforms which can be used to raise money for projects from a wide range of sources, including the general public. In recent years, some of these platforms have partnered with grant-making charities, local authorities and companies to boost the funding available to applicants and streamline the grant application process. Two notable examples of this practice are Spacehive and The Good Exchange.

Established in 2012, Spacehive is a crowdfunding platform with a focus on projects that improve public spaces. Funding initially comes from supporters and friends of the project, with over £3.3 million in additional funding available from grant-makers, local councils and businesses, including the likes of Esmée Fairbairn Foundation, The Westway Trust, Barclays and Manchester City Council. So far, over 450 projects have received funding, and success stories have included a London sculpture walk and a project to turn a Peckham railway line into a park. (Spacehive, 2018)

The Good Exchange, another fundraising platform, is open to any registered charity or group operating for public benefit in the UK. The organisation was established in 2016 and in its first year facilitated the distribution of £4.7 million to good causes. The platform uses technology to streamline the grant application process. Applicant organisations looking for funding just have to complete a single online application form, which is then automatically matched to the funding criteria of multiple funders, cutting down the time charities spend making speculative applications. This is particularly useful for smaller charities that do not have the resources to employ professional fundraising teams. Amounts raised can be match funded by funders, which helps give donors and fundraisers an incentive to work together and raise money more quickly.

In 2018, The Miss Lawrence Trust was announced as a new funder on The Good Exchange. The trust usually makes grants totalling around £100,000 per year and has to process hundreds of applications manually. One of the trustees, Jonathan Bastable explains:

> The main draw to The Good Exchange was the ability to simplify our paper-based system of processing grant applications. The platform allows us to streamline the annual shortlisting of applications, and also enables us to delve deeper and with greater ease into our applicants' objectives, while also enabling us to see the support they've received from other funders and donors. The platform provides a great deal of transparency and it also greatly simplifies matters for applicants, who now have to complete just one application form for consideration.
>
> **The Good Exchange, 2018**

Social media

Over the past two decades or so, organisations within the charity sector have become increasingly adept at exploiting the opportunities offered by digital technologies and the web. Of the grant-makers listed in this edition of *Major Trusts*, almost 60% have their own website. Many of these websites are used to accept and process applications, as well as provide essential information about grant programmes, including deadlines, eligibility criteria and application procedures.

Apart from providing a simpler, quicker and less costly means by which funding applications can be submitted, digital technologies also offer the possibility for grant-makers to advertise their grant programmes and promote the impact of their funding to a much wider audience than would otherwise be possible. While many grant-makers choose to do this using their own website, a growing number of funders are also utilising social media platforms such as Facebook, Instagram and Twitter. Of the funders listed in this edition of *Major Trusts*, almost 15% have Twitter profiles, nearly 11% have Facebook pages, and 3.6% have Instagram accounts. Often these accounts are used to promote and celebrate the important work of the funder's beneficiaries but are also on occasion used to share information about funding opportunities. As such, following grant-makers' social media activities can provide fundraisers with a simple and convenient means of keeping up to date with the latest news and updates from multiple funders at once.

Given the growing use of social media by grant-makers, for the first time, this edition of *Major Trusts* includes details of grant-makers' Twitter, Facebook and Instagram accounts. This information can be found at the top of each entry alongside the grant-makers' contact details and web address.

Applying for grants

Writing and assessing grant applications can be an incredibly time-consuming process, with every unsuccessful application representing a significant waste of resources for both the charity and funder alike. Despite this, each year thousands of hours continue to be wasted by applicants and grant-makers completing and processing applications that stand little or no chance of being successful. Given the limited resources available to both, making the grant-making process as efficient as possible – by reducing the number of ineligible applications submitted to funders – should be in the interests of everyone, but how to achieve this is not always clear.

On the one hand, of course, it is the responsibility of the charities themselves to ensure that the time they dedicate to fundraising is used as efficiently and effectively as possible. Publications such as this one, as well as online resources such as DSC's funding websites, can help charities to identify grant-makers that may be relevant to their causes. However, it is also important that charities carefully tailor their applications for each funder and only submit applications which they genuinely believe to have a good chance of success.

On the other hand, DSC has long argued that it is also the responsibility of the grant-makers themselves to help to minimise the administrative burden of the grant-making process, by providing clear guidance on the types of projects that they would be willing to fund and making their application processes as simple and proportionate as possible. This can be especially important in situations where grant programmes are likely to be competitive or likely to receive a high number of applications.

From a practical perspective, there are a number of things that grant-makers can do to help reduce the number of ineligible applications they receive. Firstly, and most simply, grant-makers may choose to provide applicants with a simple list of eligibility criteria, outlining their geographical area of benefit and focus, as well as details about the types of organisations or activities that they will or will not fund. By being open and honest about their funding preferences, grant-makers can help prospective applicants to make a more informed judgement about their chances of success and so determine for themselves whether completing an application would be a worthwhile use of their time.

Technically savvy grant-makers may choose to take this concept one stage further and provide applicants with the option of testing their eligibility using an interactive 'eligibility checker'. Usually presented in the form of an online questionnaire, this option enables applicants to determine their suitability to apply for funding in just a few clicks, and in some cases, may also be used to restrict access to application forms submitted by those organisations which have met the grant-maker's criteria.

Next, a less technical (but no less effective) alternative adopted by many grant-makers, is to invite prospective applicants to contact them by phone or email prior to completing a full application. Often a short email exchange or brief telephone conversation is enough for applicants to determine whether their project fits within the priorities of the funder, which can help them avoid wasting time writing applications that are unlikely to be accepted.

Finally, some grant-makers may choose to use a two-stage application process, whereby applicants are initially required to submit a much shorter version of the application form before completing a full application if invited to do so. By using the much simpler first stage of the application process to create a shortlist, grant-makers can help to minimise the time wasted by unsuccessful applicants. This option is particularly useful for grant-makers that require applicants to complete lengthy or detailed applications such as those that fund medical or scientific research funding.

During the process of researching this edition of *Major Trusts*, DSC collected data about the information that grant-makers provide to applicants as well as the nature of their application processes. Analysis of the data collected reveals that of the funders accepting unsolicited applications, around 55.5% provided a clear list of eligibility criteria; 11.1% offered applicants the option to check their eligibility using an online eligibility checker; 27.9% welcomed contact from applicants prior to the submission of applications; and around 15% of funders utilised a two-stage application process.

Although some of these figures may at first glance appear to be quite low, it must be recognised that many grant-makers openly invite applications from a wide range of charities and so often choose to place no restrictions on the types of projects that they would be willing to fund. Furthermore, it should also be acknowledged that some of these solutions may only be appropriate for larger grant-makers with the staff, resources and technical expertise required to respond to enquiries, administer two-stage application processes, or create online questionnaires. Conversely, many smaller grant-makers often rely on volunteers and part-time staff and so may not have the resources needed to undertake these initiatives.

As such, while these figures provide an interesting insight into the current approach of UK grant-makers to the processing of applications, additional research is required before it is possible to draw any general conclusions or make recommendations for how UK grant-making practice may be improved.

DSC policy and campaigning

DSC's policy and campaigning activities aim to make the UK a better environment for charities to thrive and help their beneficiaries. In these activities, we act independently in the role of a concerned citizen to champion the needs of the voluntary sector. We ask critical questions, challenge the prevailing view and try to promote debate on issues we consider to be important.

Grants for Good campaign

Grants for Good is a joint campaign between DSC, Charity Finance Group, Locality, Children England, Clinks and Lloyds Bank Foundation for England and Wales. It aims to tackle the decline in grant funding from the public sector.

Grant funding from government is essential for the work of many charities and voluntary groups. Grants can empower organisations to identify and solve problems, as well as addressing needs in a way that is centred on beneficiaries.

For over a decade now, income from government grants has been in decline. These grants peaked in 2003/04 at £6.2 billion, but in 2014/15 amounted to only £2.9 billion (NCVO, 2017). Grants are increasingly being replaced by short-term, restrictive, inflexible contracts.

The Grants for Good campaign aims to reverse this trend. Grants have many advantages, particularly for supporting smaller voluntary organisations, and can deliver better outcomes for beneficiaries. Grants are effective for:

▶ Adapting to change
▶ Empowering people
▶ Investing locally
▶ Nurturing innovation
▶ Saving time, effort and resources
▶ Supporting community
▶ Sustaining services

Many of the grant-making charities in this guide will also have been affected by the decline in government grants and the shift towards contracts. For example, the 2016/17 annual report for the Milton Keynes Community Foundation states:

> The community in Milton Keynes is becoming increasingly diverse and with the past and impending Council budget cuts, where monies will only be awarded to Voluntary Sector Organisations for initiatives that are a statutory requirement, the challenge for the Community Foundation is how we ensure that ongoing support is available to vulnerable people in our Community.
>
> **Milton Keynes Community Foundation, 2017**

Smaller charities in particular are increasingly unable to compete for larger government contracts or to find relevant funds to support their area of work – this in turn increases the pressure upon charitable grant-makers. With fewer and fewer grants available from both local and national government, charities that previously relied on this source of funding, or charities working in areas that have experienced large cuts in government expenditure (such as the arts) will have to turn to other sources for support, such as the grant-makers in this guide.

The Grants for Good campaign needs the support of charities and voluntary organisations so that we can influence commissioners and politicians, and champion the benefits of grants. There are a number of ways in which you can get involved: visit www.dsc.org.uk/grants-for-good for more information.

DSC's Big Lottery Refund campaign

The National Lottery occupies a unique place in the grant-making world. While the various distributors are statutory bodies which distribute public money (technically speaking), their activities, aims and beneficiaries have much in common with grant-making charities. Many of the readers of this guide will be familiar with the Big Lottery Fund, which distributes funding for projects that benefit communities across the UK. The fund's grants, many of which are for less than £10,000, support charities and voluntary organisations often with local, grassroots projects.

The Big Lottery Refund campaign was created in 2007, in response to a government decision to divert a huge amount of Big Lottery Fund money (£675 million in total) to put towards the infrastructure for the London 2012 Olympic Games. In total £425 million of this, which should have been used to support charities and communities, is still owed to the Big Lottery Fund. An agreement was made between the government and the London Legacy Development Corporation to pay this money back following the sales of the Olympic assets. However, both the current and previous governments have stated that this will not now happen until the 2020s or even 2030s.

We think that this situation is unacceptable. Our campaign aims to get the government to pay the money back immediately. Giving back this money now would make a huge difference to organisations and the individuals they serve, at a time when so many people are in need of support. Find out more and sign up at www.biglotteryrefund.org.uk or follow us on twitter @BigLotteryRfnd for updates.

DSC's Everybody Benefits Campaign

There is not a single person in the UK who has not, or will not, benefit from the work of a charity. DSC launched the #EverybodyBenefits campaign in 2016 to highlight the many ways in which we all benefit from charities. We want to show that if you stop and look around you, there are fantastic things happening that would not exist without charities.

We challenge you to play the #EverybodyBenefits game and see for yourself. You can download the game at www.dsc.org.uk/content/everybodybenefits – play it with your colleagues, friends, family, beneficiaries, and let us know what you think.

Campaign Against Charging Charities

In recent years, the Charity Commission has seen its budget slashed from £40m to around £21m. In January 2018 it received an extra £5 million in funding to help with the increase in demand on its core functions such as registration and compliance. However, this is only an interim solution and still not sufficient compared to what is needed. As a result, there is a debate about charging charities to plug the gap – this is something DSC opposes.

A well-resourced Charity Commission is vital for the work of charities, but we believe that diverting charitable resources to fund the regulator is wrong for many reasons. We believe that:

- Fees would be a damaging burden on charitable resources
- Fees are wrong in principle
- Fees would lead to bad regulation
- Fees would be poor value for money

To find out more about our campaign visit: www.dsc.org.uk/campaign-against-charging-charities.

References

'Miss Lawrence charitable trust partners with The Good Exchange to digitise grant application process' [press release], The Good Exchange, https://thegoodexchange.com/wp-content/uploads/2018/05/The-Good-Exchange-Press-Release-Miss-Lawrence-Trust-Final.pdf, 5 June 2018.

Milton Keynes Community Foundation Limited, *Trustees' annual report and financial statements of the Group 2016/17* [PDF], Milton Keynes Community Foundation Limited, 2017, www.mkcommunityfoundation.co.uk/files/4115/0400/5080/Group_Accounts_2016–17.pdf, accessed 23 July 2018.

'NCVO UK Civil Society Almanac 2017: Income From Government' [web page], NCVO, 2017, https://data.ncvo.org.uk/a/almanac17/income-from-government-2/#Government_grants, accessed 23 July 2018.

'Spacehive' [web page], Spacehive, 2018, www.spacehive.com, accessed 17 July 2018.

Acknowledgements

The research for this book has been conducted as carefully as possible. Many thanks to those who have made this easier, especially the funders themselves through their websites, their staff who provided additional information and the trustees and others who have helped us. Further thanks go to the Charity Commission for making the annual reports and accounts available online, and to the Office for the Scottish Charity Regulator, which has recently taken up this practice.

Disclaimer

We are aware that some of this information may be incomplete or will become out of date. We are equally sure we will have missed some relevant charities. If you come across any omissions or mistakes, or if you have any suggestions for future editions of this book, do let us know. We can be contacted at DSC's Liverpool Office Research Department either by phone on 0151 708 0136 or by email: research@dsc.org.uk.

We hope you find this latest edition to be as beneficial in its application as it has been interesting and inspiring in its preparation.

How to use this guide

The funders are listed alphabetically and the indexes are at the back of the book. There are subject and geographical indexes which will help you to identify the funders working in your field and area.

Read each funder's entry carefully before deciding to apply. Sometimes, a funder's interest in your field will be very specific or they may have strict guidelines for how to make an application. When you have drawn up a shortlist of funders for which your organisation may be eligible, we recommend that you prioritise them in order of the amount of information they have available. We think it's better to apply to a smaller number of grant-makers for which more information is available, as this means you can properly tailor your application and have a better chance of success.

It is particularly important to show awareness of all the information available from the funder, to acquire up-to-date guidelines where possible, and to target your applications with respect to each funder's published wishes where such information exists. Fortunately, there are more funders with an online presence than ever before, so it's becoming increasingly easy for them to communicate their priorities and policies.

Remember that when funders maintain specific guidelines or state that they do not accept unsolicited applications they are not just being fussy – they are trying to save themselves and applicants precious time and resources. Inappropriate and ill-considered approaches, especially those that show you have not read the published guidelines, can annoy funders and can even result in damaging your organisation's reputation. Of course, many funders continue to publish little or no additional material and the only information we have to rely on is that which is available from the Charity Commission register. Unfortunately, this may result in a waste of your time and the funder's if they reject an application that they deem to be ineligible.

Notes on the entries

These notes complement 'A typical entry' on page xii and explain how the entries are put together.

Grant-maker's name

The main areas of funding

These categories have been chosen by the authors from an analysis of the areas of work supported by the funder. They are indicative rather than definitive and are useful in a preliminary trawl through the guide. They are no substitute for a close reading of each entry.

Grant total and financial year

The most up-to-date financial information available is given here. For the majority of funders in this guide, we were able to obtain financial information from the 2016 financial year onwards. For a small number of entries, we had to use financial information from an earlier year as this was the latest available at the time of writing. In the majority of cases, this was because the grant-maker's annual report and accounts were not yet due at the Charity Commission.

Beneficial area

This is the area or areas within which the funder operates, either legally or as a matter of policy or practice. When a funder with a UK-wide remit shows an interest in a particular locality, this is noted. While the information usually comes from the funder itself, it may also arise from a pattern of grant-making identified by the authors.

The correspondent

This is the lead contact. Sometimes this is a solicitor or an accountant handling the affairs of a grant-making charity solely on a 'post box' basis, and in other cases it is the relevant department at an organisation. Other useful administrative contacts may also be given in the 'Applications' section or within the main body of text.

The main body of the entry

A summary of the funder's grant-making usually prefaces the text. Policy notes and guidelines for applicants, where available, are normally reprinted in detail. However, there are cases in which these are so lengthy or subject to change that some abridgement has had to be undertaken and, where appropriate, we direct readers to the funder's website, where extensive or up-to-date information is available. More grant-makers now analyse the distribution of their funding in their annual reports and, where available, this material will also usually be quoted in full. Some analysis has also been carried out by the authors based on grants lists accompanying the accounts.

Exclusions

Where information on exclusions is available, this section notes things that the funder will not or cannot support. Sometimes this has been gathered from the information on websites or in annual reports, or in other cases has been communicated directly to DSC by the funders themselves.

Applications

In this section we explain how to make an application to the funder. You will notice that there are some grant-makers that do not accept unsolicited applications – we include these funders to both promote transparency in grant-giving and help save the time and resources of organisations that may otherwise apply in vain for funding.

Sources of information

This section notes the sources of information we have used for the entries. If there is a website, this is usually the best starting point for information, but we also use the Charity Commission's register of charities (and for Scottish charities, the Office of the Scottish Charity Regulator) extensively.

How to apply to a funder

If you are looking for some detailed help in this area, DSC publishes books that can help, including *Writing Better Fundraising Applications*, *The Complete Fundraising Handbook*, *Effective Fundraising* and *Trust Fundraising*. However, there is no need to be daunted by the challenge of making effective applications. If your charity's work is good – and of a kind supported by the funder in question – a very simple letter (of one uncrowded A4 page or less, backed by a clear annual report and set of accounts) will probably do 90% of everything that can be done.

If there is an application form and/or detailed application requirements, simply follow them.

1) Select the right grant-makers to approach

If they fund organisations or work like yours, and you genuinely fit within any guidelines they publish, put them on your list.

2) Call them

If the entry makes this sound sensible, ring the grant-maker to check that the guidelines in this guide still apply and that the kind of application you are considering is appropriate.

3) Send in an application

Unless the grant-maker has an application form (many do not), we suggest that the main part of this should be a letter that fits easily on one side of an A4 sheet of paper (back-up materials such as a formal proposal may be necessary for a big or complex project but are usually, in our view, secondary). We suggest that the letter contains the following points.

- **A summary sentence such as:** 'We would like to reward our hardworking and valued volunteers with a training programme to develop their skills and I am writing to you requesting a contribution of £5,000.'
- **The problem the work will address:** This should normally be the beneficiaries' problem, not your charity's problem: 'Mothers of children with learning disabilities in our area get very little help from the statutory services in coping with their children's day-to-day needs. We are aware of the very helpful support you have given to similar projects and feel that the purpose of the project complements your charity's ethos and aims.'
- **What you are going to do about this:** 'Our volunteers (who have been in the same situations themselves) support and help our beneficiaries, but need and want better training, especially on home safety. Our beneficiaries, as you'll be aware, often struggle with meeting the needs of their children. This award would develop our volunteers' skills and, as a result, their experience and knowledge. This will then help us provide significantly better, more qualified support to help our beneficiaries more effectively.'
- **Details of the work:** 'We want to commission an expert from our sister charity Dean Cambridge Foundation to develop and test suitable training materials that we will be able to use.'
- **Information about your charity:** 'We attach one of our general leaflets explaining what we do, a copy of our latest annual report and accounts, and a copy of the quote received from the Dean Cambridge Foundation to supply the initial training which we can then develop (with funding we hope to be awarded from Awards for All).'
- **Repeat the request:** 'We are all very keen to see this project happen and hope that you will be able to help us.'

And that is all. Keep the style simple and informal. Where you can, handwrite the date, salutation and signature. A charity is not a business and is not impressed by applicants trying to sound like one. The best letter comes from someone who understands the new project and is going to be involved with it. In this way, they can speak authoritatively and with enthusiasm should someone from the funder call for more information. Making the letter longer will often reduce rather than increase its impact, but attaching compelling material is fine.

A letter of endorsement might also be nice; your local GP practice saying your work is wonderful, for example.

Appearance matters. It is a great help if you have a good-quality letterhead on something better than photocopy paper, and if your report and accounts and literature are of appropriately high quality for your kind of organisation. However, you don't want to give the impression that your charity spends unnecessary money on expensive materials rather than on carrying out its work.

Good luck!

A typical entry

The Fictitious Charity

🔍 Social welfare, education, health

📍 UK, with some preference for New Town

£ £1.3 million (2016/17)

CC number: 123456

Trustees: Eva Appiah; Rita Khan; Lorraine Murphy.

Correspondent: Ann Freeman, Appeals Secretary, The Old Barn, Main Street, New Town ZC48 2QQ

This charity makes grants to organisations working in the areas of social welfare (particularly homelessness), education and health. The trustees will support both capital and revenue projects; the annual report for 2016/17 stated that 'specific projects are preferred to general running costs'.

Financial information

In 2016/17 the charity had assets of £20.3 million and an income of £1.5 million. Over 200 grants were given totalling £1.3 million. Grants ranged from £5,000 to £200,000, with about half given in New Town.

Beneficiaries included: Homelessness UK (£200,000); Shelter (£150,000); Charity Workers Benevolent Society (£80,000); Learning Foundation (£50,000); New Town Citizens Advice (£10,000); Getwell Hospice UK (£5,000).

Smaller grants were given to a variety of local charities, local branches of national charities and a few UK welfare charities.

Exclusions

No grants are made to non-registered charities, individuals or religious organisations.

Applications

Apply in writing to the correspondent. The trustees meet in March and September each year. Applications should be received by the end of January and the end of July respectively.

Applications should include a brief description of the project and audited accounts. Unsuccessful applicants will not be informed unless an sae is provided.

Sources of information

Annual report; accounts; Charity Commission record; further information provided by the funder.

• **Name of the charity**

• **Summary of main activities:** what the funder does in practice.

• **Geographical area of grant-making:** including where the funder can legally give and where it gives in practice.

• **Grant total:** total grants given for the most recent financial year available.

• **Trustees**

• **Correspondent and contact details:** including telephone and fax numbers, and email and website addresses, if available.

• **General information:** a summary of the funder's policies. The amount of information here varies from funder to funder – sometimes we use subheadings to make it easier to read. These also vary depending on the particular funder and the information that is available.

• **Financial information:** the assets, ordinary income and grant total. We also mention here if we have noticed anything interesting and unusual about the figures.

• **Beneficiaries included:** a list of typical beneficiaries which indicates where the main money is going. This is often the clearest indication of what a funder is prepared to fund.

• **Exclusions:** a list of any areas, subjects or types of grant the funder will not consider supporting.

• **Applications:** this includes how to apply and, where available, when to submit an application.

• **Sources of information:** where we have obtained the information in the entry from.

Grant-makers in alphabetical order

The 1989 Willan Charitable Trust

 General charitable purposes, community development, social welfare

 Tyne and Wear, Northumberland, County Durham and Teesside

£ £477,000 to organisations (2015/16)

CC number: 802749

Trustees: Francis Chapman; Alex Ohlsson; Willan Trustee Ltd.

Correspondent: Community Foundation Tyne & Wear and Northumberland, The 1989 Willan Charitable Trust, c/o Community Foundation, Philanthropy House, Woodbine Road, Gosforth, Newcastle Upon Tyne NE3 1DD (tel: 0191 222 0945; email: general@communityfoundation.org.uk)

 www.communityfoundation.org.uk/funds/the-1989-willan-charitable-trust

The trust was established in 1989 out of funds originating from a shipping business, for general charitable purposes, with a preference for benefitting organisations in the north east of England. The 2015/16 annual report notes the following:

> In recognition of the origins of the trust fund and the economic impact that the decline of shipbuilding has had on the region, the trustees tend to concentrate their support towards causes which are active in Tyne and Wear and its immediate surrounds. The trustees favour causes which aim to ease social deprivation and/or enrich the fabric of the local community and the quality of life of individuals within that community. They may also support education where that is aimed at improving the economy in areas of deprivation.

> In considering which local causes to support and the level of support given, the trustees will also have regard to an

applicant's ability to raise funds elsewhere. Consequently, the trustees tend to weight their support towards local charitable institutions rather than national or international ones on the basis that the larger institutions enjoy higher profiles and will typically have wider access to funds.

> In cases of great need such as major natural disasters, conflicts or accidents, causes may be supported outside the trustees' normal parameters stated above.

Grant are given for core costs or projects, and awards typically range from £500 to £10,000, although there is no maximum or minimum grant. Projects where the trust represents a significant contribution to a project are prioritised. The trust can also provide in-kind support, in the form of premises for charitable organisations.

The Community Foundation Tyne and Wear and Northumberland provides administrative support to the trust's grant-making in the North East region, receiving and vetting applications for the trustees.

Financial information
In 2015/16 the trust had assets of £18.6 million and an income of £590,000. During the year, 167 grants were made, totalling £477,000, which were broken down as follows:

Sector

Taking part in community life	55	£238,500
Building our children's future	45	£141,000
Improving health	25	£78,000
Enjoying later life	5	£18,000
Caring for our environment	1	£1,000

Region

Northumberland	31	£101,000
Newcastle	19	£64,500
Durham	11	£56,000
Out of area	20	£49,000
Gateshead	13	£39,500
Hartlepool	8	£35,000
Darlington	5	£32,000
Sunderland	7	£29,500
Stockton	4	£21,500
Middlesbrough	5	£18,800
South Tyneside	2	£15,000
North Tyneside	5	£13,000
Redcar	1	£2,500

Size of grant

£1,001 to £5,000	92	£242,000
£5,001 to £10,000	27	£229,500
£1,000 or less	12	£5,400

A list of beneficiaries was not included in the accounts.

Previous beneficiaries have included: SAFC Foundation and Cancer Connexions (£10,000 each); Amble Multi Agency Crime Prevention Initiative (£6,000); Durham City Centre Youth Project, The Children's Society and the Calvert Trust (£5,000 each); Chester le Street Youth Centre (£4,000); Different Strokes North East, Northern Roots and People and Drugs (£3,000 each); Leukaemia Research and Coast Video Club (£2,000 each); Northumberland Mountain Rescue and the Association of British Poles (£1,000 each); Healthwise and Newcastle Gang Show (£500 each).

Exclusions
The website gives the following information:

> Please note that grants will not be available to fund:
> - Statutory organisations including schools or activities eligible for public funding
> - Trips abroad
> - Projects focused on:
>   - Heritage and the environment
>   - Religion and the promotion of faith
>   - Scientific and/or medical research

> Unless these address deprivation and/or enrich local communities and improve local quality of life.

> Applicants that do not provide feedback on previous awards from the 1989 Willan Charitable Trust within the required timescale will not generally be considered for further funding.

The trust will not normally consider applications from organisations with an annual income of over £1 million.

Applications

Applications should be submitted by email and include the following:

- Contact details for the applicant organisation
- A brief description of the applicant organisation, its track record and current activities
- Charity number or HMRC number if an exempted organisation, such as a Church, to evidence registration for tax purposes
- Details of the activities for which funding is sought and why they are needed
- A budget for the activities and details of any funding from other sources, stating if secured or unsecured
- Details of the charity's bank account and a copy of the most recent bank statement. The name of the account should be the name of your group and you should include the address of your bank, your sort code (six numbers) and account number (eight numbers)

Applicants should also submit a copy of latest accounts if they cannot be accessed on the Charity Commission website.

The trustees meet in March, June, September and December. Applications will generally be considered at the next scheduled meeting, provided they are received by the 15th of the preceding month.

All applicants to the 1989 Willan Charitable Trust are contacted with the outcome of their application.

In exceptional circumstances, applications may be submitted by post. In such a circumstance, envelopes should be marked '1989 Willan Charitable Trust'.

Sources of information

Accounts; annual report; Charity Commission record; funder's website.

The 29th May 1961 Charitable Trust

General charitable purposes including: arts and museums, conservation and protection, employment, education and training, homelessness and housing, leisure, recreation and young people, medical, offenders, social welfare

UK, with a special interest in the Warwickshire/Birmingham/Coventry area

£4.5 million (2016/17)

CC number: 200198

Trustees: Vanni Emanuele Treves; Andrew Jones; Elizabeth Rantzen; Paul Varney.

Correspondent: Vanni Treves, Trustee, Ryder Court, 14 Ryder Street, London SW1Y 6QB (tel: 020 7024 9034; email: enquiries@29may1961charity.org.uk)

The trust takes its name from the date on which it was established by the settlor, the late Helen M. Martin. The trustees include Mr Vanni Treves, who is a former chair of Channel 4 and senior partner at Macfarlanes Solicitors, among other senior positions.

The trustees give the following concise description of its grant-making policy, aims and objectives in their annual report for 2016/17:

> The 29th May 1961 Charitable Trust is a general grant making trust. The policy of the trustees is to support a wide range of charitable organisations across a broad spectrum. Although for disclosure purposes grants are analysed into separate categories, the trustees are interested in funding initiatives which meet their selection criteria regardless of the charitable area into which the grant falls. Grants are made for both capital and revenue purposes. Some grants are one-off, some recurring and others spread over two or three years. The majority of grants are made to organisations within the United Kingdom and preference is given, where possible, to charities operating in the West Midlands and in particular the Coventry and Warwickshire area. The trustees do not typically fund projects outside the UK.

Financial information

In 2016/17 the trust had assets of £119 million and an income of £3.79 million. Grants were approved to 351 organisations totalling £4.5 million and broken down as follows:

Arts and museums	27	£1.4 million
Social welfare	135	£1.16 million
Leisure, recreation and young people	84	£685,500
Homelessness and housing	33	£419,500
Employment, education and training	24	£285,000
Medical	20	£253,000
Offenders	18	£233,500
Conservation and protection	10	£101,000

Beneficiaries included: University of Warwick (£1 million); Royal Albert Hall and Victoria and Albert Museum (£50,000 each); Cleanup UK (£30,000); Ruskin Mill Land Trust (£20,000); Pathways of Chesterfield Day Centre (£15,000); Children's Food Trust (£12,000); Dorset County Hospital Charity (£5,000).

Exclusions

No grants are given to individuals.

Applications

Apply in writing to the correspondent enclosing three copies of both the most recent annual report and accounts. Trustees normally meet in February, May, August and November. Due to the large number of applications received, they cannot all be acknowledged.

Sources of information

Accounts; annual report; Charity Commission record.

The 3Ts Charitable Trust

General

UK and overseas

£329,500 (2016/17)

CC number: 1109733

Trustees: Charles Sherwood; Rosemary Sherwood; Tim Sherwood; William Medlicott; Tabitha Sherwood; Tatiana Sherwood.

Correspondent: The Trustees, PO Box 68, Knebworth, Hertfordshire SG3 6UZ (email: info@3tscharitabletrust.com)

Set up in 2005, the 3Ts Charitable Trust makes grants for general charitable purposes throughout the UK and overseas. The trustees' annual report for 2016/17 provides the following information for future plans:

> The trust continues to support existing projects by the provision of further grants and to look for additional projects to fund and the trustees look to increase grant making in the future. The trustees have decided to make grants to a bedrock of causes, which comprise the majority 2017 grant recipients, with repeat grants of the same amount for the next two years.

Financial information

In 2016/17 the trust had assets of £10.9 million and an income of £207,500. The trust made 19 grants totalling £329,500.

Beneficiaries included: Imperial College SCI (£40,000); Supporting Dalit Children (£30,000); Books Beyond Words and Mary's Meals (£25,000 each); Youngminds (£15,000); Fair Trials International (£10,000); Hardman Trust (£5,000).

Applications

The trustees adopt a proactive approach in seeking worthy causes requiring support.

Sources of information

Accounts; annual report; Charity Commission record.

4 Charity Foundation

 General charitable purposes, social welfare, education, health, Jewish causes

 UK and Israel

£ £8 million (2016/17)

CC number: 1077143

Trustees: Jacob Schimmel; Verette Schimmel; Johnathan Schimmel.

Correspondent: Jacob Schimmel, Trustee, 121 Princes Park Avenue, London NW11 0JS (tel: 020 8455 0100; email: four4charities@gmail.com)

The charity was set up in 1999 with the name Les Freres Charitable Trust. In January 2008 the charity changed its name to 4 Charity Foundation. Grants are made to Jewish organisations for religious, educational, and general charitable purposes.

Financial information

In 2016/17 the foundation had assets of £21.3 million and an income of £4.5 million. Grants made during the year totalled £2.6 million.

Beneficiaries included: Ahavat Chesed-Keren (£4.4 million); Farmwood Charitable Foundation (£1 million); Mercaz Torah Vechesed Ltd (£491,000); American Jewish Joint Distribution Committee (£320,000); British Friends of Mosdos Torah Veyirah (£300,000); ImagineNations Group, Inc. (£59,000); British Friends of Shuvu (£31,000); UK Friends of Ahavas Chesed (£30,000).

Applications

The foundation does not accept unsolicited applications.

Sources of information

Accounts; annual report; Charity Commission record.

The A B Charitable Trust

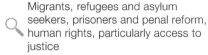 Migrants, refugees and asylum seekers, prisoners and penal reform, human rights, particularly access to justice

 UK

£ £1.12 million (2016/17)

CC number: 1000147

Trustees: Claire Bonavero; Olivier Bonavero; Philippe Bonavero; Anne Bonavero; Yves Bonavero; Athol Harley; Alison Swan Parente; Peter Day.

Correspondent: Sara Harrity, Director, c/o Woodsford 3rd Floor, 8 Bloomsbury Street, London WC1B 3SR (tel: 020 7313 8070; fax: 020 7313 9607; email: mail@ abcharitabletrust.org.uk)

 www.abcharitabletrust.org.uk

The AB Charitable Trust was established in 1990 and has a preference for funding 'unpopular' causes, particularly those that promote and defend human dignity.

The following information has been taken from the trust's website:

> ABCT supports charities that defend human rights and promote respect for vulnerable individuals whatever their circumstances. The trust is particularly interested in charities that work with marginalised and excluded people in society, with a focus on:
>
> ⯈ Migrants, refugees and asylum seekers
> ⯈ Prisoners and penal reform
> ⯈ Human rights, particularly access to justice
>
> ABCT very occasionally undertakes special initiatives related to work in these fields.

Grants are awarded to charities registered and working in the UK and tend to be one-off donations. Preference is given to charities with an annual income of between £150,000 and £1.5 million which do not have substantial investments or surpluses. Core funding is available, and most grants range from £10,000 to £20,000. Visit the trust's website for funding guidelines and deadlines.

Financial information

In 2016/17 the trust had assets of £304,000 and an income of £479,000. From 331 applications received, 79 grants were made totalling £1.12 million. They were distributed as follows:

Refugees	£565,000
Human rights	£370,000
Prisoners	£182,500

Beneficiaries included: British Red Cross Society – Families Together Initiative (£50,000); Shannon Trust and The Civil Liberties Trust (£30,000 each); Greater Manchester Law Centre (£25,000); Barnet Refugee Service, Changing Tunes and JUSTICE (£15,000 each); Asylum Welcome (£10,000); North East Prison After Care Society (£7,500); Piers Road New Communities Centre Association (£5,000).

Exclusions

ABCT does not fund charities that are principally concerned with:

⯈ Animals
⯈ Children
⯈ Environment
⯈ Formal education
⯈ Medicine
⯈ Religion
⯈ Research

Capital appeals are not normally supported, nor are charities with large national or international links.

Applications

Applications can be completed online via the trust's website. The trustees meet four times a year in in January, April, July and October to consider funding applications.

Sources of information

Accounts; annual report; Charity Commission record; funder's website.

The A Team Foundation Ltd

 Sustainable agriculture, nutrition, environment

 England

£ £289,000 (2016/17)

CC number: 1077094

Trustees: Benjamin Arbib; Tamara Arbib.

Correspondent: Paula Doraisamy, 61 Grosvenor Street, London W1K 3JE (tel: 020 3011 1100; email: info@ ateamfoundation.org)

 www.ateamfoundation.org

The A team foundation was established in 1999 to promote a 'greater understanding of the links between the consumption and production of foods and their effects on human health, social wellbeing and the environment'.

Today, the foundation supports food and land projects that are ecologically, economically and socially conscious. In addition, the foundation also seeks to 'contribute to the wider movement that envisions a future where real food is produced by enlightened agriculture and access to it is equal'.

Currently the foundation operates the following programmes:

⯈ **Inspiring nutrition:** Encouraging authentic and enlightened food production and consumption.
⯈ **Community cohesion:** Engaging communities with food to form meaningful connections to people and the land
⯈ **Education:** Disseminating the true value and interconnectivity of food and farming.
⯈ **Environmental stewardship:** Endorsing responsible land management that works in harmony with nature
⯈ **Equality:** Supporting the rights for people to work and live in dignity, providing assistance for marginalised food-growing communities

Financial information

In 2016/17 the foundation had assets of £14.5 million and an income of

£258,500. During the year, the foundation awarded grants of £289,000.

Beneficiaries included: Human Food Project (£194,000 in two grants); The Gala Foundation (£45,000 in two grants); Compassion in World Farming (£10,000); Eco Peace (£2,000); Soil Association (£1,000).

Applications
At the time of writing (June 2018) the foundation is not accepting unsolicited applications. However, if an organisation identifies that it has strong links to The A Team Foundation's funding objectives, the directors encourage the organisation to contact them via the foundation's website www.ateamfoundation.org before submitting a proposal.

Sources of information
Accounts; annual report; Charity Commission record; funder's website.

A W Charitable Trust

 Orthodox Jewish causes

 London, Gateshead, Manchester and Salford, Israel

£ £1.6 million (2015/16)

CC number: 283322

Trustees: Rabbi Aubrey Weis; Rachel Weis; Sir Weis.

Correspondent: Rabbi Aubrey Weis, Trustee, 66 Waterpark Road, Manchester M7 4JL (tel: 0161 740 0116)

This trust was established in 1981 for general charitable purposes. It is the charitable trust of Aubrey Weis, director of Aberdeen Estate Company, the owner of land and property throughout the North West. All the trustees are also trustees of The Helping Foundation which shares similar objectives to this trust.

The trust aims to support Orthodox Jewish causes and it meets this object by making grants to Jewish education and religious organisations both in the UK and abroad. Its grant-making policy is outlined in the 2015/16 annual report: 'The policy is to assist in the furtherance of Jewish education and religion, relieve poverty, assist with those in need of medical help and to alleviate hardship wherever possible.'

Financial information
In 2015/16 the trust had assets of £157.2 million and an income of £15 million. Grants to organisations were made totalling £1.6 million.

Previous beneficiaries have included: Asser Bishvil Foundation; Beenstock Home; British Friends of Kupat Hair; Chevras Oneg Shabbos-Yomtov; Friends

of Mir; Purim Fund; Toimchei Shabbos Manchester; Zoreya Tzedokos.

Applications
Apply in writing to the correspondent.

Sources of information
Accounts; annual report; Charity Commission record.

The A. H. Trust

Q Advancement of the Jewish religion, social welfare, education

 England and Wales

£ £510,500 (2015/16)

CC number: 1101843

Trustees: Elisabeth Kierszenbaum; Ivor Smith.

Correspondent: Ivor Smith, Trustee, 9 Danescroft Avenue, London NW4 2NB (email: mail@cohenarnold.com)

According to its 2015/16 annual report the objectives of the charity are as follows:

▷ The advancement and promotion of the Jewish religion including the provision of instruction or edification of the public in all its aspects and in any part of the world
▷ The relief of aged, vulnerable and impoverished persons of all ages in any part of the world
▷ The advancement of education and learning and/or establishment and/or support of schools and other institutions of Jewish learning including the establishment and support of colleges and educational establishments in all parts of the world

Financial information
At the time of writing (June 2018) the charity's latest set of accounts was unavailable. In 2015/16 the charity had assets of £328,500 and an income of £460,500. During the year, the charity awarded grants of £510,500.

Beneficiaries included: LTC Trust Co. Ltd (£260,000); Beis Hillel Trust (£20,000); Menorah High School for Girls (£16,000); Friends of Yeshivas Torah Ohr (£15,000); Ezras Hakohol Trust (£13,000); Achisomoch (£12,500).

Applications
Apply in writing to the correspondent.

Sources of information
Accounts; annual report; Charity Commission record.

The Aaronson Foundation

Q General charitable purposes, education and training, the promotion of health, social welfare, Judaism

 England and Wales, Israel, Russia, South Africa, United States of America

£ £624,000 (2016/17)

CC number: 1159385

Trustees: David Rodney; Michael Aaronson.

Correspondent: David Rodney, Trustee, First Floor Foframe House, 35–37 Brent Street, London NW4 2EF (tel: 020 3411 2001; email: lfafoundation@citroenwells.co.uk)

The Aaronson Foundation was registered with the Charity Commission in November 2014. The annual report for 2016/17 states that the foundation was established for general charitable purposes, with preference for the following causes:

▷ the prevention or relief of poverty by providing: grants, items, facilities and services to individuals in need and to charities, or other organisations working to prevent or relieve poverty
▷ the prevention or relief of poverty or financial hardship by providing or assisting in the provision of education, training, healthcare projects and all the necessary support designed to enable individuals to generate a sustainable income and be self-sufficient
▷ to assist in the treatment and care of persons suffering from mental or physical illness of any description or in need of rehabilitation as a result of such illness, by the provision of facilities for work and recreation
▷ the relief of sickness and the preservation of health by making grants and providing items, facilities and services, for medical research
▷ to advance the education of the public in general in the subject of the Jewish religion by making grants to institutions promoting knowledge and education of the Jewish religion

The main way in which the charity pursues its charitable objectives is through the provision of grants to charitable institutions and making medical research equipment available to medical researchers.

Financial information
In 2016/17 the foundation held assets of £208,000 and had an income of £717,500. Grants awarded to organisations totalled £624,000.

Beneficiaries included: Netivei Itzhak (£212,000); Jewish Learning Exchange (£45,000); Alsh Hatorah UK (£28,000); Community Security Trust (£27,500); Jerusalem Medical Ethics Forum (£27,500); Gertner Charitable Trust (£15,000).

Applications

Applications can be made in writing to the correspondent.

Sources of information

Annual report; Charity Commission record.

The Abbeyfield Research Foundation

 Research relating to older people

England and Wales

£360,500 (2016/17)

CC number: 1167685

Trustees: The Rt Revd Dr Christopher Herbert; Prof. Cameron Swift; Keith Fowler; John Robinson.

Correspondent: John Robinson, Abbeyfield Society, 2 Bricket Road, St Albans, Hertfordshire AL1 3JW (tel: 01727 734067; email: research@abbeyfield.com)

www.abbeyfieldresearchfoundation.org

The foundation was registered with the Charity Commission in June 2016 and is a branch of The Abbeyfield Society – a nationwide charity that provides housing, support and companionship in later life. The foundation's website details its aims and objectives:

> Research is one of the fundamental pillars that supports and maintains best practice in all forms of social and health care. It provides evidence to inform decisions, directs policy development and upholds the sector's credibility.
>
> Abbeyfield have always championed the needs and rights of older people and we see the potential to fund research as an extension of this. It's our research foundations aim to develop high quality services for older people through supporting individuals at varying levels in their career, from PhD students at the beginning of their research journey to established senior academics looking to support their own research teams.

Research priorities

The foundation is particularly keen to support research that effectively crosses boundaries between organisations, services and professions in the provision of 'joined up' care. The foundation has the following research priorities:

Progress and quality in the care and support of residents with dementia

- Measures to promote maintenance and development of existing and new personal relationships and of individual autonomy
- Interaction with the natural and outdoor world
- The involvement of family and informal carers and volunteers

The assessment of need, and of response to care

- The impact of geographic and socioeconomic variation on care need and provision
- The identification and development of a reliable minimum dataset for the measurement of change in the status (physical, mental, functional and emotional) of residents
- Provision of domiciliary support
- Meeting the spiritual needs of older residents

Quality and innovation in care provision

- Measures to prevent the progression of disability in care settings
- The prevention and management of falls and fractures in care settings
- The roles of volunteers in care settings
- The identification and evaluation of pastoral roles, traditional or otherwise
- Measures to assess or ensure optimal hydration and nutrition in care home residents
- Systematic and critical evaluation of the role (or not) of new technologies, including information technologies, in the delivery and quality of care

Types of grants

The foundation offers PhD studentships of around £20,000 to £30,000 per year to provide a stipend, cover fees and so on; small project grants of up to £50,000 per year to cover salaries, running costs and equipment; and pump-priming grants of up to £20,000 to cover preliminary evaluation over a year.

Financial information

In 2016/17 the foundation held assets of £339,000 and had an income of £359,500. Grants totalled £360,500.

Beneficiaries included: King's College London (£89,000); University of Sheffield (£87,500); Cardiff University (£72,500); University of Worcester (£22,800); University of Southampton (£13,900).

Exclusions

The foundation does not currently fund research using animals.

Applications

The foundation posts calls for proposals on its website, the 2018/19 call will open on 22 October 2018. Applications are made through a two-stage, peer-reviewed process. The foundation's helpful website provides detailed information on how to apply, the research priorities and the next deadline.

Sources of information

Accounts; annual report; Charity Commission record; funder's website.

Aberdeen Asset Management Charitable Foundation

 Education, disadvantaged young people, social welfare, communities

 UK and overseas where the company has a presence

£974,000 (2015/16)

OSCR number: SC042597

Correspondent: The Trustees, 10 Queen's Terrace, Aberdeen AB10 1YG (email: foundation.uk@aberdeen-asset.com)

 aboutus.aberdeen-asset.com/en/aboutus/responsible-business/aberdeen-charitable

Registered in 2011, this is the charitable foundation of Aberdeen Asset Management plc, a global investment management group, managing assets for both institutional and retail clients from some 37 offices in 25 countries. The foundation looks to work in partnership with smaller charities across the globe and, since 2012, has supported more than 400 charities. It is explained on the foundation's webpage that it seeks to give funds where they 'can be seen to have a meaningful and measurable impact'. Employees of Aberdeen Asset Management are also encouraged to contribute their time and skills in support of the foundation's charitable projects.

The foundation's two 'core focuses' – emerging markets and local communities – reflect the business' desire to give back to areas which are a key strategic focus and to build on its pattern of giving to communities in which employees of Aberdeen Asset Management live and work. The criteria for each focus is outlined on the foundation's website as follows:

Emerging Markets

Each year the Foundation will select an emerging market and focus its investment in that area. The emerging markets allocation will be focused on a small number of long-term partnerships (average duration of three years). All charities must meet the following criteria to be considered for an emerging market grant:

- UK registered
- Small to medium in size or, if a larger charity, must have an identifiable project that Aberdeen can support
- Clear focus on the promotion of education and providing wider opportunities for underprivileged young people

Local Communities

All charities applying for local community grants must meet the following criteria:

- ⟩ Be a registered charity
- ⟩ Clear connection to a community local to one of Aberdeen's offices
- ⟩ The investment should be capable of having a clear and meaningful impact, for example:
  - ⟩ Small charities where the contribution amount is significant relative to the charity's size
  - ⟩ Larger charities with identifiable project opportunities that Aberdeen could put its name to
  - ⟩ Projects which include the opportunity for Aberdeen employee involvement through volunteering
  - ⟩ Local organisations where Aberdeen can have a visible impact
- ⟩ A governance structure in place to allow Aberdeen to monitor the impact of the investment

Financial information

In 2015/16 the foundation had assets of £2.2 million and an income of £1.42 million. Donations were made amounting to £974,000, of which £210,000 was given to 'emerging markets' projects. The remaining £764,500 was distributed in local community donations from individual offices.

Exclusions

The foundation does not support political causes, parties or organisations or charities with a religious focus.

Applications

Application forms are available – along with full criteria and terms and conditions – from the Aberdeen Asset Management website. Completed forms should be returned to the foundation by email (foundation.uk@aberdeen-asset.com), and be accompanied by a PDF copy of your latest annual review. Successful applicants will be notified within three months of their application being submitted. The foundation notes that, due to the volume of applications it receives, it cannot respond to all unsuccessful applicants. Recipients of grants will be required to complete an annual impact assessment form.

Sources of information

Accounts; OSCR record; funder's website.

The Aberdeen Foundation

Q Jewish causes, education and training, health, social welfare, general charitable purposes

◉ UK and Israel, overseas including Chile and USA

£ Around £4.7 million (2016/17)

CC number: 1151506

Trustees: Irwin Weiler; Albert Friedberg; Chaya Spitz; Nancy Friedberg.

Correspondent: Yedidut Toronto, 7 Hartom Street, 2nd Floor, Har Hotzvim, Jerusalem, Israel (tel: 0526 130 910; email: aberdeenfoundation@gmail.com)

The Aberdeen Foundation was registered with the Charity Commission in April 2013. Founding trustee, Irwin Weiler, is also a trustee at Chalfords Ltd, LPW Ltd and V F Foundation Ltd, all three of which give grants for the advancement of the Orthodox Jewish religion.

The foundation's annual report indicates that it has general charitable purposes, with a particular emphasis on welfare within the Jewish community, education and training. It makes grants to charitable, educational and religious organisations in the UK, Israel and throughout the rest of the world.

Financial information

In 2016/17 the foundation had an income of £42 and a total expenditure of £5 million. We estimate that grants awarded to organisations totalled around £4.7 million. The foundation's accounts were not available to view on the Charity Commission website due to its low income.

Previous beneficiaries have included: Colegio Maimonides (£1.1 million); Ptach (£1 million) Encyclopaedia Talmudit (£770,000); Harchavat Hamaagalim (£683,000); Instituto Hebreo (£234,000); Friedberg Economic Institute (£181,000); Hapotential Haleumi (£120,000).

Applications

Unsolicited applications are not accepted. Previous annual reports have stated:

> The trustees have a clear strategic view of the types of charities they wish to support and detailed enquiries are made concerning a charity before grants are approved by the trustees. The trustees are proactive in seeking out charities that meet their criteria and do not have an open grant application process. The trustees plan to make a smaller number of large grants approved on an annual basis, and recipients are monitored closely to ensure that funds are utilised in furtherance of the projects or causes for which they were granted.

Sources of information

Accounts; annual report; Charity Commission record.

ABF The Soldiers' Charity

Q British armed forces

◉ Worldwide

£ £3.5 million to organisations (2015/16)

CC number: 1146420

Trustees: Simon Martin; Maj. General Malcolm Wood; Maj. General Robert Nitsch; Damien Francis; James Rous; Peter Baynham; Paul Hearn; Glenn Haughton; Mary Fagan; Lt General Philip Jones; Amanda Metcalfe; Lisa Worley.

Correspondent: Temidayo Ajakaiye, Director of Finance, Mountbarrow House, 6–20 Elizabeth Street, London SW1W 9RB (tel: 020 7901 8900; email: info@soldierscharity.org)

 www.soldierscharity.org

 facebook.com/soldierscharity

 @soldierscharity

Since 1944 this charity has supported soldiers, former soldiers and their immediate families. The charity's vision is: 'That all serving and former soldiers and their dependants should have the opportunity to avoid hardship and enjoy independence and dignity.'

The current policy set by the trustees is to support individuals through their regimental and corps benevolence funds, and to support other specialist charities which look after the needs of the serving and retired army community.

Grants to organisations

ABF has established guidelines for organisations, which are available to read in full on the website. They explain that the charity supports:

> All registered charities and other organisations which support the Army community, which includes veterans, serving soldiers, their families and immediate dependants, may apply.
>
> The broad range of charities/organisations supported by our charity is extensive and covers every aspect of social care including care for a disabled child, marriage guidance, hospice care, schools which have a high intake of Army children, addressing homelessness amongst former soldiers, managing post-traumatic stress disorder and helping disabled soldiers renew their sense of self-worth through sport. For example:
>
> - ⟩ Charitable organisations, in particular, with a preference to members of COBSEO/Veterans Scotland
> - ⟩ Not-for-profit organisations
> - ⟩ Community projects
> - ⟩ Housing associations and corporations

According to the 2016/17 annual report, the priorities for grants to organisations during the year were: care for older people; mental health and respite care; supported housing; education and training for employment; and welfare support.

Grants vary widely in size and scope and are considered for specific activities or programmes; they are not normally made for capital projects (such as the construction of a new building).

Grants to individuals

The charity supports around 4,500 individuals with grants each year. Cases are usually submitted through the individual's regimental headquarters. They are considered on their own merits and, according to the website, can be given for needs ranging from 'an electric wheelchair for a serving soldier's disabled son, or a stair lift for an injured former soldier, to care home fees for a Second World War veteran or a much needed holiday for a war widow and his or her young children'. See the website for more information.

Financial information

In 2016/17 the charity had assets of £77.3 million and an income of £13.2 million. Grants were made totalling £7.1 million with £3.6 million given in grants to individuals and £3.5 million given to organisations.

Beneficiaries included: Regular Forces Employment Association (£380,000); Royal Commonwealth Ex-Services League (£227,500); Erskine Hospital (£150,000); Broughton House (£86,000); Skill Force (£15,000); Spinal Injuries Association and Storybook Soldiers (£5,000 each).

Exclusions

The guidelines state:

- We are not able to accept applications from those organisations that do not support serving soldiers, veterans and their immediate families, and/or the wider Army community
- We will not normally consider any funding request made within 12 months of the outcome of a previous application, whether a grant was received or not
- Whilst we do support some educational and training activities, this does not include gap years, study trips, fundraising expeditions or sponsorship. Sponsorship referrals should be passed to the Charity's communications department
- The Charity does not normally fund specific (i.e. named) posts and salaries. Trustees will consider contributing to an organisation's core operating costs of which we recognise general salary costs will be a part of this. This is primarily because grants are single-year commitments
- Typically grants are made for a single year; however, the Charity's Trustees may consider making a grant spread over a number of years at their discretion if they feel this would be appropriate
- The Charity tends not to support umbrella organisations, preferring to support those organisations working directly with beneficiaries at a grassroots level

Applications

Full guidelines are available, along with application forms, from the website. Completed application forms should be returned to externalgrants@ soldierscharity.org. There is a helpful application checklist on the charity's website.

Sources of information

Accounts; annual report; Charity Commission record; guidelines for applicants; funder's website.

Access Sport CIO

🔍 Increasing access to sport for young people in disadvantaged communities

📍 England and Wales but in practice: London, Bristol, Manchester, and Oxford

💷 £321,000 (2016/17)

CC number: 1156819

Trustees: Paul Lee; Tim Jones; Grace Clancey; Phil Veasey; Tina Kokkinos; Mark Burgess; John Baker; Preston Rabl; Martin McPhee.

Correspondent: Sue Wheeler, Correspondent, 3 Durham Yard, Teesdale Street, London E2 6QF (tel: 020 7993 9883; email: info@accesssport.co. uk)

 www.accesssport.org.uk

 facebook.com/AccessSport

 @AccessSport

This charity was founded in 2004 and became a CIO in April 2014. Its website details its aims and activities:

Access Sport enhances the life prospects of disadvantaged children by providing opportunities to experience and enjoy the power of sport.

We do this by building thriving community sports clubs, led by inspirational volunteers, in the most disadvantaged urban areas. These clubs then provide life-changing opportunities for local, vulnerable young people, whilst creating a lasting, locally-owned community resource.

Our work supports young people aged 5–25, with a particular emphasis on under 18's who are disabled, disadvantaged or excluded from society.

We have a multi-sport approach which recognises the importance of different sports in different settings for different participants, enabling maximum inclusivity and impact – from BMX to boxing; from running to rugby; from sitting volleyball to sailing.

Our unique experience across a wide range of sports and settings in leading cities has led us, in the fourteen years since we were established in 2004, to become nationally recognised as an innovative leader in the field of community sport. In 2018 we hold particular leadership roles in the development of BMX cycling in the UK and the development of inclusive sport for disabled young people.

Programmes

Support is given through three core programmes: BMX Legacy Programme; Social Inclusion Programme; and Ignite Programme. For more information, including contact details for each programme, see the charity's website.

Financial information

In 2016/17 the charity had assets of £345,000 and an income of £1.14 million. Grants awarded to organisations totalled £321,000.

A list of specific beneficiaries was not included in the annual report and accounts.

Applications

Contact details for each of the projects can be found on the charity's website. General enquiries should be directed to the correspondent.

Sources of information

Accounts; annual report; Charity Commission record; funder's website.

Achisomoch Aid Company Ltd

🔍 Orthodox Jewish causes, general charitable purposes

📍 UK and overseas

💷 £23.7 million (2016/17)

CC number: 278387

Trustees: Jack Emanuel; Yitzchock Katz; Maurice Levenson.

Correspondent: Isaac Katz, Trustee, 26 Hoop Lane, London NW11 8BU (tel: 020 8731 8988; email: admin@ achisomoch.org)

 www.achisomoch.org

This charity was established in 1979 to advance religion in accordance with the Orthodox Jewish faith and to support general charitable purposes.

The charity's annual report for 2016/17 states that, during the year, it made grants to organisations providing benefits such as:

- Provision of basic necessities and financial support to the poor
- Relief of suffering in regard to illness and disabilities
- Jewish education and places of worship for the Jewish community

How the charity works

The following information about how the charity operates is given on its website:

Achisomoch is a Charity Voucher (cheque) agency – it is like a bank. You open an account with us and then pay money into the account. You are given a cheque (voucher) book and can then make (charitable) payments by using these vouchers.

As Achisomoch is a charity in its own right, we can reclaim the tax rebate under Gift Aid to increase the money in your account making even more available for you to distribute to charities.

Donations, via vouchers can be made only to registered charities. You get regular statements and can arrange to speak to our client services team for help or special instructions.

Financial information

In 2016/17 the charity had assets of £7.6 million and an income of £26.6 million, mainly from donations and Gift Aid receipts. Grants were made totalling £23.7 million. The following table provides an analysis of the grants given:

Advancement of health and saving of lives	£618,500
Advancement of education	£13.6 million
Relief of poverty	£3.65 million
Advancement of Jewish religion	£3.7 million
Advancement of community development	£868,500
Grants to other grant-making charities	£1.29 million

Beneficiaries included: Yesamach Levav Trust (£378,500); The Friends of Ohr Someach (£223,900); Mercaz Hatorah Netzach Yisroel (£141,500); Kollel Skver Trust (£127,500); The Chicken Soup Shelter (£121,000); Tomchei Yotzei Anglia (£104,000); Fonds Social Juif Unifié (£100,300).

Applications

Apply in writing to the correspondent.

Sources of information

Accounts; annual report; Charity Commission record; funder's website.

The ACT Foundation

 Disability, health, social welfare

Mainly in the UK, some overseas

£3.15 million to organisations (2016/17)

CC number: 1068617

Trustees: Michael Street; John O'Sullivan; Andrew Ross; Robert White; Denis Taylor; Christine Erwood; Russell Meadows; Colin Clarkson; Stephen O'Sullivan.

Correspondent: James Kerr, Secretary, 61 Thames Street, Windsor, Berkshire SL4 1QW (tel: 01753 753900; fax: 01753 753901; email: info@theactfoundation. co.uk)

 www.theactfoundation.co.uk

The ACT Foundation (ACT) was formed in 1994 and provides grants to individuals and UK-registered charities with the aim of 'enhancing the quality of life of people in need and, particularly, those on a low income who have a physical and/or mental disability or the elderly'. Its grant budget is derived from our diverse investment portfolio and the foundation does not fundraise.

The grant-making priorities of the foundation are informed by four key themes:

- **Health and Wellbeing** – supporting access to community facilities to maintain, improve and enhance general welfare
- **Independent Living at Home** – helping people to live independently in their own home for as long as possible
- **Respite** - enabling carers to take a break from the responsibility of caring for a loved one
- **Transition** – supporting the journey through education and personal development programmes into employment, long-term volunteering or other meaningful daytime activity, housing and independent living

There is no set limit to the amount of funding that can be granted. In practice however, the majority of grants awarded are around £10,000. Charities that make applications for £10,000 or more may be visited by a representative of the foundation.

Financial information

In 2016/17 the foundation had assets of £93 million and an income of £24.5 million. Grants to 207 organisations totalled £3.15 million. A further £170,000 was given in 150 grants to individuals.

Beneficiaries included: Chailey Heritage Foundation (£100,000); Alexander Devine Children's Hospice (£75,000); Centre 33, Stroud Court Community Trust (£50,000); Andover Young Carers, Golden Lion Children's Trust, Leeds MENCAP Newport Cottage Care Centre, Pear Tree School (£10,000 each).

Exclusions

According to the foundation's website, the trustees will not fund any of the following:

- Projects that are completed by the time of our decision.
- Projects that support a particular political or religious persuasion.
- Statutory services including local or national authorities, NHS hospitals or services, prisons and state schools except where the school is wholly for students with additional needs.
- Universities, further education colleges or independent schools except where the facility is wholly for students with additional needs.
- Core operating costs except in connection with setting up a new service.
- Other grant making charities except through a match funding partnership.
- Community centres and youth clubs except where those benefiting have physical and/or a mental disability, are elderly or suffering from a long-term illness.
- Overseas projects unless the project is carried out under the direct control of a UK-registered charity with a minimum of 3 years filed accounts.

Applications

Applicants are advised to visit the foundation's website in the first instance. The website provides detailed information on the application process and what to include in an application.

The trustees meet four times a year and applications can be made at any time. A letter of acknowledgement will be sent on receipt of an application and the foundation aims to make decisions on 95% of grant applications within two months and on all applications within three months.

Sources of information

Accounts; annual report; Charity Commission record; funder's website.

Action Medical Research

Medical research, focusing on children's health

UK

£2.77 million (2016)

CC number: 208701

Trustees: Charles Jackson; Valerie Remington-Hobbs; Prof. Sarah Bray; Esther Alderson; Nick Peters; Luke Bordewich; Prof. David Edwards; Prof. Nigel Klein.

Correspondent: Martin Richardson, Director of Finance, IT & Operations, Vincent House, 31 North Parade, Horsham, West Sussex RH12 2DP (tel: 01403 210406; email: info@action.org. uk)

www.action.org.uk

The history of this charity dates back to 1952, when it was set up under the name The National Fund for Poliomyelitis Research, by Duncan Guthrie. The charity was first established to find a cure for polio, an illness which affected the lives of thousands of children, including the founder's daughter. The charity funded research which helped to develop the first oral polio vaccine. Since then, the charity has spent more than £115 million on medical research and has funded breakthroughs including:

- Helping to introduce the first polio vaccines in the UK
- Discovering the importance of taking folic acid before and during pregnancy to prevent spina bifida
- Developing the use of ultrasound technology in pregnancy
- Testing the rubella vaccine
- Helping to develop the Hib meningitis vaccine which is now a routine immunisation for young children
- Pioneering a unique portable foetal heart rate monitor
- Contributing to the development of ground-breaking cooling therapy to prevent brain damage in babies

Research strategy
The charity focuses its research on the health of children, babies and young people. Its research strategy is outlined on the website:

The aim of the charity is to prevent and treat disease and disability by funding vital medical research in hospitals or research institutions across the UK.

The remit focuses on child health to include problems affecting pregnancy, childbirth, babies, children and young people. There are projects described on our website from our previous wider remit that have recently finished or have one year to run but all new applications must focus on child health.

Within child health, we support a broad spectrum of research with the objective of:

- preventing disease and disability and;
- alleviating physical disability.

Please note that our emphasis is on clinical research or research at the interface between clinical and basic science. We pride ourselves that our research is both innovative and of a high standard as judged by rigorous peer review.

Within the above criteria, we also support research and development of equipment and techniques to improve diagnosis, therapy and assistive technology (including orthoses, prostheses and aids to daily living) and we encourage applications in the field of medical engineering.

Financial information
In 2016 the charity had assets of £10.5 million and an income of £6.8 million. Grants were made totalling £2.77 million.

Beneficiaries included: Department of Pharmacology and Sir William Dunn School of Pathology both at the University of Oxford (£200,000 each); University of Manchester and St Mary's Hospital Manchester (£134,000); Molecular Immunology Unit, Institute of Child Health, London (£106,000); Royal College of Obstetricians and Gynaecologists, London (£5,000).

Exclusions
According to the charity's website it does not provide:

- Grants towards service provision or audit studies
- Grants purely for higher education, although Research Training Fellows are strongly encouraged to independently register for a PhD
- Course fees for degrees or subsistence costs
- Grants for medical or dental electives
- Grants for work undertaken outside the UK
- Any indirect costs such as administrative or other overheads imposed by the University or other Institution
- Costs associated with advertising and recruitment of staff
- 'Top up' funding for work supported by other funding bodies
- Costs to attend conferences (current Action Medical Research grant holders may apply separately as the need arises during the grant)
- General appeals from other charities. Applications would normally come directly from research teams and projects need to be passed through our scientific peer review system
- Grants for research into complementary/alternative medicine
- Grants on how best to train clinical staff
- Grants for psychosocial aspects of treatment
- Grants on social research, family relationships or socioeconomic research
- Grants for very basic research with little likelihood of clinical impact within the short to medium-term
- Applicants based in core funded units can apply but need to demonstrate added value

Applications
Full details of how to apply for both project and research grants can be found on the charity's website together with guidelines, exclusions and current closing dates.

Sources of information
Accounts; annual report; Charity Commission record; funder's website.

Action on Hearing Loss

People with disabilities

UK

£1.7 million (2016/17)

CC number: 207720

Trustees: Caroline Ashley; Carol Cole; Prof. Quentin Summerfield; Eric Roux; Richard Jones; Carol Cole; Caroline Ashley; Dr Gerhard May; Louise Craddock; Jacqueline Press; Prof. Brian Moore; Margaret Hampton; John Morgan; Dr Brian Caul; Ingrid Gallen.

Correspondent: The Trustees, 1–3 Highbury Station Road, London N1 1SE (tel: 020 7359 4442; email: informationline@hearingloss.org.uk)

 www.actiononhearingloss.org.uk

 facebook.com/actiononhearingloss

 @actiononhearing

 @actiononhearingloss

A national charity since 1911, its objects include the prevention and mitigation of deafness and the better treatment, education, training, employment and welfare of people who are deaf or hard of hearing. This includes providing high-quality support and care so people confronting deafness, hearing loss and tinnitus have their needs met. The charity also funds research to find a cure for hearing loss, and encourages the take-up of new technology and medical treatments to help manage the condition. It also 'campaigns for equality, so the people it supports can make the same life choices as everyone else'.

Grant-making
The annual report for 2016/17 provides the following information on the charity's grant-funding:

We award biomedical research grants to fund world-class research projects that will accelerate the development of medical treatments to prevent hearing loss, restore hearing and alleviate tinnitus. We also make grants to increase the numbers of trained research staff, build future research capacity and support small-scale activities that will strengthen the hearing research community. Universities, non-profit research institutes and technology-led small businesses from any country are eligible for funding, except where geographical and organisational-type restrictions are stated for specific funding schemes.

Everyone involved in the grant-application process is asked to abide by our Biomedical Research Programme's Code of Conduct and Conflict of Interest policy. We occasionally award a small number of grants for social and technical research to help provide the evidence basis for campaigning and policy development. We also award grants to develop our library collection, currently housed and managed by University College London.

Grants are generally made to organisations to facilitate research into hearing loss and tinnitus. Grants payable are payments made to third parties in the furtherance of the charitable objectives of the charity.

Financial information

In 2016/17 the charity had net assets of £10.78 million and an income of £40.29 million. Grants payable were listed in the accounts as follows:

Medical research into hearing loss – institutions	89	£1.64 million
Welfare, education and training for deaf and hard of hearing people	2	£40,000
Medical research into hearing loss – individual grants	11	£8,000

Of the total grant-funding made during the year, £1.65 million related to biomedical research projects.

In addition to the above, the charity expects to 'fund future grants totalling £2.55 million, which have been awarded subject to satisfactory reviews during the course of the project being funded'.

Beneficiaries included: University College London (£498,000); King's College London (£145,000); University of Sheffield (£83,000); Massachusetts Eye and Ear Infinity (£27,000); The Bionics University of Australia (£10,000); The Ear Foundation (£7,000); University of York (£2,000).

Applications

The charity's annual report states:

> We widely publicise our calls for grant proposals. We advertise our grant schemes on our website and through emails sent out to the research community. The proposals we receive are subjected to an appropriate level of expert peer review, typically involving independent, external reviewers and a voluntary independent grant-review panel. Each panel is made up of experts who serve for a three-year term and the panel members are listed on our website. We make the final decision about each award on the basis of this expert advice, the relevance of the research to our biomedical research strategy, and our available budget. We usually make payments every six months and review progress regularly.

Sources of information

Accounts; annual report; Charity Commission record.

The Sylvia Adams Charitable Trust

Early years preventative work, autosomal recessive conditions, development work in Kenya, Tanzania and Uganda

England and Wales, Tanzania, Kenya and Uganda

£392,500 (2016/17)

CC number: 1050678

Trustees: Richard Golland; Matthew McBryde; Alex Butler.

Correspondent: Jane Young, Director, Sylvia Adams House, 24 The Common, Hatfield, Hertfordshire AL10 0NB (tel: 01707 259259; email: jane.young@sylvia-adams.org.uk)

 www.sylvia-adams.org.uk

The Sylvia Adams Charitable Trust was founded in 1996 in line with the wishes of professional collector of antiques and art Sylvia Adams' who endowed the trust with funds from the sale of her personal collection of antiques and works of art.

Areas of work

From 1996 to 2015, grants were made to support organisations in the UK and overseas which supported children and young people, those with a disability and those living in poverty or who were socially excluded. In 2015 the trust reassessed its policies on the long-term future of the trust and regarding the causes to be supported. From 2016, the trust will primarily provide funding in the following areas:

Early years' preventative work in England and Wales

The trust supports charities in England and Wales whose work improves the life chances of disadvantaged children by investing in early intervention and preventative work. The trust has a particular focus on children up to three years old.

Grants can be one, two or three years. There is no minimum grant size however the maximum that can be awarded is £50,000 per annum.

The trust states that it is happy to consider complete or partial funding and accepts overheads as part of a budget. Successful organisations must be prepared to share learning from the funded work with other organisations, to increase the impact

Breaking down Barriers

This programme aims to enable organisations supporting families with genetic disorders, with a particular focus on autosomal recessive conditions, to reach out more effectively to those communities that are particularly at risk but currently under-served.

Because of the way this programme is managed, the trust does not accept applications for funding, however, organisations interested in becoming involved, can send an initial email of interest to kerry.leeson@alstrom.org.uk or find out more at breaking-down-barriers.org.uk.

Development work

A very limited amount of funding is made available for development work in Tanzania and Uganda. The trust typically allocates funds to organisations that it already supports.

Financial information

In 2016/17 the trust had assets of £5.2 million and an income of £203,500. During the year, the trust awarded a total of £392,500 in grants, and were distributed as follows:

Breaking down barriers	£60,000
Preventive work with 0- to 3-year-olds	£276,500
Overseas	£30,000
Trustee grants	£26,500

Beneficiaries included: Cued Speech Association, Women's Aid (£50,000); The Cedarwood Trust (£41,500); Alstrom Syndrome UK (£20,000); African Initiatives, Chance for Childhood (£15,000); Crossroads Derbyshire (£11,500); The Bendrigg Trust, PHAB (£1,000).

Applications

Applications can be made through the trust's website. At the time of writing (June 2018) the trust is only accepting applications for early years preventative work in England and Wales. There are normally two application windows per year. Check the website for the latest application information.

Sources of information

Accounts; annual report; Charity Commission record; funder's website.

The Adint Charitable Trust

Health, social welfare, disability

Worldwide, in practice UK

£309,500 (2016/17)

CC number: 265290

Trustees: Anthony Edwards; Margaret Edwards; Douglas Oram; Brian Pate.

Correspondent: Douglas Oram, Trustee, Suite 512, 571 Finchley Road, London NW3 7BN (email: adintct@gmail.com)

This trust was established in 1972 by the settlor, Henry John Edwards. Most of the grants awarded range from £5,000 or £10,000 and are given to a range charities working in the field of health, social welfare and disability.

Financial information

In 2016/17 the trust had assets of £8.6 million and an income of £183,500. Grants were made to 26 organisations totalling £309,500.

Beneficiaries included: Arthritis Research UK, Meningitis Now, Mental Health Foundation and The Lullaby Trust (£10,000 each); Missing People, The Stroke Association and WellChild (£5,000 each); National Autistic Society

(£3,500); Noah's Ark Children's Hospice (£1,000).

Exclusions
Individuals are not supported.

Applications
Apply in writing to the correspondent. Each applicant should make its own case in the way it considers best, but the application should include full details of the applicant charity. The trust states that it cannot enter into correspondence and unsuccessful applicants will not be notified.

Sources of information
Accounts; annual report; Charity Commission record.

The AIM Foundation

 Nutrition, health and well-being, young people, children

Mainly UK, with a preference for Essex. Some grants are given overseas

£322,500 (2015/16)

CC number: 263294

Trustees: Nicholas Marks; Ian Marks; Caroline Marks; Angela Marks; Joanna Precious; Philippa Bailey.

Correspondent: Sean Grinsted, Francis Clark LLP, Vantage Point, Woodwater Park, Pynes Hill, Exeter EX2 5FD (tel: 01392 667000; email: info@francisclark. co.uk)

Set up in 1971 as the Ian Roy Marks Charitable Trust, this charity changed its name to the AIM Foundation in 1993. The foundation stresses that grant-making policy is highly proactive in seeking out potential partners. The 2015/16 annual report states that it funds research, policy, prevention and support work in the following areas:

- Nutrition and Well-being – diet and life style programs to optimise cognitive health
- Young People – improving their life chances especially around the transition from school to employment
- Early Years – improving the emotional and social development of young children from vulnerable families

Grants are made for core costs, research, salaries, projects and other purposes. Further detail on each of its areas of work is given in the 2015/16 annual report.

Financial information
In 2015/16 the foundation had assets of £11.16 million and an income of £4.3 million. Grants were made totalling £322,500 and were broken down as follows:

Research and campaigning – nutrition and well-being	2	£100,000
Prevention – young people	4	£57,000
Prevention – early years	1	£50,000
Support – young people	3	£47,000
Support – community	4	£26,000
Research and campaigning – early years	1	£25,000
Support – gifts	3+	£17,700

Beneficiaries included: New Economics Foundation (£80,000); Impetus-PEF (£50,000); Essex Community Foundation (£27,000); The Wave Trust (£25,000); Health Empowerment Through Nutrition (£20,000); The Who Cares? Trust and Wells for India (£10,000 each); Families in Focus and St Clare Hospice (£5,000 each); Cirdon Sailing Trust (£2,000).

Exclusions
No grants are given to individuals.

Applications
The foundation strongly emphasises that it is proactive in its grant-making and does not, under any circumstances, consider or respond to unsolicited applications.

Sources of information
Accounts; annual report; Charity Commission record.

Ajahma Charitable Trust

 Development, poverty, human rights, health, disability, social welfare

UK and overseas

£439,000 (2016/17)

CC number: 273823

Trustees: Roger Paffard; Elizabeth Simpson; Jenny Sheridan; James Taylor; Carole Pound.

Correspondent: Suzanne Hunt, 275 Dover House Road, London SW15 5BP (tel: 020 8788 5388)

This trust was established in 1977 for general charitable purposes in the UK and overseas. The trust particularly focuses on: development; poverty; human rights; health; disability; and social welfare.

Financial information
In 2016/17 the trust held assets of £2.2 million and had an income of £60,500. During the year, the trust gave almost £439,000 in grants to 30 organisations.

Beneficiaries Included: Advocacy for Older People in Greenwich, Farm Africa and Pump Aid (£60,000); CAPE and South London Refugee Association (£12,000 each); Ashiana Network and Woman's Trust (£6,000).

Applications
The trust no longer accepts unsolicited applications. The 2016/17 annual report states: 'The Trustees have adopted a policy of seeking and considering applications for charitable funding generally from established charities. They seek to maintain a reasonable balance between charitable activities overseas and in the United Kingdom.'

Sources of information
Accounts; annual report; Charity Commission record.

AKO Foundation

Education, the arts

Norway, England, USA

£8.1 million (2016)

CC number: 1151815

Trustees: Nicolai Tangen; David Woodburn; Henrik Syse; Martin Byman.

Correspondent: David Woodburn, c/o Ako Capital LLP, 61 Conduit Street, London W1S 2GB (tel: 020 7070 2420; email: akofoundation@akocapital.com)

www.akocapital.com/40/ako-foundation

The foundation was established in 2013 by Nicolai Tangen, CEO and founder of AKO Capital LLP. The foundation receives donations from the founder and a share of profit from the company.

The foundation awards grants to charities for the following causes:

- Education
- The arts
- Local projects (North London and Norway)

In addition to charities selected for a grant by the trustees, employees from AKO Capital can also nominate a charity for a grant through the AKO Give Back Initiative. A committee of employees then selects a shortlist of around five projects, from which all employees vote to decide the distribution of grants among these charities.

Financial information
In 2016 the foundation had assets of £44.5 million and an income of £12 million. Grants were made to 16 organisations totalling £8.1 million, and were distributed in the following categories:

The arts	3	£4.7 million
Education	9	£3.2 million
AKO Give Back Initiative	4	£100,000

Beneficiaries included: Kunststiftelse AKO (£4.6 million); University of Pennsylvania (£1.1 million); Center for Human Rights and Democracy (£796,500); Stromme Foundation (£613,000); Maytree (£100,000); Bowel

Disease UK (£40,000); The Freddie Farmer Foundation (£23,000); Anne Frank Trust (£18,000).

Applications

The foundation's 2016 annual accounts state: 'The foundation does not seek applications for grants and will generally not make grants in response to unsolicited applications.'

Sources of information

Accounts; annual report; Charity Commission record; funder's website.

The Alborada Trust

 Medical and veterinary causes, research and education, animal welfare, overseas aid

UK and overseas

£2.28 million (2016)

CC number: 1091660

Trustees: Eva Rausing; David Way; Roland Lerner; Capt. James Nicholson; Robert Goff; Larry Pillard.

Correspondent: Jeremy Richardson, Secretary, Lanwades Stud, Moulton, Newmarket CB8 8QS (tel: 01638 750222; email: secretary@alboradatrust.com)

www.alboradatrust.com

This Alborada Trust was established in October 2001 and is named after the racehorse Alborada. According to the trust's website:

> The trustees' primary aims are the funding of medical and veterinary causes, research and education, welfare of animals, help with relief to disaster areas, such as Nepal and Haiti and at refugee camps. Their aims in these main areas are achieved by the award of ongoing grants to Cambridge University, a number of the leading veterinary schools and to charities such as ActionAid, Alzheimer's Research UK, The Brooke and Médecins Sans Frontières.

Smaller grants are also made available to a wide range of charitable organisations as deemed appropriate by the trustees.

Financial information

In 2016 the trust had assets of £7.5 million and an income of £74,000. The trust awarded grants made to 20 organisations worth a total of £2.28 million.

Beneficiaries included: University of Cambridge (Africa Project) (£400,000); Alzheimer's Trust (£370,000); Médecins Sans Frontières (£237,500); The Brooke Hospital for Animals (£140,000); Home of Horseracing Trust (£125,000); Animal Health Trust (£50,000); Royal Commonwealth Society for the Blind (38,000); East Anglia Air Ambulance (£25,000); Samaritans (£20,000).

Applications

According to the trust's 2016/17 annual report, 'The Trustees' funds are fully committed and unsolicited applications are not requested.'

Sources of information

Accounts; annual report; Charity Commission record.

The Alchemy Foundation

 Disability, social welfare, respite for carers, penal reform, medical research, overseas aid

UK and overseas

£401,000 to organisations (2016/17)

CC number: 292500

Trustees: Dr Jemima Stilgoe; Holly Stilgoe; Jack Stilgoe; Rufus Stilgoe; Richard Stilgoe; Alexander Armitage; Andrew Murison; Annabel Stilgoe; Joseph Stilgoe; Antoun Elias.

Correspondent: Richard Stilgoe, Trustee, Trevereux Manor, Limpsfield Chart, Oxted, Surrey RH8 0TL

The charity was established, as The Starlight Foundation, by a charitable trust deed on 14 August 1985 and is funded from Richard Stilgoe's royalties from American productions of *Starlight Express* and *The Phantom of the Opera*. The name was changed to The Alchemy Foundation on 2 June 1987. The foundation is connected to and shares trustees with The Orpheus Centre Trust, with which it co-operates in pursuit of its charitable objectives.

The 201617 annual report states that the foundation's work focuses on:

- The Alchemist Scheme (funding the costs of fundraisers assigned to other charities to assist with their fundraising efforts)
- Water projects in the developing world
- Disability (particularly mobility, access, helplines and communications)
- Social welfare (inner city community projects, disaffected youth, family mediation, homelessness)
- Personal reform
- Penal reform (work with prisoners, especially young prisoners, and their families)
- Medical research and aid (especially in areas of blindness and disfigurement)
- Individual enterprise (by helping Raleigh International, Project Trust and similar organisations to give opportunities to young people according to need)
- Respite for carers

Financial information

In 2016/17 the foundation held assets of £3.3 million and had an income of £426,500. There were 705 grants made during the year totalling £451,500, of which £401,000 was given to organisations. Donations were broken down as follows:

The Alchemist Scheme including the Orpheus Centre	£205,500
Social welfare – inner city community projects	£81,500
Disability	£68,000
Individuals on behalf of registered charities	£50,500
Other	£25,000
Respite for carers	£11,800
Penal reform and work with prisoners and their families	£7,000
Medical research into blindness and disfigurement	£2,000

A list of beneficiaries was not provided in the accounts.

Exclusions

The foundation does not fund organisations exclusive to one faith or political belief.

Applications

Apply in writing to the correspondent.

Sources of information

Accounts; annual report; Charity Commission record.

The Aldama Foundation

Arts, culture, heritage and science, amateur sport, health, social welfare, environmental protection

UK, overseas

£370,500 (2016/17)

CC number: 1126791

Trustee: The Dickinson Trust Ltd.

Correspondent: Anina Cheng, Swan House, 17–19 Stratford Place, London W1C 1BQ (tel: 020 7907 2100; email: charity@mfs.co.uk)

The foundation was established by James and Clare Kirkman in 2008. Grants are made for arts, culture, heritage and science; amateur sport; health; welfare; environmental protection in the UK and overseas.

Financial information

In 2016/17 the foundation held assets of £6.6 million and had an income of £66,500. Grants awarded to organisations totalled £370,500 and were broken down as follows:

Arts, culture, heritage and science	£201,000
Health and saving lives	£90,500
Welfare	£45,000
Education	£26,000
Amateur sport	£5,000
Other charitable purposes	£2,000
Environmental protection and improvement	£600

Beneficiaries included: National Gallery (£75,000); Liverpool School of Tropical Medicine (£60,000); Feed the Hungry (£40,500); The Fitzwilliam Museum

Development Trust (£40,000); Courtauld Institute of Art (£30,000).

Grants of under £15,000 totalled £125,000.

Applications

Apply in writing to the correspondent.

Sources of information

Accounts; annual report; Charity Commission record.

Al-Fayed Charitable Foundation

 The health, well-being and education of disadvantaged children and young people

 Mainly in the UK, but also worldwide

£ £582,000 (2016)

CC number: 297114

Trustees: Mohamed Al-Fayed; Camilla Fayed; Heini Fayed; Omar Fayed.

Correspondent: Charity Manager, 55 Park Lane, London W1K 1NA (email: acf@alfayed.com)

🌐 www.the-acf.com

🐦 @the_acf

Al-Fayed Charitable Foundation was established in 1987 by Mohamed Al-Fayed, the Egyptian business magnate. It primarily focuses its resources on the health and well-being of children and young people.

The foundation supports a range of specialist children's causes via regular donations and the provision of specialist medical equipment, play and living essentials. It also focuses on raising awareness and support for many children's hospices, hospitals and other children's charities. Examples of causes supported by the foundation are given on the website under five categories, which are: hospices; hospitals; schools; individuals; and international causes. It is further noted that 'the foundation is committed to helping make a difference. As well as financial support and co-ordinating special fundraising events, Mr Al-Fayed and Camilla give their time to meet families and give gifts to the children who attend the causes supported by the foundation'.

Financial information

In 2016 the foundation held assets of £131,500 and had an income of £609,000. Grants were made to over 28 charities during the year totalling £582,000.

Previous beneficiaries have included: Face For Children in Need (£110,000); Lotus Children Centre (£91,000); Zoë's Place (£82,500); Great Ormond Street

Hospital (£60,000); Cancer Research UK (£23,000); World Animal Protection (£11,000); Hippocrates – Health Institute (£6,300); All Terrain Wheelchairs Ltd and Fight For Peace UK (£5,000 each); I Heart Africa (£2,000).

Applications

Applications should be made in writing and sent to the charity manager by email or post. The website advises: 'Remember to include your name, direct contact details, an overview of why you are seeking funding, a breakdown of funds sought, and – if you are sending your application by post, an sae so that we can send you a reply'. Applications are considered on a monthly basis.

Sources of information

Accounts; annual report; Charity Commission record; funder's website.

The All Saints Educational Trust

 Projects that promote the development of education, particularly in the areas of religious education, home economics and related areas or subjects, and multicultural/interfaith education

 UK and overseas

£ £263,000 to organisations (2016/17)

CC number: 312934

Trustees: Diane McCrea; Revd Dr Keith Riglin; David Trillo; Stephen Brooker; Barbara Harvey; Dr Auger Pearce; The Ven. Stephen Welch; Prof. Anthony Leeds; Stephanie Valentine; Frances Smith; Anna Cumbers; Michael Jacob; Dorothy Garland; Revd Tim Elbourne; Derek Holloway; Michael Brackpool.

Correspondent: Mr K. D. Mitchell, Clerk to the Trustees, Knightrider House, 2 Knightrider Court, London EC4V 5AR (tel: 020 7248 8380; email: aset@aset.org.uk)

🌐 www.aset.org.uk

This trust, which is a member of the Association of Church College Trusts, makes grants annually to students and organisations. Its main purposes, which are listed on the website, are to:

- Help increase the number of new teachers with Qualified Teacher Status
- Improve the skills and qualifications of experienced teachers
- Encourage research that can assist teachers in their work
- Support specifically the teaching of religious studies and home economics and related areas (e.g. the promotion of public health and nutrition, both at home and overseas)

The trust provides two types of awards: 'personal' and 'corporate'.

Corporate awards

These grants are made in aid of projects that support religious studies or home economics teaching, or the development of education in schools and in the community. The website states that the trust favours projects 'that have the potential to result in lasting benefit, either through the intrinsic quality of the new ideas being put forward, or through the quantity of teachers and/or pupils who will share in the benefit.'

Grants are normally made to fund time-limited projects (of up to five years) and are not available for core costs or the direct funding of salaries.

More information on awards available from the trust – including on the All Saints Saxton Fellowship and on personal grants to individuals – is available from the website.

Financial information

In 2016/17 the trust held assets totalling £13 million and had an income of £733,500. The trust received 17 applications from organisations and awarded nine grants totalling £263,000. Scholarships and bursaries to individuals totalled £101,000.

Recent examples of beneficiaries of corporate awards, named on the website, include: Sheffield Hallam University (£86,000); RE:ONLINE (£67,000); Bible Reading Fellowship (£60,000); RSA 'Focus on Food' (£55,000); British Nutrition Foundation (£40,000); National Association of Teachers in Home Economics (£30,000); National Society for Promoting Religious Education (£25,000); Design and Technology Association (£20,000); Southwark Cathedral Education Centre (£15,000).

Exclusions

The trust will not support:

- General or core funds of any organisation
- Salaries
- Public appeals
- School buildings, equipment or supplies (except library resources)
- The establishment of new departments in universities and colleges
- General bursary funds of other organisations

Applications

Applicants are invited to discuss their ideas informally with the clerk before making an application. In some cases, a 'link director' is appointed to assist the organisation in preparing the application and who will act in a liaison role with the trust. The trust publicises application deadlines on its website. Completed applications are put before the awards committee in April/May, with final decisions made in June. Application forms are available on the trust's website, either in interactive or printable form.

There is a separate eligibility checker and application process for individuals. Further information can be found on the trust's website.

Sources of information
Accounts; annual report; Charity Commission record; funder's website.

Allchurches Trust Ltd

 Churches, Christian causes, heritage, general charitable purposes

 UK and Ireland

 £13 million (2016)

CC number: 263960

Trustees: Michael Chamberlain; The Rt Revd Nigel Stock; Sir Philip Mawer; Christopher Smith; The Ven. Annette Cooper; Denise Wilson; David Christie; Sir Laurie Magnus; Michael Arlington.

Correspondent: Iain Hearn, Grants Administrator, Beaufort House, Brunswick Road, Gloucester GL1 1JZ (tel: 01452 873184; email: atl@allchurches.co.uk)

 www.allchurches.co.uk

Allchurches Trust Ltd was established in 1972. Its income is derived from its wholly owned subsidiary company Ecclesiastical Insurance Group. Its aims are 'to promote the Christian religion, to contribute to the funds of any charitable institutions, associations, funds or objects and to carry out any charitable purpose'.

Grants policy
Grants are considered in response to appeals from Anglican churches, churches of other denominations and the Christian community. The trust's grants policy, which is available from the website, states that the trust 'supports appeals from churches for building and restoration projects, repair of church fabric, church community initiatives, religious charities, charities preserving the UK heritage and other charitable causes'.

The trust states on its website: 'We particularly welcome applications from less well-off parishes and for projects which benefit mission and help local communities.'

Financial information
In 2016 the trust had assets of £488.2 million and an income of £33.7 million. During the year, the trust gave over £13 million in grants to organisations. Grants were distributed as follows:

Church of England Dioceses	42	£6.4 million
Large Grants, above £6,250	122	£2.6 million
Small Grants, up to £6,250	978	£1.7 million
Special and Flagship Projects	24	£1.2 million
Church of England Cathedrals	45	£1 million
Methodist grant-giving committee grants	21	£132,500

Beneficiaries included: The Yonge Street Mission – Toronto (£300,000); The Representative Body of the Church in Wales (£182,000); The RESOLVE project (£52,000); St Philip's Dorridge and St James' Church, Bentley Heath (£35,000); St Mary's Church, Maidenhead (£20,000); St Mary's Church – Essex (£10,000); Above and Beyond – Bristol (£2,000); Caring for Life – Leeds (£1,000).

Exclusions
The trust is unable to support the following (apart from in exceptional circumstances):

- Charities with political association
- National charities
- Individuals
- Appeals for running costs and salaries
- More than one appeal from the same applicant within a 24-month period

Applications
Applications should be submitted online via the trust's website, where the grants policy and terms and conditions can also be found. The website advises:

To make your application stand out from the crowd follow our tips and advice.

When describing your project make sure it includes:

- The work you want to do
- Who will benefit
- How you will achieve on-going viability

Your applications will catch the attention of our Trustees if:

- It has vision and illustrates enthusiastic support
- It aims to bring improvements in areas of greatest need
- It demonstrates financial sustainability, and how you plan to keep up the good work

Sources of information
Accounts; annual report; Charity Commission record; funder's website.

The Allen & Overy Foundation

 Disaster relief, access to justice, access to education, employment and training

London, Northern Ireland, India, Nepal, Syria, Tanzania, Uganda

£1.5 million (2016/17)

CC number: 1153738

Trustees: Mark Mansell; Andrew Wedderburn-Day; Jane Finlayson-Brown; Jane Townsend; Philip Mansfield; Annelies van der Pauw; Christopher Mainwaring-Taylor.

Correspondent: The Trustees, One Bishops Square, London E1 6AD (tel: 020 3088 0000; email: allenoveryfoundation@allenovery.com)

www.allenovery.com/corporate-responsibility/charitable-giving/Pages/Local-charitable-giving.aspx

Allen & Overy is a large international law firm with its headquarters in London. Its foundation is funded by contributions from all Allen & Overy partners around the world. Around 75% of funds are allocated to support local projects with the remaining 25% being donated to international causes.

The following information about the two grant programmes has been taken from the foundation's website:

Global Grants Programme
The Foundation is funded by contributions from all of A&O's partners worldwide and supports:

- Our global charity partnership
- Disaster relief efforts
- Three or four charities a year through a global grants programme

Grants can be given for up to three years and 20% may be ring-fenced for core costs.

Local Charitable Giving (London)
The Foundation in London is administered by the London Grants Committee, which is made up of partners within the London office and a member of the Pro Bono and Community Investment team. The London Grants Committee makes donations to charities that meet one or more of the following criteria:

- Charities which work to promote access to justice in the UK
- Charities which support and develop projects focusing on issues of education, employment and training based in or benefiting those in Tower Hamlets or Hackney
- Charities to which Allen & Overy volunteers have made a significant contribution by participating in their activities or providing pro bono and volunteering support

The average grant size is £5,000 and may be given for projects or core costs.

Financial information
In 2015/16 the foundation held assets of £599,000 and had an income of £1.6 million. Grants awarded to organisations totalled £1.5 million.

Beneficiaries included: Build Africa (£143,500); Charities Aid Foundation (£100,000); Equal Rights Trust (£25,000); Liberty and the Civil Liberties Trust (£12,000); London Legal Support Trust (£10,000); First Story Ltd (£8,100); Just For Kids Law and Mind (£5,000 each); Action Against Hunger (£1,000).

Applications
The Allen & Overy Foundation (London) – Application forms are available from the correspondent by email. Application guidelines are on the foundation's website, along with the next deadline. The committee meets to consider grants in March and October.

Global Grants Programme – Applications should be made in a letter of no more than two pages – details of what to include are given on the website. Refer to the website for information on when the next round of funding will open.

Sources of information
Accounts; annual report; Charity Commission record; funder's website.

D C R Allen Charitable Trust

🔍 Disadvantaged young people

📍 UK

£ £373,500 (2016/17)

CC number: 277293

Trustees: Julie Frusher; Martin Allen; Colin Allen.

Correspondent: Julie Frusher, Trustee, Estate Office, Edgcote House, Edgcote, Banbury, Oxfordshire OX17 1AG (email: georgia.edwards@edgcote.com)

This trust makes grants for a wide range of charitable purposes but is particularly interested in supporting charities, organisations or projects which help disadvantaged young people. Projects aiming to help young people progress towards a more fulfiling lifestyle are of special interest.

Grant-making policy
Grants may be made to fund capital expenditure as well as operational expenses. Small and medium-sized charities are favoured and well established nationally known charities are less likely to be considered. Grants in 2016/17 were typically in the range of £1,000 to £5,000, but larger grants may

be considered, particularly in respect of specific or innovative capital projects. A high proportion of grants are made to new applicants and such applications continue to be encouraged.

Financial information
In 2016/17 the trust had assets of £5.26 million and an income of £445,500. There were 67 grants made totalling £373,500. The grant total was higher than previous years, due to additional funding received from the settler. Grants were distributed for the following purposes:

Youth projects	£126,000
Hardship alleviation	£93,500
Medical care/treatment	£59,000
Disability	£43,500
Education	£25,000
Community	£13,700
Arts	£8,100
Medical research	£5,000

Previous beneficiaries have included: Centrepoint and NORPIP (£25,000 each); Greenham Community Trust, Designability and Suffolk Young Carers (£10,000 each); Home-Start UK and Demand (£5,000 each); Brainwave (£3,500); Pelton Youth Project (£3,000); Choysez (£2,500).

Exclusions
Individuals; funding of services usually provided by statutory sources; causes outside the UK; evangelical or worship activities; animal welfare; medical research; heritage conservation/preservation; arts or collections.

Applications
Applications should be made by email to Georgia Edwards at the email address listed in the Correspondent section. The trustees normally meet monthly, so decisions can be made fairly promptly.

It is not possible for the trustees to respond to unsuccessful applicants, so if no positive response has been received within eight weeks of the application date, then applicants may assume that they have not been successful.

Sources of information
Accounts; annual report; Charity Commission record; information previously provided by the funder.

The Allen Trust

🔍 Social welfare

📍 Worldwide

£ Around £350,000 (2016/17)

CC number: 1146388

Trustees: Tony Allen; Andreas Triteos.

Correspondent: Tony Allen, Trustee, Oakmead Farm, Ockham Lane, Cobham, Surrey KT11 1LY (tel: 020 8939 3905)

Registered in March 2012, the trust appears to focus mainly on social welfare.

The settlor of the trust, Tony Allen, made his fortune through the A and A Group Ltd insurance broker; he is also the founder of African Revival.

Financial information
In 2016/17 the trust had an income of £7,900 and a total expenditure of £381,500. Due to the trust's low income its accounts were not available to view on the Charity Commission website. We therefore estimate that grants awarded to organisations totalled around £350,000.

Previous beneficiaries have included: African Revival (£29,000); Jubilee Life Ministries (£10,000); Tamama Construction (£5,000); Chairna Christian Institute (£3,500); Diocese of Maridi (£3,500); Church Mission Society Ireland (£2,500); Len Treneary (£2,000).

Applications
Apply in writing to the correspondent.

Sources of information
Charity Commission record.

Alzheimer's Research UK

🔍 Alzheimer's research

📍 UK

£ £12.7 million (2016/17)

CC number: 1077089

Trustees: Shirley Cramer; Rupert Evenett; Prof. James Fawcett; David Mayhew; Michael Cooper; Nicholas Antill; Christopher Carter; Prof. Rob Howard; Giles Dennison; Dr Ruth McKernan.

Correspondent: Lizzie Ashley-Webb, 3 Riverside, Granta Park, Cambridge CB21 6AD (tel: 01223 824581; email: enquiries@alzheimersresearchuk.org)

🌐 www.alzheimersresearchuk.org

 facebook.com/AlzheimersResearchUK

 @ARUKnews

Alzheimer's Research UK funds biomedical research in order to build an understanding of the causes of dementia and to improve diagnosis, prevention and treatment.

The charity's mission is to support research that will improve the lives of people living with dementia now and in years to come. It aims to achieve this objective by focusing on following four goals:

▹ **Understand:** Increasing knowledge and understanding of the diseases that cause dementia

- **Diagnose:** Improving diagnosis of dementia
- **Reduce Risk:** Reducing the risk of developing dementia
- **Treat:** Developing treatments, ensuring they get to patients and ultimately preventing dementia

The charity encourages applications that:

- Address fundamental gaps in knowledge of disease processes
- Have a translational path or vision
- Are collaborative and transparent
- Ensure reagents and data are shared with the scientific community

Funding is directed towards both translating scientific discovery into patient benefit and in growing the research base. A significant proportion of the charity's funding is allocated towards response-mode applications. The charity notes however, that social or carer-focused research falls outside its remit.

At the time of writing (June 2018) the charity offered a total of 19 grants schemes. Full details of all available grant schemes including deadlines, eligibility criteria and application procedures are available on the charity's website.

Financial information

In 2016/17 the charity had assets of £8.5 million and an income of £30.4 million. During the year, the charity awarded research grants worth a total of £12.7 million to 28 organisations.

Beneficiaries included: University of Cambridge (£3 million); University College London (£2.9 million); University of Exeter (£1 million); University of Edinburgh (£178,000); University of Dundee (£75,000); Spanish National Center for Biotechnology (£5,300).

Exclusions

Eligibility criteria vary between grant schemes; specific details are provided in the charity's eligibility document which is available to download via the website.

Applications

Initial applications should be submitted via the website, where full details of the grants approval process and guidelines for each of the charity's grant schemes can be found.

Sources of information

Accounts; annual report; Charity Commission record; funder's website.

Alzheimer's Society

🔍 Research into dementia

📍 UK

💷 £8.6 million (2016/17)

CC number: 296645

Correspondent: Research Team, 43–44 Crutched Friars, London EC3N 2AE (tel: 020 7423 5136; email: grantenquiries@alzheimers.org.uk)

 www.alzheimer's.org.uk

 facebook.com/alzheimerssocietyuk

 @alzheimerssoc

 @alzheimerssoc

The Alzheimer's Society supports people in England, Wales and Northern Ireland affected by any form of dementia, as well as investing in research into dementia and campaigning to improve understanding and influence policy.

Grants programme

The charity funds research across all areas of dementia and has two funding streams: biomedical; and care, services and public health. The information on these two funding streams has been taken from the charity's website:

Biomedical

The scope of research to be considered by this funding stream includes:

- Research that predominantly utilises cellular, animals models of disease or post-mortem brain tissue. For instance, to investigate aetiology or potential therapeutics for dementia
- Research that predominantly utilises genomic, proteomic or other 'omics' approaches
- Research that seeks to discover or validate biomarkers in a research setting, including psychometric tests, to be utilised in diagnosis or monitoring of disease progression
- Translational research that bridges between basic and clinical research
- Early-stage clinical investigations of pharmacological agents, vitamins or other small molecule compounds for the delay, prevention or treatment of dementia or associated behavioural symptoms

Care, services and public health research funding stream

The scope of research to be considered by this funding stream includes:

- Research focused on identifying or modifying novel or established lifestyle risk factors for dementia
- Research that predominantly seeks to understand the burden of dementia at an individual or population level
- Psychological, social or assistive technology interventions focused at improving the care, support or management of people with dementia or those affected by dementia

- Research concerning quality of life of those affected by dementia
- Research to investigate models of service delivery in primary care, care homes and hospitals
- Research into end of life care and delivery
- Evidence synthesis or systematic reviews related to the management of people with dementia

The charity highlights several areas that it would prefer to fund on its website. In 2018 there are two areas that the charity hopes to receive more applications in – real-world utility of biomarkers and drug repurposing.

Financial information

In 2016/17 the charity held assets of £35 million and had an income of £103.6 million. Grants to 56 organisations totalled over £8.6 million.

Previous beneficiaries have included: University College London (£2.25 million); University of Glasgow (£1.8 million); University of Cambridge (£800,000); Queen's University Belfast (£400,000); University of East Anglia (£219,000); Medical Research Council (£75,000); World Dementia Council (£31,000); Cambridge and Peterborough NHSFT (£2,000).

Exclusions

Refer to the website for exclusions from individual funding schemes.

Applications

For information on how to apply to one of Alzheimer's Society's current grant schemes, refer to the website. Funding calls are advertised on the website and applications should be submitted online. All applications that fulfil the eligibility criteria will be scientifically peer reviewed and lay reviewed by Research Network volunteers – a group of over 280 people who care for those with dementia, or who have it themselves. Applications will be shortlisted based on those reviews. Shortlisted fellowship applicants will be invited to interview and all applicants will be given the opportunity to respond to reviewer comments. Applications, reviews, and rebuttals will then be considered by the Grant Advisory Boards and feedback is provided to all applicants.

Comprehensive guidelines for applicants can be downloaded from the website and the charity welcomes contact prior to submitting an application. The charity advises that potential applicants should sign up to its research funding updates newsletter where it advertises new funding calls and opportunities.

Sources of information

Accounts; annual report; Charity Commission record; guidelines for applicants; funder's website.

Amabrill Ltd

 Orthodox Jewish causes

UK, with a preference for the north west of London

£ £2.96 million (2016/17)

CC number: 1078968

Trustees: Charles Lerner; Frances Lerner; Israel Grossnass; Irving Lerner.

Correspondent: Frances Lerner, Trustee, 1 Golders Manor Drive, London NW11 9HU (tel: 020 8455 6785; email: mail@venittandgreaves.com)

The principal activity of this charity is the advancement of education and religious practice in accordance with the teachings of the Orthodox Jewish faith. The charity also supports 'the relief of poverty and suffering experienced by those who believe in the Jewish faith'.

The annual report for 2016/17 explains that:

> Grants are made both for capital purposes, – which can include buildings, equipment and educational material – and towards the general running costs of the grantee institution. Other grants are made for the relief of poverty and these are only made after appropriate certification has been seen. (An independent organisation has been set up in North West London to verify the identity and means of Orthodox Jewish persons for this purpose.)

Financial information

In 2016/17 the charity had assets of £8 million and an income of £5.36 million. Grants were made totalling £2.96 million and were distributed as follows:

Education	£1.03 million
Social welfare	£994,500
Advancement of the Jewish faith	£925,000

Beneficiaries included: The Society of Friends of the Torah (£395,500); Kahal Chassidim Bobov (£226,000); Age Concern Witney (£180,000); Chevras Mo'oz Ladol (£122,200); Yesamach Levav (£112,500) Achisomoch Aid Company Ltd (£88,500); Moreshet Hatorah (£75,600) Emuno Educational Centre (£75,000); Friends of Sanz Institutions (£69,000).

Applications

Apply in writing to the correspondent. The 2016/17 annual report explains:

> Appeal letters are received from, and personal visits made by representatives of Jewish charitable, religious and educational institutions. These requests are then considered by the trustees and grants are made in accordance with the trustees' decisions...All applications receive the fullest and most careful consideration.

Sources of information

Accounts; annual report; Charity Commission record.

Viscount Amory's Charitable Trust

 Social welfare, older people, education, Christian churches

 UK, primarily in Devon

£ £372,000 to organisations (2016/17)

CC number: 204958

Trustees: Sir Ian Heathcoat Amory; Catherine Cavender.

Correspondent: Secretary to the Trustees, The Island, Lowman Green, Tiverton, Devon EX16 4LA (tel: 01884 254899; email: office@vact.org.uk)

 www.vact.org.uk

The trust's annual report 2016/17 states:

> The objectives of the trust are to donate the annual investment income to charitable institutions or other organisations primarily to benefit the inhabitants of the County of Devon; to assist young people, the poor and aged; and to advance education. The trustees invite or respond to applications from a wide variety of charities or groups promoting charitable causes. Their preference is to support smaller groups, mostly in the South West of England, which do not have access to sophisticated fundraising campaigns and on which a relatively small donation may have a significant effect.

Financial information

In 2016/17 the trust had assets of £14.2 million and an income of £424,000. During the year, the trust awarded 205 grants totalling £372,000 broken down as follows:

General	100	£191,000
Educational	91	£147,000
Religious	14	£37,500

Beneficiaries included: Rona Sailing Project (£95,000); Exeter Cathedral (£34,500); Blundell's School (£29,500); Exeter Northcott Theatre (£22,000); Tiverton and Mid-Devon Museum Trust (£9,000); Age UK Mid-Devon (£5,000).

Exclusions

Applications from individuals for grants for the relief of poverty. Applications for grants or short-term loans for individuals' immediate needs or wants.

Note that the trustees do not consider applications from individuals unless as part of an activity sponsored or promoted by an organisation.

Applications

The following information is taken from the trust's website:

The trustees do not issue application forms. Applications should be by letter, not by email, please, and include the following:

- Your contact details including postal and email addresses
- General background information about your appeal
- The nature of the sponsoring or associated organisation
- The total amount you are looking to raise
- How much has been raised to date
- How you propose raising any shortfall
- Any further information you feel would be relevant for the attention of the trustees

Sources of information

Accounts; annual report; Charity Commission record; funder's website.

The AMW Charitable Trust

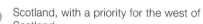 General charitable purposes, young people, music, health and medical charities

Scotland, with a priority for the west of Scotland

£ £204,000 (2016/17)

OSCR number: SC006959

Trustee: The Trustees.

Correspondent: The Trustees, c/o KPMG LLP, 319 St Vincent Street, Glasgow G2 5AS

The trust supports charities in Scotland with a priority given to the west of Scotland. It supports a range of charitable purposes, particularly: young people; music; health and medical charities.

Financial information

In 2016/17 the trust had assets of almost £5.2 million and an income of £199,000. Grants were made to 41 organisations, totalling £204,000.

Beneficiaries included: Glasgow Caledonian University (£10,000); Crohn's and Colitis UK (£8,000); CLIC Sargent Scotland (£6,000); Scottish International Piano Competition (£2,000); Lothian Autistic Society (£1,000).

Exclusions

No grants are given for individuals, or to organisations outside Scotland.

Applications

Apply in writing to the correspondent. The trustees usually meet about twice a year to consider applications. Appeals are not acknowledged and the trust only advises successful applicants.

Sources of information
Accounts; annual report; OSCR record.

The Anchor Foundation

 Christian charities addressing social inclusion, particularly through healing and the arts

UK and occasionally overseas

£204,000 (2016/17)

CC number: 1082485

Trustees: Revd Michael Mitton; Revd Robin Anker-Petersen; Nina Stewart; Sue Mayfield.

Correspondent: The Secretary, PO Box 21107, Alloa FK12 5WA (tel: 0115 950 0055; email: secretary@ theanchorfoundation.org.uk)

 www.theanchorfoundation.org.uk

This foundation was registered with the Charity Commission in September 2000. The foundation's website describes its work as 'supporting Christian charities concerned with social inclusion, particularly through ministries of healing and the arts'.

Grant-making policy
Grants of between £500 and £10,000 in any one year are awarded for projects in the UK and overseas. The trustees favour organisations whose boards demonstrate equal opportunities. Applications are considered for capital and revenue funding. Only in exceptional circumstances will a grant be given for building work. It is not the normal practice of the charity to support the same project for more than three years (projects which have had three consecutive years of funding may apply again two years after the payment of the last grant). Organisations with a number of projects operating are advised to choose a single project for their application.

Financial information
In 2016/17 the foundation had assets of almost £7.8 million and an income of £237,500. Grants totalled £204,000.

Beneficiaries included: Fountain of Life Ministries (£7,500); YMCA Downslink (£6,000); Stirling Baptist Church (£4,000); Christian Solidarity Worldwide (£3,000); Scottish Churches Housing Action (£2,000); DNA Networks (£750).

Exclusions
No grants are awarded to individuals. Building work is only funded in exceptional circumstances.

Applications
An initial application form can be completed online at the Anchor Foundation's website, where full guidelines for applicants are also available. If the trustees decide that they are interested in your application, you will be contacted and asked to send further relevant information such as a project budget and your organisation's annual accounts. Applications are considered at trustees' meetings held twice a year in April and October and need to be received by 31 January and 31 July respectively. Successful applicants will be notified as soon as possible after trustees' meetings – usually before the end of May or the end of November. Unsuccessful applicants may re-apply after 12 months.

Sources of information
Accounts; annual report; Charity Commission record; funder's website.

The Andrew Anderson Trust

 General charitable purposes, Christian activities, education, health, overseas aid

UK and overseas

£860,000 (2016/17)

CC number: 212170

Trustees: Fiona West; Colleen Rosser; Andrew Robertson Anderson; Margaret Anderson; Ann Anderson.

Correspondent: Andrew Anderson, Trustee, 1 Cote House Lane, Bristol BS9 3UW (tel: 0117 962 1588)

This trust is established for general charitable purposes. In the 2016/17 annual report, the trustees stated that: 'As in previous years, the trust has provided financial support for a wide range of charitable causes benefitting the public, with emphasis on religious activities, education/training, medical/ health/sickness and overseas aid/famine relief.'

Financial information
In 2016/17 the trust had assets of £12.69 million and an income of £497,000. Grants awarded to organisations totalled almost £860,000, including a 'special' grant of £500,000 and with a further £159,000 awarded in grants to individuals. A list of beneficiaries was not provided in the accounts and no details could be found relating to the special grant of £500,000.

Previous beneficiaries have included: Aycliffe Evangelical Church, Christian Medical Fellowship, Concern Worldwide, Emmanuel Baptist Church – Sidmouth, Fellowship of Independent Evangelical Churches, Good Shepherd Mission, Kenward Trust, Latin Link, Proclamation Trust, Rehoboth Christian Centre – Blackpool, Scientific Exploration Society, St Ebbe's Parochial Church Council – Oxford, St Helen's Church – Bishopsgate, TNT Ministries, Trinity Baptist Church – Gloucester, Whitefield Christian Trust, Weald Trust and Worldshare.

Applications
Unsolicited applications are not accepted.

Sources of information
Accounts; annual report; Charity Commission record.

Andrews Charitable Trust

 Social welfare, Christian causes

UK and overseas

£330,500 (2016)

CC number: 243509

Trustees: David Westgate; Nicholas Wright; Helen Battrick; Paul Heal; Alastair Page; Elizabeth Hughes; Chris Chapman; Marcus Olliffe; Ami Davis; Alison Kelly; Ruth Knagg; Jon Charlesworth.

Correspondent: Sian Edwards, Director, The Clockhouse, Bath Hill, Keynsham, Bristol BS31 1HL (tel: 0117 946 1834; email: info@andrewscharitabletrust.org. uk)

www.andrewscharitabletrust.org.uk

Established in 1965, the trust is funded by dividends from Andrews and Partners, a group of companies with activities including estate agents, letting agents, property management and financial services.

According to the trust's 2016 annual report, the objects of the trust are:

▶ The advancement of the Christian religion including the declaration of eternal life
▶ The relief of sickness, poverty and distress in any part of the world as an expression of Christian love

The trust has three funding programmes:

Early Stages Ventures - ACT searches out and receives proposals from young social venture organisations with innovative ideas to tackle issues of sickness, poverty and distress. It provides seed corn funding during the early stages of setting up a new organisation, as the vehicle for change.

Christian Innovation Grants – small grants are provided to Christian individuals and organisations for promoting and sharing the Christian faith and providing practical help for disadvantaged and marginalised people within communities, as a demonstration of the Christian faith and principles.

Establish grants - the initiative, to be known initially as [establish] will see ACT as the principal shareholder of Andrews Property Group, working in collaboration with the business. It is designed to combine the resources and charity support skills of ACT with the professional knowledge and expertise of the property business to give young people a roof over their heads and support in finding work or training. The aim is for 50 properties to be purchased across the entire footprint of our estate agency branch network over the next 50 years, or sooner if funding allows. Each house will hopefully provide accommodation for 3 to 4 young people on their transition into work.

Financial information
In 2016 the trust had assets of almost £15 million and had an income of £2 million. During the year, the trust gave around £330,500 in grants to organisations. Grants were distributed as follows:

Dementia	£102,000
Jobs for ex-offenders	£70,000
Relief of poverty	£55,000
Education	£50,000
Christian	£28,500
Ending violence against women	£25,000

Beneficiaries included: Dementia Adventure (£102,000); The Together Group (£70,000); 2nd Chance (£50,000); Ekklesia (£34,500).

Applications
The trust only accepts applications for its Christian Innovation Grants programme which provides small grants to Christian organisations that promote the Christian faith and provide practical help for disadvantaged and marginalised people within communities. Applications to this programme can be made online.

Sources of information
Accounts; annual report; Charity Commission record; funder's website.

Anglo American Group Foundation

 Community development, education and training, environment, health (particularly HIV/AIDS) and social welfare, international development

UK (London) and overseas (including Brazil, Chile, Colombia, Peru, China, India, Mozambique and Zimbabwe)

£498,000 (2016)

CC number: 1111719

Trustees: Duncan Wanblad; Jon Samuel.

Correspondent: Laura Dunne, Anglo American plc, 20 Carlton House Terrace, London SW1Y 5AN (tel: 020 7968 8888; email: aagf@angloamerican.com)

www. angloamericangroupfoundation. org

The foundation was established in 2005 by Anglo American plc, a multinational mining company. The foundation's website states that: 'Anglo American seeks to ensure that its impacts contribute to sustainable livelihoods in the communities in which it operates and the foundation was founded on the same principles'.

The foundation receives donations from, but is independent of, the Anglo American group of companies and supports development initiatives in the areas where the company has operations, projects or representative offices. These include: UK (London, in the City of Westminster, Southwark and Lambeth); Brazil; Chile; Colombia; Peru; China; India; Mozambique; and Zimbabwe.

Grant-making policy
As explained on its website, the foundation 'prefers to fund specific projects or components of projects within the overall activities of an organisation that are a priority area in need of support' and that 'have clearly defined objectives with quantifiable outcomes'. The main objective is to promote sustainable livelihoods.

The foundation tends to provide funding to a selected range of projects on a sustained basis. Applications are welcomed from charitable organisations associated with the following areas:

- Education and training
- Environment
- HIV/AIDS and welfare
- International development
- Community development (in London)

The foundation also distributes funding by matching funds raised for charities by employees in the Anglo American London and Luxembourg offices.

Financial information
In 2016 the foundation had assets of £50,000 and an income of £2.3 million. In total the foundation awarded grants of £498,000.

Beneficiaries included: Technoserve (£440,000); Rockwatch (£48,000).

A full list of beneficiaries was not given in the accounts; however, further case studies are provided on the foundation's website.

Exclusions
The foundation only funds registered charities and does not support:

- Animal charities
- Armed forces charities
- Community interest companies (CICs)
- Educational fees

- Expeditions overseas
- General health charities
- Hospital trusts
- Individuals
- Music festivals and choirs
- Political or quasi-political bodies
- Religious organisations (other than community outreach)
- Trade unions

Support is not provided for projects in South Africa, where funding is handled by the Anglo American Chair's Fund.

Applications
Apply in writing to the correspondent. The trustees meet quarterly.

Sources of information
Accounts; annual report; Charity Commission record; funder's website.

Anguish's Educational Foundation

Education and training for young people

Norwich and the parishes of Costessey, Hellesdon, Catton, Sprowston, Thorpe-next-Norwich and Corpusty

£241,000 to organisations (2016/17)

CC number: 311288

Trustees: David Fullman; Brenda Ferris; Geoffrey Loades; Philip Blanchflower; Dr Iain Brooksby; Jeanne Southgate; Heather Tyrrell; Peter Shields; Michael Flynn; Lesley Grahame; Christine Herries; Cllr Karen Davis; Cllr Marion Maxwell.

Correspondent: Jean Browne, Lead Grants Officer, Norwich Charitable Trusts, 1 Woolgate Court, St Benedicts Street, Norwich NR2 4AP (tel: 01603 621023; email: info@ norwichcharitabletrusts.org.uk)

 www.norwichcharitabletrusts.org.uk

The foundation is named after Thomas Anguish, who lived between 1536 and 1617 and was a merchant of the City of Norwich and Mayor. He left money in his will to set up the foundation in 1611. The foundation is now administered alongside Norwich Consolidated Charities, the Norwich Town Close Estate Charity and the Marion Road Centre Trust. Collectively, they are informally known as the Norwich Charitable Trusts.

Grants are predominantly available for individuals in the beneficial area, to cover the costs of school uniforms, trips, extracurricular activities and school or university fees. Grants are also available for local organisations working with disadvantaged children in order to improve their educational attainment.

Examples of successfully funded projects include equipment for a theatre show, funding for summer programmes, support services and the training of staff. Salaries and core costs can be funded and applications are accepted from registered charities, schools and community interest companies.

Financial information

In 2016/17 the foundation held assets of over £24 million and had an income of £908,500. During the year, £669,000 was given in grants, the majority of which was awarded to individuals. Grants were made to 13 organisations and totalled £241,000.

Previous beneficiaries have included:

The Garage Trust (£53,000 in two grants); Bowthorpe Children's Centre, Clover Hill Primary School, The Clare School (£30,000 each); Parkside Community Trust (£20,000); Into Opera (£18,000); Family Matters Norfolk CIC (£15,000); St Edmunds Society (£14,000 in two grants); Assist Trust (£10,000); Eating Matters and Greener Growth (£5,000 each); The Chermond Trust (£860).

Applications

Apply in writing to the correspondent.

Sources of information

Accounts; annual report; Charity Commission record; funder's website.

The Annandale Charitable Trust

General charitable purposes

UK

£417,000 (2016/17)

CC number: 1049193

Trustees: Carole Duggan; HSBC Trust Company (UK) Ltd.

Correspondent: The Trustees, HSBC Trust Company (UK) Ltd, Second Floor, 1 The Forum, Parkway, Whiteley, Fareham PO15 7PA

This trust has general charitable purposes and supports a range of UK charities.

Financial information

In 2016/17 the trust had assets of £13.86 million and an income of £427,000. During the year, 101 grants totalling £417,000 were awarded to organisations.

Beneficiaries included: British Heart Foundation (£14,200); Redwings Horse Sanctuary (£7,900); Independent Age (£7,300); Marie Curie Cancer Care, Tommy's Baby Charity and Victim Support (£7,000 each); St Barnabas Hospice (£2,200).

Applications

The trustees have previously stated that they have an ongoing programme of funding for specific charities and all funds are fully committed.

Sources of information

Accounts; annual report; Charity Commission record.

Anne Duchess of Westminster's Charity

Equestrian welfare, horse and racing-related charities, accommodation and housing, religious activities, education and training, medical research, health and sickness, disability, economic and community, development and employment, environment, conservation and heritage, military welfare

UK, with preference for Cheshire and the Highlands

£270,500 (2016/17)

CC number: 245177

Trustees: Timothy Marshall; Sir Michael Ridley; Andrew Clowes; Mark Ridley; John Wilson; Richard Henniker-Wilson; Annabel James; Lady Clare Daresbury.

Correspondent: Kate Williams, Charity Manager, Eaton Estate Office, Eaton Park, Eccleston, Chester CH4 9ET (tel: 01244 684433; email: enquiries@adwc.org.uk)

www.adwc.org.uk

Anne Duchess of Westminster set up this charity bearing her name in 1965 and on her death in 2003 the charity was the principle beneficiary of her will. The charity's website states that: 'the majority of the grants made by the charity have been made since this date and exceed £3 million'.

The following information is taken from the charity's website:

The Trustees of the Charity aim to assist charities with objectives that reflect Anne Duchess' own interests and causes located in areas in the UK in which she lived: Cheshire and its surrounding areas (including the Wirral, Merseyside and North Wales) and the Highlands of Scotland in addition to military charities (in recognition of Anne Duchess' wartime service in the FANY and her family's military connections).

Anne Duchess had a lifelong interest in riding and horses and she became well known as the owner of the great steeplechaser Arkle. Her connections to racing continue with her Charity's support of many horse and racing-related charities and the Charity's Race Day. However, donations to non-equine related charities form a large and important part of what the charity does.

Grants are made to registered charities and community interest companies benefitting people in Cheshire and surrounding areas and the Highlands of Scotland, with the exception of military welfare charities. The charity prefers to support small/medium-sized charities rather than national charities (although applications from relevant local branch may be considered). Grants are given on a one-off basis (up to £10,000, including start-up and running costs) or made over one to three years (up to £15,000). The charity also has the capacity to make a few 'major' grants at the trustees' discretion.

Financial information

In 2016/17 the charity held assets of £7.4 million and an income of £140,000. Grants totalling £270,500 were made, distributed as follows:

Economic and community development and employment	£87,500	21	32.3%
Medical research and health	£64,000	13	23.7%
Disability	£60,000	24	22.1%
Military welfare	£37,500	5	13.9%
Accommodation and housing	£7,500	2	2.8%
Environment, conservation and heritage	£5,000	1	1.0%
Education and training	£3,500	3	1.3%
Religious activities	£3,500	2	1.3%
Animal welfare	£2,000	1	0.7%
Total	**£270,500**	**72**	**100%**

Approximately 73% of the grants were distributed in the Cheshire, North Wales, Merseyside and Liverpool areas; 9% in the Highland Region and 18% elsewhere.

Beneficiaries included: Dementia UK and Wirral Youth Zone (£25,000 each); Missing People (£7,500); Combat Stress, National Horseracing Museum and St Luke's Hospice – Cheshire (£5,000 each); Highlands Small Communities Housing Trust (£2,500); Straight Talking (£1,500); Cheshire Furniture Reuse and Deafblind Scotland (£1,000 each); See Communications CIC (£750); Woodlands Community Centre (£500).

Exclusions

The charity does not fund:

- General appeals or letters requesting donations
- Organisation that do not have charitable aims
- Overtly political projects
- Individuals (or organisations applying on behalf of an individual)
- Student fees/bursaries
- Projects taking place or benefitting people outside the UK
- Projects/work benefitting people outside the specific geographical criteria unless they relate to military welfare

◗ Organisations that have applied unsuccessfully within the previous 12 months

◗ Organisations which have been awarded a grant within the previous two years

◗ Grant applications seeking the entire costs of a project (the charity will not be a sole funder)

Applications

At the time of writing (June 2018) the charity's website notes the following:

> During 2018 we are conducting a strategic review of our grant-making programmes and therefore our grants programme is suspended until 1st November 2018. During this period we will not be able to accept or consider any applications.
>
> Please check this page for updates, the launch of the new funding strategy and revised online application form.

Sources of information

Accounts; annual report; Charity Commission Record; funder's website.

The Anson Charitable Trust

 General charitable purposes

 UK, with a preference for Buckinghamshire

£ £732,000 (2016/17)

CC number: 1111010

Trustees: George Anson; Kirsty Anson; Lady Sarah Pauncefort-Duncombe.

Correspondent: George Anson, Trustee, The Lilies, High Street, Weedon, Aylesbury HP22 4NS (tel: 01296 640331; email: ansonctrust@btinternet.com)

The trust was set up in 2005. It supports general charitable purposes, although there appears to be a preference for work with children and older people, conservation and heritage projects and health and medical research.

Financial information

In 2016/17 the trust held assets of £558,500 and had an income of £187,500. During the year, it made 327 grants totalling £732,000. Some organisations received more than one grant.

Beneficiaries included: MK Gallery (£250,000); Asthma UK (£10,000); ABF The Soldier's Charity (£5,000); Listening Books (£3,000); Send A Cow (£2,000); Child Bereavement UK, RNLI, Shelter for Homeless and The Organic Research Centre (£1,000 each); Clean Rivers Trust (£500); Buckinghamshire Historic Churches Trust (£100); RHS (£50).

Applications

Apply in writing to the correspondent.

Sources of information

Accounts; annual report; Charity Commission record.

The Apax Foundation

 Social entrepreneurship, relief of poverty, education

♀ UK and overseas, with a focus on disadvantaged communities

£ £1.16 million (2016/17)

CC number: 1112845

Trustees: Sir Ronald Cohen; Peter Englander; Rohan Haldea; Simon Cresswell; David Marks; John Megrue; Shashank Singh; Mitch Truwit; Jason Wright.

Correspondent: Kate Albert, Apax Partners, 33 Jermyn Street, London SW1Y 6DN (email: apax.foundation@apax.com)

 www.apax.com/responsibility/apax-foundation

The Apax Foundation is the corporate charity for Apax Partners LLP. The foundation channels the firm's charitable giving and receives a percentage of the firm's profits and carried interest.

The following is taken from the foundation's annual report:

> The charity's objects are:
>
> ◗ the relief of financial hardship, either generally or individually, of people living in socially and economically deprived areas in the UK and overseas through the provision of grants, goods or services
>
> ◗ the advancement of education
>
> ◗ to further such other purposes which are charitable in accordance with the law of England and Wales as the trustees think fit

According to the foundation's website, its main focus is social entrepreneurship:

> Social entrepreneurship is the main focus of the Apax Foundation's charitable giving. We support a range of charities, large and small, working to help people in deprived communities to lift themselves out of poverty through enterprise. The Apax Foundation has made total cumulative donations of £3 million to charities working in this field.
>
> Social entrepreneurship was chosen as the focus for the Apax Foundation's major grant giving as it is the natural extension of what Apax does commercially and builds on the firm's history of support in that area, most notably as one of the founders of Bridges Ventures. It is also an area where some of the Foundation's Trustees have significant experience. This provides us with a steady flow of introductions to leading charities in the field, both from within the firm and from our wider network.

The foundation tends to make a small number of larger donations, and a larger number of grants of £10,000 or less.

As well as making grants, the foundation also runs a matched giving scheme for Apax employees fundraising for charitable causes.

Financial information

In 2016/17 the foundation had assets of £25.8 million and an income of £1.8 million. Grants were made totalling almost £1.16 million and were distributed as follows:

Social enterprise and relief of hardship	£470,000
Other charitable purposes	£436,500
Education	£256,00

Beneficiaries included: Opportunity Network (£291,000); Impetus – The Private Equity Foundation (£215,000); Mosaic (£87,000); Grameen America (£74,000); StreetSquash (£20,500); Aga Khan Foundation (£20,000); Pilotlight (£10,800).

Donations of £10,000 or less totalled £215,500.

Applications

Apply in writing to the correspondent. The following information is provided in the foundation's 2016/17 accounts:

> To ensure that the Charity reaches out as widely as possible in fulfilment of its objectives, the Apax Foundation's grant application process is open to all charities operating in all countries. The sole restriction is that the work of those organisations must be focused in the Charity's primary fields of education or the relief of poverty through the stimulation of entrepreneurship.
>
> The Apax Foundation's Trustees review grant applications received from all charities which meet these criteria and grants are awarded on the basis of the Trustees' evaluation of: the charity's effectiveness in achieving its aims, the number of beneficiaries reached, the sustainability of the charity's programmes, the strength and stability of its management team and internal processes, and the long-term public benefits that would flow from the deployment of a grant from the Apex Foundation.

Any further enquiries can be directed to Kate Albert, the foundation's manager by email: apax.foundation@apax.com.

Sources of information

Accounts; annual report; Charity Commission record; funder's website.

The John Apthorp Charity

 Education, social welfare

 Hertfordshire, Bedfordshire and Buckinghamshire

(£) £408,000 (2016)

CC number: 1102472

Trustees: John Apthorp; Duncan Apthorp; Justin Apthorp; Kate Arnold.

Correspondent: Jenny Dunford, 29 Newlands Avenue, Radlett, Hertfordshire WD7 8 EJ (email: johnapthorpcharity@hotmail.com)

🌐 www.johnapthorpcharity.org

This is the charity of John Apthorp CBE, OBE who founded the frozen food chain Bejam (which he later sold to Iceland) and co-founded Wizard Wine which became Majestic Wine. Established in 2004, the objects of the charity are 'the advancement of education, the advancement of religion and the relief of poverty and suffering'. In 2010 the charity received a donation to the value of £4.3 million from the Milly Apthorp Charitable Trust (John's mother) which greatly increased the grant-making capacity of this charity. In 2012 the charity also received new assets of £29,000 upon the closure of John Apthorp Charitable Trust (Charity Commission no. 289713).

Grant-making policy

Only registered charities can apply. The grant needs to be used for the benefit of residents of Hertfordshire, Bedfordshire and Buckinghamshire in England. National charities can apply but projects must be for the specific beneficial area. Grants will usually be given for one-off capital expenditure such as equipment or vehicles, but the charity will also consider pilot projects. Unless applicants can demonstrate an exceptional need, the charity is unlikely to fund organisations which have received funding from the charity in past two years. The charity occasionally makes a small number of grants to individuals.

Financial information

In 2016 the charity held assets of £12.07 million and had an income of £483,000. Grants were made to 33 organisations during the year totalling £408,000.

Beneficiaries included: St Albans Museums and Galleries Trust (£75,000); RAFT (£50,000); Home-Start Watford, Isabel Hospice (£20,000 each); Queen Elizabeth Scholarship Trust (£18,000); St Mary's Watford (£15,000); Friends United Network, Henderson Hub Company (£10,000 each); Tall Ships

Trust (£1,500); Herts Inclusive Theatre (£500).

Exclusions

The following will not be funded:

- Charities that have large unrestricted reserves
- Salaries and core costs
- Ongoing costs

Applications

Given the range of projects supported there is no standard application form. Instead applicants are asked to contact the charity by email, providing the following information:

- Charity number
- An overview of the project
- Any time constraints on the project
- Amount requested including a detailed breakdown
- Amount raised so far (if any)
- The total cost of the project
- Beneficiaries of the project
- To whom a cheque should be made payable if successful
- Supporting documents

Applications are considered at trustee meetings which are held every three to four months.

Sources of information

Accounts; annual report; Charity Commission record, funder's website.

The Architectural Heritage Fund

 Heritage

 UK (excluding the Channel Islands and the Isle of Man)

(£) £1.1 million (2016/17)

CC number: 266780

Trustees: John Duggan; Kate Dickson; Myra Barnes; Richard Keen; Liz Peace; David Hunter; Suzanne Snowden; Susan Brown; Adebayo Alao; Karen Latimer; Eleanor Hunter.

Correspondent: Regional Project Support Officers, 3 Spital Yard, Spitalfields, London E1 6AQ (tel: 020 7925 0199; email: ahf@ahfund.org.uk)

 www.ahfund.org.uk

 facebook.com/archhfund

 @ArchHFund

The Architectural Heritage Fund promotes the conservation and sustainable re-use of historic buildings across the UK. The fund offers loans, grants and advice to projects that can bring social and economic benefits to communities that need them the most.

Eligibility

The fund makes grants and loans to charitable organisations to help find sustainable uses for historic buildings. The website states that grants are given for constituted charities or social enterprises, although unincorporated organisations may be considered for Project Viability Grants.

Grants

Grants can be awarded to assess the viability of a project or to help fund development costs. The following information on the four grants programmes run by the fund is taken from the website:

Project Viability Grant
Maximum £5,000

Project Viability Grants (PVG) are to fund studies to look at potential uses for a building and at its current condition, and produce a Viability Report to a standard template. Successful completion of this will be used to judge whether applicants can then apply for the AHF's Project Development Grant funding, and can be used to secure further funding elsewhere.

Project Development Grant
Maximum £25,000

The Project Development Grant (PDG) scheme is intended to assist an organisation to cover some of the costs of developing and co-ordinating a project and taking it towards the start of work on site.

To qualify, an organisation must have established that the end use of the project is likely to be viable and have decided to take the project forward.

Scottish Community Development Grant
Maximum £50,000

In Scotland, thanks to additional funding from Historic Environment Scotland, projects that are community-led are eligible to apply to the new Community Development Support Grant for up to £50,000 per project.

Cywaith Legacy Fund
Maximum £30,000

In Wales, thanks to an asset transfer from Cywaith: Gwynedd Buildings Preservation Trust this fund is open to community-led organisations operating in Gwynedd, Anglesey and Conwy to find sustainable new uses for historic buildings. We will prioritise projects which will make a significant social impact. Grants of up to £5,000 are available and up to £25,000 in exceptional circumstances. Organisations which are interested in this fund should contact the Support Officer for Wales prior to submitting an application.

Full guidance notes for each programme are provided on the fund's website.

Loans

The fund also provides loans for charitable organisations to acquire or restore a building, as well as social investment into relevant enterprises. Further information is given on the website.

The AHF also produces The Heritage Funding Directory, in partnership with The Heritage Alliance: www. heritagefundingdirectoryuk.org.

Financial information
In 2016/17 the fund had assets of £14.1 million and an income of £1.9 million. A total of 120 grants were offered, amounting to £1.19 million. Of this, a number of grants were withdrawn. The resulting total of 99 grants charged was £1.1 million, distributed as follows:

Project development	42	£926,500
Project viability	57	£182,000

The fund also made new loans totalling £1.85 million and loan extensions totalling £590,000 during the year.

Beneficiaries included: Scottish Veterans' Garden City Association (£69,000); David Livingstone Trust (£25,000); Govan Workspace Ltd (£10,000); Ridge Foundation CIC (£5,000); Wiveliscombe Town Hall Trust (£2,900).

Exclusions
According to the fund's guidelines, grants are not given to:
- Private individuals
- Local authorities and other public sector bodies (except in cases outlined in 4.8 above)
- Universities, colleges and other mainstream educational institutions including independent schools
- For-profit companies, unless in a partnership led by a not-for-profit organisation
- Unincorporated organisations (e.g. charitable trusts and associations) that are not intending to incorporate
- Organisations established primarily for the benefit of their members (e.g. co-operative societies)
- Organisations with fewer than three Trustees or Directors who are not spouses or partners or otherwise related to each other
- Ltd liability partnerships
- Churches or other places of worship, where the building will remain in use primarily as a place of religious worship – defined as hosting more than six religious services per year and therefore qualifying for VAT relief
- Projects that mainly involve enhancing or facilitating existing uses within a building. Work intended to test and develop new uses for disused or derelict parts of a partly occupied building is eligible, however
- Capital costs (such as building repairs, installation of services, landscaping, access improvements or heritage interpretation displays)
- Retrospective costs (i.e. the cost of work or activities that will take place prior to us notifying you of our decision on your application)

Applications
Applications can be made via the fund's website. For advice on a project, contact your relevant regional support officer, the contact details of whom are provided on the fund's website.

Sources of information
Accounts; annual report; Charity Commission record; funder's website.

Ardbarron Trust Ltd

 Awareness and understanding of the Christian gospel, social welfare, health care, literacy

Worldwide, with a preference for the UK

£3.4 million (2016)

CC number: NIC101111

Trustees: Martin Agnew; Geoffrey Agnew; John Agnew; Malcolm Johnston.

Correspondent: John Agnew, Trustee, PO Box 49, Hightown Avenue, Newtownabbey, County Antrim BT36 4RT (tel: 028 9034 2733)

The trust makes grants for social welfare, the advancement of religion and health care worldwide with a preference for the UK. The trust received all of its income from the Henderson group of companies which includes Henderson Wholesale Ltd and Henderson Retail Ltd.

Financial information
In 2016 the trust held assets of £120.8 million and had an income of £3.4 million. Grants to 269 organisations totalled £3.4 million and were broken down as follows:

Advancement of religion	£2.1 million
Social welfare	£512,000
Health care	£501,00

Beneficiaries included: J33 Trust (£341,000); Echoes of Service (£230,000); Christian Missionary Charitable Trust (£208,000); Sandes Soldiers Home (£93,000); Crescent Church (£71,000).

Applications
Apply in writing to the correspondent.

Sources of information
Accounts; annual report; Charity Commission for Northern Ireland record.

The Ardeola Charitable Trust

 General charitable purposes

UK

£476,000 (2016/17)

CC number: 1124380

Trustees: Graham Barker; Joanna Barker; William Hiscocks; Prof. John Cornwall; Coutts & Co.

Correspondent: The Trustees, Coutts & Co., Trustee Department, 6th Floor, Trinity Quay 2, Avon Street, Bristol BS2 0PT (tel: 020 7663 6825; email: couttscharities@coutts.com)

This trust was established in 2008 for general charitable purposes. The main beneficiary each year is Target Ovarian Cancer.

Financial information
In 2016/17 the trust had assets of £7.5 million and an income of almost £806,500. Grants were made to nine organisations during the year totalling £476,000.

Beneficiaries included: Target Ovarian Cancer (£300,000); St Francis Hospital (£75,000); Royal National Theatre (£60,500); University of Oxford – Ashmolean (£26,000); British Library (£5,000); British Museum (£3,000).

Applications
Apply in writing to the correspondent, although potential applicants should note that the trust's main beneficiary is connected with the trustees.

Sources of information
Accounts; annual report; Charity Commission record.

The John Armitage Charitable Trust

 General charitable purposes, medical causes, arts and culture, social welfare, education, young and older people, religion

England and Wales

£1.97 million (2016/17)

CC number: 1079688

Trustees: John Armitage; Catherine Armitage; William Francklin; Celina Francklin.

Correspondent: John Armitage, Trustee, c/o Sampson West, 12–14 Mitre House, London EC3A 5BU

Established in 2000, this is the trust of John Armitage, co-founder of Egerton Capital, the City-based hedge fund. The 2016/17 annual report states that the current priorities for the trust are the following: disadvantaged children and youth support, including parenting support; education; medical care; arts and culture; prisoners and young offenders; and religious organisations.

Financial information
In 2016/17 the trust held assets of £72.8 million and had an income of £2.07 million

Grants were made to 71 organisations totalling £1.97 million. Grants were distributed as follows:

Youth support	14	£439,000
Other	14	£322,000
Museum and arts	14	£207,500
Parenting support	7	£215,000
Education	6	£208,000
Medical research/care	6	£193,000
Religion	6	£180,000
Support for former offenders	4	£178,000

Previous beneficiaries have included:
Greenhouse Schools, Policy Exchange and Westminster Abbey Foundation (£100,000 each); Winston Churchill Memorial Trust (£50,000); Independence at Home (£36,000); Bibury with Winson Parish County Council (£25,000); Wicken Parish County Council (£15,000).

Exclusions

The trust does not generally provide funding for long-term capital projects, although exceptionally the trustees may support suitable projects.

Applications

This grant-maker no longer accepts unsolicited applications and Sampson West have been instructed to return to sender any future applications received.

Sources of information

Accounts; annual report; Charity Commission record.

The Armourers' and Brasiers' Gauntlet Trust

 Materials science, general charitable purposes

 UK, with some preference for London

£ £336,000 (2016/17)

CC number: 279204

Trustees: Prof. William Bonfield; David Davies; Anthony Pontifex; Anthony Beare; Christopher Weston-Simons; Michael Goulette.

Correspondent: Anne-Marie Clift, Charity & Partnership Manager, Armourers' Hall, 81 Coleman Street, London EC2R 5BJ (tel: 020 7374 4000; email: charities@armourershall.co.uk)

🌐 www.armourershall.co.uk/funding-grants

🐦 @armourerbrasier

The charity, which acts as the charitable arm for the Worshipful Company of Armourers and Brasiers, was set up in 1979. The trust supports the following:

▪ Science education in schools
▪ Research in materials science – especially projects that closely align with the ancient craft of working with metals and materials

One-off grants of between £500 to £1,500 are available for registered small charities whose work can be categorised as follows:

▪ Community development and the armed forces
▪ Children, young people and general education
▪ Health and medical charities
▪ The arts, particularly arms or armour
▪ Christian mission or human rights

Applicants should:

▪ Be charities registered in the UK (with the Charity Commission of England Wales, the Scottish Charity Regulator or the Charity Commission for Northern Ireland)
▪ Be operating either nationally throughout the UK or in London (defined as within the M25)
▪ Have had income below £500,000 in the last financial year for which full accounts are available

Grants to support science education in schools are for projects that encourage students to take up scientific careers, particularly in materials science. Primary schools can receive £600 and secondary schools can receive £1,000.

The trust also funds schemes for materials science students with a number of companies, including Rolls Royce plc and Tata Steel plc. PhD or EngD students can apply for travel grants to present their research at academic conferences and undergraduate students can apply for help with the cost of industrial placements.

Financial information

In 2016/17 the trust held assets of almost £8 million and had an income of £480,500. Grants awarded to organisations totalled £336,000. During the year, the trust awarded 139 grants totalling £70,000 to individuals.

Previous beneficiaries have included:
Daylight Christian Prison Trust and Fields of Battle 14–18 (£1,000 each); St Mary-le-Bow Young Homeless Project and The Young Urban Arts Foundation (£750 each); Crackerjacks Children's Trust (£630); Anorexia and Bulimia Care, Braille Chess Association, London Wheelchair Rugby Club and Shepherds Bush Families Project (£500 each).

Exclusions

The following information is taken from the trust's website:

Applicants **should not**:

▪ Have received a grant from the Armourers and Brasiers Gauntlet Trust in the previous year ending 31st March as we do not give recurrent grants
▪ Be applying for general maintenance, repair or restoration of buildings
▪ Be applying for sponsorship as individuals

▪ Be applying for the benefit of an individual
▪ Be applying for charities or projects outside the UK

Applications

Applications should be completed online using the form on the trust's website. You will be asked some questions to verify your eligibility before you can access the full form. As part of the application process you will be asked to upload your most recent financial statements. If you are a new charity and do not yet have audited accounts, you should upload your budget and/or business plan for the year. The trustees meet three times a year in February, May and September (application deadlines are posted on the website).

Sources of information

Accounts; annual report; Charity Commission record; funder's website.

The Arsenal Foundation Ltd

 Education, sport, health and medical causes, disability, social welfare

📍 Islington, Camden, Hackney, Barnet, Walthamstow and Hertsmere

£ £1.2 million (2016/17)

CC number: 1145668

Correspondent: Svenja Geissmar, Trustee, Highbury House, 75 Drayton Park, London N5 1BU (email: thearsenalfoundation@arsenal.co.uk)

🌐 www.arsenal.com/thearsenalfoundation

The Arsenal Foundation was established in 2012 as a grant-giving organisation with the mission to help young people in North London and around the world fulfil their potential.

Guidelines

The following information was taken from the foundation's website:

Priority is given to the following areas of need:

▪ Education (including academic, social, physical education and skills training)
▪ Sports capable of improving health
▪ Medical
▪ Sickness and the relief of suffering
▪ Disability
▪ Poverty
▪ Individual misfortune

The following is a non-exhaustive list of potential beneficiaries or groups of beneficiaries:

▪ Organisations connected to Arsenal FC
▪ Charity or community projects connected to Arsenal FC
▪ Projects that have been developed by Arsenal FC's community team
▪ Staff-initiated projects
▪ Supporter-initiated projects

- Projects where The Foundation's donation, even though relatively small, will make a difference
- Projects where the gesture of support from a charity associated with Arsenal FC can have a greater effect than the money itself
- Football-linked campaigns or public bodies
- Projects where the person requesting a donation is doing something active to raise money for the cause
- Projects where the person is playing a significant and voluntary role in raising money for the charity
- Awards to reward success or achievement in areas of endeavour that fall within the objectives of The Foundation
- Where funds are donated to The Foundation for a specific project or purpose and The Foundation acts as a partner and makes an additional contribution

The Gunners Fund
The aim of The Gunners Fund is to support charities in the boroughs of Islington, Camden and Hackney by offering smaller grants of up to £2,500 that can make a big difference to the community. The priorities and objectives of the fund are the same as those of the foundation.

Financial information
In 2016/17 the foundation held assets of £1.7 million and had an income of £1.9 million. Grants awarded to organisations totalled £1.2 million and were broken down as follows:

Save the Children	£565,500
Other grants	£452,500
Local pitch projects	£88,000
Manchester Emergency Appeal	£50,000
Willow	£50,000
Islington Giving	£1,800

Exclusions
UK-based charities only.

Applications
Application forms are available to download from the foundation's website, along with grant-making guidelines. The foundation states that it is unable to respond to all of the applications it receives, due to the high volume, so if you do not receive a response within one month, you should assume that you have been unsuccessful.

Sources of information
Accounts; annual report; Charity Commission record; funder's website.

Arthritis Research UK

Research into arthritis and related musculoskeletal diseases

UK

£20 million (2016/17)

CC number: 207711

Trustees: Prof. David Isenberg; Phillip Gray; Dr Sylvie Jackson; Tom Hayhoe; Prof. Jonathan Cohen; Dr Rodger Macmillan; Karin Hogsander; Juliette Scott; Alex Hesz; Sarah Lamb; Ian Walters; Peter Anscombe; Prof. Martijn Steultjens.

Correspondent: Research Department, Copeman House, St Mary's Court, St Mary's Gate, Chesterfield S41 7TD (tel: 0300 790 0400; email: research@ arthritisresearchuk.org)

 www.arthritisresearchuk.org

 facebook.com/arthritisresearchuk

 @ArthritisRUK

 @arthritis_research_uk

This charity was established in 1936. Also known as ARC, its long-term commitment is to:

- Prevent arthritis
- Find a cure
- Transform the lives of those with arthritis

In order to achieve its commitments, the charity funds high-quality scientific and medical research into all types of arthritis and musculoskeletal conditions, provides information, and campaigns on behalf of people who are affected by the illness. The charity works in partnership with other organisations and aims to influence others in order to address important issues for people who are living with arthritis.

Strategic areas of focus to 2020
ARC's website defines its six areas of focus as:

- Find and engage: Find and engage people with arthritis to increase reach and the number of people seeking help from us
- Inform and support: Deliver our personalised offer so people feel informed and supported
- Influence: Influence the local and national environment, piloting new activity so that we improve the environment and provisions for people with arthritis
- Research: Deliver impactful research into prevention, treatment and cure that transforms people's lives
- Organisation: Develop the organisation's infrastructure, capacity, capability and skills
- Income: Raise income that is integrated with our activities and allows us to do more

Research funding
At the time of writing (June 2018) the following information was provided on the charity's website:

Our approach to funding is to support exceptional research that aims to prevent the onset of arthritis, develop a cure for

arthritis and transform the lives of those with arthritis. In 2015 we defined our strategic focus to 2020, to improve the quality of life for people with arthritis so they can say I am in control, independent and recognised. We support researchers to find the breakthroughs that help people break free from the limits of arthritis.

Our remit covers all conditions which affect the joints, bones and muscles, including osteoarthritis, rheumatoid arthritis, back pain and osteoporosis. We support basic discovery, translational, clinical and health research via a breadth of funding instruments, including programmatic, institutional and personal awards.

Research is evaluated by three thematic subcommittees – disease, treatment and health who help us to plan, fund and monitor research. This helps to us to meet our commitment that the research we fund has maximum impact for people with arthritis and to ensure this happens as rapidly as possible.

Arthritis Research UK is currently funding around 300 grants covering all types of arthritis and ranging from basic laboratory science through to large clinical trials. The 'Information for grant applicants' on the charity's website gives details of current funding opportunities open for application and their closing dates.

Financial information
In 2016/17 the charity had assets of £206.79 million and an income of £28.87 million. The total grants awarded and 'recognised within the accounts' is recorded as £20 million.

Beneficiaries included: Design Council (£217,000 in two grants); University of Manchester (£202,000 in four grants); University of Oxford (£106,000 in five grants); King's College, London (£118,000 in five grants); The Royal Veterinary College (£6,000 in two grants); Sheffield Hallam University, (£4,000 in one grant).

Exclusions
Applications for welfare and social matters will not be considered.

Applications
All applications for Arthritis Research UK funding must be received through its online grant management system, Grant Tracker. Information on currently open 'calls for applications' can be found on the website, where details of changes to the charity's research funding will also be updated as they become available. Arthritis Research UK's research department can be contacted for more support or advice by emailing research@ arthritisresearchuk.org. The annual report for 2016/17 provides the following details of the application process:

Applications for funding are received via our online grant system in response to a specific grant call. Applications received are then validated and in accordance with the requirements of the Association of Medical Research Charities (AMRC), they are subject to external peer review. The applications and the expert peer review comments are then considered by independent review panels, which make a recommendation on whether to make an award or reject the application. The review panels have a core membership of research experts and patient insight partners. All reviewers are checked for any conflicts of interest prior to being asked to review an application. Once applications have been recommended for an award they are approved in accordance with our schedule of authority, and letters of award are then issued.

Sources of information
Accounts; annual report; Charity Commission record; funder's website.

Arts Council England

 Arts and culture

England

£666.5 million (2016/17)

CC number: 1036733

Trustees: Veronica Wadley; Dame Rosemary Squire; Prof. Roni Brown; Kate Willard; Sukhy Johal; Tessa Ross; Paul Roberts; Elisabeth Murdoch; George Mpanga; Andrew Miller; Catherine Mallyon; Michael Eakin; David Joseph; Maria Balshaw; Sir Nicholas Serota.

Correspondent: Enquiries Team, 21 Bloomsbury Street, London WC1B 3HF (tel: 0845 300 6200; email: enquiries@artscouncil.org.uk)

 www.artscouncil.org.uk

 facebook.com/artscouncilofengland

 @ace_national

 @aceagrams

Arts Council England invests public money from the government and National Lottery to support activities across the arts, museums and libraries in England. The council's work is described on its website: 'We champion, develop and invest in artistic and cultural experiences that enrich people's lives. We support activities across the arts, museums and libraries – from theatre to digital art, reading to dance, music to literature, and crafts to collections.'

In 2010 after 'widespread consultation with the arts and cultural sector', Arts Council England published a strategy to guide its investment in the ten years until 2020. The strategy, which was revised in 2013, is titled 'Great Art and Culture for Everyone' and has five key goals, which are outlined both on the website and in the council's detailed annual report. They are:

1   Excellence: 'Excellence is thriving and celebrated in the arts, museums and libraries'
2   For everyone: 'Everyone has the opportunity to experience and to be inspired by the arts, museums and libraries'
3   Resilience and sustainability: 'The arts, museums and libraries are resilient and environmentally sustainable'
4   Diversity and skills: 'The leadership and workforce in the arts, museums and libraries are diverse and appropriately skilled'
5   Children and young people: 'Every child and young person has the opportunity to experience the richness of the arts, museums and libraries'

Grant programmes
Funding programmes are regularly added and closed. At the time of writing (June 2018), open funding programmes included:

- **Arts Council/V&A Purchase Grant Fund:** This fund supports the purchase of a wide range of material for the permanent collections of non-nationally funded organisations in England and Wales. Grants of between £500 and £500,000 are available. Grants may be made of up to 50% of the purchase price
- **Arts Impact Fund:** A new fund demonstrating the potential for social investment in the arts, offering repayable finance to art organisations in England that can show how they are sustainable, and have great artistic ambition
- **Capital – Small Grants:** This fund supports organisations to be more resilient by having the right buildings and equipment to deliver their work.
- **Developing your Creative Practice:** A new development fund designed to support independent creative practitioners to ensure excellence is thriving in the arts and culture sector. Grants of £2,000 to £10,000 are available.
- **Project grants:** A new open access programme for arts, museums and libraries projects, funded by the National Lottery. The fund will support thousands of individual artists, community and cultural organisations. Grants of between £1,000 and £100,000 are available.

Financial information
In the 2016/17 accounts, the auditors explain that:

> We prepare separate accounts for our Grant-in-Aid and Lottery distribution as required by the Secretary of State for Culture, Media and Sport. We do not prepare a full set of consolidated accounts due to the differing accounting policies we are required to follow under the two separate accounts directions. However, to give a better understanding of our activities, we have prepared the following illustrative results for the two accounts combined for the 2015/16 and 2016/17 financial years.

We have used the financial information contained in the summary results as this applies to all of the council's income and expenditure over the financial period.

In 2016/17 the council had assets of £210 million and an income of £724 million. We have taken £666.5 million as the total of grants made during the year. This figure is the sum of the net Grant-in-Aid commitments (£475.1 million), other Grant-in-Aid arts expenditure (£3.8 million) and net Lottery grant commitments (£187.4 million).

Beneficiaries included: Halle Concerts Society (£2.1 million); The Audience Agency (£420,000); The Hall for Cornwall Trust (376,000); Thames Festival Trust (£150,00) Tate Gallery (£121,000); Whitworth Art Gallery (£69,000); Watts Gallery (£41,000); Barbican Centre Trust (£5,000).

Exclusions
Exclusions may vary depending upon the specific grant programme. Guidance relevant to each programme is available to download from the Art Council's website.

Applications
There is a helpful 'Funding finder' facility on the council's website which allows users to browse the funding programmes operated by the council. This facility provides links to application forms and guidance as well as details about eligibility criteria and deadlines. Note that funding programmes open and close and that programmes are regularly added and removed from the site.

Sources of information
Accounts; annual report; Charity Commission record; funder's website.

Arts Council of Northern Ireland

 Arts and culture

 UK and Ireland (but projects must benefit people of Northern Ireland)

£10 million (2016/17)

Trustees: John Edmund; Dr Katy Radford; David Alderdice; Anna Carragher; Noelle McAlinden; Katherine McCloskey; Paul Mullan; Dr Siún

Hanrahan; Dr Leon Litvack; Roisin Erskine; Cian Smyth.

Correspondent: The Arts Development Department, 1 The Sidings, Antrim Road, Lisburn BT28 3AJ (tel: 028 9262 3555; email: info@artscouncil-ni.org)

 www.artscouncil-ni.org

 facebook.com/ArtsCouncilNI

 @ArtsCouncilNI

The council's website provides the following information.

The Arts Council of Northern Ireland (ACNI) is the development and funding agency for the Arts in Northern Ireland. it distributes public money and National Lottery funds to develop and deliver a wide variety of arts projects, events and initiatives across Northern Ireland.

From theatre and literature to art in the community, it works in partnership with hundreds of artists, arts organisations and venues. 'Art has the ability to reach across boundaries, inspiring, teaching and bringing people together.' The ACNI's mission is to 'place the arts at the heart of our social, economic and creative life'.

Details of all funding programmes and grants awarded can be found on the council's website.

Financial information
In 2016/17 the council had negative assets of -£2.9 million and an income of £1.4 million. 'Expenditure on the arts', according to the 2016/17 accounts, totalled £10 million.

Previous beneficiaries have included: BEAM Creative Network (£31,000); Ulster Orchestra Society (£15,000); Waterside Theatre Company Ltd (£12,000); Arts Care (£10,000); Play Resource Warehouse (£8,000) and In Your Space (NI) Ltd (£4,000).

Applications
Information on what funding is currently available, guidelines and full details of how to apply can be found at the Arts Council of Northern Ireland website.

Sources of information
Accounts; annual report; Charity Commission record; funder's website.

Arts Council of Wales (also known as Cyngor Celfyddydau Cymru)

 Arts and culture

 Wales

£ £28.62 million (2016/17)

CC number: 1034245

Trustees: Marian Jones; Alan Watkin; Dr Philip George; Richard Turner; John Williams; Dr Lesley Hodgson; Michael Griffiths; Melanie Hawthorne; Andrew Miller; Dafydd Rhys; Andrew Eagle; Iwan Bala; Kate Eden; Dr Rachel O'Rhiordan.

Correspondent: Information Team, Bute Place, Cardiff CF10 5AL (tel: 029 2044 1301; email: information@ artscouncilofwales.org.uk)

 www.arts.wales

 facebook.com/celfyddydau

 @Arts_Wales_

Arts Council of Wales, which was established by Royal Charter in 1994 to fund and develop the arts in Wales. According to the council's website, its vision is 'a creative Wales where the arts are central to the life of a nation'. The majority of the council's income comes from the Welsh Government and it also distributes money on behalf of the National Lottery. Where possible, the council raises money from a range of other sources across the public and private sector.

Strategy
The council's strategy is made up of three words: make, reach and sustain. Its website describes how this strategy is delivered:

Make:

1. Creating the environment for the arts to flourish

2. Increasing the value of international cultural exchange to the arts in Wales

Reach:

3. Finding new opportunities, ways and places for people to enjoy and take part in the arts

4. Developing the creativity of children and young people

Sustain:

5. Encouraging innovation, resilience and sustainability

6. Protecting and growing the economic base for the arts in Wales

7. Demonstrating the value of the arts

8. Making the Arts Council an efficient and effective public body

Funding
The 'Apply for funding' page on the council's website contains information on a wide range of funding opportunities for organisations and individual creative professionals, including funding which is available from other sources. Each funding scheme has specific guidelines and eligibility criteria. Helpful questionnaires on the council's website allow interested organisations and individuals to quickly determine their eligibility.

Financial information
In 2016/17 the council had assets of £2.6 million and an income of £35.7 million. We have taken our grant total for 2016/17 from the combined figures for 'value of grants' (£28.62 million). Grants were distributed as follows:

Theatres and arts centres	£6.8 million
Theatre production and presentation	£6.4 million
Opera	£4.7 million
Creative learning through the arts	£2.1 million
Visual and applied arts	£1.7 million
Dance	£1.7 million
Music	£1.3 million
Arts and young people	£1.1 million
Community arts	£1.1 million
Literature	£717,000
Strategic awards	£659,000
Circus and carnivals	£188,000
Disability arts	£160,000

Beneficiaries included: Welsh National Opera (£4.38 million); National Theatre Wales (£1.55 million); Aberystwyth Arts Centre (£518,500); Ballet Cymru (£244,000); Disability Arts Cymru (£160,000); Blackwood Miners' Institute (£125,000); Broughton Primary School, Coychurch Llangrallo Primary (£10,000).

Applications
See the 'Apply for funding' section on the council's website for details of available funding, guidelines and other important information.

The website further states:

> We also offer funding advice at fortnightly funding advice sessions or through bookable phone sessions...You'll be able to book 30 minute slots with our officers to discuss your project ideas and make general funding enquiries. They will also be able to offer you guidance on eligibility and how best to apply for a grant. To book a place you will need to contact the information team at information@ artscouncilofwales.org.uk or by phoning on 0845 873 4900.

Information about upcoming funding advice sessions can also be found on the 'Our events' section of the council's website.

Sources of information
Accounts; annual report; Charity Commission record; funder's website.

Ove Arup Partnership Charitable Trust

🔍 General charitable purposes

📍 UK

💷 £435,500 (2016/17)

CC number: 1038737

Trustee: Ove Arup Partnership Trust Corporation Ltd.

Correspondent: Stephanie Wilde, Ove Arup & Partners, 13 Fitzroy Street, London W1T 4BQ (email: stephanie. wilde@arup.com)

This trust was first established by a trust deed in January 1978 and was registered with the Charity Commission in 1994. The annual report for 2016/17 explains that the trust 'is not in receipt of a regular income and relies on gifts from Arup Group Ltd'.

Income from the company is used to make charitable donations to charities. Donations are made for a wide range of purposes and particularly education, social care, health, welfare, disaster relief, poverty alleviation, local community development, sustainability, the environment and technology.

Grant-making policy

As the annual report explains, grants are made for causes and charities 'that operate in areas related to Arup's skills and business activities where these are aligned with Arup's values, as expressed in Ove Arup's 'Key Speech', of doing socially useful work and of being engaged in activities for the benefit of society at large'.

When making a decision, the trustee takes into account the size and structure of the recipient organisation in relation to the size of the donation 'in order to maximise the impact and effectiveness of that donation'.

Financial information

In 2016/17 the trust had assets of £17,700 and an income of £438,000, almost all of which was received in the form of a donation from Arup Group Ltd. During the year, donations were made totalling £435,500.

Beneficiaries included: The Ove Arup Foundation (£175,000); The Prince's Trust (£23,500); Engineers for Overseas Development (£20,000); Architecture Sans Frontieres, Habitat for Humanity Great Britain (£10,000 each); Borders Children's Charity (£500).

Applications

Apply in writing to the correspondent.

Sources of information

Accounts; annual report; Charity Commission record.

The Asda Foundation

🔍 Sport and recreation, community development, general charitable purposes

📍 England and Wales

💷 £5.1 million (2016)

CC number: 1124268

Trustees: Gerald Oppenheim; John Cookman; Ann Rocks; Carolyn Heaney; Alison Seabrook; Jane Earnshaw; Jason Martin; Andrew Murray.

Correspondent: Julie Ward, Foundation Manager, Asda House, Great Wilson Street, Leeds LS11 5AD (tel: 0113 243 5435)

 www.asdafoundation.org

 @asdafoundation

The Asda Foundation is Asda's charitable trust. It supplements the good causes that colleagues support locally, as well as a number of bigger ad-hoc projects in local communities. It also manages all funds raised for national charities and monies raised in Asda House.

The foundation's main objective is to make donations to local good causes. They fund a wide range of causes which their colleagues are involved in, including everything from local charities and playgroups to football teams.

According to the foundation's website:

'The Foundation works in partnership with other charities tackling issues within local communities and supporting charities made a real difference to thousands of people across the UK.'

Financial information

In 2016 the foundation had assets of £8 million and an income of £7.7 million. Grants totalled £5.1 million with £663,000 awarded to Asda's national campaigns.

A further £4.4 million was donated to other organisations.

Beneficiaries included: Leeds Community Foundation (£380,000); Silver Line (£375,000); Run for All (£145,000); Children in Need (£83,000); Leeds Rhinos (£41,500); The Salvation Army (£4,400); Smart Money Credit Union (£1,500); Age UK (£1,000).

Applications

There is an eligibility checker and 'store locator' on the website.

If your application fits the Asda Foundation guidelines, applying could not be simpler, please contact your local store or depot and speak to the Community Champion – to see if this is

something they would like to be involved with and support.

Sources of information

Annual report; Charity Commission record; guidelines for applicants; funder's website.

The Asfari Foundation

🔍 Empowerment of young people, civil society development, humanitarian relief

📍 UK, Syria, Lebanon and Palestine

💷 £3.5 million (2016)

CC number: 1116751

Trustees: Ayman Asfari; John Ferguson; Sawsan Asfari; Adeeb Asfari; Dr Marwan Muasher.

Correspondent: The Trustees, Unit A, 1–3 Canfield Place, London NW6 3BT (tel: 020 7372 3889; email: info@ asfarifoundation.org.uk)

 www.asfarifoundation.org.uk

The foundation's mission is to help young people make a valuable contribution to society by empowering them through education; research and the power of free thinking. The foundation also encourages the development of civil society, as well as providing humanitarian relief in emergencies in its target countries (mainly Syria, Lebanon, Palestine and the UK). The foundation does all its work through partnerships with other organisations. The foundation achieves this through its three programmes:

▷ Youth Empowerment Programme
▷ Civil Society Programme
▷ Relief Programme

Further information about each of the foundation's programmes is given on its website.

Research is also supported through the foundation's three programme areas and through partner organisations.

The foundation's website states that it makes grants 'to reputable, registered and experienced local and international organisations that work on education, civil society, and humanitarian relief'. Grants are given for anywhere between £3,000 and £7 million, but on average are between £20,000 and £50,000.

Work in the UK

The foundation's website states:

The Foundation supports organisations working with disadvantaged young people in the UK, partners with British organisations to host scholars from its Middle Eastern target countries, partners with think tanks and research organisations, and supports British INGOs working with young Palestinians, Syrians and Lebanese people in the Arab region.

Financial information

In 2016 the foundation had assets of £13.5 million and an income of £5.1 million. Grants awarded to organisations totalled £3.5 million and were distributed as follows:

Civil society	£1.5 million
Relief	£1.7 million
Youth empowerment	£331,000

Beneficiaries included: Chatham House (£340,000); Save the Children and International Rescue Committee (£250,000); The Syria Campaign (£117,500); The Hands Up Foundation (£37,500); The Circle of Women (£19,000).

Exclusions

The foundation does not fund individual students directly.

Applications

The foundation's website states:

> The Asfari Foundation is coming to the end of a Strategic Review which aims to assess the impact of its work to date to determine what will be most useful to our partners going forward. When the review is finalised, we will be able to give a clear idea of what projects we will fund and where in the future. The review will be finalised during March. We encourage you to check our website where the new strategy will be made available and which will show information about the application criteria and process.

At the time of writing (April 2018) the application criteria and process had not changed. The foundation's website states that organisations can apply at any time, or in response to a particular call for applications. It also identifies potential partners proactively. After reading the programme pages of the website, as well as its grant-making information, the foundation states that potential applicants should apply in the following way:

> If you think your organisation meets the objectives of a particular programme and its values match those of the Foundation, we recommend that you send a short email to info@asfarifoundation.org.uk with a short introduction of your organisation and the project, including the total budget and how much you would ask the Foundation to fund. Alternatively, you could fill out the concept note which you can download [on the website].

Sources of information

Accounts; annual report; Charity Commission record; funder's website.

The Ashden Trust

 Environment, homelessness, sustainable regeneration, community arts

 UK and overseas

 £967,500 (2016/17)

CC number: 802623

Trustees: Sarah Butler-Sloss; Robert Butler-Sloss; Judith Portrait.

Correspondent: Robert Bell, Director, The Peak, 5 Wilton Road, London SW1V 1AP (tel: 020 7410 0330; email: ashdentrust@sfct.org.uk)

 www.ashdentrust.org.uk

This is one of the Sainsbury Family Charitable Trusts, which share a joint administration. They have a common approach to grant-making which is described in the entry for the group as a whole.

The trust supports work relating to climate change, sustainable development, or improving the quality of life in poorer communities. Grants are made under seven categories:

- Sustainable development – international
- Sustainable development – UK
- Sustainable regeneration
- People at risk
- Arts and sustainability
- Social investment fund
- Low carbon fund

Grant-making review

At the time of writing (June 2018), the website states:

> Until April 2017, the Trust is undertaking a review of its work over the last 26 years and is not inviting any grant applications. During this period, as well as undertaking a review, the Trust will continue its work with the Climate Change Collaboration and Divest Invest and establish a new low carbon enterprise fund.

Refer to the website for up-to-date information on funding available from the trust.

Financial information

In 2016/17 the trust had assets of £37.9 million and an income of £1.2 million. Grants awarded to organisations totalled £967,500.

Beneficiaries included: Client Earth (£100,000); Carbon Tracker (£40,000); Greenpeace (£30,000); Influence Map (£20,000); Centre for Sustainable Energy and Superkidz (£10,000 each); Tipping Point (£5,000).

Applications

The trust's website states: 'we do not accept unsolicited approaches, unless they are exceptional proposals which closely fit our specific areas of interest'.

Sources of information

Accounts; annual report; Charity Commission record; funder's website.

The Ashley Family Foundation

 Art and design, textiles, local community projects in Wales, education

 UK, with preference for Wales

£289,000 (2015/16)

CC number: 288099

Trustees: Oriana Baddeley; Emma Shuckburgh; Martyn Gowar; Laura Ashley; Sue Timney; Anita George; Jeremy McIlroy.

Correspondent: Mia Duddridge, Administrator, 6 Trull Farm Buildings, Trull, Tetbury, Gloucestershire GL8 8SQ (tel: 0303 040 1005; email: info@ ashleyfamilyfoundation.org.uk)

www.ashleyfamilyfoundation.org.uk

In 1986, a year after the sad death of Laura Ashley, her family officially established The Laura Ashley Foundation. The change of name to The Ashley Family Foundation took place in 2011.

The following information about the foundation's approach is taken from the foundation's website:

> The ethos of the Foundation is primarily to strengthen rural communities, particularly those within Wales. Both in terms of the social and environmental aspects alongside giving back to the communities that helped the family develop the *Laura Ashley* company into an international success. Added to this are the promotion and support of traditional family values often retained within rural communities.
>
> Developing the company in rural Mid-Wales had a significant impact upon the local economy and the social well-being of its people with increased employment opportunity and the valued team spirit of the workforce. A commitment to maintaining these aspects remains within the activities of the foundation, with many grassroots voluntary groups benefiting from its funds.

Funding

The following information is taken from the foundation's website:

> The Ashley Family Foundation (formerly The Laura Ashley Foundation) continues to award grants to projects that fit with the family ethos of protecting rural communities and encouraging participation in the arts, particularly that of textiles.
>
> We are keen to fund good small scale arts projects in England and Wales and welcome proposals from small scale

community textile museums/ organisations.

Although we have no set limit to the amount that can be awarded, we do favour requests that are below £10,000. Funding is awarded on the context of the project and awards of £500 can make a difference to some recipients.

The foundation favours applications for core costs over capital costs. Funding is generally awarded for one-off projects, although the foundation will consider funding for up to three years. Around half of the funds each year are awarded to projects in Wales. The foundation considers requests from 'registered charities, unincorporated organisations and community groups with a constitution or terms of reference and a charitable purpose'; organisations that are not registered charities should contact the foundation before applying, to discuss eligibility.

Financial information
In 2015/16 the foundation had assets of £12.8 million and an income of over £362,000. During the year, £289,000 was given in grants to over 50 organisations. Of this, the annual report states that, in Wales: £57,500 was given to community and social welfare projects and £38,000 was given towards arts, crafts and textile projects; and outside Wales: £57,500 was awarded to community and social welfare projects; and £43,500 was awarded to arts projects.

Beneficiaries included: University of the Arts – Chelsea (£39,000); Shakespeare Link (£12,500); FareShare (£15,000); Wyeside Arts Centre (£10,900); National Portrait Gallery (£10,000); Crisis (£5,000); Margam Youth Centre (£2,000); Eglwys Newydd Haford Church and Montgomeryshire County Music Festival (£500 each).

Exclusions
The foundation does not give grants for:

- Individuals
- Business ventures
- Overseas projects
- Religious projects
- Dance-related projects
- Direct funding for schools
- Retrospective funding

Applications
There is a two-stage application process. Applications can be made on the online form on the foundation's website, throughout the year, and are assessed in line with the guidelines also available from the foundation's website. The foundation welcomes telephone calls from potential applicants (Andrea Powell, Community Foundation in Wales: 029 2037 9580). Deadlines for the year are detailed on the website.

Sources of information
Accounts; annual report; Charity Commission record.

Asthma UK

 Research into the causes, prevention, management and treatment of asthma

UK

£2.65 million (2015/16)

CC number: 802364

Trustees: Jane Tozer; Prof. Ian Hall; John Tucker; Dr Robert Wilson; Mary Leadbeater; Martin Sinclair; Kate Clarke; George Anson; Dr Paul Hodgkin; Prof. Sir Lewis Ritchie; Jean-Francois Bessiron; James Bowes.

Correspondent: Research Team, 18 Mansell Street, London E1 8AA (tel: 0300 222 5800; email: info@asthma.org. uk)

 www.asthma.org.uk/research/for-researchers

 facebook.com/AsthmaUK

 @asthmauk

Asthma UK's long-term mission is simply 'Stop asthma attacks. Cure asthma'. The charity fights asthma in three ways, by:

- Funding world class research
- Campaigning for change on issues that affect people who have asthma
- Providing expert advice and support

Research strategy
Asthma UK's research strategy will fund, support, and partner on projects that address one of 15 research priorities that are listed on the website, on the charity's Asthma Research Roadmap. The topics within these priority areas can be broadly divided into six themes, which are:

- Asthma biology
- Asthma types
- Asthma treatments
- Asthma management
- Asthma diagnosis
- Asthma prevention

Funding opportunities
Grants are available for

- **Senior Fellowships** – clinical fellowships are available for up to £250,000 and basic fellowships for up to £225,000, both for up to five years
- **Studentships** – up to £100,000 for four years to provide foundation training for graduates
- **Project Grants** – up to £300,000 for up to three years to tackle priority areas of asthma research
- **Innovation Grants** – up to £50,000 for up to 18 months to explore original or new ideas

The charity also funds two laboratory-based research centres, the Asthma UK Centre for Applied Research and the MRC-Asthma UK Centre in Allergic Mechanisms of Asthma.

Financial information
In 2015/16 the charity held assets of £6.8 million and had an income of £8.8 million. Research grants to institutions totalled £2.65 million. The cost of charitable activities totalled £7.1 million and were broken down as follows:

Research	£3.7 million
Advice and support	£2.5 million
Improving care	£905,000

Grants were awarded to projects at the following institutions: Imperial College of Science, Technology and Medicine (£2 million).

Applications
Details of current funding opportunities can be found on the website. Applications are accepted through the charity's online research management system. The website also states 'for further information about these awards and if you would like to be kept informed about future funding opportunities, contact the Research Team at research@asthma.org.uk'.

Sources of information
Accounts; annual report; funder's website.

Aston-Mansfield Charitable Trust

Community development

The borough of Newham

£398,000 (2016/17)

CC number: 208155

Trustees: Christopher Keen, Chair; Andrew West; Bernard Tyler; Stephen Wright; Revd Paul Regan.

Correspondent: Eileen Da-Silva, Accountant, Durning Hall, Earlham Grove, Forest Gate, London E7 9AB (tel: 020 3740 8114; email: eileen.da-silva@ aston-mansfield.org.uk)

 www.aston-mansfield.org.uk

 facebook.com/AstonMansfield

@A_McOmms

The objective of the trust is to 'develop for the public benefit, the community wealth of east London and promote a diverse and inclusive society in which all are free to participate'. This goal is primarily achieved by making significant grants to Aston-Mansfield, a sister charity to which AMDT is connected, although some smaller grants are also awarded to other projects, within the objectives and area of benefit of the charity.

Financial information

In 2016/17 the trust had assets of £14.7 million and an income of £537,500. Grants were made totalling £398,000 and were broken down into the following categories:

Community buildings	£237,000
Health and education	£116,000
Community development	£33,000
Religious activity	£12,000
Housing activities	£50

There was no list of grant beneficiaries included within the accounts.

Exclusions

Revenue funding for salaries and maintenance is unlikely to be given. No national appeals and no grants are given to individuals.

Applications

Applicants for grants should apply in writing to the correspondent. There are no guidelines and no application forms.

Sources of information

Accounts; annual report; Charity Commission record.

Atkin Charitable Foundation

 Social welfare, health, education, general charitable purposes

 UK and Israel

£975,000 (2016/17)

CC number: 1112925

Trustees: Barry Gold; Raymond Harris; Ross Atkin; Celia Atkin; Edward Atkin; Lara Atkin.

Correspondent: Raymond Harris, Trustee, 16 Rosemont Road, London NW3 6NE (tel: 020 7472 6500)

The Atkin Charitable Foundation is a grant-making charity established in January 2006 and funded by private donations from the Atkins family. Its objects are the relief of poverty, distress and sickness, the advancement of education, the protection of health and for any other charitable purpose.

Financial information

In 2016/17 the foundation had assets of £5.4 million and an income of almost £975,000. Grants awarded to organisations totalled £976,000 which figure includes £157,500 of grants below £8,000 which were not listed individually in the accounts.

Beneficiaries included: Victoria and Albert Museum (£120,000); Henry Jackson Society (£100,000); Roundhouse

Trust (£75,000); Royal Opera House (£40,000); London Symphony Orchestra (£30,000); Design Museum and Refuge (£20,000 each); Magan David Adom UK, Marie Curie Foundation and UJIA Survivors' Appeal (£10,000 each).

Applications

Apply in writing to the correspondent.

Sources of information

Accounts; annual report; Charity Commission record.

Autonomous Research Charitable Trust (ARCT)

 People who are disadvantaged, empowering people and improving quality of life, general charitable purposes

Mainly London and overseas

£397,500 (2016/17)

CC number: 1137503

Trustees: Jonathan Firkins; Andrew Crean; Donald Betson; Rif Huque-Iverson.

Correspondent: Nicki Fletcher, Trust Administrator, c/o Moore Stephens, 150 Aldersgate Street, London EC1A 4AB (tel: 020 7334 9191; email: nicki.fletcher@moorestephens.com)

This trust was established in 2010 for general charitable purposes. It is the charitable trust of Autonomous Research LLP, a company that provides intelligence on banking and insurance companies. The company donates a share of its profits – according to previous research, around 5% – to charitable causes through this trust, as well as through its US foundation, Autonomous Research Foundation US (ARFUS).

The 2016/17 annual report states that the trust's core aims are:

▶ To help disadvantaged people get a step up in life
▶ To empower people to improve the quality of their lives
▶ To focus our resources upon a small number of key partner charities, both in London and abroad, where we feel we can make a difference and establish long-term relationships

It is further explained that the trust works towards these aims and objectives by:

▶ Providing funding to other recognised charitable institutions
▶ Providing mentoring, business and career advice and a variety of other hands-on roles which the Trustees believe would ultimately be a benefit to the public

Grant-making policy

The trustees' report states the following information about the grant-making process:

> At the beginning of each year, the Trustees will consider and agree a short list of charities that are to be Core Partner Charities for that year. Specific support will be directed to these organisations, with meetings and other feedback being sought, as well as considering other worthy causes that fall within the criteria and aims of the trustees. Alongside the Core Charity Partners the charity maintains discretional funds for ad hoc distributions'.

Unsolicited applications are accepted, but the trustees do receive a high number of grant applications which, in line with the Trustees' grant making policy, are mostly unsuccessful. The Trustees prefer to support donations to charities whose work they have researched and which is in accordance with the aims and objectives of the charity for the year. Financial circumstances will be relevant only in determining the amount of an award.

Financial information

In 2016/17 the trust held assets of £161,500 and had an income of £402,000. Grants were made to 32 organisations and totalled £397,500.

Beneficiaries included: Five Talents (£200,000); Food Cycle (£107,000); The October Club (£35,000); Facing the World and Renewable World (£10,000 each); Miss Isle School of Sailing (£2,500); Bloodwise (£1,500); The Parish of St Michael's Cornhill (£1,300); Cancer Research, NSPCC and Plan International UK (£1,000 each).

Grants for less than £1,000 were awarded to six organisations and totalled £3,200.

Applications

Applications may be made in writing to the correspondent. Unsolicited applications are accepted but are unlikely to be successful; the trustees prefer to take a proactive approach to their grant-making.

Sources of information

Accounts; annual report; Charity Commission record.

The Avon and Somerset Police Community Trust

Community safety and quality of life, crime reduction and prevention

The Avon and Somerset Constabulary area

£190,500 (2016/17)

CC number: 1076770

Trustees: Patricia Hunt; Paul Hooper; Beatrice Salter; Mary Prior; Janet

Trotter; Alan Bell; Sean Connolly; Sue Mountstevens.

Correspondent: Tracey Clegg, Trust Manager, PO Box 37, Valley Road, Portishead, Bristol BS20 8QJ (tel: 01275 816240; email: tracey.clegg@ avonandsomerset.police.uk)

 www.avonandsomerset.police.uk/ services/police-community-trust

The Avon and Somerset Police Community Trust was formed in July 1999 to provide people with a unique opportunity to invest in projects that improve the safety and quality of life within the Avon and Somerset Constabulary area, with particular emphasis on helping young people, people who are vulnerable and older people.

The trust aims to:

- Protect local people and property from crime
- Reduce anti-social behaviour
- Educate young people on the dangers of drug, alcohol and solvent abuse
- Increase community safety for all, but especially young people, people who are vulnerable and older people
- Divert young people away from crime and anti-social behaviour, encouraging their growth into responsible young adults
- Build good community relations

The trustees favour projects that:

- Promote safety and quality of life in the Avon and Somerset Constabulary area
- Through the prevention of crime and disorder, protect young people, people who are vulnerable and older people from criminal acts
- Advance education, including that related to alcohol, drugs, solvent abuse, community relations and responsible citizenship

The trust has a number of funds, supporting community crime prevention/reduction initiatives, including:

- Commissioner's Community Action Fund – grants of up to £3,000 for community projects supporting the priorities of the Police Crime Plan
- Road Safety Fund – grants of up to £5,000 for road safety projects
- General Fund – grants of up to £1,000 to support the trust's aims (as previously listed)

Further information about each of the funds available is provided on the trust's website.

The trust also provides free hi-vis jackets for primary schools in the area.

Financial information

In 2016/17 the trust had assets totalling £473,000 and an income of £159,500. Grants totalled £190,500.

Previous beneficiaries have included: Bobby Van Scheme (£54,500); Hartcliffe and Withywood Angling Club, Stand Against Violence, The National Smelting Co. Amateur Boxing Club, Henbury Football Club and Priory Community Association (£1,000 each); Sandford Scouts (£880); Wolverhampton Playing Fields and Thornbury Sea Cadets (£600 each); Oasis Community Club (£500) and Clevedon YMCA and Bath and North East Somerset Youth Offending Team (£250 each).

Exclusions

The trust does not support:

- Individuals, including students
- Expeditions
- Bursaries or scholarships
- Replacement of statutory funding
- Building works
- Projects that fall outside the constabulary's geographical area
- Further applications within three years

Applications

Applications can be made on a form available to download, together with criteria and guidelines, from the trust's website (www.avonandsomerset.police. uk).

For further information about the trust or advice on obtaining or completing the application form contact the Trust Manager who, the website states, will happily talk through any problems you may have in filling out the form.

The trustees meet quarterly to consider applications. Grants in support of major projects are routinely reviewed and awarded by the trustees at the commencement of each financial year at their April meeting.

Sources of information

Accounts; annual report; Charity Commission record; guidelines for applicants; funder's website.

Awards for All (see also the Big Lottery Fund)

 General charitable purposes

 UK

£ £67.6 million (2016/17)

Correspondent: (See 'Applications' section further in the entry) Big Lottery Fund, 1 Plough Place, London EC4A 1DE (tel: 0345 410 2030; email: general.enquiries@awardsforall.org.uk)

 www.awardsforall.org.uk

Awards for All is a Big Lottery Fund grants scheme funding small, local community-based projects in the UK. Each country in the UK administers its own programme. The following information is reproduced from the Awards for All's guidelines shared by all countries:

Who can apply?

You can apply if your organisation is a:

- Voluntary or community organisation
- Registered charity
- Constituted group or club
- Community interest company (CIC)
- Social enterprise
- School
- Statutory body (including town, parish or community council)

We cannot accept applications from:

- Individuals
- Sole traders
- Organisations that are aimed at generating profits primarily for private distribution
- Organisations based outside the UK
- Applications made by one organisation on behalf of another

What's it all about?

National Lottery Awards for All offers funding from £300 to £10,000 to support projects and activities that matter to people and communities. While the projects we fund usually last for up to 12 months, we know that some can take a little longer, and other grants are for one-off events. Please note we can only fund your organisation for a maximum of £10,000 within a 12-month period and you can only hold one grant at a time. If you're looking for inspiration, you can use our funding finder to see what we've funded www.biglotteryfund.org.uk/funded-projects.

What are we looking for?

National Lottery Awards for All has three funding priorities and your project idea must meet at least one of these.

- Bring people together and build strong relationships in and across communities
- Improve the places and spaces that matter to communities
- Enable more people to fulfil their potential by working to address issues at the earliest possible stage

It's important to us that you involve your community in the design, development and delivery of the activities you're planning, so please tell us how you've done this. We believe this will help your project to be better supported by the energy and strengths that exist within your community and it is more likely to be successful as a result. By community, we mean people living in your local area, people who share a common interest, or people who experience similar barriers and issues. We are keen to support smaller organisations. To achieve this, we'll take your organisation's income into consideration as part of our overall decision. We would like as many people as possible to benefit from National Lottery funding.

We expect all applications to:

- **Be open to new people getting involved.** This means that it should be easy for someone to join your group or take part in activities you're running. There shouldn't be any barriers, such as the need for someone to be recommended by a current member. We understand that sometimes there's a good reason why your activity isn't open to everyone, if so, please tell us about it in question eight of your application.

- **Support equal opportunities and challenge discrimination.** You can find our equalities principles on our website www.biglotteryfund.org.uk/equalities.

- **Be completed by the organisation applying.** Some businesses promote their services, may offer consultancy services, imply that they are acting on The Fund's behalf, or even complete an application form for you. We do not allow this or feel it's necessary. This does not relate to the useful guidance and support that agencies such as Community Voluntary Services provide to many of our applicants.

Financial information

The annual report for 2016/17 states that: 'Through Awards for All, in 2016/17 we gave out £67.6 million to more than 7,000 projects, providing grants for amazing initiatives led by local people.'

Details of all previously funded projects can be found at: www.biglotteryfund.org.uk/funded-projects.

Exclusions

Visit the individual country's webpages for full details of those organisations/projects/activities that Awards for All programmes exclude.

Applications

There is no closing date for National Lottery Awards for All, applications can be made at any time. However, it is important to submit your application at least 12 weeks before your project will start. This is because it takes around ten weeks to reach a decision on your application, and if you are successful, a further two weeks to pay out funding.

All information, application forms and guidelines are available online. If you need further support or have any questions get in touch with the organisation. Note that there are separate offices for each region and you should contact the most appropriate one – see details on the website.

Sources of information

Accounts; annual report; funder's website.

The Bacit Foundation

 Cancer research

UK

£2.4 million to organisations (2016/17)

CC number: 1149202

Trustees: Martin Thomas; Catherine Scivier; Thomas Henderson; Rupert Adams.

Correspondent: Martin Thomas, Trustee, 91 Gower Street, London WC1E 6AB (tel: 020 7968 6460; email: mt@bacit.co.uk)

Registered in October 2012, the foundation supports medical research, specifically cancer research and related diseases. Other charitable causes may also be supported.

Financial information

In 2016/17 the foundation held assets of £2.4 million and an income of £3.5 million. Grants were made to 22 organisations totalling £2.4 million.

Beneficiaries included: Cancer Research UK (£185,000); The Institute of Cancer Research (£151,500); Maggie's (£110,500); Downside Up (£108,000); Child Women for Women International (£102,000); Beating Bowel Cancer (£99,500); Scope and The Rwanda Hope Foundation (£99,500 each).

Applications

Unsolicited applications are not accepted. The foundation's Charity Commission record states that: 'The foundation grants those funds to charities selected by its trustees in furtherance of the foundation's objects, in proportions determined each year by shareholders of Bacit Ltd'.

Sources of information

Accounts; annual report; Charity Commission record.

Backstage Trust

 Performing arts

UK

£6.4 million (2016/17)

CC number: 1145887

Trustees: Lady Susan Sainsbury; Dominic Flynn; David Wood.

Correspondent: Kathryn Thompson, North House, 27 Great Peter Street, London SW1P 3LN (tel: 020 7072 4498; email: info@backstagetrust.org.uk)

The trust was established in February 2012 by Lady Susan Sainsbury for general charitable purposes. In practice, the trust's priorities are focused on the arts, particularly theatre and the performing arts. Lady Sainsbury is the deputy chair of both the Royal Shakespeare Company and the Royal Academy of Music, and she and her husband, Lord David Sainsbury of Turville, are high-profile patrons of the arts.

What the trust supports

The trustees' report for 2016/17 provides the following information:

> The primary focus of Backstage's grant programme is on projects in the live performing arts, mainly theatre. Most grants are awarded proactively and stem from the broad spectrum of Trustees' interests in the field. Backstage can only offer assistance to registered charities or to activities which have clear charitable aims; the trust cannot directly fund individuals.

> The main focus of the grants made by Backstage is on projects in the performing arts. The majority of grants awarded since the Trust was established come under one of the following:

- Financing consultant advice to help with professional development of small scale arts organisations
- Assisting live arts projects involving disadvantaged children and young people
- Feasibility studies for capital projects
- Consultant advice on fundraising, a case for support and recruiting development staff

Financial information

In 2016/17 the trust held assets of £1.8 million and had an income of £3.5 million. Grants awarded to organisations totalled £6.4 million.

Beneficiaries included: Royal Academy of Music (£2.8 million); Donmar Warehouse (£500,000); Tricycle Theatre Company (£304,500); Papatango Theatre Company (£170,000); EGO Performance (£100,000); Citizens Theatre (£50,000); Soho Theatre (£20,000); The Bike Shed Theatre (£18,000).

Grants of under £15,000 totalled £242,000.

Applications

Apply in writing to the correspondent. A proposal for support should be relevant, realistic and demonstrate a clearly expressed set of aims. It should contain a realistic expression of potential viability and ideas for how the organisation would augment charitable funding. The 2016/17 annual report states:

> Applicants should demonstrate the potential viability of their project, and provide evidence showing that the organisation has the capacity to use charitable funding in the most effective way. Trustees will want to see evidence of fundraising plans, and to know that while Backstage might act as catalyst to encourage other grant-giving bodies, it should not be regarded as a sole funder.

Sources of information

Accounts; annual report; Charity Commission record.

The Baily Thomas Charitable Fund

 People with learning disabilities

UK

£2.9 million (2015/16)

CC number: 262334

Trustees: Prof. Sally-Ann Cooper; Prof. Anne Farmer; Suzanne Marriott; Kenneth Young; Jonathan Snow.

Correspondent: Ann Cooper, Secretary to the Trustees, c/o TMF Management (UK) Ltd, 400 Capability Green, Luton LU1 3AE (tel: 01582 439205; email: info@bailythomas.org.uk)

 www.bailythomas.org.uk

This fund is dedicated solely to the well-being of those with learning disabilities. It combines one or two major funding programmes with an extensive programme of generally one-off medium and smaller grants, which are divided between revenue and capital costs.

The fund gives the following general guidance on its useful and informative website:

> The Baily Thomas Charitable Fund is a grant making registered charity which was established primarily to aid the research into learning disability and to aid the care and relief of those affected by learning disability by making grants to voluntary organisations working in this field.
>
> Learning disabilities (intellectual disabilities), and autism are our priorities for funding. We consider projects for children or adults. We do not give grants for research into or care of people with mental illness, dyslexia, dyspraxia nor ADHD, if they do not also have learning disabilities (intellectual disabilities).

Grants are made to registered or exempt charities. The fund is linked with The Rix-Thompson-Rothenberg Foundation; applications should not be made to both, and recipients of a grant from either trust should not re-apply within two years.

General grants

General grants of over £250 are made towards capital and revenue costs, for both specific projects and general core costs. Grants are usually awarded on a one-off basis, but occasionally new projects are funded for two or three years. Examples of what may be funded are given on the website.

Small grants

Small grants of up to £5,000 are considered under the same guidelines as the general grants, which are given on the website.

Research grants

Grants can be given towards research in the area of learning disabilities that the fund supports. Funding can be given for 'directly incurred costs of research', including salary costs of researchers employed on the project. Guidelines are given on the website.

Doctoral Fellowships

Up to two fellowships will be awarded each year to support promising researchers to complete a PhD on a topic relevant to people with learning disabilities (intellectual disabilities). Further guidance can be found on the charity's website.

Financial information

In 2016/17 the fund had assets of £89.2 million and an income of £1.8 million. During the year, the fund awarded 338 grants totalling £2.9 million which were broken down as follows:

Main grants – major running costs/ revenue costs	£895,000
Research projects	£799,500
Small grants – running costs/ revenue costs	£486,000
Main grants – major capital building/refurbishment costs	£293,500
Main grants – other running costs/ revenue costs	£247,500
Main grants – equipment costs	£79,000
Small grants – equipment costs	£71,000
Rix-Thompson-Rothenberg Foundation grant-making	£70,000
Small grants – capital building/ refurbishment costs	£22,000
Main grants – other capital building/refurbishment costs	£20,000

Beneficiaries included: Queen's University Belfast (£123,500); Development Trust and The JPK Sussex Project (£100,000 each); Rix-Thompson-Rothenberg Foundation (£70,000); Avon Riding Centre for the Disabled, Ferring Country Centre and The Hextol Foundation (£30,000 each); Autism East Midlands and Nansen Highland (£20,000 each).

Exclusions

Grants are not normally awarded to individuals. The following areas are unlikely to receive funding:

- Hospices
- Minibuses except those for residential and/or day care services for people with learning disabilities
- Advocacy projects
- Arts and theatre projects
- Conductive education projects
- Swimming and hydrotherapy pools
- Physical disabilities unless accompanied by significant learning disabilities
- Grants for acquired brain injury unless the resulting learning disabilities occur early in the developmental period (i.e. birth, infancy or childhood), impacting on brain maturation and development and learning in childhood
- Community interest companies
- Qualitative research studies

Applications

Applications should be made using the form on the fund's website. Comprehensive guidelines for each grant scheme are also provided on the website. Handwritten applications are not accepted.

Small grant applications are considered every month. General grant applications are considered in March, June and November and applications should be submitted by 1 December, 1 March and 1 August respectively. Research grant applications are considered in June and November and should be submitted by 1 February or 1 August.

Sources of information

Accounts; annual report; Charity Commission record; funder's website.

The Baird Trust

 Maintenance and repair of churches and halls of the Church of Scotland

Scotland

£290,500 (2017)

OSCR number: SC016549

Trustees: Lt Col Charles Ball; The Hon. Mary Coltman; Maj. J. Erskine; Revd Dr Johnston McKay; Alan Borthwick; Dr Alison Elliot; Luke Borwick; Walter Barbour; Lt Col Richard Callander.

Correspondent: Iain Mowat, Secretary, 182 Bath Street, Glasgow G2 4HG (tel: 0141 332 0476; email: info@bairdtrust.org.uk)

 www.bairdtrust.org.uk

The Baird Trust was founded by James Baird in 1873. This is a Scottish charity assisting the funds and schemes of the church in Scotland, and in particular the work of home mission, church extension, religious education and the support of active and retired ministers and their families.

There are two categories of grants for organisations: general grants, awarded for project costs; and grants awarded for repairs, renovations or new buildings of churches or church halls.

Financial information

In 2017 the trust had assets of £11.7 million and an income of £405,000. Grants were awarded totalling £290,500.

Beneficiaries included: Beith Parish Church (£10,000); Cadzow Parish

Church (£6,000); Alyth Parish Church (£5,000); Lairg Parish Church (£3,000); Motherwell Baptist Church and River Church – Elgin (£2,000 each).

Applications
Application forms can be downloaded from the website and submitted either by email or post. The trustees meet on a quarterly basis.

Sources of information
Accounts; annual report; OSCR record; funder's website.

The Rachel Baker Memorial Charity

 The arts, particularly classical music

England and Wales

£300,000 (2016/17)

CC number: 1162913

Trustees: Hugh Richards; Nicholas Moxon; Robin Daniels.

Correspondent: Kirsty McEwen, Clerk, c/o Higgs & Sons, Unit 3, Waterfront Business Park, Dudley Road, Brierley Hill DY5 1LX (tel: 01384 327322; email: kirsty.mcewen@higgsandsons.co.uk)

The Rachel Baker Memorial Charity was registered with the Charity Commission in July 2015. According to the charity's accounts its objects are, 'to apply the income, and all or such part or parts of the capital, at such time or times, and in such a manner as the trustees in their absolute discretion see fit, towards the promotion, maintenance and advancement of the education of the public in classical music. Particularly (but not limited to) making grants and awards to support charities or individuals (for exclusively charitable purposes) engaged in or concerned with the advancement of the arts, in particular (but not limited to), classical music'.

Financial information
In 2016/17 the charity had an income of £24,000 and a total expenditure of £319,500. Full accounts were not available to view on the Charity Commission website due to the charity's low income. We therefore estimate that grants totalled around £300,000.

Previous beneficiaries have included: City of Birmingham Symphony Orchestra and Young Classical Artists Trust (£125,000 each).

Applications
Details of how to apply for grants are available from the clerk. Applications must be on the charity's standard application form. Application forms should be completed and returned along with any relevant information to the clerk at least four weeks before the meeting at which the application is to be considered. The trustees usually meet at the end of May and at the end of October.

Sources of information
Accounts; annual report; Charity Commission record.

The Balcombe Charitable Trust

 Education, environment, health and welfare, specifically young people (up to the age of 29) who are not in education, employment or training

UK

£375,000 (2016/17)

CC number: 267172

Trustees: R. A. Kreitman; Patricia M. Kreitman; Nicholas Brown.

Correspondent: Jonathan Prevezer, c/o Citroen Wells, Devonshire House, 1 Devonshire Street, London W1W 5DR (email: jonathan@balcombetrust.org.uk)

 www.balcombetrust.org.uk

This trust generally makes grants in the fields of education, the environment and health and welfare. When the trust's investment income dropped in 2015/16 the trustees decided to narrow the trust's focus of funding. The trust is now concentrating on supporting innovative projects for young people (up to the age of 29) who are not in education, employment or training (NEETs). The trust's 2016/17 annual review states, 'The decision to move our focus onto UK charities was difficult but necessary to achieve a better reach for our objectives. Over the coming year the trustees will assess and discuss this implementation and decide in which direction we will move forward.'

At the time of writing (June 2018) the trust's website states:

The Trust will not be accepting any new grant applications until 1st October 2018 at the earliest. Further information will be posted in September, so we suggest you make a note to come back and check for an update. We are currently committed to more than 20 new multi-year projects focusing on young people in the UK who are not in education, employment or training (NEET). Our efforts will therefore be concentrated on assessing these projects and deciding on the future direction of the Trust's funding

Financial information
In 2016/17 the trust had assets of almost £30 million and an income of £450,000. During the year, the trust made grants to 27 charities. Some of these were continuing awards from earlier commitments but the new projects included coaching support for vulnerable young women, life skills programs for homeless young people, literacy and numeracy projects in prisons and a variety of initiatives supporting homeless or unemployed young people and refugees in various parts of the UK. Grants awarded totalled £375,000 and were distributed in the following categories:

Health and welfare	£189,000
Environment	£145,500
Education	£40,500

Beneficiaries included: Durrell Wildlife Conservation Trust (£50,000); Blue Ventures Conservation (£43,000); The 999 Club Trust (£45,000); Leuka (£20,000); Martlets Hospice Ltd (£10,000); Mary How Trust (£5,000); Freedom from Torture (£3,000); St Basils (£2,000).

Exclusions
No grants are given to individuals or non-registered charities.

Applications
Apply in writing to the correspondent.

Sources of information
Accounts; annual report; Charity Commission record.

The Ballinger Charitable Trust

 Health, development and well-being of young people, older people, cultural/arts projects

North east of England

£2.3 million (2016)

CC number: 1121739

Trustees: Diana Ballinger; John Flynn; Andrew Ballinger; Nicola Crowther.

Correspondent: Nicola Crowther, Trustee, PO Box 166, Ponteland, Newcastle upon Tyne NE20 2BL (tel: 0191 488 0520; email: info@ballingercharitabletrust.org.uk)

www.ballingercharitabletrust.org.uk

The Ballinger Charitable Trust was founded in 1994 and seeks to support charities, voluntary organisations and community groups through grants and funding.

The trust's website states that the trust currently makes grants to projects in the north east of England, supporting the following causes:

▶ Health, development and well-being of young people
▶ Older people
▶ Cultural/arts projects based in the north east of England

The websites states that:

> There is no minimum or maximum threshold to the funding that can be applied for. However, please consider the genuine costs of your proposal, any other grants awarded, or have been applied for elsewhere. We may also need to review your budget. The larger the fund applied for, the greater the amount of detail we may require.

Applicants can re-apply to the trust after a period of 12 months.

The 2016 annual report also states the following about the trust's approach:

> The Trustees recognise the deep economic and social needs in the region and that the financial donations they are able to make cannot meet that need. To extend support the Trustees have built on their experience of working together and funding charities in the North East over the last ten years to:
>
> ▶ Help charities collaborate to gain access to funding
> ▶ Connect with other funders both to reduce multiple applications by chanties to multiple funders and to bring new funders to the attention of local charities
> ▶ Identify where governance and management changes can enable people to realise their ambitions for their charity
>
> We expect these relatively new areas of work to continue

Financial information

In 2016 the trust had assets of £35.2 million and an income of £3.2 million. Grants awarded to organisations totalled £2.3 million.

Beneficiaries included: Age UK Gateshead (£185,500); Alzheimer's Society (£140,500); Youth Focus North East (£50,000); Streetspace (£35,500); Rape Crisis Tyneside and Northumberland, Sunderland Bangladesh International Centre and Woodhorn Museum (£25,000 each); Hexham Youth Initiative (£23,000); Royal Voluntary Service (£20,000); Real Deal Plus Ltd (£10,000).

Smaller grants were not listed in the accounts.

Exclusions

The trust does not fund sponsorship of any kind.

Applications

Applications for grants of up to £5,000

Applications should be made in a letter, sent by post to the PO Box address provided. Decisions are made twice a year, usually in late June and December, after which all applicants will be notified of the outcome.

Applications for grants of above £5,000

Applicants should first complete the initial application form on the website. You will be contacted shortly afterwards to either:

▶ Issue you with a unique user name and password giving access to the full application form, (note these details may be used for one full application only)
▶ Advise that your initial application has been unsuccessful

Applications can be submitted at any time; decisions on full applications are made by the trustees at their meetings in February, June September and November.

Sources of information

Accounts; annual report; Charity Commission record; funder's website.

The Bamford Charitable Foundation

 General charitable purposes

UK and overseas, but mainly within a 40-mile radius of Rocester

£ £290,500 (2016/17)

CC number: 279848

Trustees: The Lord Bamford; Lady Bamford.

Correspondent: D. G. Garnett, Administrator, c/o J. C. Bamford Excavators Ltd, Lakeside Works, Denstone Road, Rocester, Uttoxeter ST14 5JP (tel: 01889 593140)

Established in 1980 the foundation supports general charitable purposes with a preference for charities supporting children and young people, animal welfare and health and those that are within a 40-mile radius of Rocester, Staffordshire.

Financial information

In 2016/17 the foundation had assets of over £1.1 million, an income of £41,000 and made 15 grants totalling £290,500.

Beneficiaries included: Barbados Children's Trust and Denstone Foundation (£100,000 each); Racing Welfare (£20,000); Save The Children (£10,000); Checkley Parochial Church Council (£7,500); Woman vs Cancer (£5,000); Buttle UK, Panama Wildlife Conservation and Staffordshire Clubs for Young People (£1,000 each).

Applications

Apply in writing to the correspondent. The 2016/17 accounts state: 'Successful applicants are required to demonstrate to the trustees that the receipt of the grant is wholly necessary to enable them to fulfil their own objectives.' As well as responding to applications, the trustees also proactively identify potential grant recipients.

Sources of information

Accounts; annual report; Charity Commission record.

Banbury Charities

General charitable purposes, education, social welfare

Banbury and its surrounding area

£ £212,000 to organisations (2016)

CC number: 201418

Trustees: Judy May; Julia Colegrave; Angela Heritage; Nigel Morris; Helen Madeiros; Colin Clarke; Martin Humphries; Jamie Briggs; Kieron Mallon; Valerie Fisher; Tom Blinkhorn.

Correspondent: Nigel Yeadon, Clerk to the Trustees, 36 West Bar, Banbury, Oxfordshire OX16 9RU (tel: 01295 251234)

Banbury Charities is a group of eight registered charities:

▶ Bridge Estate Charity: for the benefit of local inhabitants where public support is not available.
▶ Countess of Arran's Charity: to promote education and to assist people in preparing for, entering upon, or engaged in any profession or trade by providing outfits, payment of fees or travel expenses to enable them to earn a living.
▶ Banbury Almshouse Charity: to provide and maintain almshouse accommodation.
▶ Banbury Sick Poor Fund: to supply special foods and medicines, medical comforts, extra bedding, fuel and medical and surgical appliances. The fund offers domestic help as well as financial grants.
▶ Banbury Arts and Educational Charity: to assist schools, colleges or other institutions of further education in providing facilities for the promotion of education in the arts, literature or science, as well as young people under the age of 25 studying at such institutions.
▶ Banbury Welfare Trust: for the relief of need, hardship and distress.
▶ Banbury Poor Trust: to benefit people who are in financial need; people suffering from illness, accident, old age or incapacity; any hospital or infirmary or like institution.
▶ Banbury Recreation Charity: to provide or assist in the provision of facilities for physical recreation.

All of these charities support organisations or individuals within a five-mile radius of Banbury, apart from the Banbury Poor Trust, which makes grants within a ten-mile radius.

Under these funds, the 2016 annual report states that support has been given to: secondary and primary schools; groups supporting young people; sports clubs and recreational organisations; building projects, such as churches and community halls; charities providing support to causes such as children and young people with cancer, those who have suffered bereavement, victims of domestic abuse; a hospice; individuals in need for welfare and educational purposes.

Financial information

In 2016 the charities had assets of almost £5.9 million and an income of £414,500. Grants totalled £286,000, of which £212,000 was awarded to 66 organisations and £74,000 was awarded in 236 grants to individuals.

Beneficiaries included: Banbury Welfare Trust (£33,000); Banbury Cricket Club (£15,000); Banbury Squadron Air Cadets (£10,000); Dogs for Good (£8,700); The Mill Arts Centre £5,000); Footsteps Foundation (£2,100); See Saw (£2,000); Frank Wise School (£1,500); Banbury Citizens Advice (£1,500); Nicodemus Trust (£1,000).

Applications

Apply in writing to the correspondent.

Sources of information

Accounts; annual report; Charity Commission record.

The Band Trust

 General charitable purposes including: army and veterans, children and young people, disability, disadvantaged individuals, education and arts, older people, nursing care

UK

£632,000 (2016/17)

CC number: 279802

Trustees: Richard Mason; Bartholomew Peerless; The Hon. Nicholas Wallop; The Hon. Nicholas Wallop; Victoria Wallop.

Correspondent: Richard Mason, Trustee, The Band Trust, BM BOX 2144, London WC1N 3XX (tel: 020 7702 4243; email: rjsmason32@gmail.com)

 www.bandtrust.co.uk

The trust was established in 1976 for general charitable purposes and it supports registered charities in the UK. Grants are made towards a range of charitable causes, under the following categories, as outlined on its website:

- Army and veterans
- Children and young people
- People with disabilities or who are otherwise disadvantaged
- Education and the arts
- Older people
- Nursing care

The trustees proactively identify organisations that they wish to support.

Financial information

In 2016/17 the trust had assets of £31.9 million and an income of £1 million. During the year, grants were made totalling £632,000, broken down as follows:

People with disabilities	£162,000
Children and young people	£132,500
Educational	£78,500
Disadvantaged	£70,500
Veterans	£70,000
Hospice and hospital	£45,000
Miscellaneous	£25,500
Ex-employees	£18,200
Prisons	£17,000
Medical	£5,000
Museums and art institutions	£5,000
Older people	£4,000

Beneficiaries included: Second Chance (£30,000); Prison Reform Trust (£17,000); Creative Sparkworks and Thomas Morley Trust (£15,000 each); Charlie Wailer Memorial Trust and Volunteering Matters (£10,000 each); The Halle Concert Society (£9,000); W11 Opera (£8,000); Friends of the Elderly (£2,000).

Exclusions

Unsolicited appeals; individuals; political activities; commercial ventures or publications; retrospective grants or loans; direct replacement of statutory funding or activities that are primarily the responsibility of central or local government.

Applications

Note: The trustees identify potential recipients themselves and do not accept unsolicited applications.

The website states:

> The Trust is unable to accept unsolicited applications. Due to the increase in postage costs The Band Trust will not acknowledge unsolicited applications.
>
> All the available funds are allocated proactively by the Trustees. They are keen that applicants do not waste any charity money or The Band Trust's equally limited resources by submitting applications that have no chance of success.

Only make an application if you have been specifically invited to do so – details are on the trust's website.

Sources of information

Accounts; annual report; Charity Commission record; funder's website.

The Banister Charitable Trust

 Physical and natural environment

UK

£910,500 (2016/17)

CC number: 1102320

Trustees: Christopher Banister; Huw Banister; Coutts And Co.

Correspondent: The Trustees, Trustee Department, 6th Floor, Trinity Quay 2, Avon Street, Bristol BS2 0PT (tel: 0345 304 2424; email: couttscharities@coutts. com)

The primary objective of this trust is to promote the conservation, protection and improvement of the physical and natural environment in the UK.

Financial information

In 2016/17 the trust had assets of £11.7 million and an income of almost £1.6 million. A total of 44 grants were made, amounting to £910,500.

Beneficiaries included: Lincolnshire Wildlife Trust (£58,000 towards a nature reserve land purchase); Avon Wildlife Trust (£45,000 for a three year programme reconnecting priority grassland); Nottinghamshire Wildlife Trust (£12,000 towards management costs of woodland nature reserves); Butterfly Conservation Trust (£10,000 towards a preservation project); Smallwoods (£10,000 for a volunteer development initiative); Ancient Tree Forum (£5,000 for core costs).

Applications

Apply in writing to the correspondent.

Sources of information

Accounts; annual report; Charity Commission record.

The Bank of Scotland Foundation

Community development and improvement, financial literacy and inclusion

Scotland

£1.4 million (2016)

OSCR number: SC032942

Trustees: Philip Grant; Robin Bulloch; Sarah Deas; Sir Paul Grice; Martin Fleming.

Correspondent: Lorraine O'Neill, Finance and Grants Manager, The Mound, Edinburgh EH1 1YZ (tel: 0131 300 9006; email: enquiries@ bankofscotlandfoundation.co.uk)

www.bankofscotlandfoundation.org

The Bank of Scotland Foundation is an independent charity providing grants to local, regional and national charities across Scotland, supporting people and their local communities. The foundation receives a £2 million donation from Lloyds Banking Group each year, which is used to fund its funding programmes.

Areas of support
The foundation gives support in two core areas, which are described on the website.

The development and improvement of local communities

Within any community, there will be a diverse collection of individuals and charities tackling local issues. Some issues will be unique to the local area, others will be replicated across the country or parts of it. We feel it is important to help individuals and groups work together to ensure a better quality of life within their community. Practical ways of making this happen may include:

- Initiatives designed to encourage the involvement in the community of those too often excluded
- Working with people on low incomes, at risk from poverty or with problems finding accommodation
- Improving the standard of local facilities

Financial literacy and financial inclusion

Making informed judgements and taking effective decisions regarding money are important skills – skills which some people can find to be beyond their grasp. Building the confidence and competence of everyone about finance is a particular priority for the Bank of Scotland Foundation. In order to achieve this, we're committed to supporting financial literacy and financial inclusion right across Scotland. We aim to help make these essential skills both easy and accessible for all.

Initiatives that we are particularly interested in supporting are:

- Promoting financial awareness and money advice
- Enhancing debt counselling services within the community
- Supporting life-skills in all age groups and sections of the community

Funding programmes
The foundation has three grants programmes through which charities registered in Scotland can apply:

- **Small Grants Programme:** Grants are made to support the development and improvement of local communities. Applications are accepted for amounts between £1,000 and £10,000 and grants are awarded for one year only.
- **Medium Grants Programme:** Grants are made to support the development and improvement of local communities and financial literacy and inclusion. Applications are accepted for amounts between £10,001 and £25,000 and grants are awarded for one year only.
- **Large Grants Programme:** Grants are made to support the development and improvement of local communities and financial literacy and inclusion. Applications are accepted for amounts between £50,000 and £100,000 and grants can be awarded over one or two years.

The foundation also runs Lloyds Banking Group's Matched Giving Programme, through which employees of the group can apply for up to £1,000 for charities of their choice (up to £500 for fundraising activities and up to £500 for voluntary time given).

All funding programmes run by the foundation are subject to their own eligibility criteria and guidelines. Full information can be found on the website.

Financial information
In 2016 the foundation held assets of £454,000 and had an income of £2.4 million. Grants totalled £1.4 million and were broken down as follows:

Developing and improving local communities	96	£806,500
Money advice and financial literacy	22	£609,500

Beneficiaries of large grants included: Changeworks (£100,000); Cancer Support Scotland (£60,000).

Beneficiaries of medium grants included: Baillieston Community Care (£10,600); Parkhead Citizens Advice (£13,000); The Tree Club (£17,600); Barmulloch Community Development Company (£25,000).

Beneficiaries of small grants included: 3TFM Community Radio (£1,000); Thornhill Playgroup and Toddlers (£1,500); Daisy Drop In (£2,300); Visualise Scotland (£3,500); Project Ability (£5,000).

Exclusions
The foundation does not support:

- Discriminatory or political organisations
- The promotion of religion
- Animal charities or medical research
- Organisations that redistribute funding for grant-making to other organisations and/or individuals
- Individuals
- Advertising or sponsorship

Applications
Applications can be made via the online form on the foundation's website, where eligibility criteria and guidelines are also available. Appeals for small and medium grants can be made once every 12 months and for large grants can be submitted only after two years have passed from the receipt of an award. Unsuccessful organisations should wait one year before trying again. The submission deadlines for each programme vary – see the website for most up-to-date information.

Sources of information
Accounts; annual report; OSCR record; funder's website.

The Barbers' Company General Charities

General charitable purposes, education, particularly medical education, illness

UK, with some preference for the City of London

£227,500 to organisations (2016/17)

CC number: 265579

Trustee: Worshipful Company of Barbers.

Correspondent: Col. Malachy Doran, Clerk, Barber-Surgeons' Hall, 1 Monkwell Square, Wood Street, London EC2Y 5BL (tel: 020 7606 0741; email: clerk@barberscompany.org)

 barberscompany.org.uk

The Worshipful Company of Barbers is one of the 110 livery companies of the City of London. It is also one of the oldest, having celebrated its 700th anniversary in 2008.

The charity, which was registered in 1973, was established for general charitable purposes. The trustees favour organisations supporting the relief of suffering, particularly for those who are terminally ill, and education, particularly medical education. There is some preference for projects in the City of London, especially those relating to education.

Grants are also made to individuals, particularly those connected with the barbers' trade and the medical profession.

Financial information
In 2016/17 the charity had assets of £1.6 million and an income of £170,500. Grants awarded to organisations totalled £227,500 and a further £11,100 was given in grants to ten individuals.

Beneficiaries included: King's College London (£58,500); Phyllis Tuckwell Hospice (£30,000); University of Warwick (£10,000); Brednock Primary School, Meridian Money Advice and Orthopaedic Research (£2,000 each); Clatterbridge Cancer Charity, Independence at Home Safer London (£1,000 each).

Grants of less than £1,000 amounted to £6,100.

Exclusions

The charity does not support medical research (but it does support medical education). The website states that it avoids giving grants to 'large and well-endowed charities, for them to spend as they see fit' and that it does not tend to support 'expensive projects where our contribution would be relatively insignificant', although it may consider a contribution towards a specific part of a project (e.g. a piece of equipment).

Applications

Apply in writing, directly to the Worshipful Company of Barbers. Guidelines are provided on the website.

Sources of information

Accounts; annual report; Charity Commission record; funder's website.

The Barbour Foundation

 Community and social welfare, housing, medical causes, general charitable purposes

 Mainly North East England

 £845,500 (2016/17)

CC number: 328081

Trustees: Helen Humphrey; Dame Margaret Barbour; Nichola Bellaby.

Correspondent: Mrs A. Harvey, Grants Administrator, PO Box 21, Guisborough, Cleveland TS14 8YH (tel: 0191 427 4221; email: barbour.foundation@barbour.com)

The objects of the foundation are to support medical research and relief of illness; education of children and young people; protection and preservation of features of historical or architectural interest; and relief of individuals in need.

The foundation's grant-making focuses on supporting organisations working on community welfare, housing and social deprivation, mainly in North East England.

Financial information

In 2016/17 the foundation held assets of £11.8 million and had an income of £256,000. During the year, 552 grants were made to organisations totalling £845,500, distributed in the following categories:

Medical	£226,500
Community welfare	£140,500
Children and young people	£124,000
Housing/homeless	£86,500
The arts	£73,500
Disability	£55,000
Education	£55,000
Service charities	£25,000
Conservation/horticultural	£21,000

Older people	£14,500
Animal welfare	£13,000
Maritime	£5,700
Special appeals	£3,500
Heritage/museums	£1,000

Beneficiaries included: West End School (£62,500); Hospitality and Hope South Tyneside and North Music Trust (£50,000 each); Elton John AIDS Foundation (£20,000); RBLI (£10,000); Young Asian Voices (£5,000); Fire Fighters Charity, Jesmond Library and Middleton in Teesdale Methodist Church (£2,000 each); Byker Community Association, Evenwood Family Support Project, Northern Children's Book Festival, South Tyneside Women's Aid and West End Refugee Service (£1,000 each).

Exclusions

Support is not given for:

 Requests from outside the geographical area
- Individual applications, unless backed by a particular charitable organisation
- Capital grants for building projects

Applications

Apply in writing to the correspondent. The application should include detailed information of what the grant will be used for, a statement of accounts and the official charity number of the applicant. A main grants meeting is held every three to four months to consider applications for grants of more than £500; smaller grants are considered on a monthly basis.

Sources of information

Accounts; annual report; Charity Commission record.

The Barclay Foundation

 General charitable purposes

 UK

 £655,000 to organisations (2016)

CC number: 803696

Trustees: Sir David Barclay; Sir Frederick Barclay; Aidan Barclay; Howard Barclay.

Correspondent: Michael Seal, Administrator, 2nd Floor, 14 St George Street, London W1S 1FE (tel: 020 7915 0915; email: mseal@ellerman.co.uk)

The foundation was established in 1989 by Sir David and Sir Frederick Barclay; who own the Telegraph Media Group Ltd. The foundation's objects are broad, however according to its 2016/17 annual report, the foundation's trustees have a preference for medical research and projects which support young people, people who are ill, people with disabilities or people who are disadvantaged. Note that the foundation

has no association with Barclays Bank plc.

Financial information

In 2016 the foundation had assets of £62,000 and an income of £790,500. Grants were made to seven organisations totalling £655,000. A further £8,000 was given in grants to individuals. Grants to organisations were distributed as follows:

Aid for young people	5	£455,000
Historical preservation	1	£100,000
Medical research	1	£100,000

Beneficiaries included: Frederick Hugh Trust (£300,000); Nora Doherty Charitable Foundation (£127,500); Thrombosis Research Institute and Weidenfeld Fund (£100,000 each); Duke of Edinburgh's Foundation (£15,000); Cometa Foundation (£10,000); Reina Sophia School of Music (£2,000).

Applications

Apply in writing to the correspondent. Applications should include details of the project being proposed, the level of funding required, and details of any funds already secured. Following an initial screening, applications are selected according to their merits, suitability and the funds available. Visits are usually made to projects where substantial funds have been requested.

Sources of information

Accounts; annual report; Charity Commission record.

The Baring Foundation

 Strengthening the voluntary sector, law and human rights, LGBT+ rights in sub-Saharan Africa, participatory arts for older people

 UK and overseas

 £2.3 million (2016)

CC number: 258583

Trustees: Janet Morrison; Vicki Amedume; Emma Badman; Dr Rob Berkeley; David Elliot; Dr Alison Evans; Katherine Garrett-Cox; Lucy de Groot; Prof. Andrew Hind; James Jenkins; Poonam Joshi; Shauneen Lambe; François Matarasso; Marie Staunton; Prof. Myles Wickstead.

Correspondent: David Cutler, Director, 8–10 Moorgate, London EC2R 6DA (tel: 020 7767 1348; email: baring.foundation@uk.ing.com)

 baringfoundation.org.uk

 @Baring_Found

This foundation was established in 1969 to help improve the quality of life of people suffering from disadvantage and discrimination. Its main objective is to strengthen the voluntary organisations that serve those people, directly or indirectly, both in the UK and abroad, by making grants.

Grant programmes

Potential applicants are advised to check the website for up-to-date grant-making information and guidelines. According to the website, funding is currently being given in the following areas:

Arts

The programme focuses on 'engaging the talent, experience and enthusiasm of older people in the creative arts'. Funding is given to support participatory arts with people over the age of 60, especially those facing disadvantage or discrimination.

Applications are by invitation only, unless an open programme is advertised on the foundation's website. Activities will often be part of a partnership between organisations and the foundation currently maintains a funding relationship with all four Arts Councils in the UK. The foundation also has a partnership with the Winston Churchill Memorial Trust.

International development

This programme 'aims to support civil society organisations to address discrimination against lesbian, gay, bisexual, transgender and intersex (LGBTI) individuals and communities in sub-Saharan Africa', with a particular focus on lesbian and transgender communities. As noted on the website, the foundation designs its funding to support the work of local civil society organisations 'rather than determine their agenda'.

Applications are by invitation only, unless an open programme is advertised on the foundation's website.

Strengthening the voluntary sector

This UK-only programme is delivered in collaboration with the Legal Education Foundation and Esmée Fairbairn Foundation and is designed 'to boost engagement and to support organisations within broader civil society to embrace law and human rights-based approaches as effective tools for achieving change for individuals and communities'. It also aims to develop 'sustainable collaborations, partnerships and networks that leverage existing expertise within the sector to ensure the use of these approaches is as effective as possible'.

At the time of writing (June 2018) this programme was closed for applications.

Financial information

In 2016 the foundation had assets of £79.9 million and an income of £1.6 million. A total of 47 new grants were awarded during the year, totalling

more than £2.3 million. Grants were distributed in the following categories:

Strengthening the voluntary sector	£1.35 million
Arts programmes	£783,500
Special initiatives	£138,000
International programme	£52,000

A list of beneficiaries for 2016 was not included in the annual report and accounts.

Recent beneficiaries have included: Other Foundation (£525,000); Community Law Advice Network – Clan Childlaw (£150,000); Friends, Families and Travellers (£30,000); University of Manchester (£21,000); Astraea Lesbian Foundation for Justice (£20,000); Arts Council for Northern Ireland (£5,000); Scotswood Natural Community Garden (£4,000).

Applications

Potential applicants should in the first instance refer to the website for information on each programme, current guidelines and application information.

Sources of information

Accounts; annual report; Charity Commission record; funder's website.

The Barker-Mill Foundation

🔍	General charitable purposes, including: education, health, performing arts and culture, sport and leisure, animal welfare
📍	UK, with a strong preference for south-west Hampshire, including Southampton
£	£175,000 (2016/17)

CC number: 1045479

Trustees: Christopher Gwyn-Evans; Tim Jobling; Richard Moyse.

Correspondent: Christopher Gwyn-Evans, Trustee, The Estate Office, Longdown, Marchwood, Southampton SO40 4UH (tel: 023 8029 2107; email: info@barkermillfoundation.com)

 www.barkermillfoundation.com

 facebook.com/BarkerMFoundation

The Barker-Mill Foundation was established in 1995 from funds provided by members of the Barker-Mill family in memory of their father and grandfather, Peter Barker-Mill. Previously known as the Peter Barker-Mill Memorial Charity, the foundation provides around 80 grants a year to charities, schools, and local community groups primarily in south-west Hampshire where the Barker-Mill family has owned land for generations. In particular, the

foundation gives priority to charities working in more deprived local areas, including; Nursling and Rownhams, Redbridge, Millbrook, and Totton.

Except for exceptional applications, the foundation does not normally provide grants in excess of £5,000. Furthermore, the foundation states that under normal circumstances it will not commit itself to making a series of donations or make further donations within less than a year of a previous donation.

The foundation notes that while it will consider applications for core funding, it prefers to make grants restricted to specific projects.

Financial information

In 2016/17 the foundation held assets of £3.5 million and had an income of £80,000. Grants awarded to organisations totalled £175,000.

Beneficiaries included: Murray Parish Trust (Southampton Hospital Appeal) (£40,000); Southampton City Mission (£20,000); Nursling and Rownhams Parochial Church Council (£10,500); St Mary Magdalene Music Society (£7,000); Autism and Nature (£6,300); Hampshire and Isle of Wight Community Foundation (£5,000); Homestart New Forest, Totton and Eling Tennis Centre (£2,500 each); Waterside Archers (£500).

Exclusions

The foundation will typically not consider applications for funding from:

- Individuals
- National charities
- Charities with no connection to Hampshire

Applications

Applications should be made via the foundation's website. Guidelines are also available on the site. The trustees meet in January, April, July and October to consider applications.

Sources of information

Accounts; annual report; Charity Commission record; funder's website.

Lord Barnby's Foundation

🔍	General charitable purposes
📍	UK
£	£235,000 (2016/17)

CC number: 251016

Trustees: The Hon. George Lopes; The Countess Peel; Sir Michael Farquhar; Algy Smith-Maxwell; Laura Greenall.

Correspondent: Catherine Thomason, Secretary, PO Box 442, Market Drayton TF9 9EQ (email: lordbarnbyfoundation@gmail.com)

The settlor of the charity was the late The Rt Hon. Vernon, Baron Barnby, who settled under the terms of the trust deed a portfolio of investments. Following the death of Lady Barnby on 2 November 1988 the residue of her estate, after payment of certain legacies, was added to the foundation.

The foundation has established a permanent list of beneficiaries that it supports each year, with the remaining funds then distributed to other charities.

Financial information
In 2016/17 the foundation had assets of £5.5 million and an income of £251,500. Grants awarded to organisations totalled £235,000.

Beneficiaries included: Barnby Memorial Hall (£15,000); Countryside Learning and Farms for City Children (£10,000 each); Atlantic Salmon Trust (£7,000); Sea Cadets (£5,000); Child Autism UK (£2,000); 1st Duffield Scout Group and CLIC Sargent (£1,000); Cancer Research UK (£500).

Exclusions
Grants are not given to individuals.

Applications
Applications will only be considered if they are received in writing and accompanied by a set of the latest accounts. Applicants do not need to send an sae. Appeals are considered three times a year, in February, June and November.

Sources of information
Accounts; annual report; Charity Commission record.

Barnes Workhouse Fund

Social welfare, older people, health, recreation and leisure, education

Ancient parish of Barnes only (broadly the SW13 postal district)

£223,000 to organisations (2016)

CC number: 200103

Trustees: Caroline Kelsall; John Story; Debbie Ferreira; Michael Murison; Cllr Paul Hodgins; Carolyn Rampton; Sarah Wilson; Luke Tegner.

Correspondent: Miranda Ibbetson, Director, PO Box 665, Richmond, Surrey TW10 6YL (tel: 020 8241 3994; email: mibbetson@barnesworkhousefund.org. uk)

 www.barnesworkhousefund.org.uk

Barnes Workhouse Fund was registered with the Charity Commission in 1961 for the benefit of residents of the ancient parish of Barnes (this is, broadly speaking, the SW13 postal district). The fund owns Walsingham Lodge, a sheltered housing complex, however these funds are kept separate from the fund's main capital, which is invested for grant-making purposes.

Grants policy
The fund makes grants to organisations that can demonstrate that they fulfil the criteria of assisting residents of the ancient parish of Barnes. The trustees consider 'applications for grants such as revenue grants or grants for items of equipment or one-off projects'. The Barnes Workhouse Fund also holds reserves designated for helping with capital projects.

Grants are also made to individuals for both educational and relief-in-need purposes. See the website for more information.

Financial information
In 2016 the fund had assets of £11.3 million and an income of £721,000. Grants were made totalling £259,000, with £36,000 given to individuals.

Beneficiaries included: Castlenau Centre Project (£42,500); Richmond Citizens Advice (£34,500); Age UK Richmond upon Thames (£15,000); Crossroads Care (£13,300); Home-Start (£5,300); Holly Lodge Centre (£3,000); Richmond Adult Community College (£1,200); Barnes Music Society (£1,000 each); IO Theatre Company (£500); Barnes Christmas Lights Project (£60).

Applications
Organisations can apply using the online form on the fund's website and are advised to first read the eligibility guidelines on the website. Applications from organisations are considered at trustee meetings in January, March, May, July, September and November each year. Applications must be received by the 6th of the month preceding a meeting to be considered.

Note that the fund's office is closed during August each year.

Sources of information
Accounts; annual report; Charity Commission record; funder's website.

Barnwood Trust

 Improving quality of life for people in Gloucestershire with disabilities and mental health issues

Gloucestershire

£289,000 to organisations (2016)

CC number: 1162855

Trustees: James Davidson; Sally Pullen; Annabella Scott; Lucy Floyer-Aclan; Michael North; Prof. Clair Chilvers; Dr Jean Walters; Suzanne Beach; Shaun Parson; Rachel Robinson; Edward Playne; Benjamin Preece-Smith.

Correspondent: The Grants Team, Ullenwood Manor Farm, Ullenwood, Cheltenham GL53 9QT (tel: 01452 611292; email: grants@barnwoodtrust. org)

 www.barnwoodtrust.org

 facebook.com/BarnwoodTrust

 @BarnwoodTrust

 @barnwoodtrust

Barnwood House Trust was established in its original form in 1792 and is now governed by a Charity Commission Scheme of 17 April 2000. It is one of Gloucestershire's largest charities providing assistance to people with disabilities, including those with mental health conditions, who live in the county. Its current endowment arises principally from the sale of the land upon which Barnwood House Hospital stood until 1966.

The trust provides four types of grant, details of which have been taken from its website:

Small Grants
Grants of up £1,000 are available for organisations in Gloucestershire who work to benefit disabled people and people with mental health problems. Grants could be for new projects, pilot schemes or specific pieces of equipment. Since the sale of the hospital, the trust has developed as a provider of facilities and funding for people with disabilities. It offers grants to individuals and organisations and provides supported accommodation and day care, all of which is focused on improving opportunities and quality of life for individuals and subsequently their carers.

Sports Equipment Grants
Grants of up to £5,000 to purchase sports-related equipment for activities are available for organisations in Gloucestershire who work to benefit disabled people and people with mental health problems. Grants could be for things like rugby wheelchairs or wheelchair-accessible bikes.

Holidays and Play Schemes

Grants for holidays and play schemes are available to organisations with a demonstrable track record of providing holidays, trips or play schemes for Gloucestershire people with a disability. These grants are fast-tracked.

Community Spaces Capital Grant

As part of its funding programme, Barnwood has established a Community Spaces Capital Grant. It aims to help support communities and eligible organisations to develop and improve inclusive community spaces through building belonging.

Barnwood's vision is to create the best possible environment in Gloucestershire for disabled people and people with mental health problems to make the most of their lives. Community spaces enabling people to connect and build relationships with others where everyone is welcome, are a vital part of that environment.

'Everyone is welcome' means that particular attention is given to helping people who are usually marginalised to feel that they belong in the community; for example, those with disabilities and mental health problems.

Applying for a Community Spaces Capital Grant

To be eligible to apply for our Grant, a community space project must:

- Be linked to a clear plan both for making the space welcoming, accessible and for building a more inclusive community
- Be from 'constituted' groups or organisations that have community or charitable purposes. New groups working with a constituted group may also be eligible
- Be willing to go 'the extra mile' in terms of building belonging through bringing everyone together

Barnwood will consider funding various aspects of a community spaces project such as:

- technical advice or consultancy services
- design work
- construction costs
- refurbishment costs
- furnishings and equipment

However, the Grant cannot be used for revenue costs.

Financial information

In 2016 the trust held assets of £95.2 million and an income of £3.7 million. Grants awarded to organisations totalled £289,000 and were broken down as follows:

Community Space grants	£130,000
Small grants to organisations	£109,000
Holiday and play scheme grants	£43,000
Apprenticeship grants	£7,000

A further £646,000 was given to individuals.

Beneficiaries included: Wooton Community Sports Foundation (£70,000); Roses Theatre Trust (£60,000); Cotswold Communities First CIC (£5,000); Gloucester Crusaders Boccia Club (£4,800); South Gloucestershire and Stroud College (£2,200); Allsorts Gloucestershire (£1,500).

Applications

Application forms for organisations and individuals are available to download from the trust's website or can be requested from the correspondent.

If you would like more information on the Community Spaces fund contact one of the trust's Housing and Community Spaces Facilitators: lawrence.miller@barnwoodtrust.org or martin.hawkins@barnwoodtrust.org.

Sources of information

Accounts; annual report; Charity Commission record; funder's website.

Misses Barrie Charitable Trust

 General charitable purposes

UK, with a particular interest in Surrey, Warwickshire, Worcestershire and Scotland

£ £213,500 (2016/17)

CC number: 279459

Trustees: John Carter; Rachel Fraser; Sally Abell; Charlotte Carter; Suzanne Fraser.

Correspondent: The Trustees, Raymond Carter and Co., 14A High Street, Reigate, Surrey RH2 9AY (tel: 01737 248065; email: charlotte@raymondcarter.co.uk)

This trust was established for general charitable purposes in 1979 by the late Miss Sheila Coupar Barrie and the late Miss Moira Morrison Barrie. The trustees support various small to medium-sized charities and appear to have a particular interest in those in Surrey, Warwickshire, Worcestershire and Scotland.

Financial information

In 2016/17 the trust had assets of £7.15 million and an income of £228,500. Grants to 85 organisations totalled £213,500.

Beneficiaries included: East Neuk Festival (£25,000); Royal National Lifeboat Institution (£10,000); Brain Tumour Research and UK Athletics Ltd (£3,000 each); Edinburgh Headway Group and Friends of the Elderly (£2,000 each); Braille Chess Association, Warwickshire Hedgehog Rescue and Wellesbourne Cricket Club (£1,000 each).

Exclusions

No grants are made to individuals.

Applications

Apply in writing to the correspondent accompanied, where appropriate, by up-to-date accounts or financial information. The trustees normally meet three times a year. Due to the large amount of unsolicited applications they receive, the trustees are unable to notify unsuccessful applicants.

Sources of information

Accounts; annual report; Charity Commission record.

Robert Barr's Charitable Trust

General charitable purposes

Scotland and overseas

£ £996,000 (2016/17)

OSCR number: SC007613

Correspondent: Sandra Graham, Maclay Murray & Spens, 1 George Square, Glasgow G2 1AL (email: sandra.graham@dentons.com)

The trust makes grants for a wide range of charitable purposes and the trustees tend to mainly support charities based in Scotland. Capital projects are preferred to running costs.

Financial information

In 2016/17 the trust held assets of £889,000 and had an income of £731,000. Grants totalling £996,000 were made to organisation and were broken down as follows:

Adult and child welfare	£396,000
Arts	£225,000
Adult welfare	£110,000
Conservation	£105,000
Medical research and support	£77,000
Child welfare	£40,000
International welfare	£15,000
Environment	£10,000
Research and education	£8,000

Beneficiaries included: Prince and Princess of Wales Hospice and University of Strathclyde (£100,000 each); ME Research UK and National Theatre of Scotland (£30,000 each); Jubilee Sailing Trust (£20,000); Orkidstudio and Woodland Trust Scotland (£10,000); Sedbergh School and The Unicorn Preservation Society (£5,000 each).

Applications

Apply in writing to the correspondent. The trustees meet in March each year.

Sources of information

Accounts; annual report; OSCR record.

The Paul Bassham Charitable Trust

 General charitable purposes

 UK, mainly Norwich and Norfolk

(£) £530,000 (2016/17)

CC number: 266842

Trustees: Alexander Munro; Richard Lovett; Graham Tuttle; Patrick Harris.

Correspondent: The Trustees, c/o Howes Percival, Flint Buildings, 1 Bedding Lane, Norwich NR3 1RG (tel: 01603 762103)

This trust registered with the Charity Commission in 1974 and supports general charitable purposes through its grant-making. The 2016/17 annual report states;

- Preference is given to Norfolk charities and charitable causes and consideration is given to all applications of whatever nature provided that they are legally charitable and fulfil the public benefit requirement
- Donations will not be made direct to individuals or unregistered organisations so as to ensure that all donations are used solely for charitable purposes
- To the extent that any of the trust's annual income remains undistributed within the above, applications would be considered from charities with national or international coverage for expenditure on those charities' projects within Norfolk

The trust will mainly fund projects based in Norfolk or benefitting Norfolk.

Financial information

In 2016/17 the trust had assets of £13.2 million and had an income of £389,000. During the year, the charity awarded 158 grants to organisations totalling around £530,000.

Beneficiaries included: Norfolk Wildlife Trust (£50,000); Norfolk Community Foundation and Norfolk Hospice (£25,000 each); NCF for Norwich City College Paul and Winfred Bursary (£21,000).

Grants less than £10,000 totalled £232,000.

Exclusions

Grant are not be made directly to individuals, nor to unregistered charities.

Applications

Only in writing to the correspondent – no formal application forms issued. Telephone enquiries are not invited because of administrative costs. The trustees meet quarterly to consider general applications.

Sources of information

Accounts; annual report; Charity Commission record.

The Batchworth Trust

 Medical, humanitarian aid, social welfare, general charitable purposes

Worldwide

(£) £633,000 (2016/17)

CC number: 245061

Trustee: Lockwell Trustees Ltd.

Correspondent: James Peach, Kreston Reeves LLP, Griffin House, 135 High Street, Crawley RH10 1DQ (tel: 01209 377 615; email: james.peach@krestonreeves.com)

The trust mainly supports charities in a wide range of general charitable purposes both in the UK and overseas, with a particular interest in medical research, young people and social welfare. The 2016/17 annual report states:

> Grants to smaller charities remained a priority of the Trust during the year and in most cases the distributions so made were provided to support an innovation or a critical issue. Support for larger or national charities was predominantly to support either the ongoing work of the organisation or a particular initiative.

Financial information

In 2016/17 the trust held assets of £14.4 million and had an income of £482,500. During the year, the trust gave £633,000 in grants to organisations.

Beneficiaries included: DEC East Africa Crisis (£50,000); The Tom Bowdidge Foundation (£30,000); Oxfordshire Motor Project – TRAX (£25,000); Young Minds (£20,000); Inspire, The Forgiveness Project and Thrive (£10,000 each); The Waterside Trust (£5,000).

Exclusions

No grants are made directly to individuals.

Applications

Apply in writing to the correspondent. An sae should be included if a reply is required.

Sources of information

Accounts; annual report; Charity Commission record.

The Battersea Power Station Foundation

 General charitable purposes, community development

 Lambeth, Wandsworth

(£) £1.2 million (2016)

CC number: 1161232

Trustees: Marquess Of Salisbury Robert Gascoyne-Cecil; Rt Hon. Lord Strathclyde; Dato' Jauhari.

Correspondent: Linda Crowhurst, Grants Co-ordinator, 7 Circus Road West, Battersea Power Station, London SW11 8EZ (tel: 020 7501 0715; email: info@bpsfoundation.org.uk)

bpsfoundation.org.uk

The foundation was established in 2014 by the shareholders who are redeveloping Battersea Power Station.

The foundation works with local organisations to support projects that improve the quality of life for people who live in Lambeth and Wandsworth.

Grant-making priorities

Grants can be made to constituted groups with a charitable purpose, for revenue costs, including projects, salary costs and pilot projects. The foundation looks for four common priorities in each application:

- Sustainability
- Local impact
- Shared involvement
- Added value

Further detail is given on the foundation's website.

The Spring Fund

The website states:

> The Spring Fund helps communities in Lambeth and Wandsworth with projects that bring together residents, volunteers, businesses and local authorities to strengthen neighbourhood bonds, create new opportunities and transform lives. It's about funding smaller, grassroots community efforts that energise neighbourhoods and deliver on local goals

Grants of up to £5,000 are made to organisations working in Lambeth or Wandsworth which:

- Encourage better connections between, and amongst local communities, so people feel a greater sense of ownership and responsibility for the places where they live
- Improve the wellbeing of local people by building their confidence and strength of character
- Open up new economic opportunities for residents
- Create locally-based solutions to improve community conditions
- Motivate residents to join in with neighbourhood activities
- Improve the capabilities of local organisations to deal with neighbourhood issues

It supports organisations which are 'rooted in the local community and show a real understanding of neighbourhood issues'.

The Evolve Fund

Grants from this fund are made on a proactive basis, with the fund identifying organisations which match its own long-term vision. The website states that organisations supported under this fund are 'usually involved in projects that tackle a clear and well-researched need. Their approach is normally based around evidence of what works, and they have a good understanding of how their proposals will impact in both the short- and longer-term.' A wide range of causes are supported, often larger projects with a wider reach, although still benefitting the communities of Lambeth and Wandsworth.

In addition to these two funds, the trustees state in their 2016 annual report: 'Furthermore, we aim over the next few years to provide capacity building support to the organisations and communities we fund in order to ensure we leave a lasting legacy.'

Financial information

In 2016 the foundation held assets of £41,5000 and had an income of £224,500. During the year, the foundation made 37 grants totalling almost £1.2 million, of which six were 'learning grants'; four were from the Evolve Fund; and 27 were from the Spring Fund.

Beneficiaries included: Leap Confronting Conflict (£171,000); Chance UK (£120,000); Futures Theatre, South London Cares and Trees for Cities (£5,000 each); Citizens Advice Wandsworth (£4,800); Doddington and Rollo Community Roof Garden (£4,600); Home-Start Lambeth (£4,400); Battersea Befriending Network and The Rotary Club of Battersea Park (£1,000 each).

Exclusions

According to the its website the foundation will not fund the following:

- Individuals or causes that will benefit only one person, including student grants or bursaries
- General/round-robin appeals
- Promotion of religion and places of worship
- Replacement or subsidy of statutory funding, or for work which the foundation considers should be funded by government, such as residential and day care, housing provision, individual schools, nurseries and colleges, or a combination of any of these
- Individual campaigns
- Organisations seeking to distribute grants or funds to others
- Capital developments and individual items of equipment
- One-off events, such as conferences, seminars, galas, or summer schools
- Educational initiatives linked to the national curriculum
- Medical research or treatment, including drug and alcohol rehabilitation services
- Counselling and psychotherapy services

- Animal welfare, zoos, captive breeding and animal rescue centres
- Retrospective funding
- Work that is not legally charitable
- Organisations which have applied unsuccessfully within the previous 12 months

Applications

Applications for the Spring Fund can be made through the foundation's website. Applicants should first complete the eligibility test and they will then be sent a link to the application page. Detailed guidance, FAQs and other information is provided on the website. Applications can be made at any time and the foundation aims to respond within three months.

Applications are not accepted for the Evolve Fund, as the foundation identifies eligible organisations proactively.

Sources of information

Accounts; annual report; Charity Commission report; funder's website.

Bay Charitable Trust

 Social welfare, Jewish causes

 UK and overseas

 £692,500 to individuals and organisations (2016)

CC number: 1060537

Trustees: Ian Kreditor; Michael Lisser.

Correspondent: Ian Kreditor, Trustee, 21 Woodlands Close, London NW11 9QR (tel: 020 8810 4321)

Registered with the Charity Commission in February 2007, the objects of the trust are 'to give charity for the relief of poverty and the advancement of traditions of the Orthodox Jewish religion and the study of Torah'.

Financial information

In 2016 the trust had assets of £123,500 and an income of £512,500. Grants totalled £692,500 and were payable to both individuals and organisations.

There was no list of beneficiaries within the yearly accounts.

Applications

Apply in writing to the correspondent.

Sources of information

Accounts; annual report; Charity Commission record.

The Louis Baylis (Maidenhead Advertiser) Charitable Trust

 General charitable purposes, with some preference for: children and young people, older individuals, and disadvantaged people

 UK but mainly Berkshire, Buckinghamshire and Oxfordshire, with a preference for Maidenhead

 £253,500 (2016/17)

CC number: 210533

Trustees: John Robertson; Peter Sands; Peter Murcott; Patricia Lattimer.

Correspondent: Richard Curry, Trust Administrator, PO Box 4832, Maidenhead SL60 1JQ (tel: 01628 626333; email: lbctrust@baylismedia.co.uk)

🌐 www.baylis-trust.org.uk

f facebook.com/ MaidenheadAdvertiser

🐦 @maidenheadads

The trust was set up by Louis Baylis in 1962 in order 'to work for the good of the community, principally in the Royal Borough of Windsor & Maidenhead'. The trust was established to safeguard the newspaper, The Maidenhead Advertiser, from outside influence and provide for the newspaper's continuance as part of the civic and social life of the community it serves. Support is given to local, regional and national charities. The bulk of donations are made to benefit older and young people, although many other causes, including the arts are supported.

Financial information

In 2016/17 the trust had assets of £14.8 million and an income of £3.2 million. The trust made 131 grants totalling £253,500. The grants awarded are broken down as follows:

Local charities and organisations	84%	£212,000
Regional charities	11%	£29,000
National charities	5%	£12,500

Beneficiaries included: Maidenhead Citizens Advice (£25,000); Pearl Scan Solutions Ltd for Heritage Archiving (£20,000); Cracker Appeal (£5,000); First Maidenhead Sea Scouts (£3,250); Legacy Leisure and Maidenhead Christmas Light Committee (£5,000); Boybne Hill Cricket Club and Maidenhead Heritage Trust (£2,000); Maidenhead River Swim, Maidenhead United Reformed Church Holiday Clubs and SMILE (£1,000 each); Slough Fuelshare (£500).

Exclusions

Individuals are excluded.

Applications

Application forms are available to download on the website and should be returned to the Trust Administrator by email or post. The trustees meet four times a year to consider grants. The Trust Administrator attends the trust's offices, normally on Monday and Wednesday, and applicants are encouraged to visit the offices and speak to him.

Sources of information

Accounts; annual report; Charity Commission record; funder's website.

BBC Children in Need

 Disadvantaged children and young people (aged 18 and under)

 UK

£62.8 million (2016/17)

CC number: 802052

Trustees: Phil Hodkinson; Charlotte Moore; Peter McBride; Stevie Spring; Anne Bulford; Bob Shennan; Luke Mayhew; Donald Mackinnon; Gillian Sheldon; Matthew Baker; Joanna Berry.

Correspondent: Grants Team, Grants, BBC Children in Need, PO Box 649, Salford M5 0LD (tel: 0345 609 0015 – option 2; email: pudseygrants@bbc.co.uk)

 www.bbc.co.uk/pudsey

This charity, registered in 1989, distributes the proceeds of the BBC's annual Children in Need appeal (first televised in 1980). The BBC Children in Need's vision is that every child in the UK has a safe, happy and secure childhood and the chance to reach their potential. The charity awards grants each year to organisations working to improve the lives of disadvantaged children and young people in the UK.

Grants Programmes

The charity awards funding to projects through its Main and Small Grants programmes. The information in this part of the entry was taken from the charity's website, where full details of both programmes are available.

Main Grants

The Main Grants programme is open to charities and not-for-profit organisations applying for grants over £10,000 per year for up to three years.

Grants are given for children and young people of 18 years and under who are experiencing disadvantage through:

- Illness, distress, abuse or neglect
- Any kind of disability
- Behavioural or psychological difficulties
- Living in poverty or situations of deprivation

Small Grants

The Small Grants programme is open to charities and not-for-profit organisations applying for any amount up to and including £10,000 per year for up to three years.

Grants are given for children and young people of 18 years and under who are experiencing disadvantage through:

- Illness, distress, abuse or neglect
- Any kind of disability
- Behavioural or psychological difficulties
- Living in poverty or situations of deprivation

The website also states: 'In our Small Grants programme we are looking for projects where a relatively small amount of money can make a big difference for children and young people. We are unlikely to fund applications which top up funding for salaries or larger projects where a small grant would only make a marginal impact on its success.'

Emergency Essentials

The charity also funds the Emergency Essentials programme which provides items to meet the most basic needs of individual children who are living in severe poverty. The programme is administered by Buttle UK. See the Buttle UK website for information on how to apply for a grant.

Financial information

In 2016/17, there were 1,451 new grants awarded, totalling £62.8 million.

The charity's informative annual report and accounts included a number of helpful tables showing the distribution of active grants:

London and South East	585	£36.2 million	24%
North	553	£33.8 million	22%
Central	481	£29.7 million	19%
South West	271	£14.5 million	9%
England total	**1890**	**£114.2 million**	**74%**
Scotland	300	£17.6 million	11%
Northern Ireland	208	£10 million	7%
Wales	157	£9.6 million	6%

By principal type of disadvantage, grants were distributed as follows:

Poverty and deprivation	963	£51.8 million	34%
Disability	543	£30 million	19%
Marginalised groups	356	£23 million	15%
Distress	246	£18.8 million	12%
Illness	219	£18.8 million	9%
Abuse/neglect	158	£12.1 million	8%
Behavioural difficulties	77	£4.7 million	3%

Exclusions

Grants will not be given for/to:

- Work which statutory bodies (such as schools or local authorities) have a duty to fund
- Local government or NHS bodies
- Building projects applying for more than £20,000
- Projects which promote religion
- Fund trips or projects abroad
- Medical treatment or research
- Pregnancy testing or advice, information or counselling on pregnancy choices
- Awareness-raising work, except where it is targeted at those children or young people most at risk
- Bursaries, sponsored places, fees or equivalent
- Individuals (unless an eligible organisation is applying on their behalf or through the Emergency Essentials Programme)
- Be passed on to other organisations, for example, PTAs applying on behalf of schools
- General appeals or endowment funds
- Help with budget shortfalls or debt repayments
- Projects where the grant expenditure is due to start before the grant award date (retrospective funding)
- Organisations which have applied in the last 12 months
- Projects unable to start within 12 months of the grant award date
- Unspecified expenditure
- Organisational overheads or running costs which the organisation would incur whether the project was running or not. (Although the charity will consider funding support costs incurred as a direct result of running the project.)

Applications

Applications can be made via the charity's website which also has details of guidelines and application deadlines. If you have a general enquiry, are unsure about anything you have read or are looking for support regarding your application, contact the charity via phone or email. You can also contact your local regional or national office.

All applicants to the main grants programme need to complete an 'Initial Application' form. After this assessment successful applicants are invited to make a full application. Decisions are usually made within five months, some applicants will hear much sooner if they are not going to get a grant. For applications to the Small Grants Programme, there are four application dates throughout the year with a shortened period of consideration.

Sources of information

Accounts; annual report; Charity Commission website; funder's website; guidelines for applicants.

BC Partners Foundation

 Community development, environmental conservation, arts, education

UK and overseas

£484,000 (2016)

CC number: 1136956

Trustees: Nikos Stathopolous; Joseph Cronly; Lorna Parker; Michael Pritchard; Richard Kunzer; Cédric Dubourdieu; Francesco Loredan.

Correspondent: The Trustees, BC Partners LLP, 40 Portman Square, London W1H 6DA (tel: 020 7009 4800; email: bcpfoundation@bcpartners.com)

www.bcpartners.com/about-us/bcp-foundation.aspx

Established in 2010 for general charitable purposes, this is the foundation of private equity firm BC Partners.

The firm's website states that the foundation provides matched funding for employee fundraising initiatives and supports charities nominated by employees of BC Partners or trustees of the foundation. Employees in each office also nominate two charities each year to receive donations and volunteer support from that office.

Although it has quite general criteria, the foundation focuses support on the following areas:

- Community development including infrastructure advancements, development aid, health care improvements
- Conservation of the environment including endeavours related to pollution reduction, natural preservation, clean technologies
- Arts and education including support for educational, scholastic, or artistic programs

The foundation is principally funded by the firm and by employee donations.

Financial information

In 2016 the foundation had assets of £633,00 and an income of £508,500. Grants were made to organisations totalling £484,000.

Beneficiaries included: Private Equity Foundation (£101,000); American School in London Foundation (£50,000); Over the Wall (£20,000); Dr Challoner's School Educational Trust (£15,000); Serious Fund Children's International (£8,000); The Dolphin Society (£5,000); Pilotlight (£4,000); Jo's Trust (£2,000); Médecins Sans Frontières (£1,700);

Zoological Society of London (£1,000); Cancer Research (£440).

Applications

The foundation does not accept unsolicited applications – charities must be nominated by BC Partners employees or trustees of the foundation.

Sources of information

Accounts; annual report; Charity Commission record.

The Beaverbrook Foundation

 General charitable purposes, preservation of heritage buildings, older people, health

England

£232,500 (2016/17)

CC number: 1153470

Trustees: Laura Levi; Lord Beaverbrook; Lady Beaverbrook; Max Aitken; Rory Aitken; John Kidd.

Correspondent: Jane Ford, Secretary, 3 Queen Street, London W1J 5PA (tel: 020 7042 9435; email: jane@ beaverbrookfoundation.org)

www.beaverbrookfoundation.org

The foundation was originally established in 1954 by the first Lord Beaverbrook, a Canadian-British businessman, politician and newspaper publisher. It was re-registered as a charitable incorporated organisation in 2013. Grants are made at the discretion of the trustees for charitable purposes including those that would have reflected the interests of the first Lord Beaverbrook, including:

- The erection or improvement of the fabric of any church building
- The purchase of books, papers, manuscripts or works of art
- Care of older people or sick people

Grant-making policy

Grants are made for capital expenditure, for revenue and running costs, and for special projects. The trustees are keen to support match funding initiatives, and may make a payment conditional upon the applicant obtaining the remaining funding from other sources. The foundation is able to support all faith organisations but applications are only accepted from registered charities.

Financial information

In 2016/17 the foundation held assets of £13.4 million and had an income of £176,000. Grants awarded to organisations totalled £232,500.

Beneficiaries included: RAF Museum – Hendon and Silverstone Heritage (£50,000 each); National Motor Museum

– Beaulieu (£26,500); London Air Ambulance (£20,000); Battle of Britain Memorial Trust (£10,000); Aspire (£5,500); English National Ballet (£4,000).

Grants of under £5,000 totalled £51,500.

Exclusions

Grants cannot be made for retrospective costs.

Applications

Applications can be made via the foundation's website.

Sources of information

Accounts; annual report; Charity Commission record; funder's website.

The Beaverbrooks Charitable Trust

General charitable purposes including: education, welfare, health, mentoring and self-development, Jewish charities

UK and Israel

£1.2 million (2016/17)

CC number: 1142857

Trustees: Mark Adlestone; Andrew Brown; Anna Blackburn; Susie Nicholas.

Correspondent: Susie Nicholas, Adele House, Park Road, St Annes-On-Sea, Lancashire FY8 1RE (tel: 01253 721262; email: charitable.trust@beaverbrooks.co.uk)

This is the charitable trust of Beaverbrooks the Jewellers. The trust supports a wide range of causes throughout the UK and Israel. Its 2016/17 annual report states:

> The Beaverbrooks Charitable Trust's charitable objectives during the year of review were to provide aid and support to a broad spectrum of charities and to enable the employees of Beaverbrooks the Jewellers Ltd to support their local charities, the latter being achieved by:
>
> - making donations available to Beaverbrooks the Jewellers Ltd stores and office departments, based on a fixed amount for each employee, and allowing each team to select a worthy local charity as their recipient; and
> - matching amounts raised by individual employees for their own chosen charities.
>
> In addition, the Trustees support a wide range of charities which cover education, welfare, health, mentoring and self-development, Jewish and Israeli charities and the community as a whole.

Financial information

In 2016/17 the trust had held assets of £8.3 million and had an income of £1.1 million. Grants awarded to organisations totalled £1.2 million.

Beneficiaries included: The FED (£414,000); UJIA (£50,000); World

Jewish Relief (£30,000); Better World Charity (£25,000); Withington Girls' School (£22,000); The Christie (£20,000); Magden David Adom (£16,000); Blackpool Carers (£12,500); Friendship Circle and Royal Exchange Theatre (£5,000 each).

Applications
Apply in writing to the correspondent.

Sources of information
Accounts; annual report; Charity Commission record.

The John Beckwith Charitable Trust

🔍 Education, social welfare, art, medical research, young people

📍 UK and overseas

£ £209,000 (2016/17)

CC number: 800276

Trustees: Sir John Beckwith; Heather Beckwith; Christopher Meech.

Correspondent: Sally Holder, 124 Sloane Street, London SW1X 9BW (tel: 020 7225 2250; email: info@beckwithlondon.com)

This trust was established by British businessman Sir John Beckwith in 1987 with the aim of supporting a wide range of charitable organisations. Sir John Beckwith is the founder and chair of Pacific Investments, a multi-asset fund management group and has a number of charitable commitments, namely as founder and President of the Youth Sport Trust.

The trust's annual report for 2016/17 states: 'Donations are primarily to educational charities, the under-privileged, and charities covering overseas aid and the young'.

Financial information
In 2016/17 the trust held assets of £1.25 million and had an income of £253,500. There were 44 grants made totalling £209,000 which were distributed as follows:

Education	1	£100,000
Social welfare	37	£56,500
Art	2	£45,000
Medical research	5	£7,500

Previous beneficiaries have included: Wycombe Abbey (£100,000); Movement Disorder Speech Fund (£10,000); Royal Academy of Music (£5,000) Médecins Sans Frontières (£2,500); Prostate Cancer Charity (£2,000); Age UK, RNLI, Send A Cow and The Gurkha Welfare Trust (£1,000 each); Mind (£500); Medical Engineering Resource Unit (£300).

Applications
Apply in writing to the correspondent. The trustees aim to meet once a year to review grant applications.

Sources of information
Accounts; annual report; Charity Commission record.

Bellview Charitable Trust

🔍 Social welfare, Jewish education

📍 Worldwide

£ £1.46 million (2016/17)

CC number: 1051667

Trustees: Cheskel Landau; Jacob Friedman; Raechel Friedman.

Correspondent: Jacob Friedman, Trustee, 52 Knightland Road, London E5 9HS (tel: 020 8455 6789)

According to the its 2016/17 accounts, the Bellview Charitable Trust was established 'to support the activities of religious Jewish organisations recognised as charitable by English law both in the UK and abroad, especially those in the field of education and relief of poverty'. The trust receives income from its investment properties as well as from donations received from third parties.

Financial information
In 2016/17 the trust had assets of £2.95 million and an income of £2.6 million. During the year, the trust awarded grants totalling £1.46 million.

No list of beneficiaries was detailed in the trust's accounts.

Applications
The trust's 2016/17 accounts provide the following information:

> In making grants and donations, the Trustees use their personal knowledge of the institution, its representatives, operational efficiency and reputation. The Trustees monitor the application of the grants and donations by meeting with representatives of the institutions and obtain information as to the utilisation of funds.

Sources of information
Accounts; annual report; Charity Commission record.

Benesco Charity Ltd

🔍 Medicine, education, social welfare

📍 UK

£ £9.4 million (2016/17)

CC number: 269181

Trustees: Jonathan Ragol-Levy; David Wolfson; Andrew Wolfson; Lord David Wolfson.

Correspondent: Joanne Cowan, Benesco Charity Ltd, 8/10 Hallam Street, London W1W 6NS

Benesco Charity Ltd is a registered charity and company incorporated in 1970. The majority of its grant expenditure is given to The Charles Wolfson Charitable Trust (Charity Commission no. 238043), which is another grant-making charity. Grants are also made to charitable organisations selected by the charity and preference is given to organisations that address the needs of the Jewish community. Grants are made under the following categories:

- Medicine
- Education
- Welfare

Grant-making policy
The 2016/17 annual report notes the charity's grant-making policy as follows:

- The making of direct grants
- The provision of premises to operational charities on a rent-free or rent-reduced basis
- The provision of loans, on which the interest is in certain circumstances waived

It is considered that it is not practical to make any predetermined annual allocation between the various grant headings, especially as it is sometimes appropriate not to fully distribute in a particular year in order to accommodate large projects which extend over more than one year.

The trustees particularly fund capital or fixed-term projects.

Financial information
In 2016/17 the charity had assets of £226.9 million and an income of £7.5 million. During the year, the charity's grants expenditure totalled £9.4 million. Of this amount, £5.4 million was given to The Charles Wolfson Charitable Trust.

A list of beneficiaries was not included in the annual report and accounts.

Exclusions
It is not the usual policy of the charity to make grants to individuals.

Applications
Apply in writing to the correspondent.

Sources of information
Accounts; annual report, Charity Commission record.

The Berkeley Charitable Foundation

 Homes, jobs, skills, care

West Midlands, Warwickshire, London and the south of England

£2.3 million (2016/17)

CC number: 1152596

Trustees: Anthony Pidgley; Robert Perrins; Wendy Pritchard; Elaine Anne Driver.

Correspondent: Sally Dickinson, Head of the Berkeley Foundation, Berkeley House, 19 Portsmouth Road, Cobham, Surrey KT11 1JG (tel: 01932 584555; email: info@berkeleyfoundation.org.uk)

www.berkeleyfoundation.org.uk

The Berkeley Foundation was established by the Berkeley Group in March 2011 and became a registered charity in 2013. The foundation aims to help young people and their communities across London and in the south of England. According to its website, the foundation's grant-making focuses on the following four areas:

- Homes: helping people to access and sustain good quality housing
- Jobs: reducing barriers to work
- Skills: developing young people's talent
- Care: opportunity regardless of illness or disability

The foundation's website states that they aim to support projects that:

- Test a new approach to a problem or build on tried-and-tested work to take it to another level
- Bring about real change for individuals and organisations
- Take a gender-sensitive approach to project planning and implementation

Financial information

In 2016/17 the foundation had assets of £544,000 and had an income of £2.7 million, which includes funding from The Berkeley Group and Give As You Earn contributions. During the year, the foundation gave around £2.3 million in grants to organisations, this relates to commitments and grants to Strategic Partnerships, designated charities and grants and donations to other charities within the foundation's core focus areas.

Beneficiaries included: The Change Foundation (£495,000); Crisis and Imperial College (£450,000); Richard House Hospice and Multiple Sclerosis Trials Collaboration (£200,000 each).

Grants made under £50,000 to other charities totalled £241,000.

Applications

The foundation has stated that it very rarely makes unsolicited applications, however at the time of writing (June 2018) the foundation is seeking applications for their 'Combatting Youth Homelessness' programme. Applications can be made via its website (www.berkeleyfoundation.org.uk/grants).

Sources of information

Annual report; annual review; Charity Commission record; funder's website.

Ruth Berkowitz Charitable Trust

General charitable purposes, Jewish causes

UK and overseas

£676,500 (2016/17)

CC number: 1111673

Trustees: Philip Beckman; Brian Beckman; Philip Goodman.

Correspondent: The Trustees, 63/66 Hatton Garden, London EC1N 9LE (email: admin@ruthberkowitztrust.org)

This trust was established through the will of Ruth Berkowitz in 2001 and was registered with the Charity Commission in 2005. The purpose of the trust is to provide grants for general charitable purposes to UK-registered charities that operate at home and abroad. The current grant-making policy prefers to award modest awards to a number of organisations. There is a preference for Jewish causes.

Financial information

In 2016/17 the trust had assets of £2.6 million and an income of £41,000. Grants to 28 organisations totalled £676,500.

Children/youth/education	£396,000
Community	£180,000
Medical	£100,500

Beneficiaries included: University Jewish Chaplaincy (£69,500); Jewish Leadership Council (£65,000); Camp Simcha, Gesher, Norwood Ravenswood (£17,500 each); Aleh Charitable Foundation (£10,000); British Friends of United Hatzalah Israel, Cancer Research UK, Hatzola Northwest Trust (£7,500 each); Jewish Deaf Association (£5,000).

Applications

Apply in writing to the correspondent.

Sources of information

Accounts; annual report; Charity Commission.

Bideford Bridge Trust

 General charitable purposes

The parish of Bideford, Devon and the immediate neighbourhood

£266,000 to organisations (2016)

CC number: 204536

Trustees: Peter Christie; William Isaac; Elizabeth Jenkinson; Eric Hubber; Oliver Chope; Angus Harper; David Dark; Sally Ellis; David Brenton; Jamie McKenzie; Ruth Craigie; Dermot McGeough.

Correspondent: P. Sims, Steward, 24 Bridgeland Street, Bideford, Devon EX39 2QB (tel: 01237 473122)

The trust distributes its income for charitable purposes benefitting those resident in Bideford and its neighbourhood. Within the Scheme of the Commissioners which governs the trust, it is the policy of the trustees to make the following grants:

- To encourage education
- To encourage poor people to become more self-sufficient by assisting them in business start-up schemes
- To individual applications for charitable assistance (such as on the grounds of poverty or ill health)
- To assist the travel requirements of older and infirm people through the Torridge Taxi Voucher Scheme
- To clubs, organisations and charities
- To consider actively during the year any other appropriate significant charitable projects

Full details of limits set by the trustees and payments made are given in the annual report 2016.

Financial information

In 2016 the trust had assets of almost £16 million and an income of £788,500. Grants were made totalling £504,500, of which £266,000 was paid to organisations.

Beneficiaries included: Business Start-Ups (M. Lillis/Torridge Training Service) (£107,500); School Swimming Lessons (£35,000); Steamship Freshspring Society (£30,000); North Devon Hospice (£13,000); Bideford Amateur Athletic Club, Bideford Amateur Football Club, Bideford Amateur Rowing Club and Bideford Festivals Committee (£5,000 each); Pollyfield Community Association (£3,000); Alwington Village Hall (£1,000).

Exclusions

Computer purchases for individuals and political donations.

Applications

Apply in writing to the correspondent.

Sources of information

Accounts; annual report; Charity Commission record.

The Big Lottery Fund (see also Awards for All)

 Community, young people, welfare

 UK and overseas

£ £712.7 (2016/17)

Trustees: Peter Ainsworth; Tony Burton; Nat Sloane; Sir Adrian Webb; Maureen McGinn; Julie Harrison; Dr Astrid Bonfield; Natalie Campbell; Perdita Fraser; David Isaac; Elizabeth Passey; Rachael Robathan.

Correspondent: See the fund's website for contact details. 1 Plough Place, London EC4A 1DE (tel: 0345 410 2030; email: general.enquiries@biglotteryfund.org.uk)

 www.biglotteryfund.org.uk

The National Lottery (the lottery) was launched in 1994 and rapidly established itself as a key funder of the voluntary sector. It receives 40% of the total sums raised by the lottery which it distributes through grants to support community-focused projects. Since 2004 it has distributed over £8.5 billion in awards.

Funding programmes

At the time of writing (June 2018) the following funding programmes were open. Details of the programmes have been taken from the fund's website.

UK-wide

Awards for All – grants of £300 to £10,000 for voluntary or community organisations. Applications must meet at least one of the programmes funding priorities which are: bringing people together and building strong relationships in and across communities; improving the places and spaces that matter to communities; enabling more people to fulfil their potential by working to address issues at the earliest possible stage.

Awards from the UK Portfolio – the UK Portfolio supports UK wide ideas and projects. It tests and grows bold ideas that put people in the lead to address long-term social issues and to improve the quality of life across the UK and internationally.

England

Reaching Communities – flexible funding over £10,000 for up to five years to organisations in England who want to take action on the issues that matter to people and communities.

Partnerships – grants of over £10,000 for organisations to take joint action on issues that matter to people and communities.

Wales

People and Places – funding for capital and revenue community projects. Medium grants of £10,001 to £100,000 and large grants of £100,001 to £500,000.

Northern Ireland

People and Communities – grants of £30,000 to £500,000 to support positive change in the community.

Empowering Young People – grants of £30,000 to £500,000 to support projects that give young people aged 8 to 25 the ability to overcome the challenges they face.

Scotland

Community Assets – grants of £10,000 to £1 million to help local communities address specific inequalities or disadvantages through ownership of an asset.

Grants for community led activity – grants of £10,000 to £150,000 to support communities to improve the places in which they live and the well-being of those most in need.

Our Place – grants of £10,000 to £1 million to help communities come together to find and develop ways in which they can make a difference.

Scottish Land Fund – grants of £10,000 to £1 million to support urban and rural communities to become more resilient and sustainable through the ownership and management of land and land assets.

Financial information

In 2016/17 the fund held assets of £473.6 million and had an income of £762.1 million. There were 13,814 grants made to 10,657 organisations totalling £712.7 million. Grants were distributed as follows:

England	7,786	£509.6 million
Scotland	1,225	£75.8 million
UK-wide	1,819	£56 million
Wales	930	£44.3 million
Northern Ireland	592	£27 million

Details of all previous grants made by the fund can be found on its website or on 360 Giving.

Applications

Full details on current programmes, contacts, application forms and guidance are available on the Big Lottery Fund website.

Sources of information

Accounts; annual report; funder's website.

Percy Bilton Charity

 Disadvantaged young people, disability, mental health, older people

 UK

£ £466,000 to organisations (2016/17)

CC number: 1094720

Trustees: James Lee; Kim Lansdown; Hayley Bilton; Charles Sosna.

Correspondent: Tara Smith, Administrator, Bilton House, 7 Culmington Road, Ealing, London W13 9NB (tel: 020 8579 2829; email: percybilton@aol.com)

www.percybiltoncharity.org

The Percy Bilton Charity was founded in 1962 by the late property entrepreneur Percy Bilton, who endowed the charity with a substantial parcel of shares in Percy Bilton Ltd, which later became Bilton plc. In 1998, these shares were sold and the total proceeds invested in a diversified investment portfolio which today provides the majority of the charities income.

According to its 2016/17 annual report, the funding priorities of the charity are to:

> Support projects to provide day centres, care homes, respite care facilities, sheltered housing, independent living accommodation, educational and recreational facilities for older people and those with physical or learning disabilities or enduring mental health problems, as well as educational and recreational facilities or supported living schemes for disadvantaged young people.

Grant programmes

The charity runs two programmes for organisations:

Large Grants: one-off payments for capital expenditure of approximately £2,000 and over (the majority of grants fall within the range of £2,000 to £5,000).

Small Grants: grants of up to £500 to assist smaller organisations with immediate funding for equipment and furniture (excluding office items).

On its website the charity provides the following information about the types of capital projects it would be willing to fund:

> ▶ **Disadvantaged/underprivileged young people (those under 25):** Supported housing schemes and educational and training projects to encourage disadvantaged young people who may be homeless and/or unemployed away from crime, substance/alcohol misuse and homelessness. Facilities for recreational activities and outdoor pursuits specifically for young people

who are educationally or socially underprivileged or disadvantaged.

▶ **People with disabilities (physical or learning disabilities or mental health problems):** Residential, respite care, occupational and recreational establishments for children, young people and adults with physical or learning disabilities or enduring mental health problems.

▶ **Older people (aged over 60):** Day centres, nursing and residential homes, sheltered accommodation and respite care for the frail or sufferers from dementia or age-related disorders. Projects to encourage older people to maintain their independence.

In addition to its grant programmes for organisations the charity also provides grants to individuals who have a physical or learning disability, enduring mental health problem or who are over 65 and are in financial hardship. Previously assistance has included the provision of food parcels, clothing, white goods, beds and other essential household items. See the charity's website for full details of their individual grants programmes.

Financial information
In 2016/17 the charity had assets of £26.4 million and an income of £862,000. During the year, the charity awarded around £706,500 in grants, including £466,000 in 186 grants to organisations, and £240,500 in grants to individuals. Grants to organisations were distributed as follows:

Large grants to organisations

Young people with disabilities	£151,500
Adults with disabilities	£144,000
Disadvantaged young people	£78,000
Older people	£52,500

Small grants to organisations

Disabled and older people	£28,500
Disadvantaged young people	£11,500

Beneficiaries included: Friends of Saint Nicholas School (£7,300); Hoxton Hall (£5,000); Action4Youth (£4,900); Sport 4 Life (£3,600); Beds Garden Carers (£3,200); Friends of Grangewood Association (£3,000); Bridge Training and Development (£2,400); Bluebell Wood Children's Hospice (£1,800).

Exclusions
The charity will not consider applications for the following:

▶ Running expenses for the organisation or individual projects
▶ Salaries, training costs or office equipment/furniture
▶ Projects for general community use e.g. community centre and church halls
▶ Disabled access to community buildings
▶ Publication costs e.g. printing/distributing promotional and information leaflets
▶ Projects that have been completed
▶ Items that have already been purchased

▶ Provision of disabled facilities in schemes mainly for the able-bodied
▶ General funding/circularised appeals
▶ Pre-schools or playgroups (other than predominantly for disabled children)
▶ Play schemes/summer schemes
▶ Holidays or expeditions for individuals or groups
▶ Trips, activities or events
▶ Community sports/play area facilities
▶ Exterior works such as paving, roofing and garden landscaping
▶ Consumables (e.g. stationery, arts and crafts materials)
▶ Refurbishment or repair of places of worship/church halls
▶ Research projects
▶ Mainstream pre-schools, schools, colleges and universities (other than special schools)
▶ Welfare funds for individuals
▶ Hospital/medical equipment
▶ Works to premises not used primarily by the eligible groups

Other exclusions may apply, see the charity's website for full details.

Applications
Detailed guidance on how to make an application for each of the charity's grant schemes is provided on the charity's website.

Sources of information
Accounts; annual report; Charity Commission record; funder's website.

Binks Trust

 General charitable purposes including: education, community development, the arts, heritage, culture and science, human rights and conflict resolution, social welfare, animal welfare

Scotland

£ £749,500 (2016/17)

OSCR number: SC008849

Correspondent: The Trustees, 61 Dublin Street, Edinburgh EH3 6NL

The Binks Trust registered with the Scottish Charity Regulator in 1973 and has since awarded grants to a wide variety of charitable purposes in the area of Scotland.

Financial information
In 2016/17 the trust had assets of £8.3 million and a total income of £1.4 million. Grants to 56 organisations totalled £749,500.

Beneficiaries included: National Library of Scotland (£50,000); David Hume Institute (£43,500); Edinburgh International Festival (£30,000); Scottish Chamber Orchestra (£19,000); Sistema Scotland (£10,000); The Edinburgh Quartet Trust (£10,000); Scottish Charity Air Ambulance (£5,000); Scottish Ballet (£3,000); National Libraries of Scotland (£1,000).

Applications
Apply in writing to the correspondent.

Sources of information
Accounts; annual report; OSCR record.

The Michael Bishop Foundation

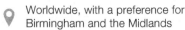 Heritage, arts and culture, human rights and social justice, health and medicine, education and training

Worldwide, with a preference for Birmingham and the Midlands

£ £2.3 million (2016/17)

CC number: 297627

Trustees: Grahame Elliott; Baron Glendonbrook of Bowdon; Timothy Bye; Martin Ritchie.

Correspondent: Pat Robinson, Staunton House, Ashby-de-la-Zouch, Leicestershire LE65 1RW (tel: 01530 564388; email: patannrob@btconnect.com)

The foundation was registered in 1987 after Sir Michael Bishop (now Baron Glendonbrook of Bowdon) of British Midland set up the foundation in 1987 by giving almost £1 million of shares in Airlines of Britain (Holdings) plc, the parent company of British Midland.

The 2016/17 annual accounts state: 'The Trustees support a broad range of charitable organisations within five main areas of focus:'

▶ Heritage
▶ Arts and Culture
▶ Human Rights and Social Justice
▶ Advancement of Health and Medicine
▶ Education and Training

These areas of focus are not exclusive, and other areas may be considered from time to time.

Financial information
In 2016/17 the foundation had assets of £30.1 million and an income of £3.2 million. Grants to 31 organisations totalled £2.3 million.

Beneficiaries included: Glendonbrook Foundation (£561,000); Birmingham Conservatoire and Black Stork Charity (£250,000 each); Attingham Trust (£175,000); Exeter Northcott Theatre (£100,000); Henshaws (£30,000); Havens Hospices (£10,000).

Applications
Apply in writing to the correspondent.

Sources of information
Accounts; annual report; Charity Commission record.

Asser Bishvil Foundation

 Jewish causes

Greater Manchester and London

£9.16 million (2016/17)

CC number: 1112477

Trustees: Daniel Orzel; S. Orzel; Chaim Simche Ehrentreu.

Correspondent: Daniel Orzel, Trustee, 88 Wellington Street East, Salford, Manchester M7 4DW (tel: 0161 792 1813; email: enquiries@asserbishvil.org.uk)

asserbishvil.org.uk

The Asser Bishvil Foundation was registered in 2005. According to its 2016/17 accounts the foundation makes grants for: 'the relief of poverty amongst persons in need and hardship in the Jewish community; the advancement of education according to the beliefs and values of the orthodox Jewish faith and the advancement of the Jewish orthodox religion'.

Financial information

In 2016/17 the foundation held assets of £1.54 million and had an income of £9.66 million. Grants totalled £9.16 million and were broken down as follows:

Relief of poverty	£5.7 million
Educational grants	£2.4 million
Religious grants	£1 million

A list of beneficiaries was not available.

Applications

According to its 2016/17 annual report: 'the charity invites applications for funding through contacting local philanthropists to contribute towards projects that both the trustees and the philanthropists feel are appropriate for the charities objects'.

Sources of information

Accounts; annual report; Charity Commission record.

The John Black Charitable Foundation

 Research into prostate cancer and Parkinson's Disease

 UK and Israel

 £1.8 million (2016/17)

CC number: 1143431

Trustees: Stephen Conway; David Taglight.

Correspondent: David Taglight, 24 Old Burlington Street, London W1S 3AW (tel: 020 7734 0424)

The foundation makes grants for medical research into prostate cancer and Parkinson's Disease in the UK and Israel.

Financial information

In 2016/17 the foundation held assets of £85.4 million and had an income of £16.9 million. Grants awarded to organisations totalled £1.8 million and were distributed as follows:

Prostate cancer in the United Kingdom and State of Israel	£770,000
Other charitable purposes in the United Kingdom and State of Israel	£770,000
Parkinson's Disease in the United Kingdom and State of Israel	£222,000

A list of beneficiaries was not available.

Applications

Apply in writing to the correspondent.

Sources of information

Accounts; annual report; Charity Commission record.

The Blagrave Trust

 Children and young people

 Berkshire, Hampshire, Sussex and Wiltshire

 £925,500 (2016)

CC number: 1164021

Trustees: Julian Whately; Timothy Jackson-Stops; Sir Paul Neave; Diana Leat; Claire Cannock; Tasneem Alom; Linda Epstein.

Correspondent: Jo Wells, Trust Director, c/o Rathbone's, 1 Curzon Street, London W1J 5FB (email: grants@blagravetrust.org)

www.blagravetrust.org

@blagravetrust

The trust was set up in 1978 and received the residuary of the estates of both Herbert and Peter Blagrave to use for charitable purposes. Today the trust supports young people aged 14 to 25 to transition successfully into adulthood.

Areas of work

The following information has been taken from the trust's website:

Our funding covers three areas of work:

- Funding to outstanding youth focused charities supporting young people aged 14–25
- Funding that supports young people to lead change themselves, have a voice in society and participate and be listened to in decisions affecting their lives
- Funding that address root causes of the issues we see manifest in young people's problems and that support advocacy, policy, research or campaigning

We believe all young people have a right to access high quality services that enables them to develop the skills, experience and capabilities they need to succeed at school, in work and in life. We prioritise work with young people whose needs are greatest and in areas where there are higher rates of poverty.

We provide core funding and therefore support organisations whose mission is clearly aligned with our own – mainly prioritising organisations that work exclusively or primarily with young people. Our minimum grant level is £10,000, maximum grant is £100,000 and our average grant amount is £25,000 to £30,000 p.a. We want to work with charities in a deep and impactful way.

Our main geographic area is in the South of England across Berkshire, Hampshire, Sussex and Wiltshire. We also fund some national programmes of work, but tend to identify these proactively ourselves.

Financial information

In 2016 the trust held assets of £38.7 million and had an income of £36.8 million due to an asset transfer. Grants to 35 organisations totalled £925,500.

Beneficiaries included: Achievement for All (£100,000); The Prince's Trust (£60,000); Barnardo's Bristol Base (£45,000); Auditory Verbal UK and Releasing Potential (£30,000 each); Urban Pursuit (£10,000).

Exclusions

Grants will not be given for:

- Capital grants or building projects
- Charities where our grant will comprise more than 20% of total turnover
- General recreational or social activities
- Promotion of religion

Applications

Applicants should complete the online 'Grant Checklist and Outline Proposal' form on the website which asks you to outline your project in no more than 200 words. The trust will then either contact you to indicate your application is not of interest, or to discuss in more detail by phone within one month. Proposals will be put forward at one of the trustee meetings in March, July or November.

Sources of information

Accounts; annual report; Charity Commission record; funder's website.

The Sir Victor Blank Charitable Settlement

🔍 Jewish organisations, general charitable purposes, the arts, health

📍 Worldwide

💷 £336,500 (2016/17)

CC number: 1084187

Trustees: Sir Maurice Blank; Lady Sylvia Blank; Simon Blank.

Correspondent: The Trustees, 53 Davies Street, London W1K 5JH (tel: 020 7403 1877; email: enquiries@ sirvictorblankcharitablesettlement.com)

Registered with the Charity Commission in December 2000, the charity makes grants to Jewish organisations and for general charitable purposes. There is some preference for the arts, health charities and cross-community work.

Financial information

In 2016/17 the charity held assets of £2.6 million and had an income of £248,000. Grants awarded to organisations totalled £336,500.

Beneficiaries included: Wellbeing of Women (£70,000); The Henry Jackson Society (£30,000); Community Security Trust (£15,000); The British Academy (£10,000); Orchestra of the Age of Enlightenment (£6,000); The National Holocaust Centre (£5,000); Listening Books (£2,500); The Howard League for Penal Reform (£1,000); The Gurkha Welfare Trust (£500).

Grants of less than £1,000 each totalled £7,900.

Applications

Apply in writing to the correspondent.

Sources of information

Accounts; annual report; Charity Commission record.

Bloodwise

🔍 Research into leukaemia, lymphoma, myeloma and other blood cancers

📍 UK

💷 £14.2 million (2016/17)

CC number: 216032/SC037529

Trustees: Prof. Frances Balkwill; Maria Clarke; John Reeve; Charles Metcalfe; Jeremy Bird; Simon Guild; Michael Prescott; Glen Lucken; Jane Stevens; Steven Prescott-Jones; Sonali Thakrar; Julia Whittaker.

Correspondent: Research Team, Bloodwise, 39–40 Eagle Street, London WC1R 4TH (tel: 020 7504 2200; email: info@bloodwise.org.uk)

 www.bloodwise.org.uk

 facebook.com/bloodwise.uk

 @bloodwise_uk

 @bloodwise

The charity was established in 1960 by the Eastwood family of Middlesbrough following the death of their daughter Susan, aged seven at the time. According to its website, the charity's mission is 'to stop people dying from blood cancer, to make patients' lives better and to stop blood cancers happening in the first place'.

Research grants

Bloodwise funds world-class research into leukaemia, lymphoma, myeloma and other blood cancers, which is carried out by researchers at universities and hospitals across the UK. The website explains: 'Our portfolio includes long and short-term research projects, career development awards and clinical trials. We now have a translational pipeline in place that covers basic biological research through to phase III clinical trials.' A list of research currently funded by the charity can be found on the National Cancer Research Institute's International Cancer Research Portfolio (cancerportfolio.org).

The following information on research grants has been taken from the charity's website:

Research projects

Proposals are considered by the Research Committee and are given through two schemes:

▶ **Project grants** – Project grants are awarded for up to £250k and up to three years, for clearly defined research projects addressing key questions in the field of blood cancer.

▶ **Programme continuity grants** – Current or recent holders of Bloodwise programme grants can apply for support to maintain core elements of their research programme, including but not limited to the retention of key research personnel.

Training and career development awards

Training and career development award applications are considered by our Training and Career Development sub-Committee, which makes funding recommendations to our Research Committee.

Previous schemes included Gordon Piller PhD studentships, Bennett fellowships for post-doctoral researchers, Clinical Research Training fellowships for haematologists training for a PhD and Lectureships.

Clinical trials

Awards are considered by the Clinical Trials Committee and are given under two schemes:

▶ **Trials Acceleration Programme (TAP) clinical trial applications** - The application process for TAP trials includes an iterative process of assessment of fit and feasibility before an application can be submitted through our grant tracker system. Please contact the TAP HUB Management team in Birmingham and the Bloodwise research team if you wish to discuss an application.

▶ **Trial-associated research projects** - This funding scheme provided support for laboratory-based research projects that are integral to clinical trials and essential for the analysis of primary and/or secondary end points and clinical outcome. We are no longer accepting applications to this scheme, but you may now apply for support for this type of project through our standard project grant scheme.

Financial information

In 2016/17 the charity had assets of £7.8 million and an income of £16 million. Research grants were approved totalling £14.2 million.

Beneficiaries included: University College London (£2.7 million); University of Cambridge (£1.6 million); Institute of Cancer Research (536,000); University of Leicester (£129,000); Royal Liverpool University Hospital (£65,000).

Applications

See the website for full information of the charity's funding schemes. All applications must be made through the online grant tracker. Grants that have been approved must be administered through a UK institution.

Sources of information

Accounts; annual report; Charity Commission record; funder's website.

The Bloom Foundation

🔍 Community development, Jewish causes, health and medical research, social welfare, international development

📍 UK, with a preference for Brighton, overseas with a preference for Israel

💷 £2.3 million (2016/17)

CC number: 1166112

Trustees: Linda Bloom; Marc Sugarman; Marcelle Lester; Adam Franks; Anthony Bloom; Philip Saunders.

Correspondent: The Trustees, 34 Jamestown Road, London NW1 7BY (email: info@thebloomfoundation.com)

The foundation was established by Tony Bloom, an online gambling entrepreneur with significant property interests. Mr

Bloom is also the owner of Brighton and Hove Albion FC and a well-known poker player.

According to its 2016/17 accounts the objects of the foundation are:

- Strengthen and educate communities and improve lives through charitable contributions, volunteering and fundraising
- Mainstream a preventative approach to health, with a particular focus on research and lifestyle-based interventions
- Create a more cohesive society in Israel, particularly through common purpose programs and advocacy, that brings together different parts of society
- Strengthen the UK Jewish community and the local Brighton community through supporting key service organisations
- Other such charitable purposes for the public benefit which are exclusively charitable under the laws of England and Wales as the Trustees may from time to time determine

Financial information

In 2016/17 the foundation held assets of £4.3 million and had an income of £3.3 million. Grants totalled £2.3 million and were distributed as follows:

Jewish community	£725,000
Medical research and welfare	£682,500
Brighton	£610,000
Disaster relief	£150,000
Israel	£58,000
International development	£26,000
Other	£3,200
Social welfare	£1,500

Beneficiaries included: Overcoming Multiple Sclerosis (£612,000); Jewish Care (£400,000); Albion in The Community (£358,500); Brighton and Hove Hebrew Congregation (£177,500); The Community Security Trust (£130,000); Save the Children (£100,000); Action Aid (£50,000); Lubavitch Foundation of Brighton (£39,500); New Israel Fund (£6,300); Israel Sport and Education (£1,800).

Applications

Apply in writing to the correspondent.

Sources of information

Accounts; annual report; Charity Commission record.

The Bluston Charitable Settlement

Jewish organisations, education, social welfare, health, research

Mostly UK

£664,500 (2016/17)

CC number: 256691

Trustees: Daniel Dover; Martin Paisner.

Correspondent: Martin Paisner, Trustee, 20 Gloucester Place, London W1U 8HA (tel: 020 7486 7760)

This charity has general charitable purposes and can make grants to support a wide range of organisations. In practice, a large number of the charity's beneficiaries are Jewish organisations.

The annual report and accounts for 2016/17 state that during the year the charity supported organisations in the following areas:

- Children's education
- Capital expenditure projects for schools and other educational establishments
- The welfare of people who are underprivileged
- Hospitals and medical institutions
- Universities, for specific research projects

Financial information

In 2016/17 the charity had assets of £10.9 million and an income of £717,500. During the year, grants totalling £664,500 were made to 29 organisations.

Beneficiaries included: The Weizmann Institute Foundation (£100,000); Jewish Care (£67,500); The Langdon Foundation (£60,000); Ohel Sarah (£50,000); Prisoners Abroad and Yeshiva Or Israel Petach Tikva (£25,000 each); Keren Hatorah (£10,000); Farms for City Children and Youth Aliyah Child Rescue (£5,000 each); Ovarian Cancer Trust (£2,500).

Exclusions

No grants are made to individuals.

Applications

Apply in writing to the correspondent. The trustees meet twice a year to consider applications.

Sources of information

Accounts; annual report; Charity Commission record.

The Boltini Trust

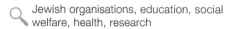

General charitable purposes, overseas aid, music, medical causes, social welfare, disadvantage, disability

UK (with a particular focus on Surrey and West Sussex) and some international support

£680,500 (2016/17)

CC number: 1123129

Trustees: Anthony Bolton; Sarah Bolton; James Nelson; Emma Nelson; Oliver Bolton; Benjamin Bolton; Fiona Bolton; Phoebe Moore.

Correspondent: Anthony Bolton, Trustee, Woolbeding Glebe, Woolbeding,

Midhurst, West Sussex GU29 9RR (email: boltinitrust@gmail.com)

This family trust was established in 2008 and supports charitable causes that the trustees think are undertaking particularly worthwhile activities and generally, but not exclusively, located within the home counties of England with a particular focus on Surrey and West Sussex. Some support is also given to charities benefitting people living in Africa, Asia and the West Indies. The trust also supports arts and musical organisations, particularly those involved in contemporary music.

Grants are generally one-off rather than recurrent.

Financial information

In 2016/17 the trust had assets of £14 million and an income of £700,000. Grants were made totalling £680,500 and broken down as follows:

Arts, music and culture	24	£255,500
International	14	£198,500
Major disasters relief funds	2	£70,000
Medical research/medical institutions	8	£54,500
Community and educational institutions	6	£54,000
Disadvantaged/disabled/ children and young people care institutions	8	£24,500
Disadvantaged/disabled homeless adult care institutions	7	£23,500

Beneficiaries included: Mondo Challenge – Nepal (£52,000); Save The Children (£45,000); Shelterbox Trust (£30,000); Sinfonietta Productions (£25,000); KSS Air Ambulance (£10,000); National Youth Orchestra (£8,500); Home-Start and Winston's Wish (£4,000 each); Petworth Community Garden and The Opera Story (£2,000 each).

Exclusions

No grants are given to individuals.

Applications

The trust's 2016/17 accounts state: 'The Trust has not thus far deemed it necessary to promote grant-making opportunities to the public and details of how to apply for a grant may be obtained by written application to the Trust's place of business.'

Sources of information

Accounts; annual report; Charity Commission record.

The Booth Charities

🔍 Social welfare, health, education, recreation and leisure

📍 Salford

💷 £419,000 (2016/17)

CC number: 221800

Trustees: John Willis; David Tully; Philip Okell; Richard Kershaw; Roger Weston; William Whittle; Richard Fildes; Alan Dewhurst; Jonathan Shelmerdine.

Correspondent: Jonathan Aldersley, Clerk to the Trustees, c/o Butcher & Barlow LLP, 3 Royal Mews, Gadbrook Road, Northwich, Cheshire CW9 7UD (tel: 01606 334309; email: jaldersley@butcher-barlow.co.uk)

The Booth Charities are two charities supporting disadvantaged people in Salford. Together they provide a wide range of support including pension payments to individuals and grants to local charities and facilities. A large number of grants go to organisations which have a direct connection with the charities and a substantial number of these institutions bear the Booth name.

Areas of work

Humphrey Booth the Elder's Charity is for the benefit of the inhabitants of Salford and is established for the relief of those in need, with a preference for people over sixty years of age; the relief of distress and sickness; the provision and support of facilities for recreation and other leisure time occupation; the provision and support of educational facilities; and any other charitable purpose.

Humphrey Booth the Grandson's Charity is established for the income to be applied in or towards the repair and maintenance of the Church of Sacred Trinity, Salford, and in augmenting the stipend of the rector of the Church. The remaining income is then applied in furtherance of the same objects as apply to the Humphrey Booth the Elder Charity.

Grant-making criteria

The charities' 2016/17 annual report states that the trustees take into account the following factors when considering applications:

- All grants must fall within one or more of the Charity's Statutory Objects of distribution
- Beneficiaries must be Salford inhabitants
- Whether the application has merit
- Whether there are sufficient funds
- An assessment of the Grant benefit in terms of the 'greatest good for the greatest number
- Socio-economic and other deprivation factors in the City of Salford from which the application derives

- Whether the stated aims of the projects are susceptible to measurement and evaluation
- Sustainability of the project and an 'exit' strategy in place from charitable funding
- The history of Grant funding from Booth Charities
- The availability of Statutory and other potential sources of funding
- Whether the application qualifies for Statutory funding

It also states that the grant distribution strategy for 2014–17 focuses on the following goals:

- Lift the level of distribution to meet increasing need in the City
- Help alleviate poverty
- Support collaborative ventures working with key stakeholders in the City, especially in those areas struggling to cope with financial hardship and deprivation

A number of charities are being supported on an annual basis in line with these goals, alongside accepting applications from other charities.

Financial information

In 2016/17 the charity had assets of almost £42 million and an income of £1 million. Grants were made to 53 organisations during the year totalling £419,000 and a further £900 was given in nine grants to individuals. Grants were broken down as follows:

Provision/support of educational facilities	10	£133,000
Relief of distress or sickness	14	£118,000
Provision of leisure and recreational facilities	13	£69,000
Sacred Trinity Church	1	£52,000
Older/poor people	27 (plus 9 individuals)	£52,000 (plus £900 to individuals)
Other charitable purposes	11	£29,500

Beneficiaries included: Salford Citizens Advice (£15,000); Heritage Project (£10,000); Humphrey Booth Music Bursary, Fairbridge programme and The Fusilier Museum (£5,000 each); Salford Institute for Dementia (£2,000); Federation of Jewish Services (£1,500); Chatsworth High School Community College (£1,000); Salford Art Club (£640); High Veterans Bowling Club (£375); Manchester University Guild of Change Ringers (£100).

Applications

Apply in writing to the correspondent.

Sources of information

Accounts; annual report; Charity Commission record.

Boots Charitable Trust

🔍 Health, social care, education and training, community development, general charitable purposes

📍 Nottingham and Nottinghamshire

💷 £187,500 (2016/17)

CC number: 1045927

Trustees: Lavina Moxley; Adrian Bremner; Una Kent.

Correspondent: James Kirkpatrick, Boots UK Ltd D90E S09, 1 Thane Road West, Nottingham NG90 1BS (tel: 07739 835909; email: james@fundingsupport.co.uk)

 www.boots-uk.com/corporate-social-responsibility/what-we-do/community/boots-charitable-trust

Registered with the Charity Commission in 1995, Boots Charitable Trust is wholly funded by Boots UK Ltd. Boots UK is part of the Retail Pharmacy International Division of Walgreens Boots Alliance, Inc. Boots became a subsidiary of the new company, Walgreens Boots Alliance, on 31 December 2014.

The trust gives to charities and voluntary organisations that benefit Nottingham and Nottinghamshire. It is explained on the Boots website that 'Supporting the Nottinghamshire community has always been important to Boots. Jesse Boot opened the very first Boots store in the mid-19th century in Nottingham, and we continue to give to local causes that are important to our colleagues and customers'.

Areas of support

The trust considers support for a wide range of charities and voluntary organisations although its main focus is on four areas which are 'very close' to the 'heart and heritage' of Boots. These areas are outlined on the website:

- **Health:** 'Both community healthcare such as homecare or support for sufferers of medical conditions as well as health education and prevention'
- **Lifelong learning:** 'For example literacy and numeracy projects'
- **Community development:** 'Such as supporting councils in providing voluntary services'
- **Social care:** 'Be it personal, social or community activities or schemes'

The website states that it also funds 'smaller voluntary organisations in Nottinghamshire which are too small to qualify for charitable status, but who still desperately need some financial support for their projects.'

Funding types

The trust's charitable giving policy states:

> The Trust will consider applications for funding for most expenditure items, including salary and running costs. Where a general overhead allocation is part of the funding requested, the method of calculation must be included. Generally, large building or construction projects will not be funded although minor structural improvements and refurbishments would be considered.

Financial information

In 2016/17 the trust had assets of £73,000 and an income of £274,500. Grants to 24 organisations totalled £187,500 and were distributed as follows:

Health	7	£57,000
Social care	6	£49,000
Lifelong learning	7	£44,000
Community development	4	£37,500

Beneficiaries included: Stonebridge City Farm (£10,000); The Friary (£9,000); Nottingham Health and Education Support (£6,900); First Story (£5,600); Cornwater Clubs and Pintsize Theatre (£5,000 each).

Note: The company also has another charity, Boots Benevolent Fund (Charity Commission no. 1046559), which provides financial help and support to serving and retired colleagues who are unexpectedly experiencing financial hardship.

Exclusions

The trust does not provide funding for:

- Projects benefitting those people outside of Nottinghamshire
- Individuals
- Organisations which are NOT registered charities and have an income or expenditure of more than £5,000 per year
- Charities seeking funds to re-distribute to other charities
- Projects for which there is a legal statutory obligation or which replace statutory funding

Applications

There is an online application form on the website, alongside guidance on eligibility. Paper application forms can also be requested on: james@ fundingsupport.co.uk or 07739 835909.

The trustees review applications on a bi-monthly basis. Applications should be received by the 7th of February, April, June, August, October and December. The website explains that the application process can take between two and four months.

Sources of information

Accounts; annual report; Charity Commission record; guidelines for applicants; funder's website.

The Borrows Charitable Trust

 Social welfare, health and saving lives, relief of poverty, armed forces, education, art, sport, culture, heritage and science, community development

England and Wales

£255,400 to organisations (2015/16)

CC number: 1140591

Trustees: Sally Borrows; Simon Borrows.

Correspondent: Simon Borrows, Trustee, Kingston Smith & Partners LLP, Devonshire House, 60 Goswell Road, London EC1M 7AD (tel: 020 7566 4000)

The Borrows Charitable Trust was registered with the Charity Commission in 2011. The trust awards grants to a wide variety of charitable causes.

Financial information

In the financial year 2016/17 the trust had assets of £7.25 million and a total income of £92,000. Grants were made to 102 organisations totalling £379,500. Grants were broken down as follows:

Social welfare	£95,000
Health and saving lives	£71,500
Relief of poverty	£70,000
Armed forces	£50,000
Education	£35,000
Arts, sport, culture, heritage and science	£34,000
Community development	£24,500

Beneficiaries included: Community Foundation for Surrey (£50,000); Bowel Cancer UK (£30,000); Footsteps International (£20,000); Royal Ballet School (£10,000); Watts Gallery (£6,100); Action Medical Research, Puttenham Church and Royal Opera House (£5,000 each).

Applications

Apply in writing to the correspondent.

Sources of information

Accounts; annual report; Charity Commission record.

The Boshier-Hinton Foundation

 Children and adults with special educational or other needs

 England and Wales

£596,500 (2015/16)

CC number: 1108886

Trustees: Thea Boshier; Dr Peter Boshier; Colin Flint; Janet Beal.

Correspondent: Peter Boshier, Trustee, Whitegates, 32 Lower Street, Horning, Norfolk NR12 8AA (tel: 01692 630695; email: boshierhinton@yahoo.co.uk)

 www.boshierhintonfoundation.org. uk

Set up in 2005, The Boshier-Hinton Foundation makes grants to organisations which advocate for support, and provide facilities for children and adults with special educational needs and other disabilities, and their families. The foundation's website states:

> The Founding Trustees are experienced in working and caring for children and adults with special needs and their families. It is also their experience that funding for projects to promote the welfare of individuals and groups of individuals continues to be difficult to obtain as grants have become more restricted and limited in recent years. The purpose of this Charity is to identify areas of need and make appropriate grants, where possible.

The foundation's application guidelines state that it welcomes projects which are 'innovative and developmental'. Although the foundation will consider funding the whole of a project, it prefers to part-fund projects in partnership with other contributors.

Financial information

In 2016/17 the foundation had assets of £1.3 million, an income of £437,000 and made 175 grants to organisations totalling £596,500.

Beneficiaries included: Signature (£30,000); SENSE (£12,300); Livability and Music Therapy Works (£5,000 each); Museum of London and Scottish Youth Dance (£3,000 each); Pathfinder Dogs (£2,600); Sheffield Mencap (£1,400); Mustard Seed Autism Trust (£1,000); Tall Ships Youth Trust (£800); Wellow Riding for the Disabled (£300).

Exclusions

The foundation will not support:

- Retrospective funding
- Capital projects, core costs or salaries
- Activities that should receive statutory funding
- Repeat grants in a period of less than two years
- Hand-written applications
- Individuals

Applications

The foundation accepts applications for grants in writing and via email, using a grant application form available to download from the website along with guidance notes. The foundation welcomes informal email enquiries prior to the submission of a formal application.

Sources of information

Accounts; annual report; Charity Commission record; funder's website.

The Bothwell Charitable Trust

Disability, health, older people, conservation

England, particularly the South East

£321,000 (2016/17)

CC number: 299056

Trustees: Paul James; Crispian Howard; Theresa McGregor.

Correspondent: Paul James, Trustee, 18 Huntingfield, Croydon CR0 9BA (tel: 01689 638980)

This trust was established for general charitable purposes and usually makes grants towards health, people with disabilities, conservation, children's and older people's causes.

Financial information
In 2016/17 the trust had assets of £4.46 million and an income of £209,500. Grants were made to organisations totalling £321,000 in the following categories, as detailed in the accounts:

Disability/social work	£114,500
Medical research	£92,500
Children's causes	£79,000
Hospices	£24,500
Other causes	£10,500

Beneficiaries were not listed in the accounts.

Previous beneficiaries have included: Arthritis Research UK, Blackthorn Trust, British Heart Foundation, ECHO International Health Services Ltd, Friends of the Elderly, Invalid Children's Aid Nationwide and Leukaemia Research Fund (£2,000 each); Brain Research Trust, British Trust for Conservation Volunteers, Childlink Adoption Society, Multiple Sclerosis Society and Riding for the Disabled Association (£1,000 each).

Exclusions
No grants are given for animal charities; overseas causes; individuals; or charities not registered with the Charity Commission.

Applications
Apply in writing to the correspondent. Distributions are usually made in twice a year.

Sources of information
Accounts; annual report; Charity Commission record.

Bourneheights Ltd

Orthodox Jewish causes

UK

£1.2 million (2015/16)

CC number: 298359

Trustees: Chaskel Rand; Esther Rand; Erno Berger; Yechiel Chersky; Schloime Rand.

Correspondent: Schloime Rand, Trustee, Flat 10, Palm Court, Queen Elizabeth's Walk, London N16 5XA (tel: 020 8809 7398)

Registered with the Charity Commission in February 1998, this charity was principally established 'for the advancement of the education of people expressing the Orthodox Jewish faith, the advance the Orthodox Jewish faith, and the relief of poverty in the Orthodox Jewish community'.

Financial information
In 2015/16 the charity held assets of £6.2 million and had an income of £1.1 million. Grants were made totalling £1.2 million.

Previous beneficiaries have included: Before Trust; Belz Synagogue; BFOT; Gevurath Ari Academy; Heaven Point; Lubavitch Mechina; Mercaz Torah Vechesed Ltd; Moreshet Hatorah; Olam Chesed Yiboneh; Telz Academy Trust; Toreth Emeth; UTA; Yeshivas Avas Torah.

Applications
Apply in writing to the correspondent. The trustees meet quarterly.

Sources of information
Accounts; annual report; Charity Commission record.

The Bowland Charitable Trust

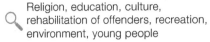

Religion, education, culture, rehabilitation of offenders, recreation, environment, young people

Mainly North West England

£2.6 million (2016/17)

CC number: 292027

Trustees: Tony Cann; Carole Fahy; Hugh Turner.

Correspondent: Carole Fahy, Trustee, Bowland House, Philips Road, Blackburn, Lancashire BB1 5NA (tel: 01254 688051; email: carole.fahy@ cannco.co.uk)

This trust, established with several large donations from the Cann family, invites applications for funding of projects from individuals, institutions and charities in particular (but not exclusively) for the promotion of education. Although its beneficial area covers the whole of the UK, in practice grants are mainly made in North West England. Most of the trust's grants are one-off, but some projects are funded over longer periods.

Financial information
In 2016 the trust had assets of £6.3 million and an income of £1.1 million. Grants awarded to organisations totalled £2.6 million and were broken down as follows:

Religious activities	£1.6 million
Educational activities	£457,500
Donations to other charities	£261,500
Cultural activities	£107,000
Rehabilitation of offenders	£99,500
Recreational activities	£75,000
Preservation of the natural environment	£12,000
Activities of young people	£2,500

Previous beneficiaries have included: Ron Clark Academy (£660,000); LEB Partnership (£306,000); The Brantwood Trust (£75,000); North Music Trust (£50,000); The Rosemere Cancer Foundation (£30,000); Blackburn Cathedral Trust (£25,000); Bowland High School (£20,000); Nazareth Unitarian Chapel (£15,000); The Lowry Centre Trust (£2,000); Ribble FM (£1,000).

Applications
The trust invites applications for funding of projects from individuals, institutions and charitable organisations. Applications can be made directly to the trustees, who meet regularly to assess them.

Sources of information
Accounts; annual report; Charity Commission record.

Friends of Boyan Trust

The advancement of the Orthodox Jewish faith, Orthodox Jewish religious education, relief of poverty in the Orthodox Jewish community

Worldwide

£487,500 to organisations (2016)

CC number: 1114498

Trustees: Jacob Getter; Mordechai Freund; Nathan Kuflik.

Correspondent: Jacob Getter, Trustee, 23 Durley Road, London N16 5JW (tel: 020 8809 6051)

This trust was established in 2006 and makes grants to support the advancement of the Orthodox Jewish faith, Orthodox Jewish religious education, and the relief of poverty in the Orthodox Jewish community.

Financial information
In 2016 the trust had assets of £68,000 and an income of £675,500. Grants were made totalling £672,500 with £487,000 given to institutions and £185,500 given to individuals.

Previous beneficiaries have included: Gomlei Chesed of Chasidei Boyan

(£84,000); Mosdot Tiferet Yisroel Boyan (£31,000); Kimcha De'Pischa Boyan (£21,000); Kimcha De'Pischa Beitar Ilit (£13,000); Chevras Mo'oz Ladol (£12,000); Kollel Avrechim Boyan, Betar Ilit (£6,000); Ezer Mikoidesh Foundation (£2,000); Beis Rizhin Trust (£1,500); Yad Vochessed (£1,000).

Applications

Apply in writing to the correspondent.

Sources of information

Accounts; annual report; Charity Commission record.

G & K Boyes Charitable Trust

 Environment, education, medical research, particularly into dementia and brain tumours, mental health, heritage

UK

£1.2 million (2016/17)

CC number: 1166015

Correspondent: The Trustees, c/o Cripps LLP, Cripps Harries Hall LLP, Number 22, Mount Ephraim, Tunbridge Wells TN4 8AS (tel: 01892 506292)

The trust was registered with the Charity Commission in 2016 and according to its 2016/17 accounts its objects are:

- The conservation, preservation, protection, and improvement of the physical and natural environment, including its woodland, rivers, lakes, flora, and fauna including birds; encouraging research into the same of publication of that research
- Promoting good citizenship amongst the public by supporting the maintenance and improvement of the grounds of the National Memorial Arboretum in Alrewas, Staffordshire
- Promoting, for the public benefit, education (including musical, social, and physical training)
- Promoting medical research for the public benefit generally and in particular in the areas of dementia and brain tumours and the publication of the results of that medical research
- Supporting the relief of those suffering from both physical and mental ill health
- The preservation, for the benefit of the nation, of land and buildings of beauty or historic interest and the preservation of furniture, pictures, and chattels of any description having national, historic, or artistic interest

Financial information

In 2016/17 the trust held assets of £4.1 million and had an income of £4.9 million. Grants to eight organisations totalled £1.2 million.

Beneficiaries included: National Brain Appeal Molly Lane Fox Unit (£751,000); National Memorial Arboretum

(£200,000); David Shepherd Wildlife Foundation (£122,000); Alzheimer's Research UK (£25,000); Berwickshire Association Voluntary Service and PSP Association (£10,000 each).

Applications

Apply in writing to the correspondent.

Sources of information

Accounts; annual report; Charity Commission record.

The Bradley Family Charitable Foundation

General charitable purposes, including Christian causes

England and Wales

£640,500 (2016/17)

CC number: 1165344

Trustees: Suzanne Beatty; Keith Bradley; Eleanor Bradley; Irene Bradley.

Correspondent: Irene Bradley, Trustee, Stoneway, Stafford Road, Penkridge, Stafford ST19 5AX

The foundation was registered in January 2016. According to the 2016/17 annual accounts the objects of the foundation are:

> To advance such charitable purposes (according to the law of England and Wales) as the Trustees see fit from time to time in particular but not limited to advancing the Christian Religion for the public benefit by making donations and grants to charities in accordance with Christian principles and for such charitable purposes in accordance with the Christian principles.

Financial information

In 2016/17 the foundation held assets of £947,500 and had an income of £1.6 million. Grants awarded to organisations totalled £640,500.

A list of beneficiaries was not available.

Applications

Apply in writing to the correspondent.

Sources of information

Accounts; annual report; Charity Commission record.

The William Brake Charitable Trust

General charitable purposes

UK, with a preference for Kent

£441,500 (2016/17)

CC number: 1023244

Trustees: Philip Wilson; Deborah Isaac; Penelope Lang; Michael Trigg.

Correspondent: Michael Trigg, Trustee, Colman House, King Street, Maidstone,

Kent ME14 1JE (tel: 01622 759051; email: michael.trigg@gillturnertucker.com)

The William Brake Charitable Trust is an unincorporated trust, which was established in 1993 with an initial gift from the late William Brake. The trust makes grants for general charitable purposes in the UK with a preference for local charities in Kent.

Financial information

In 2016/17 the trust had assets of £11.8 million and an income of 107,000. Grants awarded to organisations totalled £441,500.

Beneficiaries included: The Natural History Museum (£50,000); The Duke of Edinburgh's Award (£20,000); The Royal Agricultural Benevolent Institution (£5,000); Albion Kids Show, Dementia UK (£2,000 each); Association of Parents and Friends of Bower Grove, The Brain Tumour Charity, Disability Challengers (£1,000 each); Diabetes UK South East (£500).

Applications

The 2016/17 accounts note that, 'the charity invites applications from the William Brake family for funding of worthy registered charities each year, with a particular emphasis on local charities where the family know the charity's representative'. The trustees hold two formal meetings each year to consider grant-making.

Sources of information

Accounts; annual report; Charity Commission record.

The Tony Bramall Charitable Trust

Medical research, ill health, social welfare

UK, with some preference for Yorkshire

£247,500 (2015/16)

CC number: 1001522

Trustees: Tony Bramall; Karen Bramall Odgen; Melanie Foody; Geoffrey Tate; Anna Bramall.

Correspondent: The Trustees, 12 Cardale Court, Beckwith Head Road, Harrogate, North Yorkshire HG3 1RY (tel: 01423 535300; email: alison.lockwood@bramallproperties.co.uk)

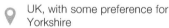

According to the 2015/16 annual report, the trust 'gives assistance to charities, organisations and individuals who are involved in carrying out medical research or involved in the care of the sick of whatever age'. Support is normally given to those causes based in

the north of England, particularly Yorkshire.

Financial information

In 2015/16 the trust had assets of £4 million and an income of £158,000. During the year, the charity gave around £247,500 in grants to organisations.

Beneficiaries included: University of Leeds – Cancer Research (£193,000); Shift.ms (£17,500); Saint Michael's Hospice (£5,600); Children with Cancer (£3,000); Wellbeing of Women (£2,500); Cystic Fibrosis Care (£2,000); Claire House Children's Hospice (£1,500); Barnardo's (£1,000); Tall Ships Youth Trust (£750); World Cancer Research (£500).

Applications

Apply in writing to the correspondent. In some cases an applicant may be visited by a representative of the trust.

Sources of information

Accounts; annual report; Charity Commission record.

The Liz and Terry Bramall Foundation

Christianity, urban and rural regeneration, relief of sickness, health, arts and culture

UK, in practice mainly Yorkshire

£5.4 million (2016/17)

CC number: 1121670

Trustees: Dr Terence Bramall; Elizabeth Bramall; Suzannah Allard; Rebecca Bletcher; Rachel Tunnicliffe; Anthony Sharp.

Correspondent: Dr Terence Bramall, Trustee, c/o Raworths LLP, Eton House, 89 Station Parade, Harrogate, North Yorkshire HG1 1HF (tel: 01423 566666)

Registered in 2007, this is the charitable foundation of Terence Bramall, former chair of Keepmoat, builders of social housing in northern and central England. It was reported that the Bramall family sold their stake in the company in 2007 for £563 million. Terence Bramall is also a director of Doncaster Rovers FC.

Areas of work

According to the foundation's 2016/17 annual report, its areas of support are:

- The benefit of the public in accordance with the statements of belief of the Church of England, and the promotion for the benefit of the public of urban or rural regeneration in areas of social and economic deprivation
- The relief of sickness
- The advancement of health
- Arts and culture

The annual report for 2016/17 also states that the foundation aims to increase the level of grants and that the grant-making policy of the foundation is being developed but it will include small donations (on application) to causes within the objectives and also larger long-term projects.

Financial information

In 2016/17 the foundation had assets of £119.9 million and an income of £2.1 million. There were grants 216 made totalling £5.4 million.

Beneficiaries included: Forget Me Not Trust (£440,000); Northern Ballet (£400,000); Birmingham University (£97,500); Rapt (£20,000); Go Kids Go (£10,000); Health for All (£8,000); Grace Kelly Ladybird Trust and Little Sisters of the Poor (£5,000 each); Radio Nightingale (£2,000); Royal Society for Blind Children (£300).

Applications

Apply in writing to the correspondent. The 2016/17 annual report states:

> Unsolicited requests from national charities will generally only be considered if there is some public benefit to the Yorkshire region.
>
> It is unlikely that the Trustees would support the total cost of a project and applicants should be able to demonstrate that funds have been raised or are in the process of being raised from other sources.

Sources of information

Accounts; annual report; Charity Commission record.

The Bransford Trust

Culture, education, sport, community, health, young people

Within 15 miles of Worcester city centre

£557,000 (2016/17)

CC number: 1106554

Trustees: Arthur Neil; Colin Kinnear; Brenda Kinnear; John Carver.

Correspondent: Julia Kirkham, 6 Edgar Street, Worcester WR1 2LR

www.bransfordtrust.org

The trust was established in 2004 for general charitable purposes. According to its website, the trust supports charitable initiatives in Worcester under the following categories, with a particular interest in the well-being of young people:

- Culture – encouraging participation in and access to performing arts, as well as supporting local heritage
- Education – particularly vocational education opportunities

- Sport – encouraging participation in sport and physical activity, and supporting associated facilities
- Community – supporting community facilities, aiming to improve the lives of local people, particularly those who are in some way disadvantaged
- Health care – benefitting the health of local people and relief of those who are in need

The trust funds local organisations (not exclusively registered charities) which undertake their activities in its area of benefit. Grants can be given for capital projects, one-off projects or events; running costs are supported, but the trust prefers to support 'initiatives designed to create a step change or expansion of an organisation's charitable activity over support for its day-to-day operating costs'. The trust expects that other sources of funding are sought and is unlikely to fund the total costs of an initiative.

The trust usually awards around £500,000 per year to organisations that apply for funding as well as to schemes initiated by the trustees. Awards are typically in the range of £500 to £5,000, although in exceptional circumstances the trust will consider applications for higher amounts.

Grant schemes

The trust currently runs two separate grant schemes:

Main Grant scheme – for applications for grant funding of all amounts. Applications made under this scheme can be submitted at any time, but will only be considered at the review meetings held in summer and winter.

Fast Track scheme – for applications of up to £1,000 each. Decisions regarding awards are made in between the six-monthly Main Grant application review meetings. Applications are reviewed regularly, although more than two awards will not usually be made per month. An organisation will not be allocated more than one Fast Track award in any two-year period.

Financial information

In 2016/17 the trust had assets of £17.4 million and an income of £937,000. Grants were made to organisations totalling almost £438,000.

Beneficiaries included: St Richard's Hospice (£157,000); Acorn Children's Hospice (£40,000); Malvern Youth Community Trust (£30,000); Worcester Festival (£20,000); Young Enterprise (£15,000); Elgar School of Music (£8,000); Severn Valley Railway Charitable Trust (£7,500); Vamos Young Children's Theatre (£5,800).

Exclusions

The trust will not support:

- Organisations outside the geographical area of benefit
- Individuals
- Commercial activities or 'for-profit' organisations
- Public sector bodies
- Retrospective funding
- Organisational costs that do not directly relate to activities delivering community benefit – e.g. restructuring costs, debt reduction, legal costs

Applications

Applications to both grant schemes should be made using the form on the trust's website – no other applications will be considered. Full guidance notes for both grant schemes are provided on the website.

Sources of information

Accounts; annual report; Charity Commission record.

The Breadsticks Foundation

Overseas aid, health care, education, children and young people

UK, Sudan, South Sudan, Kenya, Rwanda, South Africa, India, Indonesia and Laos

£1.06 million (2016/17)

CC number: 1125396

Trustees: Beatrix Payne; Dr Kirsty Le Doare; Dr Paul Ballantyne; Beatrice Roberts; Trevor Macy; Alison Burkhari.

Correspondent: Beatrix Payne, Trustee, 35 Canonbury Square, London N1 2AN (tel: 020 7288 0667; email: breadsticksfoundation@gmail.com)

 www.breadsticksfoundation.org

The foundation was established in 2008 to support organisations involved in improving the provision of health care and education. The foundation is funded by an annual grant from an individual who is known to the trustees and supports projects based mainly in the UK, Africa and Asia – in particular, the 2015/16 annual report states that it currently works in the UK; Sudan; South Sudan; Kenya; Rwanda; Zambia; Zimbabwe; South Africa; India; Indonesia; Laos. Project from other countries may be considered but are unlikely to be successful.

The foundation funds work aimed at 'improving the quality of life within marginalised communities' and is particularly interested in health; education; child and youth development. It aims to build long-term relationships with organisations, and while it does also provide project-related grants, it has a preference for providing long-term core funding.

Financial information

In 2016/17 the foundation had assets of £315,500 and an income of £1.3 million. Grants awarded to organisations totalled £1.06 million.

Beneficiaries included: Hope and Homes for Children (£250,000); Freedom From Torture (£150,000); St Mungo's Community Housing Association (£136,000); The Banyan (£75,000); School Home Support (£50,000); Brighton Oasis (£45,000); Lao Disabled Women's Development Centre and St Mary Islington Community Partnership (£35,000 each).

Applications

At the time of writing (June 2018) the foundation's website stated:

> The Breadsticks Foundation has embarked on a strategic review that will, in the long term, see a reduction in the size of grants made and a narrower focus to grant making. As a result, the Foundation will not be taking on any new grants until this process is complete, likely end 2018. Please check back then for further information.

Sources of information

Accounts; annual report; Charity Commission record; funder's website.

Breast Cancer Now

Breast cancer research

UK and Ireland

£14.6 million (2016/17)

CC number: 1160558

Trustees: Lynne Berry; Professor Trevor Powles; Professor Adrian Harris; Professor Robert Coleman; Laura Simons; Pascale Alvanitakis-Guely; Susan Johnson; Susan Gallone; Ann Pickering; Chris Copeland.

Correspondent: Hannah Hilton, 5th Floor, Ibex House, 42–47 Minories, London EC3N 1DY (tel: 0333 207 0300)

 www.breastcancernow.org

 facebook.com/breastcancernow

 @breastcancernow

 @breastcancernow

Breast Cancer Now was formed by the merger of Breakthrough Breast Cancer and Breast Cancer Campaign on 31 March 2015. The charity funds research into breast cancer. Research is focused on four key areas – risk and prevention, early detection and diagnosis, treatment and secondary breast cancer.

Grant programmes

The following information on grant programmes was taken from the charity's website.

Breast cancer risk and prevention research grants

Applications to tackle gaps in early diagnosis and prevention research.

Catalyst grants

This will bring together Europe's leading breast cancer researchers and the world's leading pharmaceutical companies to pool resources and stop women dying from breast cancer by 2050. The first partnership we've made is with Pfizer. Together we will provide exciting opportunities for breast cancer researchers across Europe.

Pilot grants

Our pilot grants allow researchers to test new hypotheses, with a view to generating preliminary data to support a full project grant application.

Project grants

Our project grants are for established researchers in the UK or Ireland who have a strong track record in their field, and who want to work in one of our priority areas.

The charity also provides PhD studentships and scientific fellowships.

Financial information

In 2016/17 the charity held assets of £10.7 million and had an income of £28.3 million. Grants awarded to organisations totalled £14.6 million.

Beneficiaries included: Breast Cancer Now Tony Robins Research Centre (£8.8 million); King's College London (£970,000); University of Manchester (£957,000); University of Dundee (£199,000); University of Belfast (£192,000); University of Cambridge (£181,000).

Applications

Applications can be made through the charity's website. Refer to the website for application deadlines.

Sources of information

Accounts; annual report; Charity Commission record; funder's website.

The Brelms Trust CIO

 Arts, education and sport, carers, conservation, debt and benefits advice, domestic abuse and sexual violence, excluded young people, homelessness, older people facing isolation, people with physical or learning disabilities, prevention of reoffending, refugees and asylum seekers, ethnic minorities, rural isolation, substance misuse, support in bereavement, support for disadvantaged communities

Yorkshire

£438,500 (2016/17)

CC number: 1153372

Trustees: Mary Cornish; Lesley Faithful; Juliet Kemp; Christine Gamble; Glynis Jones; Stephen Stroud; Alan Wallace.

Correspondent: Chris Goldson, Metro House, 57 Pepper Road, Leeds, West Yorkshire LS10 2RU (email: admin@ brelmstrust.org.uk)

www.brelmstrust.org.uk

The Brelms Trust CIO was originally set up as a charitable trust in 2007. The trust offers grants to a wide variety of charities and community groups in the area of Yorkshire. The trust aims to support 'charities working at the heart of communities to tackle disadvantage and to provide sustainable benefit to the community', particularly small and medium-sized registered charities with an income of less than £500,000 and unrestricted reserves of no more than six months. Local charities are preferred, although projects run by national charities will be considered if specific benefit to a Yorkshire community can be demonstrated, as well as local management and control of budgets. Yorkshire branches of charities controlled from elsewhere are unlikely to be supported.

Grants range from £1,000 to £5,000 a year and can be either one-off or for up to three years (totalling up to £15,000). The trust can provide funding for direct service provision, salaries, volunteer expenses and running costs – the trust does not however usually support the entire cost of a project, so expects there to be other funding plans in place.

The website cites the following examples of community issues funded by the trust: arts, education and sport; carers; conservation; debt and benefits advice; domestic abuse and sexual violence; excluded young people; homelessness older people facing isolation; people with physical or learning disabilities; prevention of re-offending; refugees, asylum seekers, and ethnic minorities; rural isolation; substance misuse;

support in bereavement; support for disadvantaged communities.

Financial information

During the year, 2016/17 trust had assets of £2.5 million and an income of £476,000. Grants to 51 organisations totalled £438,500 and were distributed as follows:

Community	13
Disability	11
Health	8
Youth	6
Older people	5
Asylum seekers and refugees	4
Environment/arts	3
BME	1

Beneficiaries included: Ruddi's Retreat (£15,000); Artworks Creative Communities (£14,600); Abigail Housing (£13,800); Bradford City of Sanctuary (£9,000); Peace Museum (£5,000); West Yorkshire Destitute Asylum Network (£4,500); Dial A Ride Scarborough (£3,000); Settle Stories (£1,800).

Exclusions

The trust will not fund: organisations without charitable status; organisations not registered at the Charity Commission; large charitable organisations with an income of £50,000 or above; national charities unless benefitting the area of Yorkshire; applications from individuals of student gap year costs; charities which send out general appeal letters for donations; organisations which advance religion or promote faith-based activities; party political organisations; animal welfare; medical research; work requiring retrospective funding.

Applications

The trust has an online application process; no paper copies or additional material must be sent. Applications are assessed throughout the year and grant awards are made quarterly.

Sources of information

Accounts; annual report; Charity Commission record; funder's website.

The Brenley Trust

 Social welfare, education

UK, southern Africa

£777,000 to organisations (2016/17)

CC number: 1151128

Trustees: Patrick Riley; Mary-Louise Brennickmeyer; Robbert Zoet.

Correspondent: Patrick Riley, Trustee, 17 Princes Drive, Oxshott, Leatherhead KT22 0UL (tel: 01372 841801; email: patrick.riley@btinternet.com)

The trust was established in 2013 and its 2016/17 accounts state: 'The trust's objectives are to support independent

charities and individuals in relation to the reduction of poverty and hardship, and the improvement of education. Grants will mainly be administered in the United Kingdom and Southern Africa.'

Financial information

In 2016/17 the trust held assets of £11.1 million and had an income of £10.1 million. Grants awarded to organisations totalled £777,000. A further £58,500 was given to individuals.

Beneficiaries included: Bridge House School (£321,000); Beyond Autism (£250,000); Tayntons (£62,000); Help2Read (£45,500); Trojan Academic Initiative (£29,000); Delmeza Children's Hospice (£17,000); Saint Augustine's Catholic Church (£2,000).

Applications

Apply in writing to the correspondent.

Sources of information

Accounts; annual report; Charity Commission record.

The Britford Bridge Trust

 General charitable purposes

Worldwide

£367,500 (2016/17)

CC number: 1160012

Trustees: Brodies and Co. (Trustees) Ltd; Adrian Frost; Dr Jane MacDougall.

Correspondent: Helen Nelson, Brodies LLP, Brodies House, 31–33 Union Grove, Aberdeen AB10 6SD (email: helen.nelson@brodies.com)

This trust, registered January 2015, supports registered charities working in a wide range of areas worldwide. It shares one of its trustees (Adrian Frost) with both The Evelyn Trust (Charity Commission no. 232891), a grant-making charity supporting medical research and health care in the Cambridge area, and The Handel House Trust (Charity Commission no. 1006009).

Grant-making policy

According to the trust's annual report for 2016/17, the trustees do not yet have a formal grant-making policy in place but will seek to review and formalise the position 'once the grant-making administration becomes more established'. In the meantime, the trustees' support is broadly focused on four primary areas, which are:

- The prevention or relief of poverty
- The advancement of education
- The advancement of health or the saving of lives
- The advancement of the arts, culture, heritage or science

The trust also has a secondary focus on the following areas:

- The advancement of citizenship or community development
- The advancement of amateur sport
- The advancement of environmental protection or improvement
- The relief of those in need, by reason of youth, age, ill health, disability, financial hardship or other disadvantage

Financial information

In 2016/17 the trust had assets of £15.45 million and an income of £5.76 million. Grants totalling £367,500 were made for the following purposes:

Advancement of health or saving lives	£167,500
Prevention or relief of poverty	£76,000
Relief of need (of young people, older people, people who are ill or who have disabilities, people facing financial hardship or people who are facing other disadvantage)	£64,000
Arts, culture, heritage or science	£50,000
Education	£10,000

Beneficiaries included: Addenbrooke's Charitable Trust (£75,000); The Egmont Trust (£62,500); London Handel Society (£50,000); Build Africa (£46,000); The Share Foundation (£25,000); Voluntary Service Overseas (£15,000); Camfed International, Médecins Sans Frontières and Survival International (£10,000 each); The Woodworks Project (£6,000); Action for Kids and Edinburgh Young Carers Project (£4,000 each).

Applications

Contact the correspondent to request an application form.

The trustees meet to review applications every three months, but requests can also be considered on an ad hoc basis by the trustees or the trust's administrators. According to the annual report for 2016/17:

The trustees will use their own knowledge of the applicants in question, in addition to considering each application on its own merits, as to whether the funding/grant sought will further and advance the trust's charitable purposes and in turn provide public benefit...If necessary the trustees will seek additional information from the applicants, such as details of specific project funding or annual accounts/ financial statements.

Sources of information

Accounts; annual report; Charity Commission record.

The British Academy for the Promotion of Historical Philosophical and Philological Studies (The British Academy)

Humanities and social sciences

UK and overseas

£28.6 million to organisations (2016/17)

CC number: 233176

Trustees: Prof. Genevra Richardson; Prof. Richard McCabe; Prof. David Abulafia; Prof. Alan Bowman; Prof. Sarah Worthington; Prof. Bencie Woll; Prof. Ash Amin; Lord Stern of Brentford; Prof. Mary Morgan; Prof. Dominic Abrams; Prof. Sally Shuttleworth; Prof. Janet Watson; Prof. Nicholas Vincent; Prof. Gillian Clark; Prof. Archibald Brown; Prof. John Baines; Prof. Roger Kain; Prof. Glynis Jones; Prof. Maxine Berg; Prof. Marianne Elliott; Prof. Michael Keating; Revd Prof. Diarmaid MacCulloch; Prof. Terence Irwin; Prof. Anne Phillips; Prof. John Scott.

Correspondent: Grants Team, British Academy, 10 Carlton House Terrace, London SW1Y 5AH (tel: 020 7969 5217; email: grants@britac.ac.uk)

 www.britac.ac.uk

The charity makes grants in the fields of humanities and social science. Awards given include those for research grants, international joint initiatives, appointments and conferences.

Full, up-to-date details of each of the funding programmes are provided on the charity's website.

Financial information

In 2016/17 the charity had assets of £20.5 million and an income of £38.3 million. During the year, the charity gave a total of £28.8 million in grants. Of this amount, £28.6 million was given to organisations and £140,500 to individuals. Grants to organisations were awarded as follows:

Fellowship	£14.9 million
Small Grants	£3 million
Overseas research facilitation	£4.8 million
Global and UK challenges	£3.5 million
Research projects	£1.8 million
Engagement awards	£501,500
Other	£11,000

Previous beneficiaries have included: University of Oxford (£3.7 million); British School at Rome (£1 million); London School of Economics (£771,500); Council for British Research in the Levant (£686,000); School of Oriental and African Studies (£285,500);

Medical Research Council (£249,000); Overseas Development Institute (£147,500); Institute for Fiscal Studies (£136,500); British Institute of Persian Studies (£114,500); Northumbria University (£86,000).

Exclusions

No loans for graduate studies. All awards are at postdoctoral level only.

Applications

Comprehensive details of grants and awards are available from the charity's website.

Sources of information

Accounts; annual report; Charity Commission record; funder's website.

The British and Foreign Bible Society

Projects that make the Bible available and accessible to people

Worldwide

£4.2 million (2016/17)

CC number: 232759

Trustees: Arfon Jones; John Griffiths; Col. Richard Sandy; Christina Rees; Peter Muir; Catherine Pepinster; Dr Bunmi Olayisade; Sue Heatherington; Paul Chandler; Alan Eccles; James Featherby; Ian Dighe.

Correspondent: The Trustees, Stonehill Green, Westlea, Swindon SN5 7DG (tel: 01793 418100; email: info@biblesociety. org.uk)

www.biblesociety.org.uk

Registered in 1964, The British and Foreign Bible Society, known simply as the Bible Society, is driven by one core belief – 'that when people engage with the Bible, lives can change – for good'.

The society works both overseas and in the UK to make the Bible available and accessible. Its website explains, 'In some parts of the world, bringing the Bible to life focuses on translation and distribution projects. Elsewhere it focuses on leadership training, or literacy programmes, or interfaith dialogue. Closer to home, in England and Wales, it focuses on advocacy effort, schools outreach and devotional resources'.

Grant-making

A large part of the society's work is carried out through grant-making to Bible societies worldwide; it is currently working alongside 146 such organisations within the United Bible Societies (UBS) network. Grants are made within an agreed strategy and within three categories: making the Bible available; making the Bible accessible; and demonstrating the Bible's credibility.

Financial information

In 2016/17 the society held assets of £24 million and had an income of £19.5 million. During the year, the society gave a total of £4.2 million in grants to organisations, of which £158,000 was given in the UK. Grants were distributed as follows:

Making the Bible available	£2.4 million
Demonstrating the Bible's credibility	£1.5 million
Making the Bible accessible	£204,000

The annual report also categorises grants as follows:

Engagement and advocacy	100	£1.45 million
Production and distribution	52	£1 million
Translation	36	£920,000
Capacity building	36	£415,000
Literacy	12	£199,000
Total international grants	**236**	**£4 million**
Other national grants	24	£74,000
Bibles to prisons, immigration centres, colleges	104	£44,000
Cambridge University library	1	£40,000
Total national (UK) grants	**129**	**£158,000**

Applications

Apply in writing to the correspondent.

Sources of information

Accounts; annual report; Charity Commission record; funder's website.

The British and Foreign School Society

Education

Worldwide

£671,000 (2016)

CC number: 312516

Trustees: Leslie Stephen; Vic Craggs; Prof. Steve Hodkinson; Stephen King; Jane Creasy; Stephen Ross; Stephen Wordsworth; E. Weale; Diana Hoy; Peter Miller; Karen Hughes; Prof. Joy Palmer Cooper.

Correspondent: Felicia Willow, Grants Manager, 32–36 Loman Street, London SE1 0EH (tel: 020 7922 7814; email: grantsmanager@bfss.org.uk)

 bfss.org.uk

Established in 1808 by Christian social reformers, the British and Foreign School Society (BFSS) makes grants for education projects in the UK and around the world.

The society prioritises projects that fall under the following themes:

▶ Teacher training, to improve educational delivery and learning

▶ The provision of learning resources and equipment
▶ The provision of classrooms and other educational facilities
▶ Support for community and supplementary education
▶ Support for education for street children and other vulnerable children
▶ Provision of appropriate ICT

Applications are accepted from organisations that have UK charitable status and educational or training institutions which have UK charitable status, or, in the case of schools, colleges, universities and churches, exempt charity status. The BFSS prefers to support smaller projects in areas of deprivation or educational disadvantage. Projects are expected to address needs for which resources from the state-sponsored education system (including the Pupil Premium in the case of UK projects) are not available or adequate. Funding is available for up to three years, after which the BFSS expects that the service will become sustainable.

In 2016 the society established a new grant programme to support the educational attainment of looked-after children and young carers in the UK. BFSS will fund projects (including staff salaries and overheads) that provide looked-after children and young carers with supplementary support that results in improved educational attainment. BFSS are especially keen to support projects that develop sustainable approaches that can be replicated at scale. Further examples and information about this funding programme can be found on the society's website.

Financial information

In 2016 the society held assets of almost £24 million and had an income of £719,000. Grants were made to 43 organisations and totalled £671,000. According to the annual report, 57% of grants were made to projects in Africa, 22% to projects in South Asia, 13% to projects in the UK, 4% to projects in Central and South America and the remaining 2% to projects in Eastern Europe and the Middle East.

Previous beneficiaries have included: Hull Children's University (£36,500); Able Child Africa (£25,500); Book Aid International (£24,500); Carefree Fostering Independence Cornwall (£19,500); Into University and Right To Play (£15,000 each); National Resource Centre for Supplementary Education (£12,700); Children Change Colombia (£5,500).

Exclusions

The following cannot be supported:

▶ Special events such as conferences or seminars or for expeditions and overseas travel

▶ Endowments
▶ Scholarships
▶ Projects for which the main requirement is funding for transport

Applications

Applications can be submitted through the online application form. A schedule of grants committee meetings can be found on the website along with detailed eligibility criteria and information on past successful projects.

Sources of information

Accounts; annual report; Charity Commission record; funder's website.

British Council for Prevention of Blindness (Save Eyes Everywhere)

Prevention and treatment of blindness

Worldwide

£260,500 (2016/17)

CC number: 270941

Trustee: BCPB Management Ltd.

Correspondent: Diana Bramson, Charity Manager, 4 Bloomsbury Square, London WC1A 2RP (tel: 020 7404 7114; email: info@bcpb.org)

 www.bcpb.org

Established in 1976, this charity, known as BCPB, funds scientific research into blindness prevention and sight restoration. BCPB supports research in the UK and overseas into the causes of blindness worldwide, as well as specific community-based disease prevention projects in financially developing countries. It also funds the training of eye care professionals from such countries.

BCPB is a part of 'VISION 2020: The Right to Sight', which is a worldwide effort led by the World Health Organisation and the International Agency for the Prevention of Blindness to eliminate avoidable blindness by the year 2020.

Research funding

The following information is taken from the charity's research strategy, which is available to download in full from the website:

Our funded research focuses on the potential to make breakthroughs in understanding and treating currently incurable eye diseases, and on operational research to improve best practice and delivery of eye care services. We only award funding to universities and hospitals in the UK.

Fellowships leading to the award of PhD or MD over 2 or 3 years – either for UK-based fellows to carry out research in a developing country, or students from developing countries who come to the UK to carry out research.

Research grants – over one or two years. These are available to clinicians, scientists or epidemiologists to develop their research ideas and generate pilot data to facilitate a future application for a substantial grant and to provide funding for a non-clinical PhD or DrPH studentship.

Research Mentorship Awards – over one year. The purpose of these awards is to build research capacity in low-income countries, give priority to applications from countries selected in 'VISION 2020: The Right to Sight' as having approximately three ophthalmologists per million population or fewer, to foster research and training links between low-income country institutions (hospitals/universities) and UK universities/NHS Trusts in order to build research capacity.

Boulter Fellowships – We support the training of a small number of applicants who come to the International Centre for Eye Health at the London School of Hygiene and Tropical Medicine to study for an MSc in Public Health for Eye Care. This course equips them with the skills and knowledge they will need to plan and implement national and regional blindness prevention programmes.

Financial information
In 2016/17 the charity had assets of £555,000 and an income of £211,500. Grants awarded to organisations totalled £260,500.

Beneficiaries included: Institute of Ophthalmology (£60,000); University of Liverpool (£16,500); University of Belfast (£12,000).

Exclusions
Unless in exceptional circumstances, the charity will not fund the individual welfare of blind people in the UK or the completion of an existing project when previous funding has ended.

Applications
BCPB's research strategy is available to download from the charity's website. Guidelines, terms and conditions, and application forms are available to download from the website in April each year and the deadline for applications is in October. The Charity Manager can be contacted for further information by email (info@bcpb.org).

Sources of information
Accounts; annual report; Charity Commission record; funder's website.

British Eye Research Foundation (Fight for Sight)

 Ophthalmology and eye disease research

UK

£3 million (2016/17)

CC number: 1111438

Trustees: Alistair Rae; Alina Kessel; Nigel Panting; Jenny Williams; Louisa Vincent; Ginny Greenwood; Fiona Hathorn; Prof. David Spalton; Barbara Merry; Prof. Roy Quinlan; Thomas Bjorn; Prof. Maria Cordeiro; Simon Craddock; Prof. Johnathan Grant; Steve Blackman.

Correspondent: Zoe Marshall, Fight For Sight, 18 Mansell Street, London E1 8AA (tel: 020 7264 3904; email: grants@fightforsight.org.uk)

🌐 www.fightforsight.org.uk

f facebook.com/fightforsightuk

🐦 @fightforsightUK

Previously known as the 'Prevention of Blindness Research Fund', Fight for Sight today 'funds pioneering research to prevent sight loss and treat eye disease'.

The charity has six research priorities:

 Developing and testing new and more effective treatments, such as cell-based, gene or drug therapies or improving surgical procedures for a range of different eye diseases and conditions

 Improving the understanding of the causes of eye diseases and conditions including the further identification of relevant genes

 Developing ways of preventing age-related macular degeneration, glaucoma, cataract and diabetic eye disease

Improving the early detection of eye diseases and conditions

Improving through eye research the quality of life for adults and children living with sight loss

Identifying and assessing emerging threats to sight

Applicants to any of the grant schemes must state which of these priorities their research will address. Further detail on the research priorities can be found in the charity's research strategy, which is available to download from the website.

Grant schemes
The foundation has a number of different grant schemes which open and close at differing times during the year. At the time of writing (April 2018) the foundation operated the following grant schemes:

▶ **Fight for Sight Award:** up to £5,000 for ophthalmologists and scientists in the UK.

▶ **Primer Fellowship Awards:** up to £60,000 tenable for one year. Open to clinical and allied health professionals.

▶ **Ophthalmology Trainee Research Network Awards:** Up to £5,000. Open to trainee ophthalmologists for clinical research in the field of ophthalmology and vision science. The awards are tenable for two years.

▶ **Small Grant Award Schemes:** up to £15,000 for clinical research studies in ophthalmology and vision science.

▶ **PhD Studentships:** up to £100,000 for PhD supervisors for three year PhD studentships.

▶ **Project Grants:** up to £170,000 for three years (or pro rate for shorter projects) for clinical and non-clinical scientists for research relevant to Fight for Sight's charitable aims – particularly research into Stargardt disease.

▶ **Fight for Sight/CSO Project Grant:** up to £200,000 for up to three years, for clinical and non-clinical researchers in Scotland researching age-related eye diseases.

▶ **MRC/Fight for Sight Clinical Research Training Fellowship:** up to three years of funding for clinically qualified professionals in the field of ophthalmology requiring registration for a research degree, usually a PhD.

▶ **Fulbright Fight for Sight Research Award:** £75,000 for one year, open to UK citizens to conduct ophthalmology research at an accredited US institution.

For further information, eligibility criteria, deadlines and guidance on each of these grants schemes, refer to the website.

Financial information
In 2016/17 the foundation had assets of £11.2 million and an income of £3.8 million. Grants made during the year totalled £3 million.

Beneficiaries included: University College London Institute of Ophthalmology (£914,000); King's College London (£208,000); University of Birmingham (£198,000); University of Liverpool (£34,000); University of Bath, University of Bristol, University of Nottingham (£15,000 each); Moorfields Eye Hospital NHS Foundation Trust (£5,000).

Exclusions
See each individual grant scheme guidance for exclusions.

Applications
Initial applications can be submitted via the foundation's website, where full details regarding the application process and deadlines can be found.

Sources of information

Accounts; annual report; Charity Commission record; funder's website.

British Gas (Scottish Gas) Energy Trust

 Fuel poverty, financial education (in relation to debt awareness and prevention)

 England, Scotland and Wales

 £2.3 million (2016/17)

CC number: 1106218

Trustees: Imelda Redmond; Andrew Brown; Daksha Piparia; Colin Trend; Peter Smith.

Correspondent: The Trustees, 3rd Floor, Trinity Court, Trinity Street, Peterborough PE1 1DA (tel: 01733 421021; email: bget@charisgrants.com)

 www.britishgasenergytrust.org.uk

The British Gas Energy Trust was established in 2004. The trust's website describes the aims of the trust as follows:

- The relief of poverty among those who are unable to meet or pay charges for the supply of energy to premises used or occupied by them
- The education of the public in relation to debt awareness and prevention
- To work with other UK trust funds and organisations to encourage good practice and consistency for the public good

The trust receives its funding solely from British Gas, who currently donate around £6 million annually. Despite this, the trust operates independently of British Gas and is governed by a board of trustees who give their time freely.

The trust fulfils its charitable objectives through the provision of grants to a range of specialist fuel debt and energy advice services across England, Scotland and Wales. There is a list of these organisations, known as 'Local Advisors', on the trust's website. In addition, the trust also makes grants to vulnerable individuals and families to clear energy and other priority household debts (such as bankruptcy fees or funeral arrears) and to purchase energy efficient white goods.

Financial information

In 2016/17 the trust had assets of £1.5 million and an income of £12.7 million. Grants totalled £12 million with £2.3 million given to organisations.

The Chair's Report 2016/17 provides the following information:

> During 2016/17, the Charity's Organisational Grants Programme continued to fund 27 organisations (including 13 Shelter locations and their

national helpline) across Great Britain. Total grants of £2.3 million funded 66 specialist advisors within 36 individual projects. Twenty three advisors worked within the Charity's 'Debt via Health' (DVH) projects, seeking to tackle fuel poverty and promote energy efficiency via the local health sector.

Beneficiaries included: Shelter (£407,000); St Helen's Citizens Advice (£90,000); Energy Project Plus (£75,000); Zinthyia (£64,000); Speakeasy (£62,500); Preston Citizens Advice, Bromley by Bow Centre (£52,500 each); Local Solutions Liverpool (£52,000); St Ann's Advice Group (£51,500).

Applications

Funding rounds for organisations are normally publicised on the trust's website and in its newsletter.

Individuals can apply via the trust's online application form. Alternatively, an application form can be downloaded and submitted via the trust's freepost address (Freepost BRITISH GAS ENERGY TRUST).

See the website for full guidelines.

Sources of information

Accounts; annual report; Charity Commission record; funder's website.

British Heart Foundation (BHF)

 Cardiovascular research

 UK

 £111.8 million (2016/17)

CC number: 225971

Trustees: Dr Doug Gurr; Andrew Balfour; Prof. Dame Anna Dominiczak; Dr Robert Easton; Rt Hon. Lord Feldman of Elstree; Daryl Fielding; Prof. John Iredale; Prof. David Lomas; Iain Mackay; Prof. Sussan Nourshargh; Peter Phippen; Prof. Liam Smeeth; Prof. Sir Kent Woods.

Correspondent: Research Funds Department, Greater London House, 180 Hampstead Road, London NW1 7AW (tel: 020 7554 0434; email: research@bhf.org.uk)

 www.bhf.org.uk

[f] facebook.com/bhf

[twitter] @TheBHF

[instagram] @the_bhf

According to its website, British Heart Foundation's mission is 'to win the fight against cardiovascular disease' and its vision is 'a world in which people do not die prematurely or suffer from cardiovascular disease'. The foundation

looks to achieve these aims by funding pioneering cardiovascular research in the UK, as well as providing information about heart disease to the British public. Currently the foundation is the biggest funder of cardiovascular research in the country.

Grant programmes
At the time of writing (April 2018) the foundation offered the following grant programmes:

- **Project Grants:** For research projects (basic science and clinical) costing up to £300,000.
- **Special Project Grants:** For research projects costing more than £300,000. This grant type supports funding for basic science research and funding for certain observational studies and studies using datasets only.
- **Programme Grants:** For long-term support on a five-year rolling basis.
- **Clinical Study Grants:** For clinical trials and some observational studies of specific patient groups costing more than £300,000 or lasting more than 3 years.
- **New Horizons Grants:** To encourage participation in cardiovascular research by scientists from outside traditional cardiovascular biology, and to bring novel expertise to the field.
- **Infrastructure Grants:** To fund essential infrastructure to support cardiovascular research in an academic institution.
- **Strategic Initiatives:** To fund strategic capital needs or a strategic appointment.
- **Translational Awards:** To support the pre-clinical development of new cardiovascular medicines and technologies so that they are attractive for follow-on funding.
- **BHF-Turing Cardiovascular Data Science Awards:** To support collaborative research between cardiovascular investigators and data scientists that could generate data science solutions to key cardiovascular problems.
- **Small Meeting Funds:** Up to £3,000 towards the support of small meetings in the UK on focused areas of cardiovascular science.

In addition to its various grant programmes the foundation also offers clinical and non-clinical fellowships as well as a range of individual awards. See the website for details.

Financial information

In 2016/17 the foundation had assets of £304 million and an income of £310.5 million. Grants awarded during the year totalled £111.8 million, including £107.5 million for research and £4.3 million for 'prevention, survival and support'.

Beneficiaries included: King's College London (£9.7 million in nine grants); University of Leicester (£5.6 million in five grants); Imperial College London (£4.8 million in five grants); UK Biobank

(£3.2 million in three grants); University of Hull (£900,000); Action on Smoking and Health (£800,000).

Applications

Applicants are asked to prepare a detailed research proposal (in Arial font size not smaller than 12 pt) that complies with the instructions and eligibility criteria outlined in the specific grant guidelines. All applications, except for Infrastructure Grants, Strategic Initiatives and Small Meeting Funds, must be submitted online using the Grants Management System (GMS) available via the foundation's website.

Applications for funding are sent to independent peer reviewers before being assessed by the relevant research grant committee. According to the foundation's website:

> Decisions are based on factors such as relevance to cardiovascular disease, scientific merit, timeliness, relationship to other work in the field, adherence to the principles of the NC3Rs guidance for reduction, refinement and replacement of use of animals, and value for money.

Each of the foundation's research grant committees meets four times a year other than the Clinical Studies Committee and the Translational Awards Committee which meet twice a year.

For full details of all current grants programme as well as information regarding eligibility criteria, application processes and deadlines, refer to the foundation's website.

Sources of information
Accounts; annual report; Charity Commission record; funder's website.

British Lung Foundation

 Research into lung diseases

UK

£2.23 million (2016/17)

CC number: 326730

Trustees: Prof. Stephen Spiro; Baroness Tessa Blackstone; Ralph Bernard; John Graham; Richard Pettit; David Gill; Stephen Holgate; Graham Colbert; Dr Francis Gilchrist; Dr Isabel DiVanna; Emily Bushby; John Loots; Teresa Burgoyne.

Correspondent: Research Team, British Lung Foundation, Lung Foundation House, 73–75 Goswell Road, London EC1V 7ER (tel: 020 7688 5555; email: enquiries@blf-uk.org)

 www.blf.org.uk

 facebook.com/britishlungfoundation

 @lunguk

 @britishlungfoundation

Established in 1984, the British Lung Foundation supports people with chest and lung diseases by funding medical research into prevention, treatment, alleviation and cure. The foundation also campaigns to improve UK air quality to meet the standards recommended by the World Health Organisation.

Research grants
The foundation has several priority areas for researchers to understand the increase in the following diseases:

- Bronchiectasis
- Chronic obstructive pulmonary disease (COPD)
- Pulmonary fibrosis
- Lung cancer
- Mesothelioma
- Children's lung disease

Research grants are given to support early stage lung researchers and to establish research networks and centres of excellence. The foundation also co-funds research with government bodies and other charities focused on specific lung conditions. Grants are available for pump-priming projects, travel costs, equipment and salaries, and are usually offered on a multi-year basis.

Financial information
In 2016/17 the foundation held assets of almost £5.3 million and had an income of £7.5 million. During the year, 19 research grants were awarded totalling £2.23 million.

Previous beneficiaries have included: University of Glasgow (£287,000); Papworth NHS Trust (£113,000); Glenfield Hospital (£100,000); University of Southampton (£40,000); Centre for Translational Inflammation Research (£23,000).

Applications
The following information is taken from the 2016/17 accounts:

> The charity invites applications for lung research projects by advertising in medical journals, on its website, through publicity at conferences and via news bulletins issued by related organisations (such as the British Thoracic Society), as appropriate. Applicants are invited to submit their proposals, which are reviewed by the Research Committee and by external peer reviewers. These evaluations are discussed by the Research Committee, which then ranks the applications in order of scientific merit and benefit to people with lung disease. Funding is granted to the top ranking grants, taking into account the research priorities of the BLF and funding available.

Sources of information
Accounts; annual report; Charity Commission record; guidelines for applicants; funder's website.

British Record Industry Trust (BRIT Trust)

 Music, performing arts, young people

UK

£1.63 million (2016)

CC number: 1000413

Trustees: Angela Watts; Geoff Taylor; Tony Wadsworth; Henry Semmence; David Sharpe; William Rowe; Simon Presswell; Jonathan Morrish; David Munns; David Kassner; Korda Marshall; Max Hole; Mel Fox; John Deacon; Rob Dickens; Andy Cleary; Maggie Crowe; Rita Broe; John Craig.

Correspondent: Maggie Crowe, Trustee, c/o BPI, Riverside Building, County Hall, Westminster Bridge Road, London SE1 7JA (tel: 020 7803 1351; email: maggie.crowe@bpi.co.uk)

 www.brittrust.co.uk

facebook.com/The-BRIT-Trust-100825950530180

 @thebrittrust

Established in 1989, the BRIT Trust is entirely funded by the British music industry, and receives a large part of its income from the profits of the annual BRIT Awards. Its mission is 'to encourage young people in the exploration and pursuit of educational, cultural or therapeutic benefits emanating from music', which it does principally through its commitments to the BRIT School in Croydon – the UK's only non-fee paying performing arts school – and to Nordoff-Robbins, which is the UK's leading independent provider of music therapy. The trust also makes small contributions to other registered charities in line with its mission statement.

Financial information
In 2016 the trust had assets of £10.45 million and an income of £1.7 million. Grants were awarded to 11 organisations totalling £1.63 million. The majority of funds awarded were given to BRIT School for the Performing Arts and Technology and Nordoff-Robbins Music Therapy which received £876,500 and £482,500 respectively.

Beneficiaries included: BRIT School for the Performing Arts and Technology (£876,500); Nordoff-Robbins Music Therapy (£482,500); East London Arts 8 Music (ELAM) (£217,000); Key4Life (£30,000); Chelsea and Westminster

Hospital (£10,000); Alcohol Research UK (£7,500); Avenues and Community Association (£6,000); Welsh National Opera (£3,300); UniBrass Foundation (£1,500).

Exclusions

The trust only supports UK-registered charities. It does not consider applications for individual grants, scholarships, capital grants or grant donations outside the UK.

Applications

Applicants are requested to complete the application form available to download from the trust's website and submit it by post or email. Applications are considered at trustee meetings.

Sources of information

Accounts; annual report; Charity Commission record; funder's website.

The Bromley Trust

 Human rights, prison reform, environmental conservation and justice

UK

£ £643,500 (2016/17)

CC number: 801875

Trustees: Peter Edwards; Jean Ritchie; Anne-Marie Edgell; Dr Judith Brett; Fiona Cramb; Terrence Davies; Adam McCormack; Susan Silk.

Correspondent: The Trustees, Studio 7, 2 Pinchin Street, Whitechapel, London E1 1SA (tel: 020 7481 4899; email: info@thebromleytrust.org.uk)

 www.thebromleytrust.org.uk

In 1989 Frederick Keith Bromley, also known as Toby, set up the Bromley Trust committed to 'offset man's inhumanity to man'. The trust supports charities concerned with human rights, prison reform and conservation and sustainability. This well-organised and focused trust also offers other organisations with similar interests and objectives the chance to participate in a network of like-minded groups.

In 2004 the Bromley Trust set up three awards in memory of the settlor. Three charities involved with prison reform were chosen for this additional support. They were the Butler Trust, the Hardman Trust and the Prison Reform Trust.

Additionally, the Koestler Award Trust, which encourages and rewards a variety of creative endeavours culminating in an annual exhibition of work from prison, probation and secure psychiatric hospitals, has named a prize after Keith Bromley as he had been such a support to their work over the years. The Bromley Trust chose nature photography

as this had been a great interest of the settlor's throughout his life. The Keith Bromley Award for Outstanding Nature Photography was presented for the first time at the Koestler exhibition in 2004.

Grant programmes

The trust's grant-making priorities are as follows:

- Human rights – particularly for refugees, those experiencing discrimination or persecution and women whose rights have been violated. The trust's focus areas are:
  - Trafficking and slavery
  - Torture and abuse
  - Persecution – including human rights defenders, journalists and immigration detainees
  - Prison reform – particularly vulnerable groups, rehabilitation and breaking the cycle of re-offending.

The trust's focus areas are:

- Prison reform
- Education and skills training of offenders

The trust's focus areas for environment are:

- Deforestation, marine conservation, biodiversity and sustainability
- Environmental justice

Visit the trust's website for further details about each grant programme.

Strategy

The website states:

The Bromley Trust is an independent grant-making foundation. We make grants to charities working in our designated focus areas, where we believe we can achieve the maximum impact. We tend to provide unrestricted funding towards organisations that wholly fall within our remit. By supporting the core costs of an organisation we can allow the charity to undertake their work to the best of their abilities. We make relatively small grants, ranging from approximately £5,000 to £20,000 per year. We fund within specific focus areas, within each of our three funding streams. This allows us to direct our funding to particular areas of need. We aim to operate in a clear and transparent fashion, and aim to make the process of applying for a grant as simple as possible. We aim to develop a close relationship with our grantees, in order to best support their work.

Guidelines

The trust's criteria for awarding grants are listed on the website as follows:

- We can only accept completed application forms. We will not consider any other form of application.
- We can only make grants to UK-registered charities, and are unable to accept any applications from other organisations.
- We will only support charities that fall within our remit and focus areas.

- We are happy to work with other grant-making foundations to support worthwhile work within our focus areas.
- We particularly encourage crossover between our different funding streams and focus areas.
- We tend to provide unrestricted support to organisations that fall wholly within our remit; if you feel that you do not entirely fit within these criteria, but wish to apply for a specific project or element of your work then please send an email to info@thebromleytrust.org.uk and we will advise you on making an application.
- As we make unrestricted grants, please do not request a specific amount, the size of our grants is made at the discretion of the trustees.
- We are a small grant-maker with limited funds and a high demand. We are only able to support a fraction of the applications that we receive.

The trust's website contains full information on recent grants to organisations, many of which are supported on a regular basis. One-off grants are occasionally made, but are infrequent. The trust prefers to give larger amounts to fewer charities rather than spread its income over a large number of small grants.

Financial information

In 2016/17 the trust held assets of almost £18 million and had an income of £711,000. There were 51 grants made totalling £643,500, which were distributed as follows:

Human rights	29	£362,500
Prison reform and prison awards	16	£206,000
Sustainability and conservation	6	£75,000

Beneficiaries included: Prison Reform Trust (£30,000); Ashden Awards (£20,000); Kalayaan, Mind in Camden, The Marine Biological Association of the UK and Yarl's Wood Befrienders (£15,000 each); Children and Families Across Borders, Hebridean Whale and Dolphin Trust, Music in Prison, Reading Agency (£10,000 each); Parents Against Child Sexual Exploitation (£5,000).

Exclusions

Grants are only given to UK-registered charities. The following are not supported:

- Individuals
- Statutory authorities, or charities whose main source of funding is via statutory agencies
- International organisations, overseas development or disaster relief
- Local conservation projects or charities that work with single species
- Drug rehabilitation programmes
- Housing programmes

Applications

Application forms are available from the trust's website and can be returned via email. Applications should not exceed eight to ten pages. All charities are visited before a grant is made. There are no deadlines. Full criteria, guidelines and application process are detailed on the website.

Currently the grant programme for environmental funding is closed.

Sources of information
Accounts; annual report; Charity Commission record; funder's website.

The Rory and Elizabeth Brooks Foundation

 International development, poverty research, higher education, social justice, visual arts

Worldwide

£ 439,000 (2016/17)

CC number: 1111587

Trustees: Elizabeth Brooks; Roderick Brooks; Bridget Fury.

Correspondent: Robyn Bryson, Orion House, 5 Upper St Martin's Lane, London WC2H 9EA (tel: 020 7024 2217; email: rbryson@mmlcapital.com)

The foundation was established and registered with the Charity Commission in 2005. The foundation receives its income through donations and legacies. According to its website the foundation currently provides support in the following areas:

- Global development and poverty research
- Higher education in the UK
- Visual arts
- Social justice

Partnership is a key consideration for the foundation and in each area of focus there are one or more partners with which Rory and Elizabeth work. Current partners include; The Rugby Portobello Trust, Justice and Care; Manchester University Global Development Institute.

Financial information
In 2016/17 the foundation held assets of £847,000 and had an income of £62,500. A total of £439,000 was donated in grants to 14 organisations, including a large donation of £333,000 to the University of Manchester – our research indicates this institution is an annual beneficiary.

Beneficiaries included: University of Manchester (£333,000); Tate Gallery (£55,000).

Applications
Apply in writing to the correspondent.

Sources of information
Accounts; annual report; Charity Commission record.

The Broomton Foundation

 General charitable purposes

East Anglia

£ £984,000 (2016/17)

CC number: 1125386

Trustees: Benedicta Chamberlain; Arthur Chamberlain; Julius Chamberlain; Robert Chamberlain; Kate Lewis.

Correspondent: The Trustees, Birketts (CRB), 24–26 Museum Street, Ipswich, Suffolk IP1 1HZ (email: admin@ broomton.org)

The foundation was established in 2008 and makes grants for general charitable purposes throughout East Anglia.

Financial information
In 2016/17 the foundation held assets of £8.6 million and had an income of £1.3 million. Grants awarded to organisations totalled £984,000.

Beneficiaries included: Riding for the Disabled (£600,000); L'Arche (£100,000); Combat Stress (£50,000); Marie Curie (£10,000); Pop Chorus (£7,700); Suffolk Wildlife Trust (£5,000).

Applications
Apply in writing to the correspondent.

Sources of information
Accounts; annual report; Charity Commission record.

Bill Brown 1989 Charitable Trust

 Health, including research into blindness, other medical research and hospices, care of older people and people who have disabilities, deaf and blind people, general welfare

UK, although support is mainly given to charities based in the south of England

£ £487,500 (2015/16)

CC number: 801756

Trustees: Graham Brown; Anthony Barnett.

Correspondent: The Trustees, BM Box 4567, London WC1N 3XX

 www.billbrowncharity.org

This trust was founded in 1989 by Percy William Ernest Brown, a civil engineer and businessman who also served in the RAF during the Second World War.

The trust's website provides the following information:

> The Trustees operate a grant giving policy with a view to making annual distributions

of approximately £475,000, including Bursary commitments which during any year can utilise approximately £300,000 of the available funds. After taking account of Bursaries and the other grants regularly made by the Trustees – most of which continue charitable interests of the late Mr Brown – there are limited funds available for distribution to other charities. A wide range of UK-Registered Charities are supported.

The Trustees are particularly interested in supporting the following areas of charitable work:

- Research into blindness
- Other medical research
- The deaf and blind
- Care of the elderly
- Care of the disabled
- General welfare
- Hospices

Financial information
In 2015/16 the trust held assets of £14.9 million and had an income of £571,00. Grants were made to 17 organisations and totalled £487,500.

Previous beneficiaries have included: Moorfields Eye Charity (£220,000 to be paid over three years); Charities Aid Foundation Trust (£75,000); Arthritis Research (£22,000); Macmillan Cancer Support and Salvation Army (£15,000 each); Crohn's and Colitis UK (£7,500); Blind Veterans UK (£5,000); Barnardo's (£3,800).

Exclusions
According to the trust's website, it does not support:

- Individuals
- Animal welfare
- Small (local) charitable causes
- Appeals from regional branches of national charities
- Wildlife and environmental conservation
- Maintenance of buildings
- Religious charities

Applications
Apply by letter confirming your registered charity number, the aims and objectives of your charity, and any other relevant facts. Applicants must also include a copy of their latest annual report and most recent audited accounts. The trustees will consider supporting specific projects, in this case provide details of the total amount required, contributions received to date and proposed timing to completion. Depending on the nature of the project, the trustees will sometimes make a grant commitment, but defer payment until assurances are received that sufficient funds have been raised or pledged. Applications will only be considered from English registered charities and the trustees concentrate on supporting charities mainly in the south of England. Applications must be received by the end of May or the end of October to be sure

of consideration at the summer and winter meetings.

Sources of information
Accounts; annual report; Charity Commission record; funder's website.

Brushmill Ltd

 Orthodox Judaism, the relief of poverty, general charitable purposes

Worldwide

£537,000 (2016/17)

CC number: 285420

Trustees: C. Getter; J. Weinberger; E. Weinberger.

Correspondent: Mrs M. Getter, Secretary, 76 Fairholt Road, London N16 5HN (email: mail@cohenarnold. com)

Established in 1982, this charity gives grants for the advancement of the Orthodox Jewish religion, the relief of poverty and general charitable purposes. It would appear that the charity mainly supports Jewish organisations.

Financial information
In 2016/17 the charity had negative assets of -£32,500 and an income of £295,000. Grants totalling £537,000 were awarded to religious, educational and other charitable organisations.

Beneficiaries included: Ezer V'Hatzalah Ltd (£283,500); Bais Rizhin Trust (£23,000); Hadras Kodesh Trust (£13,300); Beis Rochel (£12,800); The M Y A Charitable Trust (£5,000).

Applications
Apply in writing to the correspondent.

Sources of information
Accounts; annual report; Charity Commission record.

Buckingham Trust

 Christianity, churches

UK

£211,000 to organisations (2016/17)

CC number: 237350

Trustees: Richard Foot; Tina Clay.

Correspondent: Tina Clay, Trustee, Foot Davson Ltd, 17 Church Road, Tunbridge Wells, Kent TN1 1LG (tel: 01892 774774)

This trust was established by a trust deed in 1962 and makes grants in support of the advancement of religion and other charitable purposes. It is an agency charity, which means that donors are able to choose which charities receive the funds they have donated.

The trust's 2016/17 accounts state: 'The trustees and donors try to enable ordinary people to live out their faith as part of their parish community by contributing to churches and other charities, whose aim is the advancement of religion.'

Financial information
In 2016/17 the trust held assets of £747,500 and had an income of £149,000. Grants were made totalling £226,500 and were distributed as follows:

Charities	£157,500
Churches	£53,500
Individuals	£15,000

Beneficiaries included: Titus Trust (£24,500); Grace Church – Dulwich (£12,000); Tear Fund (£5,900); The Christ Church Gospel Partners Fund and Urban Saints (£1,000 each).

Applications
Apply in writing to the correspondent. Preference is given to charities of which the trustees have personal interest, knowledge, or association.

Sources of information
Accounts; annual report; Charity Commission record.

The Buffini Chao Foundation

 Education and training of children and young people, general charitable purposes

Worldwide

£332,500 (2016/17)

CC number: 1111022

Trustees: Lady Buffini; Sir Damon Buffini; Maria Hindmarsh; Sue Gutierrez.

Correspondent: Lady Buffini, Trustee, PO Box 1427, Northampton NN1 9FP (tel: 01892 701801; email: trustees@ buffinichao.com)

This foundation was established in 2005 with general charitable purposes. According to its 2016/17 annual report, the foundation's core aim is to 'support children and young people through education and training'.

Financial information
In 2016/17 the foundation had assets of £7.1 million and an income of £972,000. Grants awarded to 14 organisations totalled £332,500.

Beneficiaries included: NT Connections (£100,000); Royal Shakespeare Company (£33,500); First Give (£15,000); Build Africa (£4,000).

Applications
Apply in writing to the correspondent.

Sources of information
Accounts; annual report; Charity Commission record.

The Bulldog Trust

 General charitable purposes

UK

£203,500 (2016/17)

CC number: 326292

Trustees: Brian Smouha; Charles Hoare; Hamish McPherson; Alex Williams; Charles Jackson.

Correspondent: Mary Gunn, 2 Temple Place, London WC2R 3BD (tel: 020 7240 6192; email: info@thefore.org)

www.thefore.org

The Bulldog Trust has been funding and advice to charities for over 30 years. In March 2017 it launched its new grant-making initiative, The Fore Trust.

The Fore Trust
The Fore Trust provides unrestricted development grants and pro bono strategic supports to early-stage charities and social enterprises.

Eligibility
The trust's website states:

> The Fore provides funding to UK-registered charities, community interest companies, charitable incorporated organisations and community benefit societies with annual income of less than £500,000.

> We make unrestricted grants which have the potential to have a transformational impact on an organisation, whether by unlocking exponential growth, sustainability, efficiency or some other major step forward. We see our grants as investments in the organisations we support.

Financial information
In 2016/17 the trust held assets of £9.1 million and had an income of £1.3 million. Grants awarded to organisations totalled £203,500.

Beneficiaries included: Fully Focused (£20,500); Football Beyond and Schools of Tomorrow (£20,000 each); The Gifted (£18,000); Recycling Unlimited (£9,000); FareShare (£4,000).

The trust made 31 sundry donations of under £10,000 totalling £59,000.

Applications
Apply online through the trust's website. The trust runs three twelve-week funding rounds to coincide with the academic calendar each year. Application dates are on the trust's website. Registration is run on a first-come, first-serve basis and once the cap is reached, the round is

closed. It is recommended to register early.

Sources of information

Accounts; annual report; Charity Commission record; funder's website.

The E F Bulmer Benevolent Fund

 Relief of poverty or sickness

Herefordshire

£ £264,000 to organisations (2015/16)

CC number: 214831

Trustees: Richard Bulmer; Caroline Bulmer; Edward Bulmer; Nigel Bulmer; Andrew Patten.

Correspondent: James Greenfield, Administrator, Fred Bulmer Centre, Wall Street, Hereford, Herefordshire HR4 9HP (tel: 01432 271293; email: efbulmer@gmail.com)

 www.efbulmer.co.uk

The fund was established for the benefit of former employees of H P Bulmer Holdings plc or its subsidiary companies for a period of not less than one year, or their dependants who are in poverty, and to others for the relief of sickness and poverty.

Grants are made to organisations and groups based in Herefordshire, working for the relief of need of those living in Herefordshire. Organisations from outside the county are only supported if beneficiaries are resident in the area of benefit. Smaller groups who may have difficulty in receiving support from large national grant-makers are normally given priority. The fund supports core costs (only for one year at a time), as well as project costs and capital costs.

Small grants are occasionally also made directly to individuals in need.

Financial information

In 2016/17 the fund held assets of £15.5 million and had an income of £464,500. Grants were made totalling £330,000 of which £264,000 was paid to 74 organisations, and £19,600 to 45 individuals. Grants to 123 H P Bulmer pensioners totalled £46,000.

Beneficiaries included: Herefordshire Citizens Advice (£12,000); Herefordshire Headway (£7,500); Basement Youth Trust (£6,000); Bulmer Foundation (£5,000); Jumpstart Kidz (£4,000); Herefordshire Wildlife Trust (£3,500); Acorn Children's Hospice and Deaf Direct (£3,000 each); Happy Days (£2,300).

Grants of less than £3,000 totalled £37,000.

Exclusions

Large UK charities and those from outside Herefordshire are unlikely to be supported, unless beneficiaries are based in Herefordshire.

Applications

Application forms are available to download from the fund's website. Hard copies should be returned with a detailed two page application, organisational budget, project budget and most recent audited accounts (if not available online).

Sources of information

Accounts; annual report; Charity Commission record; funder's website.

The Burdett Trust for Nursing

 Nursing and health care

UK and overseas

£ £4.8 million to organisations (2016)

CC number: 1089849

Trustees: Alan Gibbs; Dame Christine Beasley; Bill Gordon; Andrew Martin-Smith; Dame Eileen Sills; Evy Hambro; Prof. David Sines; Dr Michael Gormley; Andrew Gibbs.

Correspondent: Shirley Baines, Charity Grants Director, Rathbone Trust Company Ltd, 8 Finsbury Circus, London EC2M 7AZ (tel: 020 7399 0102; email: administrator@btfn.org.uk)

 www.btfn.org.uk

 facebook.com/burdetttrust

 @BurdettTrust

The Burdett Trust for Nursing is an independent charitable trust named after Sir Henry Burdett KCB, the founder of the Royal National Pension Fund for Nurses. The trust was established in 2002 with the following charitable objects:

> To promote and advance education, research and training within the nursing and other healthcare professions for the benefit of the public and to promote public awareness of nursing and health issues; provide for the relief of hardship and mental or physical ill-health among nurses and other health-care professionals, and their dependants; and promote and advance the provision of nursing and other health services for the benefit of the public.

Currently funding is divided between three key areas:

> ▸ **Building nursing research capacity:** to support clinical nursing research and research addressing policy, leadership development and delivery of nursing care

> ▸ **Building nurse leadership capacity:** supporting nurses in their professional development to create a cadre of excellent nursing and allied health professionals who will become leaders of the future and foster excellence and capacity-building in advancing the nursing profession

> ▸ **Supporting local nurse-led initiatives:** to support nurse-led initiatives that make a difference at local level and are focused explicitly on improving care for patients and users of services.

Grant programmes

The trust currently operates several grants programmes:

Small Grants Programme

This programme will make small grants to projects that are nurse-led and focused on supporting the nursing contribution to health care. All projects must be focused on improving care for patients through nursing and may include multi-professional or team-working interventions. Projects may involve clinical care, environment of care, social care, leadership and/or education. Under this programme grant funding will range from £2,000 to £8,000.

Proactive Grants

This programme aims to create opportunities to engage nursing stakeholders in collaborative problem-solving and program development. Through the programme, trustees work with a wide range of public and private partners to advance the foundation's long-term goals. All proactive grants are initiated by the Burdett Trust for Nursing and the trustees do not accept unsolicited applications.

International Grants

In addition to its work in the UK, from time to time the trust also considers applications from UK-registered charities working overseas to build nurse leadership capacity or to empower nurses to make significant improvements to the patient care environment. Recently these grants have been scaled back and are currently subject to a strategic review. As such, at the present time only small applications in the region of £5,000 to £7,500 are being considered.

To maximise the impact of their funding the trustees often work in partnership with other organisations to deliver some of their grant programmes. Details of the trust's current partners can be found on the 'Our Partners' section of the website.

Financial information

In 2016 the trust had assets of £79.7 million and an income of £1.3 million. During the year, the trust awarded 63 grants to organisations totalling £4.8 million. In addition the trust also awards grants worth a total of £239,000 to individuals.

Beneficiaries included: Sue Ryder (£240,000); Commonwealth Nurses and Midwives Federation (£150,000); Junius S Morgan Benevolent Trust (£100,000); Northern Ireland Hospice (£8,000); Down's Syndrome Association (£7,900); Unity in Health (£7,500); Orchid Cancer Appeal (£6,000); Sherwood Forest Hospital NHS Trust (£2,200).

Exclusions

According to its 2016/17 annual report, the trust will not fund any of the following:

- General appeals
- Existing posts, although the trust will consider supporting new posts directly associated with a project
- Overheads of academic institutions or statutory agencies
- Organisations closely aligned to government departments (i.e. Primary Care Trusts in the NHS)
- Retrospective funding
- Funding in lieu of statutory funding
- Significant capital appeals e.g. building costs or equipment

Further programme-specific exclusions may also apply. Check the programme guidance for full details.

Applications

Guidance for each of the grants programmes is available to download from the trust's website. All applications must be submitted using the link to online application form, applications submitted by email will not be accepted. Applications will be received and assessed continually during the year and the trust aims to process grants within six weeks of receipt, although on occasion the process may take longer.

Sources of information

Accounts; annual report; Charity Commission record; funder's website.

The Clara E Burgess Charity

Children and young people, education, health and well-being

UK and overseas

£386,000 (2016/17)

CC number: 1072546

Trustee: The Royal Bank of Scotland plc.

Correspondent: The Trustees, c/o The Royal Bank of Scotland, Trust Services, 6th Floor, Trinity Quay 2, Avon Street, Bristol BS2 0PT (tel: 0345 304 2424)

The charity was registered in 1998 and makes grants to registered charities where children are the principal beneficiaries.

According to the 2016/17 annual report, grants are made towards:

> The provision of facilities and assistance to enhance the education, health and physical well-being of such children, in order that their conditions of life may be improved, but having particular regard to children under the age of 10 and those who have lost either one or both parents.

Financial information

In 2016/17 the charity had assets of £11.95 million and an income of £328,500. Grants awarded to organisations totalled £386,000.

Beneficiaries included: Norwood (£10,000); Nepal Youth Foundation UK (£8,100); British Red Cross (£5,000); Amantani, Asthma Relief, The Clatterbridge Cancer Charity, Phyllis Tuckwell Hospice Care (£4,000); Christian Aid (£2,300); Activiteens, Belvoir Cricket and Countryside Trust, Pear Tree School, Trauma Recovery Centre (£2,000 each).

Exclusions

Non-registered charities cannot apply.

Applications

Applications can be made in writing to the correspondent and are considered in January and July.

Sources of information

Accounts; annual report; Charity Commission record.

The Edward Cadbury Charitable Trust

Arts and culture, community projects, social welfare, environment and conservation, religious activities such as interfaith and multi-faith relations, education and training, medical research

Midlands region, including: Herefordshire, Shropshire, Staffordshire, Warwickshire, and Worcestershire

£372,500 (2016/17)

CC number: 1160334

Trustees: Andrew Littleboy; Charles Gillett; Nigel Cadbury; Robert Marriott; William Southall.

Correspondent: Susan Anderson, Trust Manager, Rokesley, University of Birmingham, Bristol Road, Selly Oak, Birmingham B29 6QF (tel: 0121 472 1838; email: ecadburytrust@btconnect.com)

 www.edwardcadburytrust.org.uk

The Edward Cadbury Charitable Trust was first established in 1945 by Edward Cadbury (the grandson of the founder of the chocolate company) and is linked to

The Edward and Dorothy Cadbury Trust (Charity Commission no. 1107327), which has its own separate entry. The trust in its current form was registered with the Charity Commission in 2015. The trust supports charities in the Midlands region, including Herefordshire, Shropshire, Staffordshire, Warwickshire and Worcestershire.

The trust's website states that the founder's interests in 'education, religion and social welfare, together with the Quaker values of simplicity, equality, justice, peace and care of the environment, have helped shape the current grant-making policy of the Trust'. It awards grants under the following programmes

- Arts and culture
- Community projects and integration
- Compassionate support
- Conservation and environment
- Interfaith and multi-faith relations
- Education and training
- Medical research

Grants normally range from £500 to £10,000 and are awarded on a one-off basis for a specific purpose or as part of a project. The trustees only make larger grants on an exceptional basis.

Financial information

In 2016/17 the trust held assets of over £43.1 million and had an income of £1 million. Grants totalled £372,500 and were awarded to 135 organisations in the following categories:

Community projects and integration	£115,500
Education and training	£81,500
Compassionate support	£81,000
Conservation and environment	£47,000
Arts and culture	£31,000
Research	£11,000
Interfaith and multi-faith relations	£6,000

Previous beneficiaries have included: Ashton University Medical School (£250,000); Sense (£100,000); Heart of England Community Foundation (£50,000); Dodford Children's Holiday Farm (£10,000); Birmingham Samaritans (£5,000); Trailblazers Mentoring (£4,000); Myton Hospice (£3,000); Horsham Quaker Meeting (£2,500); Relate Worcester (£2,000).

Exclusions

No grants are made to individuals or to organisations that are not registered charities.

Applications

Applications can be made by writing to the correspondent by post or email or online on the trust's website. Applications are accepted all year round and are normally considered within a three-month timescale. Letters of application should provide a clear and concise description of the project requiring funding as well as the outcomes and benefits that are likely to be achieved. The trustees also require an outline budget and explanation of how the project is to be funded initially and in the future together with the latest annual report and accounts for the charity.

Sources of information

Accounts; annual report; Charity Commission record; funder's website.

The William Adlington Cadbury Charitable Trust

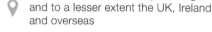 Local welfare and disability charities, environment and conservation, Quaker charities, international development

West Midlands, especially Birmingham and to a lesser extent the UK, Ireland and overseas

£745,000 (2016/17)

CC number: 213629

Trustees: Margaret Salmon; Rupert Cadbury; Sarah Stafford; Katherine Cadbury; Adrian Thomas; John Penny; Sophy Blandy; Janine Cobaine; Victoria Mohan.

Correspondent: Carolyn Bettis, Trust Administrator, Rokesley, University of Birmingham, Bristol Road, Selly Oak, Birmingham B29 6QF (tel: 0121 472 1464; email: info@wa-cadbury.org.uk)

 www.wa-cadbury.org.uk

This trust was established in 1923 for general charitable purposes. On the website the origins of the trust are described as:

William was the second son of Richard Cadbury, who, with his younger brother George, started the manufacture of chocolate under the Cadbury name. He came from a family with strong Quaker traditions which influenced his whole life. It was this Quaker ethos which underpinned his commitment to the advancement of social welfare schemes in the city of Birmingham.

William Cadbury established the trust soon after his two years as lord mayor of Birmingham from 1919 to 1921, wishing to give more help to the causes in which he was interested. One such was the building of the Queen Elizabeth Hospital, a medical centre with the space and facilities to bring together the small specialised hospitals scattered throughout Birmingham [...] He did much to encourage the city library and art gallery and a wide circle of Midland artists who became his personal friends. Through this charity, he also secured several properties for the National Trust.

As time went on, members of his family were brought in as trustees and this practice has continued with

representatives of the next three generations becoming trustees in their turn, so that all the present trustees are his direct descendants.

Grant-making policy

The trust's website outlines a clear grant-making policy:

- The William Cadbury Charitable Trust (the trust) supports charitable organisations based in the UK. If you do not have a UK base, are not registered with the Charity Commission or are applying as an individual we will not be able to help.
- Please review the Grant Programmes page in order to establish whether your project qualifies for our support. The West Midlands grant programme is sub-divided into sectors which may overlap. Please select the sector which best fits your project.
- Please ensure that your application is brief, concise and to the point. Trustees are required to undertake a large volume of reading prior to a meeting and if you have exceeded the equivalent of three sides of A4 you may be asked to re-submit a shortened application.
- Trustees will consider applications for core costs as well as for development/project funding.
- If the trust has supported you in the past, please briefly describe the outcome of the most recent project to receive our support.
- Grant applications can be submitted online or, if preferred, by post.
- Applications are considered by trustees on a regular basis and small grants (up to a maximum of £2000) are awarded monthly.
- Trustees meet in May and November to award approximately twenty large grants at each meeting, ranging in value from £10,000 to £20,000 with an occasional maximum of £50,000.
- Grants are normally awarded on a one-off basis and repeat applications are not usually considered within two years of the award.
- UK bodies legally exempt from registration with the Charity Commission can apply and small grants are occasionally made to unregistered groups in the West Midlands (who must nevertheless have a constitution, an elected committee and a bank account controlled by two or more committee members).
- We normally respond to appeals within six weeks of submission. If at that stage your appeal has been shortlisted for a large grant you may be asked to provide additional information and, if you have not already done so, to complete our online application form. Trustees may also ask to visit certain shortlisted applicants.
- Applicants selected from the shortlist for consideration at the next half-yearly meeting will be notified in the month prior to the meeting.
- Successful applicants are asked to provide a receipt upon payment of the grant and a report on the project for which funding has been given. This

should be made within the year. It need not necessarily be more than two sides of A4 but should include information regarding the number of beneficiaries and what you have observed as the strengths and weaknesses of the project. This will be kept on file for reference if further applications are made.

- All applicants will receive a response from the trust whether or not their application has been successful.

Grant programmes

Birmingham and the West Midlands

- *Community action* – community-based and organised schemes (which may be centered on a place of worship) aimed at solving local problems and improving the quality of life of community members
- *Vulnerable groups* – vulnerable groups include the elderly, children and young people, the disabled, asylum seekers and similar minorities
- *Advice, mediation and counselling* – applicants must be able to point to the rigorous selection, training and monitoring of front line staff (particularly in the absence of formal qualifications) as well as to the overall need for the service provided
- *Education and training* – trustees are particularly interested in schemes that help people of working age develop new skills in order to re-enter the jobs market
- *Environment and conservation* – projects which address the impact of climate change and projects to preserve buildings and installations of historic importance and local interest
- *Medical and healthcare* – covers hospices, self-help groups and some medical research which must be based in and be of potential benefit to the West Midlands
- *The arts* – music, drama and the visual arts, museums and art galleries
- *Penal Affairs* – *restorative justice, prison-based projects and work with ex-offenders aimed at reducing re-offending. (Penal reform used to be supported on a UK-wide basis but, because of the volume of appeals received, this programme is now restricted to the West Midlands)*

United Kingdom

- *The religious society of friends* – support for groups with a clear Quaker connection and support for the work of the Religious Society of Friends in the UK

Ireland

- *'Peace and reconciliation'*

International development

- The International grant programme is heavily oversubscribed and since the Trust can only support a small proportion of the appeals received trustees have decided to concentrate available funds on organisations with which the Trust has close and well established links. Ad hoc appeals are unlikely to be successful. All applicants must have UK charity registration.

- *Africa* – the international development programme is concentrated on West Africa and work to reduce poverty on a sustainable basis in both rural and urban communities – schemes that help children access education are also supported
- *Asia and Eastern Europe*
- *South America*

Financial information

In 2016/17 the trust had assets of £37.2 million and an income of £976,000. Grants were made totalling £745,000 and were broken down as follows:

West Midlands	76%
International development	15%
UK	7%
Ireland	2%

The trust's financial accounts lists beneficiaries of grants over £2,000.

Previous beneficiaries have included: United Purposes (£90,000); Britain Yearly Meeting of the Religious Society of Friends (£25,000); Diabetes UK and Bilston Resource Centre (£20,000 each); Orchestras for All (£12,000); Langley House Trust (£10,000); Stafford Historic Buildings Trust (£5,000); Birmingham Settlement (£3,000).

Exclusions

The trust does not fund:

- Individuals (whether for research, expeditions, educational purposes or medical treatment)
- Projects concerned with travel, adventure, sports or recreation
- Organisations which are based outside the UK

Applications

Applications can be submitted via the trust's online application form on its website. Alternatively, they can be made in writing to the correspondent, including the following information:

- Charity registration number
- A description of the charity's aims and achievements
- The grant programme being applied to
- An outline and budget for the project for which funding is sought
- Details of funds raised and the current shortfall
- If the organisation has received funding from the trust before, provide brief details of the outcome of this project

There is no requirement to send your charity's annual report and accounts as the trustees will refer to the accounts held online by the Charity Commission. Applications are considered on a continuing basis throughout the year. Small grants are assessed each month. Large grants are awarded at the trustees' meetings held twice annually, normally in May and November. Applicants whose appeals are to be considered at one of the meetings will be notified in advance.

Sources of information

Accounts; annual report; Charity Commission record; funder's website.

The Cadbury Foundation

 Education, training and employment, sport, sustainable environment, general charitable purposes

UK and overseas

£582,500 (2016)

CC number: 1050482

Trustees: Jonathan Horrell; Eoin Kellett; Glenn Caton; Michael Taylor; Lisa Crane.

Correspondent: Kelly Farrell, Community Affairs Manager, PO BOX 12, Bourneville, Birmingham B30 2LU (tel: 0121 787 2421; email: kelly.farrell@ mdlz.com)

www.cadbury.co.uk/cadbury-foundation

The Cadbury Foundation was established in 1935 in recognition of the company founders George and Richard Cadbury and their investment in the welfare of their employees and wider community. In 2010 Kraft Foods Inc. gained control of Cadbury plc. Two years later the corporation was divided into Kraft Food Group plc and Mondelez, which together now fund the Cadbury Foundation.

The Cadbury Foundation's grant-making strategy focuses on larger projects so that it can generate the greatest impact. The foundation also contributes to communities near the company's operations, so that where possible donations can be backed up with employee volunteering work and gifts in kind.

Grants are made under the following four pillars:

- **Skills Development** – giving an awareness of the world of work and enhancing the ability of young people and disadvantaged adults to gain and sustain employment
- **Olympic and Paralympic Legacy** – to build stronger, healthier communities through sport
- **Source Projects** – supporting the development of sustainable cocoa growing communities where Mondelez International sources its cocoa and coffee beans
- **Employee Passions** – some funds are reserved for employee-related grants and cash match where Company volunteers can either have their fundraising efforts matched, or where they can bid for a grant to support the work of a chosen charity

In its 2016 accounts the foundation provides the following information regarding its grant-making policy:

In considering projects for support, the Foundation considers value-for-money in terms of attaining maximum community benefit. The Foundation is guided in making its selections for grant-giving by the demonstration of factors such as genuine community need, benefit for 'at risk' client groups or areas of social deprivation and those who will obtain the maximum community benefit from an association with the charity.

The Foundation also works with major community partners to develop clear objectives and assess outcomes. Outcome measurements might include: number of people reached by the project, improvement in performance levels, evaluation rating by recipients, impact of the charity's involvement and community partner efficiency.

Financial information

In 2016 the foundation had assets of £143,000 and an income of £637,000 which included £600,000 from Mondelez UK Holdings and Services Ltd. Grants to 31 organisations totalled £582,500.

Employee passions	£232,000	40%
Skills development	£225,500	39%
Olympic and Paralympic legacy	£125,000	21%

Beneficiaries included: Taste of Work, British Paralympic Association (£100,000 each); Grocery Aid, Northside Partnership (£50,000 each); The Prince's Trust (£30,000); Sheffield Wildcats, Erme Valley Riding School for the Disabled, Trinity Homeless, Belvedere Youth Club (£5,000 each); High Acres Woodcraft Folk (£2,000).

Applications

The foundation actively seeks out projects to support and therefore cannot accept any unsolicited requests for funding. The 2016 annual report explains that, 'it is partly the elimination of 'token' grants in response to applications that has enabled the Foundation to provide more substantial support – and 'really make a difference' – in its chosen areas of activity'.

Sources of information

Accounts; annual report; Charity Commission record; funder's website.

The Barrow Cadbury Trust

 Criminal justice, migration, social and economic justice

UK and overseas, with a preference for Birmingham and the Black Country (Wolverhampton, Dudley, West Bromwich, Smethwick or Sandwell)

£3.86 million (2016/17)

CC number: 1115476

Trustees: Erica Cadbury; Anna Southall; Nicola Cadbury; Helen Cadbury; Catherina Pharoah; Tamsin Rupprechter; Harry Serle; John Serle; Stephen Skakel; Binita Mehta; Esther McConnell.

Correspondent: The Trustees, Kean House, 6 Kean Street, London WC2B 4AS (tel: 020 7632 9060; email: general@barrowcadbury.org.uk)

www.barrowcadbury.org.uk

The trust was established by Barrow Cadbury and his wife Geraldine in 1920. Barrow was the son of John Cadbury, founder of the Cadbury chocolate business. Barrow and Geraldine were inspired by Quaker beliefs and used their increasing wealth to tackle social problems including juvenile crime and urban poverty.

Charitable activities

The trust promotes social justice through grant-making, research, influencing public policy and supporting local communities. The following themes are prominent across the trust's work:

- Strengthening civil society
- Putting equality at the heart of everything
- Addressing gender-based disadvantage
- Addressing racism in all its forms
- Promoting sustainable development

Grant programmes

The programme priorities are based on social objectives that are of particular concern to the trust. These are based on the existing strengths of work previously funded and current or possible areas of policy development. Projects will be chosen that the trust believes will help to achieve tangible shifts in policy and practice.

The trust's work is divided into three main areas of interest:

- Criminal justice
- Migration
- Economic justice

Criminal justice

The website notes:

> Through its Criminal Justice Programme, Barrow Cadbury Trust's principal aim is to strengthen the evidence base for structural and practical change for young adults and women that will support rehabilitation and desistance from crime. All projects funded by the Trust in this programme will be expected to include a perspective on gender and race, and seek to enable the voices of those directly affected to be heard.

Our objectives for the next five years are:

- Supporting for the Trust's T2A initiative, seeking to further develop the evidence base for effective, distinct approaches for young adults throughout the criminal justice system, from point of arrest to prison resettlement and deepen its growing impact across England and Wales
- Generating and supporting initiatives that focus on gender and race within a criminal justice context: initiatives that focus on the distinct needs of girls and women involved in crime, with an emphasis on early intervention, and further work to highlight and address the disproportionate over-representation of young BAME and Muslim people at all stages of the criminal justice system
- Amplifying the voices of people with direct experience of the criminal justice system who are less frequently heard and listened to by decision-makers
- Supporting projects that shine a light on the parts of the system that are infrequently scrutinised, contentious, unacknowledged or about which little is known

Migration

According to the website:

> The Barrow Cadbury Trust believes that migrants and refugees should be treated in a fair and dignified manner. The aim of the migration programme is to promote an immigration system that is fair to both migrants and established residents and facilitate a policy and public debate on migration and integration that is based on shared values as well as evidence.

Our objectives over the next five years are:

- To promote greater understanding within communities and the fair and dignified treatment of refugees, asylum seekers and migrants
- To broaden and deepen the public debate on migration and integration and ensure that it draws on shared values as well as evidence
- To inform public policy and promote workable policies in relation to immigration and integration

Economic Justice

According to the website:

> The Barrow Cadbury Trust believes that economic systems should be fair. Financial networks and institutions should aim to build economic inclusion and not erode it. By exploring good practice and innovation in financial systems that actively promote financial inclusion we can spread creative solutions and encourage new conversations and partnerships. We consider that financial resilience and inequality in communities can only improve if economic systems operate sustainably both at a macro and local level. In a period of reduced resources and capacity at statutory and community level, we are keen to build learning to strengthen local economies and to share best practice between a range of sectors, but particularly across local authorities.

Our objectives over the next five years are to:

- To explore and support policy, research and practical interventions to build sustainable and socially just economic systems
- To support alliances to build economic inclusion; and use this learning to influence policy and practice at a local level
- To support innovative and sustainable approaches to build voice and reduce economic inequality through partnership and new thinking
- Use our resources to build movements, voice and collaboration across sectors

There are additional priorities for charities working in Birmingham. These can be viewed on the trust's website.

Financial information

In 2016/17 the trust had assets of £72.6 million and an income of £2.95 million. During the year, the trust awarded around £3.86 million in grants.

The trust approved 110 grants during the year which were distributed as follows:

Poverty and inclusion	31
Migration	30
Other	26
Criminal justice	21

Previous beneficiaries have included: ShareAction (£70,000); Citizens UK (£60,000); Fawcett Society (£57,500); Young Women's Trust (£45,000); Localise West Midlands (£44,500); Community Development Finance Association (£41,000); Uturn UK CIC (£40,000); The School for Social Entrepreneurs (£10,000).

Exclusions

The trust does not fund:

- Activities that are the responsibility of the central or local government
- Animal welfare
- Arts and cultural projects
- Capital costs for building, refurbishment and outfitting
- Endowment funds
- Fundraising events or activities
- General appeals
- General health projects
- Individuals
- Housing
- Learning disability
- Medical research or equipment
- Mental health
- Children under 16 and older people
- Physical disability

- The promotion of religion or belief systems
- Schools
- Sponsorship or marketing appeals
- Unsolicited international projects

The trust will not normally consider funding the following areas unless they are part of a broader project:

- Counselling drug and alcohol services (unless under criminal justice programme)
- Environmental projects (unless under the poverty and inclusion programme)
- Homelessness and destitution (unless for those leaving the criminal justice system or in relation to the migration programme)
- IT training
- Sporting activities

The trust asks that organisations planning a proposal that includes one of these services contact the grants team before submitting any application.

Colleges and universities can only apply under the policy and research funding streams.

Applications

Applicants should fill in the online enquiry form available on the trust's website. If invited to complete a full application form, applicants should do so via the application portal available online. You may also get in touch with the trust to discuss your eligibility. The trust does not accept unsolicited applications for work outside the UK.

Sources of information

Accounts; annual report; Charity Commission record; funder's website.

The Cadogan Charity

General charitable purposes, in particular social welfare, medical research, service charities, animal welfare, education, conservation and the environment

Worldwide, in practice, UK with a preference for London and Scotland

£2.3 million (2016/17)

CC number: 247773

Trustees: Rt. Hon. The Earl Cadogan; Countess Cadogan; Viscount Chelsea; Lady Anna Thomson; The Hon. William Cadogan.

Correspondent: Paul Loutit, Secretary, The Cadogan Group, 10 Duke of York Square, London SW3 4LY (tel: 020 7730 4567; email: paul.loutit@cadogan.co.uk)

The charity was established in 1966 for general charitable purposes and operates two funds namely, the general fund and the rectors' fund. The rectors' fund was created with a gift from Cadogan

Holdings Company in 1985 to pay an annual amount to one or any of the rectors of Holy Trinity Church – Sloane Street, St Luke's Church and Chelsea Old Church. The general fund provides support for registered charities in a wide range of areas (see below).

Financial information

In 2016/17 the charity had assets of £69.5 million and an income of £2.2 million. During the year, the charity gave a total of £2.3 million in grants. Grants were distributed as follows:

Social welfare in the community	17	£458,500
Medical research	32	£320,500
Military charities	10	£554,500
Education	13	£900,000
Animal welfare	8	£34,000
Conservation and the environment	4	£45,000

Beneficiaries included: Natural History Museum (£500,000); National Army Museum (£350,000); Royal Academy of Arts (£250,000); Alzheimer's Research UK and Barts Charity (£50,000 each); Prostate Cancer UK (£20,000); St Mary's Birnam (£15,000); YMCA England (£5,000); British Exploring Society (£2,500); Erskine (£2,000).

Exclusions

No grants are given to individuals.

Applications

Apply in writing to the correspondent.

Sources of information

Accounts; annual report; Charity Commission record.

Calleva Foundation

Education and academic research, general charitable purposes

London and Hampshire

£3.71 million (2016)

CC number: 1078808

Trustees: Caroline Butt; Stephen Butt.

Correspondent: The Trustees, PO Box 22554, London W8 5GN (email: contactcalleva@btopenworld.com)

Registered with the Charity Commission in January 2000, the foundation's Charity Commission record states that it is a 'small family trust' which supports 'local community-based projects limited to London/Hampshire'. In recent years, however, a large proportion of grants provided by the foundation have in practice been awarded for education and academic research projects, including significant donations to the Kew CF Phylogenomics Research Project and the Natural History Museum.

Financial information

In 2016 the foundation held assets £1.05 million and an income of £3.75 million. Grants awarded to organisations totalled £3.71 million.

Beneficiaries included: Kew CF Phylogenomics Research Project (£1,600,000); Natural History Museum (£1.19 million); Reading University (£650,000); Cancer UK Crick Summer Programme (£250,000); Cancer UK Crick PhD Programme (£75,000); Royal Ballet School (£28,000); House of Good Health (£16,000); University of Cape Town Trust (£7,500).

Applications

The foundation does not accept unsolicited applications.

Sources of information

Accounts; annual report; Charity Commission record.

Cannon Charitable Trust

Jewish causes, education, social welfare

Worldwide

£485,500 (2016/17)

CC number: 1080818

Trustees: Robert Tauber; Juliana Tauber.

Correspondent: Isaac Hoffman, Secretary, Ashley Works, Ashley Road, Tottenham Hale, London N17 9LJ (tel: 020 8885 9430)

The Cannon Charitable Trust was registered with the Charity Commission in 2000. According to its 2016/17 accounts the primary objective of the trust is 'to promote, encourage and provide finance for religious education and social welfare both in the United Kingdom and worldwide'.

Financial information

In 2016/17 the trust had assets of £158,500 and an income of £320,000. In total, the trust awarded grants of £485,500.

No list of beneficiaries was available.

Applications

Apply in writing to the correspondent.

Sources of information

Accounts; annual report; Charity Commission record; funder's website.

David William Traill Cargill Fund

 General charitable purposes, particularly: religious causes, medical charities, education, help for older people

Scotland

£282,500 (2015/16)

OSCR number: SC012703

Correspondent: The Trustees, c/o Miller Beckett and Jackson Ltd, 190 St Vincent Street, Glasgow G2 5SP (tel: 0141 204 2833)

The fund has the same address and trustees as two other trusts – W A Cargill Charitable Trust and W A Cargill Fund – although they all operate independently. It supports 'any hospitals, institutions, societies or others whose work in the opinion of the trustees is likely to be beneficial to the community'.

Financial information
In 2015/16 the fund had an income of £314,500 and total expenditure of £348,500. Grants awarded to organisations totalled £282,500.

Previous beneficiaries have included: City of Glasgow Society of Social Service; Colquhoun Bequest Fund for Incurables; Crathie Opportunity Holidays; Glasgow and West of Scotland Society for the Blind; Glasgow City Mission; Greenock Medical Aid Society; Lead Scotland; North Glasgow Community Forum; Scottish Maritime Museum – Irvine; Scottish Episcopal Church; Scottish Motor Neurone Disease Association; Three Towns Blind Bowling/Social Club.

Exclusions
No grants are made to individuals.

Applications
Applications may be made in writing to the correspondent, supported by up-to-date accounts. The trustees meet quarterly.

Sources of information
Accounts; annual report; OSCR record.

The W.A. Cargill Fund

 General charitable purposes

 Glasgow and the west of Scotland

£320,000 (2015/16)

OSCR number: SC008456

Correspondent: The Trustees, c/o Miller Beckett and Jackson Ltd, 190 St Vincent Street, Glasgow G2 5SP

This fund has the same address and trustees as two others, D W T Cargill Fund and W A Cargill Charitable Trust, although they all operate independently. It supports a wide remit of causes in the west of Scotland, particularly in Glasgow.

Financial information
In 2015/16 it had assets of £17.6 million and an income of £573,500. Grants awarded to organisations totalled £320,000.

Previous beneficiaries have included: Erskine (£50,000); People's Welfare Association (£25,000); High School of Glasgow (£20,000); Tenovus (£8,000); Accord Hospice (£7,000); Cancer Research UK (£5,000); The Girls' Brigade (£3,000); Glasgow Cathedral (£2,200); Volunteer Tutors Organisation (£1,000).

Exclusions
Individuals are not supported.

Applications
Apply in writing to the correspondent, including a copy of the charity's latest accounts or details of its financial position.

Sources of information
Accounts; annual report; OSCR record.

The Carnegie Trust for the Universities of Scotland

 Scottish universities

 Scotland

£2.4 million (2015/16)

OSCR number: SC015600

Trustees: Richard Burns; The Rt Hon Lord Eassie; Alison Fielding; Sir John Grant; Donald MacDonald; Sir Iain Macmillan; Sandy Nairn; Sara Parkin; Judith Sischy; Ed Weeple.

Correspondent: The Trustees, Andrew Carnegie House, Pittencrieff Street, Dunfermline, Fife KY12 8AW (tel: 01383 724990)

 www.carnegie-trust.org

 facebook.com/pages/carnegieuni

 @CarnegieUni

This trust was established by Andrew Carnegie to improve and expand Scottish universities, to help students of Scottish 'birth or extraction', and to provide research and similar grants.

'In accordance with Andrew Carnegie's wishes, the Royal Charter enables the trust to support the 14 universities of Scotland, their staff and students.' All of the trust's schemes are described in detail on its website.

Financial information
In 2015/16 the trust had assets of £74 million and an income of £3 million. Grants awarded totalled around £2.4 million.

Beneficiaries included: University of St Andrews; University of Edinburgh; University of Aberdeen; University of Dundee.

Exclusions
Applicants with no relation to Scotland, those living out with Scotland or those of no Scottish extraction will not be considered.

Applications
Details of the various schemes operated by the trust are available from its website.

Sources of information
Accounts; annual report; OSCR record; funder's website.

The Carpenters' Company Charitable Trust

 Education, general charitable purposes, older people, young people and children, people who are homeless

UK

£973,500 to organisations (2016/17)

CC number: 276996

Trustees: Peter Luton; Michael Matthews; Guy Morton-Smith; Martin Samuel.

Correspondent: Clerk to the Carpenters' Company, Carpenters' Hall, 1 Throgmorton Avenue, London EC2N 2JJ (tel: 020 7588 7001; email: info@carpentersco.com)

 www.carpentersco.com

The trust was established in 1978 for general charitable purposes. The Carpenter's Company itself was originally established as a medieval trade guild to safeguard the welfare and interests of carpenters in the City of London.

The trust's website provides the following information:

> The Carpenters' Company is a City of London Livery Company. It received its first royal charter in 1477, and was granted a coat of arms in 1466.
>
> The Company was originally established as a medieval trade guild to safeguard the welfare and interests of carpenters in the City of London. Today, charitable activities and support for the craft of

woodworking through scholarships, competitions and the Building Crafts College are the two cornerstones of its work.

The Carpenters' Company is the senior construction trade company amongst the City Livery Companies, and maintains close links with the carpentry profession and other building trades.

The trust's income is derived from a capital sum gifted by the company's corporate fund, supplemented when warranted by further grants from that fund. The majority of the trust's income each year goes to the Building Crafts College, but the trust also maintains long-standing commitments to numerous other organisations, mainly in the Greater London area. Craft causes receive a high priority when awards are considered.

Other charitable causes benefitting from grants include organisations supporting older people, young people and children and people who are homeless.

Financial information

In 2016/17 the trust had assets of £29.1 million and an income of £1.5 million. During the year, the trust awarded around £978,500 to one individual and 20 organisations. Grants were distributed as follows:

Craft activities	£816,000
Miscellaneous	£40,500
Youth and children's organisations	£30,000
City of London	£15,000
Religious organisations	£1,000

Beneficiaries included: Building Crafts College (£772,000); Carpenters and Dockland Centre and Carpenters Primary School (£15,000 each); Institute of Carpenters (£6,000).

Exclusions

Grants are not normally made to individual churches or cathedrals, or to educational establishments having no association to the Carpenters' Company. No grants (except educational grants) are made to individual applicants. Funds are usually only available to charities registered with the Charity Commission or exempt from registration.

Applications

Apply in writing to the correspondent. The consideration of grants is delegated to the Charitable Grants Committee which meets three times each year. Day-to-day management is the responsibility of the Clerk to whom applications should usually be addressed.

Sources of information

Accounts; annual report; Charity Commission record; funder's website.

Sir John Cass's Foundation

Education

Camden, Greenwich, Hackney, Hammersmith and Fulham, Islington, Kensington and Chelsea, Lambeth, Lewisham, Newham, Southwark, Tower Hamlets, Wandsworth, Westminster and the City of London

£972,500 to organisations (2016/17)

CC number: 312425

Trustees: Kevin Everett; David Hogben; Hon. Brian Barker; Paul Bloomfield; Revd Trevor Critchlow; Graham Forbes; Revd Laura Jorgensen; Helen Meixner; Jenny Moseley; Prof. Mike Thorne; Sophie Fernandes.

Correspondent: Richard Foley, Clerk/ Chief Executive, 31 Jewry Street, London EC3N 2EY (tel: 020 7480 5884; email: contactus@sirjohncass.org)

 sirjohncassfoundation.com

The foundation is one of the largest educational charities benefitting children and young people in inner London. The following information is taken from the foundation's website:

> Sir John Cass's Foundation support a wide range of educational establishments, special educational projects, grants and bursaries in and around the City of London. We have been doing this for over 250 years, for the benefit of the people of the boroughs.
>
> The Foundation was founded by Sir John Cass, in 1748, a City of London politician and philanthropist, who bequeathed his entire properties and fortune to the endeavour.
>
> The mission of the Foundation is to promote the education of young people in inner London through its grant programmes for individuals, educational institutions and organisations.

Grants to organisations

The foundation will only consider proposals from schools and organisations that benefit children or young people under the age of 25, who are:

▶ Permanent residents of named *inner* London boroughs (Camden, Greenwich, Hackney, Hammersmith and Fulham, Islington, Kensington and Chelsea, Lambeth, Lewisham, Newham, Southwark, Tower Hamlets, Wandsworth, Westminster and the City of London)
▶ From a low-income background
▶ From disadvantaged backgrounds or areas of high deprivation

Priorities

The foundation has four areas of focus for grant-giving, which are as follows:

▶ Widening participation in further and higher education
▶ Truancy, exclusion and behaviour management
▶ Prisoner education
▶ New initiatives

Widening Participation in Further and Higher Education

▶ **Aim:** to promote access to further and higher education for disadvantaged young people in inner London
▶ **Objective:** to increase the number of inner London students from disadvantaged backgrounds successfully participating in further and higher education
▶ **Priorities:** work with communities currently under-represented in further and higher education and/or hard to reach learners (e.g. care leavers or young people with learning difficulties). Applications could involve work with secondary school pupils as well as those in further education and universities

Individuals may also apply for grants in the widening participation category.

Truancy, Exclusion and Behaviour Management

▶ **Aim:** to encourage and support children and young people's attainment through initiatives that help them engage with, and stay in, education
▶ **Objectives:** to reduce truancy levels amongst pupils attending primary and secondary schools; to reduce levels of exclusions and expulsions; to improve pupil motivation, behaviour and achievement through initiatives that promote children and young people's emotional well-being and social development
▶ **Priority:** work with primary and secondary schools in challenging circumstances and/or those with higher than average truancy, exclusion or expulsion rates. Challenging circumstances could include, for example, schools in areas of high social deprivation or in special measures, as well as schools that have higher than average rates of truancy, exclusion or expulsion

Prisoner Education

▶ **Aim:** to reduce re-offending through education and initiatives that promote employability
▶ **Objectives:** to improve the literacy and numeracy skills of prisoners and ex-offenders; to help prisoners and ex-offenders gain skills and education qualifications that will help them into employment
▶ **Priority:** work with prisoners and ex-offenders that helps secure employment and prevent re-offending

New Initiatives

▶ **Aim:** to influence and improve education policy and practice, both within the Foundation's area of benefit and more widely
▶ **Objectives:** i) to test new and groundbreaking approaches to learning

that have the potential to enhance and influence education policy and practice; ii) to support work that focuses on identified needs and gaps in statutory provision

▶ **Priorities:** projects that are pioneering and original in their approach to teaching or learning and are strategic (relates to objective i.); projects addressing an identified need within a geographical area or learning establishment that are new and innovative in context i.e. must be a new initiative for the school or borough, but need not be a completely new approach to education (relates to objective ii.); projects that focus on addressing under-achievement in literacy and numeracy in primary and secondary schools (relates to objectives i. and ii.) projects seeking to attract greater numbers of young people into the teaching profession (relates to objectives i. and ii.)

Applicants should say which priority their project addresses as well as describing how their project meets that priority. Applications need not meet more than one priority but, for those that do, applicants are welcome to describe how their application meets each of the priorities.

Financial information

In 2016/17 the foundation had assets of £153.3 million and an income of £6.8 million. Grants totalled £1.06 million with £972,500 awarded to organisations and £92,000 awarded to individuals. The following table shows the breakdown of how grants were distributed:

Organisations	£622,500
Foundation's schools	£155,500
Other Cass institutions	£125,000
Individuals	£92,000
Organisations working with the foundation's schools	£70,000

Beneficiaries included: St Mary's Twickenham – First Star Programme (£100,000); University of London (£50,500); Charterhouse (£50,000); Chance UK (£35,000); Building Crafts College (£26,000); AHOY Centre (£10,000); IOE Prison Education Conference (£5,000); British Postal Museum (£4,100).

Exclusions

The foundation's website states the following:

There are many activities and costs that the Foundation will not fund. The following list gives you an idea of the type of activities and costs the Foundation cannot support:

▶ Projects that do not meet a Foundation priority
▶ Holiday projects, school journeys, trips abroad or exchange visits
▶ Supplementary schools or mother tongue teaching
▶ Independent schools
▶ Youth and community groups, or projects taking place in these settings

▶ Pre-school and nursery education
▶ General fundraising campaigns or appeals
▶ Costs for equipment or salaries that are the statutory responsibility of education authorities
▶ Costs to substitute for the withdrawal or reduction of statutory funding
▶ Costs for work or activities that have already taken place prior to the grant application
▶ Costs already covered by core funding or other grants
▶ Capital costs that are exclusively for the purchase, repair or furnishing of buildings, purchase of vehicles, computers, sports equipment or improvements to school grounds

Applications

The foundation operates a two-stage application process – an initial enquiry and a full application stage.

The following information has been taken from the foundation's website:

Stage 1
Complete and submit the initial enquiry form which is available from the foundation's website and on request from the correspondent. The form asks for:

▶ Outline information about your proposed project
▶ Information about how the project meets the foundation's priorities
▶ A summary of the project that includes the following information: the aims of the project including outputs and outcomes, how the project will be delivered; the duration of the project, including when and where it will take place; and a budget covering project costs

We will consider your enquiry and inform you, within three weeks, whether or not you may proceed to Stage 2. If we have any queries we may contact you during this time to discuss details of your project submitted in the initial enquiry form. We receive a large number of applications. Unfortunately, this means that good projects sometimes have to be refused even if they meet a priority. If we invite you to proceed to Stage 2 and submit a full application, we will send you a copy of our Stage 2 application guidelines for schools and organisations.

Stage 2
Complete your detailed application and send it to us with copies of your memorandum and articles of association (or constitution) and your organisation's latest annual report and accounts.

Assessment and decision-making process
On receipt of your application our staff may meet with you as part of our assessment process. After we have received responses to any queries and any further information requested, a report on your application will be considered by the foundation's grants committee, whose decision is final. The grants committee meets in March, June and November each year. It normally takes between two and

four months from receipt of a full application until a decision is made.

Notification of the decision
All applicants will be sent formal notification of the outcome of their applications within two weeks of the committee decision.

Successful applicants
Those who are offered a grant will be sent a formal offer letter and copies of our standard terms and conditions of grant. Copies of our standard terms and conditions of grant are available on our website. Additional conditions are sometimes included depending on the nature of the grant.

Monitoring and evaluation
Staff will contact you to clarify and agree how the outputs and outcomes for your project will be monitored and evaluated. Your project will be visited at least once during the lifetime of the grant. If your grant covers more than one year you will be asked to submit a progress report for each year. Continuation of multi-year grants is dependent upon satisfactory progress towards agreed outputs and outcomes. At the end of the grant you will be asked to provide a final report. The foundation provides guidance on the structure and content of these reports.

Unsuccessful applicants
Applying for funding is a competitive process and the foundation's grants budget is limited. Because of the high volume of applications received, good projects sometimes have to be refused, even if they meet a priority. All applications are assessed on merit. If your application is refused you can apply again twelve months after the date you submitted your last application.

Sources of information

Accounts; annual report; Charity Commission record; funder's website.

The Castansa Trust

Education, children and young people, support for people diagnosed with dementia or cancer, social inclusion, arts and culture, health, environment

The Central Belt of Scotland and Dumfries and Galloway

£440,000 (2016/17)

OSCR number: SC037414

Correspondent: The Trustees, c/o Turcan Connell, Princes Exchange, 1 Earl Grey Street, Edinburgh EH3 9EE (tel: 0131 228 8111)

 www.turcanconnell.com/the-castansa-trust

The trust was established in 2008 and according to its website, aims to provide 'early stage/catalyst funding...to encourage a business approach to philanthropy and to enable action'.

The trust makes grants to charities working in the following fields:

- Education
- Children and teenagers (specifically leadership courses and help with employment)
- Support for those diagnosed with cancer or dementia and for their families
- Social inclusion
- Culture and the arts
- Environment

Grants are usually between £5,000 and £15,000, although larger grants and multi-year commitments may be occasionally considered. The trust also provides smaller community grants which are distributed by Foundation Scotland, the Women's Fund for Scotland and Inspiring Scotland.

Financial information

In 2016/17 the trust had assets totalling £1.7 million and an income of £45,500. Grants to 56 organisations totalled £440,000.

Beneficiaries included: Inspiring Scotland (£60,000); Foundation Scotland and Women's Fund for Scotland (£33,000 each); Reform Scotland (£20,000); Children 1st and Hopscotch Children's Charity (£10,000 each); The Junction Edinburgh (£5,000); Contact the Elderly and The Seabird Centre (£2,000 each).

Exclusions

No grants are made to individuals.

Applications

Application forms are available from the trust's website, where guidance notes and quarterly deadlines are also posted. The trust only responds to successful applicants, in order to minimise administration costs.

Sources of information

Accounts; annual report; OSCR record; funder's website.

The Catholic Trust for England and Wales

 Advancement of the Roman Catholic religion

England and Wales

£644,000 (2016)

CC number: 1097482

Trustees: John Gibbs; Dr James Whiston; Kathleen Smith; Edward Nally; Revd John Nelson; Michael Prior; Edward Poyser; Nigel Newton; Dr Elizabeth Walmsley; Austin King; Revd David Roberts; Kees Kempenaar; Rt Revd Peter Brignall.

Correspondent: Rev. Christopher Thomas, Secretary, 39 Eccleston Square,

London SW1V 1BX (tel: 020 7901 4808; email: secretariat@cbcew.org.uk)

www.catholicchurch.org.uk

The trust was established in 1968 and is concerned with 'the advancement of the Roman Catholic religion in England and Wales'. According to its 2016/17 annual report, the trust works in line with the church's teachings, 'to ensure the moral and spiritual wellbeing of the individual, and to help discern the common good, being what is best for all in society'. In addition to the promotion of Catholicism, the trust also 'supports people to live out their faith through guidance at a local level as well as advancement and direction of national policy'.

Many of the bodies which receive grants from CaTEW have been established or promoted by the Bishops' Conference – a permanent body within the organisation of the Catholic Church that brings together the Bishops of England and Wales – and are charitable trusts. Furthermore, the trust's accounts note that 'the subscriptions to the Ecumenical Instruments are transferred to Churches Together in Britain and Ireland, a charitable Trust established as part of the ecumenical relations between the Churches in these countries'.

Financial information

In 2016 the trust had assets of £41.2 million and an income of £6.05 million. During the year, the charity awarded around £644,000 in grants to organisations.

Beneficiaries included: Anscombe Bioethics Centre (£100,000); Caritas Social Action Network (£90,000); Diocese of Birmingham, Diocese of Brentwood, Diocese of Clifton, Diocese of East Anglia (£12,500 each); National Board of Catholic Women (£10,000).

Exclusions

No grants are given to individuals, local projects or projects not immediately advancing the Roman Catholic religion in England and Wales.

Applications

Apply in writing to the correspondent. The trust has stated previously that it does not respond to unsolicited applications.

Sources of information

Accounts; annual report; Charity Commission record; funder's website.

Catkin Pussywillow Charitable Trust

General charitable purposes

UK

£278,500 (2016/17)

CC number: 1100036

Trustees: Barry Gold; Raymond Harris; Celia Atkin.

Correspondent: Raymond Harris, Trustee, 16 Rosemont Road, London NW3 6NE (tel: 020 8371 3000)

The trust was established by a declaration of trust dated 26 June 2003. According to its 2016/17 accounts, the trust's objects are 'the relief of poverty, distress and sickness, the advancement of education, the protection of health and other such charitable purposes as the trustees see fit'.

Financial information

In 2016/17 the trust had assets of £84,500 and an income of £156,500. Grants made to organisations totalled £278,500.

Beneficiaries included: Hampstead Theatre (£100,000); Jewish Leadership Council (£30,000); London Business School (£29,000); Royal Opera House Foundation (£20,000); King's College (£19,500); Arts 4 Dementia, Greenwide Foundation, HVP UK (£5,000 each); Friends of Sick (£3,000).

Applications

Apply in writing to the correspondent.

Sources of information

Accounts; annual report; Charity Commission record.

The Cattanach Charitable Trust

Children up to three years, their families and communities

Scotland

£388,500 (2016)

OSCR number: SC020902

Trustees: Alastair Wilson; Andrew Millington; Duncan McEachran; Helen Healy; Ian McLaughlan; Mafe Marwick; Neil Wood; Rhoda Reid; Steven Murray; Rachel Campbell; Kathy Nicholson.

Correspondent: Trust Manager, c/o The Corra Foundation, Riverside House, 502 Gorgie Road, Edinburgh EH11 3AF (tel: 0131 281 0369; email: info@cattanach.org.uk)

 www.cattanach.org.uk

The Cattanach Trust was founded in 1992 by Miss Phyllis Cattanach of

Grantown in Spey, with the wealth she had inherited from her family who had interests in the whisky industry. Following her death in 2008, Miss Cattanach left the 'residue' of her estate to the trust. Though it was established with broad purposes, the trustees have since focused the trusts grant-making using this theme statement published on its website:

> The Cattanach Trust seeks applications for projects which support children from pre-birth to three years old, who are affected by levels of relative deprivation. There is good evidence that supporting children during the first years of a child's life has the greatest positive impact on their developmental progress. Good quality services improve not only a child's life during these years, but also have substantial benefits into adolescence and adulthood. Projects should be working from a strengths-based model; the existing and potential strengths of the child, the family and the community should be recognised and should form the basis of the work. Projects must actively involve the parent(s)/main carers of the children. The Trust's view is that prioritising this age group values children in Scotland appropriately, and will make a significant contribution to Scotland's National Outcome.

Grant-making

Further information is provided on the website:

> The work you want to do must be in Scotland. You must be working with young children (under three) and their parent/families, or with a parent/families expecting a baby. Families experiencing deprivation or in crisis will be given priority. Deprivation can mean low income, poor housing, unemployment, isolation, disability or health problems, lack of family support, young parenthood, contact with the justice system, substance abuse, violence etc. The Trust is particularly interested in parenting, attachment, family support, and communication within the family, as it impacts on the healthy emotional and physical development of young children. The Trust wishes to encourage training for staff and volunteers, and may recommend training or evaluation help.

Grants can be given for projects or, for smaller organisations, core costs (including salaries and general running costs). The trust prefers to fund revenue costs and any capital funding will only be associated another aspect of revenue funding.

Amounts range between £3,000 and £25,000 (although most are around £10,000) and may be given for one, two or three years. Where fourth and fifth years are funded, the award will decrease in the final years. The trust prefers to fund a significant proportion of a project than just a small contribution, and can support matched funding within a project budget. In most cases, only one grant will be awarded to a particular organisation in a year. Where possible, any salaries should be at or above the Living Wage – if this is not the case, it will require explanation.

However, larger charities may apply for funding for multiple eligible projects within the same year – the total award given to the organisation will be up to 10% of the trust's annual funding. Larger grants will only be given in exceptional circumstances and should be discussed with the trust before applying.

Financial information

In 2016 the trust had assets of £19 million and an income of £646,000. During the year, 28 grants were made totalling £388,500 altogether.

Beneficiaries included: Working on Wheels (£33,000); Barnardo's – Paisley (£29,500); Children First (£20,000); Hawick Congregational Community Church and Home-Start Majik (£12,000 each); Hidden Garden Trust (£11,000); Step by Step – Moray (£10,000); Barra Children's Centre (£9,300).

Exclusions

Individuals; personal study or travel; hospices and palliative care; animal charities; appliances for illness or disability; organisations concerned with specific diseases; large capital projects (of more than £100,000); projects costing less than £3,000; crèches where parents are not involved; organisations or activities where religious content is compulsory for users; general appeals.

Applications

Applicants must first register on the trust's website and will then be sent a link to the application form by email. The application form contains instructions and help, although there is also a useful list of FAQs on the trust's website. Applications must be made online (those sent on paper or by email are not accepted) and must be submitted along with supporting documents, which are listed on the form. The manager can be contacted if any difficulties arise. The trustees meet four times a year, usually in February/March, May, August and November – meeting dates are posted on the website.

Sources of information

Accounts; annual report; OSCR record; funder's website.

The Joseph and Annie Cattle Trust

 General charitable purposes, particularly: older people, people with disabilities, social welfare, children with dyslexia

Hull and East Yorkshire

£325,500 (2016/17)

CC number: 262011

Trustees: Paul Edwards; Michael Gyte; Christopher Munday; S. C. Jowers.

Correspondent: Roger Waudby, PO Box 23, Patrington, Hull HU12 0WF (tel: 01964 671742; email: rogerwaudby@ hotmail.co.uk)

 www.jacattletrust.co.uk

The objective of the trust is to help vulnerable older people, socially disadvantaged people and those with disabilities change their lives, by supporting organisations which provide services in the local area. The trust does consider applications from organisations across the country, but priorities organisations in Hull and East Riding of Yorkshire. There is also a particular interest in supporting children with dyslexia.

Note that the trust will only provide support to registered organisations. The trust supports two types of application:

1   Applications by charity organisations on behalf of individuals or families (to be completed by the charity)
2   Applications for projects and work with the disadvantaged groups outlined in the trust's aims

Financial information

In 2016/17 the trust had assets of £10.2 million and an income of £348,500. During the year, the trust gave a total of £325,500 in grants to organisations.

Previous beneficiaries have included: Sobriety Project (£15,000); Dyslexia Action (£14,000); Anlaby Park Methodist Church and The Prince's Trust (£5,000 each); Hull and East Riding Institution for the Blind (£3,000); Bath Institute of Medical Engineering and Ocean Youth Trust (£2,000 each); Age UK East Riding, Longhill Primary School and Prison Fellowship (£1,000 each).

Exclusions

The trust only works with charitable bodies or statutory authorities and does not provide grants directly to individuals.

Applications

Application forms are available from the website and should include the following information:

▶ Charity details including registered number, contact details, and the latest financial statements
▶ Previous work carried out by the organisation that has supported disadvantaged people
▶ A project outline and timescale, with detailed costings and supporting information
▶ Details of any other funding applications or grants received for the project
▶ How the grant is to be spent

The trust requests application forms are completed in handwriting and returned to the correspondence address.

Sources of information

Accounts; annual report; Charity Commission record; funder's website.

The Thomas Sivewright Catto Charitable Settlement

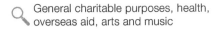 General charitable purposes, health, overseas aid, arts and music

Unrestricted (for UK-based registered charities)

(£) £252,500 (2016/17)

CC number: 279549

Trustees: Lord Catto; Olivia Marchant; Zoe Richmond-Watson.

Correspondent: The Secretary to the Trustees, PO Box 47408, London N21 1YW (email: office@tscatto.org.uk)

The charity was established in 1979 by the surviving children of The Rt Hon. Thomas Sivewright Catto, to commemorate the 100th anniversary of his birth. This charity has general charitable purposes, making a large number of smaller grants (£500) to a wide range of organisations and a few larger grants for music scholarships at selected colleges and conservatoires. There appears to be a preference for supporting medical charities and charities working with vulnerable people, for example, prisoners, refugees, and the homeless.

Financial information

In 2016/17 the charity held assets of £14.7 million and had an income of £285,500. During the year, the charity awarded 179 grants totalling £252,500. There were two exceptional grants of £50,000 to the Multiple Sclerosis Society and Parkinson's UK in response to special appeals.

Beneficiaries included: DEC East African Crisis Appeal (£4,000); Bloodwise, Fostering Network and Prisoners' Advice Service (£1,000 each); London Narrow Boat Project, The Connection at St Martin-in-the-Fields and Tools for Self Reliance (£750 each); Association of Visitors to Immigration Detainees, Big Issue, Carers Trust, Pancreatic Cancer Action, Southampton Rape Crisis and World Bicycle Relief UK (£500 each).

Exclusions

The trust does not support non-registered charities, expeditions, travel bursaries and so on, or unsolicited applications from churches of any denomination. Grants are unlikely to be considered in the areas of community care, playschemes and drug abuse, or for local branches of national organisations.

Applications

Apply in writing to the correspondent. The trustees meet quarterly to approve grants.

Sources of information

Accounts; annual report; Charity Commission record.

The Cayo Foundation

 General charitable purposes, medical research, crime prevention, armed forces, children and young people, education, the arts

UK

(£) £1.3 million (2015/16)

CC number: 1080607

Trustees: Angela McCarville; Stewart Harris.

Correspondent: Angela McCarville, Trustee, Ground Floor, 3 Devonshire Square, London EC2M 4YA (tel: 020 7248 6700)

 cayofoundation.org.uk

The Cayo Foundation provides grants and loans to registered charities for a range of charitable purposes. According to the website, the trustees are particularly interested in charities involved with 'medical research and training, the military, crime fighting, children and young people, education and the arts'.

Financial information

In 2015/16 the foundation had assets of £1.1 million and an income of £147,500. Grants were made to 28 charities totalling almost £1.3 million. A list of grant recipients was not included in the accounts.

Previous beneficiaries have included: NSPCC (£125,000); Disability

Foundation, PACT and The Royal Opera House (£25,000 each); The Prince's Foundation (£20,000); Wessex Youth Trust (£10,000); Christian Blind Mission (£6,000); Wellbeing of Women (£3,000); Institute for Policy Research and Royal Humane Society (£2,500 each); Sue Ryder Care – St John's Hospice (£1,000).

Applications

Apply in writing to the correspondent.

Sources of information

Accounts; annual report; Charity Commission record; funder's website.

The Chalk Cliff Trust

 Children and young people, social welfare, older people, disability, overseas aid, environment, arts and culture

East Sussex

(£) £690,500 (2016/17)

CC number: 1139102

Trustees: Rachel Senior; Robert Senior; Justine Senior; Sarah Hunter.

Correspondent: Robert Senior, 18 Keere Street, Lewes BN7 1TY (email: chalkclifftrust@yahoo.co.uk)

 www.chalkclifftrust.org

The Chalk Cliff Trust is a foundation set up to provide grants and donations to charities, action groups and benevolent organisations in East Sussex.

The following information has been taken from the foundation's website:

We will consider any such organisations involved in the following areas of activity :

▶ Youth schemes and activities, e.g. youth centres, clubs, arts-focused projects
▶ Concerns involved in children's activities, e.g. playgroups, kids clubs or children's education, and the relief of poverty
▶ The care of the elderly, e.g. events and activities for elderly people, or transport needs
▶ Activities for people with learning difficulties or disabilities
▶ Overseas aid, e.g. projects concerned with education, malnutrition or medical-related projects
▶ Activities concerned with the care or preservation of the environment
▶ Regional arts, music, literature and cultural projects, especially related to the groups mentioned above
▶ Other types of community initiatives

Grants available

A range of grants is available but most are in the region of £3,000 to £5,000.

Larger donations will be considered, and modest one-off payments may be appropriate for smaller concerns with low running costs or those requiring funding for a specific event.

The grants need not be specifically tied to funding projects. We are happy for the money to be used as seed capital, to help with core administration costs, or to help an organisation through a difficult time. We will respond quickly to requests and can make funds available shortly after application.

However not all applications will be successful.

Donations will normally be made to registered charities, however organisations pending registration or pressure groups will also be considered. Donations are usually made once per organisation but repeat donations may be considered in certain circumstances

Financial information

In 2016/17 the trust held assets of £5.4 million and had an income of £3 million. Grants awarded to organisations totalled £690,500.

Beneficiaries included: Glyndebourne Productions Ltd (£25,000); Brighton Dome and Brighton Festival (£10,000); Beach Without Sand Ltd (£6,300); Monday's Child UK (£4,500); Mustard Seed Relief Mission (£4,000); Time to Talk Befriending (£3,600); Parents And Children Together (PACT) (£3,200); World Cetacean Alliance (£3,000).

Applications

Application forms can be downloaded from the trust's website and should be returned to chalkclifftrust@yahoo.co.uk.

Sources of information

Accounts; annual report; Charity Commission record; funder's website.

Chapman Charitable Trust

Health and well-being, arts, culture, the natural environment

UK, with preference for North Wales, London and South East England

£336,000 (2016/17)

CC number: 232791

Trustees: Roger Chapman; Richard Chapman; Guy Chapman; Bryony Chapman; Thomas Williams.

Correspondent: Richard Chapman, Trustee, 62 Wilson Street, London EC2A 2BU (tel: 020 7782 0007; email: cct@chapmancharitabletrust.org.uk)

 www.chapmancharitabletrust.org.uk

This trust was established in 1963 and, according to its website, supports the following causes: arts; health and well-being; research; culture; natural environment.

Grants, usually of around £1,000 to £2,000, primarily focus on organisations which:

- Promote physical and mental wellbeing
- Conserve our natural environment and promote the sustainable use of resources
- Increase the accessibility of the arts, especially for young people

The trust prefers to support charities which address the root causes of problems and they welcome applications for research projects.

Where the trust gives grants for care and counselling, these are normally applied to organisations where a small grant can make a real difference.

Support is given to registered charities, mainly national charities, but local charities working in the following areas may also be supported: North Wales; London; South East England (including Hertfordshire, Cambridgeshire, Essex, Kent, East Sussex, West Sussex, Surrey and Hampshire). Charities connected to the trust's settlor or current trustees are given special consideration.

Financial information

In 2016/17 the trust had assets of £8.3 million and an income of £316,000. There were 175 grants made to organisations during the year, totalling £336,000 altogether, which were broken down as follows:

Activity, health and well-being	63	£82,000
Culture and heritage	37	£71,500
Social care	19	£69,000
Environment	28	£64,500
Education and research	28	£49,000

Beneficiaries included: Pesticide Action Network UK (£25,000); Action for Children and Fragile X Society (£12,000 each); British Film Institute (£9,000); A Rocha and Cherry Trees (£6,000 each); Wadham College (£3,000); Asthma UK and Chickenshed (£2,000 each).

Exclusions

The trust does not support:

- Individuals
- Local branches of national charities
- Animal welfare
- Sports tours
- Research expeditions
- Sponsored adventure holidays
- Overseas charities
- Community interest companies (CICs)
- Community Amateur Sports Clubs (CASCs)

Applications

Apply online using the form on the trust's website. Postal applications will not be accepted. You will be asked to provide a short paragraph giving a succinct summary of your project or organisation, it would be worth preparing this in advance. The trustees meet to consider grants twice a year in September and March. They receive a

large number of applications and regret they cannot respond to all of them – if you do not hear anything after six months, you should assume your application has not been successful.

Sources of information

Annual report; accounts; Charity Commission record; funder's website.

Sandra Charitable Trust

Animal welfare and research, environmental protection, social welfare, health, development of young people

UK, with slight preference for the South East

£496,500 to organisations (2016/17)

CC number: 327492

Trustees: Richard Moore; Michael Macfadyen; Lucy Forsyth; Francis Moore.

Correspondent: Martin Pollock, Secretary to the Trustees, c/o Moore Stephens, 150 Aldersgate Street, London EC1A 4AB (tel: 020 7334 9191)

The trust was established in 1987 to support a wide variety of beneficiaries including charities involved in animal welfare and research, environmental protection, relief of poverty and development of young people. Assistance is also given to nurses and those studying to become nurses. The trust does not accept applications from charities and organisations, as the trustees prefer to support charities that are known to them.

Financial information

In 2016/17 the trust held assets of £22.8 million and had an income of £603,500. Grants were made totalling £589,500 of which £496,500 was donated to 168 organisations. Individual nurses in training were awarded £93,500 in 123 grants.

Beneficiaries included: Scope (£35,000); The Florence Nightingale Foundation (£30,000); Arundel Castle Cricket Foundation (£25,000); Worplesdon Primary School (£12,000); Health Poverty Action, Oxfordshire Youth and Royal Horticultural Society (£5,000 each); Combat Stress (£3,000); Garsington Opera (£2,500); Mary's Meals (£1,000).

Applications

The trust states that 'unsolicited applications are not requested, as the trustees prefer to support charities whose work they have researched...the trustees receive a very high number of grant applications which are mostly unsuccessful'.

Sources of information

Accounts; annual report; Charity Commission record.

The Charities Advisory Trust

 General charitable purposes

 UK and overseas

£496,000 (2016/17)

CC number: 1040487

Trustees: Rowena Dunn, Brij Bhasin; David Russell; Leila MacTavish Mohamed.

Correspondent: Hilary Blume, Director, Radius Works, Back Lane, London NW3 1HL (tel: 020 7794 9835; fax: 020 7431 3739; email: people@ charitiesadvisorytrust.org.uk)

 www.charitiesadvisorytrust.org.uk

The Charities Advisory Trust (originally called the Charity Trading Advisory Group) was established in 1979 by Dame Hilary Blume using funds from the Home Office to provide impartial information on all aspects of trading and income generation for charities. Today the trust runs a wide range of projects, many of which are intended to help build capacity in the voluntary sector. In addition to its own projects the trust also gives around £500,000 per year to help other charities 'develop their ideas'.

According to the Charity Commission record, the objects of the charity are: to relieve poverty throughout the world; advance education; preserve buildings and monuments of architectural merit; assist charities so that they may make better use of their assets and resources both generally and in relation to trading and/or fundraising activities; and advance any other charitable purposes.

Financial information

In 2016/17 the trust had assets of almost £3.05 million and an income of £892,500. During the year, grants were awarded totalling £496,000.

No list of beneficiaries was available.

Exclusions

The trustees rarely respond to unsolicited applications for projects of which they have no knowledge. In such cases where support is given, the amounts are usually £200 or less. Furthermore, no support is given for individuals, large charities that fundraise, or missionary work.

Applications

The trustees are pro-active in looking for causes to support. They have previously stated that they are 'happy for charities to keep us informed of developments, as we do change our support as new solutions to needs emerge'. However, unsolicited applications for projects about which the trust know nothing are rarely responded to.

Applications should be submitted in the form of a letter (no more than two pages) and include:

- The aims and objectives of your organisation
- The project for which you need money
- Who benefits from the project and how
- Breakdown of the costs and total estimated costs
- How much money you need from the trust
- Other funding secured for the project
- A summary of your latest annual accounts

Sources of information

Accounts; annual report; Charity Commission record; funder's website.

Charitworth Ltd

 Religion, education, relief of poverty. In practice, mainly Jewish causes are supported

Worldwide, mainly UK and Israel

£1.26 million (2016/17)

CC number: 286908

Trustees: Samuel Halpern; Sidney Halpern; David Halpern; Relly Halpern.

Correspondent: David Halpern, Trustee, New Burlington House, 1075 Finchley Road, London NW11 0PU

This charity was set up in 1983 and makes grants to support the advancement of the Jewish religion, education and the relief of poverty. Our research suggests that support is given almost exclusively to Jewish organisations.

Financial information

In 2016/17 Charitworth Ltd had assets of £39.3 million and an income of £1.5 million. Grants were made totalling £1.26 million.

Beneficiaries included: Talmud Torah Machzikei Hadass Trust (£190,000); Side By Side School Ltd (£100,000); The ABC Trust (£80,000); Friends of Tifereth Shlomo (£30,000); Rise and Shine (£20,000).

Donations under £20,000 totalled £177,000.

Applications

Apply in writing to the correspondent.

Sources of information

Accounts; annual report; Charity Commission record.

Chest Heart and Stroke Scotland

 Research into the prevention, diagnosis, treatment, rehabilitation and social impact of chest, heart and stroke illnesses

Scotland

£26,000 (2016/17)

OSCR number: SC018761

Trustees: Dr Roger Smith; Hazel Fraser; Dr Douglas Stuart; Gill Alexander; Dr Alan Begg; Dr Gavin Boyd; Dr Charlie Chung; Prof. Martin Dennis; Theresa Douglas; Aileen Easton; Prof. Gerry Fowkes; Prof. Simon Harris; Prof. Gordon Lowe; Barbara Mitchelmore; Neil Pirie; Janet Reid; Prof. Allan Struthers; Kenneth Walmsley; Dr Keith Weston.

Correspondent: Research Committee, Third Floor, Rosebery House, 9 Haymarket Terrace, Edinburgh EH12 5EZ (tel: 0131 225 6963; email: webmaster@chss.org.uk)

 www.chss.org.uk

 facebook.com/CHSScotland

 @chsscotland

 @chsscotland

According to its website, Chest Heart and Stroke Scotland (CHSS) works to improve the quality of life for people in Scotland who are suffering from chest, heart and stroke illnesses. It does this through funding medical research, influencing public policy, and by providing advice, information and support throughout Scotland.

The following information on the charity's research strategy and priorities has been taken from its website:

Our new Research Strategy is driven by three key principles:

- **Respecting Lived Experience:** It is important to us that the research we fund matters to the people in Scotland who live with our conditions. We recognise that their experience of living with the conditions every day gives them a unique and powerful set of expertise.
- **Building Relationships:** We want to work with high quality researchers who (1) share our vision of a Scotland where fewer people have chest, heart and stroke illnesses, and those that do receive the very best possible care and support and (2) are willing to join with us to achieve this.
- **Demonstrating Impact:** We are only able to fund research because of the generous donations given to us by donors and fundraisers. We need to be able to explain how the money we

spend on research makes a difference to health and wellbeing in Scotland.

Our Priorities: What Research We Will Fund

Below, we have laid out the project types that we will prioritise in 2018–2021. In line with our charitable objectives, our funding will continue to only be available to studies that primarily cover chest conditions, heart conditions and stroke.

- **Chest Conditions:** we are proud of our history of funding research into heart conditions and stroke. While we still accept applications for these conditions, we want to ensure that chest conditions, and the hundreds of thousands of people living in Scotland with them, have a high profile and that funding from charitable sources remains available for them. We will therefore prioritise high quality applications in this area.
- **Patient & Carer Experiences and Long-Term Outcomes:** what matters to the people living with our conditions and their families and carers, matters to us. We are therefore keen to encourage research that focuses on condition and symptom management, and on what can be done to ensure that patients and carers can live the fullest lives possible.
- **Scottish-Led Research:** for many years, we have been committed to ensuring that Scotland remains a world-leader in the production of quality, life-changing medical research that is centred on the Scottish population. We continue that commitment in this strategy, by retaining our policy of normally only funding research carried out in Scottish institutions by researchers living and working in Scotland.

Financial information

In 2016/17 the charity had assets of £7.6 million and an income of £11.4 million. Research grants totalled £26,000.

Under its new 2018–21 research strategy the charity aims to invest up to £1.5 million in research.

Beneficiaries included: University of Glasgow (£15,000); Queen Margaret University Hospital (£11,200).

Applications

Information on how to apply can be found on the charity's website.

Sources of information

Annual report; accounts; OSCR record; funder's website.

The Childhood Trust

 Children's welfare

London

£489,000 (2016/17)

CC number: 1154032

Trustees: Grant Gordon; Dame Sylvia Morris; Dr Mathias Hink; David Lewis; Sonal Shenai; Lucy Capron.

Correspondent: Laurence Guinness, Chief Executive, The Workary, Chelsea Old Town Hall, King's Road, London SW3 5EZ (tel: 020 8788 9637; email: info@childhoodtrust.org)

 www.childhoodtrust.org.uk

 facebook.com/ChildhoodTrust

 @ChildhoodTrust

The Childhood Trust, which was registered with the Charity Commission in 2013, is a fundraising and grant-making charity that funds and facilitates projects run by charities, community groups and social enterprises that 'demonstrably improve' the lives of disadvantaged children of school age (4 to 18) who are living in poverty in London. The trust has an informative website, which explains: 'We believe every London child deserves the possibility of a happy, safe childhood and so we fund the very best initiatives and projects, run by charities and grassroots organisations – both large and small – that deliver vital support to the communities they serve.'

How the trust works

The trust takes a unique approach to its grant-making; it doesn't operate simply by awarding grants but rather assists in creating opportunities for the funding it provides to go further. As described on the website, it does this by matching donations and 'harnessing the power of digital fundraising'.

Furthermore, in line with its ethos which is 'to be entrepreneurial seeking innovative opportunities to reduce child poverty', the trust also offers added value support – such as skills training and marketing advice – free of charge to its partner organisations. Through this approach, the trust can assist its chosen projects to grow.

The trust's approach enables it to leverage 'more than £5 for every £1' it invests in its chosen projects.

What the trust does

The Childhood Trust looks to make an immediate difference in the lives of disadvantaged children in London. It facilitates 'best in breed projects that focus exclusively on child poverty'. The website further explains 'We do not lobby or campaign on the policies which might be causing problems for children in society, but focus first on the child who needs our help today. The Childhood Trust wants to help the 600,000 children in London who are hungry, tired, lack the will to dream or

make something of their lives, feel better today.'

In order to carry out its work effectively, the trust channels its funding into three thematic areas:

- **Practical – Ready to learn:** Ensuring that children have access to the basic necessities
- **Emotional – Safe, secure, supported:** Offering emotional support and motivation to break the cycle of poverty
- **Inspirational – Thriving, not just surviving:** Providing opportunities to try new experiences and develop new skills

Full information on these three funding areas, including examples of the kind of projects that can be supported, is detailed on the website.

Financial information

In 2016/17 the trust had assets of £83,500 and an income £625,000. Grants awarded to organisations totalled £489,000.

The trust's 2016/17 annual report explains: grants were made to a total of 72 charities during the year, collectively delivering 89 projects to vulnerable and disadvantaged children and young people. A total of £2,181,184 was raised for these projects with 94% achieving their full fundraising target compared to 78% in the previous year.

Beneficiaries included: Blooming Blossoms Trust; Clapton Common Boys Club; Embrace Child Victims of Crime; Farms for City Children; Kids Care London; Magic Breakfast; Mousetrap Theatre Projects; Shine: Support And Help In Education; StreetGames UK; Young And Inspired.

Exclusions

The trust does not:

- Fund activities that are aimed at services provided by the state
- Fund religious groups
- Offer grants other than the regular fundraising programmes that it curates
- Sponsor individuals or fund events

Applications

The trust's website states:

Charities should contact us by email at info@childhoodtrust.org.uk if they feel that the work they do is relevant to our mission – which is to alleviate the impact of child poverty across London. Charities are advised not to send speculative letters or emails to us requesting a donation as these will not be replied to.

We do not make grants directly. We mostly work with small grassroots charities to embrace digital fundraising by match-funding individual donor's gifts. There are two funding rounds each year; in December, via The Christmas Give campaign and June, via our Summer Give campaign. We make grants through both of these campaigns that are facilitated by our platform partner The Big Give.

Sources of information

Accounts; annual report; Charity Commission record; further information provided by funder; funder's website.

Children With Cancer UK

 Research into childhood cancer, welfare projects for young cancer patients and their families

 UK

£ £5.3 million (2016)

CC number: 298405

Trustees: Edward O'Gorman; Linda Robson; Sandra Mileham; Alasdair Philips.

Correspondent: Neil Meemaduma, Research Grants Manager, 51 Great Ormond Street, London WC1N 3JQ (tel: 020 7404 0808; email: research@ childrenwithcancer.org.uk)

 www.childrenwithcancer.org.uk

In the 2016 annual report, Children with Cancer UK states its aims as follows:

> Our aims are to determine the causes, find the cure and provide care for children with cancer. We fund life-saving research into the causes, prevention and treatment of childhood cancer. We fund innovative welfare projects to provide better care for young cancer patients and their families. We campaign to raise awareness of childhood cancer to protect more children and to improve the lives of young cancer patients, today and for future generations.

The charity has the following funding streams:

▶ Project grants
▶ Postdoctoral research fellowships
▶ Clinical studentships
▶ Support for conferences and meetings

Special grant calls are posted on the charity's website and in the research newsletter. The main research objectives of the charity are:

▶ To improve knowledge of the genetic and environmental causes and relevant biological mechanisms of childhood cancers
▶ To identify diagnostic and prognostic biomarkers for childhood cancers
▶ To optimise and develop more effective and less toxic treatments for children with cancer, with a special focus on those forms of cancer that still carry a poor prognosis
▶ To understand the long-term health implications of childhood cancer and its treatment

▶ To promote the dissemination of research findings to achieve maximum impact

Financial information

In 2016 the charity held assets of £10.8 million and had an income of £16.5 million. Grants totalled £5.3 million and were distributed in the following categories:

Research into prevention and causes	£3.1 million
Welfare	£1 million
Research into treatment	£1 million
Education	£194,000

Beneficiaries included: CLIC Sargent (£332,500); Bristol Children's Hospital (£250,000); Together for Short Lives (£180,000); Brainstrust (£152,000); Lifelites (£120,000); University of Nottingham (£10,000); University of Oxford (£1,000).

Exclusions

Overseas research will only be funded if it is part of a collaboration led from the UK.

Applications

For information on current funding opportunities and how to apply, refer to the charity's website.

Sources of information

Accounts; annual report; Charity Commission record; funder's website.

The Childwick Trust

 Horse racing, social welfare, health, disability, Jewish causes, education

UK – specifically the following counties: Bedfordshire, Berkshire, Buckinghamshire, Cambridgeshire, Essex, Gloucestershire, Hertfordshire, Hampshire, Kent, London and Greater London, Norfolk, Northamptonshire, Oxfordshire, Suffolk, Sussex, Surrey, Wiltshire. Also South Africa

£ £2.8 million (2015/16)

CC number: 1150413

Trustees: Clare Maurice; Mark Farmar; John Wood; Peter Anwyl-Harris; Dr Alan Stranders; Michael Fiddes.

Correspondent: Kirsty Jones, 9 Childwick Green, Childwicksbury, St Albans AL3 6JJ (tel: 01727 844666; email: kirsty@childwicktrust.org)

 www.childwicktrust.org

The trust was established in 1985 by the settlement of assets of the late founder, Mr H J Joel – racehorse owner and breeder.

Areas of work

Assistance is given exclusively to registered charities working in the counties listed (see area of benefit)

supporting people with disabilities; older people who are in need; and adults or children who are seriously ill. Support is also given towards people involved in the horse racing industry, to Jewish charities in the UK and to pre-school education projects in South Africa. The Childwick Trust controls a subsidiary charity in South Africa, The Jim Joel Fund, through which it conducts its South African-based charitable objects.

The main bulk of the support is given to health and disability causes and the next largest proportion of grants goes to charities in South Africa via the subsidiary charity. Charities connected with thoroughbred racing and breeding are next in line and Jewish charities follow. These funding preferences were set by Mr Joel in the Trust Deed in 1985 and are not changed by the trustees.

Disability, older people and serious illness

Grants are made to organisations offering care and support to people with serious illness; older people; adults and children with learning disabilities, mental health problems or physical disabilities; ex-Service personnel who are in need of care or support. Some grants may also be made for medical research.

Grants (typically between £5,000 and £30,000) can be given towards purposes such as special equipment, respite care, holidays, education and other purposes. Salaries and core costs can be supported, as well as grants towards building or refurbishment projects if at least half the total budget is already met. Hospices in the South East are also supported, including running costs.

South Africa

In South Africa, support is predominantly given to early childhood development projects with applications being administered through The Jim Joel Fund. Assistance is also provided for 'South African residents to promote education through charitable institutions in South Africa or the UK'.

Horse racing

Support is given towards the welfare of those in the racing industry who are older and retired; injured; on a low income; or young people who need support.

Jewish charities

The trust offers some support to charities which promote the Jewish faith and help the Jewish community – particularly older people, people with disabilities and children and young people. Grants are only made to charities in the UK, not Israel.

Financial information

In 2015/16 the trust had assets of £76.4 million, an income of £2.2 million and made grants totalling £2.8 million, of which £2.2 million was in the UK and £573,500 was in South Africa. Grants were broken down as follows:

Health and associated causes – UK	£1.7 million
Education – South Africa	£826,000
Racing – UK	£234,000
Jewish causes – UK	£87,000

Beneficiaries for 2016/17 were listed on the trust's website.

Beneficiaries (UK) included: Racing Welfare – Newmarket (£200,000); Rennie Grove Hospice (£35,000); National Horseracing Museum (£25,000); Youthtalk (£22,000); Combat Stress (£20,000); Together for Short Lives (£16,000); Families United Network, Gesher School, Princess Alice Hospice and Redbridge Concern for Mental Health (£15,000 each).

Exclusions

Grants are not made for:

- Complementary health and therapy projects
- Charities offering legal advice
- Charities offering counselling
- Hospices outside the south east of England
- NHS hospitals and other statutory bodies
- Universities – academic research, scholarships and bursaries
- Homelessness charities
- Projects related to drugs or alcohol addiction
- HIV/AIDS-related projects
- Charities which are part of a wider or national network – only those who are based within the South East can apply
- Individuals or organisations applying on behalf of an individual (other than in relation to South African educational grants)
- Students seeking sponsorship for educational or gap year projects
- Animal charities unless they are connected to thoroughbred racehorses
- Larger charities with widespread support are less likely to be considered unless they support local causes in Hertfordshire/Bedfordshire
- National appeals
- Conferences, seminars and workshops
- Organisations that have received a grant within the previous two years
- Causes outside the UK (apart from South Africa)

Applications

The Childwick Trust – Applications can be made using the online form on the trust's website, where deadlines for the next meeting are also posted.

The Jim Joel Fund – Potential applicants should refer to the website for details of whether funding is currently available – applications are usually due to be submitted by the end of April. Full funding guidelines for applications to fund may be requested from Giuliana Bland (PO Box 271, Jukskei Park, 2153, South Africa; tel: +27 011 704 6539; email: giuliana.jjf@iafrica.com).

Sources of information

Accounts; annual report; Charity Commission record; funder's website.

CHK Charities Ltd

General charitable purposes

UK, with a preference for the West Midlands

£2.3 million (2016/17)

CC number: 1050900

Trustees: Charlotte Percy; Joanna Prest; Katherine Lloyd; Lucy Morris; Rupert Prest; Susanna Peake; Edward Peake; Diana Acland; Pandora Morris.

Correspondent: Scott Rice, SG Kleinwort Hambros Trust Company, 5th Floor, 8 St James's Square, London SW1Y 4JU (tel: 020 3207 7041; email: scott.rice@kleinwortbenson.com)

www.chkcharities.co.uk

CHK Charities Ltd was established in 1995. The origin of the charity derives from the wish of Sir Cyril Kleinwort and his descendants, who constitute the members of the company, to devote some of their time and resources to charitable activities. The charity normally makes grants totalling around £2 million a year for a wide range of purposes across the UK, although preference is given to West Midlands and national charities.

Areas of activity

The trustees use the following programme areas to classify their grants:

- Artistic causes
- Conservation/preservation
- Countryside matters and animal welfare and disease
- Care of older people
- Crime prevention
- Treatment and care of people with disabilities
- Drug prevention and treatment
- Education
- Employment and job creation
- *General medical research – *(note, the trustees do not normally support general medical research projects, but do occasionally consider appeals for areas where they have specific knowledge)
- General welfare and social problems
- Homelessness/housing
- Hospices
- Hospital/nursing home building and equipment
- Miscellaneous
- Population control
- Research into blindness
- Research into deafness
- Care of young people

Types of grant

One-off Grants:
The trust aims to 'make a difference'; it does not support individuals or very small and narrowly specialised activities but, on the other hand, it tries to avoid 'bottomless pits' and unfocused causes. Therefore grants made on a one-off basis will be towards core costs for a specific project. This could include specialist equipment for a project or help with running costs.

Conditionally Renewable Grants:
Grants made for more than one year can be towards start-up costs, for a specific item in the applicant's budget (i.e. a salary) or towards the costs of a particular project. These are subject to annual progress reports.

Large Grants (over £25,000):
These are approved as a result of close knowledge of specific charities by a trustee.

Further information on the charity's funding guidelines is available on the website.

Financial information

In 2016/17 the charity had a total income of £3.3 million and assets of £109 million. Grants were made totalling £2.2 million and were broken down into the following areas:

Youth care	40	£489,000
Artistic causes	24	£266,000
Social welfare	43	£264,000
Education	20	£258,500
Disability	39	£218,000
Miscellaneous	7	£161,500
Deafness	2	£105,000
Hospices	6	£98,000
Conservation/preservation	4	£53,000
Reproductive healthcare control	2	£52,500
Blindness	8	£49,000
Care for the elderly	9	£47,500
Crime prevention	3	£37,000
Homelessness/Housing	7	£30,000
Employment	5	£22,000
Drug prevention/treatment	3	£15,000
Medical care and research	3	£14,000
Countryside/Animal welfare	2	£13,000

Beneficiaries included: Charities Aid Foundation (£120,000); St Christopher's Hospice (£75,000); Police Rehabilitation Trust (£22,000); Sick Children's Trust (£6,000); Carers Support Centre, Crisis Centre Ministries, National Youth Orchestra Of Great Britain, Royal Society For Blind Children, (£5,000 Each); Hepatitis C Trust (£4,000).

Exclusions

According to the charity's website, the following will not be considered for funding:

- organisations not registered as charities or those that have been registered for less than a year
- pre-school groups

- out of school play schemes including pre-school and holiday schemes
- 'bottomless pits' and unfocused causes
- very small and narrowly specialised activities
- community centres
- local authorities
- umbrella or grant-making organisations
- universities and colleges and grant-maintained private or local education authority schools or their Parent Teachers Associations, except if these schools are for students with special needs
- individuals or charities applying on behalf of individuals
- general requests for donations
- professional associations and training of professionals
- projects which are abroad even though the charity is based in the UK
- expeditions or overseas travel
- 'campaigning organisations' or citizens advice projects providing legal advice
- community transport projects
- general counselling projects, except those in areas of considerable deprivation and with a clearly defined client group

Applications

The charity does not have an application form, but suggests that the following guidelines be used when making an application:

- applications should be no longer than four A4 sides, and should incorporate a short (half page) summary
- applications should also include a detailed budget for the project and the applicant's most recent audited accounts (if those accounts show a significant surplus or deficit of income, please explain how this has arisen)

Additional information on the application process can be found on the charity's website.

Sources of information

Accounts; annual report; Charity Commission record; funder's website.

Christie Foundation

General charitable purposes, education, health, social welfare

Worldwide

£1.38 million (2016/17)

CC number: 1151063

Trustees: Iain Abrahams; Alexandra Christie Abrahams; Richard Stern.

Correspondent: Iain Abrahams, Trustee, 1 Mercer Street, London WC2H 9QJ (email: info@thechristiefoundation.co.uk)

The foundation was registered in 2013 and according to its Charity Commission record supports: education and training, health, social welfare and general charitable purposes. The settlor

of the foundation, Iain Abrahams, is former executive vice-chair of Barclays Bank's 'structured capital markets' unit.

The foundation's 2016/17 accounts state:

The objective of the Foundation is to provide assistance and support to charitable causes, generally and in particular, to organisations which encounter difficulty in raising funds to further their work. As the Foundation is recently formed it continues to research specific areas requiring donations. Grants are generally approved by the trustees during the board meetings. Grants may only be made for purposes which are charitable under UK law.

Financial information

In 2016/17 the foundation held assets of £18.7 million and had an income of £313,500. Grant to organisations totalled £1.38 million.

Beneficiaries included: Social Finance (£1.2 million); Project Orchid Ltd (£175,000).

Applications

Apply in writing to the correspondent.

Sources of information

Accounts; annual report; Charity Commission record.

Church Burgesses Trust

Ecclesiastical purposes, general charitable purposes

Sheffield

£1.1 million (2016)

CC number: 221284

Trustees: Peter Lee; Nicholas Hutton; Michael Woffenden; D. Booker; D. Stanley; Revd S. Hunter; Ian Walker; Prof. Peter Ainsworth; B. Hickman; Dr Julie Banham; S. Bain; David Quinney.

Correspondent: Godfrey Smallman, Law Clerk, Sheffield Church Burgesses Trust, 3rd Floor, Fountain Precinct, Balm Green, Sheffield S1 2JA (tel: 0114 267 5594; email: sheffieldchurchburgesses@wrigleys.co.uk)

www.sheffieldchurchburgesses.org.uk

The trust's website gives an account of the origin of the trust:

The charity now known as the Church Burgesses Trust has served Sheffield quietly and unobtrusively, for over 450 years. Edward VI had seized for his own use land and property belonging to the town. Protest was made but to no avail. When Queen Mary Tudor succeeded Edward, a petition was presented asking for the return of the lands. This she granted on 8 June 1554 in a royal charter which gave the land and property in trust to a new corporate body: The Twelve Capital Burgesses and Commonalty of the

Town and Parish of Sheffield in the County of York.

The website states: 'The trust seeks to respond positively to the needs of a large modern city through its support for: the parishes carved out of the ancient Parish of Sheffield; the work of Sheffield Cathedral; organisations working for the needy and the deprived, the elderly, the marginalised and for the revitalisation of inner city communities; the Church Burgesses Educational Foundation (schools, educational organisations and individuals)'.

Ecclesiastical grants

Applications from Church of England churches in Sheffield are considered by the Ecclesiastical Grants Committee. Only Anglican churches within the four Sheffield deaneries (Attercliffe, Ecclesall, Ecclesfield and Hallam) are eligible to apply. Grants can be given to support 'any activity which furthers the objectives of the Church of England', which often involves building repairs or the employment of parish-based staff. Applications from churches of other denominations can be considered by the General Charitable Purposes Committee. See the website for more information.

Other charitable support

The General Charitable Purposes Committee considers applications from a wide range of charities and groups whose activities are carried out within the city of Sheffield, to the benefit of local residents. There is a particular emphasis on:

- The relief for those who are aged, ailing, disabled, poor or otherwise disadvantaged
- The relief of distress and sickness
- The provision and support of facilities for recreation and other leisure time occupation
- The provision and support of educational facilities

The website further explains: 'Grants range in size from £500 to a maximum amount of £10,000 and can be for a complete scheme or a contribution towards a larger project. If the latter, grants are only made when a clear plan of achieving the desired goal is provided'.

The trust is not able to make grants to individuals under this heading, however individuals who are under the age of 25 can apply to the Church Burgesses Educational Foundation for specific educational help. More information is available from the website.

Financial information

In 2016 the trust held assets of £38.3 million and an income of £1.7 million. Grants were made totalling almost £1.1 million and were distributed as follows:

Cathedral expenditure	£492,000
Ecclesiastical grants to institutions	£450,000
General charitable grants to institutions	£136,500
Ecclesiastical grants to clergy	£8,500

Beneficiaries included: St Chad's Woodseats (£40,000); SDBF Mission (£18,500); St Luke's Hospice Sheffield (£15,000); Christchurch – Pitsmoor (£10,000); Cavendish Centre for Cancer Care (£6,000); Newlife Foundation (£2,500); Sheffield Street Pastors (£2,000); Carmel Care (£1,000); Broomhall Girls Youth Club (£500); Grenoside Community Association (£400).

Exclusions

Grants are not made to individuals, although individuals under the age of 25 may be able to apply for educational assistance from the Church Burgesses Educational Foundation.

Applications

Application forms and guidelines are available from the relevant page on the trust's website. Application forms must be completed and received by the Law Clerk before the beginning of the second week of December, March, June and September, along with all supporting papers. The trustees consider applications at meetings held on a quarterly basis. Applicants are normally informed of the outcome of their application shortly after these quarterly meetings.

Sources of information

Accounts; annual report; Charity Commission record; funder's website.

Church of Ireland Priorities Fund

 Church of Ireland

 The Republic of Ireland and Northern Ireland

(£) £570,000 (2016)

Correspondent: Sylvia Simpson, Organiser, Church of Ireland House, Church Avenue, Rathmines, Dublin 6, D06 CF67 (tel: +353-(0)1–4125607; email: priorities@ireland.anglican.org)

www.priorities.ireland.anglican.org

This fund was established in 1980 to fund Church of Ireland projects anywhere in Ireland. Funds are donated by individual parishes and are then allocated to causes.

The following information on the fund has been taken from its website:

Criteria

Only projects which comply with the Criteria may be funded. Before you decide to apply, it is important that you read the Criteria carefully.

Areas Currently Supported By The Fund

- **Training** – Lay and Ordained – Training in the following areas:- post-ordination, clergy in-service, lay ministry, youth ministry, children's ministry, student chaplaincy
- **Christian Education** – Development of RE in schools, children's ministry, youth work, adult education
- **Outreach Initiatives** – To encourage creative and innovative projects, which reach out to the communities our parishes serve, including church plants and missional areas
- **Innovative Ministry in a Rural Context** – To encourage creative and innovative ministry projects in the sparsely populated areas of the country, in rural or village settings

Maximising The Effect Of Grants From The Priorities Fund

In order to spread the money from the Fund as widely and fairly as possible, we try to adhere to certain conditions.

We encourage:-

- Applications for grants for 'seed capital'
- Applications for grants which will have a significant influence in attracting other funding

We try to avoid:-

- Funding for projects which are still at the planning stage, including feasibility studies
- Recurrent grant aiding
- Funding for salaries
- Financing debts
- Restoration projects for cathedrals and church buildings
- Routine renovations and repairs

Applications Requiring Recommendations

It is necessary for most projects to be vetted before they reach the Priorities Fund Committee.

These applications are recommended or not recommended by:-

- Church of Ireland Youth Department (youth projects)
- The appropriate Diocesan Council (diocesan and parish projects)

Financial information

The fund's website provides a list of '2018 allocations from the 2017 fund', with a list of grant recipients and amounts in euros. The total of these allocations was over €651,000. The website explains: 'Sterling grants have been converted to euro using the 2017 end of year rate of 0.8881.' Using this rate, the amounts allocated amount to £570,250.

Beneficiaries included: The Church of Ireland Theological Institute (€30,000); Braniel Community Church (€20,000);

Parish of Ballymacarrett (€10,000); St Patrick's Cathedral, Dublin (€5,000); Church of Ireland Youth Department (€1,000).

Exclusions

The fund tries to avoid funding:

- Projects which are still at the planning stage
- Recurrent grant aid
- Funding for salaries
- Financing debts
- Funding for cathedrals and churches
- Routine renovations and repairs

Applications

Application forms are available from the fund's website along with criteria and guidelines. Applications must be made by 31 October each year. They are considered by the Priorities Fund Committee at its meeting in February and are put forward for the Standing Committee's approval in March.

Sources of information

Funder's website; guidelines for applicants.

The Churchill Foundation

 Social welfare, health, older people, young people

 UK

(£) Around £200,000 (2016)

CC number: 1164320

Trustees: Clinton McCarthy; John Hatchard; Spencer McCarthy; Suzanne Revell.

Correspondent: Suzanne Revell, Churchill Retirement Living Ltd, Millstream House, Parkside, Ringwood BH24 3SG (tel: 01425 462132; email: enquiries@churchillfoundation.co.uk)

www.churchillfoundation.co.uk

The foundation was registered with the Charity Commission in November 2015 and is the corporate foundation of Churchill Retirement Living.

The foundation's website states that it supports local communities as well as national charities in three core areas:

- The relief of sickness, disease and human suffering
- The promotion of health amongst the elderly
- The support and wellbeing of the young

The foundation has two programmes:

Annual Partnership Programme

We pick two or three charities each year which we support not only financially, but by generating exposure via Churchill Retirement employees, business partners, owners and Churchill Foundation events.

87

Small Grants (£50 to £2,000)

Applications for small grants are open all year round. Applicants must be referred by Churchill Retirement colleagues, owners or business partners. All small grant donations have to be signed off by the trustees on a quarterly basis.

Financial information

In 2016 the foundation had an income of £265,500 and a total expenditure of £246,500. Full accounts were not available to view on the Charity Commission website and we therefore estimate that grants totalled around £200,000.

A list of beneficiaries was not available.

Applications

Application forms for both programmes are available to download from the foundation's website and should be returned by email. Small grant applicants must be referred by Churchill Retirement colleagues, owners or business partners.

Sources of information

Accounts; annual report; Charity Commission record; funder's website.

The CIBC World Markets Children's Foundation

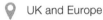 Children affected by disability, illness, social deprivation or life-limiting conditions

UK and Europe

£218,000 (2016/17)

CC number: 1105094

Trustees: Mark Beels; Martin Autotte; Andrew Ryde; Samantha Orozco; Sarah Heavey; Rob Tuffnell; Sonia Beardsmore.

Correspondent: The Trustees, Canadian Imperial Bank of Commerce, 150 Cheapside, London EC2V 6ET (tel: 020 7234 6387; email: ukchildrensmiracle@cibc.co.uk)

 www.cibc.com/ca/miracleday/international/childrens-foundation.html

CIBC World Markets is the investment banking subsidiary of the Canadian Imperial Bank of Commerce. The CIBC Children's Foundation was established in 1984 to raise funds for children's charities around the world. The website states that 'since inception, £150 million has been raised to improve the quality of life of thousands of children affected by disability, illness, social deprivation or life-limiting conditions'. The company has an annual fundraising day, CIBC Miracle Day, where employees donate their fees and commissions to the foundation. In London, employees also raise funds through events throughout the year.

Eligibility criteria

The foundation supports UK or European registered charities which have 'a record of achievement or potential for success' in line with the foundation's goals of supporting the health, welfare and education of children. Organisations should have an income of less than £5 million a year, and provide tangible benefit to children and communities in the UK/Europe. The foundation particularly favours charities where there is potential for employees to offer in-kind volunteering support.

Financial information

In 2016/17 the foundation held assets of £34,000 and had an income of £220,000. Grants totalled £218,000 and were awarded to ten organisations.

Beneficiaries included: Become, Tommy's and Winston's Wish (£70,000 each); Teens and Toddlers (£5,000); Dame Hannah Rogers Trust, Evelina London Children's Hospital, National Deaf Children's Society, SEWA and Sick Children's Trust (£500 each); Shishukunj (£250).

Exclusions

The following categories of requests would typically not be considered for funding:

- Individuals
- Political or advocacy groups
- Private schools
- Groups that limit their activities to benefitting people of a designated ethnic or religious affiliation
- Endowments or funds given permanently to a foundation so it may produce its own income for grant-making purposes
- Multi-year projects or commitments
- Charities with an annual income over £5 million
- Charities which have already been supported by the foundation in the last five years

Applications

The following is taken from the 2016/17 annual report:

Charities meeting the Foundation's objectives that are known to; or which contact; or are recommended to the Foundation are placed on a database and are invited to submit a funding proposal to the Foundation's Selection Committee. All proposals received that are fully compliant with our donation criteria are circulated to the Selection Committee for review. Charities are then short-listed by the selection committee and short-listed candidates are invited to present. The Selection Committee then makes a decision on the number of charities to be supported and those charities that receive the greatest number of votes from the various members are chosen for support.

These choices are then ratified by the Trustees before the charities are informed of their success. Additional smaller one-off donations may be made directly or indirectly (either on a one-off donation basis or by matching sponsorship efforts of CIBC London employees) to charities meeting the criteria and objectives of the Foundation at the discretion of the Trustees and must be duly approved.

Sources of information

Accounts; annual report; Charity Commission record; funder's website.

The City Bridge Trust (Bridge House Estates)

 General charitable purposes

Greater London

£18.1 million (2016/17)

CC number: 1035628

Trustee: The Corporation of the City of London.

Correspondent: David Farnsworth, Chief Grants Officer, City of London Corporation, PO Box 270, Guildhall, London EC2P 2EJ (tel: 020 7332 3710; email: citybridgetrust@cityoflondon.gov.uk)

www.citybridgetrust.org.uk

The City Bridge Trust is the grant-making arm of Bridge House Estates which is responsible for the maintenance of London Bridge, Southwark Bridge, Blackfriars Bridge, Tower Bridge and Millennium Bridge. In 1995 a scheme was agreed by the Charity Commission which enabled the trust to use its surplus income (after meeting its responsibilities for the maintenance and replacement of the bridges) for charitable purposes benefitting the inhabitants of Greater London. This currently amounts to around £20 million per year.

The trust's grants are largely made under its Investing in Londoners scheme, which includes a number of different grants programmes, including:

- English for Speakers of Other Languages
- Improving Londoners' Mental Health
- Improving London's Environment
- Making London More Inclusive
- Making London Safer
- Older Londoners
- Reducing Poverty
- Resettlement and Rehabilitation of Offenders
- Strengthening London's Voluntary Sector
- Eco-audits
- London Youth Quality Mark Awards

The trust makes grants to registered charities, community interest companies, charitable companies, exempt or excepted charities, and registered charitable industrial and provident societies or charitable co-operatives.

There is no minimum or maximum revenue grant but the trust will not contribute more than 50% of an organisation's income in a year, and applications for more than £5,000 require a detailed proposal.

Grants can be given for either running costs or capital costs but not both. Grants for running costs can be funded for up to three years, although in exceptional cases, strategic projects may be funded for up to five years. Capital grants for accessibility improvements are only considered for up to £100,000 and for existing community buildings, where total development costs of less than £10 million in total. Grants of up to £5,000 can be given for disability access audits or equalities training or consultancy to help develop projects.

Full details of the specific requirements for each programme are available on the trust's website.

Financial information
In 2016/17 the trust had assets of over £1.3 billion and an income of £34.1 million. During the year, the trust awarded grants to 209 organisations totalling £18.1 million

Grants were distributed as follows:

Investing in Londoners programme	£12.7 million
Strategic initiatives	£3.4 million
CBT 20th Anniversary Grants	£800,000
Stepping Stones Fund	£700,000
Partnership programmes	£500,000

Beneficiaries included: Disablement Association of Barking and Dagenham (£122,000); PAC-UK (£106,000); Tender Education and Arts (£100,500); Havelock Family Centre (£100,000); Chaos Theory (£99,500); South London Botanical Institute (£76,500); Somali Welfare Trust (£42,000).

Exclusions
The following are not funded:

- Political parties
- Political lobbying
- Non-charitable activities
- Work which does not benefit the inhabitants of Greater London
- Individuals
- Grant-making bodies to make grants on behalf of the trust
- Schools, PTAs, universities or other educational establishments (except where they are undertaking ancillary charitable activities specifically directed towards one of the agreed priority areas)
- Medical or academic research
- Churches or other religious bodies where the money will be used for religious purposes
- Hospitals

- Projects which have already taken place or building work which has already been completed
- Statutory bodies
- Charities established outside the UK
- Residential care services or residential facilities, except for short-term emergency accommodation

Grants will not usually be given to:

- Work where there is statutory responsibility to provide funding
- Organisations seeking funding to replace cuts by statutory authorities, except where that funding was explicitly time-limited and for a discretionary (non-statutory) purpose
- Organisations seeking funding to top up on under-priced contracts
- Work where there is significant public funding available (including funding from sports governing bodies)

Applications
Applications have to be made through the online portal on the trust's website. Appeals sent by post, fax or email are not considered and any draft or initial proposals sent by email or via the enquiry form are not reviewed. Applicants will need to submit supporting documentation and may be contacted for further details or visited by a Grants Officer as part of the assessment process. The Grants Committee meets regularly and applications are accepted throughout the year for all current funding programmes. It normally takes about four months from the receipt of an application until the final decision is made. All applicants are advised in writing of the Grants Committee's decision within a few days of the relevant Grants Committee meeting. Most programmes do not have a deadline. Unsuccessful applicants can re-apply one year after the date that a rejected application was received.

See the website for a full list of supporting documents required and for detailed step-by-step guidance on the application process.

Applicants are encouraged to contact the trust for initial guidance before making an application, and the trust can also offer feedback on unsuccessful applications.

Sources of information
Accounts; annual report; Charity Commission record; funder's website.

J A Clark Charitable Trust

 Young people, women's empowerment, general charitable purposes, overseas aid

 UK and overseas

£627,500 (2016)

CC number: 1010520

Trustees: William Pym; Thomas Clark; Aidan Pelly; Odette Clark Campbell.

Correspondent: Lynette Cooper, Trust Secretary, PO Box 1704, Glastonbury, Somerset BA16 0YB

jaclarktrust.com

The J A Clark Charitable Trust was established in 1971 by John Anthony Clark as a family charitable trust.

Following a recent review of the trust's activities the trustees have identified two areas they wish to support during the current strategic period (2017–2022):

- Women's Empowerment in Africa and Asia
- Disadvantaged Youths in deprived areas of the UK, specifically East London and the North East

Grants programmes
At the time of writing (June 2018) the trust operates the following three grants programmes:

- **Women's empowerment programme:** Aims to empower extremely poor, deprived and marginalised women in Africa and Asia. The programme supports work on women's economic empowerment and women's rights in rural areas of the following eight countries: Ethiopia, Kenya, Tanzania, Zambia, Afghanistan, Cambodia, Indonesia, and Pakistan.
- **Youth programme:** Focused on mentoring vulnerable people who are not in education employment or training, and finding them routes to employment or education.
- **Family fund:** A proportion of the trust's grant-making budget is reserved for individual members of the JAC Family to reach out to organisations they have personally identified and are keen to support. The trustees do not accept unsolicited applications for this programme.

Financial information
In 2016 the trust had assets of £19.2 million and an income of £603,500. Grants were made totalling £627,500 and were broken down as follows:

Women's empowerment		
programme	10	£310,000
Family fund	9	£214,500
Youth fund	3	£73,000
Other grants	10	£30,000

Beneficiaries included: Christian Aid (£22,000); Conflicts Forum (£20,000); Community Music (£17,500); Concern Universal, Inner City Scholarship (£15,000 each); MSF Syrian Appeal (£14,000); Peacock Gym (£7,500).

Applications

Apply in writing to the correspondent.

Sources of information

Accounts; annual report; Charity Commission record; funder's website.

The Roger and Sarah Bancroft Clark Charitable Trust

🔍 General charitable purposes, education, religion

📍 UK, Somerset

£ £472,000 (2016)

CC number: 211513

Trustees: Alice Clark; Martin Lovell; Caroline Gould; Priscilla Goldby; Robert Robertson.

Correspondent: Mel Park, c/o C. & J. Clark Ltd, 40 High Street, Street, Somerset BA16 0EQ (email: mel.park@clarks.com)

The Roger and Sarah Bancroft Clark Charitable Trust was set up by a trust deed in 1960. The trustees' annual report for 2016 states that the trustees invite applications for grants from the public and meet regularly to decide which applications to support. In the past grants have been made to Religious Society of Friends and associated bodies, charities connected with Somerset and those supporting education. The trustees do consider other applications for funding, and at present are providing grants to educational institutions for postgraduate training.

Financial information

In 2016 the trust had assets of £9.38 million and an income of £2.9 million. There were 146 grants made to organisations totalling £472,000, broken down as follows:

Other grants	£304,500
Educational grants	£80,500
Religious grants	£68,000
Somerset grants	£18,800

Beneficiaries included: AHSS Royal High School Planning Appeal (£30,000); Quaker Peace and Social Witness (£13,000); The Art Fund, University College London, University of Bristol (£10,000 each); The Society for the

Protection of Ancient Buildings (£7,000); Royal Academy of Music (£5,000); Royal School of Needlework and The Woodworks Project (£1,000 each); Book Aid International (£500).

Applications

Apply in writing to the correspondent.

Sources of information

Accounts; annual report; Charity Commission record.

Clark Foundation

🔍 Education, training, health, arts, environment, recreation

📍 There is a preference for areas where there are significant numbers of employees of C and J Clark and its subsidiaries

£ £568,500 (2016/17)

CC number: 313143

Trustees: Gloria Clark; Judith Derbyshire; Martin Lovell; Richard Clark.

Correspondent: Lesley Hide, Trust Manager, c/o Clarks International, 40 High Street, Street, Somerset BA16 0EQ (tel: 01458 842553; email: trustgrants@clarks.com)

Established in 1959, this foundation is connected to the shoe retail company C&J Clark Ltd. The foundation prefers to make grants for one-off capital projects or for organisation start-up costs. Grants are given in areas where there are significant numbers of employees or ex-employees of C&J Clark Ltd. This has recently been expanded to areas overseas which are close to where there are employees in companies supplying shoes to C&J Clark Ltd. National appeals are only supported if there is a local element.

Financial information

In 2016/17 the foundation held assets of £16.2 million and had an income of £491,500. During the year, the foundation made 146 grants totalling £568,500 for the following purposes:

Education	24	£109,000
Welfare	52	£103,500
Religion	11	£103,000
Medicine	16	£79,500
Countryside	12	£79,500
Arts	8	£40,500
Overseas	2	£5,800
Poverty	1	£500
Older people	1	£500
Family	1	£250

Beneficiaries included: Strode College (£98,000 in two grants); Street Baptist Church (£35,000); Heads Up Somerset (£15,000); St Margaret's Somerset Hospice (£11,300); Radstock Museum, South Lakes Citizens Advice and Ston Easton Parish Council (£5,000 each);

Prickles Hedgehog Rescue (£2,000); Ashcott Primary School, Curry Rivel Village Hall and Street and Glastonbury Carers Support Group (£500 each); Life Cycle UK (£250); Yeovil Netball Club (£150).

Exclusions

No grants are given to individuals.

Applications

Apply in writing to the correspondent. The trustees meet quarterly although applications for amounts up to £750 may be made by the trust manager between meetings.

Sources of information

Accounts; annual report; Charity Commission record.

The Clore Duffield Foundation

🔍 Arts, culture, heritage and museums, Jewish charities, health, social welfare

📍 UK, with larger grants going to London-based institutions

£ £7.5 million (2016)

CC number: 1084412

Trustees: Dame Vivien Duffield; Melanie Clore; James Harding; David Harrel; Richard Oldfield; Jeremy Sandelson.

Correspondent: Sally Bacon, Executive Director, Unit 3, Chelsea Manor Studios, Flood Street, London SW3 5SR (tel: 020 7351 6061; fax: 020 7351 5308; email: info@cloreduffield.org.uk)

 www.cloreduffield.org.uk

The Clore Foundation was founded in 1964 by the late Sir Charles Clore, one of Britain's most successful post-war businessmen and one of the most generous philanthropists of his day. Following his death in 1979, his daughter, Vivien Duffield, became chair of the foundation and created her own foundation in 1987 with the aim of continuing and consolidating her family's history of philanthropy. The two charities were merged in 2000 to become The Clore Duffield Foundation.

The foundation is a grant-making charity which concentrates its support on cultural learning, creating learning spaces within arts and heritage organisations, museums and galleries which provide access to cultural activities for people who would not normally take part. Some support is also given towards health and social welfare. Support towards enhancing Jewish life is mainly focused on JW3: London's Jewish Community Centre.

Grants programmes

Clore Learning Spaces: Since 2000 the foundation has funded more than 50 museums, gallery, heritage and performing arts learning spaces across the UK. These range from £2.5 million Clore Learning Centres in national museums, to grants of less than £50,000 to fund small Clore Studios with local museums. Further guidance is given on the foundation's website.

Main grants: The foundation awards grants ranging from £10,000 to over £1 million to registered charities and local authority cultural organisations. Although the foundation does provide grants for some health and social welfare projects, the majority of support is directed towards the cultural sector, and in particular to cultural learning and to museum, gallery, heritage and performing arts learning spaces. Furthermore, the majority of funding is for capital projects – only a small number of grants are made each year for programme funding. The foundation also prefers to pay grants over a number of years, particularly for large-scale projects.

Clore Poetry and Literature Awards: The foundation's smaller grants programme awards funding to participatory learning projects which engage children and young people (under 19 years of age) with poetry and literature in exciting ways. Grants of between £1,000 and £10,000 are awarded to schools and educational institutions, arts organisations, community groups and other charitable organisations.

Other initiatives: As well as making grants, the foundation runs a number of other initiatives. These include the Clore Leadership Programme, which aims to strengthen leadership across the cultural sector; the Clore Social Leadership Programme, which aims to support third sector leadership; and JW3: London's Jewish Community Centre. It has also undertaken research into areas relevant to its work.

Financial information

In 2016 the foundation had assets of almost £42.4 million and an income of £1.75 million. Grants awarded to organisations totalled £7.5 million. They were distributed as follows:

Arts, heritage and education	£3.9 million
Jewish support	£1.85 million
Leadership training	£997,000
Health and social care	£722,000

Beneficiaries included: JW3 Trust Ltd (£1.6 million); New College, Oxford (£250,000); Grange Park Opera and Royal Academy of Arts (£200,000 each); National Theatre (£187,500); The Art Room (£133,000); Royal College of Art, Anna Freud National Centre for Children and Families (£100,000 each);

University of Oxford Graduate Scholarship in the Humanities (£99,000); Tate Liverpool (£30,000); British Library, Tate (£5,000 each); Royal Trinity Hospice (£1,000).

Exclusions

The foundation does not support:

- Projects outside the UK
- Individuals
- General appeals or circulars
- Applications made by email
- Retrospective funding

The foundation rarely funds:

- Staff posts
- Local branches of national charities
- Academic or project research
- Conference costs

Further exclusions apply to the Poetry and Literature grants scheme – refer to the website for further information.

Applications

Main grants

Applications should be made in a letter of no more than two sides of A4, written on headed paper with contact details and charity number clearly displayed. The website states that applications should include the following information:

- A title (of no more than fifteen words) for the project/programme for which you are requesting funding
- A brief overview of the work of your organisation
- A concise account of the project you are seeking funding for
- A clear statement of the sum you are seeking from the Foundation and the total cost of the wider project if applicable
- No annual accounts or additional information should be included at this stage

Applications should not be sent by recorded delivery and the foundation will only respond if a standard-sized (110mm x 220mm), stamped, self-addressed envelope is provided. If your application is to be given further consideration, an application form will be supplied. Email applications are not accepted. Main grants are awarded twice a year, in June/July and November/December, but applications are accepted on a rolling basis. Further guidance is given on the website.

Poetry and Literature Awards

Grants are considered at least once a year – refer to the website to see when the next funding round is open.

Sources of information

Accounts; annual report; Charity Commission record; funder's website.

The Clothworkers' Foundation

 General charitable purposes, particularly: disability, disadvantaged young people, dramatic arts, textiles, disadvantaged minority communities, older people, conservation, domestic and sexual violence, homelessness, visual impairment, alcohol and substance misuse, prisoners and ex-offenders

UK

£ £5.2 million (2016)

CC number: 274100

Trustees: Anne Luttman-Johnson; Dr Carolyn Boulter; Michael Jarvis; Hanif Virji; Melville Haggard; Joanna Dodd; Andrew Blessley; Alexander Nelson; John Wake; Dr Lucy Rawson; Nicholas Horne; John Coombe-Tennant.

Correspondent: Jocelyn Stuart-Grumbar, Chief Executive, Clothworkers' Hall, Dunster Court, Mincing Lane, London EC3R 7AH (tel: 020 7623 7041; email: foundation@clothworkers.co.uk)

 foundation.clothworkers.co.uk

The Clothworkers' Company is an ancient City of London livery company, founded in 1528 and the twelfth of the 'Great Twelve' companies. One of the functions of livery companies was to support their members in times of need. As they grew wealthier, they were also able to benefit outsiders. The Clothworkers' Company acquired a number of trusts, established by individual benefactors for specific charitable ends. These totalled over 100 by the twentieth century. In addition, the company has always made payments to good causes from its own funds.

The Clothworkers' Foundation was set up in 1977 by the company as the independent arm for the whole of its charitable work. The foundation's early income came from a leasehold interest in a City of London property, 1 Angel Court. Subsequent funding from the company, together with the sale of the long leasehold interest in Angel Court in 1994, represents the assets of the foundation which are substantially invested in stocks and shares. Income from these investments, together with unrestricted donations from the company, is given away each year to a wide range of charities. During its first 35 years, the foundation has made grants totalling around £100 million.

Main and small grants programmes

The foundation's main grants programme and small grants programme both focus on the following areas:

▶ Alcohol and substance misuse
▶ People with disabilities
▶ Disadvantaged minority communities
▶ Disadvantaged young people
▶ Domestic and sexual violence
▶ Older people
▶ Homelessness
▶ Prisoners and ex-offenders
▶ Visual impairment

Awards from both programmes are given to UK-registered charities and non-profit organisations and grants can be given for the purchase of specific capital items including buildings; fittings, fixtures and equipment or vehicles. Main grants are awarded to organisations with an income of less than £15 million; the average grant is around £25,000 and there is no limit on total project cost. Small grants are awarded to organisations with an income of less than £250,000; the average grant is £7,000 and the maximum grant is £10,000; the total project cost must be no more than £100,000.

Other grants programmes

The foundation also has a number of grants programmes which are not open to application. Areas supported have included: autism; Better Futures initiative; conservation; dramatic arts; maths; visual impairment in developing countries, however, the themes and priorities change periodically. Grants are also made to a few, selected organisations on a regular basis, as well as to academic projects focusing on textiles.

Financial information

In 2016 the foundation had assets of £180.2 million and an income of £6.8 million. During the year, the foundation awarded 262 grants to organisations totalling £5.2 million. Grants were distributed as follows:

Disability	£1.5 million
Disadvantaged young people	£866,000
Homelessness	£641,500
Disadvantaged minority communities	£512,500
Textiles	£460,000
Older people	£367,500
Prisoners and ex-offenders	£182,000
Visual impairment	£172,500
Other	£158,500
Better Futures	£150,000
Dramatic arts	£150,000
Alcohol and substance misuse	£81,000
Conservation	£63,000
Domestic and sexual violence	£34,500

Beneficiaries were not listed in the accounts; however, the 2017 annual review, available on the foundation's website, details recent beneficiaries.

Beneficiaries included: The Aldingbourne Trust (£110,000); Ambitious about Autism (£100,000); North London Samaritans and Stable Family Home Trust (£50,000 each); Greenhouse Sports (£40,000); Ufton

Court (£33,100); Sulgrave Club (£30,000); Buttle UK and Cardiff YMCA (£25,000 each).

Exclusions

The foundation does not fund non-capital costs. This includes:

▶ Salaries
▶ Overheads
▶ Training
▶ Volunteer expenses
▶ Rent
▶ Lease of property or equipment
▶ Websites
▶ Databases/software
▶ Professional fees

Nor is funding given for the following:

▶ Hospices/NHS charities
▶ Events
▶ Grant-making organisations
▶ Medical research or equipment
▶ Overseas work, even if the organisation is UK-registered
▶ Projects to create or refurbish charity shops
▶ Projects which have already been declined from funding by the foundation
▶ General mailings
▶ Emergency appeals
▶ Political projects
▶ IT equipment which will only be used by staff/volunteers and not by service users
▶ Schools, colleges or universities, unless they work exclusively with disabled people or people with learning difficulties
▶ Organisations with an annual income of more than £15 million
▶ Arts or education projects, unless they work exclusively with people from the groups described in the foundation's programme areas
▶ Students or any individuals (other than professional conservators)
▶ Organisations that have received a grant in the last five years
▶ Organisations that promote a particular religion or only provide services for people of a particular faith

Applications

Applications must be made using the online form which can be accessed, along with guidelines and an eligibility quiz, on the website. Final decisions are made within eight weeks for small grants, or within six months for main grants.

Sources of information

Accounts; annual report; Charity Commission record; funder's website.

Richard Cloudesley's Charity

 Churches, medical causes, social welfare

 North Islington, London

£ £866,500 to organisations (2016/17)

CC number: 205959

Trustee: Richard Cloudesley Trustee Ltd.

Correspondent: Melanie Griffiths, Director, Office 1.1, Resource for London, 356 Holloway Road, London N7 6PA (tel: 020 7697 4094; email: info@richardcloudesleyscharity.org.uk)

🌐 www.richardcloudesleyscharity.org. uk

The charity was founded in 1518 by the will of Richard Cloudesley. He left the rent from a 14-acre field in Islington, London, to be used for the benefit of residents of Islington parish. The field was in Barnsbury and its centre was what is now Cloudesley Square. The significant endowment of the charity derives from the original piece of land left by Richard Cloudesley.

The governing document is now a Charity Commission Scheme of 2 July 1980 which says that half of the net income from the original endowment is to be applied for the 'relief in sickness' of people in need by providing items, services or facilities which are calculated to alleviate suffering or assist their recovery. The other half of the income is to be used for making grants towards 'the upkeep and repair of the fabric of, and the maintenance of services in, the Parish Church of the Ecclesiastical Parish of St Silas Pentonville and any churches of the Church of England in the area of the Ancient Parish of Islington'.

Church Grants

The beneficiaries of the Richard Cloudesley's Charity Church Grant programme are 21 Church of England churches in the area.

The charity holds two rounds of applications each year, in spring and autumn.

Guidance notes, available from the charity's website, set out the principal criteria used to assess applications, the general policy and the application process. There is also a helpful FAQ section.

To make a grant application, any qualifying church's representative should complete an application form.

Health Grants

The charity's health and welfare funding also provides grants to organisations that offer support to people with health needs and/or who have disabilities and are living in poverty in the area of benefit. The charity addresses its 'Sickness Object' by supporting sustainable organisations that demonstrate initiative in tackling health issues. According to the 2016/17 annual report, following a review in December 2015, the trustees agreed that the charity's Health Grants Programme 2016–19 should focus on two broad priority areas:

▷ Enabling the effective treatment and recovery of vulnerable people experiencing mental ill health
▷ Improved mental and/or physical health and well-being of vulnerable people with a health condition, particularly those living with a disability or long-term ill health

The trustees also agreed that there would be three distinct funding streams within the Health Grants Programme – Main Grants, Small Grants and Strategic Grants.

In March 2016, through its new Main Grants fund the charity agreed multiple-year grants of £349,300 towards six organisations through this programme. In each case funding covers a three-year period from 1 April 2016 to 31 March 2019 and is designed to cover a particular project objective.

In June 2016, the charity launched a new Small Grants fund inviting online applications from organisations for grants of up to £10,000. In September 2016, grants totalling £102,970 were awarded to 11 organisations, the majority of which had not previously received funding from the charity. These grants will support vulnerable Islington residents in a number of different ways.

Welfare Grants
Since 2 April 2013, there has been a new local scheme in place in Islington to help individuals, called the Resident Support Scheme. Details of the scheme are available on the Cripplegate Foundation and Islington Council websites.

Commemorating 500 years
The annual report informs us that 2017 marks the 500th anniversary of Richard Cloudesley's bequest. The charity is marking this significant anniversary in a number of ways, the main one of which is the awarding of special anniversary grants. The charity agreed a budget of £1,125,000 for these grants and hoped to award the majority of these during the 2017/18 fiscal year. These were to be in addition to the charity's normal grants budget for the year of £900,000.

The anniversary grants budget for churches is £625,000 and for health and welfare is £500,000; the difference is designed to help address an imbalance in the level of reserves held for the church and health and welfare sides of the charity's grant-making.

In addition during 2016/17 the trustees have undertaken a number of projects to mark this anniversary and thereby promote the charity's activities in particular to potential grant recipients. The major activities undertaken have been:

▷ The refurbishment of Richard Cloudesley's tomb at St Mary's Islington
▷ An anniversary service in commemoration of Richard Cloudesley's gift and 500 year legacy, at which an address was given by the Bishop of Stepney
▷ Commissioning Dr Cathy Ross to undertake further research into and write a report on the 500 years of Richard Cloudesley's legacy in Islington
▷ The production of a history booklet and some information banners, which are touring the borough of Islington during the anniversary year

Financial information
In 2016/17 the charity had assets of over £45 million and an income of £1.4 million. Grants made during this financial year totalled £945,500 and of this amount £79,000 was awarded to individuals.

Beneficiaries included: Islington Giving (£120,000); Islington Law Centre (£105,000); St Augustine, Highbury New Park (£71,000); Cranstoun and Help on your Doorstep (£12,000 each); Solace Women's Aid (£10,000); Asylum Aid and Centre 404 (£8,000 each); St Mary, Hornsey Rise (£1,700).

Applications
Applicants should write to the correspondent requesting an application form.

Sources of information
Accounts; annual report; Charity Commission record; funder's website.

CMZ Ltd

🔍 Orthodox Jewish education, social welfare

📍 UK, Israel and the United States

£ £2.46 million to organisations (2016/17)

CC number: 1087870

Trustees: Ephraim Gottesfeld; P. Schneebalg; S. Steinmetz.

Correspondent: Binyomin Goldberg, Secretary, 206 High Road, London N15 4NP (tel: 020 8801 6038)

CMZ Ltd is a company limited by guarantee and is governed by Memorandum and Articles of Association dated 24 March 2000. According to its 2016/17 accounts:

The objects of the charity are the advancement of the Orthodox Jewish religion, to aid in the provision of, and improvement of, educational facilities and to assist in the alleviation of poverty of, in particular, the Orthodox Jewish community. The charity's funds are utilised in supporting other charities with similar objectives especially in helping persons in conditions of need, hardship and distress in the Orthodox Jewish community and the advancement of the Orthodox Jewish religion.

Financial information
In 2016/17 the charity had assets of £136,500 and an income of £3.2 million. During the year, the charity awarded grants worth a total of £3.17 million, with £2.46 million given to organisations and £710,000 provided to individuals.

Beneficiaries included: The Lolev Charitable Trust (£231,303); Mifal Hachesed Vehatzedokoh (£109,383); Yesamach Levav Trust (£113,231); Friends of Beis Soroh Schneirer (£62,659); Chavorat Aveichim Noam Shabat (£196,000); One Heart Lev Echod (£125,076).

Applications
According to the charity's 2016/17 accounts:

The charity makes grants and donations to registered charitable entities and individuals, on production of a letter of approbation from a qualified Rabbi or Vaad Hatzdokoh, that meets the criteria as defined by its charitable objectives. It also operates a voucher system whereby each donor is given the equivalent amount in books and vouchers out of which the donor makes donations to charitable entities and individuals of their choice that meets criteria as defined by CMZ Ltd's charitable objects.

Sources of information
Accounts; annual report; Charity Commission record.

The Coalfields Regeneration Trust

🔍 Community regeneration, social welfare, health, employment, education and skills, young people, older people

📍 Coalfield and former coalfield communities in England, Scotland, and Wales

£ £857,000 (2016/17)

CC number: 1074930

Trustees: Wayne Thomas; Sylvia Wileman; Nicholas Wilson; Peter McNestry; Dawn Davies; Michael Clapham; Terence O'Neill; Robert Young; Nicky Stubbs; Trudie McGuinness.

Correspondent: Louise Dyson, Secretary, 1 Waterside Park, Valley Way,

Wombwell, Barnsley S73 0BB (tel: 01226 272810; email: info@coalfields-regen.org.uk)

 www.coalfields-regen.org.uk

 facebook.com/CRTEngland

 @coalfieldsregen

The Coalfields Regeneration Trust is an independent charity dedicated to the social and economic regeneration of coalfield communities in England, Scotland and Wales. It was set up in 1999 in response to a recommendation by the government's Coalfields Task Force Report. The report highlighted the dramatic effects that mine closures had, and continue to have, on communities in coalfield areas.

The trust provides advice, support and financial assistance to community and voluntary organisations which are working to tackle social issues at a grassroots level within coalfield communities. It is closely connected with the areas it serves, operating through a network of staff based at offices located within coalfield regions themselves. The trust's mission is: 'to champion and strengthen coalfield communities, generate resources to respond to their needs and deliver programmes that make a positive and lasting difference'.

Areas of work
According to its website, the trust's work falls into the following areas:

- Improve health
- Support community enterprise
- Provide opportunities for children and young people
- Provide practical help and community investment
- Deliver employment, skills and training programmes

The 2016/17 annual report states the trust's strategic goals for 2016–19:

- Employment – develop pathways to increase the number of people in work
- Skills – grow the skills of people to increase their opportunities
- Health – support activities that improve the health and well-being of all age groups

The trust runs a number of programmes providing grants, community investment programmes and voluntary sector support in England, Scotland and Wales. For full and detailed information on the trust's various programmes, see the trust's website.

Financial information
In 2016/17 the trust had assets of £34.6 million and an income of £4.6 million. Grants awarded during the year totalled £857,000.

A list of beneficiaries was not provided in the 2016/17 accounts.

Previous beneficiaries have included: Aylesham Neighbourhood Project (£210,000); Haswell and District Mencap Society – The Community Anchor (£98,000); Derbyside Rural Community Council – Wheels to Work (£89,000); The Cornforth Partnership – The Reach project (£75,000); Nottinghamshire Independent Domestic Abuse Link Workers (£66,000); Stoke-on-Trent and District Gingerbread Centre Ltd – Peer Mentoring (£37,000); St John's Church – A Building in Which to Serve Our Community (£10,000); Mansfield and Dukeries Irish Association – Luncheon Club (£5,000); City of Durham Air Cadets – Achieving Duke of Edinburgh's Awards (£3,800); Thornycroft Art Club – Christmas Tree Exhibition (£520).

Exclusions
The following will not be supported through the Coalfields Community Investment Programme:

- Individuals
- Private businesses
- Unregistered/unincorporated organisations
- Statutory bodies, including local authorities, town/parish councils, schools or colleges
- Organisations considered to be in a poor financial position or with financial management systems which are not in good order
- Companies limited by shares
- 'Friends of...' groups benefitting statutory bodies
- Organisations not established in the UK
- Organisations not based in/not working predominantly in eligible coalfield areas
- National organisations (as defined in governing document)
- Organisations with an unrestricted income of above £250,000

Check the website for exclusions from any of the trust's programmes; the guidance notes provide a more detailed list.

Applications
Application details are different for each programme; details can be found on the trust's website, where guidance notes are also available. Applicants can contact their regional teams to find out more information or to discuss an application.

Sources of information
Accounts; annual report; Charity Commission record; funder's website.

The John Coates Charitable Trust

 General charitable purposes, with preference given to: education, arts and culture, children, environment, health

UK, mainly southern England

£428,000 (2016/17)

CC number: 262057

Trustees: Gillian McGregor; Rebecca Lawes; Phyllida Youngman; Catharine Kesley; Claire Cartledge.

Correspondent: Rebecca Lawes, Trustee, 3 Grange Road, Cambridge CB3 9AS (tel: 01223 301354)

The trust was established in 1969 and mainly makes grants to large national charities or to small charities that are of personal or local interest to the trustees. Grants are made for general charitable purposes, with some preference for the following:

- Education and training
- Health
- The relief of poverty
- Arts, culture and heritage
- Science
- Environment and conservation

Financial information
In 2016/17 the trust had assets of £13.9 million and an income of £468,000. During the year, the trust awarded a total of 84 grants to organisations totalling £428,000.

Beneficiaries included: The Lymington Museum Trust (£15,000); Combat Stress, The Geffrye Museum and Royal Hospital for Neuro-Disability (£10,000 each); Sebastian's Action Trust (£8,000); The Money Charity and St Mungo's (£5,000 each); Arundel Castle Cricket Foundation (£2,000); Citizens Advice Torridge, North and Mid-Devon (£1,000).

Exclusions
Grants are given to individuals only in exceptional circumstances.

Applications
Apply in writing to the correspondent.

Sources of information
Accounts; annual report; Charity Commission record.

Denise Coates Foundation

Health and welfare, education and training, medical research, disaster relief, arts and culture, community development

UK and overseas

£5.9 million (2016/17)

CC number: 1149110

Trustees: Denise Coates; John Coates; Peter Coates; Simon Adlington; James White; Simon Galletley.

Correspondent: Simon Galletley, Trustee, c/o RSM Tenon, Festival Way, Festival Park, Stoke-on-Trent, Staffordshire ST1 5BB (tel: 0845 600 0365)

Registered in September 2012, the foundation's objects are general charitable purposes, although there is a stated preference for 'community participation in healthy recreation'. It formerly shared its name with Bet365 (Ltd), which was set up by Denise Coates. Her father, Peter Coates, also a trustee, is Chair of Stoke City FC, of which Bet365 Ltd is also a major shareholder.

The foundation's Charity Commission record states, at the time of writing (April 2018), that it distributes 'funds in support of local, national and international charitable activities, exclusively charitable according to the laws of England and Wales'.

Financial information
In 2016/17 the foundation had assets of £186.3 million and an income of £51.6 million. Grants to 20 organisations totalled £5.9 million and were broken down as follows:

Health and welfare	£3.4 million
Education and training	£1.5 million
Medical research and development	£660,500
Community development	£194,000
Arts and culture	£164,000
Disaster relief	£7,000

Beneficiaries included: The Donna Louise Trust (£2.75 million); University of Manchester – Jodrell Bank Visitor Centre (£500,000); Chronic Disease Research Foundation (£488,000); mothers2mothers (£317,000); Douglas Macmillan Hospice (£272,500); The University of Sheffield (£151,000).

Applications
Apply in writing to the correspondent. The annual report for 2016/17 states: 'Charities are invited to present proposals to the Foundation's Trustees detailing how a grant would be used and the benefits that it would deliver. The Trustees assess how the proposal aligns to the Foundation's objectives in order to determine whether or not to award a grant.'

Sources of information
Accounts; annual report; Charity Commission record.

The John S Cohen Foundation

General charitable purposes, in particular music and the arts, education, environment

Worldwide, in practice mainly the UK

£513,000 (2016/17)

CC number: 241598

Trustees: Dr David Cohen, Chair; Imogen Cohen; Olivia Cohen; Veronica Cohen.

Correspondent: Diana Helme, Foundation Administrator, PO Box 21277, London W9 2YH

The foundation awards grants to organisations in support of general charitable purposes mainly in the UK but also worldwide. The foundation has a particular interest in supporting higher education, music, the arts, and the built and natural environments. Any grants awarded by the foundation must produce an outcome that is of the public benefit.

Financial information
In 2016/17 the foundation had assets of £11 million and an income of £606,500. During the year, the foundation awarded a total of £513,000 in grants to organisations. Grants were distributed as follows:

Arts	53	£251,500
Education	54	£195,000
Conservation and environment	12	£45,500
Social and medical	12	£21,000

Beneficiaries included: New Writing North (£65,000); Royal Opera House (£25,000); British Museum (£13,000); Tate Foundation (£10,000); Royal Festival Hall (£7,500); Science Museum (£4,000); Young Vic (£3,000); Concern Worldwide (£2,000); World Jewish Relief (£1,000); Jewish Council for Racial Equality (£800).

Applications
Applications are made in writing to the correspondent. Each application is reviewed and discussed, to ensure it meets the charity objectives, and whether the application meets the requirements in terms of the benefits it gives.

Sources of information
Accounts; annual report; Charity Commission record.

The R and S Cohen Foundation

Education, social welfare, the arts

Worldwide

£700,000 (2016)

CC number: 1078225

Trustees: Lady Sharon Harel-Cohen; Sir Ronald Cohen; Tamara Harel-Cohen; David Marks; Jonathan Harel-Cohen.

Correspondent: Martin Dodd, 3–4 Stanley Crescent, London W11 2NB

The R and S Cohen Foundation was established for general charitable purposes in 1999 by Sir Ronald Cohen, chair of Bridges Ventures Investment Company.

The objectives of the foundation as detailed in the Trust Deed are as follows:
- The advancement of education
- The relief of persons who are in conditions of need, hardship or distress as a result of local, national or international disaster or by reason of their social and economic circumstances
- The promotion and encouragement for the public in all aspects of the arts, including painting, sculpture, theatre and music

Financial information
In 2016 the foundation had an income of £11,000 and an expenditure of £714,500. Since the foundation's income for this financial period was below the threshold set by the Charity Commission, no accounts for 2016 were available. Based upon our previous research, however, it is estimated that during 2016 the foundation awarded grants of around £700,000.

Previous beneficiaries have included: Exeter College Oxford (£1 million); The Portland Trust (£492,500); Tate Foundation (£100,000); Fight for Peace International (£75,000); B Lab UK (£50,000); Ashoka (£24,000); Victoria and Albert Museum (£15,000); Norwood (£12,500); WLS Charitable Fund (£3,000); Royal Academy of the Arts (£1,000).

Exclusions
The foundation does not provide grants to individuals.

Applications
The foundation's 2015/16 accounts state that:

The Trustees remain concerned about the volume of unsolicited approaches from other charities and the expenditure incurred by these charities in making these submissions. Accordingly, the Trustees have adopted a policy of only considering the making of grants to charitable organisations with which the Trustees have personal contact or those whose aims they support and will not respond to any unsolicited requests in the hope that this will dissuade such charities from incurring unnecessary expenditure.

Sources of information
Charity Commission record; accounts; annual report.

The Colchester Catalyst Charity

 Community health care

North East Essex

£347,500 to organisations (2017)

CC number: 228352

Trustees: Peter Fitt; Christine Hayward; Mark Pertwee; Dr Thilaka Rudra; Dr Max Hickman; Dr Naomi Busfield; Elizabeth Thrower; Keith Songhurst.

Correspondent: Peter Fitt, Trustee, 7 Coast Road, West Mersea, Colchester CO5 8QE (tel: 01206 323420; email: info@colchestercatalyst.co.uk)

 www.colchestercatalyst.co.uk

This charity supports organisations that provide services to people with medical conditions or disabilities living in North East Essex.

Grants are given to organisations for 'specific and well-defined projects, including therapeutic aids, equipment and building works for medical or nursing care', according to the charity's website. Individuals may also be awarded grants for specialised equipment, where it is not available through statutory sources (e.g. wheelchairs, mobility scooters, communication aids).

Financial information
In 2017 the charity had assets of £11.9 million and an income of £405,500. Grants awarded to organisations totalled £347,500. Grants were broken down as follows:

Charities etc.	£347,500
Respite care	£138,500
Special individual needs	£60,000
Equipment pools	£1,700

Beneficiaries included: Headway Essex (£125,000); Beacon House (£70,000); Colchester Hospital Charity (£20,000); Age Concern Colchester (£10,000); Colchester Hospital (£5,000); Parkestone Welfare Park (£2,300); Bright Lives (£1,000).

Exclusions
The charity's website states:

▶ Grants will not be made for any item or project which has already been paid for
▶ The Charity is unable to consider applications for any item where there is an obligation for provision by a statutory authority

▶ General funding or contributions to staff salaries or other running costs are excluded, but recognising the often overlooked needs of carers, the Charity will consider funding respite care provided the care period is well-defined, carefully controlled and readily monitored

Applications
Apply online via the charity's website. Application forms can also be sent out by post on request. Application deadlines can be found on the charity's website.

Sources of information
Charity Commission record; accounts, funder's website.

The Cole-Medlock Foundation

 Social welfare

Mainly overseas, with some UK work supported

£486,500 (2016/17)

CC number: 1132780

Trustees: Mark Goodman; David Medlock; Jacqueline Medlock; Peter Medlock.

Correspondent: David Medlock, St George's Lodge, 33 Oldfield Road, Bath BA2 3ND (tel: 01225 428221)

The foundation was established in 2009 and makes grants for welfare in the UK and overseas. Its 2016/17 accounts state: 'The trustees have taken the decision that the charity will concentrate on alleviating extreme poverty, in all forms, throughout the developing world through sustainable development of food, infrastructure, healthcare, education and independent financial progress.'

The 2016/17 accounts further state: A number of grants were made to various charities to support clean water (WASH – water, sanitation and hygiene), renewable energy, school feeding and education projects. We have specifically targeted education for girls when looking at education projects, as evidence suggests this has a greater knock-on effect with societal development.

The projects we have supported have had a worldwide impact including Indonesia, Zambia, India, Tanzania, South Africa, Malawi, Romania, Ghana, Nepal, Mozambique and Sierra Leone.

Grants can range from £500 to £50,000 but the majority are between £5,000 and £10,000.

Financial information
In 2016/17 the foundation held assets of £13.5 million and had an income of

£1.7 million. Grants to 40 organisations totalled £486,500.

Beneficiaries included: The Boshier-Hinton Foundation (£250,000); Practical Action (£25,000); Plan UK (£10,000); Crossroads Care, Centre of Hope, Send A Cow and Stepping Stones (£5,000 each); The Haven Wolverhampton (£2,500); The Eixon Charity (£2,000); Blueprint Training and Enterprise (£1,000).

Applications
Apply in writing to the correspondent.

Sources of information
Accounts; annual report; Charity Commission record; funder's website.

The Colt Foundation

 Occupational and environmental health research

UK

£331,500 to organisations (2016)

CC number: 277189

Trustees: Jerome O'Hea; Clare Gilchrist; Patricia Lebus; Peter O'Hea; Alan O'Hea; Prof. David Coggon; Natasha Heydon; Prof. Sir Anthony Taylor; Dr Ira Madan.

Correspondent: Jackie Douglas, Director, 12 The Briars, Waterberry Drive, Waterlooville, Hampshire PO7 7YH (tel: 023 9249 1400; email: jackie.douglas@uk.coltgroup.com)

www.coltfoundation.org.uk

The foundation was established in 1978 by the O'Hea family with gifts of shares in Colt International and Associated Companies Ltd. This gift is now represented by 22% of Ordinary £1 shares in Colt Investments Ltd, which is the holding company for the Colt Group of Companies. The foundation funds research into occupational and environmental health, focusing on illnesses arising from working conditions.

The website states:

The Foundation considers applications for funding high quality research projects in the field of occupational and environmental health, particularly those aimed at discovering the cause of illnesses arising from conditions at the place of work. The Trustees are especially keen to fund research that is going to make a difference to legislation or working practices. The work is monitored by our Scientific Advisers and External Assessors to achieve the maximum impact with available funds. Grants are not made to the general funds of other charities, or directly to individual research workers, and the Trustees prefer to be the sole source of finance for a project.

The foundation also makes grants through selected universities and colleges to enable students to take higher degrees in subjects related to occupational and environmental health. PhD Fellowships are awarded each year, and the foundation is committed to support the MSc course in Human & Applied Physiology at King's College, London.

The Trustees have occasionally supported projects which fall outside this area, but these projects are very much the exception.

Donations to organisations vary from a few thousand pounds to over £100,000 and may be repeated over two to five years. Beneficiaries are well-established research institutes (awards to individuals are made through these). The foundation takes a continuing interest in its research projects and holds annual review meetings.

Financial information

In 2016 the foundation had assets of £21.6 million and an income of £1.17 million. Grants totalled £489,000 with £331,500 given to organisations and £157,500 given for student fellowships.

Beneficiaries included: University of Edinburgh (£100,500); Imperial College (£80,500 in two grants); Queen Mary University of London (£47,500); University of Southampton (£35,500 in two grants); Bradford Hill Symposium 2016 (£8,000); Nanotoxicology 2016 Symposium (£580).

Exclusions

Grants are not made for the general funds of another charity, directly to individuals or projects overseas.

Applications

Apply in writing to the correspondent. Full details of what should be included in an application can be found on the grants section of the foundation's website. The trustees meet twice a year to review applications, in the spring and in the autumn, and applications normally need to be received approximately eight weeks beforehand to be considered at the meetings. Exact deadlines can be found on the foundation's website. Applicants can submit a single sheet lay summary at any time during the year prior to working on a full application, so that advice can be given on whether the work is likely to fall within the remit of the foundation.

Sources of information

Accounts; annual report; Charity Commission record; funder's website.

Colwinston Charitable Trust

 Opera, music, visual arts, library and archive projects

UK, with a preference for Wales

£350,500 (2016/17)

CC number: 1049189

Trustees: Mathew Prichard; Martin Tinney; Sian Williams; Lucinda Prichard; Rebecca Evans.

Correspondent: Chris Bliss, Colwinston Charitable Trust, 14 Hanover Court, Midhope Road, Woking, Surrey GU22 7UX (tel: 020 7842 2000; email: colwinston.trust@ntlworld.com)

 www.colwinston.org.uk

The Colwinston Charitable Trust was established in 1995 and derives its income from the royalties from the West End production of *The Mousetrap*, the Agatha Christie play, which opened in 1952. The trust's detailed annual report for 2016/17 sets out its grant-making aims:

▷ Through its grant-making, the Trust seeks to sustain and support high quality artistic activities that add to the cultural life and experiences available in the UK and especially in Wales where over 80% of its grants are directed
▷ The funding focus is particularly, but not exclusively, directed to the support of opera, music and the visual arts, and library and archive projects in Wales
▷ Other areas may also be supported on occasion, at the discretion of the trustees

The trust makes grants to UK-registered charities for activities that must take place in the UK. The types of activities it is most likely to fund are described in the guidelines:

▷ Projects that demonstrate excellence in terms of the creative ambition – through the quality of the artistic product, the calibre of the participating artists, and the value of the artistic experience for audiences and/or participants
▷ Collaborative projects that assist organisations to share skills and expertise, and extend the range and reach of the funded activity
▷ Projects designed to develop new audiences, make the art form more widely accessible, and help embed the art form in the community
▷ Projects that specifically target families and younger people, and which help them to better understand and engage with the arts
▷ Arts educational and outreach projects associated with high quality work
▷ Distinctive, high quality festivals and events, that impact beyond a purely local level

▷ Projects that help to fill an existing gap in artistic provision in Wales
▷ The commissioning of new work, particularly to develop the careers of emerging and mid-career Welsh artists, when professionally mounted presentations of the work form part of the project
▷ Projects that may assist organisations to increase their financial sustainability

The guidelines state that:
▷ The majority of grants will be in the range of £5,000 to £20,000. Most of these grants are utilised within the year following the formal offer
▷ Larger grants are generally only awarded to organisations where a funding relationship with the Trust has been developed over several years
▷ Larger grants are more likely to be offered to fund activities that deliver strategic initiatives, and that would be unlikely to occur without the assistance of the Trust
▷ Larger grants are generally limited to organisations delivering high quality artistic activity in Wales

Financial information

In 2016/17 the trust had assets of £1.4 million and an income of £582,000. Grants were made to 22 organisations totalling £350,500.

Beneficiaries included: Valley Kids, Welsh National Opera Ltd (£40,000 each); Aldeburgh Music (£35,000); Mousetrap Foundation for the Arts (£30,000); Arts & Business Cymru, Mid-Wales Opera (£20,000 each) Cheltenham Festival (£15,000); Fishguard International Music Festival, National Manuscripts Conservation Trust (£5,000 each); Bangor Festival of Music (£3,000).

Exclusions

The trust's website states the following:
▷ An organisation may only apply for one grant, in any one financial year
▷ The Trust will only consider applications from fully UK-Registered Charities
▷ It will not consider applications from 'Friends of' charities
▷ Retrospective funding will not be considered, nor will funding for projects that have already started
▷ The Trust is unable to accept applications from individuals or for individual research or study
▷ It will not consider funding for publications, conferences and seminars, or general appeals
▷ The Trust will not fund activity that takes place outside the UK, even if the organisation is UK registered
▷ Social and community welfare organisations, where the dominant purpose is not arts, will not normally be supported
▷ Community arts projects and performances by amateur groups will not generally be considered
▷ Capital or refurbishment projects will only be considered in exceptional circumstances and only when the

applicant is an arts organisation or gallery in Wales
- Commercial recordings other than those benefiting the careers of emerging or mid-career Welsh composers

Applications

Application forms and application guidelines can be found on the trust's website. Grant applications should be received no later than 30 September for consideration at the November meeting, or 31 March for consideration at the May meeting of trustees.

Sources of information

Accounts; annual report; Charity Commission record; guidelines for applicants; funder's website.

Colyer-Fergusson Charitable Trust

 Disadvantaged young people, education

Kent

£ £1.2 million (2016/17)

CC number: 258958

Trustees: Nicholas Fisher; Robert North; Ruth Murphy; Rosalind Riley; James Thorne; Barbara Long.

Correspondent: David Williams, Marcar House, Parkshot, Richmond, Surrey TW9 2RG (tel: 020 8948 3388; email: grantadmin@cfct.org.uk)

www.cfct.org.uk

Established by Sir James Colyer-Fergusson in 1969, this trust's 'overarching aim is to improve the lives of people in Kent, and in particular those who are most disadvantaged and living at the margins of society'. Since it was established, the trust has supported communities in Kent through a range of funding programmes.

What the trust funds

The trustees and staff periodically review the trust's grant-making policies and funding focus. In 2013, following a consultation with the voluntary sector in Kent, it was decided that the trust's grant-making should be narrowed and focused on supporting 'young people with poverty of opportunity'.

Grants are made to a broad range of charitable organisations. Not all of the organisations supported by the trust are registered charities; for example, the trustees will also consider funding social enterprises, community interest companies (CICs), educational establishments and churches delivering community projects, as long as their work fits within the trust's funding policies.

Grant programmes

The trust directs its funds towards supporting disadvantaged young people as they make the difficult transition into adulthood. Funds are allocated through three funding programmes, which are outlined on the website:

- **Hardship Award Programme** – 'The hardship grants are aimed at disadvantaged young people living in Kent and are intended to meet the costs of practical items such as: interview clothes; course fees; tools or equipment; travel costs to a new job etc. All applicants must be referred by an approved CFCT referral partner.'
- **Investing in Young People Programme** – 'The Trust is interested in hearing from organisations that work with young people with 'poverty of opportunity'. The Trust recognises that there are many excellent organisations in Kent working with young people. However, we are interested in hearing from those where a grant from the Trust of between £15,000 and £75,000 [*the majority being between £20,000 and £50,000*] would allow them to make a significant and demonstrable difference to these young people.'
- **Funding for apprenticeships and Vocational Learning Programme** – 'The Trust is interested in hearing from organisations that can deliver apprenticeships and/or vocational education for young people with 'poverty of opportunity'. Organisations may be offering these in-house or they may have the ability to unlock employer engagement. The Trust is particularly interested in organisations that are able to meet the needs of very vulnerable and disadvantaged young people, including ex-offenders. Grants of up to £75,000 [*the majority being between £25,000 and £50,000*] may be available for outstanding and innovative projects.'

Financial information

In 2016/17 the trust had assets of £24.6 million and an income of £485,000. The trustees awarded grants totalling £1.2 million.

The trust published a detailed and helpful trustees' report for the year, which provides a breakdown of funds allocated through the three main grants programmes:

Investing in Young People	4	£555,000
Apprenticeships/vocational learning	10	£426,000
Hardship Awards	215	£74,000*

*awarded to individuals

Beneficiaries included: Kent Community Foundation (£120,000); Cyclopark Trust (£105,000); Rising Sun Domestic Violence and Abuse Service

(£60,000); St Mildred's Abbey (£50,000); Communities Food CIC (£40,000); Books Beyond Words (£25,000); Fixers/Public Service Broadcasting Trust (£20,000); The Who Cares? Trust (£5,000).

Exclusions

According to its website, the trust cannot support:

- Individuals – unless they are made via one of our referral partners as part of our 'Hardship Awards' Programme
- National charities receiving widespread support
- Statutory bodies
- Hospitals and health authorities
- Medical care, medical equipment or medical research
- Academic research, scholarships or bursaries
- Animal charities
- The promotion of religion
- The restoration or conservation of buildings
- Work outside of Kent
- Endowment appeals
- Work that has already taken place i.e. retrospective funding
- Round-robin, widely circulated appeals

Applications

Full guidance and application forms are available on the trust's website.

Sources of information

Accounts; annual report; Charity Commission record; funder's website.

Comic Relief

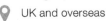 Tackling poverty and social injustice, children and young people, women and girls, community development

UK and overseas

£ £74.4 million (2016/17)

CC number: 326568

Trustees: Michael Harris; Colin Howes; Dhananjayan Sriskandarajah; Richard Curtis; Timothy Davie; Theo Sowa; Harry Cayton; Tessy Ojo; Diana Barran; Tristia Clarke; Suzie Aplin; Saul Klein; Tom Shropshire; Charlotte Moore; Alex Reid; Sue Black.

Correspondent: Ruth Davison, Grants Director, 1st Floor, 89 Albert Embankment, London SE1 7TP (tel: 020 7820 2222; email: grantsinfo@ comicrelief.com)

 www.comicrelief.com

 facebook.com/comicrelief

 @comicrelief

 @comicrelief

Since 1985 Comic Relief has raised around £500 million to tackle poverty and social injustice in the UK, Africa, and more recently in some of the poorest countries in other parts of the world. This entry is primarily concerned with grant-making in the UK.

In 2002, Comic Relief started a second initiative, Sport Relief. Half of its income goes to the International Children and Young People's programme, the other half to projects in the UK that are using sport to increase social cohesion and inclusion. The charity also administers Robbie Williams' Give It Sum Fund for community-based projects in his home area of North Staffordshire.

The charity principally receives its income through the generosity of the public via its Red Nose Day fundraising event. This is held every two years in partnership with the BBC, and the extent of the grant-making depends entirely on the success of the preceding event.

Comic Relief's vision is 'A Just World Free from Poverty, where everyone is safe, healthy educated and empowered' which it looks to achieve by 'working in partnership with people and organisations to create solutions to challenges together'.

Grants strategy

In May 2016, Comic Relief launched a refreshed grants strategy, which was described in the charity's press release as being 'in response to an ever-changing environment to enable Comic Relief to respond faster to the complex world we live in and maximise the impact made both in the UK and overseas'.

The grants strategy, which has four programme areas, connects the charity's work in the UK and internationally and sits under the Global Goals for Sustainable Development (www.globalgoals.org), which challenge 'governments, companies and communities to respond urgently to poverty and inequality'. The four programme areas, which are described in full on the Comic Relief website, are:

- Investing in children and young people to be ready for the future. Priorities are:
  - Good quality, safe, ongoing education
  - Protection from violence, conflict and abuse
  - Building young people's enterprise and leadership
- Empowering women and girls so they're safe and free to lead the lives they choose. Priorities are:
  - Tackling violence
  - Helping women work and ensuring equality
  - Leadership
- Improving health and well-being of vulnerable and disadvantaged people. Priorities are:
  - Helping people access quality health and well-being services

- Tackling stigma and discrimination
- Helping people take control of their health
- Building stronger communities in areas of disadvantage, deprivation and poverty. Priorities are:
  - Connected communities
  - Productive communities
  - Empowered communities

Full information on Comic Relief's programme areas is available from the website.

Funding initiatives

Details of currently open funding initiatives – including eligibility criteria, important dates and application processes – in the UK and around the world, can be found on the informative Comic Relief website. Examples of funds which were listed on the website at the time of writing (June 2018) included: 'Tackling Violence against Women and Girls'; 'Core Strength'; and 'Financial Inclusion at the Margins'.

Financial information

In 2016/17 the charity held assets of £117 million and an income of £104.7 million. Grants were allocated amounting to £74.4 million, of which £21.6 million was given in the UK and £52.1 million internationally. A further £706,000 was given for global awareness, education and social change. Of 374 new grants approved in the year, 250 were in the UK and the remaining 124 international. The annual report notes that the UK Community Foundations administered a further 1,382 small grants through the Core Strength initiative.

Grants in the UK were awarded as follows:

Building stronger communities	£10.5 million
Improving health and well-being	£4.7 million
Empowering women and girls	£3.4 million
Investing in children and young people	£2.3 million
The BT Supporters Club	£650,000
Special initiatives	£55,000

Exclusions

We would recommend that applicants read the full eligibility policy on the charity's website (www.comicrelief.com/grants/policies). We have included the following information, which was taken from the policy, as a general indication of what the charity does not support.

Comic Relief does not support or fund:

- General appeals
- Individual and group sponsorship
- Marketing appeals
- Proposals for bursaries from individuals
- Proposals from individuals for the funding of study or attainment of qualifications
- Activities which evangelise or proselytise

- Organisations which adopt a partisan political stance or activities which are party political
- Organisations that advocate the use of violence as a means to campaign or influence public opinion

Furthermore, Comic Relief will 'not usually fund building costs or the purchase of vehicles, land or heavy equipment unless it can be clearly shown that such expenditure is proportionately small in relation to the overall budget and adequately justified as essential to the proposed activity'.

The charity is also 'very unlikely' to fund one-off conferences or workshops. However it is able 'to fund conferences, workshops and other gatherings as part of a longer-term project where, for example, it can be shown that such events will help to bring about improvements in the implementation and outcomes of projects, influence wider policy development, or share knowledge and experience with interested parties'.

There are further restrictions for applicants who have previously submitted unsuccessful applications to the charity.

Note that individual funding initiatives also have their own various eligibility criteria.

Applications

Applications are made online via the charity's website, where full guidance is also provided. Potential applicants must register and complete Stage 1 of the process, an initial proposal. Applicants are shortlisted from those successfully completing Stage 1.

Sources of information

Accounts; annual report; Charity Commission record; guidelines for applicants; funder's website.

Community First

Community, built heritage and environmental projects, community transport, sport and leisure, jobs and business development

Wiltshire and Swindon

£518,500 (2016/17)

CC number: 288117

Trustees: Piers Dibben; Dr Martin Hamer; James Moody; Brian Clake; Edward Heard; Jane Rowell; Anthony Pooley; Peter Duke; Steven Boocock.

Correspondent: Grants Team, Unit C2 Brecon Business Centre, Hopton Park, Devizes, Wiltshire SN10 2EY (tel: 01380 732802; email: grants@communityfirst.org.uk)

www.communityfirst.org.uk

Community First was founded in 1965 as the Community Council for Wiltshire and later registered as a charity in 1983. It is part of the Action with Rural Communities in England network (ACRE). The charity has three main focus areas:

- Strengthening communities
- Encouraging enterprise
- Tackling disadvantage

Grants programmes

The charity has four grant programmes:

The Landfill Communities Fund – capital funding for local community, heritage and environmental projects in specific areas where local landfill operators sites or depots are located.

Plain Action and Vale Action LEADER Programme – European funding to increase rural jobs, help businesses grow and support the local economy in the north-west corner of Wiltshire and Salisbury Plain and surrounding areas.

Lace Up Wiltshire – funding for projects in Wiltshire that encourage inactive people to become more active as well as improving access to sport and leisure activities for disadvantaged people, women, over 55s and disabled people.

Wiltshire Community Transport Development Fund – support for existing community and voluntary transport groups to provide a wider range of services; enable communities to trial new services which assist local people to better access local facilities; and to support the establishment of wholly new community and voluntary transport groups.

Financial information

In 2016/17 the charity had assets of £291,000 and an income of £1.6 million. Grants awarded to organisations totalled £518,500.

Previous beneficiaries have included: Royal Wootton Bassett Sports Association (£67,000); Swindon Supermarine Football Club (£45,000); Wroughton Parish Council Play Area (£37,500); West Dean Village Hall (£23,500); Salisbury Museum (£20,000); River Bourne Community Farm Café (£18,000).

Exclusions

Grants are not awarded to individuals or private companies. General appeals for non-specific works are not eligible.

Applications

Landfill Communities Fund – in the first instance download and complete the expression of interest form from the website then email to grants@ communityfirst.org.uk. If you have been advised that your project is eligible for funding, then download and complete the application form on the website, and submit with supporting documents as specified in the form.

Plain Action and Vale Action LEADER Programme – full details of the application process and application forms can be found at: www.plainaction. org.uk

Lace Up Wiltshire – application packs can be downloaded from the Community First website.

Wiltshire Community Transport Development Fund – for further information contact the Community Transport team at Community First on 01380 722475 or email: transport@ communityfirst.org.uk.

Sources of information

Accounts; annual report; Charity Commission record; funder's website.

Congregational & General Charitable Trust

 Protestant churches, in particular those of the United Reformed and Congregational denominations

 UK

(£) £333,000 (2017)

CC number: 297013

Trustees: Revd David Coote; Margaret Atkinson; Revd William Adams; Revd Pamela Ward; Jacqueline Haws; John Holmes; Revd Margaret Tait; Alastair Forsyth.

Correspondent: Trish Thorpe, Trust Administrator, PO Box 1111, Lincoln LN5 0WJ (email: enquiries@candgtrust. org.uk)

 www.candgtrust.org.uk

The trust was established in 1956 as the charitable arm of the Congregational & General Insurance Company and was reformed in 1987 as a separate entity, but still receiving support from the company. In 2016 the trust became completely independent of the company.

The aim of the trust is to make grants for building maintenance and towards the capital costs of community projects to support Protestant churches, in particular those of the United Reformed and Congregational denominations.

Grants

Grants are given for capital projects involving building work, including repairs, improvements and extensions. Examples of what has been supported before include assistance with damaged roofs or water ingress, accessibility adaptations, and lighting or heating support. The trust can also make grants for to church community projects for capital costs – such as food banks, youth clubs or other community groups.

Amounts range between £500 and £10,000 and are usually given for around 10% of the total project cost; projects with a total cost of over £1 million are not considered.

The website states that the trust is considering funding professional advice on capital projects for churches planning and executing building projects – from architects or quantity surveyors, for example. It is also exploring the possibility of awarding grants specifically for work with an environmental benefit, such as solar panels, insulation or double glazing.

Financial information

In 2017 the trust held assets of £15.3 million and had an income of £458,500. Grants totalling £333,000 were made to 51 churches across England, Scotland and Northern Ireland.

Applications

Application forms can be downloaded from the trust's website, where upcoming deadlines are also posted, along with guidance on what to include in your application. Completed forms can be submitted by email or post. Grants are considered on a quarterly basis.

Sources of information

Accounts; annual report; Charity Commission record; funder's website.

Martin Connell Charitable Trust

(Q) General charitable purposes

(Q) Scotland

(£) £280,000 (2016/17)

OSCR number: SC009842

Correspondent: The Trustees, Dentons UK and Middle East LLP, 1 George Square, Glasgow G2 1AL

The trust supports general charitable purposes in Scotland.

Financial information

In 2016/17 the trust held assets of £8.8 million and had an income of £294,000. Grants to 173 organisations totalled £280,000.

Beneficiaries included: The Sick Kids Friends Foundation (£5,000); Combat Stress and Tenovus Scotland (£4,000 each); Leonard Cheshire Foundation (£3,000); Lupus UK and Upward Mobility (£2,000 each); Fife Young Carers, Fight for Sight and Scottish Ballet (£1,000 each).

Applications
Apply in writing to the correspondent.

Sources of information
Accounts; annual report; OSCR record.

The Thomas Cook Children's Charity

 Children's health and education

UK and overseas

Around £1.2 million (2016)

CC number: 1091673

Trustees: Chris Mottershead; Jamie Queen; Simon Lindsay; Bill Scott; Matthew Harding; James Montgomery.

Correspondent: Aoife McDonogh, Charitable Relations Manager, Thomas Cook Ltd Unit 15–30, The Thomas Cook Business Park, Coningsby Road, Bretton, Peterborough PE3 8SB (tel: 01733 416731; email: thomascook. childrenscharity@thomascook.com)

 thomascookchildrenscharity.com

 facebook.com/tcccharity

 @TCCcharity

The charity was set up by Thomas Cook UK and Ireland travel company, with the aim of 'improving children's lives and benefiting the communities in which they live' in the UK and overseas.

The charity receives income from donations by Thomas Cook customers and from the fundraising activities of Thomas Cook employees, as well as from the group itself, which also provides logistical and administrative support to the charity.

According to the website, the charity supports projects that benefit children in the following categories:

- Improving education facilities
- Improving facilities that provide well-being and healthcare

The charity also supports disasters and emergency relief efforts, although there is no nomination process for this category, and grants are made at the discretion of the trustees. Grants have also previously been provided for equipment and sport.

Financial information
In 2016 the charity had an income of £909,000 and an expenditure of £1.39 million. At the time of writing (June 2018) the charity's most recent set of accounts was unavailable, however, based upon the charity's previous record of grant-making it is estimated that the charity awarded grants of approximately £1.2 million.

Previous beneficiaries have included: Alder Hey (£150,000); Royal Manchester Children's Hospital (£125,000); CLIC Sargent (£100,000); SOS Children (£50,000); Whizz-Kidz (£28,500); Welfare Concern (£10,000); Riding for the Disabled (£3,000); Tiny Tims (£1,000); The Seb Goold Trust (£500); Pure O2 (£50).

Applications
The 2015 annual report states that applications can be made by: Thomas Cook UK and Ireland customers; employees of Thomas Cook UK and Ireland; members of the public; and charities themselves. Those wishing to nominate a charity can contact the correspondent by email or alternatively submit an online form available on the 'Get involved' section of the charity's website.

Sources of information
Accounts; annual report; Charity Commission record; funder's website.

The Ernest Cook Trust

 The education of children and young people in the areas of: the environment, rural conservation, arts and crafts, literary and numeracy. Research is occasionally funded

UK

£1.95 million (2016/17)

CC number: 1146629

Trustees: Andrew Christie-Miller; Harry Henderson; Simon Eliot; Sir Bertie Ross; Mary Riall; Jennifer Greenwood.

Correspondent: The Secretary, The Estate Office, Fairford Park, Fairford, Gloucestershire GL7 4JH (tel: 01285 712492; email: admin@ernestcooktrust. org.uk)

 www.ernestcooktrust.org.uk

 facebook.com/ernestcooktrust

The trust was founded by the philanthropist Ernest Cook in 1952 to support outdoor learning, conservation and the management of the countryside. The trust makes educational grants for projects that benefit children and young people. It is unusual in that it is a land-based trust that owns and manages 22,000 acres of landed estates in Buckinghamshire, Dorset, Gloucestershire, Leicestershire and Oxfordshire.

Grant-making policy
According to the trust's website, grants can be awarded to registered charities, schools and not-for-profit organisations for projects that support young people's interest 'either in the countryside and the environment, the arts (in the broadest sense), or in science, or aiming to raise levels of literacy and numeracy'. All applications are expected to link in with either the National Curriculum or with recognised qualifications.

There are two grant programmes:

- **Small grants** – between £100 to £4,000 – usually pump priming or educational resources for small groups, state schools and registered charities. Applications can be made throughout the year and are considered bi-monthly, however the trust advises that applications be submitted six months in advance of the project's expected start date.
- **Large grants** – between £5,000 to £12,000 – usually for comprehensive education programmes, environmental projects or arts, crafts and architecture projects. Applications are reviewed twice a year: in April the trustees consider projects related to the arts, crafts and architecture; in September the trustees consider projects covering the environment and countryside. Projects related to literacy, numeracy and science are considered at both meetings.

Research grants are occasionally made, and salaries for education officers can be part-funded by the trust.

Financial information
In 2016/17 the trust held assets of £181.5 million and had an income of £4.7 million. Grants were made totalling £1.95 million with a small amount of £2,100 going to individuals. During the year, 556 grants were awarded with the majority being made in through the large grants programme. Grants were made for the following purposes:

Environment and countryside	£750,000
Arts, crafts and architecture	£687,000
Literacy and STEM	£481,500
Other	£29,000

Details of individual beneficiaries were not included in the trust's 2016/17 annual report, however recipients of grants from 2017 are detailed on the trust's website.

Previous beneficiaries have included: National Literacy Trust, The Story Republic (£10,000 each); Bumblebee Conservation Trust (£9,900); Carymoor Environmental Trust (£9,000); Forest of Avon Trust (£5,600); Ignite! (£5,500); Marine Conservation Research (£4,500); Clio's Company (£3,000); Great Chart Primary School (£2,200); Endelienta (£1,000).

Exclusions

According to the trust's website grants are not made:

- retrospectively
- to pre-school groups, individuals, agricultural colleges, independent schools or local authorities
- for building work, infrastructure or refurbishment work
- for youth work, social support, therapy and medical treatment, including projects using the arts, environment or literacy & numeracy for these purposes
- for projects related to sports, outward bound type activities or recreation
- for overseas projects
- for Wildlife Trusts and for Farming & Wildlife Advisory Groups other than those based in counties in which the ECT owns land (Buckinghamshire, Dorset, Gloucestershire, Leicestershire and Oxfordshire)

Applications

Application forms are available to download from the trust's website. Small grant applications are considered bi-monthly. Large grant applications are considered twice a year in spring and autumn. Check the trust's website for application deadlines and the types of projects being considered.

Sources of information

Accounts; annual report; Charity Commission record; funder's website.

The Catherine Cookson Charitable Trust

General charitable purposes, education, environment and animals, arts and culture, religion, health and disability, children and young people, older people

UK, with some preference for north east England

£970,000 (2016/17)

CC number: 272895

Trustees: Peter Magnay; David Hawkins; Hugo Marshall; Jack Ravenscroft; Daniel Sallows.

Correspondent: Peter Magnay, Trustee, Thomas Magnay & Co., 8 St Mary's Green, Whickham, Newcastle upon Tyne NE16 4DN (tel: 0191 488 7459; email: enquiries@thomasmagnay.co.uk)

catherinecookson.com/trust

The Catherine Cookson Trust supports a wide range of activities including education and training, environment and conservation, arts and culture as well as general charitable purposes. In particular the trust supports work with young or disadvantaged people. The trust's website states that 'the trust's principal aim is to identify and meet local needs in the area

of North East England'. Grants awarded are between £250 and £100,000.

Financial information

In 2016/17 the trust had assets of £32.3 million and an income of £1.1 million. During the year, the trust awarded around £970,000 to 233 organisations. Grants were distributed as follows:

Medical, health and sickness	40	£246,000
Arts and culture	32	£224,000
Disability	22	£119,000
Education and training	17	£148,000
Other	47	£65,000
Religious activities	29	£12,700
Children and young people	42	£157,000
Animal welfare	4	£1,400

Beneficiaries included: RNIB (£100,000); Alzheimer's Research UK (£95,000); Marie Curie (£50,000); Dame Allan's School (£35,000); National Museum of the Royal Navy and Seeing Ear (£10,000 each); The Breamish Hall (£4,000); Blind Veterans Association (£1,000); Rainbow Trust and Tall Ships Youth Trust (£500); Durham Wildlife Trust (£250); British Hen Welfare Trust (£100).

Exclusions

The website states:

> The Trustees as a matter of general policy do not consider applications which would involve the Trust in core funding or ongoing financing. The Trust does not provide funding for applications with a foreign element nor does it in general consider personal applications or applications for Sports Clubs/Associations.

Applications

There is no standard application form but written applications, enclosing an sae should be sent to the correspondence address provided. There is no set format or time limit for applications, which enables many groups to apply for a grant. Charities interested in applying should complete the short online form which is available on the trust's website.

Sources of information

Accounts; annual report; Charity Commission website.

The Alice Ellen Cooper Dean Charitable Foundation

General charitable purposes

Mainly Dorset and west Hampshire, some national and overseas

£930,000 (2016/17)

CC number: 273298

Trustees: Linda Bowditch; Douglas Neville-Jones; Rupert Edwards; John Bowditch; Alastair Cowen; Emma Blackburn.

Correspondent: Rupert Edwards, Trustee, Unity Chambers, 34 High East Street, Dorchester, Dorset DT1 1HA (tel: 01305 251333; email: rupertedwards@edwardsandkeeping.co.uk)

The foundation was established for general charitable purposes in 1977 with an initial gift by Alice Ellen Cooper Dean and supplemented by a legacy on her death in 1984.

The foundation supports a wide range of charitable causes and its objects are 'the relief of poverty, distress and sickness and the advancement of education, religion and charitable purposes of benefit to the community', according to the 2015/16 annual report. Donations are only made to registered charities, with a preference for organisations benefitting the community in Dorset and West Hampshire. The majority of grants are in the range of £1,000 and £10,000 each.

Financial information

In 2016/17 the foundation held assets of around £31.9 million and an income of £1.3 million. Grants were made to 148 organisations, totalling £930,000 altogether, distributed in the following categories:

Charitable organisations in Dorset and West Hampshire	£557,500
Other national charitable organisations	£187,000
National charitable organisations benefitting Dorset and West Hampshire	£118,000
UK charitable organisations for overseas projects	£68,000

Beneficiaries included: Dorset County Hospital NHS Foundation Trusts (£100,000); Dorset Natural History and Archaeological Society (£50,000); Marie Curie Cancer Care (£13,000); Alcohol Education Trusts, Barnardo's and Read Easy (£10,000 each); Wessex Warriors Powerchair Football Club (£7,500); Msaada Cow Project (£5,000); Safe Partnership (£3,000); Community Hope of the Holy Fire (£2,500); St John's Church, Holdenhurst (£1,000).

Exclusions

Grants are awarded to registered charities only. No grants are given to individuals.

Applications

Apply in writing to the correspondent. Telephone calls are not welcome. Applications are considered from both local and national charitable organisations, with local charities given top priority and national charities only supported occasionally as funds permit. The trustees meet regularly through the year to consider applications.

Applications should include a summary of the project, costs, financial accounts and details of fundraising activities. Trustees may visit grant recipients.

Sources of information

Accounts; annual report; Charity Commission record.

Co-operative Community Investment Foundation

 General charitable purposes, education, relief of poverty, community development, children and young people

 UK

 £497,500 (2016)

CC number: 1093028

Trustees: Shelia Malley; Saleem Chowdhery; Martin Rogers; Daniel Crowe; Jamie Ward-Smith; Andy Phelps.

Correspondent: Steve Fowler, Secretary, 9th Floor, 1 Angel Square, Manchester M60 0AG (tel: 0161 834 1212; email: foundation@co-operative.coop)

 www.coopfoundation.org.uk

facebook.com/Co-op-Foundation-156348321640279

@Coop_Foundation

Established in 2000, the Co-operative Community Investment Foundation is administered by the Co-operative Group and funded by its members who have agreed to donate some of their profit share to the foundation. According to its 2016 accounts, the objects of the foundation are to support projects that contribute to the relief of poverty, the advancement of education or other charitable purposes that benefit the communities in which businesses of the Co-op operate.

In 2016 the foundation concluded a major strategic review of its activities. The new strategy defines the following three priorities for the next three years:

- To champion young people's ability to contribute positively to their communities and help strengthen their sense of belonging
- To invest in disadvantaged communities' capacity to overcome social, economic or environmental challenges
- To build our reputation as a trusted charity with a co-operative difference, uniting with others to make sustainable impact in communities

To achieve these goals, the foundation works with a UK-wide network of partners to deliver a wide range of projects and programmes which address its strategic and thematic objectives. Specific funding and partnership

opportunities vary each year and will be advertised on the foundation's website.

Financial information

In 2016 the foundation had assets of £16.3 million and an income of £1.5 million. During the year, the foundation awarded eight grants worth a total of £497,500.

Beneficiaries included: Manchester Metropolitan University (£59,500); The Royal Exchange, Youth Focus: North East, Envision, The Prince's Trust (£20,000 each); Ovalhouse, Young Scot (£5,000 each).

Applications

Funding rounds for specific programmes open periodically during the year and will be advertised on the foundation's website.

Sources of information

Accounts; annual report; Charity Commission record; funder's website.

The Gershon Coren Charitable Foundation (also known as The Muriel and Gus Coren Charitable Foundation)

 General charitable purposes, Jewish causes

 UK and financially developing countries

 £349,000 (2016/17)

CC number: 257615

Trustees: Walter Stanton; Anthony Coren; Muriel Coren.

Correspondent: Muriel Coren, Trustee, 5 Golders Park Close, London NW11 7QR (email: graham.weinberg@mhllp.co.uk)

This foundation, established in 1968, makes grants to registered charities, particularly Jewish organisations, for a wide range of charitable purposes.

Financial information

In 2016/17 the foundation held assets of £206,500 and had an income of £278,000. Grants totalled £349,000 and were awarded to 43 organisations.

Beneficiaries included: Gategi Village Self Help Group (£130,000); Youth Aliyah Child Rescue (£40,000); JNF Charitable Trust (£30,000); UK Torenet (£10,000); Association for Sustainable Urban Development (£7,000); Jewish Care and UK Jewish Film (£5,000 each); St Joseph's Hospice (£2,500); RNLI (£2,000); British Friends of Rambam Centre and National Trust (£1,000 each).

Applications

Apply in writing to the correspondent.

Sources of information

Accounts; annual report; Charity Commission record.

The Evan Cornish Foundation

 Human rights, social and economic inequality, education, health, criminal justice system, older people, refugees and asylum seekers, homelessness

 North of England, overseas

 £1.1 million (2016/17)

CC number: 1112703

Trustees: Rachel Cornish; Barbara Ward; Sally Cornish.

Correspondent: Rachel Cornish, Trustee, The Innovation Centre, 217 Portobello, Sheffield S1 4DP (tel: 0114 224 2230; email: contactus@ evancornishfoundation.org.uk)

www.evancornishfoundation.org.uk

The Evan Cornish Foundation was created by the widow and four daughters of businessman Evan Cornish who died in 2002.

UK applications

Applications are accepted from charities, not-for-profits and community interest companies. Projects should benefit people living in northern England and meet the aims of the foundation.

The foundation has eight main aims, details of which have been taken from its website:

Human Rights

We consider applications for projects which:

- fight injustice by combating violations of Human Rights (as defined by the Universal Declaration of Human Rights)
- support the victims of these violations and their dependants
- empower people to protect their own human rights

Social and Economic Inequality

We consider applications for projects which:

- work towards food sovereignty; through improvements to local food production and markets, movement building and/or policy work
- address the root causes of social and economic inequality and advocate for policy change, empowering people and communities
- support sustainable livelihoods
- address gender inequality

Education

We consider applications for projects which:

- benefit excluded children or those at risk of exclusion
- address the gender gap in access to education

- support enrichment of education to promote human rights and social cohesion and improve young people's self-esteem

Health

We consider applications for projects which:

- support people with mental health issues, promote better understanding, address inequality and work to eradicate stigma
- support women's health
- improve maternal and new-born health
- work to avoid sight loss, improve vision impairment and support a better quality of life for people with sight issues and blindness

Criminal Justice System

We consider applications for projects which:

- promote prisoners' wellbeing, ensuring people are treated humanely and with dignity
- inspire prisoners and enrich their lives through creative and innovative programmes
- assist vulnerable people at risk of imprisonment, particularly women and young people
- work with people on their transition from prison, helping them to resettle and become independent from the Criminal Justice System

Elderly People

We consider applications for projects which:

- support the wellbeing of older people with particular emphasis on maintaining independence and alleviation of isolation
- improve the quality of life of older people through home-based services, social networks and meeting places

Refugees & Asylum Seekers

We consider applications for projects which:

- advocate on behalf of refugees and asylum seekers
- improve the quality of life for asylum seekers, destitute asylum seekers, refugees and vulnerable migrants
- promote social and community cohesion

Homelessness

We consider applications for projects which:

- engage and support the vulnerable who are homeless or at risk of becoming homeless
- provide crisis support
- improve people's quality of life, relieving hardship and distress

Organisations from the rest of England and the UK can apply if:

- Your project is unique in the UK
- Your project involves advocacy/policy work
- Your people affects people in the UK prison system

Overseas applications

International applications will be prioritised which: promote tolerance and equality for women; combat human rights violations. International applicants must have a registered UK office.

Financial information

In 2016/17 the foundation held assets of £11.4 million and had an income of £239,000. A total of 160 grants totalling £1.1 million were made during the year.

Beneficiaries included: Civil Liberties Trust (£150,000); Migrant Resource Centre Asylum Aid (£10,000); Sight Savers (£8,000); Centre for Criminal Appeals (£7,500); RECOOP (£7,300); Prisoners Education Trust (£7,200); Age UK – Dudley and North of England Refugee Service (£5,000 each); Abigail Housing (£4,200); Diversity Role Models (£1,500).

Exclusions

The foundation is unable to support the following activities:

- Building work or repairs
- Political activities and purpose
- Animal welfare
- Medical research
- Individuals/gap year students
- Holiday club providers
- Religious organisations/religious or evangelical causes
- Organisations which discriminate internally or externally based on faith

The trustees will consider applications from organisations that grew from a religious basis but now have a multi-faith and secular approach. Organisations must not discriminate on the grounds of faith. Trustees, staff, volunteers and beneficiaries should not be required to be of any particular faith. Organisations should work with people of all faiths as well as those with no faith.

Applications

Applications can be made through the foundation's website. The trustees meet three times per year. Check the foundation's website for application deadlines.

Sources of information

Accounts; annual report; Charity Commission record; funder's website.

The Corporation of Trinity House of Deptford Strond

 Social welfare and training for seafarers, maritime safety and education

 UK

£ £1.8 million (2016/17)

CC number: 211869

Correspondent: Graham Hockley, Trinity House, Tower Hill, London EC3N 4DH (tel: 020 7481 6900; email: graham.hockley@thls.org)

 www.trinityhouse.co.uk

The charity was incorporated by Royal Charter in 1514. According to its website it is: 'dedicated to safeguarding shipping and seafarers, providing education, support and welfare to the seafaring community with a statutory duty as a General Lighthouse Authority to deliver a reliable, efficient and cost-effective aid to [a] navigation service for the benefit and safety of all mariners.'

Grants are made to charities that support the welfare of seafarers, ex-seafarers and their dependants. Some charities are supported on a long-term basis with either a three year rolling basis or a three-year fixed period. Some charities are supported on an ad-hoc basis in response to specific applications.

Financial information

In 2016/17 the charity held assets of £272 million and had an income of £9.4 million. During the year, the charity awarded around £1.8 million in grants to 21 organisations.

Beneficiaries included: Sailors' Children's Society (£173,000); Shipwrecked Fishermen and Mariners' Royal Benevolent Society (£145,000); Seafarers UK (£117,000); Marine Society and Cadets (£100,000); Jubilee Sailing Trust (£109,500); Nautilus UK (70,500); Sunderland Aged Merchant Seamen's Homes and Veterans' Aid (£50,000 each); Apostle of the Sea (£20,000); Apostles of the Sea (£17,600); Seafish (£14,000); The Not Forgotten Association (£12,000); The High Tide Foundation (£7,500).

Applications

Apply in writing to the correspondent.

Sources of information

Accounts; annual report; Charity Commission record; funder's website.

Corra Foundation

 Social welfare

 Scotland, Zambia, Rwanda and Malawi

 £17.96 million (2017)

OSCR number: SC009481

Correspondent: Connie Williamson, Grants Manager, Riverside House, 502 Gorgie Road, Edinburgh EH11 3AF (tel: 0131 444 4020; email: hello@corra. scot)

 www.ltsbfoundationforscotland.org. uk

 facebook.com/CorraFoundation

 @corrascot

The foundation is one of four Lloyds Banking Group charities, covering England and Wales, Scotland, Northern Ireland and the Channel Islands. The foundation is an independent grant-maker; its relationship with Lloyds Banking Group is outlined on the website:

> A covenant was agreed between Trustee Savings Bank and Trustee Savings Bank (TSB) Foundation for Scotland in 1985, making provision for Scottish communities to benefit from their share of 1% of the Group's pre-tax profits (Scotland's share being 19.46% of the total). In 1997 Lloyds Bank and TSB Group merged. This significantly increased our income and the foundation became the largest Scottish independent grant-making trust. In early 2010 Lloyds Banking Group gave notice on the agreement and the final payment will be received in February 2018.

What the foundation does

The foundation works to improve the lives of disadvantaged individuals and communities with the following mission: 'to make a difference to the lives of individuals and communities in Scotland, by encouraging positive change, opportunities, fairness and growth of aspirations, which improve quality of life'. It has three strategic objectives:

- To be the best grant maker we can be – Grant-making is at the heart of what we do and we want to do it as well as possible, with an open and accessible approach
- To get alongside communities – We are working differently, including with communities we don't historically reach, and others with a big appetite for change
- To share expertise – We will use our 30+ years experience in grant making to support others
- Partnership – We want to make a bigger difference to people by working together with others

Foundation programmes

The following programmes are available from the foundation, as stated on the website.

Henry Duncan Awards

The foundation's main grants programme was renamed in 2010 in honour of the Rev. Henry Duncan, the founder of the first Trustee Savings Bank.

In order to be eligible to apply for a grant, charities must have an annual income of less than £500,000 and be working to deliver programmes or services which are clearly aimed at improving quality of life for people in their community who are facing disadvantage. According to the website, awards of up to £7,000 are made on a one-off basis to charities working with people 'who may typically be experiencing challenging family circumstances, disability, mental ill health, abuse or poverty'. Grants are awarded for projects addressing a wide range of issues, a list of which can be found in the guidance notes on the foundation's website.

The foundation's website explains that trustees are particularly interested in projects supporting:

- Vulnerable children and young people
- Isolated older people
- Carers
- Families in poverty
- People affected by disability or mental health issues

Funding can be awarded for core costs, such as salaries or running costs, or project funds. The trustees will also consider applications for small capital costs such as equipment.

Partnership Drugs Initiative

The Partnership Drugs Initiative (PDI) was established in 2001 to support work carried out by the voluntary sectors with children and young people who are affected by issues associated with substance abuse. The initiative is delivered in partnership with the Scottish Government and The Robertson Trust. According to the foundation's website, the initiative specifically looks to:

- Increase the well-being of children and young people (0 to 25) in Scotland affected by alcohol and other drugs
- Help develop and influence both local and national policy

In 2014 the PDI adopted a new strategic direction addressing four specific areas, which are: identifying and addressing geographical gaps; identifying and addressing thematic gaps; disseminating learning; and optimising funding.

The PDI is based around building relationships between 'policy makers, local partners and projects to ensure collectively we can make a positive difference to children and young people affected by drugs and alcohol'. It is further explained that 'PDI works closely with all potential and supported groups to help us improve our approach and understanding of what it takes to make a difference to children and young people. Support for groups is offered by sharing our learning and knowledge from other groups and partners'.

The initiative targets three areas, which are outlined on the website:

- Children and young people affected by parental substance issues (alcohol and other drugs)
- Pre-teen children who are at higher risk of developing issues relating to alcohol and other drugs
- Young people in need of support due to their own alcohol or drug issue

It is further explained that 'PDI provides funding support and will contribute up to a maximum of 50% towards the overall costs of delivering a project/ service that will help improve outcomes for children and young people. You can apply for up to three years'.

Full information, including how to make an initial application, is provided on the website.

Managed programmes

The foundation also administers and manages programmes on behalf of other organisations. At the time of writing (May 2018) these included:

Scottish Government International Development Small Grants Programme

The aim of the programme is to build capacity and upscale small international development organisations so they have the ability to bid for funding through its International Development Fund (IDF) and also those of other funders. Project grants of £60,000 over three years and feasibility grants of up to £10,000 are available. Projects should be based in one of the Scottish Government's partner countries – Malawi, Zambia or Rwanda.

The Children, Young People, Families, Early Intervention and Adult Learning and Empowering Communities Fund

The foundation is working in partnership with the Scottish Government to deliver this fund.

The core elements of the CYPFEIF aspect of the fund, which the website states 'aims to improve outcomes for children, young people and their families', are:

- Promote the Getting it right for every child (GIRFEC) well-being indicators and the implementation of UN

Convention on the Rights of the Child (UNCRC).

▷ Delivery of prevention and early intervention activities.

▷ Improving parenting capacity and family support.

The website further explains that the ALEC element of the fund 'supports third sector organisations to deliver outcomes that improve opportunities for adult learning and building community capacity'. This fund has the following objectives:

▷ Prevention and early intervention through adult learning and community capacity building.

▷ Supporting the delivery of lifelong, learner-centred adult learning as outlined in the Adult Learning in Scotland Statement of Ambition.

▷ Using asset-based approaches to work with adult learners or with communities to plan and co-design learning or capacity building opportunities.

Both core funding and project funding are available through the CYPFEIF and ALEC Fund. See the website for full information.

Financial information

In 2017 the foundation had assets of £19.7 million and an income of £22.4 million. Grants were awarded totalling £17.96 million.

Previous beneficiaries have included: Relationships Scotland (£1.1 million); Action for Children (£880,000); Barnardo's (£150,000); Sleep Scotland (£38,000); Circle (£35,000); Woodcraft Folk Scotland (£8,500); People First (£3,500); Fairfield Sports and Leisure Club (£1,500); Forth and Tay Disabled Ramblers (£750).

Exclusions

Each programme has its own criteria. Refer to the foundation's website for more information.

Applications

Application forms for all programmes, complete with comprehensive guidance notes and application deadlines, are available from the foundation. Foundation staff are always willing to provide additional help.

Sources of information

Accounts; annual report; OSCR record; funder's website.

Country Houses Foundation

🔍 Heritage

📍 England and Wales

💷 £552,000 (2016/17)

CC number: 1111049

Trustees: Oliver Pearcey; Nicholas Barber; Norman Hudson; John Parsons; Mary King; Andre Jardine; Jeremy Musson.

Correspondent: David Price, Secretary, Sheephouse Farm, Uley Road, Dursley, Gloucestershire GL11 5AD (tel: 0845 402 4102; email: info@countryhousesfoundation.org.uk)

🌐 www.countryhousesfoundation.org.uk

The main aims of the foundation are to support the preservation of buildings of historic or architectural significance together with their gardens and grounds, for the public benefit.

The following information has been taken from the foundation's website:

Types of project funded

The CHF gives grants for the repair and conservation of rural historic buildings and structures located in England and Wales, including where appropriate their gardens, grounds and outbuildings. We would normally expect your building or structure to be listed, scheduled, or in the case of a garden included in the English Heritage Register of Parks and Gardens. However, we may also make grants to projects that involve an unlisted building in a conservation area which we judge to be of sufficient historic or architectural significance or importance.

Our definition of 'rural' includes all buildings and structures in the countryside and other rural buildings which have subsequently been overtaken by, and embedded in, urban and suburban development.

In addition, to qualify for any grant you must be able to show that:

▷ there is a compelling need for the work you want to undertake to be done within the next 2 to 3 years

▷ the project will enhance our historic environment

▷ there will be appropriate public access

▷ there is a financial need for the grant

▷ the project can proceed within a reasonable time frame (i.e. 1–2 years)

▷ the project is sustainable with a suitable conservation and/or business plan.

A grant is unlikely to be awarded without this information.

We aim to make grants for projects which are ready to proceed (i.e. can be started within 1 to 2 years) but which either do not qualify for funding from any of the mainstream sources or have been awarded only partial funding and require

significant further funds to complete the resource package.

We will also consider making grants to 'kick start' a project but will expect your other funding to be in place within 1–2 years.

Who can apply for Country Houses Foundation grants?

The CHF accepts applications for grants from either organisations or private individuals. The applicant must have legal responsibility for the repair of the historic building, its gardens and grounds.

We would normally expect applicants to own the building or estate, or to hold a full repairing lease with not less than 20 years to run. If this is not the case you should be able to demonstrate that you have a legally binding agreement to acquire such a building or estate.

How much are Country Houses Foundation grants for?

The minimum CHF grant on offer is £1,000 and the maximum is for £250,000 but an award of this size is only made under exceptional circumstances. Most of our grants are for less than £50,000.

We do not specify that this funding has to be matched, however we will expect you to make some contribution from your own resources. The CHF also expects applicants to have considered (and where appropriate to have applied for) other sources of funding.

We also expect the project to be sustainable in the longer term and will want to know what arrangements or plans you have to ensure that future repair and maintenance is properly funded.

Financial information

In 2016/17 the foundation had assets of £12.4 million and an income of £320,500. Grants were awarded to 21 organisations and totalled £552,000.

Beneficiaries included: Duncombe Park (Doric Temple) (£25,500); Headstone Manor (£24,000); Bramall Hall (£40,000); Watton Priory (£12,000); Milton Manor (£11,700); Compton Verney, Llanthony Secunda Priory (£10,000 each); Avington Park (£9,000).

Exclusions

According to its website, as a general rule, the foundation does not make grants for:

▷ Buildings and structures which have been the subject of recent purchase and where the cost of works for which grant is sought should have been recognised in the purchase price paid

▷ Projects which do not principally involve the repair or conservation of a historic building or structure

▷ Churches and chapels unless now or previously linked to a country house or estate

▷ Alterations and improvements, and repairs to non-historic fabric or services

▷ Routine maintenance and minor repairs

▷ General running costs

- Demolition unless agreed as part of a repair and conservation programme
- Rent, loan or mortgage payments
- Conservation of furniture, fittings and equipment except where they are themselves of historic or architectural significance, have a historic relationship with the site, are relevant to the project, and can be secured long-term from sale or disposal
- Work carried out before a grant offer has been made in writing and accepted

Applications

The foundation requires applicants to complete a pre-application form to confirm that projects fit its criteria. Pre-application forms and application forms along with detailed guidelines regarding the foundation's application process can be found on the foundation's website.

Sources of information

Accounts; annual report; Charity Commission record; funder's website.

General Charity of Coventry

 General charitable purposes

Within the boundary of the city of Coventry

£1.3 million to organisations (2016)

CC number: 216235

Trustees: David Mason; Richard Smith; Michael Harris; Edna Eaves; Edward Curtis; Cllr Joseph Cifford; Nigel Lee; Cllr Ram Lakha; Julia McNaney; David Evans; Terry Proctor; Cllr Marcus Lapsa; Vivian Kershaw; Cllr Catherine Miks; Patricia Hetherton; James Parry; Dr Roger Davies.

Correspondent: Susan Hanrahan, Old Bablake, Hill Street, Coventry CV1 4AN (tel: 024 7622 2769; email: cov.genchar@btconnect.com)

The charity makes grants to people in need in Coventry and contributions to pensioners of the City of Coventry. It also makes grants for projects that benefit the citizens of Coventry as well as grants for medical research, education and music. The charity is also responsible for the administration of Lady Herbert's Homes and Eventide Homes Ltd which provide accommodation for older people at subsidised rents.

Financial information

In 2016 the charity held assets of £10.4 million and had an income of £1.5 million. Grants to 59 organisations totalled £1.3 million with the largest grant awarded to Coventry School Foundation. A further £98,500 was awarded to individuals.

Previous beneficiaries have included: Coventry School Foundation (£562,000); Warwickshire and Northampton Air Ambulance (£85,000); Coventry Boys' Club (£30,000); Alzheimer's Society (£20,000); Mercia MS Therapy Centre (£15,000); University Hospital Coventry and Warwickshire Charity (£7,800); Coventry Sea Cadets (£5,000); Coventry Music Museum (£4,200); St Mary Magdalene with Church of the Risen Christ (£3,700); Bardsley Youth Project (£2,000); Moor Farm Stables (£700).

Exclusions

No grants are given to organisations outside Coventry, or for holidays unless of a recuperative nature.

Applications

Apply in writing to the correspondent. Applications are not accepted directly from the general public for relief in need (individuals).

Sources of information

Accounts; annual report; Charity Commission record.

The Sir Tom Cowie Charitable Trust

 General charitable purposes, rural communities, natural environment, heritage, social welfare

 City of Sunderland and County Durham

£260,500 (2016/17)

CC number: 1096936

Trustees: Peter Blackett; David Gray; Lady Diana Cowie.

Correspondent: Loraine Maddison, Grants Administrator, Estate Office, Broadwood Hall, Lanchester, Durham DH7 0TN (tel: 01207 529663; email: lorraine@sirtomcowie.com)

 www.stcct.co.uk

The primary purpose of the trust is to fund projects which provide opportunities for young people and improve quality of life in less affluent communities in Sunderland and County Durham. The trust is keen to support projects 'looking to link people living in the rural environment with the countryside and the natural environment'. Support is also given to projects proposing to conserve and maintain historic and important buildings and projects looking to conserve and maintain wildlife and, particularly, threatened species in the region.

The trust primarily supports projects in the city of Sunderland, the area of Derwentside in County Durham, and the valleys of Teesdale and Weardale.

Each year the trust awards £20,000 to the University of Sunderland Development Trust Futures Fund to provide bursaries to final year students.

Financial information

In 2016/17 the trust held assets of £5.6 million and had an income of £136,500. Grants were made to nine organisations and totalled £260,500.

Beneficiaries included: Beacon of Light Ltd (£200,000); Butsfield and District Young Farmers (£20,000); Castletown Primary School (£10,100); Asthma Relief (£4,900); St Bede's RC Academy (£2,300); Upper Teesdale Agricultural Support Services (£2,100); Outward Bound Trust (£350).

Exclusions

The trust does not make grants to:

- Projects outside the city of Sunderland and County Durham geographical region
- Individuals in any capacity
- National and international charities seeking partial funding for large projects

Applications

Application forms can be completed and submitted on the trust's website, or downloaded and returned to the mailing address. Applications should clearly state who the target users are, what the projected outcomes are and how many people will benefit from the grant.

The trust's website also states that applicants should give details of:

- The organisation – explaining its charitable aims and objectives, and giving its most recent annual income and expenditure, and current financial position (please do not send a full set of accounts)
- The project requiring funding – why it is needed, who will benefit and in what way
- The project budget – breakdown of costs, any money raised so far, and how the balance will be raised
- At this stage please do not send supporting books, brochures, DVDs, annual reports or accounts

Sources of information

Accounts; annual report; Charity Commission record; funder's website.

Dudley and Geoffrey Cox Charitable Trust

Medical research, young people, welfare, education and training, particularly in relation to construction or engineering

In order of preference: West London, the whole or part of Greater London, the South East; UK national charities or local charities meeting certain criteria may be supported (see further in the entry)

£227,500 (2015/16)

CC number: 277761

Trustees: Ian Ferres; Bill Underwood; Peter Watkins; John Wosner; Peter Magill; Michael Boyle.

Correspondent: c/o Giles Hutchinson, Charities Officer, Merchant Taylors' Company, 30 Threadneedle Street, London EC2R 8JB (tel: 020 7450 4440; email: charities@merchant-taylors.co.uk)

www.merchant-taylors.co.uk/ charities/charities-the-dudley- and-geoffrey-cox-charitable-trust

This trust was established under the name The Haymills Charitable Trust in 1979 by the late Dudley Cox and his son Geoffrey Cox. The trust is now known as Dudley and Geoffrey Cox Charitable Trust (to represent the endowment given by its settlors) and is administered by the Merchant Taylors' Company.

Areas of work
The trustees make grants to registered charities working in the following areas outlined on the trust's website:

- Medical research projects
- Young people
- Welfare – relating to 'improving the wellbeing, living conditions, comfort or general flourishing of particular groups of people who are burdened in some way' (examples include homelessness, people in prison, isolated older people, and people who are in financial hardship)

Grants for medical research are usually up to £5,000 and grants for young people and welfare typically range from £5,000 to £20,000 in a single year (although larger amounts can be considered if a proposal improves a charity's resilience or efficiency, or makes it better at achieving its charitable purposes, or will have a positive effect beyond its beneficiaries).

The trust also makes grants to help with the costs of formal education, although it does not accept unsolicited applications within this category. The trustees instead prefer to direct support exclusively to a list of educational

institutions which have a long-term connection with either the settlors or the Haymills group of companies, or with the construction industry.

Funding preferences (young people and welfare)
The trust's website details specific preferences for organisations applying within the categories of young people and welfare.

Geographical
Due to the historic links between the Haymills group of companies and West London, the trust's first preference is to support work which mainly or exclusively benefits the London boroughs with postcodes beginning with W, SW or NW. Its second preference is for work benefitting the whole or other parts of Greater London, and its third is for work in the South East.

According to the website, local charities outside these areas 'only have a chance of receiving funding in these categories for something which directly involves training beneficiaries in an aspect of engineering or construction'. National charities may only receive funding for a particular project within West London, or for a request which is strongly linked to engineering or construction.

Charity size and finances
The trustees' first preference is to support charities with an annual income of less than £100,000. Charities with an annual income of between £100,000 and £500,000 are the second preference.

National charities have been supported with projects that would make a significant difference to people living in West London and where there was no one else likely to provide anything similar.

Type of work
The trust has a preference for applications relating broadly to education or training, especially if it relates to construction or engineering, and even more so if the beneficiaries are likely to be from lower-income backgrounds.

The trustees' first preference is to fund either projects which have a clear outcome or proposals which will improve the charity's resilience, efficiency or ability to achieve its charitable purposes, or which will have a broader impact beyond its beneficiaries. However, core costs can also be supported.

Financial information
At the time of writing (June 2018) the latest accounts available for the trust were for 2015/16.

In 2015/16 the trust had assets of almost £7.4 million and an income of £246,500.

Grants totalled £227,500 and were distributed in the following categories:

Youth and welfare	24	£115,000
Medical	12	£65,000
Education	6	£47,500

Beneficiaries included: Merchant Taylors' School – Geoffrey Cox Scholarships (£40,000); Alzheimer's Research (£10,000); Childhood First, Cure Parkinson's Trust, Dream Arts, MS Society and Vision Care for the Homeless (£5,000 each); Derma Trust (£4,000); Acton and West London College (£300).

Exclusions
Applications from individuals are not accepted, nor are applications relating to beneficiaries outside the UK, environmental work or animal welfare.

Applications
In the first instance, see the trust's website for full details of funding preferences and guidance. All applications must be made using the online application form, which can be found on the website. Any application received by post or email will not be considered. Applications should be submitted between February and August. They will be shortlisted in September, and decisions are made in October or early November. Applicants will be notified of a decision on 15 November.

Sources of information
Accounts; annual report; Charity Commission record.

CRASH

Building projects for homelessness charities and hospices

UK

£311,500 (2016/17)

CC number: 1054107

Trustees: Alan Brookes; Michael Chaldecott; Jonathan Turk; Anthony Giddings; Kevon Corbett; Fiona Duncombe; Ian Bolster; Alastair Bell; Francois Morrow.

Correspondent: Francesca Roberts, The Gatehouse, 2 Devonhurst Place, Heathfield Terrace, London W4 4JD (tel: 020 8742 0717; email: froberts@crash. org.uk)

 www.crash.org.uk

 @CRASHcharity

CRASH is the charity of the construction industry and was previously known as the Construction Industry Relief, Assistance and Support for the Homeless and Hospices Ltd. The charity supports homeless charities and hospices with their building projects by providing pro bono expertise, building materials and cash sourced from its patron companies.

The charity helps with all scales of project – from complete refurbishments, new builds and extensions, to minor alterations or decoration of existing facilities. Grants range from £5,000 to £50,000.

Financial information

In 2016/17 the charity held assets of £689,000 and had an income of £1.2 million. Grants to 16 organisations totalled £311,500. A further £489,500 was donated in gifts-in-kind.

Beneficiaries included: Spitalfield Crypt Trust (£40,000); Edinburgh Cyrenians (£30,000); Highlands Homeless Trust (£20,000); Emmaus – Hastings and Rother (£5,000); Cirencester Housing for Young People (£4,200); The Manna Daycentre (£3,300).

Exclusions

CRASH can only accept applications that relate to buildings. Organisations must be a UK-registered charity.

Applications

Applications can be made through the charity's website. The charity's website states:

> Please call CRASH in advance of making your application to discuss your project and the ways in which CRASH may be able to help. Our experience shows the earlier CRASH is involved in the planning and construction process, the greater the impact of our help.

Sources of information

Accounts; annual report; Charity Commission record; funder's website.

The Elizabeth Creak Charitable Trust

🔍 Agricultural education, life sciences education

📍 UK, with preference for Warwickshire

£ £817,000 (2016/17)

CC number: 286838

Trustees: John Hulse; Nicholas Quilter Abell; Johnathan May.

Correspondent: John Hulse, Trustee, 27 Widney Road, Knowle, Solihull B93 9DX (tel: 01564 773951; email: creakcharity@hotmail.com)

The Elizabeth Creak Charitable Trust was established in 1983 and supports agricultural education in the UK, with preference for Warwickshire. The trust was set up by the late Elizabeth Creak, who passed away in 2013. Elizabeth was mentored by her uncle, Clyde Higgs, who had built up a thriving 2,000-acre dairy farm in Warwickshire that

Elizabeth inherited in 1963. Elizabeth was well respected among the farming community and was invited on the boards of many charitable organisations including the Royal Agricultural Society, The Stoneleigh Abbey Trust and the Stratford Society. She was also the first female chair of the National Farmers Union in Warwickshire and became the first female High Sheriff of Warwickshire. Elizabeth was also interested in and a keen supporter of local craftsmen, artists and the theatre.

As stated in the 2016/17 annual report:

> The principal aim of the Trust is to provide support and encourage new blood in farming through education and other means and finance projects to help agriculture succeed and ultimately thrive in a challenging modern environment.

The trust provides grants to organisations and funds Clyde Higgs Scholarships for agri-food-related courses, including MScs and PhDs, at various universities. The trust also funds the Chair in Food Security position at the University of Warwick. Preference is given to organisations that have a proven track record of supporting agricultural causes.

Financial information

In 2016/17 the trust held assets of £28.3 million and had an income of £1.27 million. Grants were made in the year totalling £817,000 and can be categorized as follows:

Life sciences education	48.9%	£384,000
Agricultural national support	27.4%	£215,000
Capital projects	19.1%	£150,000
Other local	4.6%	£36,000

Previous beneficiaries have included: Harper Adams (£525,000); Reading University (£70,000); Hampton Lucy Parochial Church Council and Studley College (£30,000 each).

Grants to institutions below £25,000 totalled £162,000.

Applications

The trustees usually meet every two months to consider grant applications. Apply in writing to the correspondent.

Sources of information

Accounts; annual report; Charity Commission record; further information provided by the funder.

Creative Scotland

🔍 The arts, film and creative industries

📍 Scotland

£ £40.3 million (2016/17)

Trustees: Robert Wilson; Iain Aitchinson; David Brew; Karen Forbes; Erin Forster; Sheila Murray; Cate

Nelson-Shaw; Barclay Price; Karthik Subramanya.

Correspondent: Enquiries Service, Waverley Gate, 2–4 Waterloo Place, Edinburgh EH1 3EG (tel: 0845 603 6000; email: enquiries@creativescotland.com)

 www.creativescotland.com

Creative Scotland is a public body supporting the arts, screen and creative industries across the whole of Scotland, on behalf of everyone who lives, works or visits there. It redistributes income from two primary sources – the Scottish Government and the UK National Lottery – having taken on the funding responsibilities and investment strands of the Scottish Arts Council in 2010.

Funding programmes

Creative Scotland's website outlines its four main funding programmes:

Regular Funding

Regular Funding is one of Creative Scotland's main funds for arts and creative organisations in Scotland, offering stable long-term funding support. It will fund ongoing running costs, helping organisations to plan, operate and deliver their work over three years. It can also be used to help the organisation change or develop their future plans.

Open Project Funding

This fund is run by Creative Scotland for artists, groups, and creative organisations looking to apply for money to support them on their artistic or creative projects.

Anyone can come to Creative Scotland with their ideas, and this fund will support a wide range of things, from small one-off events to longer programmes of work that can last for up to two years.

The types of things that this fund will support include:

- Projects which are about helping an artist to develop their skills
- Projects that create something new and high quality, in any art form
- Projects which are aiming to present high quality work to audiences, or projects which try to develop and reach new audiences for the arts
- Projects which encourage more people to take part in artistic and creative activity

Targeted Funds

Targeted Funds are funds which exist to support specific activities – as opposed to funds which are more general, supporting any activity and open to anyone to apply to.

They are usually set up to help support a specific art form or type of work, or to help meet a strategic need or gap. Often the funding has only been made available because the money is 'ring-fenced' – meaning that it can only be used to fund that activity and nothing else.

Funds Delivered by Partners

Funds Delivered by Partners are funds which Creative Scotland supports but the application process is overseen by another partner organisation.

This activity can include funding programmes which other organisations deliver for us, as well as training programmes, prizes, awards or residencies that we've funded and other partners are delivering.

Financial information

In 2016/17 Creative Scotland held assets of £6.8 million and had an income of £3.1 million. Grants totalled £40.3 million and were broken down as follows:

Regular Funded Organisations	£26.9 million
Scottish Government	£11.3 million
Targeted funding	£1.2 million
Capital Grants	£536,000
Open Project Funding	£375,000

Beneficiaries included: Youth Music Initiative (£7.6 million); Expo Fund (£1.8 million); Sistema (£415,000); Festivals Edinburgh (£200,000); Get Scotland (£50,000).

Applications

For all information regarding grant applications visit Creative Scotland's website.

Sources of information

Accounts; annual report; funder's website.

Credit Suisse EMEA Foundation

🔍 Young people's education

📍 Countries where Credit Suisse has offices in Europe, the Middle East and Africa

💷 £1.6 million (2016)

CC number: 1122472

Trustees: Stefano Toffolo; Patrick Flaherty; Michelle Mendelsson; Nicholas Wilcock; Markus Lammer; Colin Hely-Hutchinson; Mark Ellis; Marisa Drew; Marc Pereira-Mendoza; Angus Kidd; Guy Varney; Natalia Nicolaidis.

Correspondent: Kate Butchart, Corporate Citizenship Team, Credit Suisse, 1 Cabot Square, London E14 4QJ (email: emea.corporatecitizenship@credit-suisse.com)

The foundation was established by Credit Suisse and channels the group's corporate citizenship activities in Europe, the Middle East and Africa.

According to the 2016 accounts, the foundation supports 'innovative organisations providing opportunities to youth through education' and 'projects and organisations that aim to improve the educational attainment,

employability and aspirations of young disadvantaged people'.

Grants are usually made to registered charities (although other charitable organisations may be considered occasionally). The foundation looks to provide funding for two to five years if possible and 'follow on funding' may be offered to charities which meet the foundation's priorities effectively. Grants may be given for specific projects or for core costs and salaries.

The foundation also makes grants for the Credit Suisse group's Charity of the Year programme, and occasionally for other charities nominated by employees.

Financial information

In 2016 the foundation had assets of £1.6 million and an income of £1.8 million, most of which came from Credit Suisse AG, with a small amount from investments. Grants were made to 11 organisations totalling £1.6 million.

Beneficiaries included: Teach First (£657,000); Frontline (£255,000); St Giles Trust (£220,500); Fundación Exit (£97,000); Institute for Teaching and The Access Project (£30,000 each).

Exclusions

According to the foundation's 2016 accounts, grants will not be made for the following purposes:

- To directly replace or subsidise statutory funding or for activities that are the responsibility of statutory bodies
- Administration and costs not directly associated with the application
- Individuals
- Promotion of religious or political causes
- Holidays
- Retrospective funding
- General appeals
- Animal welfare
- Festivals, sports and leisure activities

Applications

Apply in writing to the correspondent.

Sources of information

Accounts; annual report; Charity Commission record.

The Crerar Trust

🔍 Health, social welfare

📍 Scotland

💷 £529,500 (2016/17)

CC number: 221335

Trustees: Patrick Crerar; Jeanette Crerar; James Barrack; Sheila Crerar.

Correspondent: Patrick Crerar, Newmains, Stenton, Dunbar, East Lothian EH42 1TQ (email: clerk@crerartrust.com)

The trust was established with shares from the company formerly known as North British Hotels Group, for general charitable purposes. Giving is concentrated in areas where the company operates, mainly Scotland, although one hotel is located in Otley, North Yorkshire. The trust's only source of income is from its investment in Crerar Hotels Group Ltd.

The trust has a non-trading subsidiary trust, the North British Hotel Cancer and Leukaemia in Childhood Edinburgh Trust.

Financial information

In 2016/17 the trust had assets of £10.9 million and an income of £231,000. In this financial year the trust awarded £529,500 in grants to 74 organisations.

Beneficiaries included: The Hospitality Industry Trust and Scotland Yard Adventure Centre (£25,000 each); Funding Neuro (£20,000); Homeless World Cup (£15,000); Robert Gordon University Foundation (£10,000); Over the Wall (£5,000); Nil by Mouth (£4,000); Cosgrove Care (£3,000); Edinburgh International Book Festival (£1,500); Action on Hearing Loss Scotland (£800).

Exclusions

No grants are given to individuals.

Applications

Apply on an application form available from the correspondent.

Sources of information

Accounts; annual report; Charity Commission record.

England and Wales Cricket Trust

🔍 Cricket, community development, young people

📍 England and Wales

💷 £10.5 million (2016/17)

CC number: 1112540

Trustees: C. Duncan Fearnley; Rear Admiral Roger Moylan-Jones; Ian Lovett; Ebony-Jewel Rainford-Brent; Tom Harrison; Scott Smith.

Correspondent: Claire Harris, Lord's Cricket Ground, St John's Wood, London NW8 8QZ (email: claire.harris@ecb.co.uk)

 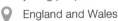 www.ecb.co.uk

Established in 2005, the England and Wales Cricket Trust is the charitable arm of the England and Wales Cricket Board. The ECB website states:

> The England and Wales Cricket Trust (EWCT) promotes community participation in cricket as a means of promoting and improving health – which is a charitable purpose. The EWCT also promotes work to improve provision of cricket in schools, clubs and other youth cricket activities. Activities funded by the EWCT must benefit the community not just a small group or elite. This is a primary obligation of an applicant when applying the funds provided by EWCT.

Grant schemes

Small grants scheme

Cricket clubs can apply for a small grant (from £1,000 to £4,000) towards the purchase of any relevant products or materials (and associated professional labour costs) under one of the following project themes:

- Covers
- Kitchen and social area
- Energy/water consumption
- Flood defence measures

Interest-free Loan Scheme

The trust runs the scheme through which it finances capital projects 'to help create a sustainable future for cricket'. Loans are given in support of projects within the following areas: buildings; equipment; fine turf; land purchase for cricketing purposes; and non-turf. A minimum of 10% partnership funding is required from the applicant.

All ECB-affiliated cricket clubs and other organisations that can demonstrate achievement/delivery of the trust's charitable aims can apply. The ECB website further states that 'ECB Clubmark registration or accreditation is not a requirement'.

Detailed information on all current schemes, including guidance notes and application forms can be found on the ECB's website.

Financial information

In 2016/17 the trust had assets of £42.6 million and an income of £10.5 million. Grants, excluding governance costs, were made totalling £10.5 million.

A list of beneficiaries was not provided in the trust's accounts.

Applications

To apply to the ECB small grants scheme, applicants should contact their local County Cricket Board (CCB) and request an application form and guidance notes.

Applicants wishing to apply to the EWCT Interest Free Loan Scheme should firstly download and read the guidance notes from the ECB's website. If they believe that their project is eligible for funding, applicants should then download, complete and return an expression of interest form, also available on the ECB's website.

Sources of information

Accounts; annual report; Charity Commission record; funder's website.

Cripplegate Foundation

General charitable purposes including: young people, social isolation, mental health and well-being, advice and access to services, supporting families, financial inclusion

London borough of Islington and part of the City of London

£1.7 million (2017)

CC number: 207499

Trustee: Cripplegate Foundation Ltd – Sole Corporate Trustee.

Correspondent: Programme Team, 13 Elliott's Place, Islington, London N1 8HX (tel: 020 7288 6940; email: grants@cripplegate.org.uk)

 www.cripplegate.org

 @cripplegatefdn

The first recorded gift to the Church of St Giles without Cripplegate was by the Will of John Sworder dated 2 April 1500. Cripplegate Foundation was established in 1891 by a Charity Commission Scheme which amalgamated all the non-ecclesiastical charitable donations previously administered as separate trusts. The early governors of the foundation built an institute on Golden Lane, containing reading and reference libraries, news and magazine rooms, classrooms, a theatre and even a rifle range. The institute was run until 1973, when it was closed and the foundation became a grant-making charity.

The original beneficial area of the foundation was the ancient parish of St Giles, Cripplegate, to which was added in 1974 the ancient parish of St Luke's, Old Street. On 1 April 2008, a Charity Commission Scheme extended the foundation's area of benefit. This now covers the Parish of St Giles, Cripplegate in the City of London and the former parish of St Luke, Old Street (both as constituted by the Act of Parliament of the year 1732–3), and the London Borough of Islington.

The foundation now

Cripplegate Foundation is an independent charity with the vision 'of a society where everyone has the opportunity to live a rewarding and fulfiled life free from poverty and inequality'. By funding voluntary organisations and working in partnership with others, the foundation works to bring about change which will positively transform the lives of some of Islington's most disadvantaged residents.

The foundation's priorities are:

- Improving the voluntary sector's ability to serve local residents
- Building the resilience of vulnerable residents
- Increasing the resources available in Islington
- Influencing policy and practice that affects Islington

Future plans

The 2017 annual report provides the following information on the foundation's future priorities:

> Reflecting the Foundation's commitment to continual learning, priority areas for 2018 will respond to external opportunities and change. In 2018 key priorities for the Foundation will be:
>
> - Strengthening and developing partnerships and collaborations which are at the heart of the Foundation's approach to effecting change in Islington
> - Sharing learning this year we plan to share learning from our Development Partners, Catalyst and Young Catalyst programmes. We aim to inform and influence a range of audiences including Islington voluntary organisations and public services, Islington Giving supporters, funders and policy-makers
> - Influencing others by convening meetings with grantees, stakeholders and those interested in Islington, and creating change through innovative approaches to grant making
> - Maximising our assets by reviewing the use of our building and developing our Governor and staff assets
> - Strengthening Islington Giving by developing our approach to fundraising so that staff, Governors and Board members can more effectively advocate and support Islington Giving and bring more resources into the borough
> - Communicating impact by improving how we tell the human stories of our work
> - Developing our 2019–2021 strategy which will identify opportunities to make the most impact for Islington residents

Grant-giving programmes

The foundation gives grants to organisations through its own grants programme as well as those it administers in partnership.

Main Grants Programme – support for organisations with substantial, flexible and often long-term funding to enable them to effectively reach local residents.

Islington Council Community Chest – funding of up to £5,000 per year for voluntary organisations that work with Islington residents expcriencing poverty and/or isolation.

111

Catalyst – a small grants scheme run in collaboration with Cloudesley, enabling residents to pursue opportunities they could otherwise not afford.

Development Partners – the foundation's four development partners work together to find innovative, effective ways of helping Islington residents.

Islington Giving – shines a light on the issues of poverty and inequality and harnesses resources to address them.

Financial information

In 2017 the foundation had assets of £40.4 million and an income of £2.19 million. Grants awarded to organisations, listed at Appendix 3 to the financial statements for 2017, totalled £1.7 million. Grants to organisations categorised by theme were as follows:

Confronting social isolation	£541,500
Investing in young people	£329,500
Financial inclusion capability	£311,500
Mental health and well-being	£278,000
Advice and access to services	£223,000
Supporting families	£168,000

Beneficiaries included: Help on Your Doorstep (£165,000); The Brandon Centre (£73,000); The Claremont Project (£38,000); CASA Social Care and Solace Women's Aid (£10,000 each); Spitz Charitable Trust (£4,000); House of AMAU (£700).

Exclusions

Eligibility criteria of each of the foundation's programmes are provided on the website.

Applications

Details of the application process and deadlines for each programme can be found on the foundation's website. Updates on funding opportunities can be found on the foundation's Twitter profile.

Sources of information

Accounts; annual report; Charity Commission record; funder's website.

The Cross Trust

Religion, education, training, relief of poverty

UK and overseas, in particular Japan, New Zealand, Scotland and South Africa

£423,500 to organisations (2016/17)

CC number: 1127046

Trustees: David Lilley; Jenny Farmer; Douglas Olsen; Michael Farmer.

Correspondent: James Foskett, Cansdales, Bourbon Court, Nightingales Corner, Amersham HP7 9QS (tel: 01494 765428; email: mailto@cansdales.co.uk)

The objects of the trust are to advance any religious or other charitable object, including the support of any religious or charitable institution or work for the furtherance of religious or secular education, to advance the Christian faith in the United Kingdom or overseas, the relief of the poor and needy and comfort of the sick and aged.

Financial information

In 2016/17 the trust had assets of £262,500 and an income of £338,500. Grants to 14 organisations totalled £423,500. A further £108,000 was given to individuals.

Beneficiaries included: The Message Trust (£150,000); George Whitefield College (£100,000); Musk Ministry Foundation (£37,500); The A Trust (£12,500); West London Mission (£10,000); Diocese of York (£6,000).

Applications

Apply in writing to the correspondent.

Sources of information

Accounts; annual report; Charity Commission record.

The Peter Cruddas Foundation

 Children and young people

UK, with a particular interest in London

£404,000 (2016/17)

CC number: 1117323

Trustees: Rt Hon. Lord Young of Graffham; Peter Cruddas; Martin Paisner.

Correspondent: Stephen Cox, Foundation Administrator, 133 Houndsditch, London EC3A 7BX (tel: 020 3003 8360; email: s.cox@petercruddasfoundation.org.uk)

www.petercruddasfoundation.org.uk

Established in December 2006, this is the charitable foundation of Peter Cruddas, founder of City financial trading group CMC Markets, who has pledged to donate at least £100 million to good causes during his lifetime.

The foundation's website provides the following information about its funding priorities:

The Foundation gives priority to programmes designed to help disadvantaged and disengaged young people in the age range of 14 to 30, to pursue pathways to Education, Training and Employment with the ultimate aim of helping them to become financially independent.

Preference will be given to the support of projects undertaken by UK-registered charitable organisations (currently not community interest companies or social

enterprises), in England and Wales only, for the benefit of such people.

The foundation's priority funding streams are listed on its website as:

- Pathways/support for young disadvantaged or disengaged young people in the age range 14 to 30 into education, training or employment
- Work experience/skills projects for young people aged 16 to 30
- Youth work in London; particularly evening work for disadvantaged young people aged 16 to 30

Financial information

In 2016/17 the foundation held assets of £341,000 and had an income of £792,000. The majority of the income came in donations from CMC Markets UK plc (£75,000) and Peter Cruddas (£675,000). Grants to 22 organisations totalled £404,000.

Beneficiaries included: Royal Opera House Foundation (£200,000); Ort UK (£25,000); Ovarian Cancer Action (£10,000); Duke of Edinburgh Trust (£5,000); Wings South West (£4,900); Tall Ships Youth Trust (£1,000); HemiHelp (£500).

Exclusions

The following are excluded: capital projects; community interest companies; and social enterprises.

Applications

Application forms are available to download from the foundation's website (www.petercruddasfoundation.org.uk).

The foundation provides guidance on how to complete the application form, also available on the website. Application forms must be sent by email.

Sources of information

Accounts; annual report; Charity Commission record; guidelines for applicants; funder's website.

Cruden Foundation Ltd

Social welfare, medical, arts, education, heritage and conservation

Scotland

£326,000 (2016/17)

OSCR number: SC004987

Correspondent: The Trustees, Baberton House, Juniper Green, Edinburgh EH14 3HN

Cruden Foundation Ltd is the company charity of Cruden Ltd, one of the largest independent development and construction groups in Scotland.

The object of the foundation is to support and contribute to institutions for the benefit of the community. According to the Cruden Ltd website, the foundation supports small and medium-sized charities in Scotland.

Financial information

In 2016/17 the foundation had assets of £10 million and an income of £680,000. Grants awarded to organisations totalled £326,000 and were broken down as follows:

Medical	£103,000
Social welfare	£99,500
Arts	£92,000
Education	£17,500
Heritage/conservation	£14,500

Beneficiaries included: Edinburgh International Festival (£20,000); Marie Curie Cancer Care (£12,500); The Edinburgh Clothing Store (£10,000); The Cure Parkinson's Trust (£9,500); Scottish Ballet (£5,000); Habitat for Humanity GB (£3,500); St Columba's Hospice (£3,000); Bobath Scotland (£2,500).

Applications

Applications can be made in writing to the correspondent and should be accompanied by most recent accounts.

Sources of information

Accounts; annual report; OSCR record.

The Ronald Cruickshanks Foundation

 General charitable purposes

 UK, particularly Faversham and Folkstone

(£) Around £195,000 (2016/17)

CC number: 296075

Trustees: Susan Cloke; Ian Cloke; Jan Schilder.

Correspondent: Ian Cloke, Trustee, Rivendell, Teddars Leas, Etchinghill, Folkestone CT18 8AE (tel: 01303 862812; email: ian@iancloke.co.uk)

The settlor of this charity died in 1995 leaving his shareholding in Howe Properties Ltd to the foundation, under the terms of his will. The foundation's objects are to provide general charitable and educational assistance as the trustees deem suitable with the knowledge of the wishes given to them by the settlor in his lifetime. The assistance is to include those in poverty and need in Folkestone and Faversham and their surrounding areas.

Financial information

In 2016/17 the foundation had an income of £7,000 and a total expenditure of £202,500. As the income was below the required threshold, no annual report is available for this financial year. However, based on previous years, we estimate the total awarded in grants to be £195,000.

Previous beneficiaries have included: Demelza House Children's Hospice and The Pilgrims Hospice – Canterbury (£10,000 each); Parish Church of St Mary and St Eanswythe – Fabric Fund (£8,000); Folkestone Town Mayor's Christmas Fund and Jesuit Missions (£4,000 each); Battersea Dogs and Cats Home (£3,000); Alkham Valley Community Association, Folkestone Heritage – Folkestone Museum, Teenage Cancer Trust and Wheelchair Users' Group (£1,000 each); Disability Information Services Kent – DISK, Highview School, The Lee Smith Research Foundation and The Royal British Legion – National (£500 each); Shelter (£250).

Applications

Apply in writing to the correspondent. The foundation's annual report for 2015/16 further explains:

> The Trustees meet as and when necessary although always in late October or early November each year to review the many requests for assistance before determining the annual distributions which are issued on, or as close to, the anniversary of the Settlor's death on the 7th December.

Our research suggests that applications should be received by the foundation by the end of September.

Sources of information

Accounts; annual report; Charity Commission record.

CSIS Charity Fund

 Grants are made to UK organisations that are wholly or partly devoted to assisting civil and public servants and their families with social welfare or health needs

 UK

(£) £701,000 (2016)

CC number: 1121671

Trustees: Gillian Noble; Charles Cochrane; Ray Flanigan; Beryl Evans; Kevin Holliday; Christopher Furlong; Tunde Ojetola; Sally Bundock; Julia Wood; Craig Pemberton; Rebecca Gooch; Tom Hoyle; Daniel Hewitt.

Correspondent: Helen Harris, Secretary, 7 Colman House, King Street, Maidstone, Kent ME14 1DD (tel: 01622 766963; email: helenharris@csis.co.uk)

(globe) www.csischarityfund.org

The CSIS Charity Fund was originally a benevolent fund established over 100 years ago by the name of the Civil Service Widows and Orphan's Fund. Its aim was to provide grants to support the dependants of deceased policy holders of the Civil Service Insurance Society (CSIS), a not-for-profit insurance intermediary that provides insurance products to civil and public servants.

The fund later changed its name in 2009 to the CSIS Charity Fund after establishing itself as a charitable company and now has a grant fund of over £750,000 per year to distribute among civil and public service charities and other charitable causes. The fund's income is mostly derived from the annual trading surplus of the CSIS.

The fund supports projects that benefit the dependants of deceased CSIS policy holders and any former, serving or retired civil and public servants in hardship or distress.

Grants

The fund's grant-making policy is available to download from the website. It details the trustees' priorities, which are currently stated as follows:

- To provide continuing financial support to the widows and other dependents of deceased policy holders of the Civil Service Insurance Society (CSIS), which the charity supports with annual grants and help with specific costs such as phone bills, replacing cookers, etc.
- To continue to provide general support to the Charity for Civil Servants for their hardship grants
- To provide support to the other civil and public service charities with which CSIS Charity Fund has had a long standing relationship, most notably the BT Benevolent Fund, the Rowland Hill Fund and the Civil Service Retirement Fellowship, smaller welfare organisations and benevolent funds that provide support to civil and public servants and their dependants, and other charities and not-for-profit organisations which have a clear and direct link with the public services

The fund makes the majority of its grants to civil and public service charities, although it does not exclusively do so. The trustees will also consider making grants to other organisations, such as hospices that work with beneficiaries that include 'former, serving and retired civil and public servants and their dependants and which are very clearly and directly relieving need, hardship and distress'.

The trustees have some preference for funding less popular organisations, without access to other substantial income, where the fund's grant will make a significant difference. Grants tend to be, where possible, unrestricted and are usually one-off payments or short-term commitments. Funding may be considered for equipment or training as long as a clear benefit to beneficiaries can be demonstrated.

Beneficiaries

Beneficiaries

According to the fund's website 'who constitutes a civil or public servant has a wide interpretation in the charity's objects' and includes:

▶ Employees of government departments
▶ Government agencies and non-departmental public bodies
▶ The forces
▶ The NHS
▶ Teachers
▶ Local government employees
▶ Railway workers
▶ Privatised bodies that were formerly part of the civil service (such as BT and the Post Office) whose pensioners were civil servants when they were working

Some preference is given to projects that support the above beneficiaries who are experiencing ill health or disability; family crisis; and/or who are older people or carers. A list of organisations that have previously received a grant is available on the fund's website.

Financial information

In 2016 the fund had assets of £2.5 million and an income of £844,500. Grants awarded to organisations totalled £701,000 and grants to individuals totalled £26,000. Grants were broken down as follows:

Major public sector charities supported by the fund for several years	£296,500
Smaller public sector charities and trade union welfare funds	£278,500
Hospices	£71,500
Smaller charities supported by the fund for several years	£55,000
Widows of deceased CSIS policy holders	£26,000

Beneficiaries included: The Charity for Civil Servants (£125,000); Railway Benefit Fund (£70,000); Hospice UK (£50,500); Rowland Hill Fund (£50,000); Relatives and Residents Association and Veterans Aid (£10,000 each); National Federation of Occupational Pensioners: NFOP (£8,000); Music in Hospitals (£1,000).

Applications

Contact the fund's secretary in the first instance.

Sources of information

Accounts; annual report; Charity Commission record; guidelines for applicants; funder's website.

Cullum Family Trust

🔍 Specialist education for children with autism

📍 Surrey

💷 £531,500 (2016/17)

CC number: 1117056

Trustees: Ann Cullum; Claire Cullum; Peter Cullum; Simon Cullum.

Correspondent: Peter Cullum, Trustee, Wealden Hall, Parkfield, Sevenoaks TN15 0HX

The trust was established in 2006 by the entrepreneur, Peter Cullum. The 2016/17 annual report states that the aim of the trust is to:

Meet the need identified by Surrey County Council and the NAS to provide specialist education targeted at children in Surrey who are on the autism spectrum, but who typically have good cognitive ability. Because of their autism, many of these children lack the necessary social and communication skills to prosper in mainstream educational settings and are often excluded for extended periods.

Financial information

In 2016/17 the trust had assets of £29.6 million and an income of £1.4 million. Grants awarded to organisations totalled £531,500.

Beneficiaries included: National Autistic Society (£377,000); The Sussex Community Foundation (£100,000); Born Free Foundation (£19,000); Canine Partners and London Philharmonic (£5,000 each).

Applications

Apply in writing to the correspondent.

Sources of information

Accounts; annual report; Charity Commission record.

The Cunningham Trust

🔍 Medical research

📍 Scotland

💷 £247,000 (2016/17)

OSCR number: SC013499

Trustees: Dr D. Corner; A. C. Caithness; Dr D. McD. Greenhough.

Correspondent: The Trustees, Murray Donald Drummond Cook LLP, Kinburn Castle, St Andrews, Fife KY16 9DR

This trust's main purpose is the encouragement of medical research and the relief of suffering. Since it was set up, in 1984, the income has been committed to medical research, mainly at Scottish university medical departments. It supports specific projects rather than giving general funding to research bodies.

According to its 2016/17 accounts the trust's objects are:

▶ To support research into the diagnosis, cause, treatment and the prevention of disease and illness and to support and encourage facilities for the diagnosis, investigation, control and treatment of disease and illness

▶ To assist and co-operate with Public Bodies, Universities, medical practitioners (general or otherwise), voluntary and charitable organisations and others in efforts to provide facilities for furthering the relief of suffering, distress or illness
▶ To consider applications for funds and to make grants of funds, whether by way of regular grants of income, capital sums, special grants, continuing grants, endowment and maintenance of fellowships or any combination thereof for the fundamental purpose of this Trust and that whether directly or indirectly through any other Trust or Association

Financial information

In 2016/17 the trust had assets of £10.3 million and an income of £268,000. Three grants were made to two organisations totalling £247,000.

Beneficiaries included: University of St Andrews (£164,000 in two grants); University of Edinburgh (£82,500).

Exclusions

Grants are unlikely to be made available to non-regular beneficiaries.

Applications

Apply in writing to the correspondent.

Sources of information

OSCR record.

Itzchok Meyer Cymerman Trust Ltd

🔍 Orthodox Jewish religion and education, social welfare, relief of sickness, general charitable purposes

📍 UK and Israel

💷 £492,000 (2016/17)

CC number: 265090

Trustees: H. Bondi; Mrs S. Cymerman; Sara Heitner; Ian Heitner; Michael Cymerman; Leonard Bondi; Bernard Hoffman; Leonard Bondi; Michel Gehler.

Correspondent: Ian Heitner, Trustee, 497 Holloway Road, London N7 6LE

The trust was established in 1972 and its objectives are the advancement of religion and education in accordance with the Orthodox Jewish faith, the relief of people who are sick and in need, and general charitable purposes.

Almost all the trust's grants are to Jewish charitable organisations, although, occasionally, grants to individuals in need are also made. Many grants are given to the same organisations each year.

Financial information

In 2016/17 the trust had assets of £17.8 million and had an income of £1.6 million. During the year, the trust gave a total of £492,000 in grants to organisations. Grants were distributed as follows:

Advancement of religion	£201,000
Education	£106,000
Relief of poverty	£165,000
Medical care and research	£21,000

Beneficiaries included: Russian Immigrant Aid Fund (£230,500); Ichud Mosdos Gur (£68,000); Friends of Gur Foundation Israel (£62,000); Society of Friends of the Torah Ltd (£20,000).

Grants under £20,000 totalled £112,000.

Applications

Apply in writing to the correspondent.

Sources of information

Accounts; annual return; Charity Commission record.

The D'Oyly Carte Charitable Trust

  Arts, medical welfare, environment

UK

£1.24 million (2016/17)

CC number: 1112457

Trustees: Jeremy Pemberton; Francesca Radcliffe; Julia Sibley; Henry Freeland; Andrew Jackson; Michael O'Brien; Andrew Wimble.

Correspondent: Grants Administrator, 6 Trull Farm Buildings, Tetbury, Gloucestershire GL8 8SQ (tel: 020 3637 3003; email: info@ doylycartecharitabletrust.org)

 www.doylycartecharitabletrust.org

The trust was founded in 1972 by Dame Bridget D'Oyly Carte, granddaughter of the founder of both the Savoy Theatre and the Savoy Hotel. The trust supports general charitable causes connected with the arts, medical welfare and the environment. Certain charities in which the founder took a special interest continue to be supported on a regular basis.

The D'Oyly Carte Charitable Trust is entirely separate from the aims and objectives of The D'Oyly Carte Opera Trust.

Grants programmes
The following information is taken from the 'Grant-making Priorities 2015–18' section of the trust's 2016/17 annual report and accounts.

The Arts

- Promoting access to and education in the arts, with a particular focus on choirs, performing arts, music and drama
- Projects that involve disadvantaged or marginalised young people, people with disabilities or special needs, and the wider community

Medical Welfare

- Providing music and art therapy to improve the quality of life for older people or those with disabilities in palliative care or hospices, and especially in hospices that operate on a low income and/or in remote parts of the UK
- Holidays and respite breaks for young carers
- Support for charities seeking to rehabilitate young people on the fringes of society to improve their employability and diminish the risk of social exclusion

The Environment

- Conservation of the countryside and its woodlands, with emphasis on the encouragement of voluntary work and projects that include young people
- Protection of species and habitats under threat in the UK
- Heritage conservation within the UK based on value to, and use by the local community for example finding new uses for buildings of architectural and historic merit to encourage the widest possible cross-section of use
- Rural crafts and skills in heritage conservation, with emphasis on increasingly rare skills that would otherwise be lost
- Social and therapeutic horticulture, particularly projects for people living with disabilities or ill-health

Grants start at around £500. The majority of grants are for amounts under £5,000 although some can be for larger amounts. Grants are usually made by the trust on a one-off basis although fixed-term grants are also agreed from time to time for a maximum period of three years, particularly in respect of bursary funding for educational establishments, mainly in the arts sector, and to help newly created charities become established. Recipients of these grants are required to report regularly to the trust for monitoring purposes.

The trustees have continued their commitment to make grants to charities that do not have a high profile in order to create significant impact on the work of the charities concerned. Recognising the day-to-day funding needs of these charities, the trustees also consider applications for core costs.

Financial information

In 2016/17 the trust held assets of £57.5 million and had an income of £1.48 million. There were 386 grants made totalling nearly £1.24 million which can be broken down as follows:

Arts	£602,000
Medical welfare	£523,000
Environment	£162,500

Beneficiaries included: City and Guilds of London Art School (£10,000); Brighton Early Music Festival (£5,000); Ardent Theatre Company, Blackheath Concert Halls, British Liver Trust,

Chelsea and Westminster Health Charity, Garden Organic (£3,000 each); Cancer Focus Northern Ireland (£2,000 each).

Exclusions

The trust is unlikely to support the following:

- Advocacy
- Animal welfare
- Campaigning or lobbying
- Capital projects (unless a specific element falls within the trust's remit)
- Community transport organisations or services
- Conferences and seminars
- Counselling and psychotherapy services
- Cultural festivals
- Drug abuse or alcoholism rehabilitation
- Educational projects linked to the National Curriculum
- Endowments
- Exhibitions
- Expeditions and overseas travel
- Friend/PTAs
- General and round-robin appeals
- Individuals
- Large national charities
- Medical research
- NHS hospitals for operational and building costs
- Organisations that are not Registered Charities (or accepted as Exempt Charities)
- Projects taking place or benefitting people outside the UK
- Recordings and commissioning of new works
- Religious causes and activities
- Routine maintenance of religious or historic buildings
- Replacement or subsidy of statutory funding or for work we consider should be funded by government
- Sport
- Umbrella organisations
- Universities, colleges and schools (other than those dedicated to the arts)
- Schools, nurseries and playgroups (other than those for special needs children)
- Works to enable a building to comply with the Disability Discrimination Act 2010

The trustees do not consider requests from charities that have had an application turned down until two years have elapsed after the date of rejection.

Applications

The trust's website states that all grant applications must be made online. If you require an accessible format of the application form than email info@ doylycartecharitabletrust.org stating your preferred format. The trust's website lists the relevant submission dates and has detailed guidelines on how to apply. The trustees usually consider applications three times a year in March, July and November.

Sources of information

Accounts; annual report; Charity Commission record; further information provided by the funder; funder's website.

The Daiwa Anglo-Japanese Foundation

 Anglo-Japanese relations

UK and Japan

£293,000 to organisations (2016/17)

CC number: 299955

Trustees: Lady Barbara Judge; Paul Dimond; Sir Peter Williams; Prof. Richard Bowring; Yusuke Kawamura; Masaki Orita; Shigeharu Suzuki; Prof. Hirotaka Takeuchi; Stephen Barber; Dr Victoria Tuke; James Harding.

Correspondent: Jason James, Director General and Secretary, 13–14 Cornwall Terrace, London NW1 4QP (email: grants@dajf.org.uk)

 www.dajf.org.uk

 facebook.com/DaiwaFoundation

 @DaiwaFoundation

 @daiwafoundation

The Daiwa Anglo-Japanese Foundation was established in 1988 with a benefaction from Daiwa Securities Co. Ltd. The foundation's purpose is to support closer links between Britain and Japan. It does this by:

▪ Making grants available to individuals, institutions and organisations to promote links between the UK and Japan in all fields of activity

▪ Enabling British and Japanese students and academics to further their education through exchanges and other bilateral initiatives

▪ Awarding of Daiwa Scholarships for British graduates to study and undertake work placements in Japan

▪ Organising a year-round programme of events to increase understanding of Japan in the UK

Daiwa Foundation Japan House, the London-based headquarters, acts as a centre for UK-Japan relations in Britain by offering a wide programme of lectures, seminars, book launches, courses and exhibitions as well as meeting rooms for Japan-related activities and facilities for visiting academics.

The foundation is represented in Japan by its Tokyo office, which provides local assistance to Daiwa scholars and administers grant applications from Japan. It also handles general enquiries and forms part of the network of organisations supporting links between the UK and Japan.

The foundation awards grants to individuals and organisations in the UK and Japan in all areas of the visual and performing arts, the humanities, the social sciences, science and engineering, mathematics, business studies and education (including schools and universities) and grassroots and professional groups.

The foundation's website provides a useful summary of its grant-making programmes.

Daiwa Foundation Small Grants

Grants of £2,000 to £7,000 are available to individuals, societies, associations or other bodies in the UK or Japan to promote and support interaction between the two countries. Daiwa Foundation Small Grants can cover all fields of activity, including educational and grassroots exchanges, research travel, the organisation of conferences, exhibitions, and other projects and events that fulfil this broad objective. New initiatives are especially encouraged and the foundation will consider grants for pump-priming projects.

Daiwa Foundation Awards

Awards of £7,000 to £15,000 are available for collaborative projects that enable British and Japanese partners to work together, preferably in the context of an institutional relationship. Daiwa Foundation Awards can cover projects in most academic, professional, arts, cultural and educational fields. (Applications in the field of science can also be considered.)

Daiwa Adrian Prizes

Daiwa Adrian Prizes are awarded in recognition of significant scientific collaboration between British and Japanese research teams in the field of pure science or the application of science. They acknowledge those research teams who have combined excellence in scientific achievement with a long-term contribution to UK-Japan relations.

Daiwa Foundation Art Prize

The Daiwa Foundation Art Prize is an open submission prize which offers a British artist a first solo exhibition at a gallery in Tokyo, Japan. The winner is awarded a £5,000 participation fee plus travel and accommodation costs for a period in Japan to coincide with the opening of the exhibition. The artist will also be offered introductions to key individuals and organisations in the Japanese contemporary art world.

Financial information

In 2016/17 the foundation held assets of £41.7 million and had an income of £391,000. Grants totalled £321,500 of which £293,500 was awarded to 88 organisations and the remaining £28,000 was awarded to ten individuals.

Previous beneficiaries have included: Royal College of Art (£7,000); Osaka International Cancer Center (£4,000); Abandon Normal Devices, Holbrook Primary School – Wiltshire, Henry Moore Foundation and Postcode Films (£3,000 each); University of York (£2,100); Starfish Kitchen (£2,000).

Exclusions

See the foundation's website for detailed exclusions for each grant programme. The foundation will typically not fund the following:

▪ General appeals
▪ Capital expenditure (e.g. building refurbishment, equipment acquisition, etc.)
▪ Salary costs or professional fees
▪ Commissions for works of art
▪ Retrospective grants
▪ Replacement of statutory funding
▪ Commercial activities

Applications

Application forms are available to download from the foundation's website where you can also find details of deadlines, further guidance and eligibility criteria. For Daiwa Foundation Small Grants and Daiwa Foundation Awards, there are two application deadlines each year, 31 March (for a decision by 31 May) and 30 September (for a decision by 30 November). However, the foundation encourages applicants to submit their applications as early as possible.

Sources of information

Accounts; annual report; Charity Commission record; funder's website; guidelines for applicants.

Baron Davenport's Charity

 Almshouses, hospices and residential homes for older people, children/ young people, older people

Birmingham and the West Midlands counties – applicants must reside within 60 miles of Birmingham Town Hall

£601,000 to organisations (2016)

CC number: 217307

Trustees: William Colacicchi; Sue Ayres; Martin Easton; Lisa Bryan; Peter Horton; Alec Jones; Ashvin Pimpalnerkar; Victoria Milligan.

Correspondent: Kate Slater, Charity Administrator, Portman House,

5–7 Temple Row West, Birmingham
B2 5NY (tel: 0121 236 8004; email:
enquiries@barondavenportscharity.org)

 www.barondavenportscharity.org

Established in 1930 by Mr Baron
Davenport, the charity is now governed
by a Charity Commission Scheme dated
16 April 1998.

The distribution of the charity's income
is set out in the 2016 annual report.

The income of the charity is distributed
as follows:

- £2,500 for each trustee (other than the
  ex-officio trustee) to nominate for
  charitable purposes
- £10,000 to the Bishop of Birmingham
- £10,000 to the Chief Minister of the
  Birmingham Hebrew Congregation

Of the remaining income:

- 30% to charities benefitting children
  and young persons under 25 years of
  age in Birmingham and West Midlands
  Counties
- 30% to almshouses, homes for aged
  persons or hospices in Birmingham
  and West Midlands Counties
- 40% in the relief and assistance of
  necessitous widows, spinsters and
  divorced or separated women
  abandoned by their partners and the
  children of any of the same persons
  under 25 years of age who are in
  reduced financial circumstances.
- The Trustees may also give grants to
  charitable institutions or organisations
  having for one of their principal objects
  the benefit of any of the necessitous
  persons qualified as aforesaid.

Grants to organisations

The charity makes grants to: almshouses,
hospices and residential homes for older
people; organisations benefitting
children/young people; and
organisations supporting older people.

Grants are awarded for special projects,
equipment and running costs. Some
organisations are funded in consecutive
years, but every grant must be separately
applied for each year; there is no
automatic renewal.

Financial information

In 2016 the charity had assets of
£34.3 million and an income of
£1.4 million. Grants awarded to
organisations totalled £601,000.

Beneficiaries included: Acorns
Children's Hospice Trust (£24,000);
Compton Hospice, Zoë's Place Trust
(£20,000 each); Douglas Macmillan
Hospice (£15,000); Lench's Trust,
Rainbow Children's Hospice,
Shakespeare Hospice, Stonehouse Gang
(£10,000 each).

Exclusions

Statutory services including state schools
(unless these are specifically for pupils
with disabilities), local authorities,

prisons, NHS hospitals or services;
universities and further education
colleges; start-up organisations that have
not yet produced their first year's
audited accounts; retrospective
expenditure; capital appeals for places of
worship unless these are primarily for
community use, such as an adjoining
church hall or clearly defined
community area within a place of
worship; medical research.

Applications

Applications can be made through the
charity's website. Applications are
considered twice yearly and distributions
are made at the end of May (spring) and
at the end of November (autumn).
Applications for the spring distribution
should be received no later than
15 March and for the autumn no later
than 15 September. No more than one
application be made in each 12-month
period.

Sources of information

Accounts; annual report; Charity
Commission record; funder's website;
further information provided by the
funder.

The Davidson Family Charitable Trust

 Jewish causes, general charitable
purposes

England and Wales

£1.1 million (2015/16)

CC number: 262937

Trustees: Gerald Davidson; Maxine
Davidson; Eve Winer.

Correspondent: Gerald Davidson,
Trustee, 58 Queen Anne Street, London
W1G 8HW (tel: 020 7224 1030)

Established in 1971, this is the trust of
Gerald Davidson, director of Queen
Anne Street Capital and Wolfe
Properties, and his family. The trust
makes grants for a wide range of
purposes and, in the main, supports
Jewish organisations.

Financial information

In 2016/17 the trust had assets of
£223,500 and an income of £1.1 million.
During the year, the trust awarded a
total of £1.1 million in grants to
organisations. Grants were distributed as
follows:

Welfare	£1 million
Education	£24,000
The arts	£10,000
Medical	£1,700
Religious organisations	£1,000

Beneficiaries included: The Jerusalem
Foundation (£1 million); Community
Security Trust (£24,000); City Pregnancy
Counselling and Psychotherapy

(£17,000); Centre for Jewish Life and
Victoria and Albert Museum (£10,000);
Centre Point (£7,500); Fine Giving
(£5,000); Western Marble Arch
Synagogue (£1,000); Israel Guide Dog
Centre (£100).

Applications

Apply in writing to the correspondent.

Sources of information

Accounts; annual report; Charity
Commission record.

The Gwendoline and Margaret Davies Charity

Visual and performing arts, education,
young people, health, social welfare,
general charitable purposes

Wales

£222,500 (2015/16)

CC number: 235589

Trustees: Lord David Davies; David
Lewis; Dr Denis Balsom; Dr Janet Lewis;
Thomas Williams.

Correspondent: Susan Hamer, Secretary,
Plas Dolerw, Milford Road, Newtown,
Powys SY16 2EH (tel: 01686 625228;
email: daviescharities@gmail.com)

The charity was established by the
Davies sisters in 1934. The daughters of
an industrialist and philanthropist, the
sisters began to collect art while
travelling in Europe before the outbreak
of the First World War. They amassed a
sizable collection of Impressionist and
post-Impressionist art which they
bequeathed to the National Museum of
Wales. In the early 1920s, the sisters
bought Gregynog Hall in
Montgomeryshire where they founded a
press and started hosting the Gregynog
Music Festival, which celebrated classical
music and poetry. Margaret donated
Gregynog to the University of Wales for
use as an arts centre. As well as being
patrons of the arts, the sisters opened
their home to artists fleeing the war.

The charity continues to support
projects that were started by the sisters,
or inspired by them, with a particular
interest in the visual and performing
arts, education, projects for young
people and, to a lesser extent, health and
social welfare causes. Applications must
be for organisations and projects that
would benefit Welsh people.

Financial information

In 2015/16 the charity held assets of
£7.4 million and had an income of
£258,500. Grants were made to over 35
organisations and totalled £222,500.

Beneficiaries included: University of
Wales (£50,000); Welsh National Opera

(£25,000); David Davies Memorial Institute (£15,000); Gregynog Festival (£10,000); Home-Start Blaenau Gwent (£5,000); Drama Association of Wales (£3,700); Llandrindod Foodbank (£2,500); Centre for Alternative Technology (£1,800); Montgomeryshire Music Festival (£1,000).

Grants for less than £1,000 totalled £8,000.

Exclusions

Grants are made to registered charities only.

Applications

The trustees consider appeals on an individual basis. There are no application forms as the trustees prefer to receive letters from applicants setting out the following information: whether the organisation is a registered charity; details of the reason for the application – the type of work and so on; the cost; how much has been raised so far towards the cost; the source of the sums raised; a copy of the last audited accounts if available; and any other information that the applicant may consider would help the application. Unsuccessful appeals are not informed unless an sae is enclosed.

Sources of information

Accounts; annual report; Charity Commission record.

The Hamilton Davies Trust

🔍 Education, sport and recreation, community development, regeneration

📍 Irlam and Cadishead, and Rixton-with-Glazebrook

💷 £514,000 (2016/17)

CC number: 1106123

Trustees: Neil McArthur; Graham Chisnall; Frank Cocker.

Correspondent: Mandy Coleman, General Manager, Hamilton Davies House, 117c Liverpool Road, Cadishead, Manchester M44 5BG (tel: 0161 222 4003; email: hello@hamiltondavies.org.uk)

 www.hamiltondavies.org.uk

The Hamilton Davies Trust is a grant-making charity which supports projects within the communities of Irlam, Cadishead and Rixton-with-Glazebrook. According to its website, the trust makes grants in four areas:

▶ **Community:** Grants are awarded for a wide variety of community purposes, such as 'improvements to community buildings and facilities or contribution towards rent and running costs, to uniforms or football

kits, as well as supporting a number of events'. The trustees have previously stated that they would also consider funding the provision of public art to help improve the appearance of local areas and attract visitors.
▶ **Education:** The trust supports after school clubs, educational trips and other extra-curricular activities in schools to make sure that all children can participate and develop.
▶ **Recreation:** The trust supports groups such as choirs, dance troupes and community organisations for various activities which support social inclusion and good health, and enhance the quality of life of participants. The trust has also supported young people with contributions towards equipment, holiday programmes and competitions.
▶ **Regeneration:** The trust works in partnership with 'Salford City Council and other stakeholders to boost regeneration and enhance pride in the area'. They provide grants in the community 'to those at grassroots level to improve local facilities and develop plans to enhance the area'.

Grants can range from small donations of a few hundred pounds for contributions to 'one-off type costs' such as uniforms and kits, to more substantial investments for refurbishments and building work. The trust tends to target its grants at grassroots organisations, such as schools, voluntary and community groups (including community interest companies and companies limited by guarantee), sports clubs, and local partnership bodies which support community activities and projects.

In addition to its main grants programmes, the trust also administers the Chris Stocks Fund which provides small grants to support young people to develop their skills and benefit their future employability. For full details see the trust's website.

Financial information

In 2016/17 the trust held assets of nearly £6.9 million and an income of £869,500 mostly from donations and gifts. During the year, the trust awarded 58 grants totalling £514,000.

Previous beneficiaries have included: Manchester Tech Trust (£200,000 in three grants); Manchester United Foundation (£22,000); Cadishead Primary School (£6,000); Irlam Gems (£3,000); The Meadows (£1,500); Irlam Royalettes (£500); Irlam Vets Bowling Club (£200); Salford Veterans Breakfast Club (£100).

Exclusions

Applications for projects outside the beneficial area will not be considered.

Applications

For applications for over £150 an application form can be downloaded from the trust's website.

For applications under £150, apply in writing to the correspondent detailing:
▶ A brief outline of the project and its benefits
▶ Who will be involved?
▶ How many people will be involved?
▶ Who will benefit?
▶ How many will benefit?
▶ What area will the project benefit?
▶ The amount of financial support required?
▶ Details of any other funding received or applied for

The trustees aim to inform applicants of their decision in writing within four months. The trust welcomes initial telephone calls or emails to discuss potential projects.

Sources of information

Accounts; annual report; Charity Commission record; funder's website.

The Crispin Davis Family Trust

🔍 The relief of hardship of children and young people, education, health

📍 Worldwide

💷 £218,000 to organisations (2016/17)

CC number: 1150637

Trustees: Sir Crispin Davis; Lady Jean Davis; Cripps Trust Corporation Ltd; Dr Julia Davis; Caroline Davis King; Angela Spaid.

Correspondent: The Trustees, Heartwood, Heartwood Wealth Management, 77 Mount Ephraim, Tunbridge Wells TN4 8BS (tel: 01892 701801; email: info@heartwoodgroup.co.uk)

This charity was established and registered with the Charity Commission in January 2013. Its main object is the relief of hardship among children and young people across the world who are in need of help as a result of poverty, lack of education or illness.

Financial information

In 2016/17 the trust had assets of £6.4 million and an income of £119,500. Grants to six organisations totalled £218,000 and one individual received a grant of £1,600.

Beneficiaries included: Karuna Foundation (£75,000); Educate Girls (£60,000); Tuchinde Children's Trust (£52,500 in two grants); Spark Inside

(£24,000); Glyndebourne (£5,000); Rainmaker Foundation (£1,500).

Applications
Apply in writing to the correspondent.

Sources of information
Accounts; annual report; Charity Commission record.

The Davis Foundation

🔍 Personal development, care of older people, education in music and opera, horticulture, environment conservation, religious education, religious harmony, research into racism

📍 England and Israel

💷 £2.6 million (2016/17)

CC number: 1152998

Trustees: Michael Davis; Barbara Davis; Sarah Davis.

Correspondent: Michael Davis, Trustee, 3 Beechworth Close, London NW3 7UT (tel: 020 7389 9504; email: mick@thedavisfoundation.com)

The foundation is constituted under a trust deed and was registered with the Charity Commission in 2013 to support social welfare and community cohesion.

The objects of the foundation are:

▷ Financial support for Jewish people (particularly young people) for activities that will help them grow as members of society
▷ To support organisations which provide support and care for those in need who are older or have a disability
▷ Educating the general public in the areas of opera; music; and other creative or performing arts
▷ To promote the study of horticulture, gardening and garden design; and also the appreciation of ecology, conservation and the study of flora and fauna
▷ Promoting religious harmony
▷ Promoting social inclusion
▷ Supporting organisations which provide security, advice and training to those who are involved with religious-based schools or places of worship
▷ Supporting organisations which promote good relationships between Jewish people and the rest of the community
▷ To promote good citizenship
▷ Relief for victims of racial or religious harassment
▷ Providing support for organisations which research racism

Financial information
In 2016/17 the foundation held assets of £689,500 and had an income of

£1.5 million. Grants awarded to organisations totalled £2.6 million.

Applications
Apply in writing to the correspondent.

Sources of information
Accounts; annual report; Charity Commission record.

Dawat-E-Hadiyah Trust (United Kingdom)

🔍 Advancement of the Islamic religion, education, social welfare

📍 Worldwide

💷 £1.2 million (2016)

CC number: 294807

Trustee: The 53rd Dai Al-Mutlaq, His Holiness Syedna Mufaddal Saifuddin.

Correspondent: The Trustees, 6 Mohammedi Park Complex, Rowdell Road, Northolt, Middlesex UB5 6AG (tel: 020 8839 0750; email: farazdaq@dawatuk.org)

The trust was registered with the Charity Commission in 1986 and supports the causes chosen by the Dai Al-Mutlaq, the spiritual leader of the Dawoodi Bohra community.

The trust's objects are outlined in its 2016 annual report as follows:

The objects of the Trust are to carry out such charitable purposes for the relief of poverty and the advancement of education or religion or otherwise for the benefit of mankind anywhere in the world as 'the Dai Al-Mutlaq' shall from time to time determine. These include the advancement, safeguard and protection of the Islamic religion; the advancement of learning and education in their widest connotations; the relief of poverty and help to the poor and needy; the grant and aid of medical relief and the advancement of such other religious and charitable objects as 'the Dai al-Mutlaq' shall determine.

The trust makes grants to charities in the UK and overseas, as well as to individuals in need.

Financial information
In 2016 the trust had assets of about £48 million and an income of £8.3 million. Grants totalled over £1.2 million including £1.14 million to organisations in the UK and were distributed as follows:

UK-registered charities	£1.14 million
Overseas charities	£59,000
Individuals	£26,000

Beneficiaries (UK-registered charities) included: Anjuman-e-Badri – Birmingham (£600,500); Al Jameah Al-Sayfiyah Trust (£126,000); Husaini Masjid and Mohammedi Park

Management Trust (£20,000); Anjuman-e-Jamali – Bradford (£7,400).

Applications
Apply in writing to the correspondent.

Sources of information
Accounts; annual report; Charity Commission record.

Peter De Haan Charitable Trust

🔍 Social welfare, the environment, the arts

📍 UK

💷 £482,000 (2016/17)

CC number: 1077005

Trustees: Peter Charles De Haan; Janette McKay; Dr Rob Stoneman; Opus Corporate Trustees Ltd.

Correspondent: Simon Johnson, Finance Director, Woolyard, 54 Bermondsey Street, London SE1 3UD (tel: 020 7232 5477; email: sjohnson@pdhct.org.uk)

 www.pdhct.org.uk

The trust's website states:

Founded in 1999, The Peter De Haan Charitable Trust aims to improve the quality of life for people and communities in the UK through its work with arts, environmental and community welfare organisations. Since then the Trust has donated more than £20 million to organisations working in these areas. Led by businessman and philanthropist Peter De Haan, the Trust operates under a venture philanthropy model, working closely with the organisations it supports financially and organisationally to increase their capacity and impact.

Historically the trust has awarded grants in the following areas:

▷ Arts
▷ Environment
▷ Social welfare (primarily community projects near its headquarters in South London)

In recent years the primary focus of the trust's grant-making have been the environment and in the 2016/17 accounts the trustees state that this will continue to be the case in coming year.

Financial information
In 2016/17 the trust had assets of £4.24 million and an income of £171,000. During the year, the charity awarded almost £482,000 in grants to organisations.

Previous beneficiaries have included: Leicestershire and Rutland Wildlife Trust; National Youth Theatre; Old Vic New Voices; Yorkshire Wildlife Trust.

Exclusions

The trust has previously stated that it will not accept applications for grants:

▹ That directly replace or subsidise statutory funding
▹ From individuals or for the benefit of one individual
▹ For work that has already taken place
▹ Which do not have a direct benefit to the UK
▹ For medical research
▹ For adventure and residential courses, expeditions or overseas travel
▹ For holidays and respite care
▹ For endowment funds
▹ For the promotion of a specific religion
▹ That are part of general appeals or circulars
▹ From applicants who have applied to within the last 12 months

In addition to the above, it is unlikely to support:

▹ Large national charities which enjoy widespread support
▹ Local organisations which are part of a wider network of others doing similar work
▹ Individual pre-schools, schools, out-of-school clubs, supplementary schools, colleges, universities or youth clubs
▹ Websites, publications, conferences or seminars

Applications

The trust's website states that: 'the trust is not open to unsolicited applications'; however, the trust has previously run an open application process for environmental organisations. Check the website for updates.

Sources of information

Accounts; annual report; Charity Commission record; funder's website.

The Roger De Haan Charitable Trust

General charitable purposes, particularly: arts, culture, heritage and regeneration, education, health, disability and welfare, particularly for older people, amateur sports, community development, young people, relief of poverty, overseas aid and disaster relief

East Kent and overseas

£3.3 million to organisations (2015/16)

CC number: 276274

Trustees: Sir Roger De Haan; Joshua De Haan; Lady De Haan; Benjamin De Haan.

Correspondent: Sir Roger De Haan, Trustee, Strand House, Pilgrims Way, Monks Horton, Ashford, Kent TN25 6DR

 www.rdhct.org.uk

 facebook.com/rdhct.org.uk

 @RDHCT

The Roger De Haan Charitable Trust was established in 1978 by Sir Roger De Haan, former Chair of Saga Group, and his father Sidney, Saga's founder. The trust supports a wide range of charitable causes and activities, mainly concentrated in the area around Folkestone, Hythe and the Romney Marsh in Kent.

Grant-making programmes

The trust's website states that the trust will support the following areas:

▹ education
▹ arts, culture and heritage
▹ community development and regeneration
▹ amateur sport
▹ projects to support young people
▹ health and welfare of older people

From time to time, Trustees may also provide support for other causes at their discretion.

Financial information

In 2016/17 the trust had assets of £23.6 million and an income of £2.6 million. A total of £7.5 million was awarded in grants, broken down as follows:

Sports	14	£5.7 million
Arts	26	£918,500
Community development	45	£323,000
International	5	£273,500
Health and welfare	64	£174,000
Education	11	£36,000
Heritage (including fabric of buildings)	13	£33,500
National	3	£5,000

Of the £7.5 million grants made, £7.1 million (94%) was granted to charitable causes in Folkestone and the surrounding area.

Beneficiaries included: Shepway Sport Trusts (£5.7 million); The Creative Foundation – Triennial 2017 (£666,500); British Red Cross – South African Project (£250,000); Kent Community Foundation – young people not in education, employment or training (£120,000); Queenstown Primary School, New Zealand (£17,000); Jim Jam Arts (£15,000); East Kent Railway Trust (£9,000); Volunteer Reading Help (£5,000); Hawkinge Cricket Club (£1,000); Primavera (£600).

Exclusions

Applications that are unlikely to receive support from the trust include:

▹ Those where a grant would replace or subsidise statutory funding
▹ The development of business ventures, publications or websites
▹ Conferences

▹ Those that would primarily benefit an individual
▹ Requests from students for the purpose of study or travel
▹ Funding for expeditions or overseas travel
▹ Projects that promote political or religious beliefs
▹ Animal welfare charities
▹ National charities, unless there is significant benefit to a local office or project
▹ Organisations that have already applied within the last 12 months

Applications

An application form can be downloaded from the trust's website, or requested in writing. Applicants can also apply online through the foundation's online application. The online application needs to be completed in one submission and cannot be saved, so you may wish to download the form if you need to return to add further information at a later stage.

The trustees will not normally consider unsolicited applications for medical research grants.

Repeat applications from a single organisation within a 12-month period will not normally be considered. Grants are awarded at the trustees' discretion and the trust is unable to provide feedback on applications.

Sources of information

Accounts; annual report; Charity Commission record; funder's website.

The De Laszlo Foundation

The arts, education

UK and worldwide

£477,000 (2016/17)

CC number: 327383

Trustees: Damon de Laszlo; Lucy Birkbeck; Robert de Laszlo; William de Laszlo.

Correspondent: Christabell Wood, 5 Albany Courtyard, Piccadilly, London W1J 0HF (tel: 020 7437 1982)

Established in 1987 in honour of the painter Philio de Laszlo, the foundation has the following objects:

▹ The advancement and promotion of education and interest in the visual arts with special reference to encouraging knowledge of the works of contemporary painters, in particular those of the late Philip de Laszlo
▹ To encourage research into the restoration of works of art and their preservation and the location of suitable venues for them

- To acquire and maintain a collection of the works of art of the late Philip de Laszlo and other works of art of the same or any other period
- To advance education and research generally in the areas of arts, science, economics and medicine
- To encourage the study, reproduction and cataloguing of works of art and the publication of books and literature in that respect
- To promote the founding of scholarships and prizes related to the above

Financial information

In 2016/17 the foundation held assets of £2.7 million and had an income of £751,000. Grants totalled £477,000. A complete list of beneficiaries was unavailable but the accounts provided the following breakdown of grants:

Archive Trust	£165,000
Arts	£77,500
Medicine	£68,500
Education	£60,000
Scholarships	£55,500
Science	£21,500
Economics	£17,600
Other charities	£11,500

Beneficiaries included: Action for ME; Centre for Social Justice; Duchenne Muscular Dystrophy; Durham University; English National Ballet School; Gilbert White Dates Museum; University College London; University of Southampton – Ophthalmology Department; Winchester Cathedral.

Applications

Apply in writing to the correspondent.

Sources of information

Accounts; annual report; Charity Commission record.

Debenhams Foundation

 Relief of financial hardship

UK

£971,000 (2016/17)

CC number: 1147682

Trustees: Keith Markham; Patricia Skinner; Sally Hyndman.

Correspondent: Natasha Kaursland, Debenhams plc, 10 Brock Street, London NW1 3FG (email: natasha.kaursland@ debenhams.com)

sustainability.debenhamsplc.com/ debenhams-foundation

Established in 2012 this is the charitable foundation of Debenhams Retail plc, the department store chain. The foundation receives its income from both Debenhams Retail plc and Debenhams Retail (Ireland) Ltd, as well as from Debenhams' customers, employees, suppliers and partners, and uses it to fund causes 'that focus on preserving and protecting health and relieving financial hardships primarily, but not exclusively, by making grants of money'.

It is described in the foundation's 2016/17 annual report that the foundation raises money 'through a mixture of product sales and fundraising in Debenhams stores and online, head office fundraising events (such as cake sales and cosmetic events) and supplier fundraising events such as Debenhams Foundation Ball, the Debenhams Foundation aims to primarily raise money for its key charity partners which reflect the causes that Debenhams' customers hold dear'.

The foundation supports some projects, which are monitored regularly, over multiple years, while other projects are funded on a one-off basis at the trustees' discretion.

Financial information

In 2016/17 the foundation had assets of £304,000 and an income of £1.8 million. Grants to 16 organisations totalled £971,000.

Beneficiaries included: Help for Heroes (£320,000); BBC Children in Need (£189,000); Breast Cancer Now (£184,000); Breast Cancer Ireland (£19,200); Allegra UK (£4,000); Rowcroft Hospice (£530).

Applications

The annual report for 2016/17 explains that 'charitable fundraising is generally organised locally and colleagues in store work closely with local community charities. In addition, the trustees supported major appeals this year and have co-ordinated stores' fundraising' for Debenhams' charity partners.

Sources of information

Accounts; annual report; Charity Commission record; funder's website.

The J N Derbyshire Trust

 General charitable purposes

 Mainly Nottingham and Nottinghamshire

£188,500 (2016/17)

CC number: 231907

Trustees: Peter Moore; Georgina Cowen; Rose Whittle; Charles George; Belinda Lawrie; Andrew Little.

Correspondent: Emma Hanson, Secretary, c/o RSM UK, 7th Floor, City Gate East, Tollhouse Hill, Nottingham NG1 5FS (tel: 0115 964 4450; email: emma.hanson@rsmuk.com)

The objects of the trust are 'the promotion of health, development of physical improvement, advancement of education and the relief of poverty, distress and sickness', in the City of Nottingham and more generally in Nottinghamshire. In 2016/17 grants ranged from £245 to £15,000.

Financial information

In 2016/17 the trust held assets of £5.6 million and had an income of £213,500. Grants were made to 80 organisations totalling £188,500 and were broken down into the following categories:

General charitable purpose	£35,000
Youth organisations	£32,500
Women and children	£26,500
Social welfare	£26,000
Older people	£25,500
Health	£23,500
Education	£12,200
Religious	£6,300
Medical and ambulances	£1,000

Previous beneficiaries have included: St Paul's Boundary Road – West Bridgford (£10,000); Dance4 Ltd, Jericho Road Project, Nottingham and Nottinghamshire Refugee Forum (£5,000 each); Elizabeth Finn Care (£4,600); Citizens Advice Broxtowe and Personal Support Unit Nottingham County Court (£4,000 each); Nottinghamshire Clubs for Young People (£3,300).

Exclusions

No grants are given to individuals or for the costs of study.

Applications

Application forms are available from the correspondent. Applications can be made at any time but trustees usually only meet to consider them twice a year. Details of the project are required. A reply is only given to unsuccessful applicants if they enclose an sae.

Sources of information

Accounts; annual report; Charity Commission record.

The Desmond Foundation

General charitable purposes, with a particular focus on: children and young people, Jewish causes, social welfare, health

UK and overseas

£1.06 million (2016)

CC number: 1014352

Trustees: Richard Desmond; Northern & Shell Services Ltd; Northern & Shell Media Group Ltd.

Correspondent: Allison Racher, The Northern & Shell Building, 10 Lower Thames Street, London EC3R 6EN (tel: 020 8612 7760; email: allison.racher@ express.co.uk)

Established in 1992, the RD Crusaders Foundation was renamed the Desmond Foundation in 2013. The trustees of the charity are Richard Desmond, the owner of Express Newspapers and founder of Northern & Shell, Northern & Shell Services Ltd and Northern & Shell Media Group Ltd. The accounts for 2016 explain that "RD Crusaders Ltd, a company wholly owned by [Richard] Desmond, was incorporated in December 2007 with the purpose of fundraising on behalf of the charity'.'

In recent years the foundation has awarded the majority of its grants to children's and young people's charities in the UK. Children's charities remain the focus of the foundation but consideration is given by the trustees to worthy causes outside this area.

Financial information

In 2016 the foundation had assets of £769,000 and an income of £79,500. A total of £1.06 million was awarded in 53 grants were awarded to 48 organisations:

Community	29	£704,000
Education	18	£340,000
Miscellaneous	6	£17,000

Beneficiaries include: World Jewish Relief (£258,000); Greenhouse Sports (£100,000); Fight for Sight (£50,000); Variety, the Children's Charity (£37,000); Wellbeing of Women (£15,000); Highgate School, The Wallace Collection, Miles Frost Fund (£10,000 each); The CAYO Foundation (£7,000); The Jerusalem Foundation (£5,000).

Applications

Apply in writing to the correspondent.

Sources of information

Accounts; annual report; Charity Commission record.

The Laduma Dhamecha Charitable Trust

General charitable purposes, medical equipment for hospitals, education

UK and overseas

£305,500 (2016/17)

CC number: 328678

Trustees: K. R. Dhamecha; Shantilal Dhamecha; Pradip Dhamecha.

Correspondent: Pradip Dhamecha, Trustee, The Dhamecha Group, 2 Hathaway Close, Stanmore, Middlesex HA7 3NR (tel: 020 8903 8181; email: info@dhamecha.com)

The trust was founded by the Dhamecha family who founded and operate the Dhamecha cash and carry group based in Greater London. The trust supports a wide range of organisations in the UK and overseas. The aims of the trust are listed in the annual report as being:

- To provide relief of sickness by the provision of medical equipment and the establishing or improvement of facilities at hospitals
- To provide for the advancement of education and/or an educational establishment in rural areas to make children self-sufficient in the long term
- Other general charitable purposes

Financial information

In 2016/17 the trust had assets of £2.5 million and an income of £629,500 mainly from donations including £513,000 from Dhamecha Foods Ltd. Grants totalled £1.5 million. Grants were made to UK organisations totalling £284,500 and to organisations and projects outside the UK totalling £20,500.

No further information was available on the size or number of beneficiaries during this year.

Applications

Apply in writing to the correspondent.

Sources of information

Accounts; annual report; Charity Commission record.

Diabetes UK

Diabetes research

UK

£6.3 million (2016)

CC number: 215199

Trustees: Sir Peter Dixon; Julian Baust; Noah Franklin; Dr Robert Young; Helen McCallum; Gareth Hoskin; Prof. Rhys Williams; Janice Watson; Prof. Mohamed Hanif; Sir Henry Burns; Robin Swindell; Ian King; Rosie Thomas; Dr Wendy Thomson.

Correspondent: Research Department, Wells Lawrence House, 126 Back Church Lane, London E1 1FH (tel: 020 7424 1076; email: research@diabetes.org.uk)

www.diabetes.org.uk

facebook.com/diabetesuk

@DiabetesUK

@diabetesuk

Diabetes UK works to provide care, support and information to people affected by or at risk of diabetes. It campaigns on behalf of people with the condition to ensure they receive the best quality of care from health services. The charity is also the leading UK charitable funder of diabetes research.

Research funding

Diabetes UK funds 'pioneering' research into diabetes and diabetes-related issues. Its Research Strategy 2015–2019, which is outlined on the website, has three research goals, which are:

- **Care**: to 'improve care and self-management for people living with diabetes today'
- **Cure**: to 'find ways to cure diabetes in those who have it now or develop it in the future'
- **Prevent**: to 'stop diabetes and its complications before they develop in those at risk'

Types of funding

Research funding is given in three ways:

- Money is awarded to support new ideas proposed by UK researchers
- Personal awards are given to help 'talented scientists and healthcare professionals become the diabetes research leaders of the future'
- Targeted investments are given to support research in specific areas where there are 'important gaps or opportunities'

Funding is distributed through a number of schemes, which are outlined on the website. At the time of writing (April 2018) these included:

- **Project grants**: 'To provide support for diabetes research projects for up to five years'
- **Small grants**: 'To enable researchers to undertake small research projects or pilot studies for a maximum of 12 months and £15,000.'
- **Equipment grants**: 'To enable the purchase of a specific large item of multi-user equipment necessary for diabetes-related research projects'

There are also a number of PhD studentships and research fellowships available for clinicians and scientists.

Financial information

In 2016 the charity held assets of £17.5 million and had an income of £37 million. Grants totalling almost £6.3 million were awarded to organisations. This figure represents expenditure on direct grant-funding only.

Grants were given in three research areas: Care (£4.4 million); Prevention (£1.5 million); Cure (£336,000).

Beneficiaries receiving grants over £100,000 during the year were: King's College London (£999,000); University of Glasgow (£669,000); University of Exeter (£576,000); Imperial College London (£363,000); University of Manchester (£270,000); University of York (£134,000); Queen's University Belfast (£114,000).

Applications
Potential applicants are first advised to read the 'General guidelines for research grant applicants' on the charity's website. Information on the application process and deadlines for each specific scheme is also available on the website or by contacting the charity directly.

Sources of information
Accounts; annual report; Charity Commission record; funder's website.

Dina Perelman Trust Ltd

 Orthodox Judaism, education, general charitable purposes

UK and overseas

£1 million (2017)

CC number: 274165

Trustees: Asher Isiah Perelman; Jonah Perelman; Sara Perelman.

Correspondent: Asher Perelman, Trustee, 30 Overlea Road, London E5 9BG (tel: 020 8809 2345)

This trust registered with the Charity Commission in 1977, and supports the advancement of the Orthodox Jewish faith through its grant-making. The trust's 2017 accounts state, 'The Trustees are approached for donations by a wide variety of charitable institutions operating all over England and the rest of the world. The trustees consider all requests which they receive and make donations based on level of funds available.'

Financial information
In 2017 the trust had assets of £8.9 million and an income of over £1 million. During the year, the trust awarded just over £1 million in grants to organisations. Grants were distributed as follows:

Education	£695,500
Advancement of religion	£139,500
Relief of poverty	£93,500
Advancement of health and saving lives	£41,000
Other grant-making charities	£25,500
Advancement of community development	£6,800

Beneficiaries included: The Friends of Alexander Institutions Trust (£237,000); Chevras Machzikei Mesivta (£63,000); Zedoko Vochessed Ltd (£59,500); Society of Friends the Torah Ltd (£44,000); Kehal Charedim Trust (£20,000); College for Higher Rabbinical Studies (£15,000); United Talmudical Associated Ltd (£12,600).

Sundry donations under £12,000 totalled £222,000.

Applications
Apply in writing to the correspondent.

Sources of information
Accounts; annual report; Charity Commission record.

Dinwoodie Charitable Company

 Postgraduate medical centres, medical research fellowships

UK

£550,500 (2016/17)

CC number: 1151139

Trustees: John Black; Dr Patrick Cadigan; Richard Arkle; Ian Goalen; John Pears.

Correspondent: Ian Goalen, Trustee, 4 Tytherington Green, Macclesfield SK10 2FA (tel: 01625 610549; email: dinwoodie@irwinmitchell.com)

Previously known as The Dinwoodie Charitable Settlement (Charity Commission no. 255495), the funds were transferred to Dinwoodie Charitable Company, which was registered in 2013.

Grant-making policy
The charity's grant-making policy is set out in its informative annual report for 2016/17:

> The Directors endeavour to be pro-active in pursuing the principal objective of the Charity within England of improving healthcare by advancing the development and dissemination of medical knowledge and skills, specifically by-
>
> » assisting the medical profession in enhancing opportunities for post graduate medical education primarily by additions and/or improvements to the buildings and provision of information technology equipment to post graduate medical centres
> » enabling post graduates to widen their knowledge through medical research
> » such other activities as they deem appropriate
>
> Grant making policy is reviewed in light of changes and developments in the delivery and widening of postgraduate education.

Grants have historically been given in two main areas – towards facilities within hospital postgraduate medical centres and research fellowships.

Financial information
In 2016/17 the charity had assets of £3.8 million and an income of £309,000. Grants were made totalling £550,500.

Beneficiaries included: Pennine Acute Trust (£278,000); Arthur Rank Hospice (£200,000); Royal College of Surgeons (£55,000); Royal College of Psychiatrists (£23,000); Medical Research Council (£14,500).

Applications
The trustees have previously stated that they are proactive rather than reactive in their grant-giving. Negotiating for new postgraduate medical centres and monitoring their construction invariably takes a number of years.

Sources of information
Accounts; annual report; Charity Commission record.

The Djanogly Foundation

 Jewish causes, general charitable purposes, medicine, education, the arts, social welfare

UK and Israel

£685,500 (2016/17)

CC number: 280500

Trustees: Sir Harry Djanogly; Michael Djanogly.

Correspondent: Christopher Sills, Secretary, 3 Angel Court, London SW1Y 6QF (tel: 020 7930 9845)

The foundation was established in 1980 by Sir Harry Djangoly, a wealthy businessman from Nottingham who made his fortune in the textile industry. He is a well-known benefactor of the arts and has made substantial donations to art institutions from his personal fortune.

The foundation supports developments in medicine, education, social welfare, the arts, Jewish charities and welfare of older and younger people, and is particularly concerned with funding projects that are new and may require a number of years to become established. In such cases the grant-making activity will be related to the development phases of these projects.

Financial information
In 2016/17 the foundation held assets of £5.8 million and had an income of £154,500. Grants were made to over 46 organisations and totalled £685,500.

Previous beneficiaries have included: Tate Gallery (£237,000); Nottingham Girls' High School (£125,000); Westminster Abbey (£50,000); Jerusalem Foundation (£24,500); Animal Health Trust (£16,000); Clockmakers Charity (£10,000); Art Fund (£3,000); Cromwell Museum (£1,000); Samaritans (£500); Weiner Library (£200).

Grants for less than £100 totalled £170.

Applications
Apply in writing to the correspondent.

Sources of information
Accounts; annual report; Charity Commission record.

Dollond Charitable Trust

Jewish causes, general charitable purposes

UK and Israel

£1.4 million (2016/17)

CC number: 293459

Trustees: Adrian Dollond; Jeffrey Milston; Melissa Dollond; Brian Dollond; Rina Dollond.

Correspondent: Brian Dollond, Trustee and Secretary, 3rd Floor, Hathaway House, Popes Drive, Finchley, London N3 1QF

The trust was registered with the Charity Commission in January 1986. The trust operates a broad grant-making policy, however the activities are often focused on health, education and religious activities. The annual report for 2016/17 states that although 'the constitution of the charity is broadly based, the trustees have adopted a policy of assisting in Jewish communities in Britain and Israel.'

Financial information
In 2016/17 the trust had assets of over £49.6 million and an income of £1.5 million. Grants to 155 organisations totalled £1.4 million and were broken down as follows:

Relief of poverty	£409,000
Religious education	£406,000
Education and training	£210,000
Medical, health and sickness	£186,500
Disability	£107,500
Religious activities	£64,000

A list of beneficiaries was not available.

Applications
Apply in writing to the correspondent.

Sources of information
Accounts; annual report; Charity Commission record.

The Dorfman Foundation

General charitable purposes including Jewish causes and the arts

Worldwide

£12.2 million (2016/17)

CC number: 1120714

Trustees: Lloyd Marshall; Sarah Dorfman; Amy Lux; Sophie Dorfman; Charles Dorfman; Anthony Wagerman; Peter Leach.

Correspondent: The Trustees, 22 Manchester Square, London W1U 3PT (email: charity. correspondence@bdo.co.uk)

The foundation was registered with the Charity Commission in August 2007 and has general charitable purposes, although there is a preference for Jewish causes and the arts.

Financial information
In 2016/17 the foundation held assets of £10.4 million and had an income of £100,000. Grants were made to 21 organisations and totalled £12.2 million.

Beneficiaries included: The Royal Opera House (£4 million); Jewish Care (£3.5 million); Great Ormond Street Hospital and Royal Academy of the Arts (£2 million each); Jewish Community Secondary School (£500,000); Community Security Trust (£76,000); World Jewish Relief (£10,000); Pancreatic Cancer UK (£1,000).

Applications
Apply in writing to the correspondent.

Sources of information
Accounts; annual report; Charity Commission record; funder's website.

The Double 'O' Charity Ltd

General charitable purposes including social welfare, health and education

UK and overseas

£324,000 to organisations (2016/17)

CC number: 271681

Trustees: Peter Townshend; Rachel Fuller.

Correspondent: The Trustees, c/o 4 Friars Lane, Richmond, Surrey TW9 1NL (tel: 020 8940 8171)

The trust registered with the Charity Commission in 1976, and holds the primary objective of making grants towards the relief of poverty, preservation of health and the advancement of education. The trust considers all requests for aid, and also makes grants to individuals.

Financial information
In 2016/17 the charity held assets of £148,000 and had an income of £338,500. During the year, the charity gave a total of £324,000 in grants to 24 organisations, and a further £17,000 was awarded to individuals.

Beneficiaries included: Shriners Hospital for Children (£82,500); Richmond Bridge Friendship Club (£67,500); National Association for People Abused in Childhood (£66,500); Spirit of Recovery (£36,000); Livewire Youth (£28,500); National Sailings Antigua (£10,000); Spears (£5,000); Rights to Play (£1,000) Meher Baba (£100).

Applications
Apply in writing to the correspondent.

Sources of information
Accounts; annual report; Charity Commission record.

Drapers' Charitable Fund

Education and young people, social welfare, homelessness, disability, ex-Service personnel, prisoners, textiles and heritage, general charitable purposes

England and Wales, with a special interest in areas of deprivation in Greater London; also County Derry

£2.3 million (2016/17)

CC number: 251403

Trustee: The Drapers' Company.

Correspondent: Andrew Mellows, Head of Charities, The Drapers' Company, Drapers' Hall, Throgmorton Avenue, London EC2N 2DQ (tel: 020 7588 5001; email: charities@thedrapers.co.uk)

 www.thedrapers.co.uk

The Drapers' Charitable Fund – which is the charity of The Drapers' Company, a City of London livery company – awards grants to help improve quality of life for people and their communities, particularly in Greater London. It also promotes The Drapers' Company's textile heritage and maintains its traditional support for the City of London and its historical connections with Northern Ireland.

Areas of work
According to the charity's website, current priority areas for funding are:

- **Social welfare**, including: homelessness; prisoners; ex-Service personnel; support services for older people, young people, and community and family services; and adults with disabilities, especially those with less visible disabilities such as sensory impairment, mental health problems and learning disabilities
- **Education and training:** projects which raise the aspirations or help to realise the full potential of disadvantaged young people under the age of 25 living in deprived areas of Greater London
- **Textiles and heritage**, including: textile conservation; projects within the textiles industry; and museums, memorials and monuments relating to the armed forces, the history of London or the textile trade

Within each of these areas, the charity applies criteria relating to geographical area (support is mainly given in Greater

London), particular types of project, beneficiary group or specific areas of charitable activity, for example. For further information, applicants should refer to the detailed information on the website.

Grant-making policy

The charity will only accept applications from UK-registered charities (or exempt organisations). Support is focused on small to medium-sized organisations whose total income is less than £10 million per annum. Guidelines on the charity's website state that funding is 'primarily provided for core costs, including salaries, and/or project costs to enable organisations to maintain and develop their work/services.' There is no minimum or maximum grant size, but the majority of grants awarded are normally for sums between £5,000 and £15,000, although smaller and larger grants may be considered.

Most of the grants awarded are one-off payments, but multi-year grants for up to three years may be made awarded, subject to specific conditions. Further appeals from organisations will not normally be considered for three years from the date of the final grant award.

Regular contact is maintained with recipients of grants, including an annual evaluation report, for monitoring purposes. A copy of the guidelines for applicants, which includes details of the application procedure and information required in the application, is available on the website or from Drapers' Hall on request.

Financial information

In 2016/17 the charity held assets of £65.4 million and had an income of almost £2.5 million. Grants totalled £2.3 million, of which almost £1.8 million was awarded from non-restricted funds. Included in this figure is £7,700 given in 35 awards to individuals.

The table below gives details of the grants awarded to organisations from non-restricted funds in 2016/17:

Education and young people	90	£1.05 million
Prisoner support	11	£149,500
Disability	14	£130,500
Ex-Service people	10	£129,000
Homelessness	9	£114,500
Textiles and heritage	11	£87,500
Miscellaneous	113	£70,500
Northern Ireland	2	£50,000

Beneficiaries included: Drapers' Multi Academy Trust (£245,000); Bangor University (£40,000); Blue Sky Development and Regeneration (£25,000); Onside Youth Zones and Streetscape Social Enterprise (£20,000 each); Cockpit Arts (£16,200); Clink Charity, Multiple Sclerosis Trust and Veterans Outreach Support (£15,000

each); The Textile Conservation Centre (£13,700).

Exclusions

The charity's website states that the following organisations and activities are not normally supported by the charity:

- Organisations that are not registered charities, unless exempt from registration
- Organisations with an annual income of over £10 million
- Branches of national charities or movements, or charities which are part of a federal structure
- Schools, colleges or universities
- Churches or other places of worship
- Almshouses
- Hospitals, medical centres or hospices
- Individuals, or organisations applying on their behalf
- Capital projects, appeals or major refurbishments
- Projects which do not support all members of the targeted community
- Children's disabilities, physical disabilities, medical research or medical conditions including drug and alcohol addiction, HIV/AIDS
- Arts projects unless able to demonstrate impact on prisoners, older people or those with less visible disabilities
- Environmental conservation
- Projects where the main focus is tolerance and understanding between faiths and communities, the promotion of religious beliefs or the promotion of social cohesion
- Projects supporting those experiencing domestic violence, trafficking or sexual exploitation
- Holidays or trips
- Animal welfare
- Projects taking place or whose beneficiaries are situated outside the UK
- Work that has already taken place

Applications

For full guidelines and details of the charity's current priorities, applicants should refer to The Drapers' Company website. The Charities Committee meets five times a year to review all applications which fall within the current priorities for funding. Upcoming meeting dates are published on the website and applications should be received at least four weeks before the date of the meeting (although whether an application will be considered at a specific meeting depends on the number of applications received). Successful applicants are usually notified within three weeks of the Charities Committee making a decision.

Sources of information

Accounts; annual report; Charity Commission record; funder's website.

The Dromintee Trust

 Social welfare, children and young people, health, medical research

UK and overseas

£594,500 (2016/17)

CC number: 1053956

Trustees: Hugh Murphy; Margaret Murphy; Mary Murphy; Patrick Hugh Middleton; Robert Smith; Paul Tiernan; Joseph Murphy.

Correspondent: Hugh Murphy, Trustee, 1 Westmoreland Avenue, Thurmaston, Leicester LE4 8PH (tel: 0116 260 3877; email: drominteetrust@gmail.com)

Established in March 1996, this Leicestershire-based trust principally supports organisations working in the areas of: social welfare, children's welfare; health and research into rare diseases. Grants are made to organisations operating locally, nationally and overseas, particularly in financially developing countries. Previously the trust has also supported a number of Catholic organisations.

Financial information

In 2016/17 the trust had assets of £2.8 million and an income of £391,500. A total of £594,500 was awarded to 22 organisations.

Beneficiaries included: Don Bosco – Hyderabad (£117,000); Don Bosco Seminary (£110,000); Light for the Blind (£100,000); Consolata Fathers (£30,000); Let the Children Live (£20,000); March for Life UK (£10,000); Brain Tumour Research (£10,000); Epilepsy Society (£2,000).

Exclusions

The trust does not fund gap year requests.

Applications

Apply in writing to the correspondent.

Sources of information

Accounts; annual report; Charity Commission record.

The Royal Foundation of the Duke and Duchess of Cambridge and Prince Harry

Armed forces, children and young people, conservation, mental health

UK and overseas

£4.3 million (2016)

CC number: 1132048

Trustees: Theresa Green; Edward Harley; Anthony Lowther-Pinkerton; Guy Morrison; Charles Mindenhall; Sir Keith

Mills; Simon Patterson; Lady Demetra Pinsent; Miguel Head.

Correspondent: Susan Stafford, Kensington Palace, Palace Green, London W8 4PU (tel: 020 7101 2963; email: sue.stafford@royalfoundation.com)

 www.royalfoundation.com

Registered in late 2009 with general charitable purposes, the foundation became fully operational in 2011. It is the primary philanthropic and charitable vehicle for The Duke and Duchess of Cambridge and The Duke and Duchess of Sussex.

Areas of Work
According to the foundation's website it has five main areas of work:

Armed forces - Promoting the welfare of those who are serving or who have served their country in the armed forces.

Young people – Helping children and young people to build their skills, confidence and aspirations.

Conservation - Supporting communities to protect and conserve their natural resources for future generations.

Mental health – Working to remove the stigma around mental health, and developing programmes to fill needs in the mental health sector

Early years - Supporting young children and families through The Royal Foundation

Financial information
In 2016 the foundation had assets of £9.8 million and an income of £10 million. Grants totalled £4.3 million, broken down as follows:

Disadvantaged children and young people	£2.4 million
Conservation and sustainable development	£1.1 million
Military veterans and their families	£683,000

Beneficiaries included: Epic Partners (£217,500); South African Wildlife College (£175,000); Welsh Rugby Union (£102,000); Help For Heroes Invictus Games (£50,000); Sledding 2017 (£43,000); Flying for Freedom (£42,500); Business in the Community (£35,000); East Anglia's Children's Hospices (£30,000); Flora and Fauna International (£29,500); Climb 2 Recovery (£29,000).

Applications
The foundation does not accept unsolicited applications.

Sources of information
Accounts; annual report; Charity Commission record; funder's website.

The Dulverton Trust

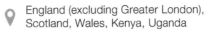

Children and young people, social welfare, conservation, heritage, peace and humanitarian support

England (excluding Greater London), Scotland, Wales, Kenya, Uganda

£2.9 million (2016/17)

CC number: 1146484

Trustees: Christopher Wills; Dr Catherine Wills; The Lord Dulverton; Tara Douglas-Home; Dame Mary Richardson; Richard Howard; The Rt Hon. The Earl of Grey Gowrie; Sir Malcolm Rifkind; The Lord Hemphill; Robert Wills.

Correspondent: Sarah Hale, Grants Manager, 5 St James's Place, London SW1A 1NP (tel: 020 7495 7852; email: grants@dulverton.org)

 www.dulverton.org

This is one of the trusts deriving from the tobacco-generated fortune of the Wills family. It has an endowment worth £85 million.

Eligibility
The trust supports registered charities, CIOs and exempt organisations that have an annual income between £200,000 and £5 million and newly registered charities.

The 2016/17 annual report states the following: 'We occasionally fund start-up charities if they can demonstrate a novel but credible approach to addressing a charitable need and have a realistic business plan. We strongly encourage cooperation or joint ventures between charities with similar objectives or beneficiary groups.'

The trusts supports activities in the following areas:

▶ Youth opportunities
▶ General welfare
▶ Conservation
▶ Preservation
▶ Peace and humanitarian support
▶ Africa

For further detail on what the trust can support within each of these categories, refer to the guidance provided on the trust's website.

Types of grant
The trust's website states:

The Trust awards both single year and multi-year grants.

▶ Single year grants are typically between £25,000 and £35,000
▶ Multi-year grants are usually for a period of 2 to 3 years, and are only awarded to charities which have previously received a Dulverton grant

We will consider applications for the following:

▶ Project costs
▶ Core funding (usually for charities which have previously received a Dulverton grant)
▶ Capital costs (usually under our preservation category)
▶ Scholarships and bursaries (usually under our preservation category)

Financial information
In 2016/17 the trust held assets of £98.8 million and had an income of £11.2 million. During the year, the trust received 292 appeals for funding, 72 of which received a grant. With multi-year grants awarded in previous years, grants totalled £2.9 million (which includes £410,000 which was distributed as minor grants by various community foundations), and were distributed among the following categories:

Youth opportunities	£1.2 million
General welfare	£787,000
Preservation	£313,000
Community Foundations	£310,000
Africa	£273,000
Conservation	£199,500
Peace and humanitarian support	£30,000
Local appeals	£25,000

Previous beneficiaries have included: Venture Scotland (£105,000); The Magdalen Environmental Trust (£93,500); Buglife (£58,000); Back on Track and Norwich Cathedral (£30,000 each); Child Bereavement UK and National Heritage Ironwork Group (£20,000 each); Parent Network Scotland and Send a Cow (£15,000 each); Tyneside Vineyard (£5,000); Cirencester Housing for Young People (£3,000); Furniture Recycling Project (£1,300).

Exclusions
The trust will not usually give grants for the following:

▶ Individuals
▶ Museums, galleries, libraries, exhibition centres and heritage attractions
▶ Churches, cathedrals and other historic buildings (except for limited support under the preservation category)
▶ Schools, colleges, universities or other educational establishments
▶ Hospices, hospitals, nursing or residential care homes
▶ Activities outside the stated geographical scope
▶ Support for charities whose main beneficiaries live within Greater London or in Northern Ireland

The trust will not normally support the following areas of activity:

▶ Regional charities that are affiliated with a national body (for example, local Scout groups)

- Health, medicine and medical conditions including drug and alcohol addiction, therapy and counselling
- Therapy and counselling
- Specific support for people with disabilities
- The arts, including theatre, music and drama (except where used as a means of achieving one of the trust's funding priorities)
- Sport, including sports centres and individual playing field projects (except where used as a means of achieving one of the trust's funding priorities)
- Animal welfare or projects concerning the protection of single species
- Research projects (unless linked to a project meeting the trust's priorities)
- Expeditions or individuals volunteering overseas
- Conferences, cultural festivals, exhibitions and events
- Salaries for specific posts (however funding salaries in the context of a multi-year grant will be considered)
- Major building projects, including the purchase of property or land
- Endowments
- Work that has already taken place (retrospective funding)

Applications

Note: The trust has asked us to emphasise that it does not accept applications via post. You should apply only through the trust's website.

Read the guidelines on the trust's website carefully, making sure that none of the exclusions apply to your charity or project, and then complete the online eligibility quiz. Only eligible organisations will be able to progress their application further. If your organisation passes the eligibility quiz, you will be provided with a link to the online application.

Applications for minor grants should be submitted to the appropriate community foundation, see the 'general' section of the website.

Sources of information

Accounts; annual report; Charity Commission record; funder's website.

Dumbreck Charity

 General charitable purposes

 Worldwide, especially the West Midlands

(£) £194,500 (2016/17)

CC number: 273070

Trustees: Chris Hordern; Hugh Carslake; Jane Uloth; Judith Melling.

Correspondent: Mrs P. Spragg, Administrator, c/o PS Accounting, 41 Sycamore Drive, Hollywood,

---

DUMBRECK CHARITY

Category	Regular grants	One-off grants	Total
Medical	2	33	£42,500
Miscellaneous	2	23	£42,500
Care of older people and those with disabilities	6	45	£40,500
Children's welfare	2	26	£26,000
Animal welfare	4	16	£19,500
Culture and the arts	0	9	£13,800
Social welfare	0	17	£9,500

Birmingham B47 5QX (email: psaccounting@hotmail.co.uk)

The trust focuses on animal welfare and conservation, children's welfare, care of older people and those with disabilities, medical causes, social welfare, arts and culture, and other general charitable purposes. A small number of grants are awarded each year to charities in Worcestershire, Warwickshire and West Midlands. Grants can be one-off or recurring and are typically for less than £2,000.

Financial information

In 2016/17 the charity held assets of almost £4.7 million and had an income of £160,500. Grants were made to 185 organisations, totalling £194,500. Grant distributions are shown in the table above.

Previous beneficiaries have included: Disasters Emergency Committee Yemen Crisis Appeal (£10,000); 2nd Warwick Sea Scout Group (£5,000); The Farm Animal Sanctuary (£3,000); Cyclists Fighting Cancer (£2,000); After Adoption, Elmhurst Ballet School and Music Therapy Works (£1,000 each); Domestic Abuse Counselling Service, Walsall Carers Centre and Warwickshire Hedgehog Rescue (£500 each).

Exclusions

No grants are given to individuals.

Applications

Apply in writing to the correspondent. The trustees meet annually in April/May. Unsuccessful applications will not be acknowledged. In general, new applications are only considered from organisations in the Midlands counties.

Sources of information

Accounts; annual report; Charity Commission record.

Dunard Fund 2016

 Classical music, architecture, visual arts, and, to a lesser extent, environmental and humanitarian projects

UK, mainly Scotland

(£) £1.7 million (2016/17)

OSCR number: SC046889

Trustees: Carol Colburn Grigor; Dr Catherine Colburn Høgel; Erik Colburn Høgel; Andrew Liddell; Peter Thierfeldt.

Correspondent: Carol Colburn Grigor, Trustee, c/o J. & H. Mitchell W.S., 51 Atholl Road, Pitlochry, Perthshire, Scotland PH16 5BU

The fund, established in 1986, is funded annually by Marlowe Holdings Ltd, of which the correspondent is both a director and a shareholder. In 2016 the Dunard Fund (SC039685) re-registered with the Scottish Charity Register as a Scottish CIO. In the past the grant total has been around £2 million and has mainly gone to classical music organisations, with humanitarian, environmental and architectural causes also being supported. As this SCIO is newly registered there are no accounts available on Companies House or the charity's OSCR record. We have assumed that the grant-making strategy will remain largely the same.

Financial information

In 2016/17 the charity had assets of £68.7 million and an income of £68.9 million. Grants totalled £1.7 million and were distributed in the following categories:

Classical music	3	£640,000
Visual arts	1	£450,000
Architectural	4	£393,000
Humanitarian and environmental	4	£177,000

Beneficiaries included: International Music and Performing Arts Charitable Trust Scotland Ltd (£640,000); National Galleries of Scotland (£450,000); The Royal Academy of Arts (£200,000); Bothwell Parish Church (£25,000); The Salvation Army (£1,000).

Exclusions

Grants are only given to charities recognised in Scotland or charities registered in England and Wales. Applications from individuals are not considered.

Applications

Apply in writing to the correspondent.

Sources of information

Accounts; annual report; OSCR record.

The Dunhill Medical Trust

 Research into ageing, the care of older people

UK

£6.5 million (2016/17)

CC number: 1140372

Trustees: Kay Glendinning; John Ransford; Prof. James McEwen; Prof. Peter Lansley; Helen Davies; Prof. Alison Petch; Claire Keatinge; Prof. Deborah Dunn-Walters; James Lorigan; Keith Sheperd; Prof. Thomas Kirkwood.

Correspondent: The Trustees, Fifth Floor, 6 New Bridge Street, London EC4V 6AB (tel: 020 7403 3299; email: info@dunhillmedical.org.uk)

 www.dunhillmedical.org.uk

The Dunhill Medical Trust (DMT) was established in 1950 by the will left by Herbert Dunhill. The trust was formally registered as a charity in the 1980s. It was established with charitable objects focused on medical research, care and facilities; specifically the research into provision of accommodation for older people; and care for older people.

The trust's website states: 'We not only fund some of the very best of the UK's academic and clinical research into understanding the mechanisms of ageing and treating age-related diseases and frailty; we also support community-based organisations that are working to enhance the lives of those who need extra support in later life.'

The following information on research grants and grants for community organisations has been taken from the trust's website:

Research

Project grants – The Trust is keen to support high quality research projects which are, perhaps, smaller than can be managed by the Research Councils or fall outside their priority themes but are important to understanding the mechanisms of ageing, treating disease and frailty and identifying and developing new and effective ways to improve the lives of older people. We are also committed to funding research into treating diseases and conditions which disproportionately affect older people but are less well-funded.

Research training fellowships – Research Training Fellowships provide funding to talented academics, clinicians and health or social care professionals who would like a future career in research aimed at improving care for older people. The awards may either be in the form of a PhD studentship or granted to experienced professionals who wish to branch into research. Research Fellows (and named early career research

assistants on our Project Grants schemes) are invited to join our Research Fellows' Network.

Community based organisations

We make grants to UK charities and community-based organisations who provide care, activities and services for older people. We particularly like to support projects which have the potential to scale up, share resources and experience with others and attract other sources of support.

Project grants - Time-limited projects which focus on the development of care and support services for older people which are innovative and/or based on evidence of best practice and which can become self-sustaining within a planned period. Priority will be given to services which are focused on older people, enhance existing mainstream services and which are not currently funded by statutory organisations elsewhere in the UK. The Trust will expect the beneficiary organisation to have a robust plan to create the ongoing revenue to maintain the service as the charitable funding diminishes and to have processes in place to ensure minimum disruption to the beneficiaries in implementing these plans.

Building and physical infrastructure grants for community-based organisations – The provision of accommodation/developments in the built environment for older people to enhance and maintain their health, well-being and independence and/or specific pieces of equipment or furnishings which can be used for the care and support of individuals (for example, installation of a hearing loop system). Priority will be given to care facilities which are focused specifically on older people and where it has not been possible to obtain the necessary funding from statutory organisations (e.g. health and social services). We will expect the beneficiary organisation to give a written commitment to bear the revenue costs of the environment and/or equipment, including its maintenance and staffing.

Capability grants - This scheme is intended to support the development of knowledge, skills and capabilities in community-based organisations, whose main beneficiaries are older people.

Some examples of what this scheme could pay for:

- Training to acquire governance, strategic development or other high level skills to assist in the development of the charity
- The development of protocols or training around risk management or quality assurance
- Feasibility studies
- Community consultations and surveys
- Business planning
- Board development and governance
- Research and evidence gathering in relation to the organisation's cause and objectives
- Capacity building for your organisation to deliver a new idea
- Needs analysis

- Skills audits of communities
- Specialist advice
- Small pilot projects
- Exchange visits within the UK to see how other projects work

Financial information

In 2016/17 the trust held assets of £141.2 million and had an income of £3.9 million. Grants were made totalling £6.5 million, with £4.2 million awarded for research and £2.3 million awarded to community-based organisations.

Beneficiaries included: Newcastle University (£1.04 million); Mid and East Antrim Agewell Partnership (£998,000); University of Liverpool (£212,500); Addenbrookes Charitable Trust (£117,000); Helix Arts (£68,000); Age UK Canterbury (£67,500); Us in a Bus (£23,000).

Applications

Applications can be made through the trust's online grants portal.

Sources of information

Accounts; annual report; Charity Commission record; funder's website.

The Charles Dunstone Charitable Trust

General charitable purposes, heritage, ex-offenders, education, young people

UK

£4.7 million (2016/17)

CC number: 1085955

Trustees: Denis Dunstone; Adrian Bott; John Gordon; Robert Clarkson.

Correspondent: The Trustees, H. W. Fisher and Company, Acre House, 11–15 William Road, London NW1 3ER (email: jtrent@hwfisher.co.uk)

Established in 2001 for general charitable purposes, this is the charitable trust of Charles Dunstone, co-founder of the Carphone Warehouse.

The trust's 2016/17 annual report states that it makes a small number of grants in the following areas:

- Improving the prospects of prisoners on release, especially through the provision of high quality 'through the gate' services.
- Making lasting improvements to the education and wellbeing of young people living in disadvantaged communities, particularly young people

The Trust also funds a small number of heritage and restoration projects which are chosen by the Trustees. Grants are likely to be made to a small number of organisations which have entrepreneurial leadership and have potential to create significant impact, either at local or national level.

The trust also provides ongoing funding to Fulwood Academy in Preston.

Financial information

In 2016/17 the trust had assets of £1.62 million and an income of £3.32 million. Grants were made totalling £4.7 million, and were distributed as follows:

Heritage and Restoration	£2.83 million
Education and training	£1.38 million
Children and young people	£346,500
Community care and 'ethnic organisations'	£102,500
Social welfare	£27,000
Medical and disability	£15,500
Other	£5,700
Arts and Culture	£3,600

Beneficiaries included: The 5Bel Charitable Trust (£2.8 million); The Fulwood Academy (£1.09 million five grants); Blue Marine Foundation (£25,000); NSPCC (£5,000); Film Aid UK, Diabetes Research (£1,000 each); Women for Women (£500); The Cairn Trust (£200); Burnham Horticultural Society (£50).

Exclusions

The trustees do not normally make grants directly to individuals.

Applications

The 2016/17 annual report states that, 'proposals are invited by the Trustees or initiated at their request. Unsolicited applications are not encouraged and are unlikely to be successful.'

Sources of information

Accounts; annual report; Charity Commission record.

The Dyers' Company Charitable Trust

 General charitable purposes

UK

£518,500 (2016/17)

CC number: 289547

Trustee: The Dyers Company.

Correspondent: Mr J. R. Vaizey, Clerk to the Trustees, Dyer's Hall, Dowgate Hill, London EC4R 2ST (tel: 020 7236 7197; email: clerk@dyerscompany.com)

www.dyerscompany.co.uk

The trust was established in 1984 and makes a large number of grants to registered charities in support of general charitable purposes. The trust gives to UK-registered charities for both one-off and long standing projects. The trust does not consider applications unless they are sponsored by one of their liverymen. The trust has several commitments to educational bursaries with schools and universities, including

Norwich School, which it reviews annually.

Financial information

In 2016/17 the trust held assets of £18.6 million and had an income of £1.9 million. Grants were made to 135 organisations and totalled £518,500. The following breakdown was provided in the 2016/17 accounts:

Education	33	£222,000
Norwich School	1	£76,500
The Dyers Craft	13	£59,000
Armed forces	7	£50,000
Health and welfare	38	£48,000
The arts	19	£21,000
Local community/Inner London	7	£15,000
The church	10	£13,200
Other	7	£13,000

Previous beneficiaries have included: St Saviour's and St Olave's School (£68,000); ABF The Soldiers' Charity (£20,000); Society of Dyers and Colourists (£15,000); Cirdan Sailing Trust (£5,000); Swan Sanctuary (£4,000); Stroudwater Textile Trust (£2,000); Association for Post Natal Illness, Clan Macpherson Museum Trust, Norfolk Archaeological Trust and Prisoners' Education Trust (£1,000 each); Southwark Cathedral (£500); St Christopher's Hospice (£200).

Exclusions

No grants are given to individuals or international charities.

Applications

The trust does not accept unsolicited applications, but members of the company can nominate charities for support.

Sources of information

Accounts; annual report; Charity Commission record; funder's website.

The James Dyson Foundation

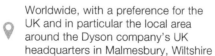 Medical research, engineering education

Worldwide, with a preference for the UK and in particular the local area around the Dyson company's UK headquarters in Malmesbury, Wiltshire

£1.39 million including organisations, bursaries and foundation awards (2016)

CC number: 1099709

Trustees: Sir James Dyson; Lady Deirdre Dyson; Valerie West; Dr Fenella Dyson.

Correspondent: Lydia Beaton, Foundation Manager, Dyson Group plc, Tetbury Hill, Malmesbury, Wiltshire SN16 0RP (tel: 01666 828416; email: jamesdysonfoundation@dyson.com)

 www.jamesdysonfoundation.com

The James Dyson Foundation was set up in 2002 to promote charitable giving, especially to charities working in the fields of science, design, and engineering education and medical research.

The 2016 annual report defines the foundation's charitable objects as follows:

- To advance education and training, particularly in the fields of design and technology. This work can take a number of forms including the free provision of support resources for teachers of design and technology in schools, the running of design engineering workshops and lectures in schools and universities, as well as bursary schemes and collaborative projects.
- To support medical and scientific research.
- To support charitable and educational projects in the region in which The James Dyson Foundation operates.

Each year, the foundation donates a number of Dyson vacuum cleaners (for raffle prizes) to charitable causes which fall within its objectives. The cost of these is included in the total grants figure. Small grants may also be made to charitable projects that share the philosophies and objectives of the foundation. The foundation also works with schools and universities, providing bursaries and educational activities and events, and runs the annual James Dyson Award, a design engineering competition for students.

Financial information

In 2016 the foundation had assets of £519,000 and an income of £9.86 million. Grants, including foundation awards and student bursaries paid to institutions, totalled £1.39 million and were distributed in three categories as follows:

Education and training	£1.21 million
Science and medical research	£171,000
Social and community welfare	£8,100

Beneficiaries included: US Education Programme (£377,500); Bath Schools Design Education Programme (£64,500); Royal College of Art (£50,000); Malmesbury School Project (£33,000); Local Community and Education Programme (£9,800).

Exclusions

According to its website, the foundation will not fund any of the following:

- Animal welfare
- Loans or funding for individuals or companies
- Sports team sponsorship

Applications

Organisations can apply by completing the online form, accessed via the contact section of the foundation's website.

Sources of information

Accounts; annual report; Charity Commission record; funder's website.

The Earley Charity

 General charitable purposes

The Ancient Liberty of Earley (i.e. the central eastern and southern part of Reading, Earley and Lower Earley, northern Shinfield, Winnersh, Sonning and Lower Caversham)

£288,000 to organisations (2016)

CC number: 244823

Trustees: Dr Deborah Jenkins; Dr David Sutton; Miryam Eastwell; Robert Ames; Philip Hooper; Mary Waite.

Correspondent: Jane Wittig, Clerk to the Trustees, The Liberty of Earley House, Strand Way, Lower Earley, Reading, Berkshire RG6 4EA (tel: 0118 975 5663; email: enquiries@earleycharity.org.uk)

www.earleycharity.org.uk

The Earley Charity was founded in 1990 and is the one of the largest local grant-making charities in central southern England. The charity makes grants to charitable and community organisations and to individuals in need. Its website states: 'The Earley Charity is one of the largest local grant-making charities in central southern England. Its object is the relief of need among elderly, disabled or poor people living in our area of benefit. The Charity's terms of reference also make it possible for us to fund community, educational, informational, cultural, sporting, recreational and social initiatives.'

Grants are made to a wide variety of organisations within the charity's area of benefit. Applications should be for one-off funding for a specific purpose. Grants normally range from £500 to £5,000. Larger grants may be awarded to organisations that the trustees know well.

Arts, Culture and Heritage

The charity has a specific programme for arts, culture and heritage. The charity's website states:

The Earley Charity is keen to promote all aspects of cultural life within our area of benefit.

To enable this, the Arts, Culture and Heritage category of grant-making has been set up to fund group activities. Through this programme we aim to:

- Promote all aspects of art, culture and heritage within our area of benefit
- Bring people together
- Promote the sharing of skills and knowledge
- Encourage people of all ages and backgrounds to try new things

Financial information

In 2016 the charity held assets of £12.46 million and had an income of almost £1.1 million. Grants made to 22 individuals totalled £6,400 and grants to 39 organisations totalled £288,000. Grants totalling £203,000 were also made under the Earley Charity Workers scheme.

Beneficiaries included: Reading Community Welfare Rights Unit (£52,000); Museum of English Rural Life (£30,000); Reading Advice Network (£22,000); Aspire2 (£10,000); Arc Youth Counselling (£3,600); Adviza (£2,000); Challengers (£1,900); Bastille Events Ltd (£500).

Exclusions

The charity does not fund the following: postgraduate education; general running/living costs; core costs; open-ended salaries; general appeals; religious activities, national organisations operating in the area of benefit without a local office; general public sector appeals (apart from in a few very exceptional cases); applications from outside the area of benefit.

Applications

Application forms can be requested via email, phone, or by completing the online enquiry form. Application forms and supporting documents should be returned to the charity by post. Check the charity's website for application deadlines.

Sources of information

Accounts; annual report; Charity Commission record; funder's website.

The Sir John Eastwood Foundation

 General charitable purposes including children with special needs, older people and people with disabilities

 Nottinghamshire

£324,500 (2016/17)

CC number: 235389

Trustees: Diana Cottingham; Constance Mudford; Valerie Hardingham; David Marriott.

Correspondent: David Marriott, Trustee, PO Box 9803, Mansfield NG18 9FT (email: sirjohneastwoodfoundation@talktalk.net)

The foundation was originally established by Sir John Eastwood in 1964, and supports general charitable purposes in Nottinghamshire. According to the trustees' report for 2016/17: 'The charity supports a number of registered charities on a regular basis by making grants each year to those particular charities. The prime target of the trustees each year is to ensure the continuance of these regular grants. Once these have been ensured, the trustees consider special projects and then other individual applications.'

Financial information

In 2016/17 the foundation had assets of £8.9 million and an income of £296,000. During the year, the foundation awarded 135 grants to organisations totalling £324,500.

Beneficiaries included: All Saints Church, Clipstone (£40,000); Yeoman Park School (£25,000); Nottinghamshire Hospice (£24,000); Warsop Youth Club (£10,000); Air Ambulance, Macmillan Cancer Support and NSPCC (£5,000 each).

Exclusions

No grants are given to individuals.

Applications

Apply in writing to the correspondent. Note that the foundation tends to supports the same charities on an annual basis.

Sources of information

Accounts; annual report; Charity Commission record.

The EBM Charitable Trust

Development of young people, animal welfare, social welfare

UK

£1.35 million (2016/17)

CC number: 326186

Trustees: Richard Moore; Michael Macfadyen; Stephen Hogg; Francis Moore; Lucy Forsyth.

Correspondent: Martin Pollock, Secretary, c/o Moore Stephens, 150 Aldersgate Street, London EC1A 4AB (tel: 020 7334 9191)

The EBM Charitable Trust was established in 1982 by the late Eric Blechynden Moller. The trustees' 2016/17 annual report states that the trust aims 'to support a wide variety of beneficiaries including charities involved in animal welfare and research, relief of poverty and youth development'.

The trust manages two funds, the general fund and the Fitz' fund. The Fitz' fund was established following the death of Cyril Fitzgerald, one of the original trustees of the charity who left the residue of his estate to the trust. The money is held as a designated fund for animal charities.

Financial information

In 2016/17 the trust held assets of £51.3 million and had an income of £1.32 million. There were 35 grants made totalling £1.35 million.

Beneficiaries included: Animal Health Trust (£250,000); Lewis Manning Hospice (£150,000); The Wavertree Charitable Trust (£60,000); Royal Veterinary College (£20,000); Missing People (£15,000); Dogs for Good (£10,000); Army Polo Association (£3,000).

Applications

The trustees state in their 2016/17 annual report:

> Unsolicited applications are not requested as the trustees prefer to support donations to charities whose work they have researched and which is in accordance with the wishes of the settlor. The trustees do not tend to support research projects as research is not a core priority but there are exceptions. The trustees' funds are fully committed. The trustees receive a very high number of grant applications which are mostly unsuccessful.

Sources of information

Accounts; annual report; Charity Commission record.

Echoes of Service

 Advancement of health, the prevention or relief of poverty, overseas aid and religious activities

 Worldwide

£ £1.8 million to organisations (2016)

CC number: 234556

Trustees: John Aitken; Dr John Burness; James Crooks; Eric Noble; Paul Young; Benjamin Scholefield; Alan Park.

Correspondent: The Trustees, 124 Wells Road, Bath BA2 3AH (tel: 01225 310893; email: echoes@echoes.org.uk)

 www.echoes.org.uk

 facebook.com/echoesinternational

 @echoesuk

The charity was founded in 1872 and works to support missionary work around the world. According to the charity's website, 'it aims to inspire and to encourage more people to get involved in mission so they can experience the positive changes brought about by the transformative power of God's work and Word'.

The charity's 2016 annual report states that its core activities fall into four main areas:

- The production of mission information for individuals and churches. This is achieved by the publication of a monthly magazine, weekly email distribution of news items, the maintenance of a website, publication of two mission bulletins per annum and the publication from time to time of mission booklets and DVDs
- The receipt and transmission of funds for mission support of individuals, specific ministries and institutions
- The provision of a wide variety of services to the personnel we support and also advice, guidance and counsel to individuals and churches on mission-related issues
- Deputation visits to churches to report on mission, and the running of seminars and mission events to create and maintain interest among our supporters

Financial information

In 2016 the charity held assets of £10.3 million and had an income of £4.3 million. During the year, the charity gave a total of almost £4.6 million in grants. Of this amount, the charity gave £1.8 million to organisations and £2.8 million to individuals. In total, 191 grants were given to organisations.

Beneficiaries included: Manara Ministries (£116,500); Opal Trust (£100,000); Lebanese Society for Education (£79,500); Operation Mobilisation (£36,500); Chitokoloki Hospital (£18,500).

Other grants paid to 182 organisations totalled £1.3 million.

Applications

Apply in writing to the correspondent.

Sources of information

Accounts; annual report; Charity Commission record; funder's website.

EDF Energy Trust

 Fuel poverty, money/debt advice, fuel debt prevention

 UK

£ £254,500 to organisations (2016)

CC number: 1099446

Trustees: Denise Fennell; Tim Cole; David Hawkes; Vic Szewczyk.

Correspondent: The Trustees, Freepost EDF ENERGY TRUST (tel: 01733 421060; email: edfet@charisgrants.com)

 www.edfenergytrust.org.uk

EDF Energy Trust, established in October 2003, makes grants to support individuals and families who are in 'need, poverty, suffering and distress

who are struggling to pay their gas and/ or electricity debts'. The trust's grants scheme is administered by Charis Grants Ltd.

Type of grants

Individuals and families

The Trust helps by giving grants:

- To clear gas and electricity debts owed to EDF Energy
- To clear gas and electricity debts owed to other suppliers.
- For Bankruptcy/Debt Relief Order (DRO), Sequestration and Minimal Asset Process fees, purchase essential energy efficient white goods and cookers (these payments are known as FAPs (Further Assistance Payments)).

The aim of the Trust is to give vulnerable individuals and families a fresh start to enable them to keep free of debt going forward. Applicants are strongly advised to seek money advice before applying to the Trust.

Organisations

In addition to the individuals and families grants programme, the trust also provides grants for organisations to support its purposes. The 2016 annual report states grants are given to organisations for the following purposes:

- Provision of specialist money/debt advice and resolving energy debt problems for all clients
- Supporting EDF Energy customers to apply to the charity where appropriate
- Promoting the Charity to local organisations, developing partnerships for referrals
- Promotion of energy debt awareness and prevention

Details of current funding opportunities are posted on the trust's website.

Financial information

In 2016 the trust had assets of almost £3 million and an income of £1.46 million. Grants were made to three organisations, (reaching over 2,000 beneficiaries), totalling £254,500. Grants were also made to 3,840 individuals and families totalling £2.8 million.

Beneficiaries included: Plymouth Citizens Advice £99,000); Talking Money – Bristol (£80,500); Thanet Citizens Advice (£75,000).

Applications

Calls for grant proposals from organisations are announced on the trust's website and in its newsletter. Alternatively, contact the trust for more information.

Sources of information

Accounts; annual report; Charity Commission record; funder's website.

The Edge Foundation

Education

UK

£ £332,000 (2016)

CC number: 286621

Trustees: Sir Kevin Satchwell; Lord Baker of Dorking; Prof. Colin Riordan; Neil Bates; Lord Adonis; Pauline Daniyan; Tobias Peyton-Jones; Sir Garry Hawekes; Andrew Stevens.

Correspondent: The Trustees, 4 Millbank, London SW1P 3JA (tel: 020 7960 1540; email: enquiry@edge.co.uk)

🌐 www.edge.co.uk

Grants of up to £100,000 are available to educational projects that focus on technical and professional learning and skills shortages in the UK. Projects should build on proven models of success or test new approaches within education and learning.

The Edge Grant Fund

Educational establishments and non-profit organisations working in the education sector can all apply.

The foundation's website states:

Projects must support Edge's plan for education and focus on technical and professional learning and skills shortages in the UK. They must also address in detail at least one of the funding themes:

Improve the design and delivery of engaging and relevant Careers Education, Information, Advice and Guidance

Support the development of Project Based Learning (PBL) and associated profound employer engagement

Support the development of a 14–19 curriculum which integrates both academic and technical/professional subjects

Support the development of innovative approaches to higher education at levels 4, 5, and 6

Ways to measure the performance of technical education.

Financial information

In 2016 the foundation held assets of £32.7 million and had an income of £660,000. Grants awarded to organisations totalled £332,000.

Previous beneficiaries of the Edge Grant Fund included: Blackburn College; Bridgwater and Taunton College; Career Ready; Doncaster Chamber of Commerce and Enterprise; St Helens Chamber; The Grimsby Institute of Further and Higher Education; The Studio Liverpool; The Studio Schools Trust.

Exclusions

Edge will not fund applications which:

▸ Are for activities or organisations that are outside the UK
▸ Are submitted by individuals or profit-making organisations
▸ Are submitted by organisations whose financial history shows serious financial deficit or are non-compliant with their regulatory body
▸ Promote religious beliefs or political opinions
▸ Request money for contingency costs, retrospective costs or recoverable VAT

Applications

Check the foundation's website for application deadlines. At the time of writing (June 2018) the foundation's website states that the next funding round will open in 2020.

Sources of information

Accounts; annual report; Charity Commission record; funder's website.

D.M.H. Educational Trust Ltd

Orthodox Jewish religion, relief of poverty, general charitable purposes

England and Wales

£ £381,000 (2016/17)

CC number: 271437

Trustees: Samuel Jacob Halpern; Sidney Halpern; Relly Halpern; David Halpern.

Correspondent: David Halpern, Trustee, 31A The Park, London NW11 7ST (tel: 020 8731 0777; email: dh@dominionltd.net)

Established in 1976, and gives grants to organisations for Orthodox Jewish causes, the prevention or relief of poverty and general charitable purposes.

Financial information

In 2016/17 the trust had assets of £2.1 million and an income of £575,000. During the year, the trust gave £381,000 in grants to organisations.

Beneficiaries included: Keren Chochmas Shloma Trust (£65,000); Talmud Torah Machzikei Hadass Trust (£50,000); The Lolev Charitable Trust (£25,000); Hadras Kodesh Trust and Society of Friends of the Torah Ltd (£20,000 each); Comet Charities Ltd (£12,000); Rise and Shine (£10,000).

Applications

Apply in writing to the correspondent.

Sources of information

Accounts; Charity Commission record.

Edupoor Ltd

Education and training, the relief of poverty, older people, illness, both mental and physical, disability, general charitable purposes

Worldwide

£ £861,000 (2016/17)

CC number: 1113785

Trustees: Alan Shelton; Michael Shelton; Benjamin Levy.

Correspondent: Michael Shelton, Trustee, Flat 10, 125 Clapton Common, Stamford Hill, London E5 9AB (tel: 020 8800 0088)

Set up in 2006, the charity is constituted as a company limited by guarantee. According to its 2016/17 accounts its objects are:

▸ The advancement in education and training through the world.
▸ The relief of poverty, old age, illness, both mental and physical and the relief of persons suffering from any disability, and such other charitable purpose as the association may time to time authorise.

Financial information

In 2016/17 the charity held assets of £29,500 and had an income of £873,5000. Grants awarded to organisations totalled £861,000.

Applications

Apply in writing to the correspondent.

Sources of information

Accounts; annual report; Charity Commission record.

The Eighty Eight Foundation

General charitable purposes, including education, cancer and dementia research and care, underprivileged Irish people, older people, artists and photographers

UK and Ireland

£ £656,000 (2016/17)

CC number: 1149797

Trustees: Stuart Walker; Ann Fitzmaurice; Claude Slatner; Neelish Heredia.

Correspondent: The Trustees, c/o Rawlinson & Hunter, 6 New Street Square, London EC4A 3AQ (tel: 020 7842 2000; email: eighty.eight@rawlinson-hunter.com)

The Eighty Eight Foundation registered with the Charity Commission in 2012. The foundation awards grants to general charitable purposes, however their 2016/17 accounts state that:

'For the time being the trustees' focus is supporting education, cancer and dementia research and care, Irish underprivileged and age concerns and exceptional underprivileged artists and photographers.'

Financial information

In 2016/17 the foundation held assets of £13 million and had an income of £210,500. Grants awarded to organisations totalled £656,000.

Beneficiaries included: The LINK South Africa (£150,000); Photographer's Gallery (£127,500); City Year (£120,000); The Sutton Trust (£80,000); Shine (£71,500).

Applications

Apply in writing to the correspondent.

Sources of information

Accounts; annual report; Charity Commission record.

The Gerald Palmer Eling Trust Company

🔍 Religion, medical research, education

📍 Berkshire

💷 £291,500 (2016/17)

CC number: 1100869

Trustees: Desmond Harrison; Robin Broadhurst; James Gardiner; Kenneth McDiarmid.

Correspondent: E. M. Crookes, Company Secretary, Eling Estate Office, Wellhouse, Hermitage, Thatcham, Berkshire RG19 9UF (tel: 01635 200268; email: charities@elingestate.co.uk)

Established in 2003, the annual report for 2016/17 states that the policy of the directors to make grants in response to specific requests giving particular emphasis to:

▶ Advancing the Christian religion
▶ Advancing medical research
▶ Relieving sickness and poverty
▶ Supporting local charities

The trust is also responsible for the management of the Eling Estate, which comprises of residential properties, farmland and woodlands.

Financial information

In 2016/17 the trust held assets of £79.18 million and had an income of almost £1.6 million. Grants were made totalling £291,500 broken down as follows:

Social welfare	£131,500
Medical research/support	£79,000
Church/religion	£43,000
Youth/education/community	£32,000
Conservation/heritage/arts	£2,000

Beneficiaries have included: Pelican Cancer Foundation (£25,000); Institute of Christian Orthodox Studies (£15,000); Convent of the Annunciation, Swings and Smiles and West Berkshire Mencap (£10,000 each).

Exclusions

No grants are given to individuals.

Applications

Apply in writing to the correspondent.

Sources of information

Accounts; Charity Commission record.

The Marian Elizabeth Trust

🔍 Children with disabilities

📍 UK

💷 £1.6 million (2016/17)

CC number: 1166932

Trustees: Maureen Edwards; Michael Edwards; Rosemary Edwards; Robert Rowley.

Correspondent: Anne Carlisle, The Enterprise Centre, Priors Hall, Corby NN17 5EU (tel: 01536 560394; email: anne@meproductions.info)

This trust was registered with the Charity Commission in May 2016. Its 2016/17 annual report states: 'The charity makes grants to charitable organisations, such as hospices, which specialise in providing care to children suffering with severe disabilities, with special focus on those with profound and multiple learning difficulties.'

Financial information

In 2016/17 the trust had assets of £1.9 million and an income of £3.5 million. Grants awarded to organisations totalled £1.6 million.

Beneficiaries included: Acorn Children's Hospice (£885,000); Rainbows Hospice (£600,000); Newlife Centre (£100,000); Rutland Rotoract Family Support Centre (£39,000).

Applications

Apply in writing to the correspondent.

Sources of information

Accounts; annual report; Charity Commission record.

The Maud Elkington Charitable Trust

🔍 Social welfare, general charitable purposes

📍 Mainly in Desborough and the county of Northampton

💷 £520,000 (2016/17)

CC number: 263929

Trustees: Roger Bowder; Michael Jones; Katherine Hall.

Correspondent: Emily Izzo, Shakespeare Martineau, Two Colton Square, Leicester LE1 1QH (tel: 0116 257 4645; email: emily.izzo@shma.co.uk)

The trust was established in 1972 and its principle aim is to distribute grants, particularly, but not exclusively, in Desborough and the County of Northampton. Grants are made to rather small projects, where they will make a quantifiable difference to the recipients, rather than favouring large national charities that have an income of millions rather than thousands. It is the usual practice to make grants for the benefit of individuals through referring agencies such as social services, NHS Trusts or similar responsible bodies.

Financial information

In 2016/17 the trust had assets of £29.3 million and an income of £695,500. During the year, the trust gave around £520,000 in grants to organisations.

Previous beneficiaries have included: Bromford Housing Association; Cancer Research UK; CARE Shangton; Charity Link; Cynthia Spencer Hospice; Elizabeth Finn Care; Launde Abbey; Leicester Grammar School – Bursary; Leicester High School for Girls – Bursary; Multiple Sclerosis Society; Nottinghamshire County Council; Phoenix Furniture; Voluntary Action Northamptonshire.

Exclusions

Only in exceptional circumstances do the trustees make grants directly to individuals.

Applications

Apply in writing to the correspondent. There is no application form or guidelines. The trustees meet every seven or eight weeks.

Sources of information

Accounts; annual report; Charity Commission record.

The Ellerdale Trust

🔍 Children, families, disability and ill health

📍 Norfolk

💷 £200,500 (2016/17)

CC number: 1073376

Trustees: Alistair Macfarlane; Paul Kurthausen; Simon Moores; Clare Cairnes.

Correspondent: Mary Adlard, The Parlour, High Street, Ketteringham, Wymondham NR18 9RU (tel: 01603

813340; email: mary.adlard@btconnect.com)

This trust was established to relieve poverty, distress or suffering in any part of the world. In practice, the majority of funding is given to local and national organisations for projects based in Norfolk. The 2016/17 annual report provides the following information about the trust's grant-making:

Funding is applied:

(a) To charities which assist children to develop in their early years, mainly up to 10 with a limit of 18, although the Trust does support some young people over that age.

(b) With preference given for applications from Norfolk charities, but the Ellerdale Trust does support applications from elsewhere in the UK.

(c) Whilst concentrating on the United Kingdom, a small proportion of grants are made to overseas charities.

Grant making is mainly directed towards children in need falling within the primary groupings of:

(i) Children who have been abused, either sexually, physically or by bullying.

(ii) Brain damaged children.

(iii) Terminally ill children.

(iv) Children requiring mobility equipment because of illness.

(v) Holidays or breaks for carers and children from inner cities.

(vi) The causes and relief of mental illness.

(vii) Children and their families suffering from life threatening illness or bereavement.

(viii) Disadvantaged children living within depressed or deprived areas.

To date the Trust has paid out a range of grants to charitable organisations. Over the last three years, the largest grant has been for £900,000 and the smallest £300.

Financial information
In 2016/17 the trust held assets of £6.8 million and had an income of £183,000. Grants were made to 43 organisations and totalled £200,500.

Beneficiaries included: Action for Kids (£24,000); NSPCC (£20,000); Mind (£17,000); East Anglia's Children's Hospices (£10,000); Bipolar UK and Norfolk and Norwich Festival (£5,000 each); CLIC Sargent, Norfolk Carers Support and Wellspring Family Centre (£2,000 each); Autism Anglia (£1,000); Africa Equipment for Schools (£500).

Exclusions
The trust does not make grants to individuals.

Applications
Apply in writing to the correspondent.

Sources of information
Accounts; annual return; Charity Commission record.

John Ellerman Foundation

Social welfare, environment, including land and marine conservation, arts including performing arts, museums and galleries

Mainly UK, also east and southern Africa

£5.4 million (2016/17)

CC number: 263207

Trustees: Sarah Riddell; Dominic Caldecott; Timothy Glass; Brian Hurwitz; Hugh Raven; Vivien Gould; Peter Kyle.

Correspondent: Dorothée Irving, Head of Grants, Suite 10, Aria House, 23 Craven Street, London WC2N 5NS (tel: 020 7930 8566; email: enquiries@ ellerman.org.uk)

 www.ellerman.org.uk

The foundation was established on the death of Sir John Ellerman in 1971 to support a wide range of charitable purposes. John Ellerman had inherited his substantial wealth from his family's business, Ellerman Lines. Today the foundation uses Sir John's legacy to make grants totalling around £5 million a year to around 150 different charities, mostly in the United Kingdom. The foundation makes grants to UK-registered charities which work nationally, not locally. For historical reasons it continues to support a few charities operating in Southern and East Africa.

The foundation's mission is 'to be and be seen as a model grant-maker to the charitable sector'. It aims to achieve its mission by managing its funds in such a way that it can both maintain its grant-making capacity and operate in perpetuity, funding nationally-registered charities so as to encourage and support those which make a real difference to people, communities and the environment. The foundation is happy to consider requests for 'hard to fund', or 'unpopular' causes and prioritises its grant-making on small to medium-sized charities as well as funding core costs.

Grant-making guidelines
Applications are accepted from organisations that work across England or the UK with an income of over £100,000. The foundation has a preference for funding smaller organisations that have reach and significance across the UK and will support core costs or projects. The foundation tends to fund organisations over multiple years rather than one-off grants. The foundation has three main funding priorities:

- Performing and visual arts, especially theatre, dance, music and museums and galleries
- The environment – with a focus on habitat management and marine conservation
- Social welfare

Financial information
In 2016/17 the foundation had assets of £142.6 million and an income of £4.1 million. During the year, the charity made 71 grants to organisations totalling £5.4 million.

Grants were broken down by category as follows:

Welfare, including overseas	£2.87 million
Arts, including regional museums and galleries	£1.35 million
Environment	£1.16 million

Beneficiaries include: Falklands Conservation (£126,000); Fishing into the Future (£100,000); Campaign for National Parks (£75,000); Bipolar UK (£60,000); Gingerbread (£50,000); Watts Gallery (£46,000); Forward Thinking (£45,000).

The average size of a grant remained the same as last year at approximately £30,000 per annum or £76,000 overall. Out of the 71 grants awarded, 60 were for core funding.

Exclusions
The website states that grants are not made for the following purposes:

- Individuals, including student grants or bursaries
- General and round-robin appeals
- Capital developments and individual items of equipment
- Promotion of religion and places of worship
- Replacement or subsidy funding, or for work we consider should be funded by government
- Individual campaigns
- One-off events, such as conferences, trips, seminars, masterclasses, summer schools, single commissions, productions or festivals
- Arts organisations and projects whose main focus is supporting and developing individuals
- Sport, leisure or individual holiday schemes
- Education, such as initiatives linked to the curriculum, arts or environmental educational projects
- Medical research or treatment, including drug and alcohol rehabilitation services
- Prisons and offenders
- Counselling and psychotherapy services

Work that does not have a national footprint or work that benefits only one location unless it has a national significance

Charities that have an income of under £100,000

Grants may be considered for charities with an income of over £10 million only if that charity is uniquely placed to meet the foundation's funding objectives. The foundation calls this the 'only they can do it' test

Please do not apply if:

Your application has been turned down within the previous 12 months

Your grant ended less than 12 months ago

You focus on a single medical area, such as an individual disease, organ or condition

You are a hospital, hospice, school, college or university, unless you are a leading university specialist unit

Applications

The following information is taken from the foundation's website:

If you are unsuccessful, we will ask you to wait for one year before you reapply. It is therefore important to make the best case you can at the first stage.

The foundation encourages informal phone calls to discuss projects and eligibility before applications are submitted. Only one application per organisation can be considered at any one time.

Stage 1

Your first-stage application should include:

1 A description of what you are seeking funding for, on no more than two sides of A4. Please include:

A brief summary of your organisation and relevant track record;

Where your work takes place, as we only support work with a national footprint;

What you would like us to fund and why you are well placed to do this work

How your proposal fits our guidelines for this category

2 A copy of your most recent annual accounts.

If your accounts show a significant surplus or deficit, high or low reserves, please explain this briefly. If the year-end date of your accounts is more than 10 months old, please include your latest management accounts

First stage applications can be submitted by post or email. Applications can be submitted at any time, unless you are applying for the annual museums and galleries fund. Applications are acknowledged and decisions made within ten weeks.

Stage 2

If we invite you to the second stage, we will ask for a more detailed application. Then we will arrange to meet you to find out more about your work.

At this second stage we aim to make a decision within three months. If your application takes longer we will be in touch.

Overseas funding

We are not currently accepting applications for overseas funding.

Our Environment category, however, provides for a small number of grants for work in UK Overseas Territories, and exceptionally for marine projects outside UK waters. We only consider applications from UK-based NGOs.

Sources of information

Accounts; annual report; Charity Commission record; guidelines for applicants; funder's website.

The Emerald Foundation

 Performing arts, animal welfare, amateur sport

West Riding of Yorkshire

£1.6 million (2015)

CC number: 1127093

Trustees: Peter Meredith; Karen Fojt; Dr Keith Howard; Timothy Ratcliffe; Melissa Fojt.

Correspondent: Sylvia Hall, Howard House, Wagon Lane, Bingley BD16 1WA (tel: 01274 777700; email: shall@emeraldinsight.com)

emeraldfoundation.org.uk

The Emerald Foundation was founded in 2008 as the charitable arm of the Emerald Global Publishing Group Ltd of which three of the trustees are directors. Keith Howard is also a trustee of Leeds Grand Theatre and Opera North Future Fund. The annual report for 2015 states that the foundations supports charities that promote:

The performing arts

Animal welfare

Sport – The Yorkshire Cricket Foundation and Leeds Rugby Foundation in particular

Financial information

The 2015 accounts were the latest available at the time of writing (March 2018). In 2015 the foundation had an income of £1.5 million which was received in donations from Emerald Global Publishing Group Ltd. Grants totalling £1.6 million were made to 38 charities in the following areas:

Performing arts	£1.1 million
Sport	£305,000
Animals	£195,000

Beneficiaries included: Opera North (£580,000); Grant Future Leeds at Leeds Grand Theatre (£166,000); Leeds Rugby Foundation and Yorkshire Cricket Foundation (£150,000 each); Whitehall Dog Rescue (£120,000); Yorkshire Cat Rescue (£10,000); The Mare and Foal Sanctuary (£5,000); Bradford Festival Choral Society, Northern Youth Theatre Company and Yorkshire Philharmonic Chair (£3,000 each); Keighley Amateurs (£1,000); Chordiality (£250).

Applications

Applications should be made in writing or via email to the correspondent. Applications are considered twice a year.

Sources of information

Accounts; annual report; Charity Commission record; funder's website.

EMI Music Sound Foundation

 Music education, with a particular focus on young people

UK and Ireland

£349,500 to organisations (2016/17)

CC number: 1104027

Trustees: Rupert Perry; David Hughes; Leslie Hill; Tony Wadsworth; James Beach; Paul Gambaccini; Richard Lyttelton; Charles Ashcroft; Jo Hibbitt; Keith Harris; Ruth Katz; Adam Barker.

Correspondent: Janie Orr, Chief Executive, EMI Music Sound Foundation, Beaumont House, Avonmore Road, Kensington Village, London W14 8TS (tel: 020 7550 7898; email: emimusicsoundfoundation@umusic.com)

www.emimusicsoundfoundation.com

facebook.com/The-EMI-Music-Sound-Foundation-119480934788116

The EMI Music Sound Foundation was established in 1997 in celebration of the centenary of EMI Records with the purpose of improving access to music education in the UK and Ireland, with a particular focus on young people.

The foundation looks to achieve its aim by providing funding in two ways:

Instrument and Equipment awards: provides grants of up to a total of £1,500 towards the purchase of musical instruments and/or equipment for individuals who are in full-time education and Schools who require the equipment to improve music education. The foundation also fund courses and training opportunities for music teachers who work within schools.

Bursary awards: provides students with assistance with fees and/or living expenses. Every year the foundation awards bursaries to students at ten chosen music colleges in the UK and Ireland. See the website for more information.

Financial information

In 2016/17 the foundation had assets of £8 million and an income of £415,500. Grants totalled £469,000 of which £119,500 was given to individuals. Grants to organisations amounted to £349,500 and were distributed in the following categories:

Donations to schools	£146,000
Schools project 2016/17	£142,500
Bursaries	£60,000
Other	£1,400

Beneficiaries included: Brighton, Bristol and London Institute of Modem Music (£10,000); Birmingham Conservatoire, Centre for Young Musicians, English National Opera, International World Music Centre, Limerick National Children's Orchestra Royal Academy of Music, London Royal Conservatoire of Scotland and National Youth Jazz Orchestra (£5,000 each).

Exclusions

According to its website, the foundation does not support:

- Applications from applicants based outside the UK or Eire
- Non-school based community groups
- Applications for tuition fees and living expenses other than as described under the Bursary Awards section on our website
- Applications over £2,000
- Applications for the funding of private instrumental lessons
- Payment of staffing costs to cover the teaching of the national curriculum or peripatetic teaching costs
- Retrospective grants

Applications

Application forms for instruments and equipment grants can be downloaded from the website, along with guidance notes. Applications should be submitted by post. Email applications are not accepted.

Bursary awards are distributed at each college's discretion based on criteria provided by the foundation. As such, applicants should contact the colleges directly if you wish to enquire about a bursary. A list of colleges who have been awarded bursary awards is listed on the foundations website.

Sources of information

Accounts; annual report; Charity Commission record; funder's website.

The Englefield Charitable Trust

General charitable purposes

Mainly the Berkshire area, also, parts of Hackney and Inverness-shire connected with the Englefield Estate

£363,000 (2016/17)

CC number: 258123

Trustees: Catherine Haig; Lady Elizabeth Benyon; Richard Benyon; Zoe Benyon; Melissa Owston; Richard Bampfylde; Richard Griffiths.

Correspondent: Alexander Reid, Secretary, Englefield Estate Office, Englefield Road, Theale, Reading RG7 5DU (tel: 01920 832205; email: charity@englefield.co.uk)

 www.englefieldestate.co.uk/ community/englefield-charitable-trust

This trust, which was established in 1968 by Sir William Benyon, supports a wide range of causes in and around Berkshire, as well as in parts of Hackney and Inverness-shire which are connected with the Englefield Estate.

Support is given in areas including: education; sport; community; social welfare and medical support; churches and faith groups; conservation and agriculture; heritage and the arts; and the armed forces.

Grants typically range from £500 to £5,000 and are usually given on a one-off basis for capital expenditure (although revenue grants will be considered). Applications from individuals for amounts up to £350 may also be considered.

Financial information

In 2016/17 the trust held assets of £16 million and had an income of £511,500. Grants were made to 131 organisations and totalled £363,000. They were distributed as follows:

Young people/education/ community	£198,000
Social and welfare/support	£56,000
Medical research/support	£40,000
Conservation/heritage/arts	£37,000
Church/religion	£19,700
Armed forces	£7,000
Overseas	£5,500

A list of beneficiaries was not included in the annual report and accounts.

Exclusions

Successful applicants should not re-apply within 12 months of receiving a grant. Individual applications for study or travel are not considered.

Applications

Applications can either be submitted directly to the trust or through the online fundraising platform The Good Exchange (www.thegoodexchange.com). Guidance notes, which are available to view in full on the trust's website, state that applications should include the following information as succinctly as possible:

- The name and address of your charity/cause, including a contact name, telephone and email and, if relevant, registered charity number
- What your organisation does
- Whether it is active in the favoured geographical areas
- What the grant is needed for
- The total cost of the project for which you are seeking funding
- How much you are asking the trust for
- How much you have raised already
- Any other funders you have applied to
- How many people will benefit from a grant from the trust, both directly and indirectly

A summary of your organisation's accounts/current financial situation should also be enclosed.

The trustees meet to consider applications twice a year, in early March and early October, and applications should be submitted by 1 February or 1 September respectively. Bank details should be included in your application as all grants are paid via BACS. Successful applicants will be informed as soon as possible. The trustees are unable to acknowledge every application or notify unsuccessful applicants.

Sources of information

Accounts; annual report; Charity Commission record.

The Enkalon Foundation

General charitable purposes, cross-community work, animal welfare, arts and culture, mental health

Northern Ireland

£523,000 to organisation (2016/17)

CC number: NIC103528

Trustees: Peter Dalton; Mark Patterson; Stephen Montgomery; John Wallace.

Correspondent: Claire Cawley, Administrator, Antrim Civic Centre, 50 Stiles Way, Antrim BT41 2UB (tel: 028 9447 7131; email: info@ enkelonfoundation.org)

 www.enkalonfoundation.org

 facebook.com/EnkalonFoundation

 @enkalonfound

The Enkalon Foundation was established following the decision of the company British Enkalon (Azko Nobel) to pull out of Northern Ireland. Azko Nobel gave a donation to start the foundation in 1985 to ease the local economic impact of the company's departure. The foundation seeks to improve the quality of life in Northern Ireland and gives to a variety of organisations such as cross-community groups, self-help groups, assistance to unemployed people and groups helping people who are disadvantaged.

The foundation welcomes grant applications from charitable organisations and individual ex-employees of Azko Nobel and their families in need in Northern Ireland, particularly within the Antrim area. The website states that 'historically the range of applicants has ranged from youth groups, senior citizens clubs, charities, self-help groups, animal welfare, arts and mental health groups'.

Grants are usually in the range of £200 to £6,000, with the average grant being between £500 and £1,000.

Financial information

In 2016/17 the foundation had assets of £7.5 million and an income of £315,000. There were 224 grants made totalling £572,500, of which 145 were distributed in the Antrim area and totalled £489,000. The rest of the grants were awarded throughout Northern Ireland. Out of the total amount of grants awarded, £523,000 went to organisations and £49,500 went to individual ex-employees and/or their families.

Beneficiaries included: Antrim Citizens Advice (£11,500); Buttle Trust and Macmillan Cancer Support (£6,000 each); Belfast Buildings Preservation Trust and NI Hospice (£5,000 each); Ulster Youth Orchestra (£2,000); Happy Days Children's Charity (£1,600); East Belfast Community Counselling Centre (£600); First Steps Women's Centre, Muslim Family Association – Belfast and South Belfast Food Bank (£500 each); Ballymena Festival (£400).

Exclusions

The foundation does not normally fund the following:

- Individuals (unless ex-employees of Azko Nobel)
- Playgroups or sporting groups outside the former Antrim Borough area
- Medical research
- Travel outside Northern Ireland

Applications

Applications can be made online via the website, where guidance notes are also available. Queries regarding the applications process can be directed to the Administrator, Claire Cawley, by telephone (07740 641166) or email (claire@enkalonfoundation.org). The trustees meet quarterly (in March, June, September and December) and closing dates for applications fall one month before the meeting. Exact dates are available from the Administrator.

Sources of information

Accounts; annual report; guidelines for applicants; funder's website; Northern Irish Charity Commission record.

Entindale Ltd

 Orthodox Judaism, education, relief of poverty

 UK and Israel

£1.5 million (2015/16)

CC number: 277052

Trustees: Allan Becker; Barbara Bridgeman; Joseph Pearlman.

Correspondent: Joseph Pearlman, Trustee, 8 Highfield Gardens, London NW11 9HB (tel: 020 8458 9266)

This charity was registered with the Charity Commission in June 1979. The trustees' annual report (2015/16) states that the charity's objects are to 'advance religion in accordance with the orthodox Jewish faith'. The charity does this through its grant-making to charitable organisations with similar aims.

Financial information

In 2015/16 the charity had assets of £18.3 million and an income of £1.9 million. Grants were made to organisations totalling £2.1 million.

Beneficiaries included: Yesamach Levav Trust (£96,500); The Society of Friends of the Torah Ltd (£40,000); Friends of Seret Wiznitz (£50,000); Chevras Bikur Cholim (M/C) Ltd (£23,000); Friends of Mir Charitable Trust (£18,000); Friends of Yeshivat Bnei Reem (£15,000); Kollel Shomrei Hachomoth (£5,500); Leeds Jewish Educational Centre (£750).

Applications

Apply in writing to the correspondent.

Sources of information

Accounts; annual report; Charity Commission record.

Epilepsy Research UK

 Research into epilepsy

 UK

£630,000 (2016/17)

CC number: 1100394

Trustees: Barrie Akin; David Cameron; Dr Yvonne Hart; John Hirst; Simon Lanyon; Prof. Mark Rees; Prof. Mark Richardson; Harry Salmon; Dr Graeme Sills; Judith Spencer-Gregson; Prof. Matthew Walker; Mary Gavigan; Bruno Frenguelli.

Correspondent: Delphine van der Pauw, Research Manager, Chiswick Town Hall, Heathfield Terrace, London W4 4JN (tel: 020 8747 5024; email: delphine@eruk. org.uk)

 www.epilepsyresearch.org.uk

Epilepsy Research UK was formed in 2007 through the merger of the Epilepsy Research Foundation and the Fund for Epilepsy. According to its website, the charity 'supports and promotes basic and clinical scientific research into the causes, treatment and prevention of epilepsy'. It is the only national charity in the UK which is dedicated exclusively to funding research into epilepsy. Since its creation the charity has allocated almost £8 million in research grants.

The charity's website states that:

> Epilepsy Research UK invests in research into all areas of epilepsy giving priority to those areas which have the potential to produce results in immediate problem areas, including: research leading to improvements in the accuracy of diagnosis; and research into improving the treatment and quality of life of the patient. Epilepsy Research UK also supports basic scientific research and operates a fellowship programme to encourage scientists to pursue a career in epilepsy research. The aim is to support innovative research, of the highest scientific merit, that has the greatest potential for patient benefit.

Grant Programmes

- **Project Grants:** Grants of up to £150,000, to support a research project lasting a maximum of three years. Applications are also accepted for smaller sums to support the purchase of equipment, student fees and salaries for non-tenured principal applicants.
- **Fellowship Awards:** Grants of up to £250,000, over one to three years, to support fellowships. Fund covers fellows' salaries, support staff and project running costs.
- **Pilot Grants in Epilepsy:** Grants of up to £30,000 to support pilot or start-up studies lasting no more than two years. These can include research costs, equipment and salaries; however, there must be a clear emphasis on the generation of new/preliminary data. The project must be a novel piece of research and not part of a project or fellowship already funded by Epilepsy Research UK or any other funding body.

Financial information

In 2016/17 the charity had assets of £794,500 and an income of £1.4 million.

A total of £630,000 was awarded in seven grants during the year.

Beneficiaries included: University College London (£420,500 four grants); University of Manchester (£150,000); St George's Hospital – London (£30,000); University of Warwick (£29,500).

Exclusions

According to the charity's website:

> Epilepsy Research UK only supports medical and scientific research into epilepsy at academic and medical institutions in the UK. We do not fund research elsewhere. Project grants cannot be used to support standalone meetings, conferences or workshops. All applicants should be graduates in medicine, one of the sciences allied to medicine, engineering or mathematics. They should be resident in the United Kingdom and affiliated to an academic institution in the United Kingdom.

Applications

Application forms, together with criteria, guidelines and application deadlines are available to download on the charity's website.

Sources of information

Accounts; annual report; Charity Commission record; guidance for applicants; funder's website.

The Eranda Rothschild Foundation

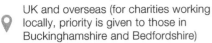

🔍 Education, medical research, the arts, social welfare

📍 UK and overseas (for charities working locally, priority is given to those in Buckinghamshire and Bedfordshire)

£ £2.4 million (2016/17)

CC number: 255650

Trustees: Sir Evelyn de Rothschild; Lady Lynn Forester de Rothschild; Anthony de Rothschild; Jessica de Rothschild; Sir Graham Hearne; Sir John Peace; Ben Elliot.

Correspondent: Gail Devlin-Jones, Secretary, PO Box 6226, Leighton Buzzard, Bedfordshire LU7 0XF (tel: 01296 689157; email: secretary@ erandarothschild.org)

🌐 www.erandarothschild.org

Established in 1967, this is one of the charitable foundations of the de Rothschild finance and banking family.

The foundation supports registered charities working in medical research, education and the arts. Social welfare is also supported, particularly if it is work that is known to the trustees.

For charities that work on a local basis, the trustees give priority to those in Buckinghamshire and Bedfordshire.

Financial information

In 2016/17 the foundation held assets of £122 million and had an income of almost £5.1 million. There were 93 grants made during the year totalling £2.4 million, distributed as follows:

Health, welfare and medical research	28	£931,000
Education	36	£829,000
The arts	29	£650,000

A complete list of beneficiaries was not included in the accounts, but the website lists all of the organisations that the foundation has supported.

Beneficiaries included: Alzheimer's Drug Discovery Foundation; Arts and Heritage Alliance Milton Keynes, Autism Speaks; Films Without Borders; Give a Book; Royal Institute of International Affairs; Unicorn Theatre; Vision Care for Homeless People; Wellbeing of Women.

Exclusions

No grants are made to individuals, organisations which are not registered charities or capital appeals (unless of personal significance to the trustees).

Applications

The trustees prefer applications to be made using the online form on the foundation's website. Applications are considered at meetings held three times a year, usually in February/March, June/July and October/November. Charities should make only one application per year. Online applications are acknowledged automatically and every applicant will be notified of the trustees' decision (this may take several months). The foundation's website notes that it always receives more applications than it is able to fund.

Sources of information

Accounts; annual report; Charity Commission record; funder's website.

The Esfandi Charitable Foundation

🔍 Jewish causes

📍 UK and overseas

£ £351,500 (2016/17)

CC number: 1103095

Trustees: Joseph Esfandi; Denise Esfandi.

Correspondent: Joseph Esfandi, Trustee, 36 Park Street, London W1K 2JE (tel: 020 7629 6666)

Set up in 2004, this foundation supports general charitable purposes, although

there is a preference for Jewish causes and organisations.

Financial information

In 2016/17 the foundation held assets of £39,500 and had an income of £62,500. Grants totalled £351,500.

Beneficiaries included: Kollel Chabad (£65,000); Hand to Hand (£35,000); Chazak Ltd (£25,000); British Friends of Migdal Ohr, Chozok, Community Security Trust, Jewish Care, and United Jewish Israel Appeal (£25,000 each); The Covenant and Conservation Trust (£15,000).

Applications

Apply in writing to the correspondent.

Sources of information

Accounts; annual report; Charity Commission record.

The Essex Youth Trust

🔍 Services for and education of people under 25

📍 UK

£ £326,000 (2016/17)

CC number: 225768

Trustees: Julien Courtauld; Revd Canon Duncan Green; Claire Cottrell; William Robson; Lady Julia Denison-Smith; Michael Dyer; Richard Wenley; Michael Biegel; Julie Rogers.

Correspondent: Jonathan Douglas-Hughes, Clerk, c/o Gepp and Sons, 58 New London Road, Chelmsford, Essex CM2 0PA (tel: 01245 493939; email: douglas-hughesj@gepp.co.uk)

The Essex Youth Trust comprises three charities administered under a scheme of the Charity Commission dated 24 February 1993. The three charities are Essex Home School for Boys, The Charity of George Stacey Gibson and the Charity of George Cleveley.

The trust's objectives are the advancement of education for people under the age of 25 who are in need of assistance. According to the 2016/17 trustees' report, preference is given to those who are in need owing to 'being temporarily or permanently deprived of normal parental care or who are otherwise disadvantaged'. Furthermore, the trustees' report states that the trust favours organisations which:

> Develop young people's physical, mental and spiritual capacities through active participation in sports and indoor and outdoor activities. As a result they are particularly supportive of youth clubs and other organisations which provide facilities for young people to take active part in an assortment of activities as well as single activity organisations.

Grants are usually made on a one-off basis.

Financial information
In 2016/17 the trust held assets of over £8.8 million, most of which is held as permanent endowment, and had an income of £396,000. Grants to 39 organisations totalling £326,000 were made.

Beneficiaries included: Essex Boys' and Girls' Clubs (£72,500); Cirdan Sailing Trust (£50,000); Stubbers Adventure Centre (£45,000); North Avenue Youth Centre (£16,800); Chain Reaction Theatre Company (£13,000); SOLID (£12,000); Sea Change Sailing Trust (£7,000).

Grants for less than £10,000 totalled £100,000.

Exclusions
No grants are given to individuals.

Applications
Apply using a form available from the correspondent. The trustees meet on a quarterly basis.

Sources of information
Accounts; annual report; Charity Commission record.

The Evelyn Trust

 Medical research, health and well-being

Cambridgeshire

£962,000 (2016/17)

CC number: 232891

Trustees: Julia Squir; Adrian Frost; Jeremy Newsum; Amy Agnew; Catherine Thomas; Rebecca Fitzgerald; Jeremy Pemberton; Will Dawkins; Bill Pike; Trevor Baglin.

Correspondent: Bill Pike, Trustee, PO Box 223, Saffron Walden CB10 9BP (tel: 01799 542708; email: evelyntrust@aol.com)

www.evelyntrust.com

Established as a charity in 1920, the Evelyn Trust owned and managed the Evelyn Hospital in Cambridge. The trust aims to support a broad range of projects, but is mainly interested in supporting medical research and health and well-being projects that deliver transformational change, especially pilot or demonstration projects.

Grants are one-off for a particular project and are available to non-profit making organisations, not individuals. Funding can be for capital and people costs relating to frontline work. The trust's website states, 'We are keen to work with people and organisations that want to help us do more or to co-fund

projects, particularly those in Cambridgeshire who wish to give to research and would value working with us.'

Grant programmes
The trust has two main grant programmes:

Medical research grant
The trust is especially interested in projects with a clear clinical impact, or that can deliver transformational change or increase inter-disciplinary working. The trust considers that one of its primary goals is to develop young or newly-established researchers, and to help them to generate data for more substantial bids to larger grant-giving bodies. Grants are usually in the range of £10,000 and up to a maximum of £250,000. This trust awards medical grants for:

- **Clinical research projects** – towards the cost of specific, planned and well managed medical research programmes. The Evelyn Trust particularly favours younger or less established researchers and pilot or demonstration projects that have yet to meet the proof of principle required by larger funding bodies
- **Capital projects** – towards the cost of new buildings or extensions or for the renovation of existing buildings, as well as contributions towards the cost of new capital equipment required for a specific purpose
- **Research training fellowships** – The Evelyn Trust supports the Cambridge Research Training Fellowship programme and there is a separate application process for this. Visit the website for guidance. Applications are usually invited for these awards in the first quarter of each year

Health and well-being grants
Healthcare projects that support and inform population health and well-being in Cambridgeshire, usually in the range of £10,000 up to a maximum of £250,000. There is a rolling small grants programme under which applications in the range £4,000 to £10,000 can be considered at any time. While welcoming other applications, the trust particularly encourages applications that:

- Support young people within families with mental health, alcohol, violence or substance abuse issues
- Assist working age adults with long-term conditions and healthcare communities that support these issues
- Enable older people to receive help and support in the community rather than needing to go into hospital or long-term care

For more information on funding guidelines, see the trust's website.

Financial information
In 2016/17 the trust had assets of £25.8 million and an income of £919,500. During the year, the trust gave £962,000 in grants to organisations. Grants were distributed as follows:

Medical research grants and fellowships	4	£726,000
Medical treatment and health/ well-being	18	£315,000
Grants for buildings/facilities for – medical teaching/ healthcare	-	

Of this amount, grant funding credited to expenditure in respect of earlier years' grants totalled £78,500.

Beneficiaries included: The University of Cambridge (£197,000); Home-Start Cambridgeshire (£106,500); Cambridge and Peterborough NHS Foundation Trust (£50,000); Little Miracles (£22,500); The Meadows Children and Family Wing (£5,000).

Exclusions
The trust does not support:

- Projects where alternative funding from a non-charitable organisation is available
- Research funding for fields already well supported by other charities, including some heart and cancer work
- Projects submitted by well-established researchers with good funding track records and alternative funding sources
- Projects that are submitted by established research charities to raise research funds
- Ongoing overheads, administrative or maintenance costs, VAT or professional fees
- General funds, non-specific appeals, endowment funds, conduit organisations or appeals by circular
- Costs of meetings, conferences, conference fees, exhibitions, concerts, travel, expeditions
- Organisations based outside the object area
- Research that will involve live animals
- Individuals
- Support on an ongoing basis
- The purchase of land
- Causes with a strong political association

Applications
Health and well-being projects – There are two stages in the grant application process. Firstly, applicants must download the applications form which is available on the trust's website. Once completed, the application form can be sent to the correspondent via post or email. The application deadline is 30 November each year. Applicants can arrange to meet and discuss the project with the trust from February to April. If the trustees decide they are able to consider the project further, they will

wish to extend their enquiries by requesting a detailed explanation of the work to be done, how it will be achieved and the results and outputs that are being sought, as well as more detailed financial information, annual reports and accounts, and for capital projects copies of estimates, building plans, photographs, artists' impressions, etc.

Medical Grants – There are two stages in the grant application process. Applicants must firstly complete an 'outline application for a medical research grant'. The outline medical research application form brings together basic information to enable the trustees to confirm whether or not the Evelyn Trust is able to consider the application further. Outline applications may be submitted at any time up to a deadline date of 30 November preceding the grant year beginning from, usually, the following July. These are reviewed by Trustees at their January meeting. Applicants will then be notified whether they have been invited to submit a full application or been declined. Grants can be sent via post or email.

Sources of information

Accounts; annual report; Charity Commission record; funder's website.

The Eventhall Family Charitable Trust

 General charitable purposes

 UK, with a preference for the north west of England

£ £573,500 (2016/17)

CC number: 803178

Trustees: Julia Eventhall; David Eventhall.

Correspondent: The Trustees, PO Box 490, Altrincham WA14 2ZT (email: efct@rectella.com)

The Eventhall Family Charitable Trust was established in 1986 and uses investment income to support a wide range of charitable causes.

Financial information

In 2016/17 the trust had assets of £3.3 million and an income of £86,500. In total the trust awarded around £573,500 in grants.

A list of beneficiaries was not included in the annual report and accounts. However, it was noted that during the year the charity made donations of £378,633 to The Federation of Jewish Services, a registered charity of which David Eventhall is also a trustee

Previous beneficiaries have included: Aish Hatorah; ChildLine; Clitheroe Wolves Football Club; Community Security Trust; Guide Dogs for the Blind;

International Wildlife Coalition; Only Foals and Horses Sanctuary; Royal National Lifeboat Institution; Sale Ladies Society; Shelter; South Manchester Synagogue.

Applications

Apply in writing to the correspondent. Note, however, that the trust has previously stated it only has a very limited amount of funds available.

Sources of information

Accounts; annual report; Charity Commission record.

The Eveson Charitable Trust

 People with physical disabilities, (including people who are blind or deaf), people with mental disabilities, hospitals and hospices, children who are in need, older people, homeless people, medical research

Herefordshire, Worcestershire, and the county of West Midlands (covering Birmingham, Coventry, Dudley, Sandwell, Solihull, Walsall and Wolverhampton)

£ £2.01 million (2016/17)

CC number: 1032204

Trustees: David Pearson; Martin Davies; Louise Woodhead; Bill Wiggin; Richard Mainwaring; Judith Millward; The Bishop of Hereford; Vivien Cockerill.

Correspondent: Alex Gay, Administrator, 45 Park Road, Gloucester GL1 1LP (tel: 01452 501352; fax: 01452 302195; email: admin@eveson.plus.com)

🌍 www.eveson.org.uk

The trust was established in 1994 by a legacy of £49 million from Mrs Violet Eveson to support the following causes:

- People with physical disabilities (including those who are blind or deaf)
- People with mental disabilities
- Hospitals and hospices
- Children in need
- Older people
- People who are homeless
- Medical research
- General charitable purposes

Grants are restricted to the geographical areas of Herefordshire, Worcestershire and the county of West Midlands. The trust does not instigate programmes of its own, but responds to the applications which it receives. Grants vary in amount but the average size of grants is around £7,000 to £8,000.

Financial information

In 2016/17 the trust had assets of £88.8 million and an income of

£1.4 million. Grants were made to 290 organisations totalling £2.01 million, and were categorised as follows:

Social Care and Development	201	£1.06 million
Health Care	77	£850,500
Accommodation	12	£103,500

Beneficiaries included: Acorns Children's Hospice Trust (£60,000); Myton Hamlet Hospice (£19,000); Bloodwise (£15,000); Action Medical Research, Alzheimer's Research UK, Diabetes UK, The Scar Free Foundation (£10,000 each); Birmingham PHAB Camps (£7,000); Revitalise (£6,000).

Exclusions

The trust cannot support the following:

- Individuals, even if such a request is submitted by a charitable organisation
- Retrospective applications
- Applications for funding towards the installation of special facilities in existing community buildings and churches for people with disabilities
- Applications which fall outside the existing objects and policies of the trust

Applications

Applications should be submitted on the trust's standard application form which is available upon request from the correspondent. These must be completed and returned to the trust's office in Gloucester at least six weeks before the trustees' meeting. A copy of your latest annual report and accounts must be included with the application. The trustees meet quarterly to discuss applications, usually at the end of March and the beginning of July, October and January. Trustees will only consider one application per year from any one applicant.

Sources of information

Accounts; annual report; Charity Commission record; funder's website.

The Exilarch's Foundation

🔍 General charitable purposes, social welfare, education, Jewish causes

📍 Worldwide (mainly UK, Israel and Iraq)

£ £4.2 million (2016)

CC number: 275919

Trustees: David Dangoor; Elie Dangoor; Robert Dangoor; Michael Dangoor.

Correspondent: David Dangoor, Trustee, 4 Carlos Place, Mayfair, London W1K 3AW (tel: 020 7399 0850)

This foundation was established in 1978 by Sir Naim Dangoor, who was an Iraqi Jewish businessman. During his life, Sir Naim Dangoor gave away millions of pounds to educational, health and religious causes. After he passed away aged 101 in November 2015, his son David took over the role of the foundation's 'Exilarch'.

The trustees have designated a £10 million fund to support the re-establishment of a Jewish community in Iraq. The initial stages of this long-term project are to fund educational and religious institutions, primarily in Baghdad.

The foundation has made grants to a wide range of charitable organisations under the following headings: social welfare (particularly community development; monotheism; hospitals, medical education and research; ethics; and general); and education (particularly university/college; and sundry).

Financial information

In 2016 the foundation had assets of £84.5 million and an income of £5.4 million. Grants made during the year totalled almost £4.2 million and were distributed within the following categories:

Social welfare	**£2.82 million**
Community development	£2.1 million
Hospitals, medical education and research	£664,500
General	£12,500
Education	**£1.37 million**
University/college	£1.3 million
Sundry	£52,500

Beneficiaries included: Jewish Care (£1 million); Jewish Leadership Council (£450,000); British Exploring Society (£360,000); Discovering Faith (£200,000); Guy's and St Thomas' Charity (£100,000); Action Medical Research (£91,000); Chazak (£31,000); The Royal Marines Charity Trust Fund (£15,500); Duke of Edinburgh's Award (£10,000).

Applications

Apply in writing to the correspondent.

Sources of information

Accounts; annual report; Charity Commission record.

The Expat Foundation

 Children and young people, older people, education, social improvement

UK and Africa

£415,500 (2016/17)

CC number: 1094041

Trustees: Patricia Wolfston; Janet Cummins; Gill Weavers; Caroline Coombs; Dirk van Dijl; Jan Knight.

Correspondent: Janet Cummins, Trustee, 127 Ellesmere Road, London NW10 1LG (tel: 020 3609 2105)

The Expat Foundation was established in 2002. The foundation's Charity

Commission record states that in the UK it focuses on 'improving the lives of disadvantaged children and young people and improving the quality of life of elderly people, particularly providing opportunities for mental and social engagement'. In Africa there is a focus on supporting 'long-term initiatives in areas such as education and social improvement'.

According to previous research, the foundation is prepared to fund seed projects and start-ups.

Financial information

In 2016/17 the foundation had assets totalling £1.2 million and an income of £514,000. Grants awarded totalled almost £451,500.

Previous beneficiaries have included: School-Home Support and Leap Confronting Conflict (£50,000 each); Build It International (£20,000); FixIt UK Ltd (£13,000); Read International (£8,000); Microloan Foundation (£6,000); Zambia Orphan Aid UK (£5,900); Choir With No Name (£5,000); Family Holiday Association (£2,500).

Exclusions

The foundation does not support medical charities.

Applications

The foundation's Charity Commission record states that its funds are currently fully committed.

Sources of information

Accounts; annual report; Charity Commission record.

Esmée Fairbairn Foundation

 Arts, children and young people, environment, social change, food

UK

£40.5 million (2017)

CC number: 200051

Trustees: James Hughes-Hallett; Edward Bonham Carter; Tom Chandos; Joe Docherty; Prof. David Hill; John Fairbairn; Beatrice Hollond; Sir Thomas Hughes-Hallett; Kate Lampard; Stella Manzie; Sir Jonathan Phillips; Eleanor Updale.

Correspondent: The Grants Team, Kings Place, 90 York Way, London N1 9AG (tel: 020 7812 3700; fax: 020 7812 3701; email: info@esmeefairbairn.org.uk)

 www.esmeefairbairn.org.uk

 @esmeefairbairn

Ian Fairbairn established the foundation in 1961 (renamed Esmée Fairbairn

Foundation in 2000). He was a leading city figure and his company, M&G, was the pioneer of the unit trust industry. Ian Fairbairn endowed the foundation with the greater part of his own holding in M&G, and in the early years the majority of grants were for economic and financial education.

His interest in financial education stemmed from his concern that most people had no access to stock exchange investment, and were therefore precluded from investing their savings in equities and sharing in the country's economic growth. It was precisely this concern that had led him into the embryonic unit trust business in the early 1930s.

The foundation was set up as a memorial to Ian Fairbairn's wife Esmée, who had played a prominent role in developing the Women's Royal Voluntary Service and the Citizens Advice before being killed during an air raid towards the end of the Second World War. Her sons Paul and Oliver Stobart contributed generously to the original trust fund, as co-founders.

The foundation's website and its annual report and accounts provide a wealth of information for anyone with an interest in this charity.

The foundation's mission is 'to improve the quality of life for people and communities in the UK both now and in the future' which it does 'by supporting organisations that work in the arts, children and young people, the environment, and social change'.

Aims

The website explains that:

> We only fund work that is designed to have wider benefits – beyond the direct participants and the life of a project. We try to fund work which tackles root cases: which uncovers a need or prevents it from happening in future. Or work which sets out to change future thinking and practice more widely – from art forms, to public opinion, to government policy. For example, individual case work might make a real difference to young refugees, but unless it also sets out to have a lasting and wider influence beyond those young refugees, we won't fund it.

The foundation's main aims, detailed in its document 'Funding Strategy 2015–19, are to:'

- Reveal the unseen and challenge the unpopular
- Strengthen and connect communities for change
- Catalyse system change
- Unlock and enable potential

Funding priorities

The foundation's website states that its Funding Strategy was developed with trustees, staff, stakeholders and grantees and informed by external research and analysis. 'Esmée does not fund according to programmes or prescriptive criteria. We are driven by our aims. Each is effective individually. Together, over time, they can combine to build powerful impact. This is our 'theory of change'.'

The foundation provides funding across five main areas: arts; children and young people; environment; social change; and food. The foundation's website explains: 'Across all our funding we aim to unlock and enable potential, back the unorthodox and unfashionable, build collective networks and catalyse system change.'

The online document 'Guidance for Grant Applicants' dated May 2017 outlines the foundation's funding priorities within the main areas:

Arts

- Art with a social impact
- Supporting emerging talent
- Organisations at a pivotal point of social change, community cohesion or participation

Children and young people

- Improving support for disadvantaged children and young people
- The rights of vulnerable children and young people
- Addressing the root causes of low educational attainment and challenging behaviour
- Empowering young leaders
- Young people leaving care

Environment

- Connecting people with nature and environmental issues
- Nature conservation on land and at sea
- Countering the effects of damaging activity
- Lesser known plants, animals and organisms

Social change

- Participation – marginalised and excluded individuals and groups
- Place – revitalising community life
- Injustice – systemic change around injustice and inequality

Food

- Innovation in alternative approaches
- Food and well-being
- Working towards a more coherent food sector

Types of support

Support is given in three ways – grants, social investment and Grants Plus – which are outlined on the website.

- **Grants:** 'Our grants support organisations' core or project costs, including staff salaries and overheads. We do not fund building or equipment costs, or individuals.

2016 grants ranged from £5k to £3.9 million (median average £96,000), with support lasting one to five years (47% were for three years).'

- **Social investment:** The foundation provides charities and other not-for-profit organisations with different types of repayable finance with 'the aim of creating social impact'
- **Grants Plus:** The foundation provides additional support for recipients of its grants and social investments in three ways: free support (such as use of the foundation's central London meeting rooms); skills support; and strategic support

More information on each of these forms of support is available from the website.

Other Funds

The foundation operates a number of funds in partnership with other bodies, which enables particular regions, communities, sectors or issues to be targeted. Current funding partnerships are detailed on the website.

Financial information

In 2017 the foundation held net assets of £996 million with an income of £6.1 million. The financial review for the year stated: 'During 2017 the Foundation spent £44.6 million in funding towards a wide range of work. The majority of our funding in 2017 was distributed through grants and we also made a number of social investments.' Grant funding excluding all costs is listed in the accounts as £40.5 million.

Grants Plus work where the foundation supported 150 organisations with training and consultancy totalled £449,500. The TASK Fund (Trustees' Area of Special Knowledge) distributed 129 grants totalling £1.08 million.

The total funding by sector (excluding TASKs and Grants Plus) was as follows:

Social change	90	£12.2 million
Environment	45	£8.1 million
Arts	72	£7.5 million
Children and young people	44	£6.9 million
Food	20	£3.7 million

Of the 1,963 eligible applications received in the year, 1,631 were turned down at the first stage and 61 were turned down at the second stage. The foundation approved 271 applications during the year.

Beneficiaries included: Compassion in World Farming (£503,500); Right to Succeed (£300,000); Eating Better (£286,000); Collective (£165,000); Trees for Life and Vi-Ability Education Programme (£150,000 each); Kettle's Yard, University of Cambridge (£120,000); Forest of Dean Sculpture Trust (£80,000); Lads Need Dads (£40,000); Global Action Plan (£15,000).

Exclusions

The foundation's website states that the following exclusions apply to all sectors:

- Organisations with a regular annual turnover of less than £50,000
- Organisations without at least three non-executive trustees or directors
- *Work that is not legally charitable
- Work that does not have a direct benefit in the UK
- Grants to individuals, including student grants or bursaries
- *Capital costs including building work, renovations, and equipment (grants only, we may make social investments for these)
- Work that is common to many parts of the UK such as: Services that are provided in similar ways in many locations such as refuges, hostels, night shelters and standard services for homeless people, sports associations, play schemes, out of school clubs, supplementary schools, playgroups, youth clubs and general capacity building/professional development. Standard work to improve employability skills such as training on CV writing, interview skills, literacy, numeracy, ESOL courses and activities to increase self confidence. Mainstream or core activities of local organisations which are part of a wider network of others doing similar work (e.g. YMCA, MIND groups, Age UK), even if they are constituted as separate organisations. General information and advice work
- Research. The Foundation does not fund academic research unless the applicant can demonstrate real potential for practical outcomes
- Health care with a clinical basis and work which mainly deals with people's physical health, including medical research, hospices, advocacy, counselling and therapy, arts-therapy, education about and treatment for drug and alcohol misuse
- Work that is primarily the responsibility of statutory authorities. This includes residential, respite and day care, housing provision, individual schools, nurseries and colleges or a consortium of any of these, and vocational training
- We will not normally replace or subsidise statutory income although we will make rare exceptions where the level of performance has been exceptional and where the potential impact of the work is substantial
- The promotion of religion
- Animal welfare, zoos, captive breeding and animal rescue centres

*these exclusions do not apply to social investments. If you are considering investment instead of a grant please review the social investment information and contact us if you have a question.

There are also sector-specific exclusions it does not support and you should refer to the website for this information

Applications

Applications can be made at any time. Before applying, the information on the website – what the foundation funds and what it doesn't fund – should be read carefully, and the helpful online 'Eligibility Quiz' can also be taken. The foundation operates a two stage application process, which is outlined briefly on the website:

⬧ 'First stage: apply online. We acknowledge by email within a week and decide whether to take it further within a month'
⬧ 'Second stage: answer a set of questions from a Grants or Social Investment Manager. We make a decision in two to four months'

In order to make an application, an organisation must set-up an account with the foundation's online grants system. You might find it helpful to look at the grants that have been made previously and to check out the FAQ section and hints and tips before deciding to submit your application.

The foundation has also previously stated: 'You do not need to have matched funding in place before applying but where the total cost of the work you propose for funding is high you should indicate other sources of funding or specific plans to apply elsewhere'.

Note: As around 3,000 applications are received each year, the foundation's staff are unable to meet or speak with applicants before they apply. First stage applications are acknowledged within a week and the decision whether to take it to the second stage is made within a month.

Sources of information
Accounts; annual report; annual review; Charity Commission record; guidelines for applicants; funder's website.

The Lord Faringdon Charitable Trust

🔍 General charitable purposes, education, hospitals and medical treatment, museums and collections, older people, vulnerable people, arts, sciences, physical recreation, drama, research, the relief of poverty

📍 UK, with a focus on Oxfordshire

💷 £214,500 (2016/17)

CC number: 1084690

Trustees: The Hon. J. H. Henderson; S. J. Maitland Robinson; Bernard Cazenove; Edward Campbell Cottrell.

Correspondent: Sharon Lander, Secretary, The Estate Office, Buscot Park, Faringdon SN7 8BU (tel: 01367 240786; email: estbuscot@aol.com)

This trust was formed in 2000 by the amalgamation of the Lord Faringdon

First and Second Trusts. The trust supports well-run national and (in Oxfordshire) local charities.

According to the trustees' report for 2016/17, the trustees support a wide range of charitable purposes, with a preference for:

⬧ Educational Scholarships Grants
⬧ Hospitals and the provision of medical treatment for the sick
⬧ Purchase of antiques and artistic objects for museums and collections to which the public has access
⬧ Care and assistance of the aged and infirm
⬧ Development and assistance of Arts and Sciences, physical recreation and drama
⬧ Research into matters of public interest
⬧ Relief of poverty
⬧ Support of matters of public interest

The trust also supports The Faringdon Collection Trust (Charity Commission no. 203770).

Financial information
In 2016/17 the trust held assets of £9.9 million and had an income of £255,500. Grants totalled £214,500 and were awarded to 80 organisations.

Beneficiaries included: Royal Choral Society (£15,000); Greyhound Rescue West of England and Morris Memorial Hall – Kelmscott (£5,000 each); Afghanistan and Central Asian Association, Anti-Slavery International, Deptford Action Group for the Elderly and Oxfordshire Lowland Search and Rescue (£1,000 each); National Heritage Ironwork Group and St Mungo's (£500).

Exclusions
No grants are given to individuals.

Applications
Apply in writing to the correspondent. The trustees meet formally once a year. The annual report for 2016/17 explains:

Grant applications are accepted from registered charities and other recognised bodies. All grant applications are required to provide information on the specific purpose and expected beneficiaries of the grant. This information helps the charity assess how its programme of discretionary grant-making achieves a spread of benefit.

Sources of information
Accounts; annual report; Charity Commission record.

The Thomas Farr Charity

🔍 General charitable purposes

📍 Nottinghamshire

💷 £363,000 (2016/17)

CC number: 328394

Trustees: Rathbone Trust Company Ltd; Henry Farr; Amanda Farr; Philip Pruden.

Correspondent: John Thompson, Administrator, 6A The Almhouses, Mansfield Road, Daybrook, Nottingham NG5 6BW (tel: 0115 966 1222; email: thomasfarrch@btconnect.com)

 thomasfarrcharity.com

The charity was established in 1989, following the sale of the Home Brewery in Nottingham with the aim of supporting those areas where the Home Brewery had a presence. This trust makes grants to registered charities and community interest companies with general charitable purposes in Nottinghamshire, but occasionally supports causes in other parts of the UK. Grants range from £500 to £20,000, although most are for under £5,000.

Financial information
In 2016/17 the trust held assets of almost £9 million and had an income of £306,000. There were 159 grants made totalling £363,000, broken down as follows:

Community projects	£91,500
Disability	£56,000
Children	£44,500
Education	£35,000
Hospitals/health	£31,000
Youth	£21,000
Museums	£20,000
Holiday	£19,000
Armed forces	£15,000
Religion	£14,000
Older people	£9,500
Homeless	£3,000
Drug projects	£1,700
Medical research	£1,000
Sport	£1,000

Previous beneficiaries have included: Nottingham Hospitals Charity (£20,000); Clipstone Miners Welfare Community Trust (£5,000); Walking with the Wounded (£3,000); Air Ambulance Service, Incest and Sexual Abuse Survivors, Shoe Aid CIC and Windmill Community Gardens (£2,000 each); Prisoners Abroad, Missing People, Sutton Youth Radio and Young Women's Trust (£1,000); Aspley Pentecostal Church (£500).

Exclusions
The charity does not make grants for the following:

⬧ Loans or business finance
⬧ Campaigning work and projects that are primarily political
⬧ Retrospective costs
⬧ General or mail shot appeals
⬧ Replacing statutory funding

No grants are given to individuals.

Applications
The charity does not make use of detailed application forms but your

application should include the completion of a 'Grant Application Header Form' which can be downloaded from this website. Applications must be made in writing and posted (not by email) to the correspondent along with a set of your latest audited accounts. Applications are not acknowledged nor will you be notified if your application is unsuccessful. The trustees meet three times a year in March, July and November and applications for consideration at these meeting must be received by 20 January, 20 May or 20 September respectively.

The following information is taken from the website. Applications should:

- Clearly identify the name of the organisation which is making the application, its status as a registered charity or community interest company (CIC) or provide other evidence of the organisation's charitable purpose
- Explain the project or activity for which the grant is requested and how it meets the charity's policy as described in 'Grant Policy
- Explain who will benefit from the project or activity and show that the benefit is sustainable
- Identify the likely costs of the project/ activity and explain what other finance is sought or is available. The Trustees need to understand if and when the project/activity will actually go ahead
- Explain if the project/activity will be managed or organised by paid staff and/or volunteers and the numbers involved
- Confirm that you have in place and comply with any necessary 'Child Protection Policy' or 'Vulnerable Adults Policy' where relevant

Sources of information
Accounts; annual report; Charity Commission record; funder's website.

Fayre Share Foundation

 Philanthropy and voluntary sector collaboration, interfaith relations, conflict resolution

UK and overseas

£816,500 (2016)

CC number: 1090985

Trustees: Hetty Maher; Katy Ostro; Lyddon Simon; Maurice Ostro.

Correspondent: The Trustees, 62 Grosvenor Street, London W1K 3JF (tel: 0843 208 0606; email: info@ fayresharefoundation.org)

www.ostro.com/foundation

The Fayre Share Foundation was established by entrepreneur Maurice Ostro in 2000. Today the foundation supports organisations which are engaged with its priority causes, namely:

- Philanthropy
- Collaboration
- Interfaith Relations
- Conflict Resolution

Financial information
In 2016 the foundation had assets of £1.4 million and an income of £961,500. During the year, the foundation provided grants totalling £816,500.

No list of beneficiaries was available.

Applications
The Fayre Share Foundation does not accept unsolicited requests for funding. However on its website the foundation states that it may 'consider offers of partnership in its key priority areas: philanthropy, collaboration, interfaith relations, and conflict resolution'.

Sources of information
Accounts; annual report; Charity Commission record; funder's website.

The February Foundation

 Health, education, end-of-life care, environment

UK

£803,000 (2016/17)

CC number: 1113064

Trustees: James Carleton; Mark Clarke.

Correspondent: Richard Pierce-Saunderson, Chief Executive, Spring Cottage, Church Street, Stradbroke IP21 5HT (tel: 01379 388200; email: rps@thefebruaryfoundation.org)

 www.thefebruaryfoundation.org

The foundation was established in 2006 for general charitable purposes and has a broad range of interests. According to its 2016/17 annual report the foundation will make grants for:

- Charities which are for the benefit of persons who are making an effort to improve their lives
- Charities which are for the benefit of persons no longer physically or mentally able to help themselves
- Charities which have a long-term beneficial impact on the future of individuals, groups of individuals, or organisations
- Charities which protect the environment
- Small or minority charities where small grants will have a significant impact

The foundation can also make grants to companies where the acquisition of equity would be in line with the foundation's charitable objectives. There is no minimum grant. The maximum grant is usually £5,000 per award, but is

reviewed on a case-by-case basis. Less than 10% of applications are successful.

Financial information
In 2016/17 the foundation held assets £87 million and had an income of £12.3 million. There were 122 grants made to 118 organisations totalling £803,000 and were broken down as follows:

End-of-life care	53	£279,000
Healthcare and patient support	55	£237,000
Education	3	£195,000
Other	10	£85,000
Heritage	1	£7,100

A list of beneficiaries was not available.

Exclusions
The foundation's website states that it will not accept applications from the following:

- Childcare
- Citizens Advice
- Community centres
- Higher education
- Housing associations
- Individuals
- Medical research
- Minibuses
- NHS trusts
- Non-departmental government bodies
- Outdoor activity centres
- Overseas projects
- Primary education
- Scouts, Guides, Brownies, Cubs, and similar organisations
- Secondary education
- Single-faith organisations
- Sports clubs (unless they are for people with disabilities)
- Village halls
- Youth clubs and centres

Applications
Apply in writing to the correspondent. The foundation's website states:

Applications by email are given priority as the Foundation aims to operate on a paperless basis. Please send us the details and budget of the proposed project, how many people would benefit, how those benefits might be measured (not just financially), what the estimated cost of raising funds for the project is, and the full cost of raising voluntary income (especially if this is not detailed in your accounts). It is important to include in your email application full accounts for your most recent completed financial year.

Consult the foundation's website for details of additional information requirements for hospices.

Sources of information
Accounts; annual report; Charity Commission record; funder's website.

Allan and Nesta Ferguson Charitable Settlement

 Education, international friendship and understanding, world peace and development

UK and overseas

£2.9 million (2016)

CC number: 275487

Trustees: Elizabeth Banister; Prof. David Banister; James Tee; Letitia Glaister; Eleanor Banister.

Correspondent: Letitia Glaister, Trustee, Tees Law, John Street, Royston, Hertfordshire SG8 9BG (tel: 01279 322519; fax: 01279 758400; email: letitia.glaister@teeslaw.co.uk)

 www.fergusontrust.co.uk

The Allan and Nesta Ferguson Charitable Trust (registered as The Allan and Nesta Ferguson Charitable Settlement) was set up in memory of two generations of the Ferguson family to promote their particular interests in education, international friendship and understanding, and the promotion of world peace and development.

The charity supports these interests by making grants to:

▸ Charities
▸ Postgraduate PhD students who are studying at UK universities to help meet the tuition costs of their final year of study
▸ Gap year students who are travelling with a recognised organisation

Eligibility criteria

In line with the interests described above, the charity makes grants in support of projects, both in the UK and abroad, and to charitable organisations based in the UK and overseas. However, only charitable organisations registered in the UK are eligible to apply for funding.

It is further explained that:

Grants to charities will be on a matching funding basis only so that if the applicant has raised 50% of their budget the Trustees will consider awarding matching funding up to a maximum of 50%. However, if the applicant has raised less than 50% of their budget the Trustees will only consider awarding a maximum of 30% funding.

Evidence of actively seeking funds from other sources is seen by the Trustees as being a beneficial addition to any application.

Only applications for forthcoming projects can be supported.

See the website for details of eligibility requirements for PhD and gap year students.

Financial information

In 2016 the charity had assets of £27.8 million and an income of £794,500. Grants awarded to organisations totalled £2.9 million, and £72,000 was awarded to individuals. Grants to organisations were broken down as follows:

Educational projects	£1.5 million
Overseas education	£1.3 million
Educational projects encompassing world peace	£52,000

Beneficiaries included: The Open University (£998,500); Camfed (£100,000); Coventry University and Pump Aid (£50,000); Sightsavers (£30,000); International Rescue Committee (£15,000); City of Birmingham Symphony Orchestra (£10,000).

Exclusions

The charity cannot provide funding retrospectively.

Applications

Applications are only accepted if they are submitted online using the correct form. Applications set by post, email or fax will not be considered. Detailed guidance is available on the website, from where the following statement is taken:

Please do not contact us for guidance prior to making an application. All the information you require is contained here. Your application will be acknowledged but no progress reports will be given and no feedback is provided in relation to unsuccessful applications.

Applications are accepted at any time and the trustees review requests for up to £50,000 monthly. Funding requests for amounts exceeding £50,000 are considered at bi-annual trustee meetings, which usually take place in March and September.

Sources of information

Accounts; annual report; Charity Commission record; guidelines for applicants; funder's website.

The Fidelity UK Foundation

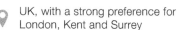 Arts, culture and heritage, community, development, education, health, environment

UK, with a strong preference for London, Kent and Surrey

£7.1 million (2016)

CC number: 327899

Trustees: Barry Bateman; Anthony Bolton; Richard Millar; John Owen; Sally Walden; Abigail Johnson; Elizabeth Bishop Johnson.

Correspondent: Sian Parry, Head of Foundations, Oakhill House, 130 Tonbridge Road, Hildenborough, Tonbridge, Kent TN11 9DZ (tel: 01732 777364; email: foundation@fil.com)

 www.fidelityukfoundation.org

The foundation was established in 1988 and primarily supports UK-registered charities based in areas where Fidelity Worldwide Investment has corporate offices: London; Kent and Surrey. Applications are also considered from elsewhere in the UK, provided the organisation is a nationally-recognised centre of excellence with national coverage.

The foundation's charitable giving is mainly in the areas of:

▸ **Arts, culture and heritage** – Including nationally significant heritage sites, internationally recognised museums and class leading organisations in the visual and performing arts
▸ **Community** – Particularly early interventions and charities which help young and/or disadvantaged people achieve their potential
▸ **Education** – Particularly initiatives which improve education outcomes for the disadvantaged, from early years through to transition to work
▸ **Health** – Including disability, palliative care and centres of excellence involved in ground-breaking research and treatments to address chronic illness (with a particular focus on investment in specialist equipment)
▸ **Environment** – Particularly preservation and sustainable initiatives that have a positive impact on the natural world

The following information is provided on the foundation's website:

Types of projects

Grantees are typically mid to large charities operating in locations in which Fidelity International has offices and other business interests. Grants are generally made to organisations with an annual operating budget in excess of £250,000. Investment is typically directed to specific projects in the following categories:

Capital improvements – Large-scale projects central to the overall growth and sustainability of the applicant, such as new construction, renovations, expansions, equipment and other initiatives that support the organisation's strategic vision.

Technology projects - High-impact technology projects that can substantially increase an organisations efficiency, effectiveness and sustainability.

Organisational development - Projects which seek to establish a new, transformational strategic path. This could include support for an initiative that helps a growing organisation achieve scale efficiencies, the development of a franchise model or helping charities to yield consolidation efficiencies through mergers

Planning initiatives - Funding for expert/external consultants to develop strategic, business, technology and other types of plans.

Grant size

Grants are made for 'significant, transformational projects' with a total budget of £50,000 or more, but the foundation does not expect to cover all the costs. Grants are one-off investments; they are rarely awarded for, or across, multiple years and will not normally be awarded to the same organisation in successive years. The minimum grant size is normally £10,000, and the majority of awards fall in the £25,000 to £100,000 range. Grants for projects with a particularly compelling investment case including significant measurable outcomes may exceed £100,000. For grants to international organisations, consult the website.

The Fidelity International Foundation

Fidelity's also has an international foundation which makes grants to organisations in countries where the company has operations and which serve beneficiaries in Continental Europe, Australia, Bermuda, China, Hong Kong, India, Japan, Korea, Singapore and Taiwan. Enquiry forms can be found on the UK foundation's website.

Financial information

In 2016 the foundation held assets of almost £233 million and had an income of £10 million. During the year, 60 grants were made totalling £7.1 million.

Grants by purpose

Arts, culture and heritage	24	£2.6 million
Health	12	£2.16 million
Community Development	13	£1.13 million
Education	9	£1.06 million
Cross Sector	2	£176,500

Grants by type of support

Information technology	27	£3.4 million
Building acquisition, development, restoration	22	£2.4 million
Organisational/development planning	4	£735,500
Core costs/programme costs	3	£428,000
Equipment	4	£170,000

Beneficiaries included: Pace2Be (£345,000); Bath Abbey (£250,000); The Mary Rose Trust (£200,000); Fulham Palace Trust (£150,000); Postal Museum (£75,000); Linden Lodge Charitable

Trust (£50,000); London Music Masters (£15,000); Sulgrave Club Ltd (£10,000).

Exclusions

Grants are not generally made to:

- Start-up, political or sectarian organisations
- Organisations which have been running for less than three years
- Individuals
- Private schools

Grants are not generally made for:

- Sponsorships
- Scholarships
- Corporate membership
- Advertising and promotional projects
- Exhibitions
- General running costs
- Replacement of dated IT hardware, routine system upgrades or ongoing website content
- Grants will not normally cover costs incurred prior to application and/or the grant being awarded

Applications

Applications should submit an initial enquiry via the foundation's website. The review process takes six to eight weeks. If you are invited to make a full application the foundation staff will request further information and possibly a site visit. Initial enquiries can be submitted at any time.

Sources of information

Accounts; annual report; Charity Commission record; funder's website.

Doris Field Charitable Trust

🔍 General charitable purposes

📍 UK, with a particular interest in Oxfordshire

💷 £401,500 (2016/17)

CC number: 328687

Trustees: John Cole; N. Harper; Wilhelmina Church; Helen Fanyinka.

Correspondent: Emily Greig, c/o Blake Morgan LLP, Seacourt Tower, West Way, Oxford OX2 0FB (tel: 01865 254286; email: emily.greig@blakemorgan.co.uk)

The Doris Field Charitable Trust was established in 1990. One-off and recurrent grants are given to large UK organisations and small local projects for a wide variety of causes and are usually below £3,000. The trust states that it favours local causes in Oxfordshire.

Financial information

In 2016/17 the trust held assets of £11.7 million and had an income of £411,000. Grants were made to 221 organisations totalled £401,500.

Previous beneficiaries have included: St Luke's Hospital (£75,000); Cancer Research UK (£30,000); Oxfordshire Sexual Abuse and Rape Crisis Centre and Riding for the Disabled (£2,000 each); Appleton Village Hall, Banbury Young Homelessness Project, Friends of Summertown Library and Women's Aid (£1,000 each); Oxfordshire Animal Sanctuary and Pavlova Wind Quartet (£500 each); Community Grocery Shop – Ascott-under-Wychwood (£450).

Exclusions

It is unlikely that grants would be made for salaries, training or higher education costs.

Applications

Potential applicants can obtain an application form from the correspondent and submit with the required information. The trustees meet three times a year to consider applications but can respond to urgent appeals if necessary.

Sources of information

Accounts; annual report; Charity Commission record.

The Sir John Fisher Foundation

🔍 General charitable purposes, with a preference for maritime projects, medicine, people with disabilities, education, music, the arts, community projects

📍 UK, with a strong preference for charities in the Furness peninsula and adjacent area

💷 £1.9 million (2016/17)

CC number: 277844

Trustees: Diane Meacock; Daniel Tindall; Rowland Hart Jackson; Michael Shields; Thomas Meacock.

Correspondent: Dr David Jackson, Secretary, Heaning Wood, Ulverston, Cumbria LA12 7NZ (tel: 01229 580349; email: info@sirjohnfisherfoundation.org.uk)

 www.sirjohnfisherfoundation.org.uk

The foundation was established in 1979 by Sir John and Lady Maria Fisher. The foundation is closely associated with James Fisher and Sons plc.

Areas of support

The foundation's website states that it supports charitable causes particularly in the six following categories:

- maritime
- medical and disability
- education
- music
- arts

‣ community projects in and around Barrow-in-Furness

Capital and revenue funding is available for up to three years. Most grants are for less than £10,000. The following information is taken from the foundation's website.

Priorities

Community Projects

In the Barrow-in-Furness and surrounding area the Foundation seeks to meet the needs of the local community and in particular the vulnerable and disadvantaged. The Trustees are likely to favour those local organisations who have sound and stable governance, and who have a strategy and considered plans for the future. In the local area community projects involving sick, disabled, children, education, family support, maritime, arts and music will receive priority.

Other causes

Outside the Barrow-in-Furness area, a very much more limited number of community causes will be supported in Cumbria and North Lancashire.

Some projects are supported nationally, particularly Maritime projects and some Music and Art projects. The foundation also supports nationally a limited amount of high quality medical research.

Financial information

In 2016/17 the foundation had assets of almost £125 million and an income of £2.4 million, of which £1.8 million was dividend income from James Fisher and Sons plc. During the year, there were 164 grants made, 143 locally and 21 nationally. Grants totalled almost £1.9 million, of which £1.1 million was given locally and £755,500 was given nationally.

Beneficiaries included: Royal National Lifeboat Institution (£500,000); Hospice of St Mary of Furness (£40,000); Cancer Care (£28,000); Dare Dance (£10,000); The CHIRP Charitable Trust (£6,400); Barrow Amateur Swimming Club (£2,000); The Eversley Choir (£1,000); Young Enterprise (£750) RSPCA (£200).

Exclusions

According to its website the foundation will not fund:

‣ Individuals
‣ Sponsorship
‣ Expeditions
‣ Promotion of religion
‣ Places of worship
‣ Animal welfare
‣ Retrospective funding
‣ Pressure groups
‣ Community projects outside Barrow-in-Furness and surrounding area (except occasional projects in Cumbria or North Lancashire or if they fall within one of the other categories supported by the foundation)

Applications

The following information has been taken from the foundation's website:

Applications should be made by submitting a completed application form, together with all relevant information (set out on the application form) to the Secretary at least six weeks in advance of the Trustees' meeting. The Trustees meet at the beginning of May and the beginning of November each year. The closing date for the May meeting is the 1st March and the November meeting is the 21st September annually'. Application forms should be obtained from the Secretary, whose contact details appear on the contacts page of this site. Alternatively please use the link below to download a Word document which you can fill in and submit by email or post.

You are always welcome to contact the Secretary for an informal discussion before submitting an application for funding.

Sources of information

Accounts; annual report; Charity Commission record; funder's website.

Fisherbeck Charitable Trust

 Christianity, homelessness, the relief of poverty, education, environment, heritage, general charitable purposes

Worldwide

£ £506,500 to organisations (2016/17)

CC number: 1107287

Trustees: Ian Cheal; Jane Cheal; Matthew Cheal.

Correspondent: Ian Cheal, Trustee, 63 Ferringham Lane, Ferring, Worthing, West Sussex BN12 5LL (tel: 01903 241027; email: ian@roffeyhomes.com)

Registered with the Charity Commission in December 2004, the Fisherbeck Charitable Trust is the vehicle for the charitable activities of the Cheal family, owners of Roffey Homes.

According to the trustees' report for 2016/17:

The Charity's objects are to encourage charitable giving from the extended Cheal family and to apply these funds to the making of grants for the following charitable objects:

‣ The advancement of the Christian religion
‣ Support the provision of accommodation for the homeless and meeting their ongoing needs
‣ The relief of poverty
‣ The advancement of education
‣ To encourage conservation of the environment and the preservation of our heritage
‣ Such other charitable objects in such manner as the trustees shall from time to time decide

Financial information

In 2016/17 the trust had assets of £472,000 and an income of £728,000. Grants totalled £512,500 of which £506,500 was given in 69 grants to organisations and a further £6,000 in one grant to individuals.

Beneficiaries included: Christian Viewpoint for Men (£55,000); Worthing Churches Homeless Project (£30,000); Release International (£21,000); Alpha International and Health Communication Resources (£10,000 each); Church Army (£6,000); Church Pastoral Aid Society and St Matthew's Church PCC Youth (£5,000 each).

Exclusions

Grants are only made to individuals known to the trust or in exceptional circumstances.

Applications

The trust does not accept unsolicited applications. The trustees have previously stated that 'all our funds are spoken for as we now have a set portfolio to a number of charities to whom we give grants each year'.

Sources of information

Accounts; annual report; Charity Commission record; further information provided by the funder.

Fishmongers' Company's Charitable Trust

 General charitable purposes, education, relief of poverty, disability

City of London and the boroughs of Camden, Hackney, Islington, Lambeth, Southwark, Tower Hamlets and Westminster

£ £535,500 to organisations (2017)

CC number: 263690

Trustee: The Worshipful Company of Fishmongers.

Correspondent: The Charities Administrator, The Fishmongers' Company, Fishmongers' Hall, London Bridge, London EC4R 9EL (tel: 020 7626 3531; email: charity@fishhall.org.uk)

www.fishhall.org.uk

The charity was established in 1972 for general charitable purposes and its focus is in the areas of education, relief of poverty and disability, fishery-related organisations, the environment and heritage. The Fishmongers' Company is one of the Twelve Great Livery Companies of the City of London, and among the most ancient of the City Guilds. As with most Livery Companies, the charity supports education and other charities.

The objects of the charity, as set out in its Trust Deed, are 'the relief of poverty, annual or other payments to poor pensioners and other poor persons, purposes of education, and general public purposes in so far as they are legally charitable'. The charity fulfils these objectives for the public benefit by means of the provision of charitable grants under the two main headings of:

▶ The advancement of education
▶ The prevention and relief of hardship

A smaller number of grants are awarded under the headings of Disability and Medical, and Heritage. The charity also provides a small number of grants for the advancement of medical science, the advancement of religious and social work in accordance with the Christian faith and fisheries.

Grant-making

The following information is taken from the charity's website:

The charity is pleased to accept grant applications in the fields of:

▶ Education in Prisons
▶ Mental Health
▶ Food and Nutrition

Preference will be given to applicants:

▶ Whose annual income does not exceed £1,000,000
▶ Requesting funding for a specific project rather than for general funds, and to those
▶ Operating within the City of London and the Boroughs of Camden, Hackney, Islington, Lambeth, Southwark, Tower Hamlets or Westminster

An application will only be considered where it:

▶ Fits clearly within one, or more, of the stated fields
▶ Is from a registered Charity, Social Enterprise or Community interest company
▶ Clearly identifies key objectives and outcomes
▶ Is made by the organisation delivering the activity, service or project. i.e. applications cannot be made on behalf of a third party

Billingsgate Christian Mission Fund

The charity makes grants from this fund for charities engaged in the fish and fishing industries and for medical research, with the following objectives stated on the website:

▶ To relieve poverty, distress and sickness among persons engaged in the Fish and Fishing Industries in the United Kingdom
▶ To advance religious and social work in accordance with the Christian Faith among persons engaged in the Fish and Fishing Industries in the United Kingdom

▶ To advance medical science, particularly by way of grants for scholarships

In 2013 the trustees merged about forty small trusts which shared the Fishmongers' Company as common trustee. The total amount transferred was £1.3 million which led to the creation of five new restricted funds:

▶ **St Peter's Hospital Fund** – for the prevention and relief of poverty
▶ **Ben Travers Fund** – for a drama scholarship in the Guildhall School of Music and Drama
▶ **Mark Quested Fund** – for the year exhibition at the universities of Oxford and Cambridge
▶ **EL Beckwith Fund** – for a music scholarship at the Royal College of Music and a sculpture scholarship at the City and Guilds of London Art School
▶ **FM Heathcote Fund** – for the benefit of the residents of Jesus Hospital, Bray

Financial information

In 2017 the charity had assets of £33 million and an income of £711,500. During the year, the charity expended around £549,500 in grants. Of this amount, £13,800 was awarded to individuals in the form of hardship grants.

Grants to organisations were broken down as follows:

Education	£456,000
Hardship	£55,700
Fisheries	£15,000
Heritage and the environment	£6,900
Disability and medical grants	£3,000

Beneficiaries included: The Gresham's Foundation (£195,500); Gresham's School (£46,000); Guildhall School of Music and Drama (£25,000); The National Lobster Hatchery (£15,000); Fishmongers' and Poulterers' institute (£11,000); City Harvest (£10,000); KeepOut (£3,000); The Lady Mayoress' Appeal (£1,000).

Exclusions

Individuals are only supported with educational and hardship grants.

Applications

Application forms are available to download from the charity's website. The following information is taken from the charity's website:

▶ Applicants are to complete and submit the online form, including all requested supporting documents
▶ Applications will be acknowledged
▶ If any further information is required, you will be contacted prior to formal assessment
▶ Following initial assessment, the strongest applications will be taken forward to the next Philanthropy Committee meeting for formal consideration

▶ All applicants will be notified of the outcome

Note the following information taken from the 2017 annual report: 'The Education and Grants Committee is currently reviewing its strategy and grant-giving policy and these guidelines may change.'

Applications are considered three times per year, in March, June and October.

Sources of information

Accounts; annual report; Charity Commission record; funder's website.

The Football Foundation

 Grassroots football, community, education

England

£ £18 million (2016/17)

CC number: 1079309

Trustees: Gary Hoffman; Roger Burden; Martin Glenn; Richard Scudamore; Peter McCormick; Rt Hon. Richard Caborn; Rona Chester.

Correspondent: Rupen Shah, Head of Finance, Whittington House, 19–30 Alfred Place, London WC1E 7EA (tel: 0845 345 4555; email: enquiries@ footballfoundation.org.uk)

 www.footballfoundation.org.uk

The Football Foundation is the UK's largest sports charity funded by the Premier League, The FA, Sport England and the government. Funds are occasionally provided by corporate partners.

The foundation's objectives are:

▶ To put into place a new generation of modern facilities in parks, local leagues and schools
▶ To provide capital/revenue support to increase participation in grassroots football
▶ To strengthen the links between football and the community and to harness its potential as a force for good in society

Grant programmes

The foundation aims to achieve its objectives through a number of programmes. At the time of writing (June 2018) the following programmes were open for applications:

▶ **Premier League & The FA Facilities Fund:** provides grants for building or refurbishing grassroots facilities, such as changing pavilions and playing surfaces for community benefit, with money provided by the Premier League, The FA and the Government (via Sport England) and delivered by the Foundation

- **Premier League & The FA Facilities Fund Small Grants Scheme:** awards grants of up to £10,000 for the provision of capital items, or to refurbish/improve existing facilities
- **Respect:** aims to ensure that football – both on and off the pitch – continues to be enjoyable, inclusive and a positive experience For All. This scheme offers clubs, leagues and schools with the opportunity to purchase Respect equipment which, if used effectively, will help us to achieve this

New grant programmes open and close regularly, so potential applicants are advised to check the foundation's website for the latest information, including detailed application instructions and eligibility terms.

There are four thresholds of grant size:

- Small grants of up to £10,000
- Medium grants for between £10,000 and £100,000
- Large grants for between £100,000 and £500,000
- Exceptional grants of over £500,000

A wide range of organisations are eligible for support, including:

- Football clubs (grassroots, professional and semi-professional) and their associated community charities
- Multi-sport clubs
- Local authorities
- Educational establishments
- Registered charities
- Not-for-profit companies limited by guarantee
- Industrial and provident societies
- Unincorporated not-for-profit organisations

Financial information

In 2016/17 the foundation held assets of £48.9 million and had a total income of £67.8 million, which the foundation receives from the professional game, and from the Department of Culture, Media and Sport via Sports England. There were 1,294 new grants made totalling £18.0 million during the year.

Beneficiaries included: Sheffield City Council (£4.4 million); Institute of Groundsmanship (£726,000); Sporting Khalsa FC (£579,500); College of Haringey, Enfield and NE London (£542,500); The Seashell Trust (£500,000); Sussex FA (£35,000); Congleton Town Ltd (£33,000); Tavistock AFC (£31,500); Wiltshire FA (£31,000).

Applications

Detailed guidance notes including a list of regional contacts are available on the website. Applications are submitted online.

Sources of information

Accounts; annual report; Charity Commission record; funder's website.

Forever Manchester

 General charitable purposes

 Greater Manchester

 £1.93 million to organisations (2016/17)

CC number: 1017504

Trustees: Michael Warner; Philip Hogben; Sandra Lindsay; Alan Mackin; Louise Marshall; Samantha Booth.

Correspondent: Communities Team, 2nd Floor, 8 Hewitt Street, Manchester M15 4GB (tel: 0161 214 0940; email: awards@forevermanchester.com)

 www.forevermanchester.com

 facebook.com/forevermanchester

 @4EVERManchester

 @4evermanchester

Forever Manchester (formerly known as The Community Foundation for Greater Manchester) raises money to fund and support community activity across Greater Manchester. The charity administers and manages a number of funds on behalf of other organisations, details of which can be found on its website.

Financial information

In 2016/17 the foundation held assets of £9.8 million and had an income of £2.5 million. Grants to organisations totalled £1.93 million and grants to individuals totalled £29,000.

Previous beneficiaries have included: Bloco Mente; Children of Jannah; Friends of Jubilee Colliery; Friends of Stockport Cemeteries; Monton Voices Community Choir; North Manchester Ladies Jewish Drama Group; Pastures New; Reddish Vale Men in Sheds; Safety4Sisters; St Mary's Friendship Club; The Seed Project.

Applications

Details of all open funds can be found on the charity's website. The website states: 'Please note we can only accept one application at a time for any project. If more than one fund is open, please call us for advice on which one would be most suitable for you to apply to.'

Sources of information

Accounts; annual report; Charity Commission record; funder's website.

Donald Forrester Trust

 Animal welfare, disability, health and medical research, seafarers and armed forces, social welfare, children and young people, older people, arts and culture, heritage, overseas aid

 UK and overseas

 £682,500 (2016/17)

CC number: 295833

Trustees: Wendy Forrester; Hilary Porter; Melissa Jones; Martin West.

Correspondent: Adrian Hollands, Secretary, 11 Whitecroft Way, Beckenham, Kent BR3 3AQ (tel: 020 8629 0089; email: ah@forrestertrusts.com)

 forrestertrusts.com/donald-forrester-trust

When Donald Forrester, a successful London business man and company director, died in 1985, his widow Gwyneth set up the Donald Forrester Charitable Trust which was established in 1986. The trust's grant-making now covers a wide range of categories. Most grants go to well known (and often, although not exclusively, national) charities and are typically for £5,000.

The trust is, for the most part, reliant on income from Films and Equipment Ltd and the increased gift aid and the maintained dividend from the company has allowed the trust to continue to increase total charitable giving.

Financial information

In 2016/17 the trust held assets of £8.4 million and had an income of £680,000. Grants were made to 140 charities, totalling £682,500 and can be categorized as follows:

Community and social welfare	35	£160,500
Overseas aid	19	£110,000
Medical relief	18	£92,500
Children and young people	16	£72,500
Disability	16	£70,000
Medical research	10	£50,000
Hospices and hospitals	6	£40,000
Older people	8	£37,000
Blindness and deafness	4	£20,000
Services and ex-services	3	£15,000
Culture, heritage and the environment	3	£10,000
Animals and birds	1	£5,000

Beneficiaries included: DEC (£25,000); St Clare Hospice (£10,000); Fenland Association for Community Transport (£7,000); Blesma, Canine Partners, Freedom From Torture, Humane Slaughter Association, Meningitis Research Foundation, The Trussell Trust and Victim Support (£5,000 each); Coldharbour Mill Trust (£2,500); North Bristol Advice Centre (£2,000).

Exclusions

No grants are given to individuals.

Applications

Historically, both the Donald Forrester Trust and the Gwyneth Forrester Trust had a policy of not accepting unsolicited grant applications. However, as explained on the website, the trustees 'have now decided to encourage applications from a wider range of charities'.

Applications should be made in writing to the correspondent, stating whether you are applying to the Donald Forrester Trust or the Gwyneth Forrester Trust. Ideally, applications should not exceed four sides of A4. Applications should include details of the impact you think a grant from the trust might make to your organisation's work. A full set of accounts is not required, however the trustees find a brief indication of an applicant organisation's financial position to be helpful. The trustees meet twice yearly in February/March and August/September, and applications should be submitted no later than 15 January and 15 July, respectively. The trust is unable to enter into correspondence with applicants.

Sources of information

Accounts; annual report; Charity Commission record; funder's website.

Gwyneth Forrester Trust

The trustees support a specific charitable sector each year. The theme for 2018 is Support of Older People. Themes in previous years have included Helping Youths and Ex-Offenders into Employment (2017), Hospices (2016), and Mental Health (2015)

England and Wales

£584,500 (2016/17)

CC number: 1080921

Trustees: Wendy Forrester; Hilary Porter; Melissa Jones.

Correspondent: Adrian Hollands, 11 Whitecroft Way, Beckenham, Kent BR3 3AQ (tel: 020 8629 0089; email: ah@forrestertrusts.com)

forrestertrusts.com/gwyneth-forrester-trust

Established in May 2000, this trust supports general charitable purposes. Each year the trust researches and identifies suitable charities within a chosen charitable sector before making grants. At the time of writing (June 2018) the theme for 2019 had yet to be decided. The theme for 2018 is 'support for older people'. Themes in previous years have included 'helping youths and ex-offenders into employment' (2017), hospices (2016), and mental health

(2015). Each year the trust distributes approximately £500,000, with grants averaging around £40,000. The trustees look favourably on charities where they feel overhead and fundraising costs are kept to a minimum.

Financial information

In 2016/17 the trust had assets of £27.4 million and an income of £764,000. In total £584,500 was awarded in grants to 20 organisations.

Beneficiaries included: Barnardo's; Bromley by Bow Centre, Mencap, Tempus Novo (£40,000 each); Get Set Girls and Langley House Trust (£20,000 each); Blyth Star (£10,000).

Exclusions

Individuals are not supported.

Applications

Historically, both the Donald Forrester Trust and the Gwyneth Forrester Trust had a policy of not accepting unsolicited grant applications. However, as explained on the website, the trustees 'have now decided to encourage applications from a wider range of charities'.

Applications should be made in writing to the correspondent, stating whether you are applying to the Donald Forrester Trust or the Gwyneth Forrester Trust. Ideally, applications should not exceed four sides of A4. Applications should include details of the impact you think a grant from the trust might make to your organisation's work. A full set of accounts is not required, however the trustees find a brief indication of an applicant organisation's financial position to be helpful. The trustees meet to consider applications in February/March, and applications should be submitted no later than 31 December. The trust is unable to enter into correspondence with applicants.

Sources of information

Accounts; annual report; Charity Commission record; funder's website.

The Fort Foundation

Health, amateur sport, education, art and culture, citizenship, community welfare, religion, environmental protection and improvement

England and Wales, with a focus on Lancashire

£201,000 to organisations (2016/17)

CC number: 1028639

Trustees: Edward Fort; Ian Wilson; Edward Drury; John Hartley; Peter Fort.

Correspondent: Edward Fort, Trustee, c/o Fort Vale Engineering Ltd, Calder Vale Park, Simonstone Lane,

Simonstone, Burnley BB12 7ND (tel: 01282 440000; email: info@fortvale.com)

The foundation was established in 1993 primarily to assist young people in Pendle Borough and local areas. It gives to organisations for the educational training of young people and it sponsors individuals on educational work in the UK and overseas. Particular areas of grant-making are listed in the table below.

Financial information

In 2016/17 the foundation held assets of £905,500 and had an income of £338,000. Grants awarded to organisations totalled £201,000 with a further £18,900 awarded to individuals.

Grants awarded to organisations were broken down as follows:

Citizenship and community welfare	£62,000
Amateur Sport	£52,500
Health	£39,500
Education	£30,500
Environmental protection and improvement	£13,200
Religion	£2,500
Art and culture	£1,200

Beneficiaries included: Community Foundation for Lancashire, The Outward Bound Trust and The 1851 Trust (£25,000 each); Lancaster University, RNLI and The Royal Yachting Association (£10,000 each); The Climate Group (£7,500); Burwain Sailing Club, Central Manchester University Hospital NHS Trust and Pendle and Craven Croquet Club (£5,000 each).

Applications

Apply in writing to the correspondent.

Sources of information

Accounts; annual report; Charity Commission record.

Four Acre Trust

Children and young people

Worldwide, with a preference for UK

£1.65 million (2016/17)

CC number: 1053884

Trustees: Mary Bothamley; Stephen Ratcliffe; John Bothamley; Taymour Ezzat; Marion Baker.

Correspondent: June Horton, Treferanon, St Weonards, Hereford HR2 8QF (tel: 01981 580002; email: info@fouracretrust.org.uk)

 www.fouracretrust.org.uk

Four Acre Trust (4AT) was founded in 1995 by John Bothamley with profits from the building industry. The trust supports charities that give children a better start in life. There is an emphasis on supporting smaller and less high

profile charities, usually with a turnover of less than £1 million.

The trust rarely supports capital projects, instead the charity's website states that most grants are made to support revenue expenses and core costs including the support of the salary costs for 'good people able to effect change in their area of work'.

Each year the trust spends around 25% of its funds on charities working internationally. Previously these funds have been used to support water, sanitation, eye and educational projects.

Financial information

In 2016/17 the trust had assets of £4 million and an income of £609,500. Grants awarded to organisations totalled £1.65 million.

Beneficiaries included: Home-Start Torridge (£689,000); First Give (£145,000); Cranfield Trust (£118,000); Scout Association (£109,000); Reachout Youth (£60,000); Education for All (£20,000); Wells for India (£15,000); Salter's Hill Charity (£11,000); Kids Kabin (£5,000); Special Needs and Parents (£1,000); Avenues Community Association (£830).

Applications

The 2016/17 accounts state: '4AT is essentially closed to new applications preferring to seek out relevant charities through thorough research. However, applications from charities that mirror our existing recipients, and meet our other policies, might be acceptable and approaches should first be made to our administrator with a very short synopsis of the support that is required.'

Sources of information

Accounts; annual review; Charity Commission record; funder's website.

The Foyle Foundation

 Arts and culture, education, libraries

UK, particularly areas outside London and the South East

£8.44 million (2016)

CC number: 1081766

Trustees: James Korner; Michael Smith; Peter Duffell; Roy Amlot; Vikki Heywood.

Correspondent: David Hall, Chief Executive, Rugby Chambers, 2 Rugby Street, London WC1N 3QU (tel: 020 7430 9119; email: info@foylefoundation. org.uk)

 www.foylefoundation.org.uk

The foundation was formed under the will of the late Christina Foyle. She was the daughter of William Foyle who, with his brother, founded the family-owned bookshop Foyles in Charing Cross Road, London, which she managed after her father's death. The foundation is an independent charity and there is no connection with Foyle's Bookshop.

The foundation gives financial support to organisations that operate in the fields of arts and education, grants mostly range from £10,000 to £50,000.

Grant programmes

Main Grants Scheme

Arts

The foundation prefers to support the performing and visual arts and will make grants for specific projects or activities. Applications for core funding will be considered but only from smaller organisations or from organisations that are not recipients of recurrent revenue funding from the Arts Council or local authorities. The following areas are supported:

- Helping to make the arts more accessible by developing new audiences, supporting tours, festivals and arts educational projects
- Encouraging new work and supporting young and emerging artists
- Building projects that improve or re-equip existing arts venues (rather than construction of new facilities, although this will not be excluded)
- Projects that reduce overheads or which help generate additional revenue

Learning

The foundation will support projects which facilitate the acquisition of knowledge and which have a long-term strategic impact. Key areas for support are:

- Libraries, museums and archives
- Special educational needs
- Projects that encourage sustainability by reducing overheads or which help generate additional revenue
- Projects and activities which increase access and widen the diversity of attenders/visitors

For state-funded schools the foundation's main initiative will be The Foyle School Libraries Scheme (special guidance notes are available from the foundation's website). Dedicated schools catering for those with Special Educational Needs (SEN) may also be supported.

The Foyle Schools Library Programme

The majority of the funding for this programme is directed toward primary schools, as there is no statutory requirement for schools to have a library. Priority will be given to funding library/reading books but not textbooks or curriculum books. Further

information and a detailed list of exclusions it available on the website.

Small Grants Scheme

Applications are accepted from charities with an annual turnover of less than £100,000 per annum. The scheme will make one-off grants of between £1,000 and £10,000 for core costs, equipment or project funding.

Financial information

In 2016 the foundation held assets of £83.2 million and had an income of £2.77 million. There were 516 grants made during the year totalling £8.44 million. Grants paid during the year and were broken down as follows:

Arts	£3.9 million
Learning	£3.7 million
Small grants	£771,000

Beneficiaries have included: Royal Academy of Arts (£250,000); King's College London (£80,000); St Albans Museums and Galleries Trust (£50,000); Octagon Theatre Trust (£15,000); Applause Rural Touring and Lewisham Education Arts Network (£10,000 each); Piper Hill Specialist Support School, Rose Green Junior School and Sandye Place Academy (£5,000 each).

Exclusions

No grants are given to individuals, organisations which are not registered charities or for international work. No retrospective funding.

Applications

Guidelines and application forms for each of the foundation's grant schemes are available to download from the foundation's website. Applications should be submitted via post. All applications will be acknowledged by email or by post within two weeks of receipt. Applications are accepted all year round, however applications for large capital projects (over £75,000) will only be considered in twice a year, in spring and autumn.

Sources of information

Accounts; annual report; Charity Commission record; funder's website.

The Elizabeth Frankland Moore and Star Foundation

General charitable purposes

UK

£275,500 (2016/17)

CC number: 257711

Trustees: R. Griffiths; Anne Ely; Dr David Spalton; Janine Cameron.

Correspondent: Marianne Neuhoff, The Elizabeth Frankland Moore and Star Foundation, c/o Neuhoff & Co.,

11 Towcester Road, Whittlebury, Towcester NN12 8XU (tel: 01327 858171; email: info@neuhoffandco.com)

The Elizabeth Frankland Moor and Star Foundation was established in 1968. The foundation aims to give grants to a range of charitable organisations and individuals. Grants range from £500 to £20,000 and the foundation states in its annual report for 2016/17: 'The grants made by the trustees are generally unrestricted as the trustees are particularly aware that for many charities meeting their basic core costs presents a significant challenge.'

Financial information

In 2016/17 the foundation held assets of £12.7 million and had an income of £348,000. Grants were made to 48 organisations (stated in the annual report), totalling £363,000. Grants were made in the following areas:

Medical research	£101,000
National Star College	£80,000
Vulnerable in society	£50,000
War veterans	£37,000
Homelessness	£35,000
Others	£16,000
The arts	£16,000
Human rights	£15,000
Hospices	£13,000

Beneficiaries included: National Star College (£80,000); Brain Tumour Research Campaign and Fight for Sight (£15,000 each); Prisoners Abroad and Salvation Army (£10,000 each); Special Forces Benevolent Fund (£5,000); The Farrers Charitable Trust (£2,000); RNLI (£500).

Applications

Apply in writing to the correspondent. The trustees meet twice a year.

Sources of information

Accounts; annual report; Charity Commission.

The Hugh Fraser Foundation

 General charitable purposes

 UK, with a strong preference for Scotland

(£) £1.8 million (2016/17)

OSCR number: SC009303

Correspondent: The Trustees, Sutherland House, 149 St Vincent Street, Glasgow (tel: 0131 228 8111)

This foundation was established in 1960 by Hugh Fraser, responsible for developing his father's shop into the retail chain now known as House of Fraser. It was founded with general charitable purposes, with a preference for educational institutions, health and arts organisations, and those working with older people, those with disabilities or the underprivileged.

The 2016/17 annual report notes that:

> The Trustees consider that grants to large, highly-publicised national appeals are not likely to be as effective a use of funds as grants to smaller and more focused charitable appeals.

> The Trustees are prepared to enter into commitments over a period of time by making grants in successive years, often to assist in new initiatives which can maintain their own momentum once they have been established for a few years.

> The Foundation makes donations to charities working in many different sectors principally hospitals, schools and universities, arts organisations and organisations working with the handicapped, the underprivileged and the aged. The Trustees are nevertheless prepared to consider applications from charities working in other fields.

Financial information

In 2016/17 the foundation held assets of £82.3 million and had an income of £2.5 million. Grants were made to 344 organisations totalling £1.8 million. In addition, four grants were made to individuals, totalling £16,000. The accounts provide the following grants breakdown:

Disadvantaged and disabled	141	£523,500
Music, theatre and visual arts	51	£390,500
Education and training	44	£337,000
Medical research facilities	26	£186,500
Conservation and environment	22	£140,500
Older people, homeless and hospices	24	£88,000
Youth organisations	16	£54,000
Miscellaneous	14	£51,000
Religion	6	£22,000

A list of beneficiaries was not available.

Exclusions

Grants are only awarded to individuals in exceptional circumstances.

Applications

Apply in writing to the correspondent. Applications should also include either a copy of your latest formal accounts if prepared or a copy of your most recent balance sheet, income and expenditure account or bank statement if formal accounts are not prepared. If you are not a registered charity you should also enclose a copy of your constitution or policy statement. The trustees meet quarterly to consider applications, usually in March, June, September and December. Applications should be received early in the preceding month in order to be considered.

Sources of information

Accounts; annual report; OSCR record.

The Joseph Strong Frazer Trust

 General charitable purposes, social welfare, education, religion, health and medical research, disability, children and young people, maritime, armed forces, wildlife

England and Wales

(£) £420,500 (2015/16)

CC number: 235311

Trustees: David Cook; Mr R. Read; William Waites; William Reardon Smith; W. Antony Reardon Smith; Ugo Fagandini.

Correspondent: The Trustees of The Joseph Strong Frazer Trust, c/o Joseph Miller & Co., Floor A, Milburn House, Dean Street, Newcastle upon Tyne NE1 1LE (tel: 0191 232 8065; email: jsf@joseph-miller.co.uk)

The trust registered with the Charity Commission in 1964 and supports general charitable purposes in England and Wales through its grant-making. The trust's 2015/16 accounts state that:

> It is the aim of the trustees to support a very wide number of good causes and charitable objects and make best use of the Trust's resources. Applications for grants are considered by the trustees and distributions are made where it is thought most appropriate and effective, to organisations within England and Wales.

Financial information

In 2015/16 the trust had assets of £14.5 million and an income of £540,500. During the year, the trust awarded 312 grants totalling £420,500. Grants were distributed as follows:

Medical and other research	63	£93,500
Caring organisations	39	£50,500
Other trusts, funds, and voluntary organisations	42	£46,500
Children	29	£38,500
Youth	31	£33,000
Hospitals and home (and connected activities)	20	£29,500
Deaf and blind	17	£29,000
People with disabilities	16	£24,000
Leisure activities, animals, and wildlife	14	£18,000
Maritime	16	£17,000
Religious bodies	9	£15,500
Armed forces	7	£12,000
Older people	3	£6,000
Learning disability	5	£6,000
Schools and colleges	1	£2,000

Beneficiaries included: St David's Church (£5,000); Seafarers UK (£2,500); Limbless Association (£2,000); National Botanical Gardens of Wales (£2,000); Spinal Injuries Association (£2,000); Combat Stress (£2,000); Headway (£2,000); Addaction (£2,000); Not Forgotten Association (£2,000); The Samson Centre for MS (£2,000); The National Brain Appeal (£2,000).

Exclusions

No grants are given to individuals.

Applications

Apply in writing to the correspondent. The trustees meet twice a year, usually in March and September. Application forms are not necessary. It is helpful if applicants are concise in their appeal letters, which must include an sae if acknowledgement is required.

Sources of information

Accounts; annual report; Charity Commission record.

Charles S French Charitable Trust

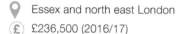 General charitable purposes, community, disability, disadvantage, medical, hospices, sports, young people, education

Essex and north east London

£236,500 (2016/17)

CC number: 206476

Trustees: William Noble; Martin Scarth; Joanna Thomas; Michael Foster; Chris Noble; Jamie Foster; Antonia McLeod.

Correspondent: William Noble, Trustee, 169 High Road, Loughton, Essex IG10 4LF (tel: 020 8502 3575; email: office@csfct.org.uk)

 www.csfct.org.uk

Established by Charles French in 1959, this trust has a policy of supporting local charities, mainly in Essex and north east London. Applications can also be considered from charities based outside this area if they can demonstrate benefit to residents within north east London, Essex, or immediate surrounding areas.

Financial information

In 2016/17 the trust had assets of £9.2 million and an income of £342,000. Grants totalling £236,500 were made to about 144 organisations and broken down as follows:

Community activities	£38,500
Disabilities/disadvantage	£38,500
Medical	£35,500
Hospices	£33,000
Sports/holidays	£30,500
Young people	£30,500
Education	£23,500
Older people	£6,000

Beneficiaries included: Loughton Youth Project (£8,000); Richard House Hospice (£3,000); Islington Centre for Refugees and Migrants (£2,000); Stratford Circus Arts Centre (£1,500); Headway Essex, Sportability and Women Together Support Group – Barking (£1,000 each).

Exclusions

Only registered charities are supported.

Applications

Apply in writing to the correspondent, including a copy of your organisation's latest accounts. Applications should be sent by standard post and are usually acknowledged by email within a few days of being received. The trustees usually meet around four times a year.

Sources of information

Accounts; annual report; Charity Commission record.

The Freshfield Foundation

Sustainable development, health, education, disaster relief

UK and overseas

£614,500 (2016/17)

CC number: 1003316

Trustees: Paul Kurthausen; Patrick Appleton Moores; Elizabeth Potter.

Correspondent: Paul Kurthausen, Trustee, BWMacfarlane LLP, Castle Chambers, 43 Castle Street, Liverpool L2 9SH (tel: 0151 236 1494; email: paul.k@bwm.co.uk)

The foundation was established in 1991 and aims to support organisations involved in sustainable development and overseas disaster relief. The 2016/17 annual report states that the trustees have decided to reduce the number of charities being supported.

Financial information

In 2016/17 the foundation had assets of £8.2 million and an income of £2.2 million. Grants were made to four organisations totalling £614,500 and were broken down as follows:

Beneficiaries included: Citizens Advice (£474,500); Sustrans (£100,000 each); Motor Neurone Disease Association, St Mungo's Community Housing Association Ltd (£20,000 each).

Applications

The foundation states that 'the process of grant making starts with the trustees analysing an area of interest, consistent with the charity's aims and objectives, and then proactively looking for charities that they think can make the greatest contribution'. With this in mind, a letter of introduction to your organisation's work may be more appropriate than a formal application for funding.

Sources of information

Accounts; annual report; Charity Commission record.

Friends of Wiznitz Ltd

Orthodox Jewish religious education, the advancement of the Orthodox Jewish religion, the relief of poverty

UK and overseas

£1.9 million (2016/17)

CC number: 255685

Trustees: Heinrich Feldman; Shulom Feldman; Ephraim Gottesfeld.

Correspondent: Ephraim Gottesfeld, Trustee, 8 Jessam Avenue, London E5 9DU

The charity supports the advancement of the Orthodox Jewish religion, Orthodox Jewish religious education and the relief of poverty. The charity also grants free use of its buildings, for educational purposes, to other Wiznitz charities in order to fulfil the above objectives.

This charity is mainly concerned with supporting major educational projects carried out by Orthodox Jewish institutions.

Financial information

In 2016/17 the charity had assets of £2.9 million and an income of £2.2 million. Grants were made totalling £1.9 million and were distributed as follows:

Religious education	£834,500
Relief of poverty	£610,500
Advancement of religion	£405,500
Grants to individuals	£72,500
Social welfare	£20,000

Beneficiaries included: Igud Mosdos Wiznitz (£550,000); Lehachzikom Velehachiyosom (£285,500); Mosdos Imrey Chaim (£143,500); Keren Lehazunas Yeladim (£86,000); Mosdos Viznitz (£54,500).

Applications

The 2016/17 annual report advises that:

In general the trustees select the institutions to be supported according to their personal knowledge of work of the institution. Whilst not actively inviting applications, they are always prepared to accept any application which will be carefully considered and help given according to circumstances and funds then available. Applications by individuals must be accompanied by a letter of recommendation by the applicant's minister or other known religious leader.

Sources of information

Accounts; annual report; Charity Commission record.

Friends Provident Charitable Foundation

 Sustainable economic development

 UK

£ £1.85 million (2016/17)

CC number: 1087053

Trustees: Hetan Shah; Joycelin Dawes; Patrick Hynes; Rob Lake; Joanna Elson; Paul Dickinson; Aphra Sklair; Kathleen Kelly; Stephen Muers.

Correspondent: Abigail Gibson, Grants Manager, Blake House, 18 Blake Street, York YO1 8QG (tel: 01904 629675; email: foundation.enquiries@ friendsprovidentfoundation.org.uk)

🌐 www.friendsprovidentfoundation. org

🐦 @fprovfoundation

Friends Provident Foundation was established as part of the demutualisation of Friends' Provident Life Office in 2001 and the flotation of Friends Provident plc. In 2011 Friends Provident changed its name to Friends Life and has been part of the Aviva Group since 2015.

The foundation's website explains that its grant-making is focused on 'exploring the role of money and financial systems as a force for social good', with the aims of:

- Encouraging 'thinking that deals with the cause of the problem'
- Transforming 'the use of financial systems so that they offer social as well as economic benefits, alleviating social disharmony and inequality'
- Pioneering 'news ways of thinking about how money is used to solve social problems'

Grants programmes

The foundation's current grants programme is 'Building Resilient Economies', through which it aims 'to contribute to a more resilient, sustainable and fairer economic system'. There are two outcomes stemming from the programme's overall aim – 'systems change' and 'local economic resilience' – and applicants are asked to which of these they wish to contribute. The outcomes are described on the foundation's website:

Systems change:

This part of the programme involves a radical assessment of how 'disruptive innovation' might change the financial system – exploring and informing changes to the regulatory, policy or other systemic level that would develop financial system innovations with the potential to deliver our aim. Projects in this category will require strong analysis of the issues and possible solutions. They will also need to develop and demonstrate methods that will effectively change policy and corporate behaviours in pursuit of wider social objectives. Our aim would be to stimulate feasible new ideas and scalable, practical examples.

Local economic resilience:

The aim of this part of the programme will be to support the development of local economic resilience. Projects should build on the technologies and approaches that currently assist localities to create economic growth and retain its value. This could be work relating to community assets, sweat equity schemes and other local resources. We expect projects in this category to build partnerships with other funders doing similar work at the local level, to learn from and share learning between local initiatives. Projects in this category should be guided by research that net did for us on local or small-scale initiatives that build economic resilience through diversity, flexibility and increasing capacity.

The NEF (New Economics Foundation) reports can be downloaded via the website.

Examples of projects which may be funded under this outcome include: 'local economics in global economies – critical analysis of the evidence on resilient economies' and 'the feasibility of collective procurement models for low income communities'.

Project approaches

The foundation is interested to know how projects will address their chosen outcome and so applicants are asked to indicate which of the following approaches they intend to take:

- **Innovation:** Development work to propose new solutions
- **Intelligence:** Research that will gather evidence to support and inform practice
- **Institutions:** The creation or maintenance of key organisations or functions that are important for building economic resilience
- **Influencing:** Exploring or piloting ways of influencing corporate, regulatory or policy players

Financial information

In 2016/17 the foundation had assets of £33.75 million and an income of £904,000. Grants were made 24 organisations totalling £1.85 million.

Beneficiaries included: IPPR – Commission for Social Justice (£200,000); Transparency International (£118,000); Community Energy Plus (£99,500); Demos (£20,000); Centre for Local Economic Strategies, Michael Jacobs – Rethinking Capitalism (£6,000 each).

Exclusions

The foundation's website states that the foundation will not fund:

- Individual or sole trader applicants
- Organisations applying on behalf of another. We require applicants to be legally independent organisations with the managerial and governance structures to contract with us for support
- Work outside the UK, unless there is a clear link to activity or benefit to people or institutions in the UK
- Work that is to benefit a narrow group of beneficiaries or which cannot be shared
- Activities to promote a specific political party
- Activity that has already happened
- General appeals

Applications

Applicants are directed to the foundation's website where details of current funding programmes, eligibility criteria, guidelines and the two-stage application process are posted.

Sources of information

Accounts; annual report; Charity Commission record; funder's website.

The Patrick and Helena Frost Foundation

🔍 General charitable purposes

📍 UK

£ £542,500 (2016/17)

CC number: 1005505

Trustees: Luke Valner; Dominic Tayler; Neil Hendriksen.

Correspondent: Neil Hendriksen, Trustee, c/o Trowers & Hamlins LLP, 3 Bunhill Row, London EC1Y 8YZ (email: asorrell@trowers.com)

The Patrick and Helena Frost Foundation was registered in 1991 to make general welfare grants to organisations as well as grants to help smaller charities that rely on a considerable amount of self-help and voluntary effort. Grants typically range between £2,500 and £15,000.

Financial information

In 2016/17 the foundation had assets of £21 million and an income of £629,500. There were 57 grants made to organisations totalling £542,500.

Beneficiaries included: Prostate Cancer UK (£15,000); Action on Addiction, Alexandra Rose Charity, Exeter Royal Academy for Deaf Education, Fauna and Flora International and Royal Trinity Hospice (£10,000 each); Acorn Christian Foundation (£5,000); The Outward Bound Trust (£2,500).

Exclusions

No grants are given to individuals.

Applications

The 2016/17 annual report notes the following: 'the Trustees of the Foundation proactively seek and select organisations to which they wish to award grants. The Trustees kindly request that unsolicited applications are not submitted as, regretfully, they will not be considered or responded to.'

Sources of information

Accounts; annual report; Charity Commission record.

The Fulmer Charitable Trust

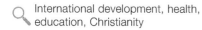 International development, health, education, Christianity

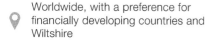 Worldwide, with a preference for financially developing countries and Wiltshire

£ £367,500 (2016)

CC number: 1070428

Trustees: Caroline Mytum; John Reis; Sally Reis; Revd Philip Bromiley.

Correspondent: John Reis, Trustee, Estate Office, Street Farm, Compton Bassett, Calne, Wiltshire SN11 8RH (tel: 01249 760410)

The Fulmer Charitable Trust was registered with the Charity Commission in 1998. The trust mostly supports organisations in the financially developing world, but also gives to UK charities, especially those working in Wiltshire. The following was taken from the trust's 2016/17 accounts:

The Settlor expressed his wish that available income should be distributed under the following 'Heads of Charity' and broadly in the proportions indicated:

- Relief of suffering hardship – 70%
- Advancement of education – 10%
- Advancement of religion – 10%
- Other charitable purposes for the benefit of the community – 10%

Financial information

In 2016/17 the trust had assets of £13.6 million and an income of £453,000. Grants awarded to organisations totalled £367,500.

Beneficiaries included: Concern Worldwide (£2,000); Action for Blind People; Action on Poverty, Alzheimer's Support Cancer Research, Chosen People Ministries, Cruse Bereavement Care, Hands Around the World and Institute for Bible Translation (£1,000 each).

Applications

Apply in writing to the correspondent.

Sources of information

Accounts; annual report; Charity Commission record.

The Funding Network

 General charitable purposes

 UK

 £494,500 (2016/17)

CC number: 1088315

Trustees: Adrian Coles; Simon Wheatley; Chrysanthy Pispinis; Michael Chuter; Robert Hewitt; Samuel Lush; Josh Babarinde.

Correspondent: Celine Gagnon, The Funding Network, 16 Lincoln's Inn Fields, London WC2A 3ED (tel: 0845 313 8449; email: info@ thefundingnetwork.org.uk)

🌐 www.thefundingnetwork.org.uk

📘 facebook.com/FundingNetwork

🐦 @FundingNetwork

The Funding Network is an open network which links donors to charitable causes and social entrepreneurs. In its 2016/17 accounts the trustees describe the charities aims as follows:

- Raise money for organisations creating social change
- Provide a public benefit by educating attendees at events about social change projects
- Encourage an increasing number of people to engage in active, intelligent philanthropy
- Help individuals make an impact by enabling them to combine their giving with others

TFN carries out its long-term objectives through hosting 'live crowdfunding' events for charitable causes and social entrepreneurs.

The charity invites non-profit organisations nominated by network members to apply for the opportunity to pitch for funds at its events. The funds raised are then passed onto the organisation by the network in the form of grants. The charity funds organisations covering a wide range of sectors, but its priorities include; crime reduction and peacebuilding, education, environment, health, human rights, inclusion and livelihoods.

Financial information

In 2016/17 the charity had assets of £244,000 and an income of £727,000. In total the charity awarded grants of £494,500.

Beneficiaries included: African Prisons Project (£24,500); Blackfordby College of Agriculture (£16,400); Refugee Support Europe (£14,400); Gravity Light Foundation (£10,600); Choir With No Name (£9,200); Bags of Taste (£8,900); The White Helmets (£7,700).

Exclusions

According to its website, the charity does not support any of the following:

- The promotion of any religion
- Organisations that are affiliated with a political party
- Individuals
- Fundraising challenges
- Organisations with a turnover of over £1.2 million

Applications

To pitch at an event, organisations must be sponsored by a Funding Network member. The charity does not share the details of its current members, however organisations that do not know a current network member can ask somebody to become a member with a view to nominating them. This could be a trustee, volunteer or someone close to the organisation, but it cannot be somebody who is in paid employment of the organisation. Once they have signed up, new members are asked to attend and donate at a network event before being eligible to sponsor an organisation.

Sources of information

Accounts; annual report; Charity Commission record; funder's website.

The Gale Family Charity Trust

 Churches, general charitable purposes

 UK, with a preference for Bedfordshire

£ £261,000 (2016/17)

CC number: 289212

Trustees: Doreen Watson; John Tyley; Warwick Browning; Russell Beard; David Fletcher; Gerry Garner; Alison Phillipson.

Correspondent: Alistair Law, Northwood House, 138 Bromham Road, Bedford MK40 2QW (tel: 01234 354508; email: galefamilytrust@gmail.com)

This trust was founded in 1984 by Horace and Marjorie Gale. According its 2016/17 accounts the main object of the trust is: 'to apply funds to charitable causes, both locally for the benefit of the community, and to larger organisations with links across the UK. Funds are also donated to local churches to further their work.'

Financial information

In 2016/17 the trust held assets of £6.6 million and had an income of £120,500 Grants were made totalling £261,000 but a list of beneficiaries was not available.

Previous beneficiaries have included: ABF Soldiers Charity; Bedford Day Care Hospice; Bedford Garden Carers, Bunyan Meeting Free Church; Cople Lower School; Happy Days; Pavenham Cricket

Club; Relate – Bedford; St John's Hospice – Moggerhanger; St Paul's Church – Bedford.

Applications

Apply in writing to the correspondent. The trustees meet every six months to award grants.

Sources of information

Accounts; annual report; Charity Commission record.

The Gannochy Trust

 Young people, social welfare

 Scotland, with a preference for the Perth and Kinross area

£3 million (2016/17)

OSCR number: SC003133

Trustees: Dr James Kynaston; Ian Macmillan; Jane Mudd; David Gray; Stephen Hay; Bruce Renfrew; Roland Bean.

Correspondent: Fiona Russell, Grants Manager, Kincarrathie House Drive, Pitcullen Crescent, Perth PH2 7HX (tel: 01738 620653; fax: 01738 440827; email: admin@gannochytrust.org.uk)

 www.gannochytrust.org.uk

The Gannochy Trust was founded in 1937 by Arthur Kinmond Bell, a whisky distiller and philanthropist, for charitable and public purposes for the benefit of the community of Perth and its immediate environs as a direct result of his family's successful whisky distilling business. The trust is also responsible for the management of the model housing estate built by Bell.

The trust's website states:

A K Bell's philanthropy has been developed into one of the more substantial grant-making trusts in Scotland. Originally, the trust contributed to worthy charitable causes solely within Perth and its immediate environs. In 1967 a Scheme of Alterations was approved by the Court of Session to expand its grant-making footprint to the whole of Scotland, but with a preference for Perth and its environs. The trust has made significant contributions to a wide variety of projects across Scotland over many years, ranging from major national flagship projects to smaller, but nonetheless important, community projects.

In July 2015 the trust released a new grant-making strategy for 2015 to 2018 which is focused on the following themes:

▶ **Inspiring Young People across Scotland** – revenue funding for activities that raise the aspirations of young people by developing their talents and skills, increasing their

employability and encouraging active citizenship

▶ **Improving the Quality of Life within Perth and Kinross** – capital and revenue funding for a general charitable purposes, with a preference for supporting disadvantaged and vulnerable people and the local community

The trust continues to make grants through its Capital Projects scheme, but this is strictly limited to the Perth and Kinross area. Only OSCR-registered charities can apply and there is a preference for smaller, community-led groups.

Financial information

In 2016/17 the trust held assets of almost £186 million and had an income of £6 million. Grants awarded to organisations totalled £3 million.

Beneficiaries of grants over £40,000 included: Perth and Kinross Council (£1.5 million); Perth and Kinrosss Country Trust (£145,000); Dundee Museums Foundation (£125,000); Perth Festival of the Arts (£75,000); Perth Methodist Church (£40,000).

Exclusions

The following are not supported:

▶ General appeals
▶ Endowment funds
▶ Statutory bodies
▶ Work benefitting people outside Scotland
▶ Work that has already taken place
▶ Individuals (and organisations applying on their behalf)
▶ Organisations with more than 12 months operating costs within their free or designated reserves
▶ Grant-making charities (unless the project has been initiated by the trust)
▶ Hospitals and health authorities; medical care, medical research or general medical equipment; palliative care (except within Perth and Kinross which should be about enhancing and not providing core care)
▶ Universities, colleges, schools, student bodies, student unions and the independent education sector (unless the project has been initiated by the trust)
▶ Academic research
▶ Pre-school groups, play schemes, after-school clubs and PTAs
▶ Personal study, travel or for expeditions, whether in the UK or abroad
▶ Animal welfare
▶ The promotion of religion
▶ Projects that are solely for the restoration or conservation of places of worship
▶ General holidays

▶ Waste disposal/landfill, pollution control and renewable energy products
▶ Political or lobbying purposes
▶ One-off events/festivals/conferences which have no element of broader community engagement
▶ Feasibility studies (unless the project has been initiated by the trust)
▶ Minibuses

Applications

There are a number of documents that applicants must complete, including an application form. These are available to download from the website, where detailed guidance notes can also be found.

According to its website the trust will be launching a new grant-making strategy in November 2018. The current strategy will run until the end of 2018.

Sources of information

Accounts; annual report; OSCR record; funder's website.

The Gatsby Charitable Foundation

 Plant science, neuroscience, technical education, Africa, public policy, the arts, general charitable purposes

 Unrestricted

£36.3 million (2016/17)

CC number: 251988

Trustees: Joseph Burns; Sir Andrew Cahn; Judith Portrait.

Correspondent: Robert Bell, Head of the Sainsbury Family Charitable Trusts, The Peak, 5 Wilton Road, London SW1V 1AP (tel: 020 7410 0330; email: contact@gatsby.org.uk)

 www.gatsby.org.uk

Established in 1967 by David Sainsbury, this is one of the Sainsbury Family Charitable Trusts (SFCT).

Areas of work

As the foundation's website explains, 'Gatsby works in areas that David Sainsbury and the Trustees are particularly passionate about and where they believe charitable funding can make a real difference.' Currently, the foundation is active in the following areas, which are outlined in the 2016/17 annual report.

▶ **Plant science:** 'to develop basic research in fundamental processes of plant growth and development and molecular plant pathology, and to encourage researchers in the field of plant science in the UK'.

- **Neuroscience:** 'to support world-class research in the area of neural circuits and behaviour, and theoretical neuroscience; and to support activities which enhance our understanding in these fields'.
- **Technical education:** 'to strengthen science and engineering skills in the UK by developing and enabling innovative programmes and informing national policy'.
- **Africa:** 'to promote economic development in East Africa that benefits the poor through support to the growth and sustainability of key sectors'.
- **Public policy:** 'to support: the Institute for Government as an independent institute available to politicians and the civil service, focused on making government more effective; and the Centre for Cities, which provides practical research and policy advice that helps cities understand how they can succeed economically'.
- **The arts:** 'to support the fabric and programming of institutions with which Gatsby's founding family has connections'.

The trustees occasionally support other charitable work which falls outside their main fields of interest. The trustees do not make grants in response to unsolicited applications or to individuals.

Financial information

In 2016/17 the foundation held assets of £396.8 million and had an income of £69.9 million. Grants payable for the year totalled £36.3 million.

Beneficiaries included: University of Cambridge (£9.05 million); Gatsby Africa (£5 million); Centre for Cities (£800,000); Chamber Orchestra of Europe (£500,000); Columbia University (£250,000); Engineering UK (£50,000); STEM Learning Ltd (£5,500).

Exclusions

No grants are made to individuals.

Applications

The trustees take a proactive approach to grant-making; generally, unsolicited applications are not considered. The annual report for 2016/17 explains that 'rather than awaiting proposals from third parties, Gatsby identifies areas for action and builds hypotheses for action which can then be tested in the field. Where successful, these can then be scaled up and rolled-out.'

Sources of information

Accounts; annual report; Charity Commission record; funder's website.

Gatwick Airport Community Trust

Children and young people, art, sports facilities, environment and conservation, community facilities, people with disabilities, older people, development of volunteering

Parts of East and West Sussex, Surrey and Kent but particularly communities directly affected by operations at Gatwick Airport. A map of the area of benefit can be seen on the website

£192,500 (2016)

CC number: 1089683

Trustees: Richard Burrett; Michael Roberts; Brian Quinn; John Kendall; Julie Ayres; Joanna Rettie; Alan Jones; Graham Knight; Christopher Townsend.

Correspondent: The Trustees, c/o Kreston Reeves, Springfield House, Springfield Road, Horsham, West Sussex RH12 2RG (tel: 07444 737518; email: mail@gact.org.uk)

 www.gact.org.uk

Established in 2002, the trust is an independent charity set up by legal agreement between West Sussex County Council, Crawley Borough Council and Gatwick Airport Ltd.

The following was taken from the trust's website:

Grants are currently awarded annually for such charitable purposes as the trustees determine within the area of benefit which covers parts of East and West Sussex, Surrey and Kent. They adopt strict criteria and channel funds for deserving projects, particularly in those areas where people are directly affected by operations at Gatwick Airport.

The normal level of grants is from £1,000 to £5,000. Occasional larger grants may be considered if the impact is targeted to benefit a significant number of people and is considered to make a valuable and noticeable difference longer term.

Priority categories for the trust when assessing a project are set out below:

- Development of young people
- Art projects including amateur drama, music, art
- Sporting facilities
- Environmental improvement and conservation
- Improvements to community facilities such as village halls
- Support for the disabled
- Support for the elderly
- Encouragement of additional volunteering or giving in the area

Financial information

In 2016 the trust had assets of £7,900 and an income of £206,500. Grants to 141 organisations totalled £192,500 and were broken down as follows:

Community and community facilities	£49,000
Sports and recreation	£37,500
People with disabilities; disadvantaged people	£34,500
Young adults	£20,500
Young children	£17,500
Arts, theatre and music	£16,000
Environmental	£9,100
Older people	£8,500

Beneficiaries included: Charlswood Parish Council (£10,000); YMCA East Surrey (£5,000); Charles Maw Trust (£3,000); Ewhurst Infant School (£2,500); Ifield Quaker Meeting (£2,000); Children's Safety Education Foundation (£1,500); 1st Hedgecourt Scouts (£1,300); Domestic Abuse Volunteer Support Services (£1,000); St Catherine's Hospice (£790); Hayward's Heath Horticultural Society (£200).

Exclusions

According to the trust's website it will not support the following:

- Projects or beneficiaries that are completely or largely outside the area of benefit
- Recurrent expenditure or running costs
- Ongoing costs, maintenance or deficits
- Repeat annual applications for similar projects
- Costs that should be funded from other sources e.g. public bodies
- Applications from organisations that have statutory responsibilities such as local authorities, hospitals, schools, unless it is a project that is over and above their core activities
- The purchase of land or buildings
- Organisations that are working to make a profit for shareholders, partners or sole owners, nor to individuals
- Individuals
- Grants will not normally be made to organisations with excess 'free' reserves
- Salaries

Applications

Application forms can be downloaded from the trust's website. Applications are invited once a year, usually between January and March. Grants are paid by the end of May. Further information can be found on the trust's website. Telephone enquiries are welcomed.

Sources of information

Accounts; annual report; Charity Commission record; funder's website.

The Robert Gavron Charitable Trust

 Health and welfare, human rights and prison reform, arts and arts education, sports and education, social policy and research

UK

£619,500 (2016/17)

CC number: 268535

Trustees: Sarah Gavron; Charles Corman; Jessica Gavron; Lady Katharine Gavron.

Correspondent: Anthony Dance, 44 Eagle Street, London WC1R 4FS (tel: 020 7400 4255; email: office@rgct.org.uk)

The trust was established in 1974 by Lord Gavron, to support general charitable purposes. At present, the trust's main focus is funding charities and organisations who support the arts; education; social policy and research; and people with disabilities. To a lesser extent, the trust also provides funding for prison reform and human rights. Grants can be provided in one-off circumstances or committed over a number of years.

The trustees prefer to make grants to organisations whose work they personally know and admire. This does not, however, mean that charities unknown to the trustees personally do not receive grants. A number of grants are made to new organisations during each financial year. These include small charities working in areas which cannot easily raise funds and which are without the resources themselves for professional fundraising.

Financial information

In 2016/17 the trust held assets of £8.7 million and had an income of £178,000. During the year, the trust awarded 39 grants to organisations totalling around £619,500.

Beneficiaries included: Mairie De Ménerbes (£84,000); Arab Israel Children's Tennis Charity (£76,000); Barbados Cricket Association (£49,000); KeepOut Crime Diversion Scheme (£20,000); National Film and Television Scheme (£15,000); Durham University Scholarship Fees (£9,000); Heart n Soul (£5,000); Holocaust Educational Trust and The Longford Trust (£3,000 each).

Applications

Apply in writing to the correspondent. The trustees meet formally approximately four times throughout the year.

Sources of information

Accounts; annual report; Charity Commission record.

Sir Robert Geffery's Almshouse Trust

 Education for children and young people, arts, communities

UK

£173,000 (2016/17)

CC number: 219153

Trustee: The Ironmongers' Trust Company.

Correspondent: Helen Sant, Charities Manager, Ironmongers' Hall, Barbican, London EC2Y 8AA (tel: 020 7776 2311; email: helen@ironmongers.org)

 www.ironmongers.org

The history of the trust dates back to the 1700s when a member of the company left a substantial endowment for almshouses in East London. The trust's website states:

> Sir Robert Geffery was twice Master of the Company and was Lord Mayor of London in 1685. Born in the village of Landrake in Cornwall, he died in London in 1704 having made his fortune in overseas trade. He left a substantial endowment for almshouses which were built in Shoreditch, east London. These were sold in 1910 to London County Council and now house the Geffery Museum. The Company then built new almshouses at Mottingham in Kent, which in turn were sold, in 1972, to the Greater London Council.
>
> Today the Trust owns two almshouses in Hampshire, one at Hook built in 1976 and enlarged in 1987 and one at Basingstoke which was opened in 1984. These provide sheltered housing for 125 retired people of limited means. There are resident Wardens at both Homes, with the overall management carried out from Ironmongers' Hall.
>
> Grants are made by the Trust for relief in need, focusing on educational projects for children and young people in disadvantaged areas. A bursary is given to support a student at the City of London School for Girls.

Financial information

According to the annual report 2016/17: 'The Ironmongers' Trust Company is the Trustee of five other charities ('the linked charities') linked to Sir Robert Geffery's Almshouse Trust by a uniting direction, made by the Charity Commission, dated 19 March 2012'. Refer to the trustees' annual report and accounts for full accounting details of the trust and its linked charities.

In 2016/17 the trust and its linked charities had assets of almost £29 million and an income of £2.1 million. Grants were made by Sir Robert Geffery's Almshouse Trust totalling £173,000. The total given in grants from the trust and its linked charities was £534,500.

Beneficiaries included: MakeBelieve Arts (£27,000); Lyric Hammersmith and St Vincent's Family Project (£25,000 each); Emergency Exit Arts (£10,000); BF Adventure (£9,600); Pompey in the Community (£6,600); The Island Trust (£5,000); The Change Foundation (£4,000); Reading Repertory Theatre (£3,800); Children North East (£3,600); Rainy Day Trust (£2,000); Hartfield Memorial Lecture (£500).

Exclusions

For full details of the trust and its linked charities' exclusions, visit the Ironmongers' website.

Applications

Refer to full details given on the Ironmongers' website.

Sources of information

Accounts; annual report; Charity Commission record; funder's website.

The Generations Foundation

 Health, family support, environment, education, hospices, overseas aid, children, people with disabilities

UK, Merton and overseas

£263,000 (2016/17)

CC number: 1110565

Trustees: Bob Finch; Stephen Finch; Rohini Finch.

Correspondent: Alison Bishop, 36 Marryat Road, Wimbledon, London SW19 5BD (tel: 020 3542 6255; email: pa@taliscapital.com)

 www.generationsct.co.uk

The foundation's website provides a useful overview of its activities:

> Generations Charitable Foundation was set up in July 2005 by the Finch Family. The foundation is funded by the family and aims to provide a better quality of life for children who need it the most; those who are disabled, disadvantaged, or struggle with ill health. The foundation supports local causes in the Borough of Merton where the family is resident and also works abroad in developing countries. The trust also supports projects for environmental protection and conservation; the central aim being to leave a gift for future generations.

Financial information

In 2016/17 the foundation held assets of £300 and had an income of £62,500.

Grants awarded to organisations totalled £263,000.

Beneficiaries included: World Land Trust (£56,000); Cure International UK (£30,000); Regenerate (£25,000); Daisy Garland (£10,000); Epiphany Trust and Partnership for Children (£5,000 each); Cancer Research UK, Charitable Staff Foundation and Diamond Centre (£500 each).

Applications

Application forms are available to download from the website. They should be returned to the foundation by email (not post), along with your organisation's latest set of accounts. The website instructs applicants to first email or telephone the foundation to ensure their request for funding is likely to be successful.

Sources of information

Accounts; annual report; Charity Commission record; funder's website.

The GC Gibson Charitable Trust

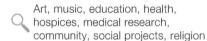

Art, music, education, health, hospices, medical research, community, social projects, religion

Worldwide

£496,000 (2016/17)

CC number: 258710

Trustees: Anna Dalrymple; Martin Gibson; Jane Gibson; Lucy Kelly; Edward Gibson; Thomas Richards Homfray.

Correspondent: Martin Gibson, Trustee, Durnsford Mill House, Mildenhall, Marlborough, Wiltshire SN8 2NG (tel: 07773 067014; email: enquiries@gcgct. org)

 www.gcgct.org

This trust was established in 1969 by GC Gibson for general charitable purposes. Grants mainly fall within the following categories: art, music and education; health, hospices and medical research; community and other social projects; and religion.

Support is given to around 200 charities each year. Applicants must be UK-registered charities but can operate anywhere in the world. The trustees prefer to support small and medium-sized charities and prioritise those they have worked with previously. However, a few new charities (typically around 10) that fall within a particular theme (which can change from year-to-year – see the website for the trustees' current area of focus) are supported each year.

Grants range between £1,000 and £10,000 and although the trustees will consider supporting capital projects, the trust's annual report for 2016/17 states

that 'the average donation of £3,000 is more suited for meeting the revenue commitments of an organisation'. Funding from the trust can be used for matched funding.

Financial information

In 2016/17 the trust held assets of £16.8 million and had an income of £656,000. Grants were made totalling £496,000 and distributed as follows:

Community and other social projects	£214,000
Health, hospices and medical research	£152,500
Art, music and education	£77,500
Religion	£52,000

A list of beneficiaries was not included in the annual report and accounts.

Exclusions

No grants are made individuals.

Applications

Applications can only be made using the online form on the trust's website. Applications are open from 1 August to around 20 August each year. Before applying, ensure you have read the up-to-date eligibility criteria on the trust's website. Applicants are usually notified of the trustees' decisions in September/ October. The trustees can be contacted by email only; they do not respond to or acknowledge letters.

Note: In previous years, the application round has closed early due to huge demand.

Sources of information

Accounts; annual report; Charity Commission record; funder's website.

The Simon Gibson Charitable Trust

General charitable purposes, with a preference for conservation, education, religious purposes, young people and older people

UK, with a preference for: Suffolk, Norfolk, Cambridgeshire, Glamorgan, Gwent, Monmouth, Powys, Carmarthen, Hertfordshire

£734,000 (2016/17)

CC number: 269501

Trustees: Bryan Marsh; George Gibson; Deborah Connor; John Homfray.

Correspondent: Bryan Marsh, Trustee, The Simon Gibson Charitable Trust, PO Box 203, Barry CF63 9FD (tel: 01446 781459; email: bryan.marsh@sgctrust. org.uk)

www.sgtrust.co.uk

The Simon Gibson Charitable Trust was set up by a settlement in 1975 by George Simon Cecil Gibson of Exning, Suffolk.

The trust's website states that it funds the following:

- Registered charities, as well as educational and religious organisations
- Local charities operating in Suffolk; Norfolk; Cambridgeshire; Glamorgan; Gwent; Monmouth; Powys; Carmarthen; Hertfordshire
- National charities, with a focus on the areas above
- Conservation charities

The trust has general charitable purposes, with a preference for organisations helping young people and older people, or those with conservational, educational or religious purposes. Grants range between £1,000 and £20,000, with most grants between £3,000 and £5,000, and can be given for both core costs and specific projects.

The website states that: 'Some of our support is provided to organisations that we have built up a relationship with over the years. However we do, each year, consider applications from new organisations that meet our criteria. If your application was unsuccessful we suggest that you wait for at least one year before trying again.'

Financial information

In 2016/16 the trust held assets of £19.5 million and had an income of £1.1 million. During the year, the trust awarded around £734,000 to organisations.

Beneficiaries included: Royal Welsh College of Music and Drama (£15,000); Ely Cathedral Appeal Fund, Insole Court and National Museum of Wales (£10,000 each); Army Benevolent Fund, Barnardo's, Flora and Fauna and Motor Neurone Disease Society (£5,000 each); Kidscape, Ronald Macdonald House Charities and Salvation Army (£3,000 each).

Exclusions

Grants are not awarded for:

- Local charities operating outside the areas specified above
- Individuals, or organisations applying on behalf of individuals
- Students seeking funding for educational or gap year projects
- Conferences, seminars and workshops
- Overseas charities, other than conservation charities or charities known to the trustees

Applications

Application forms are available to download from the website and should be returned to the trust by post. Only postal applications submitted between 1 January and 31 March are considered. The trustees meet to consider applications in spring each year.

Sources of information

Accounts; annual report; Charity Commission record; funder's website.

The Glass-House Trust

Environment, children and young people, social research, the arts

Throughout England and Wales

£576,000 (2016/17)

CC number: 1144990

Trustees: Alex Sainsbury; Judith Portrait; Elinor Sainsbury.

Correspondent: Robert Bell, Head of the Sainsbury Family Charitable Trusts, The Peak, 5 Wilton Road, London SW1V 1AP (tel: 020 7410 0330; email: info@sfct.org.uk)

www.sfct.org.uk

The trust was established in 2011 and is one of the Sainsbury Family Charitable Trusts. The Glass-House Trust concentrates on supporting a small number of projects, usually in the following areas:

- Built environment
- Child development
- Social policy
- Art

Grants are made to projects initiated by the trustees, or jointly by the trustees and the beneficiary, and to other projects which the trustees proactively seek out.

Financial information

In 2016/17 the trust had assets of £11.3 million and a total income of £251,000. Grants were made to six organisations and totalled £576,000.

Beneficiaries included: Raven Row (£350,000); Glass-House Community-Led Design (£100,000); A Space (£55,000 in two grants); Mayday Rooms (£50,000); Money for Madagascar (£20,000 in four grants); The Sainsbury Archive (£880).

Applications

Unsolicited applications are not accepted.

Sources of information

Accounts; annual report; Charity Commission record; funder's website.

The Gloag Foundation

Human trafficking, advancement of Christianity, relief of poverty, health, education

UK and overseas

£1.8 million to organisations (2016)

OSCR number: SC035799

Correspondent: The Trustees, Robertson House, 1 Whitefriars Crescent, Perth PH2 0PA (tel: 01738 633264; email: info@gloagfoundation.com)

www.gloagfoundation.org.uk

The foundation was established by Anne Gloag OBE and 'supports projects that prevent or relieve poverty and encourage the advancement of education, health and religion in the UK and overseas'.

Financial information

In 2016 the foundation held assets of £8.9 million and had an income of £2.8 million. Grants awarded to organisations totalled £1.8 million with a further £213,500 given to individuals.

Beneficiaries included: Freedom from Fistula Foundation (£1.1 million); The Balcraig Foundation (£235,000); Young Life (£131,000); Vine Trust (£29,000); Blythswood Care (£11,000); Nurses Reaching Out (£10,000); Church of Scotland (£4,000); Harper Community Initiative (£3,000); Refuge (£2,000); Befrienders Highland (£1,500); Kidz Klub Leeds, Peebles Youth Trust and Signpost International (£1,000 each).

New grants to charities totalled £929,000 and were broken down as follows:

Advancement of Christianity	£180,000
Health	£98,500
Others	£87,500
Relief of poverty	£28,000
Anti-human trafficking	£5,000

Applications

The following information has been taken from the foundation's website:

> Grants requests are reviewed throughout the year by the trustees. If you wish to request funding, please email info@gloagfoundation.com with no more than two pages of A4 which should include the following information:
>
> - The organisation – explaining its charitable aims and objectives
> - The project requiring funding – why it is needed, who will benefit and in what way
> - The funding – breakdown of costs, any money raised so far, and how the balance will be raised
>
> Further information will be requested if required so there is no need to send supporting books, brochures, DVDs, annual reports or accounts. There is no minimum or maximum grant and no deadlines or closing dates.
>
> All applications will receive a reply but we are unable to offer any feedback if an application is unsuccessful. Trustees meet quarterly.

Sources of information

Accounts; annual report; OSCR record; funder's website.

Global Charities

Children and young people

UK

£2.2 million (2016/17)

CC number: 1091657

Trustees: John McGeough; Gareth Andrews; Jonathan Norbury; Michael Connole; Joanne Kenrick; Sarah Homer; Ulrika Hogberg; Dr Justin Davis Smith.

Correspondent: Jonathan Beak, Secretary, 29–30 Leicester Square, London WC2H 7LA (tel: 0345 606 0990; email: grants@makesomenoise.com)

www.makesomenoise.com

facebook.com/globalsmakesomenoise

@makenoise

@globals_make_some_noise

Global Charities is the charitable arm of *Global*, the Media and Entertainment Group which operates some of the UK's largest and most well-known radio stations including, *Heart*, *Capital* and *Classic FM*. The charity's flagship grant-giving programme Global's Make Some Noise, raises money from Global Radio listeners, customers, and the entertainment and music industries, which the charity then distributes to support projects undertaken by small community charities, which will improve the lives of children and young people affected by disability, illness, or disadvantage in the UK.

All applicant charities must meet the following core criteria:

- Be a UK-registered charity
- Have an annual income of approximately £50,000 to £1.2 million
- Directly support children, young people and their families aged up to 25 in a community around the UK
- The children, young people and/or families supported are affected by illness, disability or lack of opportunity
- Be able to provide at least one year of filed accounts
- Be able to provide an up-to-date child protection and safeguarding policy for your charity
- Be able to identify a programme, service, role or capital project that Global's Make Some Noise programme could fund from April 2019 onwards

Financial information

In 2016/17 the charity has assets of £1.26 million and an income of £6.75 million. During the year, the charity awarded 34 grants totalling

£2.2 million. The grants were categorised as follows:

Disability	10	£601,000
Illness	6	£435,500
Lack of opportunity	6	£362,000
Mental health	5	£314,500
Bereavement	4	£278,000
Young carers	3	£218,000

Beneficiaries included: A-T Society; Cavernoma Alliance UK; Children's Liver Disease Foundation; Kids Aid; Sebastian's Action Trust; The Carer Centre for Brighton and Hove; The Lullaby Trust; Y Bont.

Exclusions

The charity does not fund any of the following:

- Activities that do not directly contribute to the welfare or development of children, young people and their families affected by illness, disability or lack of opportunity
- Local government or NHS bodies
- Projects which promote religion, politics or other activity that is not for wider public benefit
- Trips or projects abroad
- Corporate or business activity
- Individuals
- Other grant-makers or projects where funds are to be redirected to other organisations or individuals
- Projects where the grant expenditure is due to start before the grant award date (retrospective funding)

For further details on Global's Make Some Noise programme grants and full criteria visit the charity's website.

Applications

In its 2016/17 accounts the charity describes the key stages of its grant-making process as follows:

- Nomination through Global Radio's broadcast centres or expression of interest by prospective applicants on the Global Charities website
- Assessment against minimum eligibility criteria by Global Charities' staff and subsequent short-listing of prospective applicants
- Shortlist invited to apply within stated time frame
- Submission of application forms by those shortlisted. Rejection of all those not short-listed, unless the trustees or delegated Grants Panel wish to review them
- Review and assessment of application forms by independent grants panel in line with approved grant-making criteria and risk management
- Recommendations by Grants Panel are submitted to the board of trustees for ratification

If an application is successful, Global will promote and advertise the charity to raise their profile and awareness for the

project. Successful applicants will thus be required to provide:

- A case study of one or more of the young people they support
- Photographs of the young people they support and photos of their current work and projects
- Site visits to the project/charity
- Interview opportunities with staff members
- Interview opportunities young people and their families

Visit www.makesomenoise.com/whowehelp for further details.

Sources of information

Accounts; annual report; Charity Commission record; funder's website.

The Golden Bottle Trust

 General charitable purposes with a preference for the environment, health, education, religion, the arts and financially developing countries

Worldwide

£1.6 million (2015/16)

CC number: 327026

Trustee: Hoare Trustees.

Correspondent: Messrs Hoare Trustees, C. Hoare & Co., 37 Fleet Street, London EC4P 4DQ (tel: 020 7353 4522)

The trust was established in 1985 for general charitable purposes, by C Hoare and Co. bankers, the oldest remaining private bank in the UK. The trust is managed by the company, Hoare Trustees, and continues to receive most of its income from C Hoare and Co.

The objective of the trust is the continuation of the philanthropic commitments and ideals of the Hoare family. Traditionally the trust has supported causes including the arts, religion, environment, health, education, the developing world and also many charities with whom the Hoare family is familiar.

Grants range from £250 to £10,000 with larger amounts occasionally being granted, usually to the same charities that the Hoare family has funded regularly.

In addition to grant-making, the trust has invested in a number of PRIs (Programme Related Investments) in the UK and the developing world. In 2015/16 the trust made one new PRI to Big Issue Invest for £100,000.

Financial information

In 2015/16 the trust held assets of £11.9 million and had an income of £2.8 million. Grants were made totalling £1.6 million, which does not include £175,500 given by the trust to match staff fundraising.

Beneficiaries (receiving £10,000 or more) included: The Bulldog Trust (£300,000); Intermission Youth St Saviour's (£60,000); Future for Religious Heritage (£31,000); The Access Project (£20,000); Migratory Salmon Foundation (£15,000); Dawlish Garden Trust (£14,000); Royal Academy of Arts and Westminster Abbey Foundation (£12,000 each); BAT Conservation Trust, Contact a Family, Developing Artists and Royal Marsden Cancer Charity (£10,000 each).

Exclusions

No grants are given for individuals or organisations that are not registered charities.

Applications

The trust does not normally respond to unsolicited applications.

Sources of information

Accounts; annual report; Charity Commission record.

Goldman Sachs Gives (UK)

 Arts and culture, community, education, humanitarian relief, medical causes

Worldwide

£18.5 million (2016/17)

CC number: 1123956

Trustees: Jenny Evans; Robert Katz; Mike Housden; Peter Fahey.

Correspondent: Jenny Evans, Trustee, Peterborough Court, 133 Fleet Street, London EC4A 2BB (tel: 020 7774 1000)

Goldman Sachs Gives (UK) was established and registered with the Charity Commission in 2008. The income of the fund is made up of donations from affiliate and subsidiary companies of Goldman Sachs Group Inc., and also from past and present senior employees of these companies.

The charity's 2016/17 annual accounts state:

> The objects of the Fund are to promote for the public benefit the advancement of education, the relief of poverty, the advancement of religion and any other exclusively charitable purpose. In furtherance of those objects the Fund focuses on supporting charities and charitable activities that build and stabilise communities, increase educational opportunities, advance health, relieve poverty, promote the arts and culture, provide humanitarian relief and further any other charitable purposes.

Financial information

In 2016/17 the charity had assets of £93.4 million and an income of £23.2 million. A total of £18.5 million was awarded in 551 grants to institutions, broken down into the following areas of support:

Education	£7.9 million
Community	£3.1 million
Medical	£2.7 million
Humanitarian	£2.6 million
Arts and culture	£1.9 million
Other	£335,000

Beneficiaries included: Greenhouse Sports Ltd (£2.9 million); British Refugee Council (£1 million) New York University (£906,000); Grenada Schools Ltd (£750,000); Cancer Research UK (£688,500).

Applications

Applications can be made in writing to the correspondent. Please note that this is a donor-advised fund.

Sources of information

Accounts; annual report; Charity Commission record.

The Goldsmiths' Company Charity

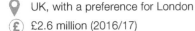 General charitable purposes, precious metal crafts

UK, with a preference for London

£2.6 million (2016/17)

CC number: 1175593

Trustees: Mark Bridges; Timothy Schroder; Martin Drury; Edward Harley; Rupert Hambro; Thomas Fattorini; Richard Agutter; George Macdonald; Dr Charles Mackworth-Young; William Parente; Michael Prideaux; Edward Braham; Victoria Broackes; Judith Cobham-Lowe; Richard Fox; Joanna Hardy; Arthur Drysdale; Lynne Brindley; Neil Carson; Arthur Johnstone Galsworthy; Jane Goad; Hector Miller; Michael Wainwright; Brig Butler; Richard Madeley.

Correspondent: The Grants Manager, Goldsmiths' Hall, 13 Foster Lane, London EC2V 6BN (tel: 020 7606 7010; email: grants@thegoldsmiths.co.uk)

 www.thegoldsmiths.co.uk/charities

 @GoldsmithsCo

The Goldsmiths' Company Charity was created following the amalgamation of 57 separate trust funds which had been built up over the centuries within the Goldsmiths' Company. Today, the charity supports a wide range of causes including, general welfare, culture and crafts, people with disabilities, and education.

Grant programmes

The following causes are supported by the charity's small grants (up to £5,000) programme:

- General welfare (including homelessness, prisoners and substance misusers)
- Culture
- Medical/people with disabilities

Large grants (up to a maximum of £30,000) are awarded to charities working in the following areas:

- Disadvantaged young people, specifically young people leaving care, young carers, young people with mental health issues, and young people suffering from homelessness (affiliated members of London Youth may be considered under the small grants category)
- The rehabilitation/resettlement of prisoners, particularly prisoner education and training, through-the-gate mentoring, employment opportunities, arts and music, women in prison, and support for prisoners' families
- Charities working to combat isolation and loneliness among older people anywhere in the UK

The charity also supports organisations working to support the goldsmiths' craft and activities previously carried out by the Goldsmiths Art Trust Fund (GATF).

Furthermore, the Goldsmiths' Company also sponsors a number of educational initiatives. These are typically directed towards primary and secondary education, science, literacy and numeracy programmes. Full details of all the charity's current education programme can be found on the website.

The company regularly reviews its grant-making policy and will update guidance on its website as necessary. As such, organisations are advised to check the website regularly for updates.

Financial information

In 2016/17 the charity held assets of £143.3 million and had an income of £13.2 million. Grants were made totalling £2.6 million including £1.1 million in support of the precious metal crafts. Grants were distributed as follows:

Support of the craft	£1.1 million
General welfare (including housing, prisoners and substance misuse)	£517,500
Education	£309,500
Youth	£307,500
Medical, welfare and people with disabilities	£141,500
Culture	£107,500
Church	£68,000

Beneficiaries included: Guildhall School of Music and Drama (£25,000); St Christopher's Hospice (£3,300); Barnet Education Arts Trust, British

Liver Trust and Hackney Migrant Centre (£3,000 each); Abbey Community Centre (£2,200); Goldsmiths and Prideaux Place Tenants Association (£500).

Exclusions

Applications are not accepted from any of the following:

- Individuals
- Overseas charities and projects taking place and/or benefiting people outside the UK
- Medical research
- Animal welfare
- Individual housing associations and tenant organisations
- Endowment schemes
- Individual churches, for maintenance of the fabric
- Individual hospices
- Individual schools or supporting associations
- Play schemes, nurseries or pre-school facilities
- Local authorities, or work usually considered a statutory responsibility
- Major building projects, or capital funding
- One-off events (such as festivals, conferences, exhibitions and community events)
- Overseas projects or trips
- Campaigning or lobbying projects, or general awareness raising work
- Membership organisations

Further programme specific exclusions may also apply. See the guidelines on the charity's website for full details.

Applications

According to its website, The Goldsmiths' Charity operates a three stage application process for large grants:

> The first stage will require an initial enquiry (phone call or email), to be made to the Grants Manager directly. The second stage will be an outline grant proposal and ideally a face-to face meeting to discuss the proposal, and the third – if judged appropriate – will result in the submission of a full application which will be assessed by the main grants committee.

Applications for larger grants are considered on the first Wednesday of February, April, July, October and December. Full applications should be received a month prior to these meetings, having already gone through stages 1 and 2.

Sources of information

Accounts; annual report; Charity Commission record; funder's website.

The Goodman Foundation

 General charitable purposes, overseas, social welfare, older people, health, disability

 UK and overseas

(£) £568,000 (2016/17)

CC number: 1097231

Trustees: Laurence Goodman; Catherine Goodman; Philip Morgan.

Correspondent: The Trustees, c/o ABP, Unit 6290, Bishops Court, Solihull Parkway, Birmingham Business Park, Birmingham B37 7YB

This foundation was registered in April 2003 for general charitable purposes by Irish businessman Larry Goodman. The objects of the foundation are:

▶ To help people on low incomes, older people and those with disabilities or ill health
▶ To support other general charitable purposes

Financial information

In 2016/17 the foundation held assets of £46.4 million and had a total income of £6.1 million. Grants were made to 39 organisations totalling £568,000 and were distributed as follows:

Poverty, older people and people with disabilities	22	£272,500
Other	12	£248,000
Overseas and disasters	4	£34,000
Children's charities	1	£12,000

A list of beneficiaries was not included in the accounts.

Applications

Apply in writing to the correspondent.

Sources of information

Accounts; annual report; Charity Commission record.

The Mike Gooley Trailfinders Charity

 Medical research, young people, armed forces

 UK

(£) £7.9 million (2016/17)

CC number: 1048993

Trustees: Mark Bannister; Tristan Gooley; Michael Gooley; Bernadette Gooley; Fiona Gooley.

Correspondent: Michael Gooley, Trustee, 9 Abingdon Road, London W8 6AH (tel: 020 7938 3143)

 www.trailfinders.com

The charity was founded by Mike Gooley the Executive Chair of the travel

company Trailfinders Ltd. The charity was created in 1995 and, according to the 2016/17 annual report, supports:

▶ Medical research
▶ Community projects which encourage young people in outdoor activities
▶ Armed forces veteran organisations

Financial information

In 2016/17 the charity had assets of £12.2 million and an income of £11.2 million. Grants awarded to organisations totalled £7.9 million.

A list of beneficiaries for the year was not available.

Previous beneficiaries have included: Alzheimer's Society (£400,000); Prostate Cancer Charity (£100,000); The Second World War Experience Centre (£40,000).

Exclusions

The charity does not make grants to overseas charities or individuals.

Applications

Apply in writing to the correspondent.

Sources of information

Accounts; annual report; Charity Commission record.

The Goshen Trust

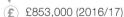 Christian projects

 England and Wales

(£) £853,000 (2016/17)

CC number: 1119064

Trustees: Jonathan Dicken; Alison Dicken; Pauline Dicken; Albert Dicken.

Correspondent: Robert Goodrum, Unit 2B, Guisley Way, Durham Industrial Park, Eaglescliffe, Stockton-on-Tees TS16 0RF (tel: 01642 790320; email: b.goodrum@masadadevelopments.co.uk)

The trust has general charitable purposes but also encourages and develops Christian projects which otherwise would not be able to reach an effective operational conclusion.

Financial information

In 2016/17 the trust held assets of £10.2 million and had an income of £456,500. Grants were made to 36 organisations totalling £853,000.

Beneficiaries included: Trans4M International (£121,000); Hope Project (£100,000); Reach Out Ministries (£62,000); Caring for Life (£46,000); Christian Institute (£30,000); Hexham Community Church (£20,000); Glasshouse Media (£7,000); Teenage Cancer Trust (£1,500); Castleton Cricket Club (£200).

Applications

Apply in writing to the correspondent.

Sources of information

Accounts; annual report; Charity Commission record.

The Gosling Foundation Ltd

 Relief of poverty, education, religion, naval and Service charities, general charitable purposes

 UK

(£) £5.1 million (2016/17)

CC number: 326840

Trustees: Hon. Vice Admiral Sir Donald Gosling; Hon. Capt. Adam Gosling.

Correspondent: Anne Yusof, Secretary, 21 Bryanston Street, Marble Arch, London W1H 7PR (tel: 020 7495 5599; email: anne.yusof@conprop.co.uk)

The foundation was established in 1985 by Sir Donald Gosling, co-founder of NCP car parks and former seafarer. The foundation's endowment derives from his personal fortune and its objects are the relief of poverty, education, religion and general charitable purposes beneficial to the community. Grants are given each year to a wide range of charities, with naval and other Service-related charities receiving substantial support.

Financial information

In 2015/16 the foundation held assets of £109.8 million and had an income of £5.4 million. There were 170 grants made to 134 beneficiaries totalling £5.1 million. Grants were broken down as follows:

Other purposes beneficial to the community	110	£2.8 million
Relief of poverty	25	£1.4 million
Advancement of education	33	£804,000
Advancement of religion	2	£10,500

Beneficiaries included: White Ensign Association (£293,000 in seven grants); Duke of Edinburgh Award (£228,000 in four grants); Marine Society of Sea Cadets and Shooting Star Chase (£100,000 each); Outward Bound Trust (£50,000); HMS Heron CAF (£26,000 in six grants); Chiltern MS Centre (£25,000); Cleanup (£10,000 in three grants).

Applications

Apply in writing to the correspondent. The grant-making policies of the foundation currently are:

▶ Applications should fall within the objects of the charity
▶ There are no minimum or maximum limit for any grant
▶ All grants will be approved unanimously by the trustees

- The charity will continue to make grants to individuals only in exceptional circumstances

The trustees meet quarterly.

Sources of information
Accounts; annual report; Charity Commission record.

Grace Charitable Trust

 Christian causes, general charitable purposes, education, medical, social welfare

UK and overseas

£647,000 (2016/17)

CC number: 292984

Trustees: Eric Payne; G. Snaith; Robert Quayle; Mark Mitchell; Robert Wright; Angela Payne.

Correspondent: Eric Payne, Trustee, Swinford House, Nortons Lane, Great Barrow, Chester CH3 7JZ

Established in 1985, the trust makes grants for general charitable purposes but has a preference for Christian-based activities and education. Grants are only awarded to charities that are known to the trustees.

Financial information
In 2016/17 the trust held assets of £2.4 million and had an income of £854,000. There were grants made to organisations totalling £647,000 which were broken down as follows:

Christian	£400,500
Education	£221,500
Social and medical	£18,700
General charitable purposes	£6,600

A list of beneficiaries was not included in the annual report.

Previous beneficiaries have included: Alpha; Euro-evangelism; International Christian College and Q3 Academies Trust.

Applications
The 2016/17 annual report states: 'The trustees administer the trust and grants are made only to charities known to the settlors.'

Sources of information
Accounts; annual report; Charity Commission record.

The Grace Trust

 General charitable purposes, with a particular emphasis on: the care and Christian education of children and young people, alleviating poverty, humanitarian relief

Worldwide

£31 million (2015/16)

CC number: 257516

Trustees: Scribefort Ltd; Aller Brook Ltd.

Correspondent: Douglas Smart, Director, Chelwood House, Cox Lane, Chessington, Surrey KT9 1DN (tel: 020 3301 3806; fax: 020 3301 3807; email: enquiries@thegracetrust.org.uk)

www.thegracetrust.org.uk

The Grace Trust was set up in 1968 by Mr John Dallow using a large proportion of the proceeds from the sale of his manufacturing business. The trust's website describes how Mr Dallow used the trust:

> To assist worthy causes both in Britain and further afield. This included supporting children's education where taught under a Christian ethos, relief of poverty, helping the preaching of the Gospel throughout the world, aiding the ill, elderly and infirm and giving financial support to those providing vital aid at the scenes of natural disasters.

What the trust supports
The website states that the trust operates on a very broad scale, at both a European and an international level. Where it does not have the expertise to provide assistance directly, it supports charities working nationally and locally in order to further its wide aims and objectives. Charities supported by the trust include those involved in, for example:

- Non-statutory emergency services and medical relief
- Disaster relief
- Childcare
- Disability support
- Essential medical research

A special emphasis is placed on supporting the care and Christian education of children and young people. As part of this effort, the trust has supported Christian schools in Britain and Europe (particularly Plymouth Brethren Christian Church schools, run under the Focus Learning Trust umbrella), in addition to schools in Africa, South America and the Caribbean.

Financial information
In 2015/16 the trust had assets of £15.5 million and an income of £100.7 million. Grants were made

totalling £31 million, of which £30.5 million was awarded to a single beneficiary, Focus Learning Trust. Of the remaining amount, £285,500 was awarded to three other educational organisations, £80,000 was awarded to one organisation for the relief of poverty, and £104,000 was awarded to 46 organisations for a wide range of other charitable purposes.

Beneficiaries included: Focus Learning Trust (£30.5 million); Balmoral Education (£137,000); Central Hardship Relief Trust (£80,000); Great Western Air Ambulance (£6,000); Oxfam – Ethiopia Food Crisis (£5,000); Prostate Cancer UK (£2,500); Redbridge Carers Support (£1,000); Clothing Solutions and Zoë's Place Baby Hospice (£500 each).

Applications
The annual report for 2015/16 states:

> The trustees recognise the importance of being outward looking and of making grants to a wide range of charities in order to demonstrate public benefit. The independent Grant Making Committee is encouraged to make grants in accordance with the criteria set out above under 'Objects of the Trust' but also to give due consideration to any applications for grants from charities. The usual checks are made to ensure that charities to whom grants are made are well run, financially sound; that their fundraising and administration costs are proportionate and moderate, and who therefore maximise the percentage of funds received that are actually applied to the relevant charitable purpose.

Sources of information
Accounts; annual report; Charity Commission record; funder's website.

The Granada Foundation

 Fine arts, recreation and leisure, education, science

North West England and parts of North Wales

£157,500 (2016/17)

CC number: 241693

Trustees: Sir Robert Scott; Philip Ramsbottom; Prof. Jennifer Latto; Virginia Tandy.

Correspondent: Irene Langford, Administrator, PO Box 3430, Chester CH1 9BZ (tel: 01244 661867; email: irene.langford@btconnect.com)

www.granadafoundation.org

The Northern Arts and Sciences Foundation was established in 1965 to encourage the study and appreciation of the fine arts and sciences and to promote education, with a particular interest in activity in the north west of England and parts of North Wales. In 1972, the name was changed to The Granada Foundation.

What the foundation funds
The foundation's 2016/17 annual report describes its charitable purposes as follows:

- 'To encourage and promote the study, practice and appreciation of the fine arts and the methods and means of their dissemination'
- 'To encourage and promote the study and application of the sciences'
- 'To promote and advance education'
- 'To provide or assist in the provision of facilities for recreation or other leisure time occupation in the interests of social welfare'

At the time of writing (June 2018) the foundation's new website was under construction; however, the 2016/17 annual report explains that the trustees 'look for imaginative proposals from organisations which will in some way make the North West a culturally richer and more attractive place in which to live and work. There is a clear preference for new projects.' Support can be given for festivals and other annual events, although such support is not automatically renewed.

Financial information
In 2016/17 the foundation held assets of £3.4 million and had an income of £35,500. Grants were made to 36 organisations and totalled £157,500. They were distributed as follows:

Appreciation of the fine arts	14	£79,500
Recreation and leisure time occupation	14	£59,500
Promotion of education	7	£16,500
Study and application of the sciences	1	£2,000

Beneficiaries included: Unity Theatre (£30,000); Blackpool Museum Trust (£20,000); Granby Four Streets Community Land Trust (£10,000); Glossop Music Festival (£3,000); Manchester Histories (£1,500); National Black Arts Alliance (£1,000).

Exclusions
Grants are not made for: general appeals; individuals; courses of study; expeditions; overseas travel; or youth clubs/community associations.

Applications
In the first instance, organisations wishing to apply should email brief details to the correspondent. If the project meet the foundation's funding criteria, a full application pack will be sent out by email.

Sources of information
Accounts; annual report; Charity Commission record; funder's website.

The Grant Foundation

 General charitable purposes, advancement of the Christian faith, education and welfare of children and young people

UK and overseas

£356,500 (2016)

CC number: 1084915

Trustees: Catherine Grant; Duncan Grant; Stuart Grant; Gary Grant; Anna Warner-McLoughlin; Alastair Grant.

Correspondent: The Trustees, The Entertainer, Boughton Business Park, Bell Lane, Amersham HP6 6GL

According to the 2016 accounts the objectives of the foundation are as follows:

- Apply funds for such charitable purposes that the Trustees may from time to time select
- The advancement of the Christian faith in the UK or overseas
- The advancement of education of children and young people, assisting with the provision of help to socially disadvantaged children and young people and assisting children and young people in financial need to receive support and training

Financial information
In 2016 the foundation had assets of £187,500 and an income of £258,000. The foundation awarded 118 grants worth a total of £356,500.

Beneficiaries included: Alpha International (£54,000 in two grants); Christians Against Poverty, Happy Child International (£10,000 each); Amersham Methodist Church (£5,000); Freedom for Life Ministries (£3,500); Christian Solidarity Worldwide and Theodora's Children's Charity (£2,500 each).

Applications
Apply in writing to the correspondent.

Sources of information
Accounts; annual report; Charity Commission record.

GrantScape

 Environment, community development, sports and recreation, social welfare

UK

£1.8 million (2016/17)

CC number: 1102249

Trustees: Antony Cox; Mohammed Saddiq; Michael Singh; Michael Clarke; Philippa Lyons; John Mills.

Correspondent: Patricia England, Secretary, Office E, Whitsundoles, Broughton Road, Salford, Milton Keynes MK17 8BU (tel: 01908 247630; email: info@grantscape.org.uk)

 www.grantscape.org.uk

GrantScape is a grants management specialist whose main activity is to redistribute donations received from landfill operators under the Landfill Communities Fund. It also delivers grants and community benefit programmes on behalf of renewable energy companies from other sectors (e.g. wind and solar energy) and provides grants administration services to other organisations. GrantScape is a company limited by guarantee and is enrolled with ENTRUST as an accredited environmental body.

GrantScape's general grant-making policy – which was introduced in January 2006 and last reviewed in March 2016 – states:

- GrantScape will only make grants in line with its charitable objects
- Grants will be made to projects that improve the environment and the life of communities
- Grants will be made on a justifiable and fair basis to projects which provide best value

Programmes are subject to their own specific criteria and guidelines. They are listed on GrantScape's website and can be filtered using the 'Grant & Project Finder' facility. Examples of funds listed on the website at the time of writing (March 2018) include the Brigg Biomass Community Fund, and the Burbo Bank Extension Community Fund.

Financial information
In 2016/17 the charity held assets of £2.4 million and had an income of £3 million. A total of 197 grants were made amounting to £1.8 million. Grants were distributed as follows:

Landfill Community Fund	64	£1.03 million
Renewable Community Benefit Fund	133	£764,867

Beneficiaries included: The Wildlife Trust for Lancashire, Manchester and North Merseyside (£20,000); Samaritans (£10,000); Allandale Community Youthworks (£8,000); Acronova Gymnastic Club (£6,000); Sudbury Gasworks Restoration Trust and Lancaster People's Cafe LPC (£5,000 each); Pirates At Art (£500).

Applications
Applicants should visit the 'Grant and Project Finder' section of the charity's website to find information on all grant programmes currently available. Applications should be made online via the website.

Sources of information
Accounts; annual report; Charity Commission record; funder's website.

The Great Britain Sasakawa Foundation

 Links between Great Britain and Japan

UK and Japan

£576,500 to organisations (2016)

CC number: 290766

Trustees: Michael French; Sir John Boyd; Ambassador Hiroaki Fuji; The Earl of St Andrews; Prof. David Cope; Tatsua Tanami; Joanna Ptiman; Prof. Yuichi Hosoya; Prof. Yorkio Kawaguchi; Prof. Janet Hunter; Prof. Ryuichi Teshima.

Correspondent: Brendan Griggs, Dilke House, 1 Malet Street, London WC1E 7JN (tel: 020 7436 9042; email: grants@gbsf.org.uk)

www.gbsf.org.uk

The foundation was established following a visit to London in 1983 by the late Ryoichi Sasakawa to discuss UK-Japanese relations. The main aim is enhance and promote a mutual appreciation of each other's culture and the foundation can make grants for activities in the following areas:

- Arts and culture
- Humanities and social issues
- Japanese language
- Medicine and health
- Science, technology and environment
- Sport
- Youth and education

The website states that although applications can be submitted in any of the above areas, it is especially keen it support projects in science and technology; medicine and health; environment and social issues; Japanese studies; and in the Japanese language. Grants are made for pump-priming and not core funding of projects.

Criteria for awards

The following is taken from the website, where you can find a more in-depth guide:

- Grants are intended to be 'pump-priming' or partial support for worthwhile projects which would not otherwise be realised, and evidence of core funding should be available before any application is made for an award
- There are no set budgets for any category of activity, but emphasis is placed on innovative projects and on those involving groups of people in both countries (especially young people) rather than individuals
- Projects originating in the UK should be submitted through the London office and those originating in Japan through the Tokyo office

- Projects for UK-Japan collaborations or exchanges should be submitted as a single project through Tokyo or London, and not as separate applications from the UK and Japanese partners
- For projects designed to extend over more than one year, the foundation is prepared to consider requests for funding spread over a period of not more than three consecutive years
- We welcome applications from previous recipients for new projects
- Awards average £1,500 to £2,000 and do not normally exceed £5,000 to £6,000 for larger-scale projects

Financial information

In 2016 the foundation held assets of £27.5 million and had an income of almost £1.18 million. Grants totalled £1.1 million, although £546,500 was paid in restricted grants to fund the Sasakawa Lectureship Programme for Japanese Studies at UK universities and for a conference programme at Chatham House, and a further £650 was awarded to one individual. The remaining £576,500 was distributed to 213 organisations. Examples of successful projects are posted on the website.

Exclusions

Grants are not made for the following purposes:

- Consumables, core costs, salaries or the purchase of materials
- Capital projects, including the purchase, construction or maintenance of buildings
- Individuals/personal projects, apart from where there is clear evidence of organisational support and a project which furthers the foundation's aims
- Student fees or travel for study, apart from PhD fieldwork in Japan (limited to £1,000 maximum), only where it is necessary for the completion of the PhD thesis – applications must be accompanied by a letter of support from the supervisor
- Medical, psychological or sociological research on humans or animals
- Projects designed to extend over more than one year (the foundation is prepared to consider requests for funding spread over a period of not more than three consecutive years)
- Completed or current projects

Applications

Full application details can be found on the website. Application forms to the London office can be found on the website, once completed they must be sent via email to grants@gbsf.org.uk. To apply to the Tokyo office, the applicant must email tokyo@gbsf.org.uk before making an application. Trustees make the final decisions on awards at meetings held in London three times a year (normally March, May and November) and Tokyo twice a year (normally April

and October). The deadline for London applicants are as follows: 15 December for a decision in early March; 31 March for a decision by the end of May; 15 September for a decision in early November. The deadline for Tokyo applicants are as follows: 28 February for a decision by the end of April; 30 September for a decision by the end of October.

The foundation's website states that they normally receive three times as many requests as they are able to grant, and that around 75% of applicants receive funding, but may receive less than originally requested.

Sources of information

Accounts; annual report; Charity Commission record; funder's website.

The Kenneth and Susan Green Charitable Foundation

 General charitable purposes, social welfare, education, health, the arts

UK

£273,500 (2016)

CC number: 1147248

Trustees: Kenneth Green; Philip Stokes; Susan Green; Sarah Scragg; Charlotte Garlick.

Correspondent: Philip Stokes, Trustee, Kenneth Green Associates, Hill House, Monument Hill, Weybridge KT13 8RX (tel: 01932 827060)

The settlor of the foundation, Kenneth Green, is Chair of Kenneth Green Associates, a company which markets and distributes luxury brands. The foundation's objects are:

- The relief of poverty
- The advancement of education
- The advancement of health and the saving of lives
- The advancement of the arts, culture, heritage and science
- General charitable purposes

Financial information

In 2016 the foundation held assets of £3.4 million and had a total income of £1.66 million. During the year, the foundation awarded £273,500 in grants to six organisations, and paid £35,500 in grants less than £10,000 (recipients of these smaller grants were not listed in the accounts).

Beneficiaries included: The Royal Opera House Covent Garden Foundation (£105,000); The Royal Ballet School (£50,000); RNLI (£25,000); The Pepper Foundation (£20,000); Paladin and The Cecchetti Society Trust (19,000 each).

Exclusions

No grants are given to individuals.

Applications

Apply in writing to the correspondent.

Sources of information

Accounts; annual report; Charity Commission Record.

The Green Hall Foundation

 Social welfare, medical, health, community projects, general charitable purposes

 UK and overseas

£ £364,500 (2016/17)

CC number: 270775

Trustees: Margaret Hall; Sue Collinson; Nigel Hall; Peter Morgan; Charlotte Footer.

Correspondent: S. Hall, 3rd Floor, International House, 41 The Parade, St Helier, Jersey JE2 3QQ (tel: 01534 487757; email: greenhallfoundation@ fcmtrust.com)

 www.greenhallfoundation.org

This foundation was established by Constance Vera Green from Yorkshire, who died in 1992. She was a well-known philanthropist who involved herself in many charitable activities and set up this foundation in 1976 to which she donated substantial financial assets.

Following the death of Colonel Henry Robert Hall in 2012, one of the long-standing original trustees, additional assets were donated to the foundation. To commemorate his contribution, the trustees decided to adopt the name The Green Hall Foundation in May 2013.

The foundation makes grants mainly in the fields of social welfare and medicine. There is a special emphasis on the needs of young people and people with mental or physical disabilities. Preference is given to funding special projects rather than to supplement funds used for general expenditure. In an average year the trustees usually make around 100 grants ranging in value from £1,000 to £10,000.

Financial information

In 2016/17 the foundation had assets of £11.47 million and an income of £404,000. The principal charity sector nominated by the trustees for the year was people with physical and mental disabilities who are aged 25 and over. Grants were made totalling £364,500 and were broken down follows:

People with disabilities and older people	45%	£163,500
Medical and social care	32%	£117,500
Children and young persons	11%	£41,500
Homeless	6%	£22,000
Church and community projects	6%	£20,000

Beneficiaries included: Hope for Tomorrow (£30,000); Lewis-Manning Hospital, Moorfields Eye Hospital, Save the Children – Rescue at Sea and The Salvation Army (£10,000 each); Acorn Villages Ltd, Queen Elizabeth's Foundation and Save the Children – Ethiopia Appeal (£5,000 each); Friends of Castledon School (£4,000); Good Companions and Langley House (£1,000 each).

Exclusions

The foundation does not make grants to individuals or for core costs and salaries.

Applications

Applications must be made online through the foundation's website. The trustees meet twice a year, in May and November. Only the first 100 applications received by the foundation will be taken forward to be considered by the trustees. The opening dates for application cycles are detailed on the website and the cycles close when the 100th application has been received.

Sources of information

Accounts; annual report; Charity Commission record; further information provided by the funder; funder's website.

Greenham Trust Ltd

 General charitable purposes

 Newbury and the surrounding area (West Berkshire and North Hampshire)

£ £1.2 million (2016/17)

CC number: 1062762

Trustees: Sir Peter Michael; David Bailey; Charles Brims; Paul Bryant; Julian Cazalet; Victoria Fishburn; Biddy Hayward; Graham Mather; Malcolm Morris.

Correspondent: Jaz Ghalley, Grants Administrator, Liberty House, The Enterprise Centre, Greenham Business Park, Newbury, Berkshire RG19 6HS (tel: 01635 817445; email: jaz@ greenham-common-trust.co.uk)

www.greenham-common-trust.co.uk

The trust was established in 1997 to provide funding for general charitable purposes in Newbury, West Berkshire and North Hampshire. Since its creation the trust has donated £40 million to over 3,000 charities. The following information is taken from the trust's website:

Poverty: Youth activities in areas of deprivation; advice services; food bank service provision

Education: Youth development projects; First Aid training; extra-curricular activities; volunteer training costs (e.g. safeguarding, health and safety)

Health and Wellbeing: Defibrillators; hospital equipment; dialysis unit; cancer unit; contribution to cost of counselling/therapy sessions; First Aid training; hospices for the terminally ill; activities for people with dementia and their carers; support for young carers

Community: Community events such as Newbury Carnival, Hungerford Victorian Event, Stockfest, CultureFest; repair/refurbishments of community buildings; playground equipment; youth clubs and activities, equipment for scouts/guides/brownies; venue hire; volunteer training costs (e.g. safeguarding, health and safety); improvements to church halls/buildings with wide community use

The Arts, Heritage and Science: Newbury's Outdoor Events programme; Culture-fest; Production costs for music events; musical instruments; local theatre group productions costs; venue hire; artiste fees for charity productions; science programmes in local primary and secondary schools

Sport: Sports equipment (not clothing); cricket nets; refurbishment of sports pavilions/shower rooms; sports event trophies; sports coaching; floodlighting; sports buildings and grounds; grounds maintenance equipment

Human Rights and Diversity: Multi cultural events; CultureFest

Environment: Restoration of Greenham Common; Environmental improvements to local areas; Flood alleviation schemes; Construction of wildlife pond as a learning resource; Restoration of ancient meadow and wildwood

Helping the Disadvantaged: Youth clubs and activities in deprived areas; contribution to costs of counselling/ therapy sessions; transport for elderly or infirm; advice services; accommodation/playschemes/skill programmes for people with learning disabilities

Wildlife: Bird watching hides; feeding stations; bird food; bird ringing; funding for protected species

Military and Emergency Services: Refurbishment to The Royal British Legion Club, replacement vehicle/ equipment for rapid response teams

Grant programmes

The trust currently operates several different grants programmes and funding schemes:

Major funding: Grants for local charities and community organisations to fund major projects. Projects previously supported include: £770,000 towards the restoration of Greenham Common; £570,000 to help save The Watermill Theatre in Bagnor; and £185,000 towards the upgrading of West Berkshire Museum

▸ **Reactive Grants**: Grants of up to £30,000 (average £2,500) for local organisations to fund a wide variety of good causes. Applications for reactive grants are considered twice a year (in spring and autumn) by the trust's Distribution Committee

▸ **Pitch to the Panel**: Each year the trust hosts a Dragons' Den style gala event during which local charities are asked to pitch for a share of £100,000. All projects are for the benefit of local people, and the trust donates a further £1 for every public vote made both online and on the night of the Pitch to the Panel event

▸ **Sports Activities Building Programme (SABP)**: The Sports Activities Building Programme (SABP) was set up by the trust in 2016 to support capital improvements to local community sporting facilities and children's play areas. The trust match-funds on a 1:1 basis any other grants and public donations made to the project, up to a maximum of 50% of the total project cost. SABP applications are considered on a quarterly basis

▸ **Trust Top Up**: The trust pledges to double public or company donations made via The Good Exchange (see below) to any projects that match its charitable criteria, up to £5,000 per project and up to £10,000 per organisation per financial year

Since 2013 the trust has also had agreements with several local councils to provide match-funding for projects which are consistent with its charitable objectives.

In addition to its grant-making activities, the trust supports local organisations more directly by subsidising accommodation rents for charities and voluntary sector organisations who are its tenants and works collaboratively with local organisations to deliver projects and services for the benefit of the local community.

Financial information

In 2016/17 the trust had assets of £62.3 million and an income of £8.3 million. Expenditure on charitable activities totalled £3.3 million. Grants made to institutions during the year totalled 1.2 million and were distributed as follows:

Community	£502,000
Youth	£187,500
Sport	£163,000
Health	£119,500
Education	£92,500
Arts	£44,500
Economic	£40,000
Older people	£27,500
Disability	£12,000

Diversity	£4,400
Nature and conservation	£3,600
Emergency services	£1,000

Beneficiaries included: Newbury Carnival (£7,000); Recovery in Mind (£6,300); Community Youth Project (£3,900); Newbury Symphony Orchestra (£3,200); Basingstoke Counselling Service (£3,000); Stockfest (£330).

Exclusions

Grants are only awarded for projects within the trust's geographical area of operation. This includes all of West Berkshire as well as the following ward areas of North Hampshire:

▸ East Woodhay
▸ Burghclere, Highclere and St Mary Bourne
▸ Kingsclere
▸ Tadley Central
▸ Tadley South
▸ Baughurst and Tadley North
▸ Pamber and Silchester

In addition, the trust will not consider applications for any of the following:

▸ Projects in retrospect
▸ Projects for items/refurbishment which are the responsibility of the applicant's landlord
▸ Projects for which statutory funding which has been withdrawn or which are considered a statutory responsibility
▸ Individuals
▸ Feasibility studies
▸ Core educational needs, i.e. books and IT equipment (except in cause of special need)
▸ Private pre-schools and nurseries that are run as a business
▸ Education of school/college/university pupils
▸ Re-turfing and re-fencing school playgrounds
▸ Organisations that do not have charitable aims
▸ Projects that will bring in profit
▸ Fundraising events
▸ Payments for membership subscriptions
▸ Provision of broadband for rural villages
▸ Cultural celebrations

There may be additional exclusions for specific schemes or funding types. Check the trust's website for full eligibility criteria.

Applications

All applications should be made through The Good Exchange – an online matching service for fundraisers and funders used by the trust to administer its grants. Full details and links to The Good Exchange portal are available on the trust's website.

If applying for major funding, it is recommended that applicants contact

the trust by phone to discuss their project in person.

Sources of information

Accounts; annual report; Charity Commission record; funder's website.

The Greggs Foundation

🔍 Social welfare, community causes, environment, general charitable purposes

📍 England, Wales and Scotland, with a preference for the north east of England, (Northumberland, Tyne and Wear, Durham and Teesside), and in the regional divisions of Greggs plc

💷 £2.5 million to organisations (2016)

CC number: 296590

Trustees: Andrew Davison; Fiona Nicholson; Richard Hutton; Lindsay Graham; Jane Irving; Tony Rowson; Roisin Curry; Karen Wilkinson-Bell; Kate Bradley.

Correspondent: Justine Massingham, Grants Manager, Greggs House, Quorum Business Park, Newcastle upon Tyne, Tyne and Wear NE12 8BU (tel: 0191 212 7626; email: greggsfoundation@greggs. co.uk)

 www.greggsfoundation.org.uk

The Greggs Foundation was registered with the Charity Commission in 1987. It is the corporate charity of Greggs plc, whose principal activity is the retailing of sandwiches, savouries and other bakery products with a particular focus on takeaway food and catering.

The latest annual report and accounts state: 'Ian Gregg (former chairman of Greggs plc) set up the foundation as a registered charity in 1987 with the aim of giving something back to the communities where Greggs plc trades, and where customers and employees live.'

The foundation makes grants to organisations throughout England, Scotland and Wales to enhance the quality of life in local communities. Divisional Charity Committees based within the regional divisions of Greggs plc also make grants on behalf of the foundation and are located in Newcastle upon Tyne; Glasgow; Gosforth; Leeds; Manchester; Birmingham; Treforest; and Twickenham.

Grant programmes

The following information is taken from the foundation's website:

North East Core Funding

Financial support is offered to help sustain and increase the capacity of organisations that are based in and support people who live in the north east of England. Awards are of up to £45,000 (up to £15,000 per year) and aim 'to increase the capacity of the organisation to provide quality services', including support for core running costs. Priority groups are: people with disabilities; homeless people; voluntary carers; older and isolated people. Any not-for-profit organisation can apply.

Local Community Projects Fund

Small grants of up to £2,000 are made to 'enable not-for-profit organisations to do something they otherwise could not afford to'. The programme is administered by seven regional charity committees based throughout England, Wales and Scotland. Any not-for-profit organisation can apply as long as the project supports a community interest and benefits people who: have disabilities; live in poverty; are voluntary carers; are homeless; are isolated older people; or those who have other demonstrable significant need. The website states:

> We are interested in projects that improve resilience within your community of interest. This can include sessional activities/respite support, equipment for sessional activities, trips and residential breaks. We are also interested in new approaches and innovative ideas as well as sustainable approaches to supporting your community of interest.

Grants are more likely to be made to local organisations based near Greggs shops. Organisations 'with a turnover in excess of £300,000 are unlikely to be successful'.

Environment Grants

Funded by the 5p levy on carrier bag sales, this fund is dedicated to 'projects that improve the physical environment in a way that will improve people's lives'. Small grants of up to £2,000 are available on a one-off basis. The fund is administered in a similar way to the Local Community Projects Fund. Any not-for-profit organisation can apply although preference is given to smaller, locally based, community-led organisations with a turnover of under £300,000. The foundation encourages schools to also apply.

Hardship Fund

Grants of up to £150 are made to individuals and families (via recognised social organisations) who live in extreme financial hardship. The grants are used to provide household goods, such as cookers, fridge freezers, clothing, beds and bedding, baby equipment and flooring.

Breakfast Clubs

The club programme was established to help primary schoolchildren to get nutritious start of their day. Through the scheme, schools in England, Wales,

Scotland or Belfast are provided with fresh bread from their nearest Greggs shop, and a grant to support start-up and ongoing costs of the initiative. There are currently over 465 breakfast clubs operating.

Financial information

In 2016 the foundation had assets of £17.7 million and an income of £3 million, of which almost £1.7 million was donated by Greggs plc. Grants totalled £2.75 million and were broken down as follows:

Environmental grants	£768,500
Major grants	£613,000
Local charity committees' grants	£512,500
Breakfast club	£250,000
Other grants	£103,000

Beneficiaries included: Belville Community Garden Trust and Montgomeryshire Wildlife Trust (£10,000 each); Team Oasis (£8,500); Hemlington Hall Academy (£2,500); Wipe Your Tears (£2,400); Be Crafty, Cruse Crew and Greenscape (£2,000 each).

Exclusions

The website provides lists of exclusions for each funding programme, check for further details.

Applications

Each grant programme has its own detailed criteria, guidelines and application process, all of which are available to view on the website.

Applications for Hardship Fund grants are only accepted via recognised social organisations, such as charities, housing associations and social services acting on behalf of a family or individual in need.

The North East Core Funding programme is very competitive with around one in five eligible applications being successful.

Similarly the Local Community Projects Fund is 'over-subscribed and there is huge competition for the grants available'. The foundation asks not to be too disappointed if it is unable to support your project. It is unable to give tailored feedback on every application but will let you know whether it has been successful as early as possible. In 2017 27% of eligible applications were awarded.

The foundation also states that the Small Environment Grants is 'likely to receive a very high number of applications and an accordingly low success rate'.

Sources of information

Accounts; annual report; Charity Commission record; guidelines for applicants; funder's website.

The Grimmitt Trust

General charitable purposes, including community development, children and young people, culture, education, medical, older people, overseas aid

The Birmingham, Dudley, Wolverhampton and Walsall postcode areas, overseas

£271,500 to organisations (2016/17)

CC number: 801975

Trustees: Sue Day; Leon Murray; David Owen; Tim Welch; Jenny Dickins; Sarah Wilkey; Phil Smith; Trevor Jones.

Correspondent: Vanessa Welch, Secretary, 151B All Saints Road, Kings Heath, Birmingham B14 6AT (tel: 07576 195955; email: admin@grimmitt-trust. org.uk)

The Grimmitt Trust was established by a trust deed in 1986. According to the trustees' report for 2016/17: 'the objects of the trust are the encouraging and strengthening of local communities, together with an awareness of national and international responsibilities particularly those within the active interest and geographical areas of the trustees and the Kite Connexion group employees.' Currently the geographical areas covered are Birmingham, Dudley, Wolverhampton and Walsall postcodes. Grants are typically one-off and are usually for less than £2,500. Larger or recurrent grants can be made on an exceptional basis.

Financial information

In 2016/17 the trust held assets of almost £9.4 million and had an income of £296,500. There were 226 grants made totalling £272,000, of which £600 was awarded to individuals. Grants were broken down as follows:

Community	94	£108,500
Culture and education	47	£54,000
Children and young people	52	£49,000
Overseas	5	£27,000
Medical and health	16	£17,600
Older people	12	£16,000

Previous beneficiaries have included: All We Can (£15,000); The King Edward's School Birmingham Trust (£10,000); The Methodist Church Selly Oak (£6,000); Christian Aid and St Basil's (£5,000 each); YMCA Black Country Group (£3,500); Acacia Family Support (£3,000); RBSA (£2,500); Birmingham Centre for Arts Therapies, Birmingham St Mary's Hospice and Shirley Methodist Church (£2,000 each).

Out of the 226 grants made, 179 were of less than £1,000 each and totalled £129,000. The trust has also authorised future grants, which are subject to the recipient fulfilling certain conditions, totalling £59,500.

Exclusions

The trust does not normally support national charities, community interest companies or social enterprises.

Applications

Applicants should contact the secretary who will advise on the best way to design a grant request and to ensure that all the necessary information is included. The trustees meet three times a year to consider applications.

Applicants must demonstrate that their project and the grant received is used in line with the trust's objectives.

Sources of information

Accounts; annual report; Charity Commission record.

The Grocers' Charity

General charitable purposes, including: the relief of poverty, children and young people, older people, disability, medicine and health, heritage and the arts, armed forces

UK, with a preference for the City of London and its surrounding boroughs, as well as in the vicinity of the churches and educational establishments it supports

£944,000 (2016/17)

CC number: 255230

Trustee: The Grocers' Trust Company Ltd.

Correspondent: Lindsay Mitchell, Charity Manager, Grocers' Hall, Princes Street, London EC2R 8AD (tel: 020 7606 3113; email: charity@grocershall.co.uk)

 www.grocershall.co.uk

The Grocers' Charity was established in 1968 with general charitable purposes. It supports a wide range of UK-registered charities.

Grant-making information

The charity prioritises applications from organisations working in the City of London and its surrounding boroughs, as well as in the vicinity of the churches and educational establishments it supports (the charity offers regular support to a fixed group of educational establishments and has patronages with thirteen churches across the UK). The main open grants scheme is the Memorial Grants programme.

According to the Grocers' Hall website, one-off grants of up to £5,000 can be awarded in the following categories: relief of poverty in young people (up to the age of 25); older people (specifically projects aimed at ending loneliness and social exclusion); disability; medicine; military (support for current and ex-Service people and their families); and

heritage and the arts (conservation of historic buildings, objects and paintings and improving accessibility to the arts). See the website for specific eligibility criteria for each area.

Financial information

In 2016/17 the charity had assets of £22.3 million and an income of nearly £1.3 million. During the year, £944,000 was awarded in 122 grants (or 90 grants excluding those to organisations with which the charity has a historic connection). Grants were distributed for the following purposes:

Education	23	£423,500
Relief of poverty	23	£214,500
Churches	19	£77,500
Disability	14	£68,500
Medicine	15	£53,500
The arts	10	£46,000
Older people and other	12	£45,000
Heritage	6	£16,600

Beneficiaries included: Home-Start North West Hampshire (£40,000); City of Pelican Cancer Foundation (£10,000); London School for Girls (£8,000); Action for Refugees in Lewisham (£5,900); The Campaign for Drawing (£3,000); iSightCornwall (£5,000); River Thames Society (£2,000).

Exclusions

Support is rarely given to the following unless there is a specific or long-standing connection with the Grocers' Company:

▸ Places of worship
▸ Educational establishments
▸ Hospices
▸ Charities whose beneficiaries are overseas
▸ Non-UK-registered charities
▸ Non-medical charities with a turnover of over £500,000
▸ Medical charities with a turnover of £15 million
▸ Individuals

Applications

Applications can be made through the Grocers' Hall website. Potential applicants must at first complete the eligibility checker on the website to determine if they are able to apply for a grant.

Sources of information

Accounts; annual report; Charity Commission record; guidelines for applicants; funder's website.

M and R Gross Charities Ltd

Orthodox Jewish causes

UK and overseas

£3 million (2016/17)

CC number: 251888

Trustees: Rifka Gross; Sarah Padwa; Michael Saberski; Leonard Lerner.

Correspondent: The Trustees of M and R Gross Charities Ltd, c/o Cohen Arnold, New Burlington House, 1075 Finchley Road, London NW11 0PU (tel: 020 8731 0777; email: mail@cohenarnold.com)

This charity makes grants to organisations within the Orthodox Jewish community in the UK and overseas.

According to the charity's 2016/17 annual report, its objects are:

▸ To foster, assist and promote the charitable activities of any institution professing and teaching the principles of traditional Judaism
▸ To advance religion in accordance with the Jewish faith
▸ To undertake, accept, execute and administer, without any remuneration, any charitable trust
▸ To give philanthropic aid to the Jewish needy

Financial information

In 2016/17 the charity had assets of £55.3 million and an income of £4.3 million. Grants were made totalling almost £3 million. A list of beneficiaries was not included.

Previous beneficiaries have included: Atlas Memorial Ltd; Beis Ruchel Building Fund; Chevras Tsedokoh Ltd; Daas Sholem; Friends of Yeshivas Brisk; Gevurah Ari Torah Academy Trust; Kehal Chareidim Trust; Talmud Torah Trust; Telz Talmudical Academy; Union of Orthodox Hebrew Congregations; United Talmudical Associates Ltd; and Yetev Lev Jerusalem.

Applications

Apply in writing to the correspondent. Applications are assessed regularly and many smaller grants are dealt with through a grant-making agency, United Talmudical Associates Ltd.

Sources of information

Accounts; annual report; Charity Commission record.

Groundwork UK

Environment, social welfare, communities

UK

£30.4 million (2016/17)

CC number: 291558

Trustees: Stuart Baker; Wendy Golland; Jenny Bradley; June Campbell; Catherine Culverhouse; Brynley Davies; Mike Master; Ian Brown; Geoff Howsego; Alan Smith; Graham Hartley; John Bland.

Correspondent: Sarah Reece-Mills, Director of Partnerships and Programmes, Lockside, 5 Scotland Street, Birmingham, West Midlands B1 2RR (tel: 0121 236 8565; email: info@groundwork.org.uk)

 www.groundwork.org.uk

 facebook.com/groundworkuk

 @groundworkuk

Groundwork UK (The Federation of Groundwork Trusts) is the national body of Groundwork Trusts, each of which is an independent registered charity, with a common set of aims, objectives and processes.

The charity states the following vision on its website:

> Big global issues – the economy, the environment – have a big local impact. We work across the UK helping communities find practical solutions to the challenges they face.

> We provide training and create jobs, reduce energy use and waste, re-connect people with nature and transform whole neighbourhoods. Step by step we'll go on changing places and changing lives until everywhere is vibrant and green, every community is strong enough to shape its own destiny and everyone can reach their potential.

The charity runs a range of programmes and projects across the UK with the following aims:

- Promoting greener living and working
- Improving people's prospects
- Creating better, greener places

Grants

While Groundwork UK does not have its own grants scheme, it administers a number of grants programmes for other organisations. The following information on grant schemes has been taken from Groundwork UK's website:

Coastal Communities Fund – The CCF encourages the economic development of UK coastal communities by giving funding to create sustainable economic growth and jobs.

Culture Seeds GLA Grant - Communities can bid for grants of between £1,000 – £5,000 community-led cultural projects in London

Tesco Bags of Help – Grants of up to £4,000 to support community projects.

HS2 Community and Business Funds - Two funds are available to local communities to help with the disruption that will be caused by the construction of Phase one of HS2 between London and the West Midlands.

London Family Fund – The London Family Fund provides grants of up to £85,000 to innovative projects that promote social integration in London.

One Stop Carrier for Causes - Grants of up to £2000 for good causes within two miles of a One Stop shop.

Clarion Housing Group Community Grants Programme – Grants of between £1,000 and £5,000 for charities, community organisations, voluntary groups and projects that primarily benefit Clarion residents.

Ministry of Housing, Communities & Local Government (MHCLG) - Support for groups to build the neighbourhood they want.

Community Business Bright Ideas Fund - Up to £20,000 grants available to local business ideas.

Community Activity Grant Programme – funding for organisations in Salford, Huntingdon and North Cambridgeshire to develop and deliver community-based activities to encourage people to become more active.

Financial information
In 2016/17 the charity held assets of £2 million and had an income of £34.4 million. Grants awarded to organisations totalled £30.4 million.

Over £28 million was distributed to over 2,000 projects through Tesco Bags of Help grants.

Applications
Check the Groundwork UK website for details of grants programmes currently being administered.

Sources of information
Accounts; annual report; Charity Commission record; funder's website.

Calouste Gulbenkian Foundation – UK Branch

 Fulfilling potential, cultural understanding, environment

UK and the Republic of Ireland

£ around £1.5 million (2015/16)

Trustee: The foundation's board of administration is based in Lisbon. Martin Essayan, the great-grandson of the foundation's founder, is trustee for the UK branch of the foundation.

Correspondent: Andrew Barnett, Director, 50 Hoxton Square, London N1 6PB (tel: 020 7012 1400; fax: 020 7739 1961; email: info@gulbenkian.org.uk)

 gulbenkian.pt/uk-branch

 facebook.com/fundacaocaloustegulbenkian

 @fcgulbenkian

 @fcgulbenkian

This foundation is largely proactive in its approach to grant-making. It currently gives funding across three themes – fulfilling potential, cultural understanding, and the environment – via four strands, which are: Transitions in Later Life; Sharing the Stage; Valuing the Ocean; and Creating the Conditions for Change.

The following information is taken from the foundation's website:

> The Calouste Gulbenkian Foundation is a charitable foundation set up in 1956 as a private institution of public utility under a special act of the Portuguese Government. Its Headquarters are in Lisbon and include the Administration, which deals with grant-giving throughout the world, the Calouste Gulbenkian Museum, housing the Founder's art collections and recognised as one of the best small museums in Europe and the Modern Art Collection, whose holdings include an extensive collection of contemporary British art. There is also an Art Library, book shop, concert and conference halls. The Foundation also maintains a Science Institute near Lisbon, a Portuguese delegation in Paris and the grant giving branch in London.

> The purpose of the UK Branch in London is to bring about long-term improvements in wellbeing, particularly for the most vulnerable, by creating connections across boundaries (national borders, communities, disciplines and sectors) which deliver social, cultural and environmental value.

> As a small branch we can be nimble but cannot provide large-scale continuous support. However, being part of one of the largest foundations in Europe, we are well positioned to address transnational issues and can act as an 'exchange' for ideas.

Financial information
According to the foundation's annual review for 2015/16, £1.67 million was expended under the four strategic strands – Sharing the Stage (£786,500); Valuing the Ocean (£366,500); Transitions in Later Life (£355,500); and Creating the Conditions for Change (£164,000), however, we were not able to determine the proportion of this figure that was allocated in grants. Based on previous years, we have made a cautious estimate and approximate that grants during this financial year were in the region of £1.5 million.

Previous beneficiaries have included: Independent Age (£300,000); Social Finance (£200,000); Pig Shed Trust (£180,000); Homeless Link and Volunteering Matters (£60,000 each); Royal Society for the Protection of Birds (£47,000); Wildlife and Countryside Link (£30,000); Contact – Manchester Young People's Theatre Ltd, Geese Theatre Company and New Philanthropy Capital (£20,000 each); The Legal Education Foundation (£6,000).

Exclusions

The UK Branch of the foundation gives grants only for proposals of a charitable kind, from registered charities or similar not-for-profit organisations in the UK or Ireland. The foundation does not fund:

▸ Work that does not have a direct benefit in the UK or the Republic of Ireland
▸ Individuals
▸ Curriculum-based activities in statutory education
▸ Student grants or scholarships for tuition and maintenance
▸ Vocational training
▸ Teaching or research posts or visiting fellowships
▸ Educational resources and equipment
▸ Gap year activities
▸ Group or individual visits abroad, including to Portugal
▸ Core services and standard provisions
▸ Routine information and advice services
▸ Capital costs for housing or the purchase, construction, repair or furnishing of buildings
▸ Equipment, including vehicles, IT, or musical instruments
▸ Scientific or medical research
▸ Medicine or related therapies such as complementary medicine, hospices, counselling and therapy
▸ Promoting religion or belief system
▸ Website development
▸ Sports
▸ Holidays of any sort
▸ Animal welfare

The website further states: 'Historically we have supported the arts, arts and science and arts education but we will not any longer consider arts applications unless they meet our current strategic aims. We never make loans or retrospective grants, nor help to pay off deficits or loans, nor can we remedy the withdrawal or reduction of statutory funding.'.

Applications

The majority of the foundation's support is proactive although funding is very occasionally given to 'a very small number of exceptional projects' that contribute to meeting the foundation's strategic strands through the open fund. At the time of writing (June 2018), however, the website stated: 'Our open fund is temporarily suspended. This is because we have recently undertaken open calls for proposals for strands of work. In general, we are proactive as opposed to reactive in identifying the partners with whom we wish to work on the basis of extensive research. However, we also scan the horizon for innovative projects using our open fund'. Refer to the website for more information.

Sources of information

Annual review; funder's website.

H & T Clients Charitable Trust

🔍 General charitable purposes
📍 England and Wales
💷 £319,500 (2016/17)

CC number: 1104345

Trustees: Hugh Lask; Ronnie Harris; Neville Newman; Charlotte Harris.

Correspondent: Hugh Lask, Trustee, 64 New Cavendish Street, London W1G 8TB (tel: 020 7467 6300)

Registered with the Charity Commission in 2004, the trust makes grants for general charitable purposes.

Financial information

In 2016/17 the trust had assets of £857,000 and an income of £437,000. The trust awarded 11 grants to organisations which totalled £319,500.

A list of beneficiaries was not available.

Applications

According to the trust's 2016/17 accounts: 'the Charity invites applications for funding of projects through various sources. The applications are reviewed by the Trustees who ensure that they are in accordance with the Charity's objectives.'

Sources of information

Accounts; annual report; Charity Commission record.

HCD Memorial Fund

🔍 General charitable purposes, environmental causes, particularly climate change
📍 UK and overseas
💷 £823,500 (2016/17)

CC number: 1044956

Trustees: Nicholas Debenham; Bill Flinn; Harriet Lear; Joanna Lear; Jeremy Debenham; Susannah Drummond.

Correspondent: Susannah Drummond, Secretary, 24 Fern Avenue, Jesmond, Newcastle upon Tyne NE2 2QT (tel: 0191 281 4228; email: hcdmemorialfund@gmail.com)

This fund was established in 1995 and makes grants to a wide range of organisations in the UK and overseas. According to the trustees' annual report, the charity usually awards grants in the following areas:

▸ The relief of human need, whether due to poverty, ill health, disability, want of education, or other causes

▸ Projects which aim to mitigate the effects of climate change.

The trustees note in their annual report that they prefer to give to small and medium-sized charities and that they are willing to permit risk taking in appropriate cases.

In addition to its grant-making activities the charity also owns a freehold woodland property in the Republic of Ireland which it uses for charitable purposes, including recreational access for the community.

Financial information

In 2016/17 the charity had assets of £636,500 and an income of £884,500. Grants were made to 41 organisations totalling £823,500.

Beneficiaries included: A Rocha and Unseen UK (£20,000 each); Refugee Women of Bristol (£15,500); Friends First, Chailey Heritage and Tiverton Market Centre (£10,000 each); Hamsey Church Restoration (£9,500).

Exclusions

The charity will not fund any of the following:

▸ Evangelism or missionary work
▸ Individuals
▸ Nationwide emergency appeals
▸ Animal, cancer and children's charities
▸ Gap year funding

Applications

Apply in writing to the correspondent. Applicants should be aware however, that the trustees prefer to seek out their own projects, and have stated that they will only very rarely responds to general or unsolicited appeals. Grants are considered by the trustees at meetings held twice a year.

Sources of information

Accounts; annual report; Charity Commission record.

Hackney Parochial Charities

🔍 Social welfare, education and training
📍 The London borough of Hackney
💷 £342,000 (2016/17)

CC number: 219876

Trustees: Mary Cannon; Cllr Geoff Taylor; Nicola Baboneau; John Parmiter; Cllr Chris Kennedy; Allan Hilton; Ifran Malik; Rob Chapman; Revd Alexander Gordon; Revd Mark Nelson.

Correspondent: Hackney Parochial Charities, 6 Trull Farm Building, Tetbury, Gloucestershire GL8 8SQ (tel: 020 3397 7805; email: hackney@ thetrustpartnership.com)

www.hackneyparochialcharities.org.uk

The charity makes grants to organisations which benefit children, young adults and people disadvantaged by poverty; community organisations can also benefit.

Financial information

In 2015/16 the charities had assets of £6.6 million and an income of £307,500. Grants awarded to organisations totalled £342,000.

Beneficiaries included: Off Centre (£45,000); Hackney Community Law Centre (£20,000); North London Muslim Community Centre Ltd (£10,000); Albion Kids Show (£5,000); Happy Days Children's Charity (£4,000); Get Set Girls (£3,000).

Grants under £2,500 totalled £342,000.

Exclusions

According to the charities' website the following are not supported:

- general appeals or letters requesting donations (Hackney Parochial Charities application forms must be used)
- local authorities or work usually considered a statutory responsibility
- schools, colleges or universities (including schools for pupils with disabilities). The Trustees will, however, consider hardship applications made by individuals
- organisations that do not provide direct services to clients (such as umbrella, second tier or grant-making organisations)
- running costs of hospices, except for project applications
- feasibility studies
- professional associations, or training for professionals
- organisations that do not have charitable aims (such as companies limited by shares and commercial companies)
- overseas trips
- family holidays (apart from project applications for group trips)
- heritage projects, unless they may be considered as educational in the broadest sense
- environmental conservation projects
- social research
- campaigning or lobbying projects, or general awareness raising work
- projects where the main focus is website development or maintenance
- IT equipment. The Trustees, will, however, consider hardship applications made by individuals
- debt of any kind

Applications

Application forms are available to download from the charity's website. Applications can be submitted at any time. The trustees meet bi-annually to consider project applications.

Sources of information

Accounts; annual report; Charity Commission record.

The Hadfield Charitable Trust

 Young people and employment, social welfare, older people, arts, environment

Cumbria

£ £335,000 (2016/17)

CC number: 1067491

Trustees: Roy Morris; William Rathbone; Alan Forsyth; Andrew Morris; Andrew Forsyth; Caroline Addison; Michael Hope.

Correspondent: Susan Berriman, Trust Administrator, Greystone House, Kings Meaburn, Penrith CA10 3BU (tel: 01931 589029; email: admin@hadfieldtrust.org.uk)

www.hadfieldtrust.org.uk

The Hadfield Charitable Trust was established in 1997 and was endowed through the generosity of one family who had been resident in Cumbria for many years. Grants are made to organisations in Cumbria to support projects in the following areas: social welfare; youth and employment; help for older people; the arts; and the environment.

Grant guidelines

The trustees believe that grants should benefit as many residents of Cumbria as possible with particular regard to those who are disadvantaged in any way. The trust can give grants of up to £5,000 but the majority of awards range from £1,500 to £3,000. The trust usually has about £100,000 to distribute at each of the three rounds of funding annually. The website notes that they normally receive 50 to 60 applications per funding round.

Preference is given to capital funding requests although revenue will be considered and ideally applications will be from a registered charity. Most grants are one-off although two and three year awards are considered occasionally for vital projects where sustainability is at risk.

Financial information

In 2016/17 the trust had assets of £8.95 million and an income of £339,000. There were 134 grants made totalling £335,000 and grants ranged from £250 to £10,000. The distribution of the grant total was as follows:

Social needs	£128,500
Youth and employment	£127,500
Arts	£59,000
Help for older people	£11,800
Environment	£7,900

Beneficiaries included: Life Education Cumbria and Maryport Amateur Boxing Club (£3,000 each); Arkwright Scholarships Trust, Cumbria Crimestoppers and Dalton Leisure Centre (£2,000 each); Cumbria Rural Choirs (£1,000); Deafblind UK (£700).

Exclusions

The following would not normally be considered for a grant:

- Individuals
- Organisations with large unrestricted reserves
- Retrospective funding
- Projects outside Cumbria
- Sponsorship
- Religious bodies or places of worship unless it can be shown that there is significant community use apart from worship
- Political organisations or pressure groups
- Statutory organisations e.g. health or education
- Expeditions
- Feasibility studies

Note that successful applicants cannot apply for two years from the date of their last award and must submit an evaluation form for their project if they wish to be considered for funding again in future.

National charities can apply but they must clearly evidence their work in Cumbria and provide an independent referee who lives in the county.

Applications

A completed application form is always required and is available from the trust's website or offices. The completed application form should be sent to the administrator together with a copy of the applicant's most recent accounts. Applications are not accepted by email. Application deadlines are always the 1st of the month preceding that of the trustees' meeting i.e. 1 February, 1 June and 1 October. If the application form gives insufficient space for your project to be described, up to two sheets of A4 paper can be accepted.

The policy of the trust is that capital funding is strongly preferred but some revenue requests will be accepted in particular circumstances.

If in any doubt about the best way to complete the application form, applicants are advised to telephone the Administrator.

In reaching their decision the trustees benefit from the advice of an Advisory Panel which meets some weeks before them to discuss the applications in detail. Panel members are chosen from across Cumbria for their knowledge and experience of the county and its charitable sector.

Sources of information
Accounts; annual report; Charity Commission record; funder's website.

The Hadley Trust

Social welfare, crime and justice, young people, social investment

UK, especially London

£3.3 million (2016/17)

CC number: 1064823

Trustees: Philip Hulme; Thomas Hulme; Katherine Prideaux; Janet Hulme; Sophie Swift.

Correspondent: Carol Biggs, Gladsmuir, Hadley Common, Barnet EN5 5QE (tel: 020 8447 4577; email: carol@hadleytrust.org)

The trust was established in 1997 for welfare purposes. According to the 2016/17 annual report it makes grants to small and medium-sized registered charities to:

> Assist in creating opportunities for people who are disadvantaged as a result of environmental, educational or economic circumstances, or [disability], to improve their situation, either by direct financial assistance, involvement in project and support work or research into the causes of, and means to alleviate, hardship.

Occasionally the trust will also support organisations that are not registered charities.

The trust aims to make grants on a long-term basis and as a result does not take on many new funding commitments. However, the trustees will always consider and respond to proposals which fit the activities of the trust.

Financial information
In 2016/17 the trust held assets of £150 million and had an income of £3.47 million. There were 76 grants made to organisations totalling £3.3 million, which were broken down as follows:

Crime and justice	39.1%	1.3 million
Hospices	18.1%	£600,000
Young people	12.1%	£402,000
Social investment	9.6%	£317,000
Medical	7.0%	£232,000
Disabilities	4.3%	£141,500
Welfare reform	4.2%	£140,000
Local	3.4%	£112,000
International	2.2%	£74,000

A list of beneficiaries was not included in the annual report.

Applications
Apply in writing to the correspondent. **Note:** Although the majority of the trust's funds are already committed, it does nevertheless still accept and consider new applications. The application process is ongoing and interested applicants may apply at any time.

Sources of information
Accounts; annual report; Charity Commission record.

Hadras Kodesh Trust

The advancement of the Orthodox Jewish religious education and faith

UK and overseas

£2.47 million to organisations (2016/17)

CC number: 1105885

Trustees: Pincus Mann; Yoel Fisher.

Correspondent: Pincus Mann, Trustee, 52 East Bank, London N16 5PZ (tel: 020 8880 8941; email: pincus@hktrust.org)

The income of this trust, registered with the Charity Commission in September 2004, is made up entirely of donations from the local Jewish community in Hackney. According to its 2016/17 accounts, the trust's objective is 'the advancement of Orthodox Jewish religious education and the Orthodox Jewish faith throughout the world and in particular by supporting the charitable activities by religious publishers'. In order to achieve its objective, the trust makes grants to a wide range of individuals and organisations for the advancement of religion and education.

Financial information
In 2016/17 the trust had assets of £236,500 and an income of £5.4 million. Grants were made amounting to £5.1 million, of which £2.47 million was awarded to organisations and £2.67 million to individuals.

A list of beneficiaries was not detailed in the annual report and accounts.

Applications
Apply in writing to the correspondent. The annual report for 2016/17 explains that, 'the trustees are approached for donations by a wide variety of charitable institutions and individuals. The trustees consider all requests which they receive and make donations based on the level of funds available.'

Sources of information
Accounts; annual report; Charity Commission record.

The Hadrian Trust

Social welfare, young people, people with disabilities, older people, women, ethnic minorities, environment, education, the arts

Tyne and Wear, Northumberland and Durham, including Hartlepool

£208,500 (2016/17)

CC number: 272161

Trustees: Pauline Dodgson; Kathryn Winskell; Jim Dias; Ian Brown; Colin Fitzpatrick; Catherine Wood; Dorothy Parker.

Correspondent: Pauline Dodgson, Trustee, PO Box 785, Whitley Bay, Tyne and Wear NE26 9DW (tel: 07815 785074; email: enquiries@hadriantrust.co.uk)

 www.hadriantrust.co.uk

The trust was established by Kathleen Armstrong in 1976 and supports charities and groups working for the benefit of the people and the environment of Tyne and Wear, Northumberland and Durham, including Hartlepool.

Grant-making information
Check the website for full details of funding priorities and deadline dates. At the time of writing (June 2018), the trustees funding priorities were listed as follows:

- Social welfare
- Youth
- People with disabilities
- Older people
- Women
- Ethnic minorities
- Environment
- Education
- The arts

Financial information
In 2016/17 the trust held assets of £6.9 million and had an income of £230,500. There were 198 grants made totalling £208,500 and broken down as follows:

Social welfare	52	£54,000
Youth charities	52	£48,000
People with disabilities/older people	41	£39,000
Education/arts	29	£28,500
Greggs Foundation	4	£20,000
Ethnic minorities	9	£9,000
Women's charities	4	£3,500
Environment	7	£6,500

The values of grants made in the year were broken down as follows:

£5,000	4	£20,000
£3,000	1	£3,000
£2,000	16	£32,000
£1,500	1	£1,500
£1,000	128	£128,000
£750	1	£750
£500	46	£23,000
£250	1	£250

A list of beneficiaries was not available.

Exclusions

The trust does not support:

- Capital projects that are for major building improvements
- Repair of buildings used solely for worship
- Animal protection charities
- Charities based outside the geographical area of interest
- National charities making general appeals
- National charities without a base in the north east of England

Applications

Applications can be made online via the trust's website. Refer to the website for application deadlines.

Sources of information

Accounts; annual report; Charity Commission record; funder's website.

Halifax Foundation for Northern Ireland (previously known as Lloyds Bank Foundation for Northern Ireland)

 Social and community needs, education and training

Northern Ireland

£1.1 million (2017)

CC number: NIC101763

Trustees: Janet Leckey; Hugh Donnelly; Janine Donnelly; James McCooe; Imelda Macmillan; Paula Leathem; Aine McCoy; Mary Keightley; Nuala Dlacz; Gillian Boyd.

Correspondent: Brenda McMullan, 11–15 Donegall Square North, Belfast BT1 5GB (tel: 028 9032 3000; email: info@halifaxfoundationni.org)

 www.halifaxfoundationni.org

Previously known as the Lloyds Bank Foundation for Northern Ireland, the foundation was renamed in 2016, due to the strong presence in Northern Ireland of the Halifax, which is part of Lloyds Banking Group. The foundation is one of four Lloyds Banking Group charities, covering England and Wales, Scotland, Northern Ireland and the Channel Islands. The foundation is an independent grant-maker, receiving its income from shares held in the banking group.

Funding objectives

The overall aim of the foundation, as stated on its website is:

To support charitable organisations within Northern Ireland to enable people, who are disadvantaged or with special needs, to participate actively in their communities.

The foundation has two main target areas to which it seeks to allocate funds:

- Social and community needs
- Education and training

Social and community needs

The foundation supports a wide range of activities and the following examples are listed on the website as a guide:

- **Community Services:** Family centres, youth clubs, older people's clubs, after schools clubs, self-help groups, childcare provision preschools and playgroups
- **Advice Services:** Homelessness, addictions, bereavement, family guidance, money advice, helplines and suicide awareness
- **People with Special Needs:** Residences, day centres, transport, carers, information, advice, and advocacy
- **Promotion of Health:** Information and advice, mental health, hospices, day care, home nursing, independent living for older people
- **Civic Responsibility:** Young people at risk, crime prevention, promotion of volunteering, victim support, mediation, rehabilitation of offenders
- **Cultural Enrichment:** Improving access and skills development in the arts and national heritage for disadvantaged people and those with special needs

Education and training

The objective is to enhance educational opportunities for disadvantaged people and those with special needs:

- **Employment:** Projects which help disadvantaged people develop their potential and secure employment
- **Life Skills:** Promotion of life skills, independent living skills for people with special needs
- **Training and Education:** Accredited, vocational or personal development training

Grant programmes

The Community Grant Programme is the foundation's main focus through which grants are made within its funding objectives. Grants currently average between £3,000 and £4,000.

In order to be eligible to apply, organisations must have an income of less than £1 million in the previous 12 months. For registered charities which have a headquarters based outside Northern Ireland, the foundation will use the figure of the income of their Northern Ireland operation to determine their eligibility.

Full guidelines for the programme are available from the website.

The Matched Giving Programme allows employees of Lloyds Banking Group to claim up to £1,000 per year for a charity they have fundraised or volunteered for, within the scheme's eligibility criteria. The foundation matches every pound raised, or donates £8 per hour of voluntary time given, for a maximum of £500 in fundraising or time given. Full guidelines are provided on the foundation's website. During this financial year, 326 awards were made under the programme totalling £120,500.

Special Initiatives is intended to support significant change occurring within the voluntary and community sector as a whole. In 2017 four awards were made totalling £27,800.

Financial information

In 2017 the foundation held £3.35 million in assets and had an income of £3.9 million. A total of almost £1.1 million was awarded in 531 grants broken down as follows:

Social and community welfare	£661,000
Education and training	£317,500
Matched giving	£120,500

Previous beneficiaries have included: Appleby Careers Project Ltd and Gleann Amateur Boxing Club (£5,000 each); Loughside FC (£4,100); Child Brain Injury Trust (£4,000); Citizenship Foundation (£3,600); Cathedral Quarter Trust, St John's Parish Church, Strabane Community Unemployed Group and Youth Hostel Association of Northern Ireland (£3,000 each); Greenpower Education Trust (£1,500); Ballynure and District Friendship Club (£700); Ballymacward Preschool Playgroup (£500).

Exclusions

The following is not supported by the foundation:

- Non-registered charities
- Organisations which have an income of more than £1 million in the previous year's accounts
- Organisations which are insolvent
- Organisations who have over 12 months reserves would not be seen as a priority
- Individuals, including students
- Animal welfare
- The environment
- Hospitals and medical centres
- Schools, universities and colleges (except for projects specifically to benefit pupils with special needs)

- Sponsorship or fundraising events either for your own organisation or another
- Promotion of religion
- Endowment funds
- Activities that are normally the responsibility of central or local government or some other responsible body
- Loans or business finance
- Travel or activities outside Northern Ireland
- Capital build (except in the case of disabled access)

The foundation is less likely to fund organisations who do not charge a nominal fee for activities.

Applications

All applications must be made online via the foundation's website, where full guidelines, including a list of supporting documentation required, are available. The Community Grants Programme is operated on a rolling basis, meaning organisations can apply at any time. It can take at least four months for a decision to be made, and applying organisations may receive a telephone call or visit as part of the application process.

Sources of information

Accounts; annual report; Charity Commission record; funder's website; guidelines for applicants.

Paul Hamlyn Foundation

🔍 Arts, education, young people, social justice

📍 UK and India

💷 £19.6 million to organisations (2016/17)

CC number: 1102927

Trustees: Jane Hamlyn; Tim Bunting; Lord Anthony Hall; Michael Hamlyn; Charles Leadbeater; James Lingwood; Janet McKenley-Simpson; Sir Anthony Salz; Claire Whitaker; Tom Wylie.

Correspondent: Grants Team, 5–11 Leeke Street, London WC1X 9HY (tel: 020 7812 3300; fax: 020 7812 3310; email: information@phf.org.uk)

 www.phf.org.uk

Paul Hamlyn was a publisher and philanthropist. In 1987 he established the Paul Hamlyn Foundation and upon his death in 2001, bequeathed the majority of his estate to the foundation, so that it became one of the UK's largest independent grant-giving organisations.

The mission of the foundation is to 'help people overcome disadvantage and lack of opportunity, so that they can realise

their potential and enjoy fulfilling and creative lives'. In particular, the foundation has an interest in supporting young people and a strong belief in the importance of the arts.

UK grants programmes

In 2015 the foundation carried out a strategic review of its UK grant-making activities which identified the following priorities:

- **Nurturing ideas and people:** Support the creation of exciting ideas by helping imaginative people nurture them
- **Arts access and participation:** Widen access and participation in the arts
- **Education and learning through the arts:** Improve people's education and learning through the arts
- **Arts evidence:** Show that the arts make a difference to people's lives
- **Investing in young people:** Support and strengthen the work of organisations working with young people experiencing disadvantage
- **Migration and integration:** Improve support for young people who migrate and for receiving communities to support better integration
- **Playing our part:** Play a role in pioneering philanthropy, both as an independent grant-maker and as a partner to others seeking to achieve social justice

Under each of these themes the foundation offers a range of funds and grants programmes, summarised below.

Ideas and Pioneers Fund: supports people with unusual or radical ideas to improve the life chances and opportunities of people in the UK. Grants of up to £10,000 (and up to £15,000 in exceptional circumstances) are available to individuals, partnerships or small organisations.

Access and Participation Fund: support organisations to test, implement and develop ambitious plans to widen access to and deepen participation in the arts. Two types of grant are available to support work at different stages of development.

Arts-based Learning Fund: support arts organisations working with schools, colleges and other education environments to improve the evidence base for their work, so that they can do more to enhance the lives, development and achievements of children and young people.

Teacher Development Fund: helps teachers to develop their skills to deliver arts in schools and to maximise the potential impact of the arts on young people. The foundation supports school-based projects to develop and spread good practice in teaching and learning in

the arts. Each year, the foundation aims to make around five grants of up to £150,000 to partnerships of arts/cultural organisations and schools who will work together for two academic years.

Youth Fund: supports organisations whose main purpose is about helping young people (aged 14 to 25) in the most precarious positions, where making the transition to adult independence is most challenging.

Shared Ground Fund: helps to explore new approaches to supporting young migrants in greatest need and/or communities experiencing high levels of migration, particularly in response to new challenges and opportunities arising as a result of policy and practice changes.

Tech for Good Fund: provides the opportunity for not-for-profit organisations who already have some technological capacity, to progress their digital innovation projects.

In addition to the grants programmes listed above, the foundation also operates several funds which are by invitation only. Full details including eligibility criteria and terms and conditions for all UK grant programmes are available on the foundation's website.

India Grants programme

In addition to its work in the UK, the foundation also works with Indian NGOs that focus on vulnerable groups in the poorest regions of the country. Funding for the foundation's India work falls into two categories:

Open grants fund: helps vulnerable communities living in priority geographical areas to improve their lives.

Lost childhoods fund: supports young people who 'run away from home and gravitate towards railways, where they are vulnerable to many forms of exploitation, trafficking, drugs and crime'.

To be eligible for funding, organisations should be local Indian NGOs with Foreign Contribution Regulation Act registration. Further details about these grants are provided on the foundation's website.

Financial information

In 2016/17 the foundation had assets of £747 million and an income of £19.4 million. During the year, a total of 220 grants were made to organisations totalling £19.6 million. A further 22 grants, amounting to £570,000 were awarded to individuals.

Beneficiaries included: Royal Liverpool Philharmonic Society (£329,000); Royal Society of Arts (£250,000); Arts Derbyshire (£175,000); Migration Museum Project (£165,000); ACTA Community Theatre Ltd (£155,000);

Digdarshika Institute of Rehabilitation and Research (£79,000) Tate Gallery (£70,000); Phoenix Dance Company, Prison Arts Foundation, Mental Health Foundation (£60,000 each); CanDo Coffee (£50,000); Fight for Peace UK (£10,000); University of Sunderland (£5,400).

Exclusions

According to the foundation's website, it will not support:

- Proposals that are only for the benefit of one individual
- Websites, publications or seminars, unless part of a wider proposal
- Funding for work that has already been delivered
- General fundraising appeals, letters requesting donations and other non-specific funding requests
- Proposals that have previously considered in the past 12 months and turned down, unless we have explicitly invited you to resubmit. Organisations that have submitted a proposal to one of our funds which has been rejected may apply to another fund for a different proposal. We will not consider the same proposal even if submitted to another fund
- Proposals about property or which are mainly about equipment or other capital items, including the restoration or conservation of buildings or habitats
- Overseas travel (including expeditions, adventure and residential courses)
- Promotion of religion
- Animal welfare
- Medical/health/residential or day care
- Proposals that benefit people living outside the UK (except for our India Programme)
- Organisations that do not have a formal constitution
- Activity that is not legally charitable
- More than one proposal to us from an individual, team or organisation at any one time
- Academic research, scholarships, bursaries, or any kind of student fees
- Loan and/or debt repayments

The foundation is unlikely to support any of the following – applicants wishing to apply for any of these should contact the foundation:

- Endowments
- Organisations that would like to use our funding to make grants
- Proposals from organisations outside the UK (except for our India Programme)
- Organisations that are for-profit
- Organisations that already have an active grant with us, unless we have explicitly invited you to submit an additional bid

Specific funding programmes may have additional exclusions – details are provided on the foundation's website.

Applications

Applications can only be submitted via the online application process. The foundation does not accept any applications that have been sent in by mail. Applicants should first complete the eligibility quiz before submitting the form online. Applications should be submitted at least three months before work is due to start, or six months for grants under the 'More and Better' scheme.

Sources of information

Accounts; annual report; Charity Commission record; funder's website.

The Helen Hamlyn Trust

 Medical, arts and culture, education and welfare, heritage and conservation in India, international humanitarian affairs, healthy aging

Worldwide

(£) £1.09 million (2016/17)

CC number: 1084839

Trustees: Lady Hamlyn; Dr Kate Gavron; Dr Shobita Punja; Brendan Cahill; Margaret O'Rorke; Dr Deborah Swallow; Stephen Lewin; Dame Alison Peacock.

Correspondent: John Roche-Kuroda, Director of Finance and Administration, 129 Old Church Street, London SW3 6EB (tel: 020 7351 7600; email: john.rochekuroda@helenhamlyntrust. org)

 www.phf.org.uk/our-work-in-the-uk/helen-hamlyn-trust

The Helen Hamlyn Trust was established in 2000 and registered with the Charity Commission in January 2001. In April 2002 the assets and activities of the Helen Hamlyn 1989 Foundation were transferred into this trust. The trust's activities fall within the aims and broad objectives of the Paul Hamlyn Foundation (Charity Commission no. 1102927).

The trust's core aims are to 'initiate and support innovative medium to long-term projects, which will effect lasting change and improve quality of life for the benefit of the public or sections of the public'. In its 2016/17 accounts, the trust lists the following current areas of activity:

- **Medical** – support innovation in the medical arena
- **Arts and culture** – increase access to the arts and support the professional development of artists from the fields of music and the performing arts
- **Education and welfare** – increase intercultural understanding; provide opportunities for young people to develop new interests and practical skills which will contribute to their education and their future lives and to create opportunities for young offenders to acquire practical skills which will support their personal development for their future lives
- **Heritage and conservation in India** – conserve heritage in India for public access and cultural activities
- **International humanitarian affairs** – support examples of good practice in the humanitarian sector
- **Healthy aging** – provide practical support to enable older people to maintain their independence for as long as possible

Additionally, the trust also awards small grants of up to £10,000 'to a wide variety of small local and regional charities where a grant of this size can make a significant difference'. The annual report notes that the trust has 'wide powers' to make grants with recommendations for projects being brought forward to the trustees and subjected to the approval by the board.

The trust provides ongoing support to a number of projects, including, its flagship education project 'Open Futures' and the Helen Hamlyn Centre for Design at the Royal College of Art.

Financial information

In 2016/17 the trust held assets of £4.86 million and had an income of £2.58 million. Grants totalled £1.09 million. In addition £281,500 was spent on direct charitable activities related to the Open Futures Trust (£215,000) and Setubal Music Festival Portugal (£66,500).

Grants were broken down into the following categories:

Education and welfare	£750,000
Arts and culture	£315,500
Medical	£18,000
Healthy Ageing	£7,500

Beneficiaries included: The Design Museum (£356,000); The Helen Hamlyn Centre for Design at the RCA (£250,000); Royal Opera House (£100,000); Oxford University (£116,000); Cini Foundation (£89,000); The Stroke Association (£15,000); Partnership for Children (£4,000); Kew Foundation (£3,800).

Applications

The trustees have previously noted that 'their energies are focused on the initiation of projects and they do not accept unsolicited applications for major grants'. Appeals for small awards may be directed to the correspondent. The trustees meet formally twice a year and informally throughout the year.

Sources of information

Accounts; annual report; Charity Commission record; funder's website.

Hammersmith United Charities

 General charitable purposes, education and training, people with disabilities, the prevention or relief of poverty, accommodation and housing, community development, recreation

 The eight northern wards of Hammersmith and Fulham

 £350,500 (2016/17)

CC number: 205856

Trustee: Hammersmith United Trustee Company.

Correspondent: Tim Hughes, Sycamore House, Sycamore Gardens, London W6 0AS (tel: 020 8741 4326; email: info@hamunitedcharities.com)

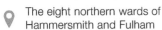 www.hamunitedcharities.org.uk

facebook.com/hamunitedcharities

@HamUnited

The charity's statement of purpose was reviewed in the 2016/17 business plan, and is unchanged. It reads:

Hammersmith United Charities invests in the people and communities in the 8 northern wards of Hammersmith & Fulham to tackle poverty, deprivation and disadvantage, building on our legacies, wisdom, learning and experience gained over 400 years.

We support local people to build their confidence and resourcefulness, develop op their own talents and skills, connect people together and strengthen relationships and neighbourliness within and across diverse communities. We achieve these aims by:

- managing vibrant sheltered housing communities for older people
- creating safe, beautiful outdoor environments managed by the Charity's community horticulturalist with the residents, for people to share and enjoy as neighbours
- funding a community based grants programme
- match-funding the Wormholt & White City Big Local with the Lottery, and
- by working with local people, organisations and businesses to make Hammersmith a great place.

Grants programme

The grants committee meets in January, May and October to consider applications, with a grants budget of £250,000. The trustees are particularly keen to fund smaller, local organisations with a very strong connection to their beneficiaries and a good knowledge of the local area. Applications should be with the trustees four weeks before their meeting, the dates of which are published on the website.

The trustees also offer 'micro grants' of up to £500 for one-off projects and activities, or for specific pieces of equipment. These are assessed on a rolling basis and the application form is much simpler than for the larger grants. You are strongly advised to contact the charity before making an application.

Financial information

In 2016/17 the charity had assets of £34.58 million and an income of £1.48 million. Grants awarded to organisations totalled £350,500.

Beneficiaries included: Soup4lunch (£16,000); London Sports Trust (£14,900); Leaf Education (£9,400); Flying Gorillas (£7,000); Silver Screen Film Club (£3,000); Folk Art Group (£1,200).

Exclusions

The charity does not make grants for religious or political causes, animal welfare or the environment.

Applications

The charity welcomes initial grant enquiries by phone or email. The charity's website states, 'we like to meet new applicants to develop a better understanding of what they are doing and we are happy to give advice about potential projects'.

Grant application forms can be downloaded from the website. The charity has three grants committee meetings each year and the dates of these and the dates by which forms must be received for each meeting are advertised on the website. Once completed, application forms must be emailed to the correspondent.

Sources of information

Accounts; annual report; Charity Commission record; funder's website.

The Hampstead Wells and Campden Trust

 Social welfare, health and disability, community development, special needs groups

 The former metropolitan borough of Hampstead

£184,500 to organisations (2016/17)

CC number: 1094611

Trustees: Gaynor Bassey; Geoff Berridge; Mike Bieber; Steven Bobasch; Linda Chung; Francoise Findlay; Revd Jeremy Fletcher; Tibor Gold; Gaynor Humphreys; Angela Mason; Chris Percy; Charles Perrin; Alison Rankin; Jenny Stevens; Alistair Voaden; Dr Christina Williams.

Correspondent: Sheila Taylor, Director and Clerk to the Trustees, 62 Rosslyn

Hill, London NW3 1ND (tel: 020 7435 1570; email: grant@hwct.co.uk)

www.hwct.org.uk

The Hampstead Wells and Campden Trust was formed as a result of the amalgamation of several trusts dating back to the 17th century. In 1880 the Campden Charity, which was founded in 1624 under the will of Lady Campden, amalgamated with the Wells Charity, which was founded in 1698 by the Earl of Gainsborough. Today the trust also administers several local parish charities, including the Wells and Campden Stock Education Foundation, the Wharrie Cabmen's Shelter Fund and the Hampstead Relief in Sickness Fund.

Grants programme

According to the 2016/17 annual report the trust's principal objective 'is to relieve need, and help people who are sick, convalescent, disabled or infirm who reside in the old Metropolitan Borough of Hampstead'. The grants programme is 'aimed at pensions, single payment grants to individuals and organisations'. Grants to organisations normally range from a few hundred pounds to around £20,000 and can help with running costs and occasionally help with capital and core costs.

Financial information

In 2016/17 the trust held assets of £16.7 million and had an income of £460,500. There were grants made totalling £496,000, of which £184,500 was awarded to 38 organisations and £195,500 to 3,321 individuals. A further 126 individuals received pension grants totalling £116,000.

Beneficiaries included: Caris Camden C4WS Homeless Project (£29,500 in two grants); Quaker Social Action (£25,000); Camden Community Law Centre (£20,000); Emmanuel Church West Hampstead and Home-Start Camden (£15,000 each); Age UK Camden (£13,400); West Hampstead Women's Centre (£12,200); Camden Psychotherapy Unit (£7,500); Beanstalk (£6,000); Hampstead Counselling Services (£5,000); The Brandon Centre (£4,000); Henna Asian Women's Group (£1,600).

Exclusions

Grants may not be made towards the payment of rates or taxes, or in principle where statutory bodies have the responsibility to help. General fundraising appeals are not supported.

Applications

Applications for up to £1,000 can be fast tracked to provide an answer within one month of the application. Use either the application form or send a letter detailing: the work to be supported, how much it will cost what you have raised already (and your sources); the type and number of people who will benefit; your links to the trust's area of benefit; information about your group; and your suitability to run and manage the work.

Applications for grants of £1,000 or more must be requested on using the trust's application form, available via the website. Applications can be made at any time. The trustees meet quarterly. Refer to the trust's website for further application guidelines.

Sources of information
Accounts; annual report; Charity Commission record; funder's website.

Hampton Fuel Allotment

 Relief in need, disadvantage, social welfare

 Hampton, Hampton Hill, Hampton Wick, Teddington, Twickenham and Whitton

(£) £929,000 to organisations (2016/17)

CC number: 211756

Trustees: Clive Beaumont; Dr Jim Brockbank; Martin Duffy; Hilary Hart; Revd Ben Lovell; Victoria Reid; Martin Seymour; Derek Terrington; Paula Williams; Mark Boyle; Richard Montgomery.

Correspondent: David White, 15 High Street, Hampton, Middlesex TW12 2SA (tel: 020 8941 7866; email: david@hfac.co.uk)

 www.hfac.co.uk

This charity was established by an Act of Parliament in 1811 and exists to support people and families in need, by making grants to individuals and grants to other organisations. The main aim of the charity is that local people will not suffer from fuel poverty.

Areas of support
The charity's objectives are:

1 The relief of need, hardship or distress of those in the area of benefit
2 Support for the sick, those recovering from illness, and people with a disability
3 Promoting the education of children and young people
4 Providing and supporting recreational and leisure time activities to improve life condition in the interests of social welfare

Grants are made to individuals in need to improve their quality of life. Assistance is given with fuel costs, the purchase of essential household items and the costs of Year 6 school trips, for

example. Full information on these grants is available from the charity's website.

Community grants are made to charities, voluntary sector organisations and community groups which provide services and activities to support people who live in the area of benefit. They are given to a wide range of organisations working in sectors including: disability; older people; children and young people; carers; mental health; and community activities.

Financial information
In 2016/17 the charity had assets of almost £60 million and an income of £2 million. Grants awarded totalled £1.8 million, comprising of £767,000 to individuals and £929,000 to 63 organisations.

Grants that were awarded to organisations were distributed into the following categories:

Other	19	£300,000
Disabilities	14	£200,500
Older people	10	£151,500
Children and young people	8	£112,500
Carers	4	£83,000
Community activities	4	£37,000
Hospitals and hospices	1	£20,000
Education	2	£16,000
Arts, sports, recreation	1	£7,500

Beneficiaries included: Richmond Citizens Advice Service (£55,000); Spear Housing Association (£40,000); Richmond upon Thames Crossroads Care (£35,000); Integrated Neurological Services (£25,000); Princess Alice Hospice (£20,000); Richmond Advice and Information on Disability (£15,000); My Life in Films (£10,000); (£7,000); Marble Hill Play Centre and Whitton Network (£4,000 each); Connaught Opera (£3,500); Still Building Bridges (£1,500).

Exclusions
The charity is unable to support the following:

- Grants to individuals for private and post compulsory education
- Adaptions or building alterations for individuals
- Holidays except in cases of severe medical need
- Decoration, carpeting or central heating
- Anything which is the responsibility of a statutory body
- National general charitable appeals
- Animal welfare
- The advancement of religion and religious groups, unless they offer a non-religious service to the community
- Commercial and business activities
- Endowment appeals
- Projects of a political nature

- Retrospective funding, both capital and revenue
- Organisations whose free reserves exceed 12 months' running costs
- Non-charitable social enterprises

Applications
Applicants are strongly advised to first read the guidance notes, which are available to download from the charity's website. Candidates who match the funding criteria should then contact the correspondent to further discuss their needs.

Sources of information
Accounts; annual report; Charity Commission record; guidelines for applicants; funder's website.

The W A Handley Charity Trust

General charitable purposes

North east of England and Cumbria

(£) £287,500 (2016/17)

CC number: 230435

Trustees: Bill Dryden; Tony Glenton; David Irvin; David Milligan.

Correspondent: The Trustees, c/o Ryecroft Glenton, 32 Portland Terrace, Newcastle upon Tyne NE2 1QP (tel: 0191 281 1292; email: davidmilligan@ryecroft-glenton.co.uk)

This trust was founded in 1963 and endowed by the late Wilfred Handley and his relatives. The trust has general charitable purposes., with grants commonly made for: the welfare of people who are disadvantaged, young people, older people, people with disabilities, maritime and armed forces causes, education, training and employment, community, historic and religious buildings, the environment, music and the arts. There is a preference for supporting organisations on a regular basis within Northumberland, Tyne and Wear, County Durham (including Hartlepool) and Cumbria (including Carlisle). Grants are normally made to registered charities (within these counties) but may also be made to national charities operating within or where their work may be expected to be of benefit to these areas.

Financial information
In 2016/17 the trust had assets of £9.8 million and an income of £232,500. During the year, the trust awarded 127 grants to organisations totalling £287,500. Out of the 127 grants awarded, 98 were made on a regular basis.

Regular annual grants totalled £162,000 and were broken down as follows:

Social care	31	£50,000
Health	24	£44,500
Arts, culture and recreation	16	£31,000
Philanthropy, volunteering and voluntary sector support	11	£11,500
Religious activities	6	£8,700
Civil society, law and advocacy	4	£5,600
Development and housing	4	£4,800
Environment and animal care	3	£4,000
Education	2	£2,000

One-off grants totalled £135,000 broken down as follows:

Social care	8	£48,500
Arts, culture and recreation	9	£37,500
Education	2	£20,000
Health	6	£16,500
Religious activities	3	£10,500
Philanthropy, volunteering and voluntary sector support	1	£2,000

Beneficiaries included: Royal Grammar High School and Percy Park Rugby Club (£10,000); Seaton Delaval Hall (£7,000); NE Youth (£6,000); Great North Air Ambulance (£5,000); Northumberland Scout Association (£3,500); Paxton House (£2,500); Alnwick Playhouse (£2,250); Citizens Advice Newcastle (£1,000).

Exclusions

Individuals; unregistered charities; awards are not normally made outside the area of benefit.

Applications

Apply in writing to the correspondent.

Sources of information

Accounts; annual report; Charity Commission record.

The Robert Fleming Hannay Memorial Charity

 General charitable purposes

Scotland

£ Around £400,000 (2016/17)

CC number: 1086811

Trustees: Christian Ward; Geoffrey Richards; Fiona Hannay.

Correspondent: The Trustees, c/o RF Trustee Co. Ltd, 15 Suffolk Street, London SW1Y 4HG (tel: 020 3696 6721; email: charities@rftrustee.com)

The Robert Fleming Hannay Memorial Charity was registered with the Charity Commission in 2001 for general charitable purposes. In previous years the charity has awarded grant under the following categories:

- The prevention or relief of poverty
- The advancement of education
- The advancement of religion
- The advancement of health or the saving of lives

- The advancement of the arts, culture, heritage or science
- The advancement of human rights, conflict resolution or reconciliation, or the promotion of religious or racial harmony or equality or diversity
- The relief of those in need by reason of youth, age, ill-health, disability, financial hardship or other disadvantage

Financial information

In 2016/17 the charity had an income of £18,100 and a total expenditure of £442,000. Due to its low income, accounts for this financial year were unavailable, however, it is estimated that the charity awarded grants of around £400,000.

A list of beneficiaries was unavailable.

Applications

Apply in writing to the correspondent. The trustees meet twice a year to consider applications and make grants.

Sources of information

Accounts; annual report; Charity Commission record.

The Haramead Trust

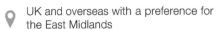 Social welfare, children and young people, education in relation to the advancement of health

UK and overseas with a preference for the East Midlands

£ £1.1 million (2016/17)

CC number: 1047416

Trustees: David Tams; Robert Smith; Winifred Linnett; Simon Astil; Victoria Duddles; Dr Mary Hanlon.

Correspondent: Winifred Linnett, Trustee, Park House, Park Hill, Gaddesby, Leicestershire LE7 4WH (email: harameadtrust@aol.com)

The Haramead Trust was established in 1995 for general charitable purposes. According to the annual report for 2016/17, the grant-giving is focused on:

- The relief of those suffering hardship or distress
- Children's welfare
- Education in relation to the advancement of health

Causes supported include children's charities, social and medical assistance, homelessness and educational needs. Support may cover capital or core costs and project expenditure.

Financial information

In 2016/17 the trust had assets of £2.4 million and an income of £1.8 million. During the year, the trust made 75 grants totalling £1.1 million. Grants were distributed as follows:

UK and Ireland	£596,500
Local Area (East Midlands)	£333,500
Developing World	£160,000

Beneficiaries included: Ireland Fund of Great Britain (£100,000); CAFOD and Charity Link (£50,000 each); Cathedral Trust for England and Wales (£30,000); Shelter (£25,000); De Montfort University (£20,000); Dogs for the Disabled and Leicester Children's Holiday Centre (£10,000 each).

Grants of less than £10,000 totalled £175,000.

Applications

Applications may be made in writing to the correspondent, providing relevant financial details of your organisation and the budget of the project for which the grant is required. The trustees meet every couple of months and may visit funded projects for monitoring purposes or to assess for future grants. All appeals are acknowledged.

Sources of information

Accounts; annual report; Charity Commission record; further information provided by the funder.

The Harborne Parish Lands Charity

 Social welfare

The ancient parish of Harborne, which includes parts of Harborne, Smethwick, Bearwood and Quinton and Wednesbury

£ £224,500 to organisations (2016/17)

CC number: 219031

Trustees: Cllr Roger Horton; Rachel Silber; Frank Wayt; Nigel Thompson; Geoff Hewitt; Buddhi Chetiyawardana; David Jeffrey; Kerry Bolister; Vic Silvester; Bawa Dhallu.

Correspondent: Peter Hardisty, Grants Officer, 109 Court Oak Road, Harborne, Birmingham B17 9AA (tel: 0121 426 1600; email: peter.hardisty@hplc.org.uk)

www.hplc.org.uk

According to the 2016/17 annual report, the origins of the charity are:

Lost in the mists of time, but it was mentioned in a document dated 1640 and may date from a bequest by Mrs Elizabeth Cowper (alias Piddock) in 1576. Today the charity owns various investments together with five almshouse properties which were part funded by the Housing Corporation. The area of benefit is the Ancient Parish of Harborne, now in the County of West Midlands and the beneficiaries are the almspeople and those in need within the parish.

The objectives of the charity are for the benefit of the almspeople and the relief of those in need who are resident in the 12 parishes which together make up the Ancient Parish of Harborne. This comprises most of Harborne and some of Quinton in the City of Birmingham, and most of Smethwick and a small part of Bearwood in Sandwell MBC. The charity has no religious affiliation and the name refers to the geographical area.

The charity provides grants to both individuals directly and to organisations which assist individuals and has referral arrangements with the housing and social services in both Birmingham and Sandwell.

The major grants awarded to organisations in 2016/17 included a manager's salary at a community day centre for older people; person-centred support for older people and older carers; and employability courses for 16- to 24-year-olds who are not in education, employment, or training (NEETs) or those at risk of NEET.

Financial information
In 2016/17 the charity held assets of £18 million and had an income of £1.4 million. There were grants made to 27 organisations totalling £224,500 and to 298 individuals totalling £51,000.

Beneficiaries included: Soho and Victoria Friends and Neighbours CIC (£18,500); Ethnic Minority Council (£15,300); West Smethwick Enterprise Family Centre (£13,600); Care Link West Midlands (£7,700); Wheelchair Recycling We Can Do (£5,000); Smethwick Mini Muslims (£2,000); Birmingham St Mary's Hospice, NICE – Centre for Movement Disorders and Women's Aid (£1,200 each).

Applications
Applications should be made on a form available from the correspondent. An exact map of the beneficial area can be obtained from the charity (or on its website) and should be consulted before an application is submitted. The following information is taken from the charity's website:

Application process:
- All applications must be made on the Charity's grants to organisations application form and submitted with a copy of the organisation's audited accounts
- Applicants are visited by the grants administrator to ensure complete understanding of the proposal
- The grants administrator prepares a report for the Board of Trustees
- Board of Trustees meet – decision made
- Letter to applicant advising of decision

The application deadlines are posted on the charity's website. The current application deadlines for 2018 are as follows:

- **Monday 5th February 2018** – Approved applicants to be notified in April
- **Monday 7th May 2018** – Approved applicants to be notified in July
- **Monday 2nd July 2018** – Approved applicants will be notified in September
- **Monday 1st October 2018** – Approved applicants to be notified in December

Sources of information
Accounts; annual report; Charity Commission record; funder's website.

The Harbour Foundation

General charitable purposes, especially: relief of poverty, refugees and homeless people, education and research, musical training, and scientific and technical postgraduate training

Worldwide, in practice mostly in the UK

£607,500 (2016/17)

CC number: 264927

Trustees: Susan Harbour; Dr Daniel Harbour; Edmond Harbour; Gideon Harbour; Harry Rich; Richard Hermer.

Correspondent: The Trustees, 1 Red Place, London W1K 6PL (tel: 020 7456 8180)

The Harbour Foundation was established in 1970. According to the trustees' report for 2016/17, 'the charity's activities consist of the making of grants to charitable organisations which are based in the UK and abroad'. Charitable objects, as established in the governing document, comprise:

- The relief of poverty, suffering and distress among refugees and other homeless people
- The advancement of education, learning and research and the dissemination of the results of such research
- To make donations to any institution established for charitable purposes according to the law of England and Wales

The annual report for 2016/17 notes that:

The emphasis on support for scientific and technical postgraduate training has been maintained and at the same time additional funds have been made available to assist organisations involved in poverty alleviation and positive social and cultural change.

The foundation also has a programme supporting postgraduates which is available to impoverished post-grad students for science and medical related degrees at the two Israeli universities: the Hebrew University of Jerusalem and Ben Gurion University of the Negev.

Financial information
In 2016/17 the foundation had assets of £20.8 million and an income of £1.1 million. During the year, the foundation awarded 42 grants to organisations totalling £607,500. Grants were distributed in following areas:

Education	4	£450,000
Arts	12	£72,000
Social organisations	16	£53,500
Relief	5	£22,500
Medical	4	£8,800
Religious bodies	1	£1,000

Beneficiaries included: Ben Gurion University Foundation and British Friends of Hebrew University of Jerusalem (£200,000 each); UCL Medical School (50,000); Ben Bodna (£15,300); East London Business Alliance (£7,500); Cure Parkinson's Trust and Suffolk Cruse Bereavement (£5,000 each).

Other grants below £5,000 totalled £7,500.

Applications
Applications can be made in writing to the correspondent.

Sources of information
Accounts; annual report; Charity Commission record.

The David and Claudia Harding Foundation

Science, the arts, community development

UK

£7.6 million (2016)

CC number: 1120878

Trustees: David Harding; Claudia Harding; Revd Richard Whittington.

Correspondent: Adrianna Whish, DCH Office, Michelin House, 81 Fulham Road SW3 6RD

The foundation was established by David Harding, founder of the Winton Group and his wife Claudia in 2007. David also established Winton Philanthropies in 2005.

The foundation makes grants to a wide range of charities including those with a particular focus on science, the arts and community development.

Financial information
In 2016 the foundation held assets of £11.4 million and had an income of £45,000. Grants awarded to organisations totalled £7.6 million. During the year, the commitment to pay two grants totalling £2.25 million was transferred to Winton Philanthropies.

Beneficiaries included: Cambridge Foundation (£3 million); Cancer Research UK (£1.25 million); Westminster Abbey Foundation (£500,000); MS Society (£250,000); Candoco Dance Company (£150,000); Kind Edward VII Hospital (£50,000).

Grants of under £50,000 totalled £1 million.

Applications

Apply in writing to the correspondent.

Sources of information

Accounts; annual report; Charity Commission record.

William Harding's Charity

 Education, social welfare

Aylesbury

£688,500 to organisations (2016)

CC number: 310619

Trustees: Les Sheldon; Anne Brooker; Freda Roberts; Penni Thorne; Roger Evans; William Chapple; Ranjula Takodra; Lennard Wakelam; Susan Hewitt.

Correspondent: John Leggett, Clerk to the Trustees, 14 Bourbon Street, Aylesbury, Buckinghamshire HP20 2RS (tel: 01296 318501; email: doudjag@pandclip.co.uk)

Under a scheme of 1978, Harding's Eleemosynary Charity and Harding's Educational Charity (both set up in the eighteenth century) merged to become William Harding's Charity. Its objects, limited to the town of Aylesbury, include:

▶ The provision of almshouses and other benefits for older people
▶ The provision of special benefits of any kind not normally provided by the local authority for any maintained school or any college of education or other institution of further education in or substantially serving the town of Aylesbury
▶ Awarding maintenance allowances tenable at any school, university or college of further education
▶ Relief in need and provision of general benefit in Aylesbury

The charity owns 35 properties in Aylesbury itself, land in or adjacent to Aylesbury and is a member of the National Association of Almshouses.

Financial information

In 2016 the charity had assets of £34.3 million and an income of £1 million. Grants paid to organisations totalled £688,500 and were broken down as follows:

Schools and educational establishments	£490,500
Individual pupil support	£340,500
Travel costs for 30+ voluntary clubs and societies	£50,500
Youth groups	£28,000
General benefit and relief in need	£20,400

Beneficiaries included: Mandeville School (£219,000); Aspire Project (£95,000); Bedgrove Junior School (£35,000); Aylesbury Youth Action (£12,500); Buckinghamshire Play Association (£10,000); Inspire All CIC (£8,300); Jigsaw Theatre Company (£2,200); Aylesbury Symphony Orchestra (£1,600); Silverdale Social Club (£1,500); Wednesday Club (£100).

Exclusions

Organisations not based in Aylesbury town are not eligible for support.

Applications

Applications may be made in writing to the correspondent. The trustees meet on a regular basis to consider applications.

Sources of information

Accounts; annual report; Charity Commission record.

The Harpur Trust

 Education, social welfare, and recreation

The borough of Bedford

£1.1 million (2016/17)

CC number: 1066861

Trustees: David Wilson; Michael Womack; Philip Wedgwood Wallace; Anthony Nutt; William Phillimore; Susan Clark; Mark Taylor; Tina BeddoesProf. Stephen Mayson; Hugh Stewart; Clive Loader; Prof. Richard Ratcliffe; Sally Peck; Dr Jennifer Sauboorah Till; Dr Anne Egan; Cllr Randolph Charles; Rhian Castell; Linbert Spencer; Shirley Jackson; Cllr Luigi Reale; Rose-Marie Wellington; Harriett Mather; Prof. Rajkumar Roy; Prof. Rebecca Taylor.

Correspondent: Lucy Bardner, Grants Manager, Princeton Court, The Pilgrim Centre, Brickhill Drive, Bedford MK41 7PZ (tel: 01234 369500; email: lbardner@harpurtrust.org.uk)

 www.harpurtrust.org.uk

 facebook.com/TheHarpurTrust

 @theharpurtrust

The Harpur Trust (also formerly known as the Bedford Charity), has been in existence since 1566 when it was founded by Sir William Harpur (1496–1573) a tailor from Bedford and later Lord Mayor of London, who created an endowment to sustain a school he had established in Bedford.

Today, the trust owns and runs four independent schools in Bedford – Bedford School, Bedford Girls' School, Bedford Modern School and Pilgrims Preparatory School. The trust is also a co-sponsor, along with Bedford College of the new Bedford Academy, and manages almshouses which provide secure, affordable accommodation for a number of the borough's disadvantaged, older citizens.

Each year the trust awards grants totalling up to £1 million to organisations which fit one or more of its charitable objects: 'education, relief of poverty, sickness or distress and recreation with a social welfare purpose'.

According to the trust's website, grants are usually awarded in three priority areas:

▶ **Transitions:** Offering preparation and support for people undergoing difficult life transitions
▶ **Resilience or psychological fitness:** Giving people the skills to manage traumatic change positively, adapting and prospering after setbacks
▶ **Isolation:** Reducing loneliness and lack of social networks among Bedford's most vulnerable residents

In addition to grants for organisations, the trust also awards a small number of individual educational grants and university bursaries.

From time to time the trust also offers additional grants programmes with separate requirements and application processes. Check the trust's website for the latest information.

Financial information

In 2016/17 the trust had assets of £170.8 million and an income of £52.8 million. Grants worth a total of £1.1 million were awarded and were distributed as follows:

Social welfare	£828,000
Education	£179,000
Recreation	£74,000

Previous beneficiaries have included: Philharmonia Orchestra (£125,000); Mind BLMK (£80,500); The Cranfield Trust (£70,000); Mid North and Bedfordshire CVS (£50,000); Chums Child Bereavement Service (£40,000); Royal Mencap Society (£30,000); Bedford Creative Arts (£21,000); Tibbs Dementia Services (£15,500); The Bedfordshire Orchestral Society (£10,000); Balliol Lower School, Putnoe Woods Preschool and SchoolReaders (£5,000 each); Arkwright Scholarships Trust (£2,000); Bedford Community Netball Club and The Polish Language and Culture Association (£1,000 each).

Exclusions

Grants are not provided for the following:

▶ Businesses
▶ Projects that promote a particular religion

- Projects considered to be the responsibility of the local authority or national government
- Projects that do not benefit the residents of the borough of Bedford
- Costs already incurred
- Trips, except in very limited circumstances

Applications

Organisations and individuals are encouraged to contact the trust informally for initial guidance on potential applications. The trust's main priorities, grant programmes and application process are also set out in the guidance notes which are available by post, email and on the trust's website.

Small grants programme

Small grant applications can be considered for:

- Up to £5,000 for a capital project
- Up to £2,000 for any other project

Organisations applying for this programme can submit a full application using an online form on the trust's website, or by downloading or requesting a form from the Grants Manager.

Larger grants programme

All other funding requests must follow the two-stage application process:

The first stage of the formal application process is to submit a preliminary proposal form. Proposals are first considered by trustees before the trust writes to applicants to discuss the outcome, offer feedback and make an invitation to submit a formal, second stage application if applicable.

The second stage application may be completed online or by filling out a hard copy form, downloadable from the website, and posting it back to the trust. Be careful to include the required additional information. The trust guidelines detail what information is required depending on the size and type of grant requested.

Applications requesting amounts of up to £5,000 are normally considered within two to three months. Grants of up to £50,000 for a single project in any one year and up to £150,000 for a project over a three-year period will be considered by the full grants committee which meets every three months. Decisions for these grants are usually made within three to six months.

Sources of information

Accounts; annual report; annual review; Charity Commission record; guidelines for applicants; funder's website.

The Edith Lilian Harrison 2000 Foundation

 General charitable purposes, health, disability, social welfare

 UK

£321,500 (2016/17)

CC number: 1085651

Trustees: Geoffrey Peyer; Clive Andrews; Paul Bradley.

Correspondent: Geoffrey Peyer, Trustee, c/o TWM Solicitors LLP, 40 West Street, Reigate RH2 9BT (tel: 01737 221212; email: paul.bradley@twmsolicitors.com)

The foundation was established in 2000 for general charitable purposes, although grant-making activities only commenced in 2008/09 after receiving almost £3.5 million from the estate of the late Edith Lilian Harrison. The 2016/17 annual report notes that 'although the trustees have unfettered discretion in identifying future grant recipients, it is likely that they will attempt to support projects which reflect their understanding of the charitable aims of Mrs Harrison'. In practice, the foundation supports general charitable purposes, particularly health, disability and social welfare.

Financial information

In 2016/17 the foundation held assets of £2.2 million and had an income of £75,500. Grants were made to 52 organisations totalling £321,500.

Beneficiaries included: Salisbury Hospice (£50,000); Salvation Army (£25,000); Age UK, Blesma, Dogs for Good and Seafarers UK (£5,000 each); Salisbury Rotary Club (£1,500).

Applications

Apply in writing to the correspondent. The trustees meet every six months. Applications for grants are normally considered in November.

Sources of information

Accounts; annual report; Charity Commission record.

The Peter Harrison Foundation

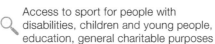 Access to sport for people with disabilities, children and young people, education, general charitable purposes

 UK, with a preference for South-East England

£1.8 million (2016/17)

CC number: 1076579

Trustees: Peter Harrison; Julia Harrison-Lee; Peter Lee; Nicholas Harrison.

Correspondent: Andrew Ross, Director, Foundation House, 42–48 London Road, Reigate, Surrey RH2 9QQ (tel: 01737 228000; fax: 01737 228001; email: enquiries@peterharrisonfoundation.org)

 www.peterharrisonfoundation.org

The foundation was established for general charitable purposes by Peter Harrison in April 1999. The following year the foundation received a capital endowment from Peter Harrison of £30 million, to which the Harrison family later contributed a further £15 million. The foundation aims to maintain the value of this capital while distributing annual income of approximately £2.2 million for charitable purposes. According to the 2016/17 annual report the aims of the foundation are to:

- Help people with disabilities or disadvantaged children/young people, principally through sport and education
- Support charitable activities which are well planned and demonstrate a high level of community involvement
- Fund projects where their grant will make a substantial difference to the charity funded
- Support projects that are likely to have a sustainable impact

Grant programmes

At the time of writing (May 2018), the foundation administers four grant-making programmes:

Opportunities through sport

This programme supports sporting activity or projects which provide opportunities for people with disabilities or who are otherwise disadvantaged to fulfil their potential and to develop other personal and life skills. Grants will often be 'one-off' grants for capital projects. The trustees will, however, also consider revenue funding for a new project or if funding is key to the continuing success or survival of an established project.

The trustees welcome applications for the following types of project:

- Projects which provide a focus for skills development and confidence building through the medium of sport
- Projects that have a strong training and/or educational theme within a sporting activity
- Projects that provide sporting equipment or facilities for disadvantaged people or those with disabilities
- Projects with a high degree of community involvement
- Projects that help to engage children or young people at risk of crime, truancy or addiction

Special needs and care for children and young people

This programme is exclusively for charities in the south-east of England and applications are accepted only from charities meeting the needs of children and young people in the following counties: Berkshire; Buckinghamshire; Hampshire; Isle of Wight; Kent; Oxfordshire; Surrey; East Sussex; and West Sussex.

The foundation does not accept applications from charities based in or operating in London, but may consider funding charities based in London for a specific project taking place in the South East area, that meets the foundation's criteria:

> Projects that work with or benefit chronically or terminally ill children, children with disabilities, and their parents and carers
> Projects that help to engage children or young people at risk of crime, truancy or addiction
> Projects organised for young people at risk of homelessness or that provide new opportunities for homeless young people

Education

This programme supports the provision of educational facilities and bursary places for children from Reigate and Redhill areas in Surrey, to enable them to attend Reigate Grammar School. This programme does not accept unsolicited applications.

Trustees' discretion

This programme supports projects that are of particular interest to the trustees that may fall outside the foundation's main aims. This programme does not accept unsolicited applications.

Financial information

In 2016/17 the foundation had assets of £47 million and an income of £2.4 million. The total amount awarded in grants was £1.8 million to 84 organisations, broken down into categories below:

Opportunities through sport	£995,000
Special needs and care for children and young people	£544,000
Trustees' discretion	£147,000
Education	£136,000

Beneficiaries included: Loughborough University (£200,000); YMCA East Surrey (£50,000); Alexander Devine Children's Hospice and Donaghmore District Community Association (£30,000 each); Access Sport CIO and Samson Centre for MS (£25,000 each).

Exclusions

The foundation does not fund:

> Requests for retrospective funding
> Activities that are primarily the responsibility of central or local government
> Individuals
> Overseas projects
> Adventure challenges or expeditions in the UK or abroad
> Projects that are solely for the promotion of religion

Applications

For its open grants programmes (i.e. 'Opportunities through sport' and 'Special needs and care for children and young people') the foundation has a two-stage application process.

Step 1: Initial enquiry

Potential applicants are asked to first read the information on eligibility and grant programmes available on the foundation's website. Eligible applicants are then requested to complete the online initial enquiry form, a link to which can be found in the 'application process' section of the foundation's website. Applications are first assessed by the foundation's staff. If it is felt the project will be of interest, they will arrange either to visit the project or phone applicants to discuss their application. Depending on the outcome of these discussions, applicants may then be invited to submit a full application. If an initial enquiry is not successful applicants will be notified by email. No feedback is given on unsuccessful applications. Note that given the large number of applications received by the foundation, it may sometimes take up to four months for an initial enquiry form to be considered.

Step 2: Full application

Applicants who have been successful at the first stage, will then receive an application form by email. Once completed and returned, application will be considered by the board of trustees. If an application is successful, the applicant will normally be contacted by telephone followed by a grant offer letter. Unsuccessful applicants will be informed by letter.

Sources of information

Accounts; annual report; Charity Commission record; guidelines for applicants; funder's website.

Edward Harvist Trust (The Harvist Estate)

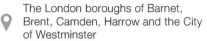

The relief and support of people resident in the areas of benefit

The London boroughs of Barnet, Brent, Camden, Harrow and the City of Westminster

£289,000 (2016/17)

CC number: 211970

Trustees: Ian Jacobs; Howard Bluston; Angela Harvey; Shafique Choudhary; Graham Old.

Correspondent: Iain Millar, London Borough of Harrow, Finance Department, PO Box 21, Civic Centre, Harrow HA1 2XY (tel: 020 8424 1450; email: treasurymanagement@harrow.gov. uk)

This trust dates back to 1610 and derives its income from its former ownership of estates on the line of the Edgware Road which it has now sold. The income is currently distributed to the constituent authorities, namely the London boroughs of Barnet, Brent, Camden, Harrow and the City of Westminster, in proportion to the length of the Edgware Road passing through the local authorities' boundaries. Each local authority has a representative on the trustee body.

The trust does not make direct grants; each local authority is responsible for the charitable allocation of its grants budget for: the relief of older and disadvantaged people; the relief of distress and sickness; the provision and support of recreational and leisure time facilities (in the interests of social welfare); the provision and support of educational facilities; and any other purposes for the benefit of residents.

Financial information

In 2016/17 the trust had assets of £10.5 million and an income of £320,000. Distributions to the five local authorities amounted to £289,000 and were made as follows:

Barnet	£88,500
Brent	£80,000
City of Westminster	£72,500
Camden	£31,000
Harrow	£16,000

Applications

Applications must be made through the appropriate local authority. At the time of writing (June 2018) there was information on the trust (such as eligibility criteria and application procedures) available on each of the five borough councils' websites. This information could be found following a search for the trust's name using the websites' search bars.

Do not write to the correspondent. There may be different criteria and application procedures imposed by the five local authorities.

Sources of information
Accounts; annual report; Charity Commission record.

The Maurice Hatter Foundation

 Jewish causes, general charitable purposes, medical research, social welfare, religion, education

 UK and overseas

(£) £713,000 (2016/17)

CC number: 298119

Trustees: Piers Barclay; Richard Hatter; Fausto Furlotti.

Correspondent: The Trustees, c/o Smith & Williamson, 1 Bishops Wharf, Walnut Tree Close, Guildford, Surrey GU1 4RA

The foundation was established in 1987 for general charitable purposes, and distributions can take the form of grants, or long/short-term loans. The trustees have five key areas they support: education, social welfare, medical research, Jewish causes and international policy research. Grants are also occasionally made to cultural or animal welfare organisations.

Financial information
In 2016/17 the foundation held assets of £12.1 million and had an income of £3.2 million, mainly from donations and legacies. Grants totalled £713,000 and were made to 31 institutions in the following categories:

Education	10	£427,500
Social welfare	12	£182,000
Medical research	6	£93,500
Religion	2	£5,000
International policy research	1	£5,000

Beneficiaries included: University College London Hospital Charity Fund (£155,000); The Work Avenue Foundation (£100,000); Royal National Orthopaedic Hospital (£75,000); Holocaust Educational Trust and Prostate Cancer UK (£7,500 each); Henry Jackson Society, Stop Ivory and The National Theatre (£5,000 each); United Synagogue (£2,500); Battersea Dogs and Cats Home (£2,000); British Heart Foundation (£1,000).

Applications
Apply in writing to the correspondent.

Sources of information
Accounts; annual report; Charity Commission record.

The Charles Hayward Foundation

 Heritage and conservation, older people, criminal justice, overseas aid

 UK and Commonwealth countries of Africa

(£) £1.46 million (2016)

CC number: 1078969

Trustees: Susan Heath; Julia Chamberlain; Caroline Donald; Richard Griffith; Alexander Heath; Brian Insch; Nikolas van Leuven.

Correspondent: Dorothy Napierala, Administrator, Hayward House, 45 Harrington Gardens, London SW7 4JU (tel: 020 7370 7063 or 020 7370 7067; email: dorothy@charleshaywardfoundation.org.uk)

 www.charleshaywardfoundation.org.uk

The Charles Hayward foundation was established 2000 when two charitable trusts the (Hayward Foundation and the Charles Hayward Trust) founded by the businessman Sir Charles Hayward were combined.

Grants programmes
The foundation currently operates two separate grant programmes:

- **Main grant programme** – social and criminal justice and heritage and conservation (available to charities with an income of more than £350,000); and overseas aid (available to charities with an income between £150,000 and £5 million)
- **Small grant programme** – social and criminal justice and older people (available to charities with an income of less than £350,000)

Both grant programmes are designed to cover both the project costs and capital expenditure. Full guidelines for each of the foundation's grants programmes are provided on the website.

Financial information
In 2016 the foundation had assets of £65.9 million and an income of £1.37 million. A total of 142 grants were made totalling £1.46 million, broken down as follows:

Social and criminal justice	£648,000	37
Heritage and conservation	£375,000	14
Overseas	£205,000	16
Small grants	£199,500	51
Miscellaneous	£34,000	24

Beneficiaries included: British Postal Museum and Archive (£50,000); Forgiveness Project (£21,000); Pump Aid and Staffordshire Women's Aid (£15,000 each); Kids Club Kampala (£12,500); Holbeck Elderly Aid (£4,000); Arts Together (£3,000); Songbird Survival

(£1,000); Bliss (£350); Salvation Army (£250).

Exclusions
The foundation only supports UK-registered charities. The website notes further that generally funding is not given for the following purposes:

- Endowments
- General appeals
- Grant-making charities
- Individuals
- Loan and deficits
- Retrospective funding (costs already incurred prior to receiving a decision from the foundation)
- Core costs

Note that individual programmes may have their own additional exclusions – see programme-specific guidelines.

Applications
Full information, including eligibility criteria and how to apply for a grant, is available on the foundation's highly informative website. Applications to the small grant programme are accepted on a rolling basis and are considered every two to three months. The main grant programme has a two-stage application process. Firstly, applications are considered by the grants committee, which recommends applications to be considered by the trustees at the second stage of the process. Trustee meetings usually take place in February, April, July and November.

Sources of information
Accounts; annual report; Charity Commission record; funder's website.

The Headley Trust

 Arts, heritage, cathedral and church restoration, health, welfare, education, overseas development

 UK and overseas

(£) £4.1 million (2016/17)

CC number: 266620

Trustees: Susan Sainsbury; Judith Portrait; Timothy Sainsbury; Sir Timothy Sainsbury; Camilla Sainsbury; Amanda McCrystal.

Correspondent: Robert Bell, Director, The Sainsbury Family Charitable Trusts, The Peak, 5 Wilton Road, London SW1V 1AP (tel: 020 7410 0330; email: info@sfct.org.uk)

 www.sfct.org.uk

This is one of the Sainsbury Family Charitable Trusts (SFCT) which share a joint administration. Like the others, it is primarily proactive, aiming to choose its own grantees, and its annual reports state that 'proposals are generally invited by the trustees or initiated at their request'.

The Headley Trust is prepared to consider unsolicited applications as long as they closely match one of the areas of interest listed below. Like many of the others in the Sainsbury group, the Headley Trust prefers to support 'innovative schemes that can be successfully replicated or become self-sustaining'.

Funding Priorities

The trust's website provides more detailed information on each priority.

Arts and Heritage UK

- Conservation of industrial, maritime and built heritage
- Regional and national museums, galleries and libraries
- Ceramics and crafts (including rural crafts)
- Arts education/outreach and access to the arts
- Archaeology – see Headley Trust Museums Archaeological Acquisition Fund

Cathedrals and Major Churches

- Restoration or repair work to the fabric of large churches and cathedrals of exceptional architectural merit

Parish Churches

- Fabric repairs to listed medieval parish churches in rural areas in England and Wales
- Provision or upgrade of parish church toilet facilities and disabled access

Arts and Heritage Overseas

- Conservation and recording of heritage (including ecclesiastical and vernacular architecture, archaeology and cultural artefacts), primarily in South Eastern Europe (Slovenia, Croatia, Albania, Macedonia, Bulgaria, Romania, Serbia, Montenegro, Bosnia-Herzegovina, Turkey), but also in Ethiopia
- Raising awareness of heritage issues in these countries, supporting the capacity of new heritage NGOs, and training the next generation of conservation and heritage professionals

Developing Countries

Development projects in sub-Saharan Anglophone Africa, under the following general headings:

- **Water** – including access to safe water, promoting better use of water resources and sanitation projects
- **Environment** – including sustainable energy, sustainable farming, forestry and livelihood development, habitat management and conservation and environmental education

- **Education and literacy** – in particular supporting pilot projects
- **Healthcare** – including care for mothers and infants and people with disabilities and trachoma prevention and treatment programmes in Ethiopia
- **Emergency Appeals** – primarily reserved for supporting communities after a disaster or emergency (at the discretion of the trustees)

Education

Mainly bursaries for:

- Vocational training in traditional crafts, conservation and heritage skills
- UK graduate students (dance) and postgraduate students (music)

Health and Social Welfare

- Ways to encourage older people to live independently for as long as possible
- Projects to improve older people's quality of life in residential care homes
- Carer's projects
- Projects that support families, including pre-schoolchildren and parenting education
- Projects that encourage volunteering
- Support for specific medical conditions (at the discretion of trustees)
- Small grants providing practical aids for people with disabilities

Financial information

In 2016/17 the trust had assets of £70.5 million and an income of £2.3 million. During the year, the trust gave £4.1 million in grants. Grants payable in the year consisted of the following:

Arts and heritage – UK	£2.1 million
Arts and heritage – overseas	£186,500
Developing countries	£272,500
Education	£262,500
Health and social welfare	£1.2 million

Beneficiaries included: Maggie's Cancer Caring Centres and Victoria and Albert Museum (£500,000 each); Dorset County Museum (£200,000); Art Fund – National Art Collections Fund and Mulberry Bush School (£100,000 each); Café Africa Trust and Lively Minds UK (£60,000 each); Southbank Sinfonia (£32,000).

Exclusions

Grants are not normally awarded to: individuals; expeditions.

Applications

A single application will be considered for support by all the trusts in the SFTC group.

Although the majority of unsolicited proposals are unsuccessful, the trust's website states that the 'trustees are prepared to consider unsolicited

proposals so long as they closely match one of [its] areas of interest' (as summarised earlier in the entry).

Applications should be sent by post with a description (strictly no more than two pages please, as any more is unlikely to be read) of the proposed project, covering:

- The organisation – explaining its charitable aims and objectives, and giving its most recent annual income and expenditure, and current financial position. Do not send a full set of accounts
- The project requiring funding – why it is needed, who will benefit and in what way
- The funding – breakdown of costs, any money raised so far, and how the balance will be raised

All applications will receive a letter of acknowledgment. If your proposal is a candidate for support from one of the trusts, you will receive a response within eight weeks of the acknowledgement. Applicants who do not hear from the trust within this time must assume they have been unsuccessful.

Sources of information

Accounts; annual report; Charity Commission record; funder's website.

The Health Foundation

🔍 Health care and public health research, training and development

📍 Worldwide

💷 £18.45 million (2016)

CC number: 286967

Trustees: Bridget McIntyre; David Zahn; Sir Hugh Taylor; Martyn Hole; Roaslind Smyth; Melloney Poole; Sir David Dalton; Branwen Jeffreys; Eric Gregory; Loraine Hawkins; Ruth Hussey.

Correspondent: Programmes Team, 90 Long Acre, London WC2E 9RA (tel: 020 7257 8000; email: info@health.org. uk)

🌍 www.health.org.uk

f facebook.com/thehealthfoundation

🐦 @HealthFdn

The Health Foundation aims to improve health and the quality of healthcare in the UK. It receives funding from an endowment, which comes from a one-off charitable donation of £560 million from the sale of the PPP Healthcare group in 1998 – one of the largest charitable donations in UK history. The website states:

We are here to support people working in health care practice and policy to make lasting improvements to health services. We carry out research and in-depth policy analysis, run improvement programmes to put ideas into practice in the NHS, support and develop leaders and share evidence to encourage wider change. Each year we give grants in the region of £18 million to fund health care research, fellowships and improvement projects across the UK – all with the aim of improving health care quality.

It is the largest charitable foundation of its kind in the UK, and it works in partnership with others to ensure that the research it funds helps to shape future health policy and practice. It works with individuals and organisations from across the UK health system, including clinicians and managers, charity sector, patient organisations, academics, national bodies and policy makers. It also works with people and organisations from around the world that have an interest in how to improve the quality of health care.

The foundation's objectives are:

- To promote medical research and the publication of the useful results of such research
- To promote medical education and training, including the education and training of nurses and other persons involved in the provision of health care or the management and administration of health care providers
- To promote the relief of sickness and disability and the preservation and protection of public health
- To promote the relief of the aged

Grants programme

Currently the foundation is focused on 'helping local people improve the quality of care and helping policy makers make better policy'.

Small, one-off awards as well as multi-year support are offered. Research teams and individuals can be assisted or the foundation can fund a fellowship. Anyone who can demonstrate that they can carry out high quality research can submit a proposal; however, applicants will need to demonstrate that those delivering the research have the necessary expertise and experience to do so. Grants can be used to cover expenses, including:

Travel costs for meetings, relevant conferences, data analysis support, transcription of interviews and focus groups, venue hire/refreshments for research meetings/focus groups, travel costs for patient and health and social care staff to attend focus groups, 'honorarium' payments for patient participants and some backfill payments for health and social care staff to participate in specific research activities but not where this would constitute covering part of the research team, or for any length of time beyond a few days.

Financial information

In 2016 the foundation had assets of £946.7 million and an income of £14.9 million. A total of 145 grants were made totalling £18.45 million.

Previous beneficiaries have included: The Commonwealth Fund (£500,000); Bangor University (£304,500); The Bromley by Bow Centre (£97,500); PROMPT Maternity Foundation (£62,000); Wirral Child and Adolescent Mental Health Service (£29,000); University of Edinburgh (£13,500); All-Party Parliamentary Health Group (£5,600).

Exclusions

Overheads are not funded. The foundation states:

We expect that the majority of funding will be spent on the direct costs covering academic/researcher time spent on projects, which can include staff who are already employed at the institution or the new staff (directly allocated cost and directly incurred cost). However, we do not provide the funding for academic backfill or teaching replacement time in addition to the direct cost.

Clinical trials and research focused on the development of new treatments are not supported; however, the research may be set within a specific clinical setting.

Applications

The foundation does not consider unprompted requests or proposals for funding. Programmes open for applications are advertised on the foundation's website. These are likely to change frequently and candidates are advised to visit the website for the most up-to-date information. You may sign up for an online account with the foundation to receive alerts when new funding opportunities go live. Application forms are available online together with full guidelines and specific requirements and deadlines for each of the programme. There is also a helpful FAQ document which should be consulted by potential applicants.

Sources of information

Accounts; annual report; Charity Commission record; funder's website.

Heart Research UK

 Research into the prevention, treatment and cure of heart disease

UK

£1.1 million (2016)

CC number: 1044821

Trustees: Paul Rogerson; Keith Loudon; Richard Colwyn; Christine Mortimer; Dr David Dickinson; Kevin Watterson; Anthony Knight; Antony Oxley; Dr Catherine Dickinson; Anthony Kilner; Paul Smith; Richard Brown; Peter Braidley; Julie Fenwick; Pierre Bouvet; Christopher Newman.

Correspondent: Samantha Turner, Suite 12D, Joseph's Well, Hanover Walk, Leeds LS3 1AB (tel: 0113 234 7474; email: grants@heartresearch.org.uk)

 www.heartresearch.org.uk

 facebook.com/heartresearchuk

 @heartresearchuk

Heart Research UK (formerly the National Heart Research Fund) was founded in 1967. The stated aims of the charity are the promotion of medical research into heart disease and related disorders and into the prevention treatment and cures of such complaints and the dissemination of any useful results. The provision of practical help and rehabilitation for those with, or vulnerable to, heart disease or any related complaint.

The objects are fulfilled by funding medical research projects at centres throughout the UK. All projects undertaken are allocated and controlled in line with the guiding principles of the Association of Medical Research Charities (AMRC). In addition, an ongoing programme is undertaken to raise awareness of the issue of heart disease and related illnesses, coupled with the promotion of healthier lifestyles through Healthy Heart community grants and initiatives in schools and workplaces. The charity has also forged partnerships with organisations and companies to promote heart health and highlight particular conditions and issues.

Types of grants

The charity's website explains that grants are awarded for research into the prevention, treatment and cure of heart disease. In addition, the charity's 'Masterclasses' provide educational and training opportunities for clinicians.

At the time of writing (April 2018) the charity offered the following grants programmes:

- **Scotland Grant:** Up to £150,000. Supports research at hospitals and universities across the Scotland.
- **Northern Ireland Grant:** Up to £150,000. Supports research at hospitals and universities across in Northern Ireland.
- **Translational Research Project Grants:** 'Up to £150,000 each. These grants aim to bridge the gap between scientific research and patient care, bringing about clinical benefits in the most efficient way. This may advance

current practice or enable innovative discoveries to be efficiently transferred into practical tools to prevent, diagnose and treat human disease'.

▶ **Novel and Emerging Technologies Grants:** 'A maximum of £250,000 is available. Research projects with an emphasis on (1) novel and emerging technologies and (2) their application to cardiovascular disease prevention and/or treatment, which can be expected to benefit patients within a foreseeable timeframe, will be considered. Appropriate approaches include tissue and bioengineering, the development and evaluation of new diagnostic and therapeutic devices, bio-imaging, nanotechnology, biomaterials, genomic and proteomic approaches, computational biology and bioinformatics. NET Grants are not appropriate for funding clinical trials'.

Information on Masterclasses and PhD studentships is also available from the website.

Financial information

In 2016 the charity held assets of £4.28 million and had an income of £2.98 million. Grants were awarded totalling £1.1 million.

Beneficiaries included: Papworth Hospital NHS Foundation Trust (£250,000); Imperial College London (£150,000); Sheffield Hallam University (£144,000); Bristol Heart Institute (£76,000); University of Liverpool (£25,000); Willowfield Parish Community Association, Blackpool FC Community Trust (£10,000); Society of Cardiothoracic Surgeons (£5,000).

Exclusions

Government and local authority funded institutions are not eligible.

Applications

Application forms, full guidelines and up-to-date deadlines for each programme can be found on the charity's website. Alternatively, the charity can be contacted directly for more information.

Sources of information

Accounts; annual report; Charity Commission record; funder's website.

The Heathcoat Trust

Relief of poverty, social welfare, education and training, health causes, children and young people, older people, local causes, general charitable purposes

Local causes in and around Tiverton, Devon

£ £144,000 to organisations (2016/17)

CC number: 203367

Trustees: Mark Drysdale; Sir Ian Heathcoat-Amory; John Stanley Smith; Susan Westlake; Julian Morgan; Nikki Wood-Wright.

Correspondent: C. J. Twose, Secretary, The Factory, Tiverton, Devon EX16 5LL (tel: 01884 254949; email: heathcoattrust@heathcoat.co.uk)

This trust was established in 1945 and makes grants for the following:

▶ The relief of financial hardship
▶ Education and training
▶ Health organisations or their buildings
▶ Local charities in Tiverton in Devon and its neighbourhood or in places where the firms John Heathcoat and Company Ltd and Lowman Manufacturing Company Ltd and their subsidiaries carry on business
▶ Other general charitable purposes

Grants are also made to individuals, employees and pensioners of the Heathcoat group of companies. Educational grants are given to children of those employees or pensioners and also to local students attending schools and colleges in Tiverton, or beyond if courses are not available locally.

Financial information

In 2016/17 the trust held assets of £25.1 million and had an income of £751,500. Grants totalled £687,500 with £144,000 being paid to organisations and the remainder to individuals.

Beneficiaries included: St Thomas the Apostle Church – Chevithorne with Cove and Tiverton Market Centre (£10,000 each); Heathcoat Social Club (£2,500); Willow Tree Theatre Company (£2,000); Cold harbour Mill Trust Ltd, Listening Books, Tiverton Citizens Advice and Tiverton Swimming Club (£1,000 each).

Applications

Applications should be made in writing to the correspondent giving as much relevant information as possible. The trustees meet regularly to consider applications for grants. There are application forms for certain education grants.

Sources of information

Accounts; annual report; Charity Commission record.

Heathrow Community Fund (LHR Airport Communities Trust)

Community development, young people, education, skills and employment, environmental protection

The areas surrounding Heathrow Airport (Ealing, Hillingdon, Hounslow, Richmond, Runnymede, Spelthorne, Slough, South Buckinghamshire, Royal Borough of Windsor and Maidenhead)

£ £523,500 (2016)

CC number: 1058617

Trustees: Alison Moore; Jason Holmes; Ian Nichol; Dr Prabhjot Basra; Michael Murphy; Andrew Kerswill; Richard de Belder; Carol Hui; Chris Johnston; Darius Nasimi; Gennie Dearman; Samina Hussain.

Correspondent: Dr Rebecca Bowden, Trust Director, c/o Groundwork South, Colne Valley Park Centre, Denham Court Drive, Uxbridge, Middlesex UB9 5PG (tel: 01895 839662; email: community_fund@heathrow.com)

 www.heathrowcommunityfund.com

 facebook.com/ heathrowcommunityfund

 @heathrowairport

BAA plc – now known as Heathrow Airport Holdings Ltd – established this trust under the name 'BAA 21st Century Communities Trust' in 1996. The majority of the trust's funding is received from Heathrow Airport Ltd (a subsidiary of Heathrow Airport Holdings Ltd) and other companies based at Heathrow Airport, as well as from money raised by fines levied on airlines for breaching noise limits.

The trust is a grant-making charity which until recently supported communities close to the airports at Aberdeen, Glasgow, Heathrow and Southampton through local community funds. However – following the sale of the airports at Aberdeen, Glasgow and Southampton – the local community funds at each of these airports no longer fall under the governance of the trust.

The primary focus of the trust is now the Heathrow Community Fund (HCF) which works to support the communities in the areas surrounding Heathrow Airport. The fund also supports the fundraising and volunteering efforts of Heathrow staff. Heathrow Airport Ltd has committed to making an annual contribution of around £750,000 to support the trust's charitable activities, all of which contribute to the trust's vision to 'Work with communities to create significant and positive social change'.

The trust carries out its grant-making with the following objectives:

- To create learning opportunities for young people and so raise their aspirations
- To break down barriers to employment through skills development
- To help protect the environment
- To support staff active in the community

Grants programmes

In support of its objectives, the Heathrow Community Fund (HCF) makes grants through five programmes.

Organisations can apply for grants through three programmes. These are:

- **Youth projects – Communities for Youth**: 'invites grant applications from organisations working on projects linked to education and economic regeneration schemes that give young people new skills and help them into employment'. Young people are generally defined as being those between the ages of 13 and 25. Grants range from £2,500 to £25,000 and are given for projects costing no more than £100,000 in total. Projects under this programme must take place in one of the following boroughs: Ealing, Hillingdon, Hounslow, Spelthorne or Slough.
- **Sustainability and environmental projects – Communities for Tomorrow**: 'invites grant applications from organisations working on environmental or sustainability projects and schemes that involve recycling, tackling climate change or improving the local environment'. Grants range from £2,500 to £25,000 and are given for projects costing no more than £100,000 in total. Projects under this programme must take place in one of the following boroughs: Ealing, Hillingdon, Hounslow, Richmond, Runnymede, Slough, South Buckinghamshire, Spelthorne or Windsor and Maidenhead.
- **Community projects – Communities Together**: 'invites grant applications from organisations looking for small amounts of funding to support projects that draw communities closer together – funding can support all sorts of community activities from gardening to sports or the arts'. Grants are awarded up to £2,500. Projects under this programme must take place in one of the following boroughs: Ealing, Hillingdon, Hounslow, Richmond, Runnymede, Slough, Spelthorne, South Buckinghamshire or Windsor and Maidenhead.

More information on these programmes, including full eligibility criteria and guidelines, is available from the fund's website.

There are also two funds to which employees can apply for support with their own charitable involvement:

- **Heathrow Active People Initiative (HAPI)**: 'Employees of Heathrow Airport Ltd are encouraged to actively volunteer for charities and community groups working in their local communities, the Trust supports this with a grant programme awarding up to £2,500 to charities for projects involving Heathrow staff volunteering'.
- **Matched Funding**: 'Employees of Heathrow Airport Ltd are also supported in their fundraising for charity by a Matched Fund scheme in which the Trust will match funds raised'.

Financial information

In 2016 the trust had assets of £694,500 and an income of £1.14 million (of which £1.04 million was received from Heathrow Airport Holdings Ltd). Grants totalled £523,500 and were distributed as follows:

Communities for Tomorrow	£188,500
Communities for Youth	£152,500
Communities Together	£97,500
Midnight Marathon	£37,000
Heathrow Active People Initiative (HAPi)	£32,000
Staff match funding	£16,000

Previous beneficiaries have included: Renfrewshire Community Sports Hub (£25,000); Hounslow Arts Trust (£10,000); LondonClyde River Foundation (£9,800); St John Olgilvie Primary School (£5,000); Linwood Active (£3,000); Southampton Mencap and Surrey Care Trust (£2,500 each); One Community (£1,000).

Exclusions

Applications which benefit individuals only, whether or not they meet the other criteria, will fail. No support is given for religious or political projects. Grants will not be made to national organisations unless the direct benefit will be felt locally and the other criteria are satisfied. The trust does not support general running costs or staff costs.

Note that each of the grants programmes are subject to their own eligibility criteria and restrictions.

Applications

Application forms and guidance notes for each of the grants programmes are available from the HCF website, where important dates for application submissions and decision-making are also listed. There are two application rounds: Round 1 involves the

submission of an expression of interest form and Round 2, a full application.

The fund's grants programmes are managed by the charity Groundwork South – the website explains that: 'Trustees and panel members live and work locally and are supported by the Trust Director and a team at Groundwork, who draw on their local knowledge and experience to help you submit a strong bid showing the full value of your work'. Decisions are made by the trustees and the review panel according to the priorities and criteria set for the funding programmes.

Sources of information

Accounts; annual report; Charity Commission record; guidelines for applicants; funder's website.

The Heathside Charitable Trust

🔍 General charitable purposes, Jewish causes

📍 UK and Israel

£ £426,000 (2016)

CC number: 326959

Trustees: Sir Harry Solomon; Lady Judith Solomon; Geoffrey Jayson; Louise Jacobs; Daniel Solomon; Juliet Solomon; Sam Jacobs; James Jacobs.

Correspondent: Sir Harry Solomon, Trustee, 32 Hampstead High Street, London NW3 1QD (tel: 020 7431 7739)

This trust was established in 1985 to support general charitable purposes, with a preference for Jewish organisations and causes. According to the 2016 annual report, the 'trustees identify organisations it wishes to support and this generally arises from direct contacts rather than speculative applications'.

Financial information

In 2016 the trust held assets of £4.4 million and had an income of £1.2 million, mostly from donations. The trust made 86 grants totalling £426,000. A list of beneficiaries was not included in the accounts.

Previous beneficiaries have included: Babes in Arms; British Friends of Jaffa Institute; CancerKin; Community Security Trust; Holocaust Educational Trust; First Cheque 2000; Jewish Care; Jewish Education Defence Trust; Jewish Museum; Joint Jewish Charitable Trust; King Solomon High School; Marie Curie Cancer Care; Motivation; Royal London Institute; Royal National Theatre; Weizmann Institute.

Applications

According to the annual report for 2016, the 'trustees identify organisations it wishes to support and this generally arises from direct contacts rather than speculative applications'. The trustees meet four times a year to discuss applications.

Sources of information
Accounts; annual report; Charity Commission record.

The Charlotte Heber-Percy Charitable Trust

General charitable purposes, animal welfare, the environment, medical and health, overseas aid, education, children and young people, the arts

Worldwide

£322,000 (2016/17)

CC number: 284387

Trustees: Joanna Prest; Charlotte Heber-Percy.

Correspondent: The Trustees, Rathbone Trust Company Ltd, 8 Finsbury Circus, London EC2M 7AZ (tel: 020 7399 0820; email: linda.cousins@rathbones.com)

The trust was set up by a deed created in 1981 to support general charitable purposes through small, one-off grants. A wide range of causes are supported, including: animal welfare, the environment, medical causes and hospices, international charities, local charities, children, education, the arts and museums.

Financial information
In 2016/17 the trust had assets of £7.6 million and an income of £299,000. Grants were made to 47 organisations totalling £322,000 and were distributed in the following categories:

General charitable purposes	£87,000
Medical, cancer and hospices	£64,500
Animal welfare and environment	£58,500
Arts and museums	£50,000
Education and children	£35,000
Local organisations	£14,000
International charities	£13,000

Beneficiaries included: Compassion in Dying (£25,000); Horation's Garden – Stanmore Hospital and Royal Shakespeare Company (£20,000 each); Brooke Hospital for Sick Animals and Wheel Power (£10,000 each); Klosters Alpine Concert Society and Songbird Survival Trust (£5,000 each); Cystic Fibrosis Trust and St Peter's Church, Upper Slaughter (£1,000 each).

Exclusions
Grants are not made to individuals.

Applications
Applications should be made in writing to the correspondent. The trustees meet on an ad hoc basis to consider applications.

Sources of information
Accounts; annual report; Charity Commission record.

Hedley Foundation Ltd (The Hedley Foundation)

Young people in the areas of recreation, sport, training, health and welfare, and outdoor education, young people who are at risk of offending, young people who have disabilities or a terminal illness, young carers

UK

£822,000 (2016/17)

CC number: 262933

Trustees: George Broke; Maj. John Rodwell; Lorna Stuttaford; Patrick Holcroft; Lt Col. Peter Chamberlin; Angus Fanshawe; Lt Col. Andrew Ford; David Byam-Cook.

Correspondent: Mary Kitto, Victoria House, 1–3 College Hill, London EC4R 2RA (tel: 020 7489 8076; email: mkitto@hedleyfoundation.org.uk)

 www.hedleyfoundation.org.uk

The Hedley Foundation was set up in 1971 and endowed from a family trust of which the principle asset was the compensation received on nationalisation of the family's collieries. The main objective of the foundation is to bring about change for the better in the lives of young people, which it looks to achieve by making grants to UK-registered charities.

The following information is taken from the foundation's website:

Priorities
The Foundation makes grants to small charities working with young people in the areas of Recreation, Sport, Training, Health and Welfare, Support and outdoor Education of young people. The Foundation is particularly keen on open air and adventure-type activities and the funding of appropriate kit and equipment. The Foundation is keen to support small charities which can demonstrate achievement in persuading and deterring at-risk young people from proceeding further down the pathway to custody. A secondary aim is to assist small charities helping with disabled and terminally ill young people through funding for specialist equipment, organised respite breaks. The Foundation also supports young carers. The Foundation provides limited bursary type funding to organisations which provide apprenticeships and specialist training for talented young people who, for want of money alone, are unable to develop their talents.

Financial information
In 2016/17 the foundation held assets of £36 million and had an income of £1.3 million. During the year the foundation gave around £822,000 in grants to organisations. Grants were distributed as follows:

Youth	£467,500
Disability	£213,000
Other	£79,500
Terminally ill and hospices	£62,000

Beneficiaries included: In2Change South Yorkshire Ltd (£50,000); English National Ballet School and the British Exploring Society (£15,000 each); Raleigh International (£10,000).

Exclusions
The foundation does not support:

- Organisations which are not UK-registered charities
- Individuals directly
- Churches, cathedrals and museums
- Exclusive charities (which only help people from specific groupings)
- Appeals for general funding, salaries, deficit, core revenue costs, transport funding
- Appeals for building or refurbishment projects

National and very large appeals are not considered.

Applications
Application forms are available to be downloaded from the foundation's website, and should be completed in typescript and sent back via post. Dates of trustee meetings are listed on the website.

Sources of information
Accounts; annual report; Charity Commission record; funder's website.

The Michael Heller Charitable Foundation

Medical, scientific and educational research, humanitarian causes

Worldwide

£195,500 (2016/17)

CC number: 327832

Trustees: Lady Morven Heller; Sir Michael Heller; W. S. Trustee Company Ltd.

Correspondent: Sir Michael Heller, Trustee, 24 Bruton Place, London W1J 6NE (tel: 020 7415 5000)

This foundation was established in 1988 and funds specific projects relating to medical research, science and educational research. This usually involves making large grants to universities for research purposes, particularly medical research. Support has also been given to humanitarian causes.

Financial information

In 2016/17 the foundation had assets of £3.9 million and an income of £272,500. Grants to institutions totalled £195,500. Grants were awarded as follows:

Education	£102,000
Humanitarian	£57,000
Research	£37,000

A list of beneficiaries was not included in the annual report and accounts.

Exclusions

No support is available for individuals.

Applications

Apply in writing to the correspondent.

Sources of information

Accounts; annual report; Charity Commission record.

The Helping Foundation

🔍 Orthodox Jewish causes, education, religion, social welfare

📍 Greater Manchester and London

£ £7.1 million (2016)

CC number: 1104484

Trustees: Rachel Weis; Rabbi Aubrey Weis; David Neuwirth; Benny Stone; Sir Weis.

Correspondent: Benny Stone, Trustee, Flat 1, Allanadale Court, Waterpark Road, Salford M7 4JN (tel: 01617 40116)

The Helping Foundation was established in 2004, and is funded primarily by donations and investment income. According to its 2016 annual report, the objectives of the foundation are as follows:

▶ The advancement of education according to the tenets of the Orthodox Jewish Faith

▶ The advancement of the Orthodox Jewish Religion

▶ The relief of poverty among older people or persons in need, hardship or distress in the Jewish Community

Financial information

In 2016 the foundation had assets of £195.3 million and an income of £42.5 million. Grants totalled £7.1 million.

Previous beneficiaries have included: Asser Bishvil Foundation (£2 million); British Friends of Ezrat Yisrael (£670,000); Notzar Chesed (£236,500); New Rachmistrivka Synagogue Trust (£201,000); TTT (£198,500); Emuno Educational Centre (£163,000); BCG CT (£105,000); Friends for the Centre for Torah Education Centre (£57,000); Toimchei Shabbos Manchester (£30,000); Gateshead Kollel (£20,000);

Beis Naduorna (£10,000); Law of Truth (£5,500).

Applications

Apply in writing to the correspondent.

Sources of information

Accounts; annual report; Charity Commission record.

Henderson Firstfruits

🔍 General charitable purposes, Christianity, social welfare, disability, children and young people, older people

📍 England and Wales, overseas

£ £243,000 (2015/16)

CC number: 1157218

Trustees: Rachel Henderson; Gareth Henderson; Elaine Elcock; Barbara Heal; Richard Gage.

Correspondent: Rachel Henderson, Trustee, Orchard House, 1 Park Road, Elland, Halifax HX5 9HP (tel: 01484 880170; email: applications@first-fruits.org.uk)

 first-fruits.org.uk

 @firstfruits2013

Firstfruits was established in 2013 by Gareth and Rachel Henderson, who are both currently trustees, after many years of charitable giving through their business, the Orchard Group. It was set up to bring more structure to their grant-giving process and to help identify a greater number of causes.

The charity's annual report states that:

> The only object for which the charity is established is the relief of those in need, by reason of youth, age, ill-health, disability, financial hardship or other social or economic disadvantage by providing grants to charities, other organisations and individuals within a Christian ethos. The Trustees consider grant applications at each Trustee meeting which propose to meet this objective.

The charities supports organisations that predominantly, but not exclusively, demonstrate a Christian ethos and provides small and medium-sized grants, as well as monthly donations and one-off specific project grants. It also supports individuals.

Financial information

In 2015/16 the charity held assets of £103,000 and had an income of £278,500. Grants totalled £243,000.

Beneficiaries included: Calderdale Community Foundation (£50,000); Inn Churches Storehouse (£30,000); Life Church (£10,000); Whizzkids (£5,000); Invisible Traffick (£4,400); Leeds Faith in

Schools (£1,600); Hope for Justice (£1,000 pcm indefinitely); Light Church Bradford (£1,000).

Applications

Application forms are available via Firstfruits' website. Completed application forms should be uploaded via a link on the website, or sent by email or post, along with the organisation's latest set of accounts. If the latest set of accounts cannot be submitted applicants should explain why this is the case.

Trustees meet on a quarterly basis in March, June, September and December to consider grant applications. The closing date for each quarter is the 15th day of the month prior to the meeting. Successful applicants will be informed shortly after the meeting and the grant will be paid.

All recipients of grants are requested to issue an impact report to the charity after 12 months which allows us to effectively assess the impact of the grant and the achievement of our objective.

Sources of information

Accounts; annual report; Charity Commission record; funder's website.

The Christina Mary Hendrie Trust

🔍 Youth charities, older people, veterans, hospices

📍 Scotland and Canada

£ £307,500 (2016/17)

OSCR number: SC014514

Trustees: John Scott Moncrief; Charles Cox; Anthony Cox; Mary Grieve; Andrew Desson; Laura Irwin; Laura Cox; Alan Sharp.

Correspondent: Audrey Souness, Trust Secretary, 1 Rutland Court, Edinburgh EH3 8EY (tel: 0131 270 7700)

 www.christinamaryhendrietrust. com

The trust was established in 1972 in by the niece of Christina Hendrie following her death in 1950. It supports charities in both Scotland and Canada with a focus on:

▶ Veterans
▶ Older people
▶ Young people
▶ Hospices

The trust's website provides the following information about what the trustees favour when considering applications:

> ▶ Smaller local organisations will be preferred to larger well-funded ones

- Charities helping greater numbers of people will be preferred to those helping only a few. Group activity is preferred to individual support
- Those involved in early intervention will be preferred
- Those helping people with limited resources are preferred to those helping a broader range of the community
- Geographical spread is important both in Scotland and Canada
- Specific projects are preferred to general funding but contributions to the cost of employing staff, community workers are acceptable
- Achieving aims through sport, organised physical activity, the arts, yoga and education are preferred
- Building projects are not generally supported
- Scottish charities will be preferred to English based charities offering services in Scotland
- In Canada, applications relating to issues facing First Nation citizens and those in remote rural areas are invited

Financial information

In 2016/17 the trust had assets of £7.8 million and an income of £123,000. Grants awarded to organisations totalled £307,500.

Previous beneficiaries have included: Alzheimer Research; Barnardo's; Befriending Networks; Combat Stress; Dance Base; Erskine Trust; Houses for Heroes; Marie Curie Cancer Care; Veterans Scotland.

Exclusions

The trust does not usually support individuals or building projects.

Applications

Applications can be made online via the trust's website. Alternatively, you can request an application form from the correspondent.

Sources of information

Accounts; annual report; OSCR record; funder's website.

Heritage Lottery Fund

Q Heritage

♀ UK

£ £432.6 million (2016/17)

Trustees: Sir Peter Luff; Maria Adebowale-Scwarte; Baroness Kay Andrews; Anna Carragher; Sir Neil Cossons; Dr Angela Dean; Jim Dixon; Dr Claire Feehily; Sarah Flannigan; Perdita Hunt; Steve Miller; René Olivieri; Dame Seona Reid; David Stocker; Dr Tom Tew.

Correspondent: The Trustees, 7 Holbein Place, London SW1W 8NR (tel: 020 7591 6000; email: enquire@hlf.org.uk)

The National Lottery was established in 1994. Proceeds from the sale of tickets provided funding for charities, the arts, sports and heritage.

Responsibility for the UK-wide distribution of National Lottery proceeds allocated to heritage was given to the trustees of the National Heritage Memorial Fund (NHMF). The Lottery-distribution arm of NHMF became known as the Heritage Lottery Fund (HLF).

Today it is a non-departmental public body accountable to parliament via the Department for Culture, Media and Sport (DCMS). This means that, although not a government department, the Secretary of State for Culture, Media and Sport issues financial and policy instructions to HLF, and its trustees report to parliament through the department. The HLF website states that its decisions about individual applications and policies are entirely independent of the government.

Heritage funding is very wide-ranging and HLF supports diverse projects with the criteria that they make a lasting difference for heritage, people and communities. There are many examples of projects funded on its informative website.

Projects

The following projects are funded:

- Buildings and monuments
- Community heritage
- Cultures and memories
- Industrial, maritime and transport
- Land and natural heritage
- Museums, libraries and archives

Grants range from £3,000 to over £5 million. The fund assesses applications based on the outcomes for heritage, people and communities that projects will achieve.

Financial information

In 2016/17 the fund held assets of £502 million and had an income of £327 million. A total of £432.6 million was awarded in grants.

Beneficiaries included: Canterbury Cathedral (£12 million); Canal and River Trust Partnership (£2.4 million); Ashmolean Museum of Art and Archaeology (£1.1 million); Norfolk County Council (£455,000); Askham Bryan College (£155,000); The Landmark Trust (£96,000); Butterfly Conservation (£58,000); Durham Wildlife Trust (£51,000); National Trust North (£15,000).

Exclusions

Private owners of heritage, including individuals and for-profit organisations, can apply under the Our Heritage grant programme only. Public benefit from

such a project must be greater than private gain.

Applications

All applications must be submitted via the online application portal. Contact the Grant Enquiries line if you need assistance to do this: 020 7591 6042/6044.

Sources of information

Accounts; annual report; funder's website.

The Hilden Charitable Fund

Q Homelessness, asylum seekers and refugees, penal affairs, disadvantaged young people, overseas development, women and girls

♀ UK and financial developing countries

£ £477,000 (2016/17)

CC number: 232591

Trustees: Catherine Rampton; Mr A. Rampton; Prof. D. Rampton; Prof. C. Rodeck; Mr J. Rampton; Prof. M. Rampton; Maggie Baxter; Elizabeth Rodeck; Ms E. Rodeck; Samia Khatun; Jonathan Branch; Robert Rampton.

Correspondent: Catherine Sotto, Office Manager, 34 North End Road, London W14 0SH (tel: 020 7603 1525; email: hildencharity@hotmail.com)

 www.hildencharitablefund.org.uk

The charity was established in 1963 by an initial gift from Anthony and Joan Rampton. Priorities in the UK are homelessness, asylum seekers and refugees, penal affairs and disadvantaged young people. For projects in developing countries, priorities are projects which focus on community development, education, and health. These priorities are reviewed on a three year cycle and may change from time to time, as dictated by circumstances. The charity has also allocated a small budget to help community groups run summer playschemes for disadvantaged communities.

The 2016/17 annual report notes that:

The aim of the fund is to address disadvantage, notably by supporting causes *which are unlikely to raise funds from public sources*, known sometimes as 'unpopular causes'. Both the UK and overseas funding policy is directed largely at supporting work at community level and funding is given to both project costs and general running costs.

The charity's website states:

Trustees are most sympathetic to funding general running, or core costs. In awarding these types of 'unrestricted' grants, Trustees believe that great value can be added, as most charities find fund raising for core costs most difficult. Trustees look to the Hilden staff team to advise applicants on funding alternatives if grant applications cannot be considered or awarded.

All grant recipients are expected to send a report on how they have made use of their funding. The charity's staff team ensure adequate grant monitoring. Feedback is given to the trustees via regular mailings as well as at the quarterly meetings. Similarly the secretary produces briefings on all aspects of grant-making and policy development within the priority areas.

Grant-making information
UK
Preference is given to charities that work at a community level with an income of less that £500,000 per year. Priorities given to different types of work within the main categories may change from time to time.

Overseas
The trustees will only consider applications from UK or overseas charities that have a history of working overseas for at least five years. There are other criteria relating to financial status that are detailed on the website. The fund encourages UK non-governmental organisations/charities to apply and in turn to direct their local partners to Hilden for grant aid. Overseas projects will either work with a UK charity partner or show relevant local legal status. The trustees wish to fund community development, education and health initiatives and particularly welcome projects that address the needs and potential of girls and women.

Summer playscheme
The fund also has a small budget to support community groups with an income of less than £150,000 to run summer play schemes for disadvantaged communities. Some priority will be given to projects which show they are inclusive of children from refugee families, and show BME involvement. The project must be for children aged 5–18 years, be based locally, and last for two to six weeks. The fund prefers to support schemes with strong volunteer support. A list of exclusions and how to apply can be found on the website.

Financial information
In 2016/17 the charity had assets of £13.8 million and an income of £409,500. During the year, the charity awarded 105 grants to organisations totalling £477,000. Grants were distributed as follows:

Asylum seekers and refugees	25	£132,300
Overseas	20	£129,500
Homelessness	14	£69,500
Penal affairs	10	£44,000
Young people	8	£37,500
Scotland	1	£37,000
Play schemes	23	£22,500
Other	4	£15,500

Beneficiaries included: Joint Council for the Welfare of Immigration, London (£20,000); Mityana Charity – Uganda; Unicef UK, Northern Nigeria (£10,000 each); Barts Health NHS Trust (£8,000); Criminon UK (£5,000); SharelSteps, Suffolk (£3,000); Families First Charity Ltd – Rugby (£2,500).

Exclusions
Grants are not normally made for well-established causes or to individuals. A full list of exclusions for each grant programme can be found on the charity's website.

Applications
Applicants should complete the application form available on the charity's website (www.hildencharitablefund.org.uk) or offices. Application forms must be submitted to the secretary by post as hard copies as forms submitted by email or other electronic means will not be considered. Applicants are advised to ensure that they have read the application guidelines at the top of the form prior to completion. Ensure adequate postage on applications.

When making an application, grant seekers should note the following guidance from the charity's website:

We expect all applicants to complete our application form. Your case for funds should be concise (no more than 2 sides of A4), but supporting documentation is essential. Please ensure your application includes enclosures of:

 Your most recent independently inspected accounts

 Your most recent annual report

 Projected income and expenditure for the current financial year

Be clear in your application form about when the proposed work is to commence, and give the relevant timetable. The trustees would prefer applicants to explain what their organisations actually do, rather than lots of information on 'need' (such as statistical information on deprivation). If statistics are included, applicants must reference the sources and use actual numbers if percentages are quoted.

Applicants from the UK applying for funds for their project partners must complete both the UK application form and the overseas partner profile form.

For applicants to the Summer Playschemes fund: applications should be sent by post along with a brief plan or timetable for the scheme and a copy of the applicant's most recent annual report and accounts which should include details of their management committee.

Potential applicants in Scotland should contact the Scottish Community Foundation, 22 Calton Road, Edinburgh EH8 8DP; Tel: 0131 524 0300; website: www.scottishcf.org.

Sources of information
Accounts; annual report; Charity Commission record; funder's website.

The Hillingdon Community Trust

Community projects, social welfare, relief of poverty, economic development, conservation of environment and heritage, unemployment, adult education and training, crime prevention, economic development

The London Borough of Hillingdon: Botwell, Pinkwell, Heathrow Villages, Townfield, West Drayton, Yiewsley

£698,500 (2016/17)

CC number: 1098235

Trustees: Isabel King; Dominic Gilham; Keith Wallis; Stephen Coventry; Carole Jones; Matthew Gorman; Jasvir Jassal; Clive Gee; Jack Taylor; Peter Money; Balwinder Sokhi; Shane Ryan; Freda Ritchie; Paul Lewis.

Correspondent: Kathleen Healy, Company Secretary and Trust Director, Barra Hall, Wood End, Green Road, Hayes, Middlesex UB3 2SA (tel: 020 8581 1676; email: info@hillingdoncommunitytrust.org.uk)

www.hillingdoncommunitytrust.org.uk

The trust was established in 2003 and its main source of funding is a deed of gift of £1 million a year for 15 years from Heathrow Airport Ltd (commencing in 2003). A requirement of the gift is that grants will benefit the community in the southern part of Borough-Hayes. The trust's 2016/17 annual report states that 'the overall objective of the trust is to contribute to the improvement of community facilities and the opportunity to participate in voluntary run organisations, leisure activities and adult learning in the London Borough of Hillingdon'.

According to the website, 'support is mainly in the form of grants but the trust also offers occasional training events and organises networking events for funded groups'. Help is given in the form of revenue or capital funding for projects and rarely to help with core costs of running an organisation.

Grant-making information
Support can be made to a range of properly constituted voluntary bodies; however for larger awards preference

may be given to registered charities. It is less likely that a grant will be made to a corporate body other than on a matched funding basis.

The trust awards two types of grant:

▶ **Small grants:** range from £100 to £7,500. Small grants typically represent 15% of the grant expenditure

▶ **Large grants:** over £7,500 for a maximum period of two years. Grants are awarded following a two-stage application procedure. For grants above £25,000, there is a preference for applicants to be registered charities

The vast majority of grants are for projects, however, the trust accepts that a grant application should aim to allow an organisation to meet all reasonable overheads relating to a project (salaries, rent, etc.). The trust's website notes that applications can be for either: 'development funding (where at least some of the core costs of an organisation are met for start-up organisations or for those undergoing significant development and change)' or 'strategic funding (where the Trust recognises the need for an organisation to exist in its area and is prepared to contribute for an agreed period of time)'.

Grants for volunteer expenses are also considered.

Preference is given to projects that:

▶ Will have the greatest impact in the six wards

▶ Have a strong community ownership, and will be delivered by organisations based in or with a proven track record of contributing to the communities in the six wards

▶ Bring in funds from other sources

▶ Involve partnership and co-operation between organisations, where this is feasible

▶ Address social need and deprivation

▶ Help strengthen voluntary bodies and support community involvement

▶ Are sustainable and provide a long-term legacy to the local communities

▶ Encourage social cohesion and integration

▶ Improve health and well-being

Financial information

In 2016/17 the trust had assets of £2.4 million and an income of over £1 million. There were 31 small grants (£179,500) and 11 main grants (£604,500) approved in the year, which totalled £698,500.

Previous beneficiaries have included: Hillingdon Law Centre (£59,000); Hounslow Arts Trust (£40,000); Action for West London (£28,000); Harlington and Ealing Citizens Advice (£26,500); Hillingdon Somali Women's Group (£11,200); Crown Centre for the Deaf

(£7,500); Children's Writers and Illustrations South London (£7,400); Heathrow Primary School (£3,900); Austin Sewing Club (£3,000); The Harlington Locomotive Society (£2,000 in two grants); Young Carers (£500).

Exclusions

Funding is not provided to the following:

▶ Individuals

▶ Public bodies or projects that should be funded by public funds (projects by voluntary bodies that will be partially financed by public bodies are considered)

▶ Religious bodies except for ancillary activities which meet one of the priorities)

▶ Organisations that have already received funding in respect of a completed project

▶ Work that has already started

▶ Political parties or lobbying

▶ Non-charitable activities

Applications

Application forms and detailed guidelines for both schemes are provided on the trust's website. Applicants are welcome to approach the trust prior to submitting a formal application. Awards are considered every second month – see the website for up-to-date deadlines.

Note: The trust is currently implementing a plan to wind down its operations. It is anticipated that final grants will be made in March 2019.

Sources of information

Accounts; annual report; Charity Commission record; funder's website.

The Lady Hind Trust

🔍 General charitable purposes, particularly social welfare and health and disability but also: churches, education, arts and culture, environment and heritage, accommodation, community groups and clubs, crime prevention

📍 England, in practice, mainly Nottinghamshire and Norfolk

£ £367,500 (2016)

CC number: 208877

Trustees: Charles Barratt; Tim Farr; Nigel Savory; John Pears.

Correspondent: John Thompson, Trust Administrator, PO Box 10455, Nottingham NG5 0HR (tel: 01476 552429; email: ladyhind@btinternet.com)

 www.ladyhindtrust.org.uk

The charity has general charitable purposes, however, the trustees have historically given support in the

following areas described on the charity's website:

▶ Charitable projects and activities in or benefitting the people of Nottinghamshire or Norfolk

▶ Activities relating to community healthcare services including home care, after care, sufferers of long-term medical conditions and the continuing care of people with disabilities

▶ Health education and prevention – promoting knowledge and awareness of specific diseases or medical conditions

▶ Lifelong learning projects helping people of any age to achieve their educational potential through supplementary schools, literacy and numeracy projects, community education, vocational/restart education for the unemployed, and alternative education for excluded school pupils

▶ Community development by helping groups to organise and respond to problems and needs in their communities

▶ Personal social services including organisations assisting individuals or families to overcome social deprivation, e.g. people who are homeless or those with disabilities and their carers, single parent and childcare groups and other family support groups

▶ Social preventive schemes covering activities which prevent crime, 'dropping out' and general delinquency, provide social care outreach services, deliver social health and safety awareness schemes

▶ Community social activities which promote social engagement for vulnerable people, mitigating against isolation and loneliness

The Lady Hind Trust and The Charles Littlewood Hill Trust (see page 251) share the same trustees and are administered together.

Financial information

In 2016 the charity had assets of £16.1 million and an income of £423,000. A total of 135 grants were made totalling about £367,500. Grants were distributed as follows:

Welfare	50	£121,000
Medical/disabilities	39	£97,000
Churches	11	£31,000
Other	11	£27,500
Education	9	£21,000
Groups/clubs	4	£21,000
Accommodation	3	£11,000
Arts	3	£11,000
Environment	3	£3,000
Heritage	1	£1,000
Services	1	£1,000

A further £22,000 was distributed in smaller grants of less than £1,000 across all categories.

Beneficiaries included: The Norfolk Churches Trust (£10,000); Framework Housing Association (£5,000); Pintsize Theatre Ltd (£3,500); 18th Nottingham Boy's Brigade (£3,000); Collingham and District Pre-School (£1,000); European Squirrel Initiative, Greenfingers Charity and Marine Conservation Society (£1,000 each); Nottinghamshire Building Preservation Trust (£1,000); Bowel Cancer UK (£1,000); Meningitis Research Foundation (£1,000).

Exclusions

The charity does not support:

◗ Organisations that are not based or specifically working in England
◗ New applications from individuals
◗ Activities that are the responsibility of the local health authority, education authority or similar body

Applications

Applications should be made in writing via post to the correspondent. The website explains that applications must be received by 20 January, 20 May or 20 September, to be considered at the trustees' meetings held in March, July and November, respectively.

Applicants should provide:

◗ The name of their organisation and its status as a registered charity or a community interest company (CIC), or provide other evidence of the organisation's charitable purpose
◗ Details of project or activity for which the grant is requested and how it meets the trust's policy
◗ Information on who will benefit from the project or activity and show that the benefit is sustainable
◗ Likely costs of the project or activity and an explanation of what other finance is sought or is available
◗ Details of how the project or activity will be managed or organised by paid staff and/or volunteers and the numbers involved
◗ A copy of their organisation's latest set of audited accounts

Applications are not acknowledged and unsuccessful applicants are not notified.

The website states that: 'The Lady Hind Trust and The Charles Littlewood Hill Charitable Trust are connected and administered in unison. Please only apply to one Trust.'

Sources of information

Accounts; annual report; Charity Commission record; funder's website.

The Hintze Family Charity Foundation

🔍 Education, Christianity, arts and culture, health, armed forces, social welfare, environment, general charitable purposes

📍 England and Wales, particularly the diocese of Southwark, overseas

💷 £9.4 million (2016)

CC number: 1101842

Trustees: Sir Michael Hintze; Sir Michael Peat; Duncan Baxter.

Correspondent: Kate Rees-Doherty, Secretary, 4th Floor, One Strand, London WC2N 5HR (tel: 020 7201 2444; email: enquiries@hfcf.org.uk)

The foundation was established in 2003 by UK-based Australian businessman, philanthropist and political patron Sir Michael Hintze, the founder and head of CQS Management, a London hedge fund. Since its inception the foundation has supported almost 200 charities. Many of the organisations receiving larger grants are those to which the founder is closely connected.

The principal objectives of the foundation are:

◗ To advance education by supporting schools, colleges and universities
◗ To support universities, libraries and art galleries and in particular to promote access for the general public to works of artistic, scientific, historic, architectural or cultural importance
◗ To support the Christian faith and institutions
◗ To relieve sickness and protect and preserve public health through projects to benefit the sick and terminally ill
◗ To further such other purposes which are charitable in accordance with the laws of England and Wales as the trustees think fit provided that in so doing the charity shall not relieve any local authority or other body from its statutory obligations

Grants can be made on a one-off or multi-year basis and the foundation can contribute to capital and revenue funding, including salaries and core costs.

Financial information

In 2016 the foundation had assets of £4.2 million and an income of nearly £9.9 million, mostly from donations. Grants totalling £9.4 million were made during the year. A total of 46 organisations were supported in the following categories:

Education	£7.4 million
Armed services	£500,000
Cultural/Arts	£362,000
Health	£231,000
Religious	£33,500

Previous beneficiaries have included: Outward Bound Trust (£100,000); Institute of Economic Affairs (£85,000); National Portrait Gallery (£83,500); Advance Charitable Fund UK, British Museum, Canterbury Cathedral Trust, The Black Stork Charity and The Prince's Teaching Institute (£50,000 each); British Film Institute (£20,000); Southwark Diocese Clergy Support Fund Campaign (£5,000).

Applications

The annual report 2016 explains that the foundation: 'invites applications for grants from charities which further the objectives of the foundation. No specific format is required for applications. Applications and potential donations identified by the Chief Executive and the trustees are considered at trustees' meetings.'

Sources of information

Accounts; annual report; Charity Commission record; funder's website.

The Henry C. Hoare Charitable Trust

🔍 Environment, welfare, education, community development, health and saving lives, animal welfare, religion, arts, culture, heritage and science, public policy

📍 UK

💷 £243,500 (2015/16)

CC number: 1088669

Trustees: Henry Hoare; Hoare Trustees.

Correspondent: Messrs Hoare Trustees, C. Hoare & Co., 37 Fleet Street, London EC4P 4DQ (tel: 020 7353 4522)

This trust was established in 2001 with general charitable purposes. Grants have been awarded in the following categories: environmental protection and improvement; health; education; citizenship and community development; animal welfare; youth, age, ill health, disability and financial hardship; religion; public policy; and the arts. One-off and annual donations are made.

Financial information

In 2015/16 the trust held assets of £4.6 million and had an income of £180,500. There were grants made totalling £243,500 to 59 organisations that were broken down as follows:

Advancement of environmental protection or improvement	£46,500
Relief in need	£42,000
Advancement of education	£42,000
Advancement of citizenship and community development	£31,000
Advancement of health and saving lives	£28,000
Advancement of animal welfare	£25,000
Advancement of religion	£22,000
Advancement of arts, culture, heritage or science	£5,000
Public policy	£2,000

Beneficiaries included: Zeal's Youth Trust (£28,000); European Squirrel Initiative (£10,000); Vincent Wildlife Trust (£5,000); Rainmaker Foundation (£2,000); Bury St Edmonds Heritage Trust, John Muir Trust and Niall Mellon Township Trust (£1,000 each); Young People Frome (£500).

Applications

The annual report for 2015/16 states that the trustees seldom grant funds to unsolicited requests for donations.

Sources of information

Accounts; annual report; Charity Commission record.

The Hobson Charity Ltd

Relief of poverty, education, recreation, health, religious activities, animals, arts and culture, environment, armed forces

England and Wales

£1.6 million (2016/17)

CC number: 326839

Trustees: Deborah Hobson; Lady Patricia Hobson; Jennifer Richardson.

Correspondent: Mark Turner, PO Box No. 57691, London NW7 0GR (tel: 020 3880 6425; email: post@hobsoncharity. org.uk)

The charity was established in 1985. It serves as the charitable vehicle of Sir Ronald Hobson, founder of Central Car Parks and later co-owner of NCP car parks with a business partner, Sir Donald Gosling, who is a fellow trustee and also a trustee of The Gosling Foundation Ltd (see page 163). Both charities are administered from the same address.

Areas of work

The charity supports a wide range of charitable causes and has the following objects:

▶ The relief of poverty, suffering and distress among older and disadvantaged people and the provision of recreational facilities and other leisure time occupation in the interests of their social welfare

▶ The advancement of education
▶ The furtherance of other charitable purposes beneficial to communities in the UK

Trustees advise that they expect project leaders to be active in seeking additional sources of funding besides those provided by the fund. Furthermore, they note that while the is no a set limit for the amount of funds that may be granted, applicants are nonetheless recommended to be specific regarding the level of funding required.

Financial information

In 2016/17 the charity held assets of £47.1 million and had an income of £2 million. Grants awarded to organisations totalled £1.6 million and were broken down as follows:

Other purposes beneficial to the community	£869,000
Advancement of education	£575,000
Advancement of religion	£120,000
Relief of poverty	£57,500

Beneficiaries included: RAF Museum Hendon (£200,000); British Library and Outward Bound Trust (£50,000 each); Chilterns MS Centre (£25,000); Bloodwise (£15,000); University of Manchester (£10,000); Animals in Need and My Life My Choice (£5,000 each); St Luke's Healthcare for the Clergy and The Vine (£1,000 each); Bethany Christian Trust and Open Country (£500 each).

Exclusions

Individuals are not assisted (except in exceptional circumstances). Unless there are exceptional circumstances the fund will also not support salaries or core costs.

Applications

The fund has no formal application process, instead a letter or email enclosing the project details together with financial information, including; the amount of funds requested, additional sources of funding, and information regarding other pending funding applications, should be submitted to the correspondent. There are no deadlines and feedback is usually given within 30 days.

Sources of information

Accounts; annual report; Charity Commission record, further information provided by the funder.

Hockerill Educational Foundation

 Education and training, Christianity

UK and overseas, with a preference for the dioceses of Chelmsford and St Albans

 £221,000 to organisations (2016/17)

CC number: 311018

Trustees: Hannah Potter; Ven. Elwin Cockett; Colin Bird; Canon Harry Marsh; Janet Scott; Revd Tim Elbourne; Jonathan Longstaff; Raymond Slade; Rt Revd Dr Alan Smith; Rt Revd Stephen Cottrell; Ven. Janet Mackenzie; Ven. Robin King; David Morton.

Correspondent: Derek Humphrey, Secretary, 3 The Swallows, Harlow, Essex CM17 0AR (tel: 01279 420855; email: info@hockerillfoundation.org.uk)

www.hockerillfoundation.org.uk

This foundation was set up following the closure of Hockerill College, which was founded in 1852 to train women teachers who 'would go to schools in the service of humanity'. When the Secretary of State for Education and Science decided in 1976 to wind down Hockerill College, the proceeds of the sale of its assets were given to this foundation to use for the purposes for which the college was created.

The aims of the foundation

The foundation makes grants in the field of education in three main areas, which are outlined on the website:

▶ 'Individual grants to support the education and training of teachers'
▶ 'Grants to organisations to support teachers and research and development in religious education'
▶ 'Grants to develop the church's educational work in the dioceses of Chelmsford and St Albans'

Generally about two thirds of the annual grant expenditure is allocated to the church's educational work in the two dioceses and the remainder to organisational and individual grants. Awards are made both in the UK and internationally.

Grants for organisations

The website provides the following information:

The Foundation makes grants to organisations and corporate bodies associated with education on Christian principles. We recognise that there is a religious dimension to all education, but the trustees would expect any activity, project or research they support to be likely to be of real benefit to Religious Education and/or the Church's educational work. They will give priority to imaginative new projects which will enhance the Church's contribution to higher and further education and/or promote aspects of Religious Education in schools.

The Foundation may make grants to organisations renewable for up to three years, or occasionally a maximum of five years, subject to the trustees being satisfied annually that the grant has been used satisfactorily. Grants for the funding of research or the appointment of staff may be paid by instalments and are subject to funds being available.

Financial information

In 2016/17 the foundation had assets of £7.3 million and an income of £316,000. Grants totalling £292,500 were paid during the year and were distributed as follows:

Diocese of Chelmsford	£100,000
Diocese of St Albans	£100,000
Individuals	£71,500
Other corporate grants	£21,000

Beneficiaries included: In the diocese of St Albans: Diocesan RE Advisor (£50,000); General Schools Administrator (£25,000); In the diocese of Chelmsford: School Governance Support (£25,000); Training placements (£10,000); Corporate Grants for Research and Development in Education: RE Council (£5,000); CACTUS (£2,000).

Exclusions

Grants are not made for general appeals, 'bricks and mortar' building projects, or 'purposes that are the clear responsibility of another body'.

Applications

Application forms are available from the website, along with full guidelines.

Sources of information

Accounts; annual report; Charity Commission record; funder's website.

The Jane Hodge Foundation

Medical care and research, education, religion

UK and overseas with a preference for Wales

£3.2 million (2015/16)

CC number: 216053

Trustees: Ian Davies; Jonathan Hodge; Adrian Piper; Karen Hodge; Helen Molyneux; Alun Bowen.

Correspondent: Jonathan Hodge, Trustee, One Central Square, Cardiff CF10 1FS (tel: 029 2078 7693; email: contact@hodgefoundation.org.uk)

The foundation was established in 1962 and its objective is to apply its income in the following areas:

- The encouragement of medical and surgical studies and research, and in particular the study of and research in connection with the causes, diagnosis, treatment and cure of cancer, poliomyelitis, tuberculosis and diseases affecting children
- The general advancement of medical and surgical science
- The advancement of education
- The advancement of religion

Financial information

In 2015/16 the foundation held assets of almost £37.7 million and had an income of £3.2 million. During the year, 112 grants were made totalling £3.2 million. Donations were broken down as follows:

Medical	57	£1.8 million
Education	23	£969,000
Other	27	£416,000
Religion	5	£30,000

Previous beneficiaries have included: The Prince's Trust (£250,000 in three grants); The Duke of Edinburgh's Award (£130,000); Bobath Children's Therapy Centre Wales (£107,500 in two grants); Valleys Kids (£80,000); Institute of Welsh Affairs (£75,000); Arts & Business Cymru (£50,000); Variety, the Children's Charity (£27,000); Breast Cancer Care (£19,500); Plan UK (£10,000); Council for Education in World Citizenship (£7,500); Meningitis Now (£6,000); Welsh Heritage Schools Initiative (£5,000).

Grants for less than £5,000 totalled £215,000.

Exclusions

Applications are only considered from exempt or registered charities. No grants are given to individuals.

Applications

Apply in writing to the correspondent. Applications for grants are considered by the trustees at regular meetings throughout the year. Applications are acknowledged.

Sources of information

Accounts; annual report; Charity Commission record.

The Holden Charitable Trust

Jewish causes, education, religion

UK, with a preference for the Manchester area

£486,000 (2016/17)

CC number: 264185

Trustees: David Lopian; Marian Lopian; Michael Lopian.

Correspondent: The Trustees, c/o Lopian Gross Barnett & Co., 6th Floor, Cardinal House, 20 St Mary's Parsonage, Manchester M3 2LG (tel: 0161 832 8721; email: david.lopian@lopiangb.co.uk)

The Holden Charitable Trust was established in 1972 and exists to receive and distribute charitable donations to worthy causes primarily within the Orthodox Jewish community.

Financial information

In 2016/17 the trust had assets of £785,500 and an income of £458,000. During the year, the trust gave almost £486,000 in grants to organisations.

A list of beneficiaries was not included within the accounts.

Previous beneficiaries have included: Broom Foundation; Friends of Beis Eliyahu Trust; King David's School; Ohel Bnei Yaakob; Ohr Yerushalayim Synagogue; The Fed.

Applications

Apply in writing to the correspondent.

Sources of information

Accounts; annual report; Charity Commission record.

P H Holt Foundation

Community development, social welfare, education, the arts, natural and built environment

Merseyside

£302,500 to organisations (2016/17)

CC number: 1113708

Trustees: Neil Kemsley, Chair; Tilly Boyce; Martin Cooke; Paige Earlam; Nikki Eastwood; Anthony Hannay; Ken Ravenscroft; Elspeth Christie.

Correspondent: Anne Edwards, 151 Dale Street, Liverpool L2 2AH (tel: 0151 237 2663; email: administrator@ phholtfoundation.org.uk)

www.phholtfoundation.org.uk

The foundation makes a large number of mostly small grants mostly in Merseyside. The original charity, the Holt Education Trust was started with a bequest from Philip Holt in 1915. Holt was of the founders of the Liverpool based Ocean Steam Ship Company Ltd.

Areas of work

The foundation's website states:

The PH Holt Foundation supports charities which aim to make Merseyside a better place to live, particularly smaller grass roots organisations that find it difficult to attract funds. We focus support on five priority themes.

To be considered for funding, your activity should meet at least one of our priority themes:

- Creating opportunities for people to contribute to their local community

- Enabling people to overcome barriers and take control of their lives
- Widening access to education for people of all ages
- Increasing engagement in the arts for marginalised or excluded groups
- Encouraging care of the natural and built environment

The majority of our grants are for specific purposes and diverse in nature. Additional qualities trustees look for in an application include:

- Making Merseyside a better place to live
- Encouraging self-help and resilience
- Developing realistic and sustainable plans
- Delivering strategic solutions
- Bringing positive change and measurable impact

Financial information

In 2016/17 the foundation held assets of £19.6 million and had an income of £270,500. Grants awarded to organisations totalled £302,500.

Beneficiaries included: Ariel Trust (£13,000); Old Roan Baptist Church (£10,000); Apex Trust (£9,000); Rampworx (£6,500); Emmaus Merseyside (£5,000); Hope Street Lt (£4,300); Rotters Community Composting (£3,000); Wirral Community Narrowboat Trust (£2,000); Stick 'n' Steps (£1,200); Merseyside Environmental Trust (£750); The Tall Ships Youth Trust (£200).

Exclusions

The foundation will not support the following:

- Religious and political causes
- General fundraising appeals
- Sponsorship of individuals
- Medical research

Applications

Application forms are available to download from the foundation's website and should be returned by email to administrator@phholtfoundation.org.uk with a copy of your latest annual report and accounts.

Sources of information

Accounts; annual report; Charity Commission record; funder's website.

The Holywood Trust

 Disadvantaged young people

 Dumfries and Galloway

£ £1.5 million to organisations (2016/17)

OSCR number: SC009942

Trustees: Valerie McElroy; John Jencks; Ben Weatherall; Amy Agnew; Clara Weatherall.

Correspondent: Richard Lye, Trust Administrator., Hestan House, Crichton Business Park, Bankend Road, Dumfries

DG1 4TA (tel: 01387 269176; email: funds@holywood-trust.org.uk)

 www.holywood-trust.org.uk

 facebook.com/The-Holywood-Trust-421320750713

The trust's primary aim is to help young people aged 15–25 years in Dumfries and Galloway. It gives grants to individuals and organisations, creating opportunities for young people in the region. Grants are made in the following areas:

- Providing opportunities for the most disadvantaged and vulnerable young people in the region
- Encouraging talented young people in Dumfries and Galloway
- Helping improve sports and cultural opportunities across the region

The website states that the trust is 'particularly interested in helping to fill gaps in provision, and to support innovative ideas. Your organisation should be appropriately constituted and demonstrate a commitment to equal opportunities.' The trust will occasionally consider supporting vulnerable younger children for preventative measures in relation to health or social disadvantage.

Grants can be made to organisations involving the wider community, including self-help groups. Some examples of what the trust has previously supported includes: youth and sporting clubs; equipment; group development activities and residential trips; programmes for activities for young people; and cultural venues or arts programmes.

Financial information

In 2016/17 the trust held assets of £125 million and had an income of almost £2.5 million. Grants to 117 organisations totalled £1.5 million.

The top three categories of grant were:

Sports and recreation	31	£548,000
Arts provision	16	£453,500
Disability	11	£343,000

Beneficiaries included: Maggie's Centres (£75,000); Aberlour Childcare Trust (£50,500); Soul Soup (£45,000); Electric Theatre Arts (£40,000); Project Scotland (£31,000); University of Glasgow (£15,000); Newton Stewart Rugby Club (£15,000); Stranraer YMCA (£10,500).

Grants of under £10,000 totalled £308,000.

Applications

Application forms are available from the correspondent or available (together with criteria and guidelines) to download from the website. The trustees usually meet every three months – normally March, June, September and December; and deadline dates for

applications are set prior to each meeting and advertised on the trust's website. There is no minimum or maximum amount for applicants to request. Organisations may submit their applications electronically but note the trust also requires a signed hard copy with all documents before the application form can be processed.

Sources of information

Accounts; annual report; OSCR record; funder's website.

The Homelands Charitable Trust

 General charitable purposes, General Conference of the New Church, medical research, care and protection of children, hospices

UK

£ £305,500 to organisations (2016/17)

CC number: 214322

Trustees: Nigel Armstrong; Revd Clifford Curry; Robert Curry.

Correspondent: Nigel Armstrong, Trustee, 4th Floor, Imperial House, 15 Kingsway, London WC2B 6UN (tel: 020 7240 9971)

The trust was established in 1962, the settlors were four members of the Curry family and the original endowment was in the form of shares in the Curry company.

Most grants are for less than £2,000. The 2016/17 annual report notes that the trust supports general charitable purposes with a bias towards:

- General Conference of the New Church
- Medical research
- Care and protection of children
- Hospices, including those for children

Financial information

In 2016/17 the trust held assets of £8.8 million and had an income of £378,500. Grants awarded to organisations totalled £305,500. The following breakdown can be found in the accounts:

Church	£111,000
Other	£93,500
Hospices	£35,500
Children	£34,500
Medical	£31,500

Previous beneficiaries have included: General Conference of New Church (£63,000); Broadfield Memorial Fund (£16,000); Friends of the Earth and RNLI (£3,000 each); Anorexia and Bulimia Care and SOS Children's Villages (£2,800 each); Benslow Music Trust, Edinburgh Young Carers Project, Riding for the Disabled and Sailors' Families Society (£1,800 each); St Luke's

Hospice (£1,500); Womankind Worldwide (£1,000).

Applications

Apply in writing to the correspondent.

Sources of information

Accounts; annual report; Charity Commission record.

Sir Harold Hood's Charitable Trust

 Roman Catholic causes

Worldwide

£781,000 (2016/17)

CC number: 225870

Trustees: Dom Hood; Lord True; Lady True; Margaret Hood; Christian Elwes.

Correspondent: Margaret Hood, Trustee, c/o haysmacintyre, 26 Red Lion Square, London WC1R 4AG (tel: 020 7969 5500; email: nlandsman@ haysmacintyre.com)

The trust was established in 1962 by the late Sir Harold Hood, who died in 2005. Sir Harold was an influential editor and director of several Catholic publications during his lifetime, a philanthropist who was involved in a number of charities and an early investor in an electronics company that later evolved into Vodafone. The trust supports Roman Catholic organisations only.

Financial information

In 2016/17 the trust had assets of £34.4 million and an income of £731,000. Grants were made to 110 organisations totalling £781,000.

Beneficiaries included: Craig Lodge Trust (£50,000); St Richard Reynolds Catholic Church (£40,000); PACT – Prison Advice and Care Trust (£38,500); St Francis Leprosy Guild (£20,000); Youth 2000 (£11,000); Little Friends Centre – Botswana and Mary's Meals (£5,000 each); Maryvale Institute, Birmingham (£3,000); Friends of Kipkelion (£2,000); Young Alive Zimbabwe (£1,500); Friends of St Michael's Primary School – Uganda and St Joseph's Home for Chronically Ill Children – South Africa (£1,000 each).

Exclusions

Grants are not awarded to individuals.

Applications

Applications may be made in writing to the correspondent, including the latest set of accounts. The trustees meet once a year to consider applications, usually in November.

Sources of information

Accounts; annual report; Charity Commission record.

Horne Foundation

 General charitable purposes, mainly education

 UK, mainly Northamptonshire and Oxfordshire

 £2 million to organisations (2016/17)

CC number: 283751

Trustees: Julie Davenport; Ros Harwood; Tina Horne.

Correspondent: Ros Harwood, Trustee, Horne Foundation, PO Box 6165, Newbury RG14 9FY (email: hornefoundation@googlemail.com)

The foundation was established in 1981 for general charitable purposes including the relief of poverty and the advancement of education. The 2016/17 annual report states that the foundation's grants policy is:

> To make substantial grants towards major educational projects that involve new buildings, once every few years and regular smaller donations to local projects in the Northampton and Oxfordshire areas and also student bursaries for higher education through Northampton schools.

Financial information

In 2016/17 the foundation had assets of almost £6.7 million and an income of £143,000. Grants totalled £2 million and were awarded to two organisations with a further £53,000 awarded to 26 individual students in Northampton schools via bursaries.

Beneficiaries included: Sutton Trust (£2 million); Just for Kids Law (£25,000).

Exclusions

The foundation prefers to support organisations without religious affiliation.

Applications

Applications can be made in writing to the correspondent at any time.

Sources of information

Accounts; annual report; Charity Commission record.

The Thomas J Horne Memorial Trust

 Hospices, medical research, people with disabilities, people who are homeless, international development

 UK and the developing world

£748,000 (2016/17)

CC number: 1010625

Trustees: Jeff Horne; Jon Horne; Emma Horne.

Correspondent: Jeff Horne, Trustee, Kingsdown, Warmlake Road, Chart Sutton, Maidstone, Kent ME17 3RP (email: cc@horne-trust.org.uk)

The trust was set up in 1992. The vast majority of support is given to hospices, particularly children's hospices, and related medical support charities. Organisations helping people who are homeless, individuals with disabilities and self-help groups in the financially developing world are also assisted.

Financial information

In 2016/17 the trust had assets of £7.1 million and an income of £815,000. Grants to 117 organisations totalled £748,000.

Beneficiaries included: World Medical Fund (£20,000); Demelza House Children's Hospice, Ellenor Lions Hospices, Prospect Hospice and St Andrew's Hospice (£10,000 each); St Catherine's Hospice and Wisdom Hospice (£7,500 each); Marie Curie Cancer Care (£5,000); Whitby Dog Rescue (£1,000).

Applications

Unsolicited applications are not accepted.

Sources of information

Accounts; annual report; Charity Commission record.

The Horse Trust

 Equine health or welfare

 UK

£285,000 (2016)

CC number: 231748

Trustees: Josh Salter; Peter Clegg; Rupert de Mauley; Bronwen Jones; Ian Bowen; Christopher Marriott; Bruce McGorum; Milly Soames; David Cook; Rupert Neal.

Correspondent: Jeanette Allen, Speen Farm, Slad Lane, Speen, Princes Risborough HP27 0PP (tel: 01494 488960; email: info@horsetrust.org.uk)

 www.horsetrust.org.uk

The trust works to improve the quality of life of horses, ponies and donkeys in the UK. One of the ways the trust achieves this is by giving grants to fund a wide range of projects that help improve horses' health or welfare. The trust mainly funds non-invasive equine veterinary research.

The trust has supported ethical research projects into a wide range of equine diseases and ailments including laminitis, sarcoids, digital flexor tendonitis, periodontal disease, drug resistance in parasites, strangles, equine herpesvirus, colic, degenerative joint disease, grass sickness and sweet itch.

199

The trustees invite applications for both research grant projects and PhDs.

Financial information

In 2016 the trust had assets of £25.1 million and an income of £2.8 million. During the year, the trust awarded £285,000 in grants to organisations in support of veterinary research.

Beneficiaries included: University of Liverpool (£91,000); AHT (£72,000); Moredun Research Institute (£43,500); RVC (£43,000); The Royal (Dick) School Veterinary Studies and Roslin Institute (£32,000).

Other grants totalled £4,300.

Applications

Apply in writing to the correspondent. The trust's 2016 annual report states the following:

Once preliminary applications have been received they are reviewed by the Scientific Committee who then short list a selection that are invited to submit a full application, These full applications are then subject to a peer review and are ranked. The Board of Trustees of The Horse Trust will then make the final funding decisions from these rankings. These will be based in part on the impact assessment report of each short listed application. The applicants will need to have demonstrated clearly the intended benefits to the UK equine population, how such benefits will be communicated to the horse owning and keeping public as well as veterinary and allied professionals and will be prompted to look at a variety of criteria when completing their reports. When the research grants are being discussed the meetings are chaired by the legally qualified trustee and all perceived, potential or actual conflicts of interest are scrupulously declared and recorded.

Sources of information

Accounts; annual report; Charity Commission; funder's website.

Hospice UK

 Hospice and palliative care

UK Throughout the UK and overseas

£ £830,000 (2016/17)

CC number: 1014851/SCO41112

Trustees: Paul Dyer; Ann Smits; Anthony Collins; Catherine Tompkins; Christine Gibbons; Christine Heginbotham; Stephen Roberts; Karen Field; John Stephen; Emma Reynolds; Stephanie Peters.

Correspondent: Grants Team, 34–44 Britannia Street, London WC1X 9JG (tel: 020 7520 8200; email: grants@hospiceuk.org)

 www.hospiceuk.org

Hospice UK's work is explained on its website:

Hospice UK is the national charity for hospice care. We champion and support the work of more than 200 member organisations, which provide hospice care across the UK, so that they can deliver the highest quality of care to people with terminal or life-limiting conditions, and support their families.

We support the breadth, dynamism and flexibility of modern hospice care by influencing government and decision makers, improving quality of care through the sharing of good practice, and providing resources, education and training, and grant programmes. We also support the development of hospice and palliative care worldwide.

Grants programmes

Grants are made by Hospice UK, both in the UK and overseas, with the intention of having a lasting impact on the provision of hospice and palliative care.

Grants programmes are funded by donations from external sources, including grant-making charities. The charity notes on its website that criteria for each grants programme are approved by the Hospice UK Governance Committee and by each individual funder. Each programme has its own specific application form, criteria, guidelines and deadlines.

In the UK, Hospice UK member organisations and their staff can apply for funding to enable them to undertake specific capital projects, to develop new or existing services, and to increase their expertise in the work that they do. Organisations which offer palliative care services but are not Hospice UK members can also apply for grants, depending on the criteria of the grant programme.

On an international basis, organisations and health professionals providing hospice and palliative care in 'resource-poor' countries can apply for funding to increase and improve the provision of care in those countries. The website explains that 'the grants are designed to help people working in palliative care to attend existing education and training programmes'.

Financial information

In 2016/17 the charity had assets of £5.3 million and an income of £5.9 million. There were 357 grants payable during the year totalling £830,000 and broken down as follows:

Grants to support rehabilitative palliative care	£570,000
Professional development grants	£192,000
Grants to support capital projects	£51,000
Other grant programmes	£17,000

Beneficiaries included: St Catherine's Hospice (£47,000); Oakhaven Hospice (£13,000); Dorothy House Hospice Care

(£10,000); Bluebell Wood Children's Hospice (£2,000); St Giles Hospice (£1,000).

Applications

Full details of open grants programmes can be found on the Hospice UK website. The grants team can also be contacted for further information.

Sources of information

Accounts; annual report; Charity Commission record; funder's website.

The Hospital Saturday Fund

 Health and medicine, disability

UK and Republic of Ireland

£ £874,500 to organisations (2016)

CC number: 1123381

Trustees: Paul Palmer; John Greenwood; Jane Dalton; John Randel; David Thomas; Mark Davies; Margaret Rogers.

Correspondent: Paul Jackson, 24 Upper Ground, London SE1 9PD (tel: 020 7202 1365; email: charity@hsf.eu.com)

www.hospitalsaturdayfund.org

The Hospital Saturday Fund is a healthcare cash plan organisation which was founded in 1873. In 1987 it established a charitable fund to support a wide range of hospitals, hospices and medical charities for care and research, as well as welfare organisations providing similar services. According to the charity's website, it can support:

- Individuals with a medical condition or disability who would benefit from assistance with the purchase of specialised equipment or from practical forms of treatment
- Registered health charities such as hospitals, hospices, medical organisations who are in need of grants for medical projects, care, research or support of medical training

The fund will also consider grants for running costs.

Financial information

In 2016 the charity had assets of £26 million and an income of £28 million. Grants totalled £915,000, including £40,500 in grants to individuals.

Donations to medical charities totalled £714,000. Donations to hospitals and hospices totalled £120,500. Donations to other causes totalled £40,000.

Beneficiaries included: Acquired Brain Injury Trust: Bloodwise, British Lung Foundation; Cerebral Palsy Plus; Lucy Air Ambulance for Children; Medical Detection Dogs; Muscular Dystrophy UK; National Eye Research Centre; National Kidney Federation; Pituitary

Foundation; Post-Polio Support Group; St John Ambulance; The Cure Parkinson's Trust; Urology Foundation.

Further details of recent grants are given on the charity's website.

Exclusions

Projects outside the UK, Isle of Man, Channel Islands and Republic of Ireland; unregistered organisations; organisations carrying out non-medically related activities.

Applications

Applications should be made using an online system on the charity's website. The Grant Making Committee meets quarterly. For the application submission dates consult the website – these vary depending on the size of grant but are generally in January, June, August and October.

Sources of information

Accounts; annual report; Charity Commission record; guidelines for applicants, funder's website.

Housing Pathways Trust

🔍 Social welfare, education and training, health, community services, domestic violence, homelessness

📍 Ealing and Brentford

💷 £276,000 (2016/17)

CC number: 211053

Trustee: Housing Pathways.

Correspondent: Grants Officer, Housing Pathways, 33 Dean Court, London W13 9YU (tel: 020 8579 7411; email: enquiries@yourpathways.org.uk)

🌐 www.yourpathways.org.uk

 facebook.com/yourpathways

 @yourpathways

Housing Pathways Trust is the amalgamation of a number of smaller charities dating back to the seventeenth century. As well as making grants to local community organisations, the trust owns 134 almshouse units.

Grant programmes

The trust has two grant programmes to help community groups and small charities in Ealing and Brentford.

The Main Grants programme covers the Ealing W5, W7 and W13, and the Brentford TW8 postcodes. At the time of writing (June 2018) the trust's website states that it will consider applications from organisations or projects that:

- Strengthen the local voluntary and community sector
- Alleviate poverty by tackling root causes
- Promote healthy living among disadvantaged groups
- Help disadvantaged people in the community to access local services
- Improve educational and employment opportunities
- Tackle homelessness
- Overcome isolation
- Support victims of domestic violence
- Provide counselling and support services
- Meet the need of disadvantaged people who have or care for those with disabilities
- Promote social cohesion and/or cross-generational activities

The trust supports full cost recovery, excluding capital costs. Grants can be made for up to three years for organisations that are able to demonstrate that they have monitored and evaluated their work, refined their approach, and have achieved their stated results. Generally, funding is limited to support small organisations with an annual income of less than £100,000 a year.

The Hopes and Dreams programme funds projects for young people in the beneficial area. Grants of up to £500 are available for individuals and groups can apply for up to £2,000.

The trust also makes an annual grant to the Ealing Deanery Synod to support the outreach and community work of Anglican churches in Ealing. Grants are normally restricted to £2,000 per project. Applicants should contact the Ealing Deanery Synod for further information.

Financial information

In 2016/17 the trust held assets of £13 million and had an income of £1.25 million. Grants totalled £276,000 of which £250,000 was awarded through the Main Grants programme. An additional £14,000 was awarded through the Ealing Deanery Synod and a further £3,000 was awarded through the Hopes and Dreams programme.

Beneficiaries included: Cultivate London (£153,500); Home-Start Ealing (£20,000); Volunteer Link (£10,000); Mind – Ealing and Hounslow (£7,300); Mindfood (£6,800); Hanwell Carnival, Our Barn Youth Club, Welshore Community Hub and West Ealing Neighbours (£5,000 each); Bless Community Church and Ealing Race and Equality Council (£4,500 each).

Exclusions

At the time of writing (June 2018) the trust's website states that the Main Grants programme will not fund:

- Projects which do not benefit the residents of Ealing and/or Brentford
- Individuals
- Projects which trustees consider ought properly to be funded by statutory funders such as local and central government and the health authority
- Commercial organisations
- Projects which have already happened
- Travel or transport costs
- Projects or organisations that exclude beneficiaries on the grounds of religious or political beliefs
- Projects or organisations that do not adhere to our equal opportunities policy
- Capital costs
- Organisations with free reserves more than three months its operational costs
- General appeals
- Academic research
- Hospitals and schools
- Ecology and animal welfare
- Applicants who have been rejected by us in the last 12 months
- Organisations that are currently receiving grant funding from us, unless this is coming to an end within the next ten months

Applications

Application forms and guidance can be found on the trust's helpful website or by contacting the Grants Officer.

Sources of information

Accounts; annual report; Charity Commission record; funder's website.

The Reta Lila Howard Foundation

🔍 General charitable purposes, with a preference for children's and young people's charities

📍 UK and the Republic of Ireland

💷 £540,000 (2016/17)

CC number: 1041634

Trustees: Alannah Weston; Charles Burnett; Garfield Mitchell; Melissa Murdoch; Claudia Hepburn; Mark Mitchell; Gregg Weston; Geordie Dalglish.

Correspondent: The Trustees, Horsmonden Business Centre, The Business Centre, Green Road, Horsmonden, Tonbridge TN12 8JS (tel: 01892 723394; email: retalilahoward@gmail.com)

The foundation was established in 1994 to support general charitable purposes. Today the foundation primarily supports a few innovative projects that benefit the physical and emotional well-being of children up to the age of 16 within the UK and Republic of Ireland. According the foundation's 2016/17 accounts, 'donations are intended to be given over a finite period', with the intention that the projects will be self-supporting once funding has ended.

Financial information

In 2016/17 the foundation had assets of £20 million and an income of £94,500. Grants were made totalling £511,000.

Beneficiaries included: Civitas (£80,000); Kids Run Free (£60,000); The Tree Council, Sense About Science (£40,000); Countryside Education Trust (£33,000); Urban Hope, Future First, Think Forward (£30,000 each); New Forest Centre (£29,000); St Albans Cathedral, Barnardo's and The Bike Project (£20,000 each); Fields in Trust (£18,000).

Exclusions

The foundation does fund any of the following:

- Individuals
- Non-registered charities
- Core costs
- Fundraising activities
- Conferences
- Student aid

Applications

The foundation does not accept unsolicited applications.

Sources of information

Accounts; annual report; Charity Commission record.

James T Howat Charitable Trust

 General charitable purposes

 Primarily Glasgow, but support can also be given to Scottish and UK-wide organisations

£ £231,500 to organisations (2016/17)

OSCR number: SC000201

Correspondent: The Trustees of James T Howat Charitable Trust, c/o Harper Macleod LLP, The Ca'd'oro, 45 Gordon Street, Glasgow G1 3PE

This trust can support a wide range of charitable causes. It primarily supports projects which are for the benefit of Glasgow and people who live there, although Scottish and UK-wide projects can be considered for small grants, especially if they can be applied locally. Grants are made to both organisations and to individuals.

Financial information

In 2016/17 the trust had assets of £6.36 million and an income of £225,500. Grants awarded to organisations totalled £231,500, including £30,000 to fund a scholarship at the University of Glasgow. Individuals were awarded a further £7,100.

Beneficiaries included: Royal Conservatoire of Scotland (£4,000); Listening Books (£2,000); Blind Veterans

UK, Carers Trust Scotland, East Glasgow Music School and Glasgow City Mission (£500 each); Foundation for Social Improvement (£250).

Exclusions

The trust's grants policy, published in the 2016/17 annual report, states that grants cannot normally be made to the following:

- Religious organisations duplicating rather than complementing existing statutory services
- Organisations running large current surpluses
- Individuals seeking medical electives, second or further qualifications, school fees, or costs incurred at tertiary educational establishments

Successful applicants in one year are unlikely to be successful in the next.

Applications

Applications may be made in writing to the correspondent and should include evidence of charitable status, current funding and how it is being used. According to the trust's grants policy, an application should demonstrate that the project for which the grant is intended is 'practical and business-like'.

Applications should include a summary of your request (no longer than one side of A4), backed up as necessary with schedules, and be accompanied by a copy of your organisation's latest accounts and/or business plan and foundation documents. The trust's grants policy also states that 'evidence of need must be produced, as should evidence that client groups participate in decision taking, and that through the applicant's work their quality of life and choice is enhanced rather than restricted'. A breakdown of costs and financial needs should be provided where possible, as should evidence of the difference a grant could make and details and outcomes of other grants applied for.

The trustees usually meet to consider grants in March, June, September and December and applications should be received by the middle of the preceding month. The trustees are unable to acknowledge unsuccessful applicants.

Sources of information

Accounts; annual report; OSCR record.

The Hull and East Riding Charitable Trust

 General charitable purposes

Hull and the East Riding of Yorkshire

£ £235,000 (2016/17)

CC number: 516866

Trustees: Kate Field; Matthew Fletcher; Adrian Horsley.

Correspondent: John Barnes, Greenmeades, Kemp Road, Swanland, North Ferriby, East Yorkshire HU14 3LY (tel: 01482 634664; email: john.barnes@ herct.org.uk)

 www.herct.org.uk

The trust was established in 1985 to give to general charitable causes for the benefit of people living in Hull and the East Riding of Yorkshire. National charities may be supported but usually only if they carry out work in the local area.

The trust's website states:

> Participation by young people under the age of 18 years, in the UK or overseas visits or projects with a leading organisation will be considered. Requests for notable buildings with a good level of community use will be evaluated.

> For significant community projects demanding major fund raising, support may be given by way of pledge, payment being conditional upon all other funds being sourced. Funding of both capital and revenue costs will be considered.

Financial information

In 2015/16 the trust held assets of £7.9 million and had an income of £201,500. A total of £235,000 was awarded in grants to 102 organisations and charities.

Beneficiaries included: Holy Trinity Church (£20,000); No Way Trust Ltd (£10,000); Marie Curie and St Andrews Children's Hospice (£5,000 each); Whizz-Kidz (£3,000); Community Church Hull and Matthew's Hub (£2,000 each); Relate (£1,800); William Wilberforce Monument Fund (£500); Lullaby Trust (£300).

Exclusions

Donations will not be made for education, political or religious purposes.

Applications

Apply in writing to the correspondent via post or email. A list of required information is available on the trust's website.

The trust's website states that 'initial telephone enquiries can be made – if necessary, a message can be left for future response'. The trustees meet twice a year – early in May and November. Appeals should be submitted by 20 April and 20 October, respectively.

Sources of information

Accounts; annual report; Charity Commission record; funder's website.

The Albert Hunt Trust

Health, homelessness, social welfare

UK

£2 million (2016/17)

CC number: 277318

Trustees: Breda McGuire; Stephen Harvey; Coutts & Co; Ian Fleming.

Correspondent: The Trustees, The Albert Hunt Trust, Wealth Advisory Services, Coutts & Co., 440 Strand, London WC2R 0QS (tel: 0345 304 2424)

The Albert Hunt Trust was established in 1979. The trustees' report for 2016/17 states that the trust's mission is as follows:

> To promote and enhance the physical and mental welfare of individuals, or groups of individuals, excluding research or the diagnosis of specific medical conditions, by the distribution of trust funds, at the sole and absolute discretion of the trustees, to charities registered in England and Wales, Scotland and Northern Ireland, that are actively engaged in that field of work.

In 2016/17 grants were given in three categories: hospices; homelessness; and health and well-being.

A very large number of modest grants are given to a wide range of organisations, both national and local, each year. The vast majority of grants are for £1,000 to £2,000 and many seem to go to new beneficiaries. There are around 50 grants for £5,000 or slightly more each year and many of these tend to go to regularly supported, national charities.

Financial information

In 2016/17 the trust had assets of nearly £63.9 million and an income of around £1.6 million. Grants were made to 637 organisations totalling over £2 million and were distributed as follows:

Health and well-being	£991,500
Hospices	£796,500
Homelessness	£298,500

Beneficiaries included: Macmillan Cancer Support – Tameside (£50,000); Hospice of the Good Shepherd (£25,000); Lakeland's Day Care Hospice (£10,000); Acorns (£5,000); Safe and Sound Homes and Hospice UK (£3,000 each); Brendoncare (£2,000); Age UK Leicestershire and Rutland (£1,000 each).

Exclusions

No funding is given for 'research or the diagnosis and treatment of specific medical conditions' or overseas work.

Applications

The 2016/17 annual report states that applications should be made in writing to the correspondent by letter containing the following:

 Aims and objectives of the charity
 Nature of appeal
Total target if for a specific project
Contributions received against target
Registered charity number
 Any other relevant factors

Appeals are considered on a monthly basis. The trust has previously stated that no unsolicited correspondence will be acknowledged unless an application receives favourable consideration.

Sources of information

Accounts; annual report; Charity Commission record.

The Hunter Foundation

Prevention and relief of poverty, education, entrepreneurialism, economic equality

UK and overseas

£2.7 million (2016/17)

OSCR number: SC027532

Trustees: Vartan Gregorian; Lady Marion Hunter; Sir Tom Hunter, Jim McMahon.

Correspondent: The Trustees, Marathon House, Olympic Business Park, Drybridge Road, Dundonald, Ayrshire KA2 9AE (email: info@ thehunterfoundation.co.uk)

www.thehunterfoundation.co.uk

facebook.com/pages/ THunterFoundation

@THunterF

The Hunter Foundation defines itself as 'a proactive venture philanthropy that seeks to invest in determining model solutions, in partnership with others, to troubling systemic issues relating to poverty eradication and educational enablement'. The objectives of the foundation are to support economic opportunity and equality by providing funding for education; entrepreneurship; and to help the prevention and relief of poverty.

Grant-making

The foundation usually works in strategic partnerships with governments, agencies, funders and individuals but does sometimes run grants programmes such as The Innovation Fund itself.

The Innovation Fund

At the time of writing (June 2018) the foundation's Innovation Fund was looking to fund ten organisations with plans to combat child poverty in their areas of Scotland. According to the fund's guidelines it is looking to fund:

 New and innovative approaches that will have an impact on reducing child poverty by 2030 in a way that helps

families to remain out of poverty for a minimum 3 year period and that is viable and sustainable practice for public sector/third sector; or

Expansion of existing proven approaches to reducing child poverty that will again have an impact on reducing child poverty by 2030 and in a way that families can remain out of poverty for a minimum 3 years and that organisations involved can sustain

Financial information

In 2016/17 the foundation held assets of £3.2 million and had an income of £3 million. Grants awarded to organisations totalled £2.7 million.

Beneficiaries included: Kiltwalk (£623,000); Entrepreneurial Scotland (£100,000); The Amber Foundation (£46,000); Coach Core (£40,000); Mary's Meals (£25,000); Home from Home (£10,000); Livingstone Volunteers (£5,000).

Applications

Applications to The Innovation Fund can be made through the foundation's website. Contact the foundation for further information on partnerships.

Sources of information

Accounts; annual report; OSCR record; funder's website.

Miss Agnes H Hunter's Trust

People with cancer, people with arthritis, people with physical or learning disabilities or mental health issues, education and training

Scotland

£347,000 (2016/17)

OSCR number: SC004843

Trustees: Walter Thomson; Keith Burdon; Alison Campbell; Elaine Crichton; Norman Dunning; John Hume; Neil Paterson.

Correspondent: Sarah Wright, Trust Manager, Davidson House, 57 Queen Charlotte Street, Edinburgh EH6 7EY (tel: 0131 538 5496; email: s.wright@ agneshunter.org.uk)

www.agneshunter.org.uk

The trust was established in 1954 to support registered charities delivering health and social welfare projects in Scotland.

Grants programmes

As stated on the website, the trustees currently support projects which:

1. Support people living with arthritis or cancer The Trust will assist a range of projects supporting people living with arthritis or cancer. Although there are no restrictions on the type of project that can be considered, the Trust does have an interest in schemes that assist with self-management and those that help people live with their condition. The Trust has, however, discontinued its assistance to hospices.

2. Help disabled people, including those affected by physical disability, visual impairment or illness Priorities include:a) Advice, support, welfare benefit schemes b) Information, awareness and self-management/education c) Employment and life-skills training

3. Help people living with mental health issues or learning disabilities Priorities are the same as those listed above.

4. Assist with the education and training of disadvantaged people The Trust will consider projects working with people aged 16 and above who have left school. Priority will be given to schemes which provide basic skills or improve employment prospects, such as life-skills, ICT, literacy and numeracy. Activities involving sports, arts and the environment may be considered only where appropriate.

Grants are awarded under one of the following programmes, with the above priorities:

- **Main Grants Programme** – grants are awarded for £4,000 or above. A limited number of grants may be awarded for two or three years. The majority of grants awarded by the trust under this programme are between £4,500 and £10,000
- **Small Grants Programme** – there are a limited number of grants under £4,000 available. Priorities are given to smaller projects where the trust's grant will cover a large proportion of the total project cost

Financial information
In 2016/17 the trust held assets of £15.1 million and had an income of £686,500. Grants awarded to organisations totalled £347,000. Grants approved during the year were broken down as follows:

Education and training/youth development	20	£143,500
Mental health and learning disabilities	18	£90,000
Physical disability and illness	13	£79,000
Arthritis and cancer care	7	£47,500

Beneficiaries included: Venture Trust (£20,000); Deafblind Scotland (£15,000); Ayrshire Cancer Support (£14,000); Rosemount Lifelong Learning (£10,000); Haven and The Yard (£8,000 each); Addaction (£6,500); Alcohol Focus Scotland (£5,000); Living Paintings (£4,000); St Vincents Therapy Garden (£1,800).

Exclusions
As the trust's website specifies, the following are not supported:

- Organisations that are not formally recognised as charities

- Organisations under the control of the UK or Scottish Government
- Projects which are primarily intended to promote political or religious beliefs
- Individuals – including students
- Expeditions, overseas travel or international projects
- Projects outside Scotland
- General appeals or circulars, including contributions to endowment funds
- Statutory requirements of local authorities, hospitals, schools, universities and colleges
- Medical research
- Clinical work within hospitals
- Animal welfare
- The breeding and training of assistance/guide dogs for blind/disabled people
- The bricks and mortar aspect of capital projects
- Initiatives focused on sports, arts or the environment except where the subject is being used as a vehicle to engage with one of the Trust's core policy groups
- Normal youth club activities

Applications
Apply online via the trust's website. Hard copy and email applications will not be processed.

Check the trust's website for Main Grants Programme deadlines.

Applications for the Small Grants Programme are assessed on a quarterly basis although there are no fixed deadlines for submissions.

Sources of information
Accounts; annual report; OSCR record; funder's website.

Huntingdon Freemen's Trust

🔍 Relief in need, education, recreation and leisure

📍 Huntingdon, including Oxmoor, Hartford, Sapley, Stukeley Meadows and Hinchingbrooke Park

💷 £294,500 to organisations and individuals (2016/17)

CC number: 1044573

Trustees: Ann Beevor; Brian Bradshaw; Jonathan Hampstead; John Hough; Kate Parker; Michael Shellens; Cllr Jill Watkin-Tavener.

Correspondent: Karen Clark, 37 High Street, Huntingdon, Cambridgeshire PE29 3AQ (tel: 01480 414909; email: info@huntingdonfreemen.org.uk)

 www.huntingdonfreemen.org.uk

The Huntingdon Freeman's Trust was formed in 1993 and provides grants to both individual residents and or organisations located who live or are based within the area covered by

Huntingdon Town Council, including Oxmoor, Hartford, Sapley, Stukeley Meadows and Hinchingbrooke Park.

Grants are paid from income earned through the trust's investments and from the farm land owned in Cambridgeshire, Norfolk and Bedfordshire. Since its creation the trust has made donations totalling £6 million. Every year about £400,000 is given in grants to individuals and organisations.

Grants are available within the following areas, which are described in full on the trust's website:

- **Relief in need** – for the benefit of children, families, pensioners, the disabled and people who are on a low income or struggling due to a variety of circumstances. Applicants may be working or in receipt of benefits, but we will need to assess your income and expenses to verify your need. We will consider grants for a variety of purposes including help with essential household items, medical and mobility equipment and adaptations. We do not normally consider grants for the payment of rent, council tax, debts, fines or funerals
- **Education** – students can apply for half their accommodation fees while at university or college. Help is also available for school equipment and educational activities
- **Recreational and leisure** – for local groups and organisations involved in sports, hobbies and the arts, we can help with the purchase of equipment, project costs, training and competitions. Help is also available for trips, organised outings and Christmas lunches

Financial information
In 2016/17 the trust had assets of £17.7 million and an income of £538,000. Grants were made totalling £294,500. No detail was given in the annual report to say how much was awarded to individuals.

Previous beneficiaries have included: Huntingdon Gymnastic Club (£50,000); Natural High Support to Youth Project (£35,000); Huntingdon Youth Centre (£17,000); The Gainsborough Foundation (£15,000); Huntingdon Volunteer Club (£10,000).

Exclusions
The trust does not fund:

- Organisations from outside the area of benefit
- Services that should be provided by government or local councils (although funding may be given to supplement these services)

Applications
Application forms can be downloaded from the trust's website. Applications are considered at monthly meetings.

Sources of information

Accounts; annual report; Charity Commission record; funder's website.

Hurdale Charity Ltd

 The advancement of the Orthodox Jewish faith, education, medical causes, the relief of poverty

 Worldwide

(£) £1.6 million (2016/17)

CC number: 276997

Trustees: David Oestreicher; Abraham Oestreicher; Jacob Oestreicher; Benjamin Oestreicher.

Correspondent: Abraham Oestreicher, Trustee, 162 Osbaldeston Road, London N16 6NJ

The charity was set up in 1978 and supports charitable activities mostly concerned with the Orthodox Jewish faith, education, medical causes and the relief of poverty. Almost all of the support is given to Jewish organisations that are seen to uphold the Jewish way of life, both in the UK and overseas.

Financial information

In 2016/17 the charity had assets of £25.8 million and an income of £1.7 million. Grants and donations totalled £1.6 million.

Beneficiaries included: Springfield Trust Ltd (£390,000); Moundfield Charities Ltd (340,000); Fountain of Chesed Ltd (£260,000); Harofeh Donations Ltd (£220,000).

Applications

Apply in writing to the correspondent.

Sources of information

Accounts; annual report; Charity Commission record.

Hyde Charitable Trust (Youth Plus)

 Financial inclusion, employment, enterprise, community welfare, social welfare

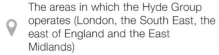 The areas in which the Hyde Group operates (London, the South East, the east of England and the East Midlands)

(£) £196,000 to organisations (2016/17)

CC number: 289888

Trustees: Geron Walker; Jonathan Prichard; Michelle Walcott; Andrew Moncreiff; Christopher Carlisle; Paul Cook; Patrick Law; Brid O'Dwyer; Jen Wight.

Correspondent: The Trustees, Hyde Housing Association, 30 Park Street, London SE1 9EQ (tel: 020 3207 2762;

email: grantsadministration@hyde-housing.co.uk)

 www.hyde-housing.co.uk/tenants/advice-and-support/the-hyde-charitable-trust

Hyde Charitable Trust (also known by its working name, Youth Plus) is a charitable company established in 1984. It works closely with Hyde Housing Association to help target its funds to the Hyde residents and communities most in need. In particular activities and services that:

▶ Promote financial inclusion
▶ Promote social and community welfare
▶ Support education, training, and enterprise
▶ Work with young people

Hyde Plus has an online funding portal which outlines the different funds available and open to organisations and individuals. The main grants programme for organisations is the Successful Places Fund which offers grants of up to £20,000 to organisations operating locally, regionally or nationally for the provision of services and activities that seek to address issues on Hyde's estates and densely populated neighbourhoods. Grants from this fund are intended to support the development and implementation of activities or services designed to mitigate or prevent social challenges that negatively impact local communities.

Financial information

In 2016/17 the trust held assets of £9.1 million and had an income of £340,000. Grants totalled £223,000 of which £27,000 was awarded to individuals. A list of beneficiaries was not included in the accounts.

Exclusions

Consult the guidance documents for each funding round for a full list of exclusions.

Applications

Information on current funding rounds and how to apply can be found on the trust's website.

Sources of information

Accounts; annual reports; Charity Commission record; funder's website.

Hyde Park Place Estate Charity

 Church maintenance, relief of poverty, health and medicine

 City of Westminster

(£) £194,000 to organisations (2016/17)

CC number: 212439

Trustees: Revd Roderick Leece; Mark Hewitt; Michael Beckett.

Correspondent: Shirley Vaughan, Clerk to the Trustees, St George's Church, The Vestry, 2A Mill Street, London W1S 1FX (tel: 020 7629 0874)

 www.stgeorgeshanoversquare.org

After paying for the cost of maintenance of the burial ground and repairs to the chapel of the parish church of St George, Hanover Square, the income of this charity is divided equally between the civil trustees and the ecclesiastical trustees.

The civil trustees apply their allocated funds to people in need, whether through poverty, disadvantage, or ill health, within the London borough of the City of Westminster. The civil trustees have ongoing relationships with a number of organisations, including City of Westminster Social Services, Age UK Westminster, and Home-Start Westminster.

The ecclesiastical trustees apply their allocated funds towards the preservation and maintenance of the district churches, or for any such ecclesiastical purposes as they see fit within the district. These grants are not open to application.

Financial information

In 2016/17 the charity had assets of £15 million and an income of £515,500. Grants totalling £194,000 were made to 47 organisations, and grants totalling £10,000 to 88 individuals, by the civil trustees.

Beneficiaries included: St George's Hanover Square PCC Voucher Scheme for the Homeless (£13,000); Age UK Westminster, Depaul UK and Marylebone Project (£5,000 each); Beanstalk and London Music Masters (£4,000 each); St Andrew's Club (£3,000); South Westminster Community Festival (£1,000).

Exclusions

No educational grants to foreign students. Grants will not be given in aid of campaigning activities, academic research, animal charities, or the furtherance of religious causes.

Applications

Apply in writing to the correspondent. The trustees meet four times a year.

Sources of information

Accounts; annual report; Charity Commission record.

IBM United Kingdom Trust

Education and training in ICT (information and communication technology)

UK, Europe, Middle East, Africa

£1.19 million (2016)

CC number: 290462

Trustees: Prof. Derek Bell; Anne Wolfe; Naomi Hill; Andrew Fitzgerald.

Correspondent: Mark Wakefield, Trust Manager, IBM United Kingdom Ltd, 1PG1, 76 Upper Ground, London SE1 9PZ (email: wakefim@uk.ibm.com)

The focus areas for IBM's community investment are the strategic and innovative use of information and communication technology (ICT) in education and training and the promotion of digital inclusion, with the broad objective of raising standards of achievement. Most activity is within the compulsory education phase. The vast majority of IBM's community investment is delivered through specific programmes initiated and developed by IBM in partnership with organisations with appropriate professional expertise. The trust gives preference to organisations concerned with people disadvantaged by poverty and/or at risk of digital exclusion. Preference is given to supporting projects and organisations in areas in which the company is based and/or where there is employee involvement.

The trust's 2016 annual report gives the following information on its objects and activities:

- The advancement of education, particularly through the use and understanding of information technology
- The advancement of research, with emphasis (though not exclusively) on information technology
- Improving the condition of life for the disadvantaged or disabled through the use of information technology
- Encouraging the use and understanding of information technology in the charitable sector
- Through the provision of information technology and related services, or otherwise, supporting the relief of poverty, the health of the community and the preservation of the environment

Based on the above objects, and with consideration for public benefit, the Trust has the following aims:

- Increasing the scope, usage and understanding of information technology through education
- Providing information technology and other services to enable not for profit organisations and the disadvantaged to acquire skills
- Promoting volunteering by IBM employees
- Providing aid in the form of technology and technical support for disaster relief
- Providing support for research at universities and other educational institutes

The Trust primarily achieves its aims by supporting the development and delivery of IBM's own community programmes, where these meet the charitable objects of the Trust. The support is delivered through the provision of grants of equipment, technical support and cash. The support is provided for IBM's community involvement programmes in the United Kingdom, and across EMEA. Additionally the Trust incurs expenditure where it directs activities in its own right, which achieve the Trust's objects.

The Trust's approach to grant making falls into two key areas:

- The provision of grants that advance both the aims of the Trust and support IBM programmes
- The provision of small grants in support of charitable organisations in the communities surrounding IBM sites

In this way the Trust seeks to achieve its aims, not only through key longer term programmes, but also through support for smaller scale initiatives by providing direct contributions, and encouraging ongoing links between charitable and educational organisations and IBM.

Financial information

In 2016 the trust had assets of £4.1 million and an income of £1 million which comprised of donations from IBM International Foundation and IBM subsidiaries. Grants were made totalling £1.19 million, and were distributed as follows:

Provision of IT and other services	£1.06 million
Increasing the use of technology in education	£60,000
Support for research	£60,000
Misc.	£4,000

The accounts give general information on the IBM programmes and initiatives which the trust supports. Five research grants were made to universities.

Beneficiaries included: Lagos State Universal Education Board (£64,000); Age Friendly Ireland (£31,000); Egyptian Ministry of Youth and Sports (£24,000); National College for Digital Skills (£21,000).

Applications

Very few unsolicited requests are considered. If you decide to submit an appeal then it should be done by email or in writing and include a brief résumé of the aims of your organisation and details of what assistance is required. Those considering making an application are advised to telephone first for advice.

Sources of information

Accounts; annual report; Charity Commission record.

Ibrahim Foundation Ltd

Community building, environment, strengthening non-profits, supporting families

UK and overseas

£306,000 (2016/17)

CC number: 1149438/SC043491

Trustees: Dr Azeem Ibrahim; Adeel Ibrahim; Aadil Butt.

Correspondent: Dr Azeem Ibrahim, Trustee, 18 Little Street, Glasgow G3 8DQ (tel: 0141 416 1991; email: info@ibrahimfoundation.com)

 www.ibrahimfoundation.com

The foundation was established in 2012 and is one of the philanthropic interests of Dr Azeem Ibrahim, an entrepreneur, academic and strategic adviser.

The 2016/17 annual report provides the following helpful information:

Grant making policy
The Charity has established its grant making policy to achieve its objects for the public benefit. The grants committee comprising of the board of trustees reviews the grant making policy annually to ensure that it reflects the Charity's objects and thereby advances public benefit.

Grants ranging between £500 and £10,000 are awarded twice a year for projects that help transform the UK. Extraordinary projects and projects of significant importance may receive grants up to and above of £50,000. Grant applications are not accepted from the same organisation in successive grant cycles.

There are no areas of focus in grant making, as the Charity believes those on the front lines in the community best understand the particular needs and where grants will bear the greatest fruits. The grant committee looks for situations where small amounts of funds will make significant impact. The Charity is particularly interested in the following areas:

Community Building Community Building grants focus on strengthening communities by engaging residents and stakeholders in a process that builds leadership and capacity from within, while respecting and valuing the rich diversity represented in our geographic region. The Charity supports efforts to build social capital – a resource defined as the web of relationships and civic participation that improves our ability to address the challenges and opportunities we face as a community. The Charity also recognises that building a community's capacity and leadership is a critical precursor to community involvement for those, who, because of language, culture or educational levels have been excluded from participation.

Environment
Scotland's residents are fortunate to live among abundant natural resources. The Charity's work aims to preserve the Scotland's biological treasures and increase environmental awareness in our communities. Scottish counties have developed amid rich, diverse ecosystems – including marine coast and fertile agricultural lands. Our environment grants seek to foster greater awareness of, access to, and stewardship of the natural treasures gracing the country. By supporting opportunities in environmental education and conservation for both children and adults, the Charity is seeking to promote greater access to the variety of hills, open space and wild areas stretching from coast to coast, an overall appreciation for the natural environment and a sense of responsible stewardship for these natural treasures.

Strengthening Non-profits
When healthy organisations have the support they need, new ideas and imaginative community solutions flourish. The Charity makes selected grants to strengthen non-profits and promote a vibrant non-profit community. Grants in this area support the mission and infrastructure of the non-profit sector as a whole. The Charity makes selected grants to management support organisations that provide services to other non-profits and build capacity within the field as a whole. Our goal is to help exemplary organizations continue to thrive within a healthy and stimulating non-profit sector.

Supporting Families
Strong families are the cornerstones of a strong community. The Charity is committed to helping families and individuals achieve self-sufficiency and the skills they need to prosper. Our funding is aimed at strengthening the human services safety net for low-income families and helping families of all kinds exercise their rights, fulfil their responsibilities and realise their full economic and social potential. We support non-profit organisations that help low-income and disadvantaged children and adults meet basic needs for food, clothing and emergency and permanent housing. The Charity also targets organisations addressing family violence, promoting expanded opportunities for persons with disabilities, and serving adults seeking to improve their economic prospects through literacy and employment development.

Financial information
In 2016/17 the foundation had assets of £24,000 and an income of £339,500. Grants awarded to organisations totalled £306,000. Charitable activities were broken down as follows:

Strengthening non-profits	£215,500
Community building	£90,500

Previous beneficiaries have included: Purifi; Asia Pacific Children's Fund; Scotland Institute; Solas Foundation.

Applications
Initial contact can be made via the foundation's website, although potential applicants should note that most funding is likely to go to projects and organisations with which the foundation and Dr Ibrahim already have an involvement.

Sources of information
Accounts; Charity Commission record; funder's website.

Impetus – The Private Equity Foundation

 Children and young people, education and training, employment

UK

£4.1 million (2016)

CC number: 1152262

Trustees: Louis Elson; Craig Dearden-Phillips; Prof. Becky Francis; Lionel Assant; Marc Boughton; Hanneke Smits; Nikos Stathopoulos; Caroline Mason; Lisa Stone; Patrick Healy; Simon Turner; Bill Benjamin; Shani Zindel.

Correspondent: The Trustees, 183 Eversholt Street, London NW1 1BU (tel: 020 3474 1000; email: info@impetus-pef.org.uk)

 www.impetus-pef.org.uk

 facebook.com/ImpetusPEF

 @ImpetusPEF

Registered with the Charity Commission in 2013, Impetus – The Private Equity Foundation was formed from the merger of the Impetus Trust and Private Equity Foundation, bringing together 16 years of experience supporting charity sustainability, effectiveness and growth through its venture philanthropy model.

Areas of work
The aim of the foundation is to improve education and employment opportunities for disadvantaged young people. According to its 2016 annual report, by 2021 its goals are to:

- Halve the gaps between disadvantaged young people and their better-off peers in GCSE/equivalent attainment and access to university
- Demonstrate and strive to reduce the gap in sustained employment between disadvantaged young people and their better-off peers

The foundation aims to achieve these goals in three ways:

- Through our investment work, we will continue to find, fund and build the most promising charities working to improve employment and education outcomes for disadvantaged young people
- Through our partnerships work, we will work alongside other private and public funders to support our charities and multiply the impact we can have on the lives of disadvantaged young people
- Through our policy work, we will influence decision makers, so that the young people we serve stay on the agenda, and have the right policies and resources devoted to them

Financial information
In 2016 the trust held assets of £9.5 million and had an income of £8.7 million. Grants were awarded to 22 organisations, totalling £4.1 million.

Beneficiaries included: ThinkForward (£1.2 million); Resurgo (£400,000); City Gateway (£320,000); Action Tutoring (£277,000); Access Project (£255,000); Family Nurse Partnership (£180,000), Dallaglio Foundation (£100,000); Workingrite (£85,000); Teens and Toddlers (£75,000); Family Links (£31,000).

Applications
Unsolicited applications are not accepted.

Sources of information
Accounts; annual report; Charity Commission record; funder's website.

The Indigo Trust

 Technology-driven development in Africa

 Sub-Saharan Africa and the UK

£1.64 million (2016/17)

CC number: 1075920

Trustees: Dominic Flynn; Francesca Perrin; William Perrin.

Correspondent: Louise Vickers, The Peak, 5 Wilton Road, London SW1V 1AP (tel: 020 7410 0330; email: indigo@sfct.org.uk)

 indigotrust.org.uk

The Indigo Trust is one of 15 charitable organisations under the Sainsbury Family Charitable Trusts. It originated through a trust deed and was registered with the Charity Commission in 1999.

The trust funds organisations that use digital technologies to improve transparency and accountability in sub-Saharan Africa. On the its website, the trust defines its mission as follows:

> The power of people and communities to effect change is heavily dependent upon

the level of information that they can access. Information enables them to make informed decisions and hold authorities to account. We believe that mobile and web technologies have the power to transform how people access, share and create information.

Following a recent strategic review, international grants (usually £10,000 to 20,000) are now almost solely made to:

▶ Projects and organisations that leverage the power of mobile and web technologies, to foster active, informed citizens and accountable governments

▶ Civic tech communities and innovation hubs that use information communication technologies for positive social change

The trust generally prefers to support smaller or early-stage projects and applications from groups working on issues such as parliamentary monitoring, corporate transparency, freedom of information, and democratic engagement are particularly encouraged to apply.

In addition to its international work, the trust also provides grants supporting more open and effective philanthropy in the UK as well as grants to local community charities in London. The trust notes however, that unsolicited proposals will not be considered for these funding streams.

Financial information

In 2016/17 the trust had assets of £10.87 million and an income of £1.4 million. There were 51 grants made totalling £1.64 million, including grants made in the UK and under the Open Philanthropy programme.

Information technologies	40	£1.47 million
UK local grants	8	£101,000
Open Philanthropy	3	£76,000

Beneficiaries included: Hive Colab (£81,500); Parliamentary Monitoring Group (£70,000); 360 Giving (£50,000); British Library (£48,500); MySociety (£40,000); Open Data Durban (£29,000); Campaign for Freedom of Information and Publish What You Fund (£20,000 each) Maya Centre (£2,000).

Exclusions

The trust does not provide funding for any of the following:

▶ Sponsorship requests from individuals, e.g. expeditions, scholarships, etc.
▶ ICT training or skills
▶ ICT equipment costs, e.g. purchasing computers or tablets
▶ Large, international NGOs
▶ Costs for events, such as workshops, conferences or meetings

Applications

Applications for web and technology driven projects in Africa should be submitted via email. To apply for this grant, you must be an African based organisation undertaking charitable work in Ghana, Kenya, Nigeria, South Africa, or Uganda.

Application templates are available to download on the trust's website, however if you choose to construct your own application, include the following:

▶ Between two and four pages of A4
▶ A brief history and background of your organisation
▶ An overview of the project
▶ A rough budget for the project
▶ How you plan to evaluate and monitor the project

Other documents, such as accounts, brochures and registration documents, are not necessary at this time. Applications can be submitted at any time of the year.

Unsolicited applications for the Open Philanthropy and UK Local (London) programmes are not accepted.

Sources of information

Accounts; annual report; Charity Commission record; guidelines for applicants; funder's website.

The Worshipful Company of Information Technologists

 People who are disadvantaged, disabled and socially excluded, education, information technology

 UK

 £252,000 (2017)

CC number: 1113488

Trustees: Jo Connell; Geoffrey Squire; David Morriss; Mark Holford; Dr Elizabeth Sparrow; Bill Kennair; Kerri Mansfield; Anthony Buxton; Gary Moore.

Correspondent: Eleanor MacGregor, Charity Co-ordinator, 39a Bartholomew Close, London, EC1A 7JN (tel: 020 3871 0255; email: eleanor@wcit.org.ok)

 www.wcit.org.uk/apply_for_a_grant.html

facebook.com/WCIT.Livery

@it_livery

The Worshipful Company of Information Technologists is the 100th livery company of the City of London, and registered the charitable arm of the company with the Charity Commission in 2006. The charity provides education

of IT skills; helps to shape the IT industry and its commerce; and also runs a social activity fellowship programme.

The mission of the charity is to use IT skills to make a difference.

The priority areas for the charity are:

▶ To enhance opportunities for young people through more effective education
▶ To improve the quality of life for those who are disadvantaged, disabled, or socially excluded
▶ To help charities and other not-for-profit organisations get the best out of IT
▶ To improve the understanding of IT and its capabilities to the wider public

The charity also provides pro bono IT support for charities and social enterprises.

Financial information

In 2017, the charity had assets of £7.3 million and an overall income of £386,000. Grants were made to 31 organisations and totalled £252,000.

Beneficiaries included: Lilian Baylis Technology School (£50,000); Thames Reach Homeless Charity (£42,000); Founders4Schools (£22,000); The Charity IT Association (£21,000); Gresham College (£11,300); Lifelites (10,000); The Bar Pro Bono Unit (£6,300); AbilityNet (£5,500).

Applications

All applications should be submitted via a grant application form which can be downloaded from the website.

Applicants for grants under £5,000 are requested to provide:

▶ A document proving charitable status (which must relate directly to the applicant organisation)

Applicants for all grants of £5,000 and over are requested to provide:

▶ Most recent audited or independently examined accounts
▶ Memorandum and articles of association/constitution
▶ Contact details of an external referee who can be contacted to provide a reference on the charity's effective project or service delivery (who should be external to the organisation and be happy to be named, and not related to any applicant staff or volunteer)

Applicants for all grants of £10,000 and over are requested to provide:

▶ Most recent annual report or minutes of AGM
▶ If the organisation is new, the minutes from the meeting when the constitution was formally adopted are acceptable

Contact details of three external referees who can be contacted to provide a reference on the charity's effective project or service delivery (who should be external to the organisation and be happy to be named, and not related to any applicant staff or volunteer)

Sources of information

Funder's website; further information provided by the funder.

The Ingram Trust

 General charitable purposes

UK and overseas, with a preference for Surrey

£601,500 (2016/17)

CC number: 1040194

Trustees: Christopher Ingram; Clare Maurice; Janet Ingram; Jonathan Ingram; Sally Ingram.

Correspondent: Joan Major, Ground Floor, 22 Chancery Lane, London WC2A 1LS (email: theingramtrust@nqpltd.com)

The Ingram Trust was established in 1994. According to the trust's 2016/17 annual report, the grant-making policies of the charity are:

▸ To support specific projects which can include identifiable costs for equipment required, special services or projects
▸ Generally, beneficiaries will be major national and international charities together with some local ones in the County of Surrey
▸ The majority of grants will be made for periods of 3 to 4 years at a time in order to assess more satisfactorily grant applications and monitor progress

Financial information

In 2016/17 the trust had assets of £10.9 million and an income of £251,000. There were 30 grants made in the year totalling £601,500. Many beneficiaries are supported on a regular basis.

Beneficiaries included: WWF UK (£60,000); The Royal National Theatre (£40,000); Almeida Theatre Company Ltd and Queen Elizabeth Foundation for Disabled People (£35,000 each); Kew Gardens Apprenticeship Scheme and Unicef UK (£25,000 each); Transform Housing (£20,000); Disability Challengers (£12,500); The Princess Alice Hospice (£10,000); Cherry Trees – Respite Care (£5,000).

Exclusions

The trust does not support any of the following:

▸ Non-registered charities;
▸ Individuals;

▸ Charities specialising in overseas aid (except those providing more permanent solutions to problems)
▸ Animal charities (except those concerned with wildlife conservation)

Applications

Apply in writing to the correspondent.

Sources of information

Accounts; annual report; Charity Commission record.

The Inman Charity

General charitable purposes, medical causes, social welfare, disability, older people, hospices, armed forces

UK

£298,000 (2016)

CC number: 261366

Trustees: A. L. Walker; Belinda Strother; Neil Wingerath; Prof. John Langdon; Michael Mathews.

Correspondent: Neil Wingerath, Trustee, BM Box 2831, London WC1N 3XX

www.inmancharity.org

The charity supports general charitable purposes through their grant-making, with a particular interest in providing assistance for:

▸ Medical research
▸ Care of older people
▸ General welfare
▸ Hospices
▸ Deaf and blind individuals
▸ Care of people with physical and mental disabilities
▸ Armed forces

Financial information

In 2016 the charity had assets of £5.4 million and an income of £352,000. There were 64 grants made to organisations totalling £298,000 broken down as follows:

Medical – research	13	£80,000
Welfare and people with disabilities	17	£69,500
Older people	9	£43,000
Social – hospices	9	£36,500
Social – deaf and blind individuals	9	£32,000
Bursary fund	1	£20,000
General and armed forces	6	£17,000

Beneficiaries included: Hospice UK (£10,000); Brain Research Trust (£6,000); Diabetes UK, Contact the Elderly, Deafblind UK and Independent Arts (£5,000 each); York Blind and Partially Sighted Society and Nottinghamshire Hospice (£4,000 each); Live Music Now (£3,000); Kent Search and Rescue (£2,000).

In addition, the charity makes a regular payment (currently £20,000 per annum) to the Victor Inman Bursary Fund at

Uppingham School of which the settlor had been a lifelong supporter.

Exclusions

Individuals; young children and infants; maintenance of local buildings (such as, churches and village halls); animal welfare; wildlife and environmental conservation; religious charities.

Applications

Applications should be made in writing to the correspondent and should include:

▸ A letter confirming the registered charity number
▸ Aims and objectives of the organisation
▸ Latest annual reports and audited accounts
▸ Total amount required for the project
▸ Funding, if any, received to date
▸ Timeline of completion

Only successful applicants will be contacted.

Sources of information

Accounts; annual report; Charity Commission record; funder's website.

Integrated Education Fund

Integrated education

Northern Ireland

£369,000 (2016/17)

CC number: NIC104886

Trustees: Ken Cathcart; Grainne Clarke; David Cooke; Marie Cowan; Roderick Downer; Barry Gilligan; Errol Lemon; Richard Lemon; Paddy McIntyre; Michael McKernan; Ellen McVea; David Thompson; Dorothee Wagner; Mary Roulston; Barbara McAtamney.

Correspondent: The Trustees, Cleaver Fulton & Rankin, 48–50 Bedford Street, Belfast BT2 7FW (tel: 028 9027 1723; email: info@ief.org.uk)

 www.ief.org.uk

 facebook.com/ IntegratedEducationFund

 @IEFNI

This fund, which is also known by the abbreviation IEF, was established in 1992 with funding provided by EU Structural Funds, the Department of Education Northern Ireland, the Nuffield Foundation and the Joseph Rowntree Charitable Trust. The fund provides funding to support the development and growth of integrated education in Northern Ireland.

The IEF's website explains that it 'seeks to bridge the financial gap between starting integrated schools and securing full government funding and support', which it does by making grants to support 'the establishment of new schools, the growth of existing schools and those schools seeking to become integrated through the transformation process'.

Grant-making programmes
The charity has various grant-making programmes open, the following is a brief summary of each. See the website for further details.

1 **Transformation** – grants of up to £2,500 for schools exploring transformation or already undertaking transformation

2 **Carson Awards** – awards and prizes for children of integrated schools for completed creative projects with the theme What Integrated Education Means To Me

3 **Support Grants for Transformed Schools** – grants from £15,000 to £75,000 to support schools that have already transformed and integrated

4 **The Trust Programme** – grants for integrated schools to embed the integrated ethos within the school. Each grant-making programme has its own rounds and deadlines for applications, see the website for eligibility and closing dates.

Financial information
In 2016/17 the fund had assets of £2.45 million and an income of £882,000. In total the fund gave £369,000 in grants, including:

£123,500 donated through the Transformation programme, £45,500 donated through the Support Grants programme, £40,000 donated through the Carson Awards and £53,000 donated through the Trust programme.

A list of beneficiary schools was not available.

Applications
See the fund's website for full information of current grant-making programmes.

Sources of information
Accounts; Charity Commission for Northern Ireland record; funder's website.

International Bible Students Association

Q Jehovah's Witnesses, overseas aid

Q Worldwide

£ £7.5 million (2016/17)

CC number: 216647

Trustees: Stephen Papps; Paul Stuart Gillies; Karl Snaith; Ivor Darby; Jonathan Manley.

Correspondent: The Trustees, IBSA House, The Ridgeway, London NW7 1RN (tel: 020 8906 2211)

The association was registered with the Charity Commission in 1964. According to the 2016/17 annual report:

> The object of the Association is to promote the Christian religion as practiced by the body of Christians known as Jehovah's Witness, by supporting congregations of Jehovah's Witnesses and others in connection with their spiritual and material welfare in Britain and abroad within the charitable purposes of the Association. This is achieved by:
>
> ▶ The purchase and distribution of religious literature, free of charge
> ▶ The arranging of conventions for Bible education
> ▶ Financially assisting legal entities of Jehovah's Witnesses with similar aims and objectives, both foreign and domestic
> ▶ Paying expenses for and taking care of living arrangements for some members of the Worldwide Order of Special-full-time Servants of Jehovah's Witnesses

Financial information
In 2016/17 the association held assets of £121.7 million and had an income of £29.6 million. Grants totalled £7.5 million worldwide including £650,000 in the UK. A list of beneficiaries was not included within the accounts; however, the 2016/17 accounts state: 'Material grants (in the context of grant-making) were made to the following institutions: Jehovas Zeugen in Deutschland K.d.ö.R, Germany – £6.5 million (this would appear to be an on-going annual grant); The Kingdom Hall Trust £650,000.'

Applications
Apply in writing to the correspondent.

Sources of information
Accounts; annual report; Charity Commission record.

Investream Charitable Trust

Q Jewish causes, education, social welfare, medical, older people, general charitable purposes

Q Worldwide, with a preference for the UK and Israel

£ £555,000 (2016/17)

CC number: 1097052

Trustees: Mark Morris; Graham Morris.

Correspondent: The Trustees, Investream Ltd, 38 Wigmore Street, London W1U 2RU (tel: 020 7486 2800)

The trust was established in 2003 and derives its income from Investream Ltd and its subsidiary undertakings. The

trust's objectives are the advancement education, the relief of poverty and illness, and general charitable purposes. It would appear that the trust mainly makes grants in support of Jewish charities.

The annual report for 2016/17 states:

> The Trustees have adopted a policy of making regular donations to charitable causes, having regard to the level of the Trust's annual income. They regularly appraise new opportunities for direct charitable expenditure and from time to time make substantial donations to support special or capital projects.

Financial information
In 2016/17 the trust had assets of £216,500 and an income of £865,000. Grants awarded to organisations totalled £555,000 and were broken down as follows:

Education	£298,000
Community and care of older people	£219,000
Medical	£38,500

Beneficiaries included: The Belz Foundation (£65,000); Camp Kef (£42,000); United Jewish Israel Appeal (£40,500); Menorah High School for Girls Foundation Trust (£39,500); Torah and Chesed (BH) Ltd (£38,000); Beis Hillel Trust (£35,000).

Applications
Apply in writing to the correspondent.

Sources of information
Accounts; annual report; Charity Commission record.

The Ireland Fund of Great Britain

Q Social welfare, Irish community, education, peace and reconciliation, arts and culture, young adults, older people

Q The Republic of Ireland and Northern Ireland

£ £538,500 (2016/17)

CC number: 327889

Trustees: Seamus McGarry; Michael Casey; Ruairi Conneely; Zach Webb; Rory Godson; Garrett Hayes; Kieran McLoughlin.

Correspondent: Katie Norris, Grants Manager, Can Mezzanine, 7–14 Great Dover Street, London SE1 4YR (tel: 020 3096 7897; email: knorris@irlfunds.org)

🌐 www.theirelandfunds.org/great-britain

f facebook.com/IrelandFundsGreatBritain

🐦 @IrelandFundsGB

Founded in 1976 by Sir Anthony O'Reilly and a number of key American businessmen, *The Worldwide Ireland Funds* is an international philanthropic network operating in 12 countries. The Ireland Funds' mission is to be the largest network of friends of Ireland dedicated to supporting programs of peace and reconciliation, arts and culture, education and community development throughout the island of Ireland. The Ireland Fund of Great Britain (IFGB) is a branch of this network and a UK-registered charity.

The IFGB was established in 1988 and distributes funding to community groups, voluntary organisations, charities and educational establishments that, according to the 2016/17 accounts, 'promote wellbeing, community and culture across Great Britain, including those that best support Irish communities'. Awards are made through the Small Grants Round (up to €/£7,000 in Ireland only) and through the Flagship Grant Round, which awards multi-year funding of up to €/£100,000 over a two-year period. When a grants round is open for application, guidelines and deadlines are published on the website and a number of grant workshops are run across Ireland for potential applicants to receive fundraising advice and training.

Areas supported include:

▶ **Education** – projects that widen access to and participation in tertiary education for under-represented groups, funding for research in tertiary institutions, promoting learning opportunities for students of all ages
▶ **Community Development** – projects for people with mental and physical health problems, community integration, development of entrepreneurial skills, sport and leisure projects, and the protection of the natural environment. Support is also available for programmes that care for older people, disadvantaged young people and capacity building for non-profit organisations
▶ **Arts and Culture** – projects that promote Irish culture and heritage, including the preservation of uniquely Irish art and artefacts, the protection of Irish heritage sites and resources, and increasing public access to sites and arts organisations
▶ **Peace and Reconciliation** – organisations working to address sectarianism and violence in Northern Ireland by promoting understanding and respect for varying cultural and religious values, and by addressing the problems caused by long-term employment and inadequate opportunities in education, employment and personal development

Financial information

In 2016/17 the charity held assets of £434,500 and had an income of £841,500, largely from donations. Grants were awarded to 35 organisations and totalled £538,500. The following breakdown was provided in the accounts:

Education	£202,000
Community development and relief of poverty	£202,000
Sharing and developing Irish arts and culture	£134,500

Previous beneficiaries have included: University of Limerick Foundation and Munster Rugby Academy (£138,500); University of Limerick Foundation (£81,500); Southwark Irish Pensioners Project (£40,500); Immigrant Counselling and Physiotherapy (£11,600); Solace Women's Aid (£9,100); Birmingham Irish Association, Irish Woodland Trust and Music Network (£5,000 each); Glasnevin Cemetery Museum (£4,000); Conradh Na Gaelige (£1,900).

Exclusions

The charity has separate exclusions for both the small grants programme and the flagship grants programme. Generally the following are excluded:

▶ General appeals – assistance must be sought for clearly specified purposes
▶ Individuals, including the cost of tuition or student fees
▶ One-off events and festivals
▶ Debt and retrospective costs

For a complete list of exclusions, consult the guidelines on the charity's website.

Applications

Application should be completed through the online process on the charity's website. Guidance and deadlines for expressions of interest are advertised online, as well as information on successfully funded organisations and the charity's grant workshops and resources. Applicants can only submit one application per organisation per year. For current deadlines and eligibility criteria for each of the rounds see the website.

Sources of information

Accounts; annual report; Charity Commission record; funder's website.

The Ironmongers' Company

 Disadvantaged children and young people, schools, heritage, ironwork projects

 UK

£ £534,500 (2016/17)

CC number: 1039950

Trustee: The Ironmongers' Trust Company.

Correspondent: Helen Sant, Charities Manager, Ironmongers Hall, Barbican, London EC2Y 8AA (tel: 020 7776 2311; email: helen@ironmongers.org)

 www.ironmongers.org

The Ironmongers' Company can trace its origins back to 1300 and is one of the Great Twelve Livery Companies of the City of London. The company administers a number of charitable trusts that make grants to organisations throughout the UK. Grants are made to schools, charities supporting disadvantaged children and young people and iron projects. The charity's website provides detailed guidance on the company's three areas for grant-making:

Disadvantaged children and young people – educational projects for disadvantaged children and young people under the age of 25 in the UK. Items of equipment will be considered only where a full explanation is given of how they will support this activity. The Company is particularly interested in enabling primary age children to develop a strong foundation for the future. Projects could, for example, support special educational needs, address behavioural problems or promote citizenship, parenting or life skills. Preference will be given to projects piloting new approaches where the outcomes will be disseminated to a wider audience. Grants typically range from £200 to £10,000.

Iron Projects – projects that promote the ironwork craft, or conserve historic ironwork. Grants are made to registered charities, churches or schools and cannot be made to individuals or for retrospective costs. The Company prefers to fund entire projects or specific elements of a project, with the majority of grants being under £5,000.

Schools – The Company works in partnership with the Church of England's education division to identify schools in areas with high levels of deprivation who need funding for non-statutory equipment or activities. Unsolicited applications are currently not accepted from schools.

Financial information

In 2016/17 the company held assets of £28.9 million and had an income of £2.1 million. Grants awarded to organisations totalled £534,500.

Beneficiaries included: Drake Music Scotland (£8,400); Scunthorpe CE Primary School and St John's CE Primary School (£7,500 each); Charterhouse Railings, Haworth Riding

For the Disabled (£6,400); Creative Sparkworks (£4,000); King Edward VI School (£2,300); Mid Suffolk Light Railway (£2,000).

Exclusions

Exclusions may vary depending on the specific grant programme. Refer to the company's website for full details.

Applications

Application forms and details of the application process for each fund can be found on the charity's website.

Disadvantaged children and young people: Complete an application summary sheet, available to download on the website, to be returned together with a description of the project (no more than three A4 pages on both sides). The appeals committee meets twice a year in March and October with deadlines 15 December and 31 July respectively. Applications are not accepted by email. The company asks applicants to enclose a copy of your most recent audited accounts if they are not available from the Charity Commission's website.

Iron projects: Applications should be made in writing, preferably by email to helen@ironmongers.org, including full details of the project – guidance on what should be included is given on the website. The website states that it is expected that 'any conservation of historic ironwork to follow the National Heritage Ironwork Group's Conservation Principles (see www.nhig.org.uk)' – applications should confirm that projects will meet these standards. The iron committee meets at the end of April, with deadline for applications 31 March.

Schools: At the time of writing (April 2018), the website states: 'Funds are currently committed to existing partnerships. All Diocesan Directors of Education will be notified when the Company is actively seeking new partner schools. Appeals are not accepted directly from individual schools.'

Sources of information

Accounts; annual report; Charity Commission record; funder's website.

The J Isaacs Charitable Trust

General charitable purposes, particularly young people, education, older people, community development, health care

England and Wales

£975,000 (2016/17)

CC number: 1059865

Trustees: Jeremy Isaacs; Joanne Isaacs; Helen Eastick; Vincent Isaacs.

Correspondent: The Trustees, JRJ Group, 61 Conduit Street, London W1S 2GB (tel: 020 7220 2305)

The charity was registered with the Charity Commission in 1996 and receives donations from Mr J Isaacs alongside its investment income. Its objectives are as follows:

▪ Care for children
▪ Education
▪ Well-being of the older people
▪ Tolerance in our community
▪ Healthcare

Financial information

In 2016/17 the trust held assets of £15.3 million and had an income of £527,500. In total £975,000 was awarded in grants. The grants were distributed as follows:

Healthcare	£344,000
Education	£322,500
Other	£205,500
Care for children	£78,500
Tolerance in the community	£24,500

Beneficiaries included: Community Security Trust (£100,000); Norwood (£75,500); Tate Gallery and United Jewish Appeal (£70,000 each); The Trustees Imperial College Healthcare, Cancer Research UK (£33,000).

Applications

Apply in writing to the correspondent.

Sources of information

Accounts; annual report; Charity Commission record.

The Isle of Anglesey Charitable Trust

General charitable purposes

The Isle of Anglesey

£771,000 (2016/17)

CC number: 1000818

Trustee: Isle of Anglesey County Council.

Correspondent: The Trustees, Head of Function (Resources), Isle of Anglesey County Council, County Offices, Llangefni, Anglesey LL77 7TW (tel: 01248 752602; email: garethjroberts@ anglesey.gov.uk)

The Isle of Anglesey Charitable Trust was established by the Isle of Anglesey Borough Council, a forerunner of the County Council, to administer investments purchased from funds received from Shell (UK) Ltd when the company ceased to operate on Anglesey. The County Council has 30 elected members who, when acting as trustee, meet separately from their meetings as a local authority.

According to the its annual report 2016/17 the trust has the following charitable objectives:

▪ The provision of amenities and facilities
▪ The preservation of buildings
▪ The conservation and protection of land
▪ The protection and safeguarding of the environment

The trust operates a small grants scheme (less than £8,000) and a large grant scheme (more than £8,000), each of which accepts applications once a year. In addition, the trust also allocates funding for the annual running costs of village halls and the maintenance and development of community and sporting facilities.

Financial information

In 2016/17 the trust had assets of £21.8 million and an income of £611,000. Grants were made to 64 organisations, totalling £771,000.

Beneficiaries included: Beaumaris Leisure Centre and Llanddona Village Hall (£45,000 each); Canolfan Ucheldre (£30,000); Anglesey Central Railway Ltd, Cwmni Tref Llangefni (£25,000 each); Holyhead Boxing Club, Holyhead Sea Cadets, Ynys Mon and Gwynedd Mind (£20,000 each).

Exclusions

Individuals and projects based outside Anglesey are excluded from applying.

Applications

Apply in writing to the correspondent. Application forms can be downloaded from the council's website. Applications can be made by organisations who have received funding within the previous five years, but these will only be considered once all other applications have been considered and if there is funding available.

Sources of information

Accounts; annual report; Charity Commission record; guidelines for applicants.

The ITF Seafarers' Trust

Seafarers, their families and dependants

Worldwide

£1.7 million (2016)

CC number: 281936

Trustees: Paddy Crumlin; Dave Heindel; Stephen Cotton; Lars Lindgren; Brian Orrell; Abdulgani Serang; Jacqueline Smith.

Correspondent: Thomas Abrahamsson, ITF House, 49–60 Borough Road,

London SE1 1DR (tel: 020 7940 9305; email: info@seafarerstrust.org)

 www.seafarerstrust.org

This trust, established in 1981, makes grants to organisations catering for the social welfare of seafarers of all nations, their families and dependants.

Grant-making information

The trust's website provides the following grants guidelines on its website:

Who can apply?

- Any registered charity, non-profit, educational institution and trade union interested in welfare work for seafarers, their families and other maritime workers in any part of the world
- It is not our policy to award grants to individual seafarers or their dependants. In exceptional circumstances the Trust has provided humanitarian aid and assistance. Nonetheless, such grant applications must always be submitted by organisations and not individuals. Application forms submitted by individuals will not be considered

Your organisation must:

- Have a proven record of dealing with seafarers and maritime workers' welfare
- Demonstrate a thorough knowledge of the facilities already available for the seafarers in the port where you might be based
- Be able to demonstrate that your project is sustainable
- Be capable of demonstrating that the project will improve seafarers and/or their families' health and well being irrespective of nationality, creed, race, language, sex or rank
- Have a constitution or a set of rules defining the aims and operational procedures of your organisation
- Have a bank account in the name of the organisation

What types of grants are available?

- Capital costs (vehicles, equipment, etc.)
- Training and education
- Health and medical
- Feasibility studies
- Research
- Conferences
- Operational support

Financial information

In 2016 the trust had assets of £49.7 million and an income of £5.2 million. Grants totalled £1.7 million and were broken down as follows:

Vehicles	£594,000
Training for those working with seafarers and their families	£401,000
Health for seafarers	£78,000
Research into welfare provision for seafarers	£75,000
Buildings, internet, communications and telecommunications	£62,000
Raising awareness of seafarers rights	£52,000
Furniture and equipment	£44,500
Financial help (personal assistance and special monetary assistance)	£30,000
Other	£14,000

Beneficiaries included: International Seafarers Welfare And Assistance Network (£245,000); World Maritime University (£238,000); Hunterlink Global (£78,000); Merchant Navy Welfare Board (£30,000); International Maritime Organization (£22,000); Stella Maris Apostolado Mar Bilbao (£2,800).

Exclusions

According to the trust's website the following are not likely to be supported:

- Retrospective funding for completed projects
- Deficits which have already been incurred
- Projects which promote particular religious beliefs
- Recurring costs
- Individuals

The trust awards grants for humanitarian aid and assistance only in exceptional circumstances.

Applications

Applications have to be made online on the trust's website, where full criteria and guidelines are also available. Applications must be supported by an ITF affiliated seafarers' or dockers' trade union.

Requests for small grants (between £500 to £75,000) may take about two to six months to proceed and for large grants (over £75,000) the process can last 3 to 12 months.

Sources of information

Accounts; annual report; Charity Commission record; funder's website.

The J J Charitable Trust

🔍 Environment, literacy, social change

📍 UK and overseas

💷 £781,000 (2016/17)

CC number: 1015792

Trustees: John Sainsbury; Mark Sainsbury; Judith Portrait; Lucy Guard.

Correspondent: Robert Bell, Sainsbury Family Charitable Trusts, The Peak, 5 Wilton Road, London SW1V 1AP (tel: 020 7410 0330; fax: 020 7410 0332; email: info@sfct.org.uk)

 www.sfct.org.uk

The J J Charitable Trust is one of 17 charities under the Sainsbury Family Charitable Trusts. It was established through trust deed, and registered with the Charity Commission in 1992. The trust seeks to fund registered charities, and grants are usually in the range of £5,000 to £200,000. The main areas of interest to the trust are:

- Literacy – helping to improve the effectiveness of literacy teaching in compulsory education for children with learning difficulties, e.g. dyslexia; and also for ex-offenders or those at risk of offending
- Social and cultural change towards more sustainable lifestyles – finding creative approaches that visualise a sustainable future in positive ways; innovate economic models that support sustainable lifestyles; and the role of the media in communicating climate change and sustainability
- Environmental projects in Africa – particularly community based agriculture projects, creating more environmental sustainability

The trust is also committed to investing in forestry, microfinance, renewable energy, and clean technology infrastructures. It also works closely with the Ashden Trust and the Mark Leonard Trust on the Climate Change Collaboration.

In its 2016/17 annual report, it is noted that it is the trustees' objective is 'to support innovative schemes with seed-funding, leading projects to achieve sustainability and successful replication'.

Financial information

In 2016/17 the trust held assets of £43.8 million and had an income of £1.1 million. A total of £781,000 was awarded to 30 organisations. Grants were distributed as follows:

Environment UK	28	£740,000
Literacy support	1	£36,000
General (including net payments)	1	£5,000

Beneficiaries included: Carbon Tracker (£60,000); Royal Society of Arts (£31,000); Greenpeace and Influence Map (£30,000 each); Climate Change Collaboration (£16,200); Centre for Sustainable Energy and Thomas Dane Gallery (£10,000 each).

Exclusions

Grants are not made to individuals.

Applications

Generally, proposals are invited by the trustees or initiated at their request. The trust stresses very few unsolicited applications are successful. However, should you wish to apply, the following must be provided:

- A description of your charity, including aims and objectives, and the most recent annual report including income and expenditure
- An outline of the project requiring funding
- The budget of the project, including cost breakdown

⮚ The timescale of the project
⮚ A plan of how you plan to measure the success and impact of the project

Completed applications should be sent to proposals@sfct.org.uk or to the correspondent address.

Sources of information
Accounts; annual report; Charity Commission record; funder's website.

The Jabbs Foundation

🔍 General charitable purposes including medical research, education, family relationships and the prevention of crime

📍 UK, with a focus on the West Midlands

💷 £664,000 (2015/16)

CC number: 1128402

Trustees: Robin Daniels; Alexander Wright; Ruth Keighley.

Correspondent: The Trustees, PO Box 16067, Birmingham, West Midlands B32 9GP (tel: 0121 428 2593)

The foundation was registered in 2009 for general charitable purposes. The objectives of the foundation as set out in the Trust Deed are widely drawn and state that 'the objects are to advance for the public benefit any purpose which is exclusively charitable at law'. The trustees have to date focused on several areas of public benefit in making grants:

⮚ Medical research
⮚ Education
⮚ Enhancing personal, family and community relationships in the West Midlands
⮚ Organisations providing support to vulnerable members of society and organisations which aim to prevent people entering the criminal justice system
⮚ Research into the health of trees and forests and encouraging the planting of new trees where these offer educational opportunities

Financial information
In 2015/16 the foundation had assets of £351,000 and an income of £429,000. Grants were made totalling £664,000 and were broken down as follows:

Grants to enable direct medical research	£311,500
Grants to other charitable organisations	£240,000
Grants to academic institutions	£112,500

Beneficiaries included: University of Liege (£259,500); University of Birmingham (£110,500); Anawim – Women Working Together (£104,500). Smaller grants of £50,000 or less totalled £189,500.

Applications
Apply in writing to the correspondent.

Sources of information
Accounts; annual report; Charity Commission record.

The Frank Jackson Foundation

🔍 Education, environmental research

📍 South Africa and UK with a preference for Suffolk

💷 £804,000 (2016/17)

CC number: 1007600

Trustees: Amanda Taylor; Pete Brown; Tim Seymour; David Tennant; Thomas Sheldon; Mary-Anne Gribbon.

Correspondent: Lisa Mills, Administrator, 24 Taylor Way, Great Baddow, Chelmsford CM2 8ZG (tel: 01245 474418; email: frankjacksonfoundation@live.co.uk)

🌐 www.frankjacksonfoundation.org.uk

The Frank Jackson Foundation was established by the late Mr Frank Jackson M.B.E., a well-known businessman and philanthropist from Woodbridge in Suffolk.

The objectives of the foundation are 'to benefit, through education, the disadvantaged and to support world-class research in institutions of higher learning'.

Each year the foundation awards a small number of 'core grants' of significant value to organisations which support these objectives. In addition, to its core grants programme the foundation also offers a larger number of smaller grants to a wide spectrum of causes which reflect the interests or expertise of the trustees. Grants are mainly given to organisations and projects based in South Africa and Suffolk.

Financial information
In 2016/17 the foundation had assets of £25.35 million and an income of £581,500. During the year, the foundation awarded grants totalling £804,000 to 44 organisations.

Beneficiaries included: Cordwalles Preparatory School (£85,500); Wolfson College (£80,000); Oriel College Development Trust (£70,000); Baker Dearing Trust and Suffolk Community Foundation (£50,000 each); Island Trust and Pioneer Sailing (£15,000 each); Gresham College Trust (£11,300), Winston Churchill Memorial Trust (£9,000).

Applications
According to its website, the foundation does not accept unsolicited applications for funds. Instead the trustees prefer to actively seek out good causes which meet the foundation's aims. If you believe your organisation's work aligns closely with the aims of the foundation, then it is recommend that you contact the foundation by email, summarising in a paragraph how your work meets the foundation's charitable objectives.

Sources of information
Accounts; annual report; Charity Commission record; funder's website.

John James Bristol Foundation

🔍 Education, health, older people, general charitable purposes

📍 Bristol

💷 £1.8 million (2016/17)

CC number: 288417

Trustees: Joan Johnson; David Johnson; Elizabeth Chambers; John Evans; Andrew Jardine; Andrew Webley; Dr John Haworth; Peter Goodwin; Nicola Parker.

Correspondent: Louise Henderson, Chief Executive, 7 Clyde Road, Redland, Bristol BS6 6RG (tel: 0117 923 9444; fax: 0117 923 9470; email: info@johnjames.org.uk)

🌐 www.johnjames.org.uk

👍 facebook.com/JohnJamesFdn

🐦 @JohnJamesFdn

The foundation was established in 1983 by John James, a businessman and philanthropist, who was born and lived in Bristol until his death in 1996. It makes grants to charitable organisations whose work benefits residents of Bristol. According to John's sentiments, the foundation's main aim is to benefit as many residents of the city as possible and so the trustees make every effort to grant money diversely in each financial year.

Areas of work
The main areas of focus for the foundation are education, health and older people, which were all supported by John James during his life. The website stresses that 'links with the past are however coupled with a strong vision for the future needs of Bristol and its residents'.

Financial information
In 2016/17 the foundation had assets of £78.3 million and an income of £2.3 million. Grants totalled £1.8 million and were categorised as follows:

Education	£1.06 million
Health	£497,500
Older people	£212,000
General	£11,700

Beneficiaries included: Bristol Aero Collection Trust (£200,000); Lifeskills (£107,000); Hawkspring (£50,000); Badminton School (£30,000); Bristol Refugee Rights (£25,000); Bristol Grammar School (£3,000); The Nest (£2,000); Shelter (£1,900); The Almhouse Association (£1,500); The Canynges Society (£1,000).

Applications

The trustees meet quarterly in February, May, August and November to consider appeals received by the 15th of January, April, July and October, respectively. There is no formal application form and appeals must be submitted by post, to the chief executive of the foundation. Appeals should be no more than two sides of A4. All appeal applications are acknowledged, stating the month in which the appeal will be considered by the trustees.

Sources of information

Accounts; annual report; Charity Commission record; funder's website.

The Jerusalem Trust

 Christianity, including education, overseas work and Christian art

 Worldwide

£ £4.4 million (2016/17)

CC number: 285696

Trustees: The Rt Hon Sir Timothy Sainsbury; Lady Susan Sainsbury; Dr Hartley Booth; Phillida Goad; Dr Peter Frankopan; Melanie Townsend; David Wright.

Correspondent: Robert Bell, Director, The Peak, 5 Wilton Road, London SW1V 1AP (tel: 020 7410 0330; email: info@sfct.org.uk)

 www.sfct.org.uk

The Jerusalem Trust is one of 17 Sainsbury Family Charitable Trusts. It originated through a deed of appointment and was registered with the Charity Commission in 1982.

The objects of the trust are to advance the Christian religion and promote Christian organisations, and the charitable purposes and institutions they support; and also to advance Christian education and learning.

The trust's website states that its priorities are:

Evangelism and Christian mission in the UK

- Christian projects that develop new ways of working with children and young people, including children who have little or no contact with the church
- Support for Christian youth work
- Evangelistic projects, especially new and emerging evangelists
- Work with prisoners, ex-prisoners and their families

Christian education

- The development of Christian curriculum resource materials for schools in RE and across the curriculum
- Support of RE as a subject, both in curriculum development and teacher training
- Support, training and retention of Christian teachers in all subjects
- Adult lay Christian training and education
- Projects which encourage Christians in leadership in schools

Christian evangelism and relief work overseas

- Priority areas are Anglophone sub-Saharan Africa, Ethiopia, Jordan, Syria, Lebanon, Egypt, Iraq and Iran
- Programmes which support theological training colleges
- Programmes which build capacity of local churches through the training of the laity and clergy
- Translation of Christian books and materials
- Provision of aid to the persecuted church

Christian media

- Media projects promoting Christianity in the UK, North Africa, and the Middle East
- Training and networking projects for Christians working in the media
- Creative use of digital media and the internet to promote Christianity
- Jerusalem Productions, which enters into co-productions with national broadcasters and runs the annual Jerusalem Awards for Christian radio and internet productions

Christian art

- Commissions of works of art for places of worship

It should be noted that while the trust does accept unsolicited applications, funding can only be provided if the proposals closely fit the trust's areas of interests. The trustees prefer to seek out organisations and projects to support.

Financial information

In 2016/17 the trust had assets of £93.9 million and an income of

£3.05 million. Grants awarded to organisations totalled £4.4 million.

Beneficiaries included: National Society for Promoting Religious Education (£490,000 in two grants); Auckland Castle (£333,500); Tearfund (£265,500); Safe Families for Children (£175,000); Salmon Youth Centre (£100,000); CAFOD (£97,500); Frontier Youth Trust (£65,000).

Applications

While unsolicited applications are usually unsuccessful, they are accepted if the work being carried out is closely aligned with the aims of the trust.

Sources of information

Accounts; annual report; Charity Commission record; funder's website.

The Jerwood Charitable Foundation

 Arts and culture

 UK

£ £777,000 to organisations (2016)

CC number: 1074036

Trustees: Katharine Goodison; Rupert Tyler; Juliane Wharton; Timothy Eyles; Thomas De Sivrac Grieve; Lucy Ash; Philippa Hogan-Hern; Vanessa Engle; Catrin Griffiths.

Correspondent: John Opie, Deputy Director, 171 Union Street, Bankside, London SE1 0LN (tel: 020 7261 0279; email: info@ jerwoodcharitablefoundation.org)

www.jerwoodcharitablefoundation. org

The Jerwood Charitable Foundation was established in 1998 with general charitable purposes. In 1999 it took over the administration of a number of initiatives of the Jerwood Foundation (the parent company), including the Jerwood Applied Arts Prize, Jerwood Choreography Award and Jerwood Painting Prize.

In 2005 the charitable foundation became completely independent after receiving the final endowment donation from the Jerwood Foundation. Nevertheless, the foundation retains close ties with all of the Jerwood family.

The current aims of the foundation are to support the development of talented and dedicated individuals at transitional stages of their careers. This is delivered primarily through partnerships with outstanding arts organisations throughout the UK.

Its main objectives include:

- To support artists and arts producers, particularly in the early stages of their careers

- To support the wider infrastructure of arts organisations and the arts sector
- To respond positively to those taking artistic risks
- To maintain an open, responsive strand of funding

Grant programmes

The foundation is a major sponsor of a wide range of arts and culture projects, particularly those which involve rewards for excellence and the encouragement and recognition of outstanding talent and high standards, or which enable an organisation to become viable and self-financing. Single performances or arts events, such as festivals, are rarely sponsored and grants towards the running or core costs of established arts organisations are not normally made.

The foundation states that there should be no expectation of grant level as all applications will be assessed on merit and need. Both individuals and organisations are supported, including bodies that are not registered charities (providing the project meets the charitable foundation's aims).

Funding for organisations is provided through two programmes:

Large Grants – £10,000 and over

Through this programme the foundation aims to develop strategic approaches to supporting artists and arts professionals by nurturing artistic or professional development programmes founded and run by established arts organisations. In addition, the foundation supports 'new collaborations, commissioning initiatives, research and development initiatives which either enable experimentation or generate new work'. Occasionally, the foundation may also fund research into sectoral and/or policy issues which affect artists. The foundation's website notes that 'these projects tend to be developed proactively or through ongoing conversation with potential applicants, and always respond to key needs and issues within arts sectors'.

Small Grants – up to £10,000

Through this programme the foundation seeks to 'explore new relationships, work directly with individual practitioners, take risks and support research and/or development for future ideas'.

In addition to these two grants programmes the foundation also offers a wide range of bursaries and funding opportunities for individual artists. See the foundation's website for full details.

Financial information

In 2016 the foundation had assets of £28.6 million and an income of £1.3 million. There were grants made totalling £1.14 million, including £777,000 to organisations. Grants to

organisations were categorised as follows:

| Large grants | 22 | £657,500 |
| Small grants | 14 | £119,500 |

Beneficiaries included: Young Vic: Jerwood Assistant Directors (£50,000); Pacitti Company: SPILL Artist and Producer Development (£35,000); Gate Theatre: Jerwood Young Designers and Situations: Artist Development (£30,000 each); Yorkshire Dance: Artists Curating Dance (£27,000); South East Dance: Dramaturg in Resistance (£25,000); Serious Music: Take Five Edition XII (£20,000); Camden People's Theatre: Home Run (£9,500).

Exclusions

The following are not funded:

- Non-arts projects
- Building or capital costs (including purchase of equipment)
- Projects involving those who have not yet left formal education
- Academic study or course fees, or any associated costs
- Formal or informal education or community participation work
- Projects which support artists who are not resident in the UK
- General rehearsal, touring, production or staging costs for performances or exhibitions
- Retrospective awards or funding for retrospective activity
- Grants towards the purchase of musical instruments
- Projects in the fields of religion or sport
- Animal rights or welfare appeals
- Social welfare
- General fundraising appeals
- Appeals to establish endowment funds for other charities
- Medical research
- Environmental or conservation projects
- Medical or mental health projects

The foundation may, where there are very exceptional circumstances, decide to waive an exclusion.

Applications

The foundation asks potential applicants to study carefully the information available on its website prior to making a formal applications or calling for an advice. Those interested in funding should get in touch with the foundation via email or phone to discuss potential application. Further application information is available on the website.

Sources of information

Accounts; annual report; Charity Commission record; funder's website.

Jewish Child's Day (JCD)

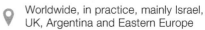 Jewish children who are disadvantaged, suffering or in need of special care

 Worldwide, in practice, mainly Israel, UK, Argentina and Eastern Europe

£ £777,000 (2016/17)

CC number: 209266

Trustees: June Jacobs; Joy Moss; Stephen Moss; Virginia Campus; Frankie Epstein; Susie Olins; David Collins; Amanda Ingram; Gaby Lazarus; Dee Lahane; Charles Spungin; Dee Lehane; Gary Cohen; Melvyn Orton.

Correspondent: Natasha Brookner, Grants and Events Manager, First Floor, Elscot House, Arcadia Avenue, London N3 2JU (tel: 020 8446 8804; email: natasha.brookner@jcd.uk.com)

🌐 jcd.uk.com/projects-grants

f facebook.com/jewishchildsday.uk

🐦 @JewishChildsDay

This charity was established in 1947 to encourage Jewish children in the UK to help less fortunate Jewish children who were survivors of the Nazi holocaust. The charity exists to improve the lives of Jewish children, in the UK, Israel or elsewhere overseas, who for any reason are suffering, disadvantaged or in need of special care. The charity's website notes that, although in the main Jewish children are the beneficiaries, this should not exclude non-Jewish children.

The charity gives grants to registered charities running programmes which help these children, awarding grants for items of equipment or specific projects. All grants must directly benefit children up to the age of 18. Grants are generally for between £500 and £5,000. Jewish Child's Day will support projects from all sections of the Jewish community.

Financial information

In 2016/17 the charity had assets of £507,500 and an income of £1.2 million. Grants awarded to organisations totalled £777,000.

Beneficiaries included: Netanya (£128,500); Federation of Jewish Services (£45,000); Arugot (£39,000); Beit Uri (£27,000); Cystic Fibrosis (£10,000); Yeladim (£5,000); Shaarei Tzedek (£4,800); Youth Space (£2,500); SOS Children's Villages (£2,000).

Exclusions

Grants are not awarded for:

- Individuals
- Capital projects

- General running costs
- Building or maintenance of property
- Staff salaries

Applications

To apply for a grant contact the correspondent to discuss in the first instance. Applications must be supported by audited accounts in English or with the main heading translated into English. and provide a breakdown of items and related costs that are being applied for. Applications should be submitted by 31 December, 30 April and 31 August for consideration in March, June and October, respectively. Organisations with dedicated UK fundraising operations must disclose this in the application. Applicants are visited by a representative of the charity where possible. The charity has a useful and informative website.

Sources of information

Accounts; annual report; Charity Commission record; funder's website.

The Elton John AIDS Foundation (EJAF)

HIV/AIDS welfare and prevention

Worldwide

£8.4 million (2016)

CC number: 1017336

Trustees: Anne Aslett; David Furnish; Sir Elton John; Johnny Bergius; Rafi Manoukian; Scott Campbell; Evgeny Lebedev; Graham Norton; Dr Mark Dybul; Tracy Blackwell.

Correspondent: Anne Aslett, Trustee, 1 Blythe Road, London W14 0HG (tel: 020 7603 9996; email: grants@ejaf.com)

 london.ejaf.org/grants

The Elton John AIDS Foundation was established in 1993 to empower people infected, affected by or at risk of HIV/AIDS and to alleviate their physical, emotional and financial hardship, to enable them to improve their quality of life, live with dignity and exercise self-determination.

The foundation funds a range of services for those living with or affected by HIV/AIDS including education, peer support, medical care, income generation, counselling and testing. It supports operational research but not pure medical research. Particular emphasis is given to the most disadvantaged or high risk groups, both nationally and internationally, and to community driven programmes that place people living with HIV/AIDS at the centre of service provision.

Grant programmes

The grants provided by the foundation can be divided into two categories:

Key Vulnerable Populations

Support is targeted at people who are at higher risk, such as men who have sex with men, sex workers and people who inject drugs. This comprises of three funds:

- **LGBT Fund** – a partnership between EJAF, the U.S. President's Emergency Plan for AIDS Relief (PEPFAR), and UNAIDS, small grants are available where LGBT people face discrimination, stigma and violence
- **Pioneer Grants** – to support a specific initiative focusing on an individual key population at higher risk within an individual country. Grants may be multi-year and there is no limit on the amount. The following criteria must be fulfilled:
  - Focus on service delivery
  - Catalytic in nature
  - Scalable in design
  - Innovative
  - Operate within one of the programme countries
  - Able to track changes for example access to condoms
- **Flagship Programmes** – to target a specific vulnerable group through a number of related initiatives within an individual country. These programmes look to genuinely 'close a gap' for a specific vulnerable group by engaging in a number of activities ranging from service delivery to advocacy. Due to the complex nature of this programme it is not open for applications; the foundation will proactively identify partners

Large Scale and Grassroots Initiatives

To complement the focus on key populations at risk, the foundation also supports regional and global initiatives that impact large numbers of people living with or at risk of HIV.

- **Support Grants** – to be targeted at groups within the general population that the foundation has been invested in for a long time, namely vulnerable girls, women and children. The following criteria must be fulfiled:
  - aligned with the UNAIDS elimination agenda (Getting to Zero) and/or the UNAIDS Global Plan
  - allow for a unique EJAF contribution
  - already be working at scale
  - applications for this programme are by invitation only
- **Robert Key Memorial Fund** – Established in the memory of Robert Key MBE (1947–2009) co-founded the UK arm of the EJAF with Sir Elton.

- open to organisations that can demonstrate an immediate, tangible benefit for individuals living with HIV
- applications can be made for awards of up to £10,000 per year on a rolling basis, for single or multi-year programmes
- must operate in one of the foundation's programme countries (Botswana, Cameroon, Cote D'Ivoire, Democratic Republic of the Congo, Ethiopia, Ghana, Kenya, Lesotho, Malawi, Mozambique, Nigeria, South Africa, Tanzania, Uganda, Zambia, Zimbabwe, China, India, Indonesia, Myanmar, Thailand, Vietnam, Russian Federation, Ukraine and the UK)

Financial information

In 2016 the foundation had assets of £16.3 million and an income of £10.7 million. Grants were made totalling £8.4 million and were distributed as follows:

Pioneer grants	£4.3 million
LGBT fund	£3 million
Support grants	£556,000
Advocacy grants	£430,000
Robert Key Memorial Fund	£60,000

Beneficiaries included: International HIV/AIDS Alliance (£2.9 million); The Population Council (£900,000); India HIV/AIDS Alliance (£850,500); Healthright International (£612,500); Doctors of the World (£600,000); APOPO (£595,500).

Exclusions

Exclusions vary for each programme. Check the foundation's website for full details.

Applications

Application information and guidelines vary for each programme, see the foundation's website for full details.

Note: Grants for projects in the Americas and Caribbean are made by the foundation's New York-based sister organisation. For further information and to apply for a grant from the Elton John AIDS Foundation (New York), visit the website (ejaf.org/newyork).

Sources of information

Accounts; annual report; Charity Commission record; funder's website.

St John's Foundation (Bath)

Health and well-being, housing, isolation, poverty, relationships, employment and skills

Bath and North East Somerset

£765,000 to organisations (2016)

CC number: 201476

Trustee: St John's Hospital Trustee Ltd.

Correspondent: John Thornfield, 4–5 Chapel Court, Bath BA1 1SQ (tel: 01225 486427; email: grants@ stjohnsbath.org.uk)

www.stjohnsbath.org.uk/funding-support

facebook.com/stjohnsbath

@stjohns1174

St John's Hospital began life in 1174 when Bishop Reginald Fitzjocelyn established a refuge for the poor and vulnerable in his parish. Since then the charity has continued to provide support and accommodation to the local community.

Eligibility

Charities supporting people and communities who live Bath and the surrounding area. Applications must fall under one of these key social issues: Health and Wellbeing; Poverty; Housing; Relationships; Employment and Skills and Isolation.

Types of grant

Grants of up to £40,000 for a maximum of three years can be applied for through the Project Supporting funding stream. Other Funding Streams include: Core Funding – £20,000 available for a maximum of three years, Pilot Project Funding – £20,000 available for a 12-month project and Business Development Funding – £40,000 available for 12-month project and Community Awards – £2,000 available for unregistered charities and community groups.

Applications are also welcomed from individuals and families who have reached a crisis point in their lives.

Financial information

In 2016 the charity had assets of £130.8 million and an income of £5.5 million. Grants totalled £1 million with £765,000 awarded to organisations and £232,000 awarded to individuals.

Beneficiaries of over £15,000 included: Sporting Family Change (£90,000); Jamie's Farm (£39,500); Cycling Projects (£24,500); Bath City Farm, Three Ways School and Triumph Over Phobia (£20,000 each).

Applications

There is an online system where applications can be made on for each of the above funding streams.

Applications on behalf of an individual or family should be made by a professional referrer such as a professional support worker or registered charity.

Sources of information

Accounts; annual report; Charity Commission record; further information provided by the funder; funder's website.

The Johnson Foundation

General charitable purposes, education, health, social welfare, children and young people, community development, families

Liverpool and the Merseyside area

£293,500 (2016/17)

CC number: 518660

Trustees: Christopher Johnson; Peter Johnson.

Correspondent: Kate Eugeni, Trust Administrator G6 Pacific Road Business Hub, 1 Pacific Road, Birkenhead, Wirral CH41 1LJ (tel: 0151 650 6987; email: kate@johnsonfoundation.co.uk)

The foundation's main aim is to support charitable activities in Liverpool and its surrounding neighbourhood. Grants are made for general charitable purposes, although the foundation prefers to support education, health, families, young people and social welfare. The trustees prefer to make grants to small charities with little or no professional funding.

Financial information

In 2016/17 the foundation held assets of £3.8 million and had an income of £160,500. Grants totalled £293,500.

Beneficiaries included: Pacific Road Enterprise Hub (£150,000); Feeding Birkenhead (£60,000); Upton Hall School (£7,500); North West Cancer Research (£5,500); Helping Young People Everywhere (£5,000); Autism Initiatives (£3,400); Hoylake Community Centre (£3,100); Claire House Children's Hospice (£2,000); Children's Adventure Farm Trust (£1,500); Birkenhead Gang Show (£1,000).

Exclusions

Grants are not normally given to individuals.

Applications

Applications can be made in writing to the correspondent. The trustees meet monthly.

Sources of information

Accounts; annual report; Charity Commission record.

The Joicey Trust

General charitable purposes

The county of Northumberland, the old metropolitan county of Tyne and Wear and Eastern Borders region

£227,500 (2016/17)

CC number: 244679

Trustees: R. Dickinson; Lord Joicey; The Rt Hon. Lady Joicey; Hon. Andrew Joicey; The Hon. Mrs K. Crosbie Dawson.

Correspondent: Andrew Bassett, Appeals Secretary, Joicey Trust, One Trinity, Broad Chare, Newcastle Upon Tyne NE1 2HF (tel: 0191 279 9676; email: appeals@thejoiceytrust.org.uk)

 www.thejoiceytrust.org.uk

The Joicey Trust provides grants to organisations in support of general charitable purposes. The trustees will consider any applications from their main beneficial area – that is, the County of Northumberland, the old Metropolitan County of Tyne and Wear and the Eastern Borders Region. As a minor part of the trust's activities, it provides grants to individuals from the beneficiary area who undertake overseas charitable activities for a minimum of six months 'in country'.

Financial information

In 2016/17 the trust had assets of £8.7 million and had an income of £311,500. During the year, the trust gave 121 grants to organisations totalling £227,500. The trust's 2016/17 accounts state, 'The majority of the grants continued to be for amounts of under £5,000 and to provide practical support for small community groups based in the North of England.'

Beneficiaries included: Greggs Foundation (£10,000); Northumberland Theatre Company (£5,000); Barnabas Safe and Sound, Comfrey Project and Gateway into the Community (£3,000 each); Bede Foodbank Newcastle West (£2,000); Lesbury Village Hall (£1,500); North of England Refugee Service Ltd (£1,000); Tyneside Women's Health Project (£750); Voluntary Services Overseas (£300); Success4All (£150).

Exclusions

The only applications that the trustees will not normally support are ones in respect of medical research.

Applications

To apply, visit the website where an enquiry form is available. Upon completion, a redirection to the link to the full application will automatically happen. Papers and supporting documents must be supplied with the application. The deadlines are 30 November and 31 May each year, but early applications are encouraged. Informal contact prior to application is welcomed.

Sources of information

Accounts; annual report; Charity Commission record; funder's website.

The Jones 1986 Charitable Trust

People with disabilities, older people, children and young people, medical research, health, education, social welfare, community development

Primarily Nottinghamshire

£662,500 (2016/17)

CC number: 327176

Trustees: Robert Heason; John Pears; David Lindley; Richard Stanley.

Correspondent: David Lindley, Trustee, c/o Smith Cooper Ltd, 2 Lace Market Square, Nottingham NG1 1PB (tel: 01154 54300)

The trust was established in 1986 with general charitable purposes. It primarily supports causes in the Nottinghamshire area and its grants programme supports charities assisting people with disabilities, medical research into disabilities, and organisations working to improve the welfare of older and young people. The trust also funds education and community projects. The trust prefers to develop a relationship with the organisations funded over an extended period of time. Awards are considered for both capital and/or revenue projects as long as each project appears viable.

Financial information

In 2016/17 the trust held assets of £21 million and had an income of £1.6 million of which £757,000 derived from a legacy donation. A total of £662,500 was awarded in grants to 73 organisations, broken down as follows:

Older people	5	£269,000
Children and young people	20	£182,500
Health and disability	14	£82,000
Community	35	£67,500

Previous beneficiaries have included: Radford Care Group (£225,000); Ruddington Framework Knitters Museum (£30,000); Age UK (£20,000); Children's Bereavement Centre (£6,500); Pintsize Theatre Company and Switch Up CIC (£5,000 each); Carlton St Paul's PCC and Eco Works (£3,000 each); Bestwood and Bulwell Foodbank, Broxtowe Women's Project, Clipstone

Miners' Welfare and Sneinton Town Football Club (£2,000 each).

Exclusions

Grants are not made to individuals.

Applications

Applications may be made in writing to the correspondent. The trustees invite applications for grants by advertising in specialist press.

Sources of information

Charity Commission record; accounts; annual report.

The Muriel Jones Foundation

General charitable purposes

UK and overseas

£1.1 million (2016/17)

CC number: 1135107

Trustees: Richard Brindle; Katie Brindle; Coutts & Co.

Correspondent: The Trustees, Coutts & Co. Trustee Department, 6th Floor, Trinity Quay 2, Avon Street, Bristol BS2 0PT (tel: 0345 304 2424)

This foundation was established in 2010 with the aim to support general charitable purposes in the UK and abroad. Previous annual reports have shown a preference for environmental, welfare and human rights charities (note this is an observed trend and not exclusively stated priority).

Richard Brindle is chief executive of Bermuda-based insurance company Lancashire Holdings and is also a trustee of Crossflow Ltd, a charity which supports people in the countries of the Himalayas through the advancement of health and education.

Financial information

In 2016/17 the foundation had assets of £7.7 million and an income of £155,000, mostly from donations. There were 25 grants made to 13 organisations totalling £1.1 million.

Beneficiaries included: Médecins Sans Frontières (£200,000); Crossflow (£157,500); Anti-Slavery International (£125,000); Animals Asia Foundation (£100,000); Epatoma Foundation (£41,500); FareShare (£30,000); Guide Dogs for the Blind (£26,500).

Applications

Apply in writing to the correspondent.

Sources of information

Accounts; annual report; Charity Commission record.

The Jordan Charitable Foundation

General charitable purposes, health, disability, heritage, the environment, animals, economic development and community development

UK, with a preference for Herefordshire and Sutherland

£631,000 (2016)

CC number: 1051507

Trustees: Sir George Russell; Ralph Stockwell; Christopher Bliss; Anthony Brierley; Snowport Ltd; Parkdove Ltd.

Correspondent: Ralph Stockwell, Trustee, 8th Floor, 6 New Street Square, New Fetter Lane, London EC4A 3AQ (tel: 020 7842 2000; email: jordan@ rawlinson-hunter.com)

The Jordan Charitable Foundation was established in 1995. The foundation's grant-making policies are guided by the original intentions of the founders. Awards are made to UK national charities and also to charities that are local to the county of Herefordshire and, in particular, charities operating within the city of Hereford. The foundation also makes awards to a much lesser extent to charities in Sutherland, Scotland, as there is a connection between the founders and this area.

In the foundation's 2016 accounts the trustees list the following as areas of priority for funding:

- Medical equipment
- Medical research
- Grants to elderly people
- Grants to help disabled people, including disabled children
- Grants for animal welfare
- Grants to assist in the maintenance of Hereford Cathedral

The trustees are willing to assist with both capital and revenue costs. Support may be given as a one-off grant or over a period of time. Since 1995 the foundation has made grants totalling over £12 million.

Financial information

In 2016 the trust had assets of £64.7 million and an income of £997,000. A total of £631,000 was awarded in grants to 49 organisations, broken down by location as follows:

Herefordshire	51%	£323,000
UK	47%	£299,000
Sutherland	2%	£9,000

Beneficiaries included: St Michael's Hospice Development Trust (£250,000); Canine Partners for Independence (£15,000); Royal National Lifeboat Institution (£15,000); Hereford Riding for the Disabled (£15,000); Wildfowl and Wetlands Trust (£10,000); St John Ambulance (£10,000); Atlantic Salmon

Trust (£5,000); War Memorials Trust (£5,000); British Diabetic Association (£5,000); Motor Neurone Disease Association (£5,000); International Animal Rescue (£2,000).

Applications

Applications may be made in writing to the correspondent. The trustees meet four times a year.

Sources of information

Accounts; annual report; Charity Commission record.

Anton Jurgens Charitable Trust

 General charitable purposes, social welfare, health, children and young people, education, vulnerable people

 UK, with a preference for the south-east of England

 £185,000 (2016/17)

CC number: 259885

Trustees: Maria Edge-Jurgens; Frans Jurgens; Steven Jurgens; Paul Beek; Frans Tilman; Hans Veraat.

Correspondent: Maria Edge-Jurgens, Trustee, c/o Saffery Champness, 71 Queen Victoria Street, London EC4V 4BE (tel: 020 7841 4000)

This trust was established in 1969 to support general charitable purposes and help organisations working for vulnerable people. In practice, social welfare, children's and health groups feature prominently in the grants, as do organisations based in the south-east of England.

Financial information

In 2016/17 the trust had assets of £9.2 million and an income of £240,500. Grants were made to 63 charities totalling £185,000.

Beneficiaries included: Bemerton Community (£5,000); Engineering Development Trust (£4,000); First Light Trust (£3,000); Root and Branch – Westmill (£2,000); Ickle Pickle's Children's Charity (£1,200); Wipe Your Tears Children's Charity (£1,000); Recital Artists' Trust (£500).

Applications

Applications may be made in writing to the correspondent. The trust's 2016/17 annual accounts state: 'The charity invites applications for funding of projects from charitable organisations. The applications are then considered by the Trustees, at twice yearly meetings in June and October.'

Sources of information

Accounts; annual report; Charity Commission record.

The Ian Karten Charitable Trust

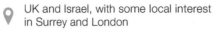 People with disabilities, education and training, Jewish causes

 UK and Israel, with some local interest in Surrey and London

 £724,500 (2016/17)

CC number: 281721

Trustees: Timothy Simon; Angela Hobbs; David Fullerton; Anthony Davis; Sally Cooke; Alexandra Davis; Nigel Flint.

Correspondent: Timothy Simon, Trustee, PO Box 386, Lymington SO41 1BD (tel: 01590 681345; email: kartentrust@aol.com)

www.karten-network.org.uk

@kartennetwork

The trust was established in 1980 to support the Jewish community in the UK and Israel as well as social welfare, assistive technologies for people with disabilities and education. According to the 2016/17 annual report the trust is currently concentrating on supporting the following two areas:

CTEC Centres

Improving the quality of life and independence of people with severe physical, sensory, cognitive disability or mental health problems by providing Karten Centres where people are supported to use Technology and Assistive Technology in learning, working and/or residential contexts. Centres are typically established by and located in Specialist Colleges of Further Education or Adult Services host charities concerned with the provision of education, employment, health, rehabilitation and daily living services for people with one or more of the above-mentioned disabilities.

The trustees will not consider funding any new centres other than in very exceptional circumstances. Applications for grants for centres are limited to a maximum of £25,000.

Scholarships and bursaries

The support of higher education by funding studentships for studies and research at universities in the UK and Israel and posts at Southampton University and Birkbeck College, University of London.

Awards are mainly given through the educational institutions and can be for higher and postgraduate education.

There is also a modest budget for small grants that can be made to select registered charities, mostly in London or Surrey.

Financial information

In 2016/17 the trust held assets of £14.4 million and had an income of £464,000. Grants totalled £724,500. The accounts note that during the year no scholarships were committed to individual scholars. Grants for scholarships and bursaries totalled £100,000 and went to three educational institutions. The remaining £624,500 went to CTEC centres and other charities.

Previous beneficiaries have included: The Woolf Institute (£100,000); Cedar Foundation Northern Ireland (£50,000); Ono University Israel (£26,500); Vision North Somerset and Young Epilepsy Lingfield (£25,000 each); Jewish Care (£1,500); The Anne Frank Educational Trust, Community Security Trust, Institute for Jewish Policy Research and Surrey Care Trust (£500 each).

Applications

Our previous research indicates that the trust only considers grants to charities supported in the past. Grants are no longer being made for new CTEC centres; however existing centres may be able to apply for additional or upgraded equipment – check the trust's website for the next application deadline. The trustees meet every six months to review the accounts and to discuss any proposed donations, scholarships and bursaries.

Sources of information

Accounts; annual report; Charity Commission record; funder's website.

The Caron Keating Foundation

 Cancer care and research

UK

£11,000 (2016/17)

CC number: 1106160

Trustees: Michael Keating; Gloria Hunniford.

Correspondent: Mary Clifford Day, Secretary, PO Box 122, Sevenoaks, Kent TN13 1UM (tel: 01732 455005; email: info@caronkeating.org)

www.caronkeating.org

Registered with the Charity Commission in October 2004, this foundation is a fundraising charity that aims to target and financially assist 'small but significant' cancer charities and support groups.

The foundation's overall aim is to help small cancer charities in their work with professional carers, complimentary healing practitioners as well as groups that provide support and advice to cancer patients and the people closest to them who are affected by the disease.

Financial information

In 2016/17 the foundation held assets of £901,500 and had an income of £163,500. Only two charities were supported in the financial year due to the ill health of the trustees. However, the annual report states that a further £300,000 was awarded to 71 charities shortly after the year end.

Previous beneficiaries have included:

Action Cancer (£30,000); Hope For Tomorrow (£25,000); Leicestershire and Rutland Organisation for the Relief of Suffering (£10,000); Cancer Support (£4,000); Hull and East Riding Breast Friends and Rotherham Cancer Care Centre (£3,000 each); Kids Cancer Charity (£2,000); Cyclists Fighting Cancer (£1,000).

Exclusions

No grants are given to individuals.

Applications

Apply in writing to the correspondent.

Sources of information

Accounts; annual report; Charity Commission record; funder's website.

The Kay Kendall Leukaemia Fund

 Research into leukaemia and patient care

 UK

(£) £5.1 million (2016/17)

CC number: 290772

Trustees: Judith Portrait; Timothy J. Sainsbury; Charles Metcalfe.

Correspondent: Robert Bell, The Peak, 5 Wilton Road, London SW1V 1AP (tel: 020 7410 0330; email: info@kklf.org.uk)

 www.kklf.org.uk

This charity was established in 1985 following the death of James Sainsbury in 1984. The trust provides funding for research into leukaemia, and other relevant studies on related diseases. In 2008, the trust instigated a new programme of patient care and patient centred projects associated with blood diseases. The trust also helps to support first class clinicians and scientists who wish to pursue a career in haematological research by providing junior and intermediate level fellowships, depending on the level of research already obtained.

Project Grants

Research grants are normally awarded for projects of up to three years'

duration. It is intended that the KKLF funding should not be the core funding of any research group – grants are usually awarded to give additional support to programmes already underway, the aim being to further strengthen activities which are already of high quality. It follows that the KKLF will accept proposals from groups which already have support from other agencies.

Requests for support for basic science programmes may be considered. Proposals which are closely related to the prevention, diagnosis, or therapy of leukaemia and related diseases are particularly encouraged.

Other funding

Capital funding

Requests for capital grants for leukaemia research laboratories or for clinical facilities for leukaemia will be considered either alone or in conjunction with proposals for the support of research and/or patient management. Capital requests must give a budget estimate of costs, together with a full justification.

Equipment grants

Requests for single large items of equipment will be considered. Requests must give detailed cost estimates and a full scientific justification.

Clinical care

Requests for clinical support must give full costing and a detailed explanation of how this support will enhance the existing service and/or research activities.

Financial information

In 2016/17 the charity had assets of £18.1 million and an income of £532,000. Grants awarded to organisations totalled £5.1 million.

Beneficiaries included: University of Cambridge (£666,500); University College London Cancer Institute (£258,000); University of Leeds (£176,500); University of Glasgow (£80,000); Full Circle Fund (£35,000); Paterson Institute for Cancer Research (£19,500); London Cancer Haematology Pathway Board – University College London (£3,000).

Exclusions

The charity does not support the following: circular appeals for general support; phase three clinical trials; and project grant applications submitted simultaneously to other funding bodies will not be accepted. Tenured or non-time-limited appointments will not be supported.

Applications

A preliminary letter or telephone call to the administration offices of the Kay Kendall Leukaemia Fund may be helpful to determine whether or not a proposal

is likely to be eligible. Application forms are available by contacting the charity's office.

Research Proposal

Applicants should complete the approved Application Form and include a research proposal (aims, background, plan of investigation, justification for budget.) The research proposal should be 3 to 5 single-spaced pages for project grants (excluding references, costings, and CVs). Applications should be submitted by email in addition to providing a hard copy with original signatures. The trustees will take account of annual inflation and of salary increases related to nationally negotiated pay scales and these should not be built into the application.

Salaries should generally be on nationally agreed scales.

The trustees may, from time to time, set special conditions for the award of a grant.

Final decision on the award of a grant is made by the trustees, having taken into account advice from their scientific advisers.

The trustees consider proposals twice each year, normally May and October. To allow for the refereeing process, new full proposals for the May meeting should be received by 28 February and for the October/November meeting by 15 July. Late applications may be deferred for 6 months.

Sources of information

Annual report; accounts; Charity Commission record; funder's website.

The Kennedy Trust For Rheumatology Research

 Research into rheumatic and related muscoskeletal diseases

 England

(£) £5.7 million (2015/16)

CC number: 260059

Trustees: Professor John Richard Batchelor; Sir Gregory Winter; Margaret Frost; Professor Hill Gaston; Jennifer Johnson; Professor Sir Ravinder Maini; James Davis; Professor Stephen Holgate; David Paterson; Dame Nicola Davies; Rodney Hornstein.

Correspondent: Sue Preston, The Kennedy Trust For, Rheumatology Research, 26–28 Hammersmith Grove, London W6 7BA (tel: 020 8834 1562; email: enquiries@kennedytrust.org)

 www.kennedytrust.org

The trust's mission is to investigate study and carry out research into the causes and means of treatment of rheumatism and allied diseases.

According to the trust's annual report:

> The Kennedy Trust was founded in 1965 by Mathilda Kennedy, daughter of the founder of Marks & Spencer (Michael Marks), and her husband Terence to support the establishment of the first Institute of its kind designed specifically to serve the needs of researchers investigating the fundamental causes of rheumatic and related musculoskeletal diseases. Since then, the Trust has focused its support on the Kennedy Institute of Rheumatology, now part of the Medical Sciences Division of the University of Oxford, by facilitating and funding research at the Institute.

Financial information

In 2015/16 the trust had assets of £257 million and an income of £37.2 million. During the year, the trust gave £5.7 million in grants. Grants were distributed as follows:

Capital/infrastructure	48%
Research projects	18%
Studentships	16%
Laboratory support	12%
Research fellowships	4%
Institute core research costs	2%

Beneficiaries include: The Kennedy Institute at Oxford University.

Applications

According to the trust's website:

> The Trust is committed to supporting research into rheumatism and allied diseases. At present this is done by means of supporting the work of scientists in the Kennedy Institute of Rheumatology at the University of Oxford. The Trust is also exploring the funding of new research and facilities outside of the Kennedy Institute.

Sources of information

Accounts; annual report; Charity Commission record.

The Kennel Club Charitable Trust

 Science, welfare, and education projects to benefit dogs

UK

£880,000 (2016)

CC number: 327802

Trustees: Michael Herrtage; Bill King; Dr Andrew Higgins; Steven Dean; Jennifer Millard; Graham Hill.

Correspondent: The KCCT Administrator, 10 Clarges Street, Piccadilly, London W1J 8AB (tel: 020 7518 6874; email: kcct@thekennelclub.org.uk)

 dogcharityblog.org.uk

 @TheKennelClubUK

The trust will consider grant applications for science, welfare, and education projects to benefit dogs.

The trust's website states:

> Specifically, and in accordance with its Trust Deed, KCCT provides funds for three purposes:
>
> ▪ To promote the advancement of education and science by furthering research into canine diseases and hereditary disorders of dogs
> ▪ To promote the quality of life of human beings by promoting dogs as therapeutic and practical aids to humans
> ▪ To promote the relief of suffering of dogs that are in need of care and attention.

Financial information

In 2016 the trust held assets of £2.6 million and had an income of £435,000. There were grants made to 52 organisations totalling £880,000.

Beneficiaries included: Animal Health Trust (£316,500 in four grants); University of Surrey (£49,500); Canine Partners (£20,000); Ability Dogs for Young People (£18,500); Ryedale Dog Rescue (£10,000); Style Acre (£8,000); Friends and Rotherham Dog Rescue (£2,000 each).

Exclusions

The trust's website states:

> ▪ Generally, pure building costs or requests from organisations whose concern is not predominantly with the dog (e.g. general animal sanctuaries) are not supported
> ▪ Grants are rarely made to individuals or to organisations having a political objective

Applications

Applications should be made in writing to the correspondent providing the latest accounts (and registered charity number, if applicable) and clearly stating the details of the costs for which you are requesting funding, for what purpose and over what period of time. The trustees meet four times a year usually in April, June, September and December. Your application will be assessed at the first available meeting once all the required documentation has been received. Make sure that you have included the following:

> ▪ Specific details of the precise amount of funding sought
> ▪ Latest set of audited accounts
> ▪ Three quotes (where building work is planned)

Scientific project proposals should be made on a separate application form available to download from the trust's website.

Further guidance is available from the trust's website.

Sources of information

Accounts; annual report; Charity Commission record; funder's website.

The Kensington and Chelsea Foundation

 Arts, families and children, disability and mental health, health and sport, education and young people, homelessness, environment, older people, employment and opportunities

 Kensington and Chelsea

 £469,500 (2016/17)

CC number: 1125940

Trustees: Jonnie Beverley; Cynthia Dize; Jeremy Raphaely; Michael Bach; Clare Ferguson; Lucinda Stafford-Deitsch; Jennifer Greenbury; Mark Garraway; Martin Morgan.

Correspondent: The Trustees, 111–117 Lancaster Road, London W11 1QT (tel: 020 7229 5499; email: team@thekandcfoundation.com)

thekandcfoundation.com

facebook.com/kandcfoundation

@kandcfoundation

The foundation provides grants and in-kind support for charities and community groups that benefit the people of Kensington and Chelsea.

Financial information

In 2016/17 the foundation held assets of £274,000 and had an income of £707,500. Grants to 52 organisations totalled £469,500.

Beneficiaries included: St Cuthbert's Centre (£32,500); Glass Door (£27,000); Chelsea Community Hospital School (£25,500); Age UK Kensington and Chelsea (£19,000 each); Full of Life (£10,000); Response Community Projects (£2,000); Chelsea Community Hospital School and Wormwood Scrubs Pony Centre (£1,000 each); Portobello Dance (£500); New Horizons (£360).

Applications

Charities which have worked with the foundation before should download the Charity Information Form from the foundation's website. Charites that have not worked with the foundation before should first ring or email the foundation.

Sources of information

Accounts; annual report; Charity Commission record; funder's website.

The Kentown Wizard Foundation

 Children and young people suffering from life limiting conditions and terminal illness and their families

Worldwide, with a preference for the UK

£871,000 (2016/17)

CC number: 1163956

Trustees: David Bamber; Kenneth Townsley; Richard Ingle; Kathryn Graham.

Correspondent: Margaret Ingram, Metro House Ltd, Unit 14–17, Metropolitan Business Park, Preston New Road, Blackpool FY3 9LT (tel: 01253 446923; email: enquiries@kentownwizard.org)

The foundation was set up by millionaire Ken Townsley in 2015. Ken was a baggage handler at Blackpool Airport before going on to start Blackpool based Gold Medal Travel which he later sold to Thomas Cook for an estimated £87 million. In 2016/17 he gifted assets with a total value of £55.8 million to the foundation on a permanent endowment basis.

The foundation focuses on children and young people suffering from life limiting conditions and terminal illness and their families.

Financial information

In 2016/17 the foundation held assets of £64 million and had an income of £57.2 million. Grants awarded to organisations totalled £871,000 and were broken down as follows:

Wish-granting charities	£400,000
Charities providing respite care, end of life care and other support	£271,000
Medical charities working overseas	£200,000

Beneficiaries included: Dreams Come True, Make a Wish and Operation Smile (UK) (£200,000 each); Rainbow Trust (£100,000); Brian House (£75,000); Kids Cancer Charity (£56,000); Donna's Dream House (£40,000).

The 2016/17 accounts cover an 18-month period.

Applications

Apply in writing to the correspondent.

Sources of information

Accounts; annual report; Charity Commission record.

Keren Association Ltd

 General charitable purposes, Jewish causes, education, religion, social welfare

 UK and overseas

£13.7 million (2016/17)

CC number: 313119

Trustees: Mrs S. Englander; Mr S. Englander; E. Englander; H. Weiss; N. Weiss; Jacob Englander; Pinkus Englander.

Correspondent: Mrs S. Englander, Trustee, 136 Clapton Common, London E5 9AG (email: mail@cohenarnold.com)

The charity was established in 1961 and supports general charitable purposes, including the advancement of education and the provision of religious instruction and training in traditional Judaism. Assistance is also given to Jewish people who are in need.

Financial information

In 2016/17 the charity had assets of £48.6 million and an income of £16.7 million. Grants were made totalling £13.7 million.

Beneficiaries included: Friends of Mercaz Hatorah Belz Macnivka (£3.7 million); United Talmudical Associates Ltd (£574,500); Emuno Educational Centre Ltd (£333,000); Crownhost Ltd (£98,000); Edupoor Ltd (£92,000); Keren Yitomei Mishpahat Eizenberg (£51,500).

Other grants totalled £1.9 million.

Applications

Applications may be made in writing to the correspondent. The annual report for 2016/17 states that 'the trustees consider all requests which they receive and make donations based on the level of funds available'.

Sources of information

Accounts; annual report; Charity Commission record.

E And E Kernkraut Charities Limited

 The advancement of the Orthodox Jewish faith, education, general charitable purposes

 UK and overseas

 £908,500 (2016/17)

CC number: 275636

Trustees: Eli Kernkraut; Esther Kernkraut; Joseph Kernkraut; Jacob Kernkraut.

Correspondent: Eli Kerndkaut, Trustee, The Knoll, Fountayne Road, London

N16 7EA (tel: 020 8806 7947; email: mail@cohenarnold.com)

The charity was established in 1973 and makes grants to support the advancement of the Orthodox Jewish faith, education and general charitable purposes.

Financial information

In 2016/17 the charity had assets of £5.7 million and an income of £1.1 million. Grants were made totalling £908,500.

Beneficiaries were not listed in the annual report and accounts.

Applications

Applications may be made in writing to the correspondent.

Sources of information

Accounts; annual report; Charity Commission record.

The Kiawah Charitable Trust

 Overseas aid, children and young people, education

 UK and India

£249,500 (2016/17)

CC number: 1107730

Trustees: Peter Smitham; Lynne Smitham; Andrea Jackson.

Correspondent: Lynne Smitham, Trustee, PO Box 7563, London WC1 3XX (tel: 020 7242 2022)

Registered in 2005, the trust's objectives according to the trust's 2016/17 annual report are as follows:

- Supporting organisations and initiatives that help adolescent girls to become healthy, educated, empowered and confident, and promote gender equity
- Building evidence and best practice of scalable initiatives and programs that help adolescent girls live in a gender equal world
- Helping to build stronger charitable organisations who can successfully scale their work with adolescent girls or work to improve gender equity
- Focusing on the most disadvantaged and vulnerable individuals and communities in India
- Supporting disadvantaged and vulnerable young people nationally and overseas

Grant-making policy

In line with their current strategy, the trust will consider supporting organisations that can demonstrate:

- Compelling evidence of program success and deep impact on their beneficiaries

- That they have worked at some level of scale and are keen to work at greater scale
- That they have effective leadership, policies and management practices
- That they are experienced in norm change at a community, wider district, or national level

Financial information

In 2016/17 the trust had assets of £4.1 million and an income of £1 million. The trust provided grants worth a total of £249,500, the majority of which was given to the Dasara – adolescent girls empowerment program (£210,500).

Beneficiaries included: Dasara – adolescent girls empowerment program (£210,500); Family Links (£33,000); Hospice in the Weald (£5,000).

Applications

Apply in writing to the correspondent. The trustees consider any applications received for grants but also adopt a proactive approach in seeking worthy causes requiring support.

Sources of information

Accounts; annual report; Charity Commission record.

Kidney Research UK

🔍 Kidney research

📍 UK

💷 £5.9 million (2016/17)

CC number: 252892

Trustees: Adrian Akers; Dr Adnan Sharif; Andrew Tripp; Anna-Maria Steel; Dr Charles Tomson; David Prosser; Deirdre Jennings; Federica Pizzasegola; Prof. Fiona Karet; Iain Pearson; Prof. Jeremy Hughes; Dr Jill Norman; Prof. John Feehally; Julia Moross; Tom Kelly; Prof. Sunil Bhandari.

Correspondent: Research Operations Team, Nene Hall, Peterborough Business Park, Lynch Wood, Peterborough PE2 6FZ (tel: 0300 303 1100; email: grants@kidneyresearchuk.org)

🌐 www.kidneyresearchuk.org

 facebook.com/kidneyresearchuk

 @Kidney_Research

📷 @kidney_research_uk

Kidney Research UK funds research with the aim of improving the understanding of kidney disease, its causes, treatment and management. It has a vision of lives 'free from kidney disease', which it looks to achieve by:

- Funding and delivering life-saving research into kidney diseases

- Improving treatments for people with diseases and enhancing their quality of life
- Increasing awareness of kidney health

What the charity funds

The charity offers a wide range of support for kidney research through the following types of grants:

- Research project grants
- Innovation grants
- Senior (non-clinical) fellowships
- Training (clinical) fellowships
- Postdoctoral (non-clinical) fellowships
- PhD studentships
- Intercalated degree
- Allied Health Professional fellowships
- Kidney Research UK – Stoneygate Research Awards (project and innovation)
- Kids Kidney Research Paediatric Research Awards (project and innovation)
- Jointly funded fellowships (these are listed on the website)

Financial information

In 2016/17 the charity had assets of £9.7 million and an income of almost £9.4 million. During the year, the charity committed £5.9 million in research grants.

Grants were given to fund projects at universities, hospitals and other research institutions.

Applications

Applications must be submitted through the online portal, which can be found on the charity's website. Hard copy application forms are not accepted. A user guide on how to apply is accessible once you have logged into the online portal.

To access the online grants management system or for an overview of the charity's application and review process, the types of grants available and dates of funding rounds, see www. kidneyresearchuk.org/research/apply-for-funding. For more advice and help, contact the Research Operations Team.

Sources of information

Accounts; annual report; Charity Commission record; funder's website.

The King Henry VIII Endowed Trust – Warwick

🔍 General charitable purposes

📍 The former borough of Warwick only

💷 £240,500 (2016)

CC number: 232862

Trustees: Neil Thurley; Gerry Guest; Stephen Copley; Rupert Griffiths; Kathryn Parr; John Edwards; Ian Furlong; Revd David Brown; Michael Peachey; Marie Ashe; Stephen Jobburn; Susan Grinnell.

Correspondent: Jonathan Wassall, Clerk and Receiver, King Henry VIII Endowed Trust, 12 High Street, Warwick CV34 4AP (tel: 01926 495533; email: jwassall@kinghenryviii.org.uk)

 www.kinghenryviii.org.uk

The trust was founded in 1545 and changed its name in July 2003 having formerly been called The Warwick Municipal Charities The Charity of King Henry VIII.

The trust's website specifies that grants can be made for the following purposes, provided they are for the benefit of the inhabitants of the Old Borough of Warwick:

- The repair of historic buildings
- The relief of older people, those who are infirm and people in need
- The improvement of social welfare, recreation and leisure facilities
- The support of educational facilities

Awards are made to both individual residents of the town and organisations benefitting such people. Assistance is also given to educational projects provided by organisations for Warwick Town LEA Schools (such request should be submitted by the school). The geographical criterion is strict – it mostly covers the CV34 postcode district but there are exceptions (see the application guidelines available from the trust's website).

The trust's website states that:

> 50% of its distribution benefits the 5 Anglican churches in Warwick. 30% of the distribution goes to the Warwick Independent Schools Foundation (which is used for means tested bursaries for Warwick children) and the remaining 20% Town Share is available for discretionary grants that benefit the inhabitants of the Old Borough of Warwick.

The church share of support provides for the parishes of St Mary, St Nicholas, St Michael's (Budbrooke), St Paul's (Warwick) and All Saints (Emscote).

According to the application guidelines, the trust will not normally provide grants for 'regular annual revenue expenditure but it is prepared to consider assisting the start-up of a project by providing instalment funding for a period not exceeding three years'.

Trustees have, in recent years, prioritised grants that support young people. Over 50% of the Town Share distribution has benefitted young people (including schools).

Financial information

In 2016 the trust had assets of £31.2 million and an income of £1.2 million. During 2016 the trust distributed a total of £1.1 million to beneficiaries with £526,500 being distributed to the five Anglican churches in the town, £336,500 to the Warwick Independent Schools Foundation. £245,500 in grant was given in discretionary grants to beneficiaries in the town of Warwick, of this amount, £5,000 was awarded to two individuals.

Grants from the Town Share were made to 37 different organisations.

Beneficiaries of the 'Town Grants' included: Warwick Apprenticing Charities (£30,000); Warwick Corps of Drums (£25,000); Myton School (£20,000); Aylesford School (£12,800); Woodloes Senior Citizens Association (£2,800); Dogs for Good (£1,000).

Exclusions

Grants are not given for projects outside the beneficial area or retrospectively for projects which have already taken place. The website notes that 'the trustees have only limited powers to make grants for projects for which central or local government has a financial responsibility'.

Applications

Application forms are available to download from the trust's website or can be requested from the correspondent. They should be returned by post or email. There are detailed guidelines and criteria, available from the trust's website. The trustees consider grants quarterly, in March and June (appeals should be received at the beginning of the month) and September and December (requests should be received by mid-August and November, respectively). The outcome of your application is normally communicated within a week following a meeting.

In the case of an emergency, applications may be fast-tracked (provided such urgency is made clear on the application). Organisations that provide educational projects for schools should note that the application needs to be made by the recipient school.

Sources of information

Accounts; annual report; Charity Commission record; guidelines for applicants; funder's website.

King/Cullimore Charitable Trust

 General charitable purposes

Worldwide

£650,000 (2016/17)

CC number: 1074928

Trustees: Peter Cullimore; Alastair McKechnie; Christopher Gardner; Richard Davies; Jil Pye.

Correspondent: Peter Cullimore, Trustee, Cullimore, 52 Ledborough Lane, Beaconsfield, Buckinghamshire HP9 2DF

This trust was established in 1998 to support general charitable purposes anywhere in the world.

Financial information

In 2016/17 the trust had assets of £9 million and an income of £6 million. During the year, the trust awarded grants of £650,000. A list of beneficiaries was not published.

Previous beneficiaries have included: Alexander Devine Children's Hospice (£500,000); RAFT (£25,000); Countryside Learning and Medical Detection Dogs (£20,000 each); Alzheimer's Research UK; Asthma UK, Demand, Duke of Edinburgh Award, Mind, Parents Against Child Exploitation and SENSE (£10,000 each); Play Kenya (£9,000); Wired Cornwall (£8,000); Orangutan Foundation (£6,500); Drednought Centre, Everyday Art and Sussex Snowdrop Foundation (£5,000).

Applications

No new applications are currently being accepted.

Sources of information

Accounts; annual report; Charity Commission record.

The Mary Kinross Charitable Trust

 Relief of poverty, advancement of education, medical research, community development, young people, offenders/ex-offenders, health, including mental health

UK

£1.06 million (2016/17)

CC number: 212206

Trustees: Elizabeth Shields; Fiona Adams; Dr Neil Cross; Gordon Hague; Elizabeth Barber; David Milne.

Correspondent: Fiona Adams, Trustee, 36 Grove Avenue, Moseley, Birmingham B13 9RY (email: marykinrossct@gmail.com)

This trust, established in 1957, makes grants in the areas of the relief of poverty, advancement of education, medical research, community development, young people, people who have offended and health, including mental health issues. Grants made under the heading 'youth' tend to be made with crime prevention in mind.

The trust prefers to work mainly with a group of charities with which it develops a close connection, led by at least one of the trustees. It describes its grant policy in the 2016/17 annual report as follows:

> The Trustees wish to continue the policy of the Founders which was to use the Trust income to support a few carefully researched projects, rather than make many small grants. The fields of work chosen reflect the particular interests and knowledge of Trustees and at least one Trustee takes responsibility for ensuring the Trust's close involvement with organisations to which major grants are made.

> During the year, grants have been made in the fields of medical research, youth, penal affairs, health and mental health.

Financial information

In 2016/17 the trust had assets of £43 million and an income of £848,500. The 2016/17 annual report states that: 'Grants paid in the year totalled £1,060,340 and commitments until 31 March 2021 now stand at £1,055,500. There have been 21 grants paid of £10,000 or above and totalling £1,010,300...There have been 14 grants of lesser sums paid totalling £50,040.' We have used the figure of £1 million as the total grants paid in 2016/17. Grants were distributed as follows:

Medical research	8	£482,500
Youth	10	£365,000
Penal affairs	6	£72,000
Health	4	£59,500
Mental health	2	£55,000
Miscellaneous	6	£26,500

Beneficiaries included: Bendrigg Trust (£265,000); Juvenile Diabetes Research Foundation (£100,000); Bipolar UK (£35,000); Growing Well (£20,000); Citizens Advice Enfield (£17,000); Circles UK (£15,000); Prison Radio Association (£2,000); Eve Brook Scholarship Fund (£1,000).

Exclusions

Individuals are excluded.

Applications

Under the trust's current grant-making policy, a high majority of unsolicited applications are unsuccessful, as most new organisations are recommended by the trustees or the chair. However, should an organisation wish to submit an application, it must be done in writing. Telephone calls and emails are discouraged.

Sources of information
Accounts; annual report; Charity
Commission record.

The Kirschel Foundation

 Jewish causes, medical, health and disability needs, disadvantaged individuals, education and training

 UK

£ £316,000 (2016/17)

CC number: 1067672

Trustees: Laurence Kirschel; Ian Lipman; Steven Pinshaw.

Correspondent: Pritesh Patel, 26 Soho Square, London W1D 4NU (tel: 020 7437 4372)

This foundation was established in 1997 and states its objective as 'the promotion of internal spirituality and harmony which leads to positive thought and action'. In practice, the charity mainly makes grants to Jewish organisations, social welfare in the Jewish community and medical causes.

Financial information
In 2016/17 the foundation had assets of £1,400 and an income of £310,000. Grants totalled £316,000.

Beneficiaries included: Aharat Shalom Charity Fund (£68,000); Jewish Learning Exchange (£33,000); Gateshead Academy for Torah Studies (£20,000); Friends of Lubavitch Scotland (£18,000); Jewish Care (£15,000); Kisharon (£10,000); Sumatran Orangutan Society (£6,000); Ovarian Cancer Action (£1,000).

Applications
Apply in writing to the correspondent.

Sources of information
Accounts; annual report; Charity Commission record.

The Ernest Kleinwort Charitable Trust

 Environmental conservation, wildlife, general charitable purposes, reproductive health

 UK, Sussex

£ £1.75 million (2016/17)

CC number: 229665

Trustees: Marina Rose Kleinwort; Sir Richard Kleinwort; Alexander Hamilton Kleinwort; Rt Hon Edmund Christopher; Lord Chandos; Charlie Mayhew; SG. Kleinwort Hambros Trust Company (UK) Ltd.

Correspondent: The Trustees, SG Kleinwort Hambros Trust Company (UK) Ltd, 5th Floor, 8 St James's Square,

London SW1Y 4JU (tel: 020 3207 7337; email: ekctadmin@kleinwortbenson.com)

 www.ekct.org.uk

The trust was established in 1964 by Sir Ernest Kleinwort. The following information was taken from the trust's website:

EKCT aims to 'make a difference'. The trustees will consider all applications that fall within the trust's area of activity from charities that are registered in the UK.

Principal support is given to charities working in the following areas:

1 Charitable work in the county of Sussex
2 Wildlife and Environmental Conservation (UK and International)
3 Reproductive Health (International)

The trustees use the following programme areas to classify their grants:

▷ Care of the Elderly
▷ Disability
▷ General Welfare
▷ Hospices
▷ Reproductive Health (International)
▷ Wildlife and Environmental Conservation (UK and International)
▷ Youth

Grant-making
The trust's website states that:

Grants will be considered for start-up costs, core costs or for a specific project for which applicants have requested support. This could include a contribution towards a building/refurbishment project, purchase of specialist equipment or other similar capital expenditure, or assistance with running costs.

The trust provides small grants (£5,000 and under); medium grants (£5,001 to £10,000); and large grants (£10,001 and over). See the trust's website for details on closing dates and how to apply, as each grant varies.

Financial information
In 2016/17 the trust had assets of £62 million and an income of £1.5 million. During the year, the trust awarded 145 grants to organisations, supporting 59% of all applications. Grants awarded to organisations totalled £1.75 million.

Beneficiaries included: Chailey Heritage Foundation (£150,000); Tusk Trust (£140,000); Galapagnos Conservation Trust (£76,000); EIA – Environmental Investigation Agency (£60,000); St Wilfred's Hospice (£50,000); Winston's Wish (£30,000); Natural History Museum (£25,000); Action for Deafness (£5,000); Carousel (£2,000); Over the Wall (£1,000).

Exclusions
The trust's website states that it will not fund the following:

▷ Large national charities having substantial fundraising potential, income from legacies and or endowment income
▷ Organisations not registered as charities in the UK, or those registered less than a year
▷ Pre-school groups
▷ Out of school play schemes, including holiday schemes
▷ Charities not funded by any other charity
▷ Very small and narrowly specialised activities
▷ Local authorities
▷ Individuals
▷ Charities applying on behalf of individuals
▷ General requests for donations
▷ Expeditions or overseas travel
▷ 'Campaigning' organisations
▷ Charities whose main aim is to raise funds for other charities with substantial cash reserves
▷ Animal rescue or animal welfare organisations

Applications
Firstly, complete the eligibility questionnaire. If you are eligible, application forms are available to be completed online on the trust's website.

Small grants: applications are accepted and considered throughout the year.

Medium grants: applications are accepted four times per year, during the following periods:

▷ 4 January to 11 February
▷ 18 April to 19 May
▷ 10 July to 20 August
▷ 9 October to 19 November

Large grants: applications are accepted twice per year, during the following periods:

▷ 4 January to 4 March
▷ 10 July to 10 September

Sources of information
Accounts; annual report; Charity Commission record; funder's website.

The Sir James Knott Trust

 General charitable purposes

Durham, Gateshead, Hartlepool, Newcastle upon Tyne, North Tyneside, Northumberland and South Tyneside

£ £1.36 million to organisations (2016/17)

CC number: 1001363

Trustees: Oliver James; John Cresswell; Fiona Sample; Ben Speke.

Correspondent: Vivien Stapley, Secretary, 16–18 Hood Street, Newcastle upon Tyne NE1 6JQ (tel: 0191 230 4016; email: info@knott-trust.co.uk)

 www.knott-trust.co.uk

This trust was founded and registered with the Charity Commission in 1990 to act as an independent grant-making-charity. The aim of the trust is to improve the conditions for people living and working in the north east of England (note, the trust does not cover the areas of Darlington, Stockton-on-Tees, Middlesbrough, Redcar, or Cleveland).

The trust supports a wide range of charitable causes, including:

- Arts and culture
- Community issues and events
- Conservation and environment
- Education and training
- Public services
- Health and sport
- Heritage and historic buildings
- Housing, homelessness, and hardship
- Maritime
- Public service
- Service related charities

Grants are awarded at the trustees' discretion, three times a year. Since 1990, the trust has made over 8,500 grants totalling over £27.8 million.

Financial information
In 2016/17 the trust had assets of £51.6 million and an income of £1.6 million. A total of £1.36 million was awarded to organisations and individuals, with £2,000 going to individuals.

Beneficiaries included: St John's College – Durham University (£30,000); Aged Merchant Seamen's Homes (£25,000); Duke of Edinburgh's Award (£7,000); Beacon Hill Arts (£5,000); Alnwick Playhouse (£4,000); Fawdon Community Library, Guide Association-Durham South and Hartlepool Foodbank (£3,000 each); Rape Crisis Tyneside and Northumberland (£2,500); Berwick Youth Project (£2,000).

Exclusions
The trust does not provide funds for:

- The replacement of funding withdrawn by local authorities
- Organisations that do not have an identifiable project within the beneficial area

Applications
Applications need to be submitted in writing to the correspondent, giving a description of the need and providing all the relevant supporting information regarding your organisation as well as a copy of the latest annual report and accounts (see the website for an extensive list of details which the trust expects to find in your appeal).

The trustees normally meet in spring, summer and autumn. Applications need to be submitted at least three months before a grant is required. Successful applicants may re-apply after 18 months following a receipt of grant; unsuccessful applicants can try again after 12 months.

The trust welcomes initial enquires by phone or email and 'endeavours to acknowledge all applications'. The outcome of the application is communicated within two weeks following the meeting.

Sources of information
Accounts; annual report; Charity Commission record; funder's website.

Kollel and Co Ltd

 Jewish causes, relief of poverty, religious education, general charitable purposes

Worldwide

£943,500 (2016/17)

CC number: 1077180

Trustees: Simon Low; Judith Weiss; Rachel Kalish.

Correspondent: Simon Low, Trustee, 7 Overlea Road, London E5 9BG (tel: 020 8806 1570)

This charity was established in 1999 with the following objects:

- The advancement of education and religion in accordance with the doctrines of the Jewish religion
- The relief of poverty
- General charitable purposes

Financial information
In 2016/17 the charity had assets of £9.9 million and an income of £2.6 million. Grants were made totalling £943,500 to organisations.

Beneficiaries included: Ezer V'hatzolah (£84,500); Here 2 Help (£57,000); Talmud Torah D'Chasidi Gur (£49,500); Chevras Maoz Ledol (£54,000); Rise and Shine (£50,000).

Applications
The annual report for 2016/17 states that, 'grants are made upon application by the charity concerned...in amounts thought appropriate by the directors/trustees.'

Sources of information
Accounts; annual review; Charity Commission record.

Kolyom Trust Ltd

Jewish religion, education and welfare

Worldwide

£3.15 million (2016/17)

CC number: 1112084

Trustees: Leopold Zahn; Isaac Bamberger; Hyman Weiss.

Correspondent: Leopold Zahn, Trustee, 44 Stanley Road, Salford M7 4HN (tel: 0161 740 5998)

The Kolyom Trust was registered with the Charity Commission in 2005. According to its 2016/17 annual report the objects of the trust are 'the advancement and furtherance of the Jewish Religion and Jewish religious education and the alleviation of poverty amongst Jewish community throughout the world'.

Financial information
In 2016/17 the trust had assets of £1.55 million and an income of £3.4 million. During the year, the trust awarded grants totalling £3.15 million. Grants were distributed as follows:

Relief of poverty	£2 million
Education grants	£821,500
Religious grants	£347,500

No list of beneficiaries was available.

Applications
According to the trust's annual report 2016/17: 'The charity invites applications for funding through contacting local philanthropists to contribute towards projects that both the trustees and the philanthropists feel are appropriate for the charities objects.'

Sources of information
Accounts; annual report; Charity Commission record.

The KPMG Foundation

Children and young people, young offenders, education and training, employment

England, Scotland and Wales

£1.23 million (2016/17)

CC number: 1086518

Trustees: Robin Cartwight; Peter Sherratt; Christine Gilbert; David Woodward; Fahad Raja; Rachel Hopcroft; Melanie Richards.

Correspondent: Melanie Richards, Trustee, KPMG LLP, 15 Canada Square, Canary Wharf, London E14 5GL (tel: 020 7311 4733; email: kpmgfoundation@kpmg.co.uk)

 home.kpmg.com/uk/en/home/about/corporate-responsibility/kpmg-foundation.html

@kpmg_foundation

Established in 2001, the KPMG's Foundation's objective is to unlock the potential of children in the UK who, for primarily social reasons, have not achieved their educational potential.

To date the foundation has helped over 30,000 children improve their literacy, and has awarded £10.8 million to 68 charitable projects.

On its website former trustee and KPMG UK Chair Simon Collins states that the foundation has a particular focus 'on early intervention and education significantly helps to unlock the potential of individuals and communities. As trustees, one of our key objectives is to improve the outcomes of children in care and children in deprived families.'

Applications are particularly encourages from projects which:

▶ Focus primarily on improving access to education, training and employment
▶ Demonstrate that early intervention can prevent problems further downstream
▶ Build on a thorough understanding of the core issues facing the most disadvantaged children and how their lives could be transformed
▶ Utilise the Foundation's convening and collaboration power by bringing others together around an issue (funders, policy makers, academics etc.)
▶ Demonstrate potential to evidence success over the long-term through rigorous evaluation and quantitative metrics
▶ Enhance the work of the Foundation through leveraging the power of KPMG and the skills of its staff
▶ Focus on outcomes as opposed to focusing on what is being done
▶ Have the potential to be scalable; and
▶ Will leverage other funds and be sustainable

The foundation's impact report available on the website gives an extensive list and further details of projects supported in the past as well as currently assisted initiatives.

Financial information

In 2016/17 the foundation had assets of £6.3 million and an income of £851,500. There were 13 grants made totalling £1.23 million. Grants were distributed as follows:

Children and young people in deprived families	9	£1.1 million
Children and young people on edge of care, in care or leaving care	3	£89,000
Young offenders and those at risk of offending	1	£37,000

Beneficiaries included: Barnardo's (£569,000); Future First (£150,000); Working Chance (£101,000 in two grants); Family Rights Group (£50,000); Enabling Enterprise (£40,000); Education Endowment Foundation (£21,500).

Applications

According to the website, the director and advisor to the foundation 'pro-actively seeks projects to support and does not accept any unsolicited applications'. The trustees can also make referrals to the director of the foundation should they identify a programme or charity that fits with the foundation's objectives.

Sources of information

Accounts; annual report; Charity Commission record; funder's website.

The Kreitman Foundation

 General charitable purposes, environment, education, medical research, health and social welfare

UK

£425,500 (2016/17)

CC number: 269046

Trustees: Richard Luck-Hille; Anna Harford; Emma Walker.

Correspondent: The Trustees, Citroen Wells, Devonshire House, 1 Devonshire Street, London W1W 5DR (email: jonathan.prevezer@citroenwells.co.uk)

The foundation was established in 1975 as the Jill Kreitman Charitable Trust, it changed its name to the Luck-Hille Foundation and in 2009 changed it again to The Kreitman Foundation. The foundation mostly supports projects in the fields of the environment (marine/land conservation), education, medical research, health and welfare. It makes grants to registered charities or charitable organisations which are exempt from charitable registration, based in the UK.

Grant-making

At the time of writing (June 2018) the foundation's website states:

Currently we have high levels of funding commitments to medical research and, as a result, we are unlikely to enter many new partnerships this year.

Nevertheless we are committed to the continued fulfilment of our charitable objectives and so are constantly engaging with both fundraisers, exports and those working on the ground to learn and monitor landscapes and explore possible future opportunities within them. We are currently looking broadly at the environment and human welfare as possible new areas to focus on and hope

to be able to publish further specifics in time.

We would like to hear from new organisations but ask that any initial introduction be kept as concise as possible. Should we then wish to explore in more depth we will progress dialogue looking more extensively at the work you are doing (and/or proposing doing), what you hope to achieve, what measurements (general and specific) you expect might represent progress in that direction and so on. We would also be keen to look at any external factors/systems you think might interact with and potentially affect your objectives.

Financial information

In 2016/17 the foundation had assets of £3.3 million and had an income of £56,000. During the year, the foundation gave a total of £425,500 in grants to organisations.

Beneficiaries included: Institute of Cancer Research (£200,000); Wellington College (£100,000); The Tennis and Racket Associations Ltd (£28,000); Royal Marsden Hospital (£18,900); Middlesex University (£16,500).

Exclusions

Grants are not normally made to individuals.

Applications

Applications may be made in writing to the correspondent. The trustees seem to have a list of regular beneficiaries and it may be unlikely that any new applications will be successful.

Sources of information

Accounts; annual report; Charity Commission record.

The Neil Kreitman Foundation

Arts and culture, education, health, social welfare

Worldwide, in practice UK, USA and Israel

£18.7 million (2016/17)

CC number: 267171

Trustees: Neil Kreitman; Gordon Smith.

Correspondent: Gordon Smith, Trustee, Citroen Wells & Partners, Devonshire House, 1 Devonshire Street, London W1W 5DR (tel: 020 7304 2000)

The foundation was established in 1974 and makes grants to registered or exempt charities for general charitable purposes, with favour for arts and culture, education, health and social welfare. The foundation has also given to Jewish charities in previous years. In 2005/06 the foundation received £15 million from the Kreitman Foundation when it ceased operating.

Financial information

The 2015/16 annual report lists the foundation's accounts in US dollars, which has been converted to pound sterling on 14 June 2018 using XE.com (www.xe.com/currencyconverter).

The foundation held assets of £28,500 and had an income of £109,500. A total of £18.7 million was awarded in grants to 11 organisations, in areas broken down as follows:

Arts and cultural activities	£18.4 million
Health and welfare activities	£78,000
Educational activities	£128,000

Beneficiaries included: Monimos Foundation (£17.6 million); The Ashmolean Museum (£750,500); University of Oxford Development Trust Fund (£127,500); Freud Museum London (£46,500); The British Film Institute (£14,500); Victoria and Albert Museum (£14,500); The School of Oriental and African Studies University of London (£465).

Exclusions

No grants are given to individuals.

Applications

Apply in writing to the correspondent.

Sources of information

Accounts; annual report; Charity Commission record.

Kusuma Trust UK

 Education, research and advocacy, community projects

India, Gibraltar and the UK

£1.7 million (2016/17)

CC number: 1126983

Trustees: Anurag Dikshit; Prashant Jain; Dr Soma Pujari; John Rhodes.

Correspondent: Andrew Arthurson, 5th Floor, 55 New Oxford Street, London WC1A 1BS (tel: 020 7420 0650; email: info@kusumatrust.org)

 www.kusumatrust.org

 @KusumaTrustUK

Kusuma Trust UK was established in 2008 by Dr Soma Pujari and her husband Anurag Dikshit, who both serve as trustees. The trust's website explains that its mission is to 'facilitate and increase access to education and other life opportunities for children and young people, with a focus on the most economically disadvantaged'. Through its work, it aims to 'break the inter-generational cycle of poverty' by enabling children and young people to realise their potential. The trust also supports innovation and new developments in education, research and advocacy.

Strategic priorities

The 'Strategy 2015–18' document, which is available from the website, explains that education is central to the trust's strategy and that research and advocacy are also priorities. It outlines the two priority areas.

Education

Our focus is to improve education outcomes for young people in secondary and higher education. We address major obstacles in secondary and higher education for motivated young people from the most disadvantaged backgrounds. Our grants contribute to a range of outcomes, including improvements in student attainment, teaching quality and community engagement, and an increased number of young people pursuing higher education and gaining employment.

Our priority interventions focus on teacher professional development, school governance and management, parent and community involvement, scholarships, career development support for young people, and widening access to educational resources. Points of transition during education and entry into employment receive special attention.

Research and advocacy

Research with a focus on baseline and outcome measures is integrated into projects supported by the Trust. This is reinforced with qualitative research to understand the impact on beneficiaries, including multiplier effects and unintended outcomes that are as important as the intended outcomes. We also support research to better understand the obstacles in education and the causes of educational failure. Evidence generated from research is used to shape our grant making, and influence the practices and policies of implementers, other donors, government and policy bodies.

Grant-making

Kusuma UK makes grants to partner organisations whose work aligns with its strategy, quoted above. Through their small grants programme, Kasuma Trust provide grants of up to a maximum of £10,000 for organisations that enable disadvantaged young people to have more opportunities in education or employment. Registered charities in England can apply for to the small grants programme.

Geographic focus and beneficiaries

Through its work, the trust targets: young people from disadvantaged backgrounds, teachers and government education officials; programmes that engage parents and communities; and appropriate higher education institutions, universities and centres of excellence.

The trust operates in two districts in India – Sambalpur in Odisha and Hardoi in Uttar Pradesh. It also supports initiatives at a national level and with relevance to the national policy.

The trust also operates in Gibraltar supporting education projects, community initiatives and charities that enhance life in the country.

Support in the UK is focused on areas based on 'significant economic and other deprivation' indicators. These areas include declining coalfield, mining, industrial and coastal communities.

Financial information

In 2016/17 the trust had assets of £369.3 million and an income of £3 million. A total of 15 grants were made amounting to £1.7 million. Grants were broken down as follows:

Education in India	1	£1 million
Gibraltar	1	£349,000
UK projects	9	£311,000
Research in India	4	£92,500

Beneficiaries included: Kusuma Foundation (£1 million); Kusuma Trust Gibraltar (£349,000); Children of St Mary's Intensive Care (£100,000); Sutton Trust (£27,300); Royal Parks Foundation (£15,000).

Applications

Details of future funding opportunities will be post on the trust's website.

Sources of information

Accounts; annual report; Charity Commission record; funder's website.

The Kyte Charitable Trust

 Sport, community support, education, healthcare, children, international aid

UK

£254,000 (2016/17)

CC number: 1035886

Trustees: David Kyte; Tracey Kyte; James Kyte; Ilana Kyte; Max Kyte.

Correspondent: David Kyte, Trustee, First Floor, Nations House, 103 Wigmore Street, London W1U 1QS (tel: 020 7486 7700)

The trust was established in 1994 and supports general charitable purposes across the UK. The trust only makes grants to organisations.

Financial information

In 2016/17 the trust had assets of £146,000 and an income of £250,000 from donations and legacies. Grants were made totalling £254,000 and broken down as follows:

Sports	£161,500
Community support	£51,500
Educational support	£19,000
Healthcare	£12,700
Children	£6,500
International aid	£2,800

Previous beneficiaries have included:

Maccabi London Brady Recreational Trust (£73,500); Jewish Care and United Jewish Israel Appeal (£25,000 each); Jewish Community Secondary School Trust (£22,500); Community Security Trust (£20,000); Presidents Club (£15,000); Chai Cancer Care (£7,200).

Applications

Apply in writing to the correspondent.

Sources of information

Accounts; annual report; Charity Commission record.

Ladbrokes Coral Trust

 General charitable purposes, healthcare, education, community projects

UK

£304,500 (2016)

CC number: 1101804

Trustees: Karen Thraves; Shaun Giblin; Stuart Whitwell; Simon Reynolds; Grainne Hurst; Nick Batram.

Correspondent: Rachael Edwards, 5th Floor Zig Zag Building, 70 Victoria Street, London SW1E 6SQ (tel: 020 8429 7777; email: charity@ladbrokes.co.uk)

Ladbrokes Coral Trust was established in 2003. Formerly known as Ladbrokes in the Community Charitable Trust, the charity changed its name to Ladbrokes Coral Trust from in May 2017, following the merger between Ladbrokes and certain businesses of Gala Coral Group Ltd. Its funding comes not from the Ladbrokes company, but via the fundraising efforts of the head office and shop staff, customers and 'Event Days'.

The trust's record on the Charity Commission's website states that support can be given to a range of causes 'with the overriding requirement being that the causes supported operate and serve the community in which the shops and businesses of Ladbrokes Coral group plc operate'.

According to the annual report for 2016, grants are commonly given in the following categories:

▶ **Health:** 'Principally research/ treatment, hospice services and disability support'
▶ **Education:** supporting people who are disadvantaged or who have disabilities

▶ **Community:** with a focus on projects for people who are older or homeless or social activity projects for people who are at risk

Financial information

In 2016 the trust had assets of £127,000 and an income of £302,500. Grants were made totalling £304,500 and were distributed under the following categories:

Hospices and hospitals	£169,500
Social welfare	£131,500
Other	£1,000
Environment and animals	£300

Previous beneficiaries have included:

Cancer Research UK; Children with Cancer UK; Coalfields Regeneration Trust; Marie Curie Cancer; Starlight Charity.

Applications

In the first instance, the support of a local shop should be secured in raising funds on behalf of a cause. The trustees meet every month 'to consider grant requests from shop and head office fundraisers and registered charities'.

Sources of information

Accounts; annual report; Charity Commission record; funder's website.

John Laing Charitable Trust

 Education, community regeneration, young people, homelessness, with a particular emphasis on day centres, general charitable purposes

UK and, occasionally, countries where John Laing Group plc operates

£907,000 to organisations (2016)

CC number: 236852

Trustees: Christopher Laing; Sir Martin Laing; Lynette Kridge; Alexandra Gregory; Benjamin Laing; Christopher Waples; Daniel Partridge; Stewart Laing.

Correspondent: Jenny Impey, Trust Director, 33 Bunns Lane, Mill Hill, London NW7 2DX (tel: 020 7901 3307; email: jenny.impey@laing.com)

🌐 www.laing.com/top/corporate_ responsibility/john_laing_ charitable_trust.html

The trust was established in 1962 by John Laing Group plc, and 'infrastructure investor' and asset management company.

The trust provides an avenue for John Laing plc and its subsidiaries to make charitable donations and provide welfare support to existing and former employees as well as helping charitable organisations. Charitable activities of the trust are split into the following fields:

▶ Welfare
▶ Charitable donations
▶ Staff applications
▶ Named funds

Areas of work

Although the trust was established with general charitable purposes, the trustees have placed priority on the following areas:

▶ Education
▶ Community regeneration, which includes causes relating to older people
▶ Disadvantaged young people
▶ Homelessness with a particular emphasis on day centres

Historically the trust has tried to match its areas of donations to sectors allied to the company's business. The trust supports charitable activity in the areas in which the company operates. This is primarily in the UK, although grants are also awarded to organisations working in Australia and the USA.

Grant-making policy

According to the website donations normally range from £250 to £25,000, with only up to a dozen charities receiving more than £10,000.

As of May 2015, the trust no longer accepts unsolicited applications.

Financial information

In 2016 the trust had assets of £62.3 million and an income of £2.3 million. There were grants awarded during the year totalling £1.6 million, of which £907,000 was awarded to over 50 organisations. Grants made to around 376 individuals totalled £664,000 (most individuals received more than one grant throughout the year).

Beneficiaries included: NWG Network (£79,000); Leap (£50,000); Coram (£40,000); Hertfordshire Groundwork (£37,500); The Prince's Trust (£34,500); Business in the Community (£33,000); Young Enterprise (£30,000); Atlantic College (£26,000); Manchester Settlement (£25,500); Cumbria Community Foundation, Mosaic, The Silverline and Alzheimer's Research UK (£25,000 each).

There are also other four charities set up by the Laing family and administered at the same address – for more information see www.laingfamilytrusts.org.uk.

Exclusions

Grants are not made to individuals or organisations whose main purpose is animal welfare.

Applications

Unsolicited applications are no longer accepted. However, the website does state: 'Minor Grants of up to £1,000 are administered for us by selected Community Foundations granting to small charities operating locally in the following regions: Wiltshire and Swindon; Lancashire and Merseyside; Oxfordshire; Essex; Leicestershire and Rutland.'

The charity takes a pro-active approach in seeking out eligible organisations for its other grant-making activities.

Sources of information
Accounts; annual report; Charity Commission record; funder's website.

Maurice and Hilda Laing Charitable Trust

 Promotion of Christianity, relief in need

UK and overseas

£3.67 million (2016)

CC number: 1058109

Trustees: Andrea Currie; Peter Harper; Simon Martle; Paul van den Bosch; Ewan Harper; Charles Laing; Stephen Ludlow.

Correspondent: Belgin Wingrove, Grants Manager, 33 Bunns Lane, Mill Hill, London NW7 2DX (tel: 020 8238 8890; email: info@laingfamilytrusts.org.uk)

www.laingfamilytrusts.org.uk/maurice_hilda_laing.html

This trust was established in 1996 and is mainly concerned with the advancement of the Christian religion and relieving poverty, both in the UK and overseas. The trust is administered alongside the Beatrice Laing Trust, the Martin Laing Foundation and the Kirby Laing Foundation with which it shares members of staff and office space; collectively they are known as the Laing Family Trusts.

In practice, grants by the trust fall into three main categories:

- **Advancement of the Christian Religion:** to promote Christian faith and values through evangelistic, educational, ministerial and media activities at home and overseas
- **Relief of Poverty in the UK:** to express Christian faith through practical action to help people in need, for example, people with disabilities, homeless individuals, those in ill health, young and older people or people who have offended
- **Relief of Poverty Overseas:** to relieve poverty overseas, with a particular emphasis on helping children who are vulnerable or at risk, advancement of education of women, the quality of health care, HIV/AIDS help and education of children in Africa. In most cases, these grants to overseas projects are made through UK-registered charities which are expected to monitor and evaluate the projects on behalf of the trust, providing progress reports at agreed intervals

Our research indicates that in 2006 the trustees made the decision to work towards winding up the trust by 2020. As such, there will be a controlled increase in the level of future grant expenditure. The trustees are making a number of significant investments to a small number of organisations that they will proactively invite to apply. Charities can still apply for the small grants programme.

Financial information
In 2016 the trust had assets of £24.8 million and an income of £846,000. During the year, a total of 98 awards were made which totalled £3.67 million. Grants were distributed as follows:

Religion	44	£1.6 million
Overseas aid	25	£924,500
Children and youth	5	£498,500
Social welfare	18	£384,000
Miscellaneous	3	£190,000
Health and medicine	3	£84,000

Beneficiaries included: University of Roehampton (£250,000); Fegans Child and Family Care (£176,000); Sue Ryder Care (£25,000); Ethiopiaid (£12,000); Great Lakes Outreach (£10,000); Arundel and Brighton Diocesan Trust (£9,600); Derby City Mission, Friends of the Belarusian Children's Hospice UK, Willowfleld Parish Community Association (£5,000 each).

Exclusions
The trust's website states that in general the following organisations and projects are not supported:

- General appeals or circulars
- Campaigning or lobbying activities
- Umbrella, second tier or grant-making organisations
- Professional associations or projects for the training of professionals
- Feasibility studies and social research
- Individual sponsorship requirements
- Grants to individuals for educational, medical or travel purposes including gap year projects and overseas exchange programmes
- Summer activities for children/young people or after-school clubs
- State maintained or independent schools other than those for pupils with special educational needs
- Uniformed groups such as Scouts and Guides
- Costs of staging one-off events, festivals or conferences
- Animal welfare
- Core running costs of hospices, counselling projects and other local organisations
- Church restoration or repair (including organs and bells)

Applications
An application to any of the four Laing family trusts is considered by all and directed to the most appropriate one. Appeals should be made by post (three to four pages) long providing the following:

- Contact details
- Confirmation of charitable status
- A clear overview of the charity s aims and objectives
- Precise details of the project for which funding is sought including:
  - Project activities
  - Proposed start and end date
  - A detailed budget breakdown
  - Fundraising strategy: anticipated sources of funding, funds already secured, plans for securing the shortfall
  - Arrangements for monitoring and evaluating the project
  - A copy of the charity's most recent annual report and audited accounts.

Applicants should wait at least 12 to 18 months before re-applying following an unsuccessful application.

Sources of information
Accounts; annual report; Charity Commission record; funder's website.

Christopher Laing Foundation

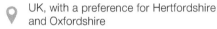 General charitable purposes, arts and culture, sports, environment, health and disability causes. There is a particular preference for organisations supporting adults with disabilities

UK, with a preference for Hertfordshire and Oxfordshire

£423,000 (2016/17)

CC number: 278460

Trustees: Christopher Laing; Diana Laing; Peter Jackson; John Keeble; Michael Laing.

Correspondent: Vince Cheshire, Director of UK Private Client Services, TMF Management (UK) Ltd, 400 Capability Green, Luton, Bedfordshire LU1 3AE (tel: 01582 439200; email: claing_charity@tmf-group.com)

The foundation was established in 1979 by Christopher Laing, a member of the Laing family which is associated with the construction company John Laing plc. Christopher Laing remains on the foundation's board of trustees and is also a trustee of two other grant-making charities associated with members of the Laing family – John Laing Charitable Trust (Charity Commission no. 236852) and The Beatrice Laing Trust (Charity Commission no. 211884).

Areas of work

The foundation has general charitable purposes and, therefore, supports a wide range of charities. The annual report for 2016/17 states:

> At the Trustees' meeting on 28 October 2015, they decided to increase the non-exclusive priorities of the trust to charitable organisations in Hertfordshire and Oxfordshire and to those organisations supporting disabled adults. The Trustees make regular payments to a number of charitable organisations who are invited to apply on an annual basis.

Financial information

In 2016/17 the foundation had assets of £11.5 million and had an income of £404,000. During the year, the foundation awarded a total of £423,000 in grants to organisations. Grants were distributed as follows:

Social welfare	11	£167,500
Children and youth	4	£102,500
Charities Aid Foundation	-	£80,000
Cultural and environmental	3	£72,500

Beneficiaries included: The Silver Line (£75,000); The Duke of Edinburgh's Award (£50,000); Fields in Trust (National Playing Fields Association) (£40,000); Global Action Plan (£20,000); Hertfordshire Groundwork Trust (£12,500); DrugFAM (£5,000).

Exclusions

Grants are only made to registered charities.

Applications

Applications may be made in writing to the correspondent. The annual report for 2016/17 noted: 'An enormous and increasing number of requests for donations are received and unfortunately only a small proportion of these requests can be fulfilled.'

Sources of information

Accounts; annual report; Charity Commission record.

The David Laing Foundation

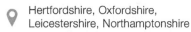

General charitable purposes, arts and culture, social welfare, health, children and young people, religion, sport, overseas aid, children and young people

Hertfordshire, Oxfordshire, Leicestershire, Northamptonshire

(£) £203,000 (2015/16)

CC number: 278462

Trustees: David Laing; Stuart Lewis; Frances Laing; Francis Barlow.

Correspondent: David Laing, Trustee, The Manor House, Grafton Underwood,

Kettering, Northamptonshire NN14 3AA (email: david@david-laing.co.uk)

The foundation was registered with the Charity Commission in 1979 to provide funding for general charitable purposes. The trust has particular favour for projects in the areas of young people; disability; and the arts, and it operates in Hertfordshire, Leicestershire, Northamptonshire, and Oxfordshire.

The 2016/17 annual report states that the foundation intends to continue providing support to the Community Foundations in Northamptonshire and Hertfordshire to reach the needs of local communities.

Financial information

In 2016/17 the foundation had assets of £6.5 million and an income of £198,000. Grants were made totalling £333,000 and were broken down as follows:

General charitable purposes	£95,500
Arts and culture	£61,500
Disability/disadvantage/health/ sickness/medical	£54,000
Social welfare/sports/recreation	£49,000
Children and youth	£38,500
Religion	£31,500
Overseas aid	£3,700

Beneficiaries of over £5,000 included: Northamptonshire Community Foundation (£80,000); Royal and Derngate (£39,000); The Living Room (£30,000); Adrenaline Alley (£20,000); Crusader Community Boating (£15,000); Future Talent (£10,000).

Exclusions

No grants are given to individuals.

Applications

Apply in writing to the correspondent.

Sources of information

Accounts; annual report; Charity Commission record.

The Kirby Laing Foundation

General charitable purposes, arts and culture, health causes and medical research, social welfare, Christian religion, young people, education, overseas aid

Unrestricted, but mainly UK

(£) £3.4 million (2016)

CC number: 264299

Trustees: David Laing; Simon Webley; Revd Charles Burch; Dr Frederick Lewis.

Correspondent: Elizabeth Harley, Trust Director, 33 Bunns Lane, Mill Hill, London NW7 2DX (tel: 020 8238 8890; email: info@laingfamilytrusts.org.uk)

 www.laingfamilytrusts.org.uk

The foundation was established in 1972 by Sir Kirby Laing. The foundation supports a wide range of charities in the UK and abroad, reflecting the personal interests of the founder and the current concerns of the trustees. Particular areas of interest include:

- Promotion of the evangelical Christian faith
- Education, particularly in science and engineering, and youth development
- Medical research, with emphasis on stroke and dementia
- Social and medical welfare projects, especially those benefitting older and disabled people
- Preservation of cultural and environmental heritage, and improving access to the arts for young people and the disabled
- Overseas development projects, largely supported by UK charities

The website states that the trustees are implementing a strategy to spent out their assets, during which time they will seek to identify a small number of partners. These partnerships will be at the invitation of the trust only, however the reactive small grants programme will continue (any grants below £5,000).

Financial information

In 2016 the foundation had assets of £57.4 million and an income of £2.25 million. During the year, the foundation awarded a total of £3.4 million in grants to organisations. Grants were distributed as follows:

Religion	20	£1.7 million
Children and youth	12	£694,000
Cultural and environmental	29	£401,500
Health and medicine	17	£283,000
Social welfare	3	£215,000
Overseas aid	6	£57,500
Charities Aid Foundation	-	£50,000

Beneficiaries included: University of Aberdeen (£1.2 million); St Lawrence College (£500,000); Design Museum (£100,000); Rock UK (£75,000); Parkinson's UK (£50,000); Royal Botanic Gardens Kew (£25,000); Royal Institute of British Architects (£10,000); Raleigh International (£5,000).

Exclusions

The trust's website states that in general the following organisations and projects are not supported:

- General appeals or circulars
- Campaigning or lobbying activities
- Umbrella, second tier or grant-making organisations
- Professional associations or projects for the training of professionals
- Feasibility studies and social research
- Individual sponsorship requirements
- Grants to individuals for educational, medical or travel purposes including gap year projects and overseas exchange programmes
- Summer activities for children/young people or after-school clubs

- State maintained or independent schools other than those for pupils with special educational needs
- Uniformed groups such as Scouts and Guides
- Costs of staging one-off events, festivals or conferences
- Animal welfare
- Core running costs of hospices, counselling projects and other local organisations
- Church restoration or repair (including organs and bells)

While ongoing cost of sustaining core activities is not funded, reasonable level of management costs to cover project overheads, including some employment costs, can be covered.

Applications

An application to any of the four Laing family trusts is considered by all and directed to the most appropriate one. Appeals should be made by post (three to four pages) long providing the following:

- Contact details
- Confirmation of charitable status
- A clear overview of the charity s aims and objectives
- Precise details of the project for which funding is sought including:
  - Project activities
  - Proposed start and end date
  - A detailed budget breakdown
  - Fundraising strategy: anticipated sources of funding, funds already secured, plans for securing the shortfall
  - Arrangements for monitoring and evaluating the project
  - A copy of the charity's most recent annual report and audited accounts

Applicants should wait at least 12 to 18 months before re-applying following an unsuccessful application.

Sources of information

Accounts; annual report; Charity Commission record; funder's website.

The Martin Laing Foundation

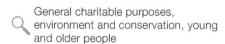

General charitable purposes, environment and conservation, young and older people

UK and worldwide, particularly Malta and Thailand, and Norfolk-based projects

£404,000 (2016/17)

CC number: 278461

Trustees: Edward Laing; Sir Martin Laing; Lady Laing; Nicholas Gregory; Colin Fletcher; Alexandra Gregory; Graham Sillett.

Correspondent: Elizabeth Harley, Trusts Director, 33 Bunns Lane, London

NW7 2DX (tel: 020 8238 8890; email: info@laingfamilytrusts.org.uk)

 www.laingfamilytrusts.org.uk

This foundation was established in 1979 by Sir Martin Laing, a grandson of Sir John Laing. It is one of the Laing Family Trusts, a group which seek to promote the Christian religion and alleviate poverty in the UK and overseas.

The foundation funds organisations and charities which have environmental and conservation-based objectives, or small community projects to benefit disadvantaged young and older people. There is a preference for Norfolk-based charities. A small number of grants are also made to overseas projects in Malta and Thailand.

Financial information

In 2016/17 the foundation held assets of £11 million and had an income of £412,500. Grants totalled £404,000 of which £75,000 was awarded to Charities Aid Foundation (CAF), who made 26 grants on the trust's behalf.

Grants made directly by the Martin Laing Trust were broken down as follows:

Religion	3	£180,000
Overseas development	6	£54,000
Cultural and environmental	5	£35,000
Health and medicine	4	£30,000
Social welfare	4	£25,000
Child and youth	1	£5,000

Donations made via CAF were broken down as follows:

Health and medicine	9	£18,400
Child and youth	6	£17,100
Social welfare	6	£11,500
Cultural and environmental	4	£9,500
Overseas aid	1	£4,000

Beneficiaries included: Diocese in Europe (£170,000 in two grants); East Anglian Air Ambulance, Huntington's Disease Association, Norfolk Wildlife Trust and The Norfolk Churches Trust (£10,000 each); Blue Elephant Theatre, Cromer and District Foodbank and Welsh National Opera (£5,000 each).

Exclusions

According to the foundation's website, the following will not be funded:

- General appeals or circulars
- Campaigning or lobbying activities
- Umbrella, second tier or grant-making organisations
- Professional associations or projects for the training of professionals
- Feasibility studies and social research
- Individual sponsorship requirements
- Grants to individuals for educational, medical or travel purposes including gap year projects and overseas exchange programmes
- Summer activities for children/young people or after-school club

- State maintained or independent schools other than those for pupils with special educational needs
- Uniformed groups such as scouts and guides
- Costs of staging one-off events, festivals or conferences
- Animal welfare
- Core running costs of hospices, counselling projects and other local organisations
- Church restoration or repair (including organs and bells)

Applications

An application to any of the four Laing family trusts is considered by all and directed to the most appropriate one. Appeals should be made by post (three to four pages) long providing the following:

- Contact details
- Confirmation of charitable status
- A clear overview of the charity's aims and objectives
- Precise details of the project for which funding is sought including:
  - Project activities
  - Proposed start and end date
  - A detailed budget breakdown
  - Fundraising strategy: anticipated sources of funding, funds already secured, plans for securing the shortfall
  - Arrangements for monitoring and evaluating the project
  - A copy of the charity's most recent annual report and audited accounts

If you were unsuccessful you should wait about 12 to 18 months before re-applying.

Sources of information

Accounts; annual report; Charity Commission record; funder's website.

The Beatrice Laing Trust

Relief of poverty, advancement of the evangelical Christian faith, social welfare, health causes, overseas aid, disadvantaged individuals, education and training

UK and overseas

£1.7 million (2016/17)

CC number: 211884

Trustees: Christopher Laing; Sir Martin Laing; David Laing; Charles Laing; Paula Blacker; Alex Gregory.

Correspondent: Elizabeth Harley, Trusts Director, 33 Bunns Lane, Mill Hill, London NW7 2DX (tel: 020 8238 8890; email: info@laingfamilytrusts.org.uk)

 www.laingfamilytrusts.org.uk

This trust was established in 1952 by Sir John Laing and his wife, Beatrice, both

now deceased. The trust's main objects are the relief of poverty and the advancement of the evangelical Christian faith in the UK and abroad. It mainly concentrates on small grants for the relief of poverty in its broadest sense.

The Beatrice Laing Trust is one of the Laing Family Trusts and administered alongside the Maurice and Hilda Laing Charitable Trust, the Martin Laing Foundation and the Kirby Laing Foundation with which it shares members of staff and office space.

In addition to the trust's own funds, the trustees are invited to make nominations to the grants committee of the J W Laing Trust, for donations totalling 20% of that trust's income up to a maximum of £400,000 per annum. These funds are used to support the advancement of the evangelical Christian faith through projects of new church building or extension or church mission activities.

Grant-making guidelines

The website details very useful information including the following:

Grant recipients include:

- Organisations, many of them Christian organisations working to express their faith through practical action to help those in need, offering direct support to the most vulnerable and disadvantaged in society, including:
  - homeless people
  - elderly people
  - ex-Service people
  - people who have offended
- Charities providing practical services to people with physical, mental and learning difficulties and their families/carers. Examples include:
  - special schools seeking to develop and expand their facilities in order to enable them to meet the needs of people with increasingly complex disabilities
  - those involved in supporting young people with complex needs in the transition into adulthood, providing supported accommodation and opportunities for training/meaningful employment
  - those seeking to provide facilities for respite care
- Organisations providing opportunities for training and development to young people, in particular those who are disadvantaged or 'at risk'
- Small-scale overseas development projects aiming to build the capacity of local partners to develop long-term sustainable solutions to local problems in countries in the developing world

Financial information

In 2016/17 the trust had assets of nearly £65.1 million and an income of £2.6 million. Grants to 213 organisations totalled almost £1.7 million and were broken down as follows:

Social welfare	88	£552,000
Religion	28	£549,500
Overseas aid	30	£202,000
Health and medicine	42	£230,500
Children and young people, including education	25	£174,500

Beneficiaries included: Diocese in Europe (£200,000); John Trotter Trust and Veterans Aid (£50,000 each); Housing Justice (£40,000); Deafblind Scotland (£25,000); Fiveways School Yeovil (£20,000); Traidcraft Exchange (£15,000); Crime Diversion Team (£10,000); Crisis Centre Ministries (£5,000); YMCA Reading (£2,000).

Exclusions

The trust's website states that in general the following organisations and projects are not supported:

- General appeals or circulars
- Campaigning or lobbying activities
- Umbrella, second tier or grant-making organisations
- Professional associations or projects for the training of professionals
- Feasibility studies and social research
- Individual sponsorship requirements
- Grants to individuals for educational, medical or travel purposes including gap year projects and overseas exchange programmes
- Summer activities for children/young people or after-school clubs
- State maintained or independent schools other than those for pupils with special educational needs
- Uniformed groups such as Scouts and Guides
- Costs of staging one-off events, festivals or conferences
- Animal welfare
- Core running costs of hospices, counselling projects and other local organisations
- Church restoration or repair (including organs and bells)

Applications

An application to any of the four Laing family trusts is considered by all and directed to the most appropriate one. Appeals should be made by post (three to four pages) long providing the following:

- Contact details
- Confirmation of charitable status
- A clear overview of the charity's aims and objectives
- Precise details of the project for which funding is sought including:
  - Project activities
  - Proposed start and end date
  - A detailed budget breakdown

- Fundraising strategy: anticipated sources of funding, funds already secured, plans for securing the shortfall
- Arrangements for monitoring and evaluating the project
- A copy of the charity's most recent annual report and audited accounts

You may also like to provide a list of other supporting documents available on request e.g. annual review, business plan, drawings for capital building projects, etc.

Applicants should wait at least 12 to 18 months before re-applying following an unsuccessful application.

Sources of information

Accounts; annual report; Charity Commission record; funder's website.

The Lake House Charity

 Young people, older people, disability, health, general charitable purposes

 UK

(£) £268,500 (2016/17)

CC number: 1126293

Trustees: Helen Perry; Gerard Maguire; Sarah Mulford; Andrew Butler-Cassar; Timothy Andrew Perry; Marcus Platt.

Correspondent: The Trustees, The Lake House Foundation, Po Box 651, Weybridge KT13 3EP (email: lakehouse.office@googlemail.com)

🌐 www.thelakehouse.org.uk

Established in April 2008 by Helen Perry who is still 'the directional force of the charity, reviewing all request for donations personally'. The objects of this charity are:

The care and support of and the provision of financial support for:

- Disabled and sick children and young people
- Children and young people suffering from emotional distress or from lack of stable family upbringing
- Children and young people suffering from social or educational disadvantages; and
- The relief of poverty and care of older people and the provision of accommodation for older people
- Such general charitable purposes as the trustees determine

The website for this grant-maker states: 'The Lake House Charitable Foundation is run by a group of friends to provide financial assistance for organisations whose primary aims are to support and care for sick and disadvantaged children and young people as well as the elderly.'

Block'em LLP was established by the Lake House Charitable Foundation trustees in which they invested to allow it to develop technologies that aid and help protect the vulnerable in today's society. The applications developed are simple to use and manage and are targeted principally for use with children (preventing cyberbullying) and also adults to use the application to prevent nuisance calls and work place bullying or threatening calls.

Financial information

In 2016/17 the charity had assets of £60,000 and an income of £276,500. It made grants to 30 organisations totalling £268,500.

Beneficiaries included: Chailey Heritage Foundation (£45,000); Shooting Star Chase (£41,000); Ellen Macarthur Cancer Trust (£15,000); Full Circle £10,000); Skill Force (£7,000); Carers Trust (£5,000); Tall Ships Youth Trust (£500).

Exclusions

The trustees review each communication on an individual basis and make a decision based on the suitability of the cause.

Applications

Apply in writing to the correspondent.

Sources of information

Accounts; annual report; Charity Commission record; funder's website.

Lancashire Environmental Fund Ltd

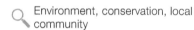 Environment, conservation, local community

 Lancashire (excluding unitary authority districts of Blackpool and Blackburn)

£ £958,500 (2016)

CC number: 1074983

Trustees: Francis McGinty; Geraint Rees; John Drury; Albert Atkinson.

Correspondent: Andy Rowett, Fund Manager, The Barn, Berkeley Drive, Bamber Bridge, Preston PR5 6BY (tel: 01772 317247; fax: 01772 628849; email: general@lancsenvfund.org.uk)

 www.lancsenvfund.org.uk

The Lancashire Environmental Fund (LEF) is a partnership between SUEZ Recycling and Recovery UK Ltd, Lancashire County Council, The Wildlife Trust for Lancashire, Manchester and North Merseyside and Community Futures.

Since its creation in June 1998 the Fund has distributed over £25 million of Landfill Communities Fund (LCF) grants to community and environmental projects which benefit the environment and people of Lancashire. The Fund is

supported financially by SUEZ Recycling and Recovery UK Ltd, Lancashire County Council and various third party funders.

The fund awards grants to environmental projects which meet the criteria specified by the Landfill Tax Regulations 1996, these include:

- The maintenance of public amenities and parks, within ten miles of a landfill site, when the work benefits the natural social or built environment
- The provision, conservation, restoration or enhancement of a natural habitat, maintenance or recovery of a species within ten miles of a landfill site
- The restoration and repair of buildings which are for religious worship, or architectural or historical interest within ten miles of a landfill site

The fund's website states that the fund has supported projects including 'improvements to community facilities, general environmental improvements, creation and management of habitats, improvements to parks, gardens, open spaces, play areas, recreational facilities, ponds, canals and rivers and natural biodiversity'. There are three grants programmes to which community and environmental groups can apply.

- Green Grants of up to £1,000
- Small Grants of up to £15,000
- Main Grants of up to £30,000

A full list of eligibility criteria and guidance notes for all grant programmes are available via the fund's website.

Financial information

In 2016 the charity had assets of £1.68 million and an income of £1.26 million. A total of 71 grants were awarded during the year, amounting £958,500. They were distributed as follows:

Community facility improvements	£447,000
General environmental improvements	£159,500
Play areas and recreational facilities	£339,500
Habitat creation and management	£58,500
Parks, gardens and open spaces	£41,000
Green grants	£10,500

Beneficiaries included: Proffitts CIC (£85,000 in three separate grants); Preston Little Theatre Co. Ltd, Longton Community Church, Community Solutions NW Ltd, Brierfield Methodist Church and St Mary's Church Gossnargh, (£30,000 each); Newground and Crawford Village Playing Fields (£26,500 each); Mid Pennine Arts (£25,000); Playground Upgrade at Bedford Park (£24,000).

Exclusions

For a comprehensive list of exclusions, applicants are advised to refer to the

guidance notes of the specific grant programme to which they intend to apply (available to download via the fund's website). Generally, however, the fund does not award grants for any of the following:

- Core costs of an organisation
- Projects that request 100% wholly revenue cost
- Retrospective funding
- Projects located in libraries; allotments; schools, nurseries and preschools; or the offices of charities, Citizens Advices, or statutory service providers
- Projects that are located in the boroughs of Blackpool and Blackburn with Darwen

Applications

Application forms and guidance notes for Green Grants are available to download via the fund's website. Applicants for Small and Main Grants are asked to first submit an expression of interest form (available to download via the website). Should their initial proposal be successful, they will be invited to submit a full application. The trustees meet on a quarterly basis. Specific information regarding application deadlines and board meeting dates are available via the website.

Potential applicants are strongly advised to visit the website and consider the guidelines before contacting the fund. Further guidance on the Landfill Communities Fund can be obtained from the regulatory body Entrust at www.entrust.org.uk.

Sources of information

Accounts; annual report; Charity Commission record; guidelines for applicants; funder's website.

The Lancashire Foundation

 General charitable purposes with a particular focus on young people and people who are severely disadvantaged

UK and overseas

£ £1.4 million (2016)

CC number: 1149184

Trustees: Michael Connor; Derek Williams; Louise Wells.

Correspondent: Michael Connor, Trustee, Lancashire Insurance Company (UK), Level 29, 20 Fenchurch Street, London EC3M 3BY (tel: 020 7264 4056)

www.lancashiregroup.com/en/ responsibility/lancashire-foundation.html

This foundation is the corporate charity of the Lancashire group of insurance companies which operates in Bermuda and London. It receives its income through an annual donation from the group.

The Lancashire Foundation forms a core part of the group's corporate social responsibility commitments and uses its resources to support local and international communities, with a particular focus on assisting young people and people who are severely disadvantaged.

Areas of support

The Lancashire Holdings Ltd website states:

> The work of the Lancashire Foundation is a crucial component of our corporate social responsibility activity. The Foundation is committed to channelling its resources in an effective way to meet the needs of our local communities and also international communities, and is particularly focused on helping young people and those severely disadvantaged in society. The Foundation recognises the financial pressure that charities face and therefore its donations are generally not tied or restricted to particular programmes or activities. We believe that the benefitting charities themselves are best placed to direct funds in the most efficient and effective way to ensure their sustainability and to meet their beneficiaries' needs. We seek to enter into multi-year arrangements with the charities we support to assist in their sustainability.

The foundation's page on the group's website explains that 'in very exceptional circumstances' additional emergency funding can be provided and that 'in certain circumstances' charities suggested by others in its market place can be supported.

Financial information

In 2016 the foundation had assets of £3.1 million and an income of £446,500. Grants to 58 organisations totalled £1.4 million.

Beneficiaries included: Médecins Sans Frontières (£391,000); St Giles Trust (£101,000); The Family Centre (£77,500); Vauxhall City Farm (£43,000); Ace Africa (£34,000); Medical Detection Dogs (£28,500); Malawi Community Hubs (£20,000); Young Enterprise (£10,000); Action Medical Research (£5,000); Brake and Skiing with Heroes (£2,000 each).

Applications

The foundation principally channels its funding through key partner charities and those nominated by staff of the Lancashire group. Its page on the Lancashire group's website explains that 'Prospective charitable organisations are asked to provide a grant application form to the staff Donations Committee, which considers their funding proposals and, if agreed, provides a

recommendation to the Trustees of the Foundation for their approval to release funds accordingly. Donations Committee members and other members of staff act as advocates for the charitable organisations that the Foundation supports throughout the year'.

Sources of information

Accounts; annual report; Charity Commission record; funder's website.

Duchy of Lancaster Benevolent Fund

General charitable purposes

Lancashire, Greater Manchester and Merseyside, and elsewhere in the country where the Duchy of Lancaster has historical links

£292,000 (2016/17)

CC number: 1026752

Trustees: Warren Smith; Lord Charles Shuttleworth; Chris Adcock; The Hon. Justice Gerald Barling; Robert Miles; Mark Blundell; Michael Stevens.

Correspondent: Timothy Crow, Secretary, 1 Lancaster Place, Strand, London WC2E 7ED (tel: 020 7269 1700; email: info@duchyoflancaster.co.uk)

 www.duchyoflancaster.co.uk

According to its 2016/17 annual report the fund aims to:

> Support charitable causes in the county palatine of Lancaster – the administrative counties of Lancashire, Greater Manchester and Merseyside – and elsewhere in the country where the Duchy has historical links (such as landed interests and the presentation of church livings).

A wide range of charitable causes and organisations are supported each year.

Financial information

In 2016/17 the fund had assets of £14.4 million and an income of £391,000. During the year, 265 grants were made totalling £292,000 and were distributed as follows:

Community help	£132,000
People with disabilities, older people and people who are unwell	£59,500
Religious causes	£55,000
Youth and education	£41,500
Miscellaneous	£3,500

Beneficiaries included: Lancaster International Youth Games and Stanley Grange Community Association (£10,000 each); Birkenhead Youth Club and Moulton College (£2,500 each); Barnardo's, Beanstalk, Contact Hostel and British Red Cross Merseyside (£2,000 each).

The Duchy of Lancaster Jubilee Trust (Charity Commission no. 1085881) is administered from the same address and mainly gives towards the Queen's Chapel of the Savoy.

Applications

Applications need to be made in writing to the appropriate lieutenancy office (see below), at any time. Applications should be by letter, including as much information as possible. All applications are acknowledged.

Lancashire lieutenancy: County Hall, Preston, Lancashire LPRI 8XJ.

Greater Manchester lieutenancy: Gaddum House, 6 Great Jackson Street, Manchester M15 4AX.

Merseyside lieutenancy: PO Box 144, Royal & Sun Alliance Building, New Hall Place, Old Hall Street, Liverpool L69 3EN.

Other grants are administered at the general office in London.

Sources of information

Accounts; annual report; Charity Commission record; funder's website.

Lancaster Foundation

Christianity, social welfare, medical, young people, community development

UK and Africa, with a local interest in Clitheroe

£2.42 million (2016/17)

CC number: 1066850

Trustees: Rosemary Lancaster; Dr John Lancaster; Steven Lancaster; Julie Broadhurst.

Correspondent: Rosemary Lancaster, Trustee, c/o Text House, 152 Bawdlands, Clitheroe, Lancashire BB7 2LA (tel: 01200 444404)

The Lancaster Foundation was established in 1997 by Dr John Lancaster, the founder of Ultraframe Ltd which specialises in the design and manufacture of conservatory roofing systems based in Clitheroe, Lancashire. He remains one of the foundation's trustees, alongside other members of the Lancaster family.

The foundation's annual report for 2016/17 states that:

> The Lancaster Foundation has been founded on Christian principles offering medical and practical support to the suffering, disadvantaged and marginalised people throughout the UK and Africa. Additionally, the foundation is committed to numerous ongoing local and national youth and community projects.

Grants are awarded at the absolute discretion of the trustees, mainly to causes personally known to them. Unsolicited requests are not considered.

Financial information

In 2016/17 the foundation had assets of £56.5 million and an income of £2.87 million. Grants were made to 52 organisations totalling £2.42 million.

Beneficiaries included: Message Trust (£392,000); Mary's Meals (£159,000); New Generation Music and Mission (£120,500); Christchurch Harpurhey (£22,000); Christians Against Poverty (£12,000); Home-Start (£8,000); Hospices of Hope (£3,000); Christian Surfers (£2,000); Children's Air Ambulance and Cancer UK (£1,000 each).

Applications

The trustees' annual report for 2015/16 states that: 'Although many applications are received, the administrative structure of the charity does not allow for the consideration of unsolicited requests for grant funding.'

Sources of information

Accounts; annual report; Charity Commission record.

The Lancaster-Taylor Charitable Trust

Education

UK and overseas

£5.9 million (2016)

CC number: 1106035

Trustees: Lindsay Diane Dodsworth; Steven Lloyd Edwards; Dr Rosalind Anita Jane Smith.

Correspondent: Matthew Derek Pintus, Macfarlanes Solicitors, 20 Cursitor Street, London EC4A 1LT (tel: 020 7831 9222)

The trust was established in 2014 and its 2016/17 annual report states that the: 'primary focus of the trust is currently on making grants to education organisations for the furtherance of educational excellence'. The income and expenditure of the trust varies significantly from year to year as large donations are received and large capital projects are periodically supported.

Financial information

In 2016/17 the trust had assets of £657,000 and an income of £160,000. Grants made during the year totalled £5.9 million. This figure included a large donation of £5.6 million to Murray Edwards College.

Beneficiaries included: Murray Edwards College (£5.6 million); Student Information Services (£204,500); Red Balloon of the Air (£10,000).

Applications

Apply in writing to the correspondent. The trustees meet regularly and decisions are made at trustees' meetings.

Sources of information

Accounts; annual report; Charity Commission record.

LandAid Charitable Trust (Land Aid)

Youth homelessness

UK

£1.3 million (2016/17)

CC number: 295157

Trustees: Robert Bould; Michael Slade; Suzanne Avery; Elizabeth Peace; David Taylor; Lynette Lackey; Timothy Roberts; Mark Reynolds; Alistair Elliot; David Erwin; Scott Parsons; Melanie Leech; Andrew Gulliford.

Correspondent: Grants team, St Albans House, 5th Floor, 57–59 Haymarket, London SW1Y 4QX (tel: 020 3102 7192; email: grants@landaid.org)

www.landaid.org

LandAid is the charity of the property industry which works to the vision of ending youth homelessness in the UK. Its key aims are:

▶ To provide accommodation and support for young people who have been homeless
▶ To profile youth homelessness within the property industry, especially where we can offer young people a platform to have their voices heard

According to its website, support is given in two main ways:

> Awarding 'grants' to exceptional small-medium sized charities working with young people who are at risk of becoming homeless, are currently homeless, or have experienced homelessness in the past. We mainly fund capital projects which provide much-needed homes and stimulating spaces for vulnerable young people.

> Brokering 'free property expertise' for charities working to end youth homelessness, including those supporting disadvantaged young people and children. We match skilled property professionals from our network of partner companies with charities in need of advice on their buildings.

Financial information

In 2016/17 the trust had assets of £743,500 and an income of £2.2 million. Grants awarded to organisations totalled £1.3 million.

Beneficiaries included: Grimsby and Cleethorpes Area Doorstep (£130,000); Depaul UK (£100,000); Methodist

Action (£86,000); New Horizon (£40,000); Homeless Link (£15,000); Housing Associations' Charitable Trust (£5,000).

Applications

In the first instance, visit the LandAid website for full information of the charity's work. Open rounds of applications for funding are advertised online. Decisions are made by the LandAid Grants Committee, which is made up of trustees and representatives of the charity's corporate partners.

Sources of information

Accounts; annual report; Charity Commission record; funder's website.

The Allen Lane Foundation

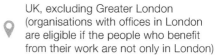

Charities supporting asylum-seekers and refugees, LGBTQ communities, migrant communities, offenders and ex-offenders, older people, people experiencing lasting mental health problems, people experiencing violence or abuse

UK, excluding Greater London (organisations with offices in London are eligible if the people who benefit from their work are not only in London)

£749,000 (2016/17)

CC number: 248031

Trustees: Zoe Teale; Juliet Walker; Fredrica Teale; Margaret Hyde; Philip Walsh; Maurice Frankel.

Correspondent: Gill Aconley, Grants Officer, 90 The Mount, York YO24 1AR (tel: 01904 613223; email: info@ allenlane.org.uk)

 www.allenlane.org.uk

The Allen Lane Foundation is a grant-making trust set up in 1966 by the late Sir Allen Lane, founder of Penguin Books, to support general charitable causes. The foundation has no connection now with the publishing company, but five of the trustees are members of the founder's family.

The foundation wishes to fund work which will make a lasting difference to people's lives rather than simply alleviating the symptoms or current problems, is aimed at reducing isolation, stigma and discrimination and which encourages or enables unpopular groups to share in the life of the whole community. As well as making grants, the foundation also hosts regular lectures in memory of Sir Allen Lane.

Aims

The foundation's website states that it aims to fund work which:

- will make a lasting difference to people's lives rather than simply alleviating the symptoms or current problems
- is aimed at reducing isolation, stigma and discrimination, and
- encourages or enables unpopular groups to share in the life of the whole community

We aim to help organisations to become sustainable, supporting running and core costs to enable them to have flexibility, security and longevity.

Beneficiary groups

The Allen Lane Foundation is interested in funding work which benefits people in the following groups, or generalist work which includes significant numbers from more than one such group:

- Asylum-seekers and refugees
- The travelling community
- Migrant communities
- Offenders and ex-offenders
- Older people
- People experiencing mental health problems
- People experiencing violence or abuse

The foundation focuses on work with adults, rather than children and young people. The website also states that in its most recent review, the trustees have taken the decision that after twenty years directly supporting the LGBT community, it will no longer retain it as one of its specific priorities.

Eligibility

Grants are only awarded to smaller organisations, including registered charities, but also other organisations that are seeking funding for a charitable project, such as constituted voluntary groups and community interest companies. People who we do not fund generally fall into:

Grant purposes

The following information is taken from the website, where further examples are also provided:

We make grants for general running costs, core costs, or specific project costs. We can also offer funding for start-up costs.

Our grants are relatively modest. The average award is around £5,000–£6,000. You can apply for funding to a maximum of £15,000 – but this is generally only offered to larger organisations.

The Foundation makes single grants, or grants split over two or three years.

If you have received a grant from us previously, you will need to wait at least 12 months following the end of the grant period before applying to us again.

Financial information

In 2016/17 the foundation had assets of £21.1 million and an income of £743,500. During the year, the foundation awarded 135 grants to organisations totalling around £749,500. The foundation's 2016/17 accounts state that 'around a third of grants offered were to organisations previously funded by the foundation'.

Beneficiaries included: Open Gate and Women's Breakout (£15,000 each); Centre for Peaceful Solutions (£14,900); CHAS Bristol (£12,000); Criminal Justice Alliance (£10,000); Futures Unlocked (£8,000); Good Morning Down (£6,000); Kilmarnock Road Children and Young People Family Centre (£5,000); LGBT Fed (£2,100); Mind Dorset (£1,000); Seniors Men's and Women's Forum (£500).

Exclusions

The following information has been taken from the foundation's website:

The foundation will not consider applications from the following groups:

- Children and young people, or families
- Individuals
- People with particular medical conditions or disorders
- People with physical or learning disabilities
- People suffering or recovering from addiction, alcohol or drug misuse
- Single nationality community groups

Grants are not awarded for the following activities:

- Animal welfare or animal rights
- Annual or one-off events or festivals
- Capital grants
- Endowments or contributions to other grant-making bodies
- General arts or cultural or language projects
- General health or healthcare
- Holidays or holiday play-schemes or day-trips
- Medical research
- Museums or galleries
- One-to-one general counselling
- Overseas travel
- Private and/or mainstream education
- Property purchase, building or refurbishment
- Publications
- Restoration or conservation of historic buildings or sites
- Sports and recreation
- University or postgraduate education
- Vehicle purchase
- Work which with Trustees believe is rightly the responsibility of the state
- Work which will already have taken place before a grant is agreed

Applications

There is no formal application form, but there is a short registration form, available from the foundation's website. Applications should be made in writing (no more than four sides of A4); details of what should be included are specified on the website. The foundation welcomes contact from potential applicants by telephone or email to discuss making an application.

The trustees meet to award grants three times a year, usually in February, June and October. Applicants should allow between two and six months for an application to be processed. The foundation will be in touch within two weeks of receiving an application to request further information, to set out a schedule for the next stage of assessment, or to notify that the application has been unsuccessful. The website states that 'any group or organisation wishing to discuss applications to benefit LGBT communities should contact Tim Cutts at the Foundation – tim@allenlane.org.uk'.

Sources of information

Accounts; annual report; Charity Commission record, funder's website.

The LankellyChase Foundation

 Prevention of homelessness, substance abuse, violence and abuse, people with mental or physical disabilities, social welfare, women and girls, ethnic minorities

UK

£4.87 million (2016/17)

CC number: 1107583

Trustees: Marion Janner; Morgag Burnett; Hilary Bunrnett; Jane Millar; Simon Tucker; Oliver Batchelor; Jacob Hayman; Darren Murinas; Robin Tuddenham; Myron Kellner-Rogers.

Correspondent: Robert Mclaurin, Greenworks, Dog and Duck Yard, Princeton Street, London WC1R 4BH (tel: 020 3747 9930; email: enquiries@lankellychase.org.uk)

 www.lankellychase.org.uk

 @lankellychase

The LankellyChase Foundation was established in 2004 following the amalgamation of two grant-making trusts, the Lankelly Foundation and the Chase Charity. The foundation's mission is to bring about change that will transform the quality of life of people who face severe and multiple disadvantages, meaning the persistent clustering of severe social harms, particularly homelessness, substance misuse, mental and physical illness, extreme poverty and violence and abuse.

Grant-making policy

The foundation has recently re-evaluated its grants policy, and is currently moving away from traditional grant-making to working in partnership with selected organisations that match its charitable aims. The foundation has details of its current partnerships listed on its website (lankellychase.org.uk/partnerships).

According to its 2016/17 accounts, the foundation's current activities are guided by four strategic objectives:

- **People:** to shape the prevailing view of disadvantage by revealing its interlocking nature, enabling people to describe themselves in their own terms and creating a litmus test for the reach and effectiveness of public systems.
- **Support:** to promote continual improvement and innovation in the support networks available to people facing severe disadvantage.
- **Systems:** to promote the systems conditions that help people who face severe and multiple disadvantage to be part of support networks.
- **Lankelly Chase:** to be an organisation that lives by its values

Financial information

In 2016/17 the foundation had assets of £145.8 million and an income of £3.67 million. During the year, the foundation awarded grants totalling £4.87 million.

Beneficiaries included: Goldsmiths University of London (£175,000); Advice UK (£133,500); Centre for Local Economic Strategies (£44,000); Locality (£40,000); Birmingham Community Healthcare NHS Foundation Trust (£22,500); Arts at the Old Fire Station (£10,000); Centre for Criminal Appeals (£5,300).

Applications

The foundation's website provides the following information: 'We are currently not investing in new funding relationships. We are spending more time with existing partners to change the systems that perpetuate severe and multiple disadvantage.'

The foundation asks organisations interested in its work to keep up-to-date through its website and on Twitter. Organisations are welcome to email the foundation if they have any specific queries.

Sources of information

Accounts; annual report; Charity Commission record; funder's website.

Largsmount Ltd

 The advancement of the Orthodox Jewish religion, the relief of poverty

 UK and overseas, namely Israel

£ £585,000 (2016)

CC number: 280509

Trustees: Simon Kaufman; Naomi Kaufman.

Correspondent: Simon Kaufman, Trustee, 50 Keswick Street, Gateshead NE8 1TQ (tel: 0191 490 0140)

This charity was established in 1979 and makes grants in line with its objects, which are: the advancement of religion in accordance with the Orthodox Jewish faith; and the relief of poverty.

The trustees' report for 2016 states: 'The charity accepts applications for grants from representatives of Orthodox Jewish charities. The Trustees consider all requests which they receive and make donations based on the level of funds available.'

Financial information

In 2016 the charity had assets of £4.7 million and an income of £956,000. Grants made during the year totalled £585,000. Donations of less than £10,000 were not listed in the accounts and totalled £17,500.

Beneficiaries included: M O Charitable Trust (£150,000); C E K Stern Charitable Trust, H P Charitable Trust and S C K Charitable Trust (£60,000 each); Friends of Wiznitz Ltd (£40,000).

Applications

Applications should be made in writing to the correspondent.

Sources of information

Accounts; annual report; Charity Commission record.

The Basil Larsen 1999 Charitable Trust

 General charitable purposes

 UK

£ £21.05 million (2016/17)

CC number: 1080493

Trustees: Mary Jane Pugsley; Bob Wightman.

Correspondent: Bob Wightman, Trustee, High House, Highlands Road, Reigate, Surrey RH2 0LA (email: bazzaschazza@hotmail.com)

The Basil Larsen 1999 foundation was established in 1999 by businessman Basil Larsen, who ran Scottish operation of the Bison concrete company and helped to develop its revolutionary construction patents. Following the death of Mr Larsen in 2014, the trust was endowed with £25 million (the majority of the businessman's fortune).

In the trust's 2016/17 accounts, it is explained that at 'recent trustee meetings, the trustees have focused their grant making on the large household named charities in the United Kingdom and intend to continue with that focus'.

The trust does not actively fundraise and seeks to continue its charitable purposes through the careful management of its existing resources.

Financial information

In 2016/17 the trust had assets of £30.26 million and an income of £1.36 million. During the year, the trust awarded grants to eight organisations totalling £21.05 million.

Beneficiaries included: British Heart Foundation, Cancer Research UK, Parkinson's UK, Prostrate Cancer UK, RNLI, Royal Marsden Hospital (£3 million each); Macmillan Cancer Support (£2.8 million); Battersea Dogs and Cats Home (£250,000).

Applications

The trustees do not consider unsolicited applications for funding.

Sources of information

Accounts; annual report; Charity Commission record.

The Lauffer Family Charitable Foundation

 Jewish causes, general charitable purposes

Commonwealth countries, Israel and USA

£ £485,000 (2016/17)

CC number: 251115

Trustees: Jonathan Lauffer; Robin Lauffer; Gideon Lauffer.

Correspondent: The Trustees, Clayton Stark & Co., 5th Floor, Charles House, 108–110 Finchley Road, London NW3 5JJ (tel: 020 7431 4200; email: jonathanlauffer13@gmail.com)

The foundation was created in 1965 and seeks to support general charitable purposes in the UK, any British Commonwealth territory, Israel, and the USA. Beneficiaries mainly include Jewish organisations; however, the annual report for 2016/17 states that all applications will be considered for funding by the trustees.

Financial information

In 2016/17 the foundation had assets of £5.7 million and had an income of £176,000. During the year, the foundation awarded 181 grants to organisations totalling around £435,000. Grants were distributed as follows:

Welfare and care of children and families	65	£149,000
Religious activities	23	£104,000
Education	38	£119,000
Medical health care	28	£31,500
Recreation and culture	23	£30,500
Environment	4	£700

Beneficiaries included: KCT (£66,500); Kehal Charedim Trust (£20,000); Tel Aviv University Trust (£18,700); Camp Simcha (£6,200); Hendon Reform Synagogue (£5,000); Teenage Cancer Trust (£4,100); Side by Side (£3,000); J Roots (£2,100); The National Holocaust Centre (£1,000).

There were 64 grants made below £1,000 which totalled almost £17,200.

Exclusions

Individuals are excluded.

Applications

Apply in writing to the correspondent; applications are considered once a year.

Sources of information

Accounts; annual report; Charity Commission record.

The Kathleen Laurence Trust

Health care, medical research, older people, children and young people

UK

£254,000 (2016/17)

CC number: 296461

Trustee: Coutts & Co.

Correspondent: Trust Manager, Coutts & Co., Trustee Department, 6th Floor, Trinity Quay 2, Avon Street, Bristol BS2 0PT (tel: 0345 304 2424; email: couttscharities@coutts.com)

The trust was founded in 1987 and supports general charitable purposes in the UK. There is some preference for medical research charities and organisations working with children and older people.

Financial information

In 2016/17 the trust held assets of £983,500 and had an income of £68,500. Grants were made to 65 organisations and totalled £254,000. The amounts given to each organisation were not specified but grants ranged from £500 to £25,000.

Beneficiaries included: Arthritis Care; British Heart Foundation; Child Bereavement UK; Children's Safety Education Foundation; Dun Runnin Rehoming Kennels; Independent Age; St George's Hospital Charity; The Movement Foundation; Young Kent.

Applications

Apply in writing to the correspondent.

Sources of information

Accounts; Charity Commission record.

The Law Family Charitable Foundation

General charitable purposes including: education, health, disability, the arts

Worldwide

£4 million (2016/17)

CC number: 1141997

Correspondent: Marie Metcalfe, c/o Caxton Europe LLP, 40 Berkeley Square, London W1J 5AL (tel: 020 7647 4057)

www.lawfamilycharitablefoundation.org

The Law Family Charitable Foundation was established in 2011 by Andrew and Zoë Law. Andrew is the Chair and CEO of Caxton Associates, a global macro hedge fund. Zoë has previously worked in the music and make-up industries and currently works as a photographer.

The foundation supports causes that are important to the founders. These include education, health, disability, and the arts.

Financial information

In 2016/17 the foundation held assets of £46 million and had an income of £28.8 million. Grants to 19 organisations totalled £4 million.

Beneficiaries included: Law Family Educational Trust (£2.9 million); Speakers for Schools (£250,000); Christie Charitable Fund (£200,000); Policy Exchange (£60,000); Hotcourses Foundation (£28,000); Outward Bound Trust (£5,000); Pink Ribbon Foundation (£500); Portsmouth Down's Syndrome Association (£100).

Applications

Apply in writing to the correspondent.

Sources of information

Accounts; annual report; Charity Commission record; funder's website.

The Betty Lawes Foundation

General charitable purposes

UK and overseas

£291,000 (2016)

CC number: 274025

Trustees: Margaret Lee; Stephen Lewin; Jane Neville.

Correspondent: Stephen Lewin, Bircham Dyson Bell, 50 Broadway, London SW1H 0BL (tel: 020 7227 7000)

The foundation was established in 1977 and makes grants throughout the UK and overseas.

Its Charity Commission record states:

> It is a grant-making charity which supports appeals and not-for-profit organisations where donations will have a real and immediate impact. [The trustees] prefer smaller charitable institutions and specialised or local branches of larger charitable institutions. However, at present unsolicited applications are not being considered.

Financial information

In 2016 the foundation had assets of £5.25 million and an income of £276,500. Grants awarded to organisations totalled £291,000.

Beneficiaries included: Humanitus Charity (£30,000); Moorfields Eye Hospital (£25,000); 1,000 Hills Community Helpers (£23,000); Farm Inspiration Trust (£10,000); Winter Comforts for the Homeless (£5,000); Winston's Wish (£2,000); Orthopaedic Research UK (£1,000).

Applications

Apply in writing to the correspondent.

Sources of information

Accounts; annual report; Charity Commission record.

The Edgar E Lawley Foundation

Medical research and education; medical care/treatment; older people; education in relation to the arts, commerce and industry; children and young people; community; disability; general charitable purposes

UK, with a preference for the West Midlands

£214,500 (2016/17)

CC number: 201589

Trustees: John Cooke; Philip Cooke; Frank Jackson.

Correspondent: Frank Jackson, Trustee, PO Box 456, Esher KT10 1DP (tel: 01372 805760; email: edgarelawley@gmail.com)

 www.edgarelawleyfoundation.org.uk

This foundation was established in 1961 by a gift from the late Edgar E Lawley. It has general charitable purposes but in particular supports organisations working in the areas of medicine, older people in need and education in relation to the arts, commerce and industry.

The foundation's area of benefit is unrestricted within the UK but it has traditionally provided particular assistance to smaller charities in the West Midlands.

The trustees prefer to award unrestricted funding, typically in the region of £1,500 per organisation, to smaller charities and non-profit organisations.

Financial information

In 2016/17 the foundation had assets of £4.85 million and an income of £206,000. Grants were made to 143 organisations and totalled £214,500.

During the year, grants were awarded in six broad areas, which were: medical, research and other miscellaneous projects; hospices; older people; children and young people; community; and disability.

Beneficiaries included: Age Concern Birmingham; Coventry Resource Centre for the Blind; Home-Start Walsall; Lambeth Mencap; Maryvale Community Project; MND Association Birmingham and Solihull; Salvation Army; Woodford Village Hall.

Exclusions

Appeals from and on behalf of individuals are not considered.

Applications

Application forms and full guidance can be downloaded from the website or requested from the foundation by email or post (together with an sae). The completed form can be returned along with any supporting information by email or post between 1 August and 31 October. The foundation's website notes that because it is the trustees' preference to award unrestricted grants, 'significant amounts of project data are not required to be submitted with grant applications'. The trustees make grant decisions in January. The foundation's website notes that it receives more than 800 requests per year but can only fund approximately 125 of them.

Sources of information

Accounts; annual report; Charity Commission record; funder's website.

The Raymond and Blanche Lawson Charitable Trust

 Arts and heritage, education, environment, health, social and economic disadvantage

 Kent and Sussex

£ £5.1 million (2016/17)

CC number: 281269

Trustees: Philip Thomas; Sarah Hill; Michael Norrie; Jennifer Thomas.

Correspondent: The Trustees, Riverside Business Centre, River Lawn Road, Tonbridge, Kent TN9 1EP (email: enquiries@lawsontrust.co.uk)

www.lawsontrust.org

The Raymond and Blanche Lawson Charitable Trust was established in 1980.

The trust has a preference for local organisations and its five key funding priorities are:

- Arts and heritage
- Education
- Environment
- Health
- Social and economic disadvantage

The trust supports the running costs of smaller charities. However the trustees are unlikely to support large national charities with overheads, preferring to devote funds to a specific project or intervention.

Financial information

In 2016/17 the trust had assets of £23.1 million and an income of £263,500. Grants awarded to organisations totalled £5.1 million.

Previous beneficiaries have included: Canine Partners, Crisis and Young Lives Foundation (£2,500 each); Kenward Trust, Teenage Cancer Charity and The Trinity Hospice (£2,000 each); Ambitious about Autism, Create Arts, Footsteps International, Jubilee Sailing Trust, Marie Curie Cancer Care and Meningitis Now (£1,000 each); British Trust for Ornithology, Great Ormond Street Hospital Charity and Let's Face It (£500 each).

Exclusions

The trust does not support:

- Individuals
- Non-registered charities
- Overseas charities
- Political parties
- Endeavours to promote religion

Applications

Applicants based in Kent seeking funding of up to £5,000 can apply to the Lawson Endowment for Kent. Further information on this fund can be found on the Kent Community Foundation's website.

The trust also has an endowment with Sussex Community Foundation. Applicants based in Sussex with an annual income of under £1 million can apply to the foundation for a grant.

National charities or charities outside the criteria for the two community foundations can apply via the trust's online application process.

Applicants should first complete the eligibility checker on the trust's website. Eligible organisations will then be provided with a link to the online application form. Applications can be made at any time as the trustees meet four times per year. Check the trust's website for meeting dates.

Sources of information

Accounts; annual report; Charity Commission record.

The Leathersellers' Company Charitable Fund

 General charitable purposes

 UK, particularly London

£ £2.2 million to organisations (2016/17)

CC number: 278072

Trustees: David Santa-Olalla; The Leathersellers Company.

Correspondent: David Santa-Olalla, Trustee, 7 St Helen's Place, London EC3A 6AB (tel: 020 7330 1444; email: dmsantao@leathersellers.co.uk)

www.leathersellers.co.uk

The fund was registered with the Charity Commission in 1979. The following is taken from the fund's website:

> The Leathersellers' Company is one of the ancient livery companies of the City of London, ranked fifteenth in the order of precedence. It was founded by royal charter in 1444 with authority to control the sale of leather within the City. The company no longer has this regulatory role, and instead devotes its energies to support for charity, education and the British leather trade.

The Company particularly welcomes applications that support the use of leather within the fashion industry, education in leather technology and the leather trade, and those working for the benefit of people in Greater London. The fund's website states: 'Last year (2016/17) we awarded £2,000,000 in charitable and educational grants. This year (2017/18) we expect to spend over £2,300,000 on deserving causes.'

Special projects, capital grants and core costs such as salaries, rent and utilities can be funded. Applicants can apply for up to four years of funding.

Grant-making programmes

Charitable grants are one of two types; a single grant or a multi-year grant. All multi-year grants are subject to annual review. The Leathersellers' Company Charitable Fund operate two grant-giving programmes for charities:

Small grants programme

The small grants programme is a fast-track grant assessment for one-off grants of up to £3,000. Applicants can expect a result within six weeks of making an application.

Main grants programme

The main grants programme is a far more thorough assessment for single and multi-year grants of £5,000 or more. A successful application can take up to nine months to receive a result.

Preference is given to London-based or national charities.

Financial information

In 2016/17 the fund held assets of £62.9 million and had an income of £1.7 million. During the year, the fund awarded a total of 384 grants totalling £2.4 million. Of this amount, £2.2 million was given in 290 grants to organisations, and £178,000 was given in 94 grants to individuals under the Leathersellers' University Exhibitions Scheme. Grants were distributed as follows:

Education	33%	£814,000
Advice and support	10%	£250,000
Disability	15%	£370,000
Leather industry-associated causes	8%	£186,000
Recreational	6%	£160,000
Medicine and health	6%	£140,000
Criminal justice and rehabilitation	5%	£123,000
Homelessness	7%	£167,000
Heritage and environment	3%	£75,000
Creative arts	4%	£92,000
Services support and rehabilitation	3%	£78,000

Beneficiaries included: Colfie's School (£313,000); Leathersellers Federation of Schools (£75,000); Beyond Autism (£40,000); FareShare (£20,000); Addiction NI (£15,000).

Grants under £15,000 totalled £962,000.

Applications

Applicants can be made using the online form on the Company's website. Applicants to the small grants programme can usually expect a decision to have been made within six weeks. Successful applicants to the main grants programme will typically have to pass through a four-stage process, which can take up to nine months:

1 Initial assessment: applicants will hear whether they have been successful or unsuccessful within six weeks or that it will go before the grants committee

2 Consideration by the grants committee: the committee meets three times a year to consider applications to the main grants programme

3 Charities grant working group assessment: applicants may be visited for a detailed assessment

4 Charities grants committee decision: a final decision will be made following a report from the working group.

Only one application can be made in a year. If a charity is in receipt of a multi-year grant or a large single-year grant, then it cannot apply for another grant for four years.

Sources of information

Accounts; annual report; Charity Commission record; funder's website.

The Leche Trust

 Preservation and conservation of art and architecture, historic collections and church furnishings, performing arts

UK

£200,500 to organisations (2016/17)

CC number: 225659

Trustees: Martin Williams; Lady Anne Greenstock; Ariane Bankes; Caroline Laing; Thomas Howard; Robin Dhar.

Correspondent: Rosemary Ewles, 105 Greenway Avenue, London E17 3QL (tel: 020 3233 0023; email: info@ lechetrust.org)

 www.lechetrust.org

The trust was founded and endowed by the late Mr Angus Acworth in 1950. It provides support to organisations in two main areas: performing arts and conservation.

The following information has been taken from the trust's website:

Performing Arts

The Trustees' priorities for music, theatre and dance are:

▸ excellence in professional performance
▸ new work, and
▸ development of young, professional artists aged 18 or over

Conservation

The Trustees support projects to conserve historic objects, collections and features of buildings and landscapes which date from the Georgian period or earlier, i.e. pre-1830s.

Projects may include acquisition costs (for objects) and conservation surveys as well as remedial work. Trustees are inclined to give grants to smaller projects, or specific elements of projects, where their contribution can make a greater impact.

In the case of churches, Trustees will consider supporting the conservation of such features as monuments, wall paintings, stained glass, and historic furniture and fittings.

Grants are also made to overseas PhD students from Developing Countries who find themselves in unforeseeable financial difficulty during the final six months of their course at a UK university. Grants are made towards living costs, not tuition fees, and the typical size of grant offered is £500 to £1,000. A list of countries is available to download from the trust's website.

Financial information

In 2016/17 the trust had assets of £6.8 million and an income of £87,000. Grants awarded to organisations totalled £200,500 with a further £48,500 awarded to individuals.

Arts	£99,000
Historic objects and collections	£45,000
Historic buildings	£36,000
Churches	£22,500

Beneficiaries included: Royal Pavilion and Museums (£6,000); The Landmark Trust (£4,000); Hay Castle Trust and Music for Youth (£2,500 each); Donmar Warehouse and Hexham Abbey (£2,000 each); Orchestra of the Swan and Southbank Sinfonia (£1,000 each).

Exclusions

The trust's general exclusions are:

▸ Schools or school buildings
▸ Student tuition fees
▸ Social welfare projects
▸ Natural environment or wildlife projects
▸ Buildings and objects in private ownership
▸ Projects promoting religion
▸ Health and medicine

Each area of work also has its own specific exclusions.

Applications

There is no formal application form and requests should be addressed in writing to the correspondent by post or email. Full details of what should be included in written applications can be found on the trust's website.

Sources of information

Accounts; annual report; Charity Commission record; funder's website.

The William Leech Charity

 Health and welfare in the north east of England, overseas aid

Northumberland, Tyne and Wear, Durham and overseas

£271,000 (2016/17)

CC number: 265491

Trustees: Adrian Gifford; Roy Leech; Richard Leech; Sir N. Sherlock; David Stabler; Barry Wallace; Revd Prof. David Wilkinson.

Correspondent: Kathleen Smith, Secretary, Diocese of Hexham & Newcastle, St Cuthberts House, West Road, Newcastle NE15 7PY (tel: 0191 243 3300; email: enquiries@ williamleechcharity.org.uk)

www.williamleechcharity.org.uk

William Leech started out as an apprentice and went on to lead large-scale building operations providing affordable housing for sections of society who had not been able to contemplate home ownership previously. In 1972 Sir William Leech set up The William Leech Property Trust (now The William Leech

Charity) and donated to it some 300 tenanted properties, the income from which was to be distributed in accordance with his guidelines.

The charity supports projects that primarily benefit people of the North East in the counties of Northumberland, Tyne and Wear and Durham. Grants may be considered for other areas if there is a substantial connection with the settlor or a local organisation.

Grant-making policy

The following information has been taken from the charity's website:

Geographical Area

Grants are normally made to organisations for work in the counties of Northumberland, Tyne and Wear and Durham. Grants for other areas are sometimes made if there is a substantial connection with the Settlor or a local organisation.

Preferred Categories

To encourage local and community-spirited people to create and sustain interest in voluntary charitable work.' 1. Organisations in which a high proportion of the work is undertaken by voluntary, unpaid workers. 2. Organisations with a close connection to the Settlor, or with districts in which William Leech (Builders) Ltd, built houses during the time when the Settlor was active in business. 3. Organisations with an active Christian involvement 4. Organisations working in deprived areas for the benefit of local people, especially those which encourage people to help themselves. 5. Organisations doing practical, new work and putting new ideas into action.

Financial information

In 2016/17 the charity had assets of £19 million and an income of £521,000. Grants to 76 organisations totalled £271,000.

Beneficiaries included: Newcastle upon Tyne Hospitals (£100,000); The Peoples Kitchen (£15,000); St Oswald's Hospice (£10,000); The Peru Mission (£5,000); Action for Children (£2,500); Children North East (£2,000); Breast Cancer Now (£500).

Exclusions

The charity's website provides the following information on exclusions:

The following will not generally receive grants. The chairman and secretary are instructed to reject them without reference to the trustees, unless there are special circumstances.

- Community care centres and similar (exceptionally, those in remote country areas may be supported)
- Running expenses for youth clubs (as opposed to capital projects)
- Running expenses of churches – this includes normal repairs, but churches engaged in social work, or using their buildings largely for 'outside' purposes may be supported

- Sport
- The arts
- Applications from individuals
- Organisations which have been supported in the last 12 months. It would be exceptional to support an organisation in two successive years, unless we had promised such support in advance
- Holidays, travel, outings
- Minibuses (unless over 10,000 miles per annum is expected)
- Schools
- Housing associations

Applications

The following information has been taken from the charity's website:

As it is the intention of the Trustees to favour support for those charities who help others by utilising the generous time and skills of volunteers, they accept applications in the short form of a letter, rather than expecting the completion of a complicated application form, which may seem daunting to some applicants.

In order to safeguard our Charity Status, it is important that we are accountable for how funds are distributed. As such, the following protocols exist for making and investigating applications.

Your applications must include:-

1. A Description of the project that the Charity is undertaking, who it hopes to help, and any evidence which will support the need for this particular project.

2. How much the project will cost, capital and revenue, with an indication of the amounts involved.

3. How much the charity has raised so far, and where it expects to find the balance.

4. The type of support sought; i.e. small grant, multiple grant, loan, etc.

5. How much does it cost to run the charity each year, including how much of the revenue is spent on salaries and employees.

Where does the revenue come from? How many paid workers are there, how many volunteers are there.

Low priority application

Applications maybe submitted via this form by filling in the details required and clicking the email button, or may be submitted by letter.

Proposed grant up to £1,000 or loan up to £10,000.

Applications for this amount must be submitted in writing to our Saville Chambers address. To aid the application process, you may simply fill in the Form below. Clicking the Print button will then Print off a letter in the correct format for submission. This letter must be printed on your letterhead. The letter must be signed. One or more of the Trustees will contact you to enquire about your application.

Please ensure you provide proof of your Registered Charity status in the application. Please ensure you have a printer installed on your computer before selecting this option.

For amounts over £5,000 trustees would need to see audited accounts

For Amounts £5000+, trustees would require to see audited accounts

Amounts over £10,000, you may follow the same process as above for the letter. Your application must be accompanied by relevant supporting documentation.

Please ensure you provide proof of your Registered Charity status in the application.

For applications of this level, full papers will be circulated to the Trustees to be discussed and approved.

Postal applications should be addressed to: Mrs Kathleen Smith, The William Leech Charity, Saville Chambers, 5 North Street, Newcastle upon Tyne NE1 8DF.

Sources of information

Accounts; annual report; Charity Commission record; funder's website.

The Legal Education Foundation

Legal education, access to employment in the legal profession, public understanding of the law, the use of technology in legal education, research into the above objectives

UK

£4.9 million (2016/17)

CC number: 271297

Trustees: Jane Reeves; Mark Harding; Edward Nally; Guy Beringer; Roger Finbow; Sally James; Timothy Dutton; Ailsa Beaton; Rupert Baron; Jonathan Freeman; David Armstrong.

Correspondent: Alan Humphreys, Deputy Chief Executive, Suite 2, Ground Floor, River House, Broadford Park, Shalford, Guildford, Surrey GU4 8EP (tel: 020 3005 5692; email: alan. humphreys@thelef.org)

 thelegaleducationfoundation.org

The origins of The Legal Education Foundation date back to the 1870s. Its purpose is 'to promote the advancement of legal education and the study of the law in all its branches'. The foundation does this by making grants to a wide variety of mostly charitable organisations working in different social, professional and academic settings and by commissioning research.

Grant-making policy

The trustees will only consider requests for funding which cover one or more of the foundation's following strategic objectives:

- To increase public understanding of the law and the capability to use it
- To advance high quality thinking, training and practice in legal

THE LEGAL EDUCATION FOUNDATION

Advance high quality thinking and practice in legal education and legal services so as to ensure legal needs are met	*Total: £1.9 million*
Legal skills and knowledge of people working in the law	£1.4 million
Developing income streams for legal services	£308,000
Legal skills and knowledge of law students	£102,000
Related research	£45,000
Increase public understanding of the law and the capability to use it	*Total: £1.5 million*
General public	£704,000
Staff in voluntary sector	£397,000
Users of advice organisations	£289,000
Young people	£187,000
Related research	£12,000
Increase access to employment in the legal profession and, in particular, advice social mobility and diversity	*Total: £1.5 million*
Increase in access to employment for law students	£1.2 million
Increase in access to employment for those from less advantaged backgrounds	£265,000

education and legal services so as to ensure legal needs are met

▶ To increase access to employment in the legal profession and, in particular, to advance social mobility and diversity

The foundation has also identified the following themes of focus and interest where applications are encouraged on its website:

1   To explore the implications of the vote for Brexit for the areas covered by our strategic objectives

2   To develop the role of social welfare legal advice needs in health settings through legal education with health professionals and development of models to expand the provision of services

Financial information

In 2016/17 the foundation held assets of £250 million and had an income of £3.9 million. During the year, the foundation had a total grant expenditure of £4.9 million. The breakdown of grants is shown in the table above.

Beneficiaries included: Law Centres Network (£302,000); The Baring Foundation (£200,000); National Family Mediation (£196,000); St Oswald's Hospice (£90,000); UCL Centre for Access to Justice (£65,000); Scottish Refugee Council (£45,000); Integrated Educations Fund – Hazelwood Integrated College (£2,000).

Exclusions

The foundation's website highlights areas which are unlikely to meet the criteria:

▶ Funding of existing mainstream academic activities or facilities in schools, universities or other educational institutions, unless it is innovative in terms of delivery or access

▶ Provision of bursaries which do not bring the possibility of structural or cultural change on the part of the institutions involved

▶ Small-scale interventions which are not subsequently scalable

▶ Funding which is likely to be viewed as a substitute for government or legal profession funding

▶ Initiatives covered by other organisations

The foundation will not support individuals or work outside the UK.

Applications

Apply on a form available from the foundation's website. The website states the following information:

For grant requests up to £100,000 there is a single-stage application process. Applicants are invited to submit applications early in order that any more detailed or missing information can be sought well before the Grants Committee meeting date.

For grant requests of £100,000 or more, an initial application must be made at least 2 months before the deadline. This is to allow for discussion with intending applicants.

We are happy to discuss proposals for funding but please note that having a discussion with staff is not a guarantee that any application will go on to be awarded a grant by the Governors. The Foundation always receives more requests than can be funded out of the available budget.

A grant timetable is posted on the foundation's website, with up-to-date application deadlines.

Sources of information

Accounts; annual report; Charity Commission record; funder's website.

The Lehman Brothers Foundation Europe

○ Children and young people, education, health

○ UK and overseas

(£) £399,500 (2016/17)

CC number: 1088535

Trustees: Peter Sherratt; John Phizackerley; Lisa Greenway; Calvert Burkhart; Ruggero Magnoni; Emily Everard Upton.

Correspondent: Emily Upton, Trustee, 25 Canada Square, London E14 5LQ

The Lehman Brothers Foundation Europe is a grant-making charity run by former employees of Lehman Brothers on a voluntary basis.

It was originally established as part of the charitable programme of Lehman Brothers. After the financial crash in 2008, several employees decided to continue the work of the charitable programmes already in place, and if possible, make new grants.

A new programme of grants has recently been established, through which the trustees intend to support charities with a focus on children, education or health. The trustees have also stated their intention to support appropriate and impactful philanthropic activities by other former Lehman employees.

Financial information

In 2016/17 the charity had assets of £3 million and an income of £141,000. During the year, the charity awarded five grants, worth a total of £399,500.

Beneficiaries included: Noah's Ark The Children's Hospice (£152,000); Laureus Foundation (£72,500); Mousetrap Foundation for the Arts and Oaklands School (£60,000 each); Greenhouse Sports (£55,000).

Applications

Apply in writing to the correspondent. According to the 2016/17 accounts, 'the charity strongly values relationships with charities where trust has been built or there are people who are known to LBFE involved in monitoring the programme'.

Sources of information

Accounts; annual report; Charity Commission record.

Lempriere Pringle 2015

○ Regeneration, community development

○ Bishop Auckland and surrounding areas

(£) £11.25 million (2016/17)

CC number: 1161516

Trustees: Jonathan Ruffer; Revd Matthew Hutton; Ashe Windham; Jane Ruffer; Nicholas Turner; Harriet Ruffer.

Correspondent: Peter Chapman, 17 Ilderton Road, Stockton-on-Tees TS18 2SR (email: jruffer@aucklandcastle. org)

The charity was established in 2015 by philanthropist Jonathan Ruffer, co-founder of Ruffer Investment

Management Ltd. The charity funds three Auckland Castle-based charities of which Jonathan Ruffer is a trustee – Auckland Castle Trust, Eleven Arches and The Zubaran Trust. The charity also funds the regeneration of Bishop Auckland and its surrounding areas.

The charity's 2016/17 accounts state: 'A major proportion of the organisation's resources is allocated to various sister trusts based at Auckland Castle, with the underlying aim of stimulating regeneration in Bishop Auckland and surrounding areas.'

'Grants have also been made to a range of other charitable projects and initiatives in other areas.'

Financial information

In 2016/17 the charity held assets of £47.4 million and had an income of £16.5 million. Grants awarded to organisations totalled £11.25 million. Of this, £3.06 million went to Auckland Castle-based trusts.

Beneficiaries included: Seedbed Christian Community Trust (£5.3 million); Archbishop of Canterbury's Discretionary Fund (£250,000); A Way Out and Harvest Charitable Trust (£25,000 each); The Vine Church (£15,000).

Various grants in Stockton-on-Tees totalled £158,000.

Applications

The 2016/17 annual report states: 'The organisation is proactive in identifying projects, ministries, charities and individuals whose work relates to the organisation's objectives, but who generally are pursuing their causes without resorting to funding via professional fundraisers.'

Sources of information

Accounts; annual report; Charity Commission record.

Leng Charitable Trust

○ Social welfare, health

◉ Tayside, primarily Dundee (and also nationally, to Scottish charities)

£ £246,500 (2016/17)

OSCR number: SC009285

Correspondent: The Trustees, c/o Thorntons Law LLP, Whitehall House, 33 Yeaman Shore, Dundee DD1 4BJ (tel: 01382 229111)

This trust supports local organisations working in Tayside, primarily Dundee. The trustees favour social welfare organisations assisting people with disabilities and people struggling with day-to-day living. National organisations can be supported as long as their work

benefits the Tayside and Dundee community.

The average amount awarded to local community organisations is around £1,500.

Financial information

In 2016/17 the trust held assets of £7.6 million and an income of £292,000. Grants awarded to organisations totalled £246,500.

Beneficiaries of grants over £5,000 included: The Salvation Army (£36,000); University of Dundee and V&A at Dundee (£25,000 each); Ninewells Cancer Campaign (£20,000); Dundee Science Centre (£12,000); Broughty Ferry YMCA (£10,000).

Grants of under £5,000 totalled £108,500.

Exclusions

Individuals going to work overseas on behalf of a charity will not normally be considered, nor will applications by organisations to raise funds just for one individual.

Applications

Apply in writing to the correspondent.

Sources of information

Accounts; annual report; OSCR record.

The Lennox Hannay Charitable Trust

○ General charitable purposes

◉ England and Wales

£ £547,000 (2016/17)

CC number: 1080198

Trustees: Christopher Fleming; Caroline Wilmot-Sitwell; Tara Douglas-Home.

Correspondent: Mrs C. Scott, Secretary, RF Trustee Co. Ltd, 15 Suffolk Street, London SW1Y 4HG (tel: 020 3696 6715; email: charities@rftrustee.com)

The Lennox Hannay Charitable Trust was established in 2000 for general charitable purposes. Grants are made to a wide variety of UK-registered charities and typically range between £1,000 and £3,000. They have previously been awarded under the following categories:

▷ Education/training
▷ Medical/health/sickness
▷ Disability
▷ Relief of poverty
▷ Overseas/famine relief
▷ Religious activities
▷ Arts/culture
▷ Sports/recreation
▷ Environment/conservation

Financial information

In 2016/17 the trust had assets of £32.3 million and an income of

£841,000. There were 64 grants made totalling £547,000. The vast majority of grants were for under £20,000.

No list of beneficiaries was available.

Applications

Applications may be made in writing to the correspondent by post. There are no deadlines. The trustees meet twice a year to discuss applications.

Sources of information

Accounts; annual report; Charity Commission record.

The Mark Leonard Trust

○ Environment, youth work, general charitable purposes

◉ Worldwide, mainly UK

£ £764,500 (2016/17)

CC number: 1040323

Trustees: Zivi Sainsbury; Judith Portrait; John Sainsbury; Mark Sainsbury.

Correspondent: Robert Bell, Director, The Peak, 5 Wilton Road, London SW1V 1AP (tel: 020 7410 0330; email: info@sfct.org.uk)

 www.sfct.org.uk

The Mark Leonard Trust is one of the 18 Sainsbury Family Charitable Trusts, which share a common administration and collectively give over £60 million a year.

According to the website the trustees focuses their grant-making on two broad areas:

▷ Sustainable agriculture and food; tackling climate change, energy efficiency and renewable energy
▷ Youth work that supports the rehabilitation of young people involved in anti-social or criminal activities, and helps remove the barriers to social inclusion

Grants are made to support innovative schemes through seed-funding with the aim of helping projects to achieve sustainability and successful replication.

The trust also works closely with the Ashden Trust and the JJ Charitable Trust on the Climate Change Collaboration, which supports projects seeking to accelerate progress towards a low-carbon society. The collaboration is flexible in what kind of projects it will fund from the development and piloting of new financing systems to market research and advocacy as long as these take account of existing experience and learning. As a general rule, the collaboration does not fund academic research, except where the research has direct and rapid policy application. Furthermore, the trustees favour projects that are designed and delivered in collaboration in order to capitalise on and develop further organisations' expertise and facilitate learning opportunities between organisations.

Since January 2015, the collaboration has supported the global Divest Invest movement – discouraging investment in fossil fuels and encouraging investment in 'climate solutions', including renewable energy, energy efficiency and storage.

Financial information

In 2016/17 the trust had assets of £19.5 million and an income of £916,000. The trust approved 26 grants totalling £764,500, some of which are payable over more than one year. Grants were distributed as follows:

Environment	£382,000
Climate Change Collaboration – capital grants	£317,500
Youth work	£47,500
General	£18,000

Beneficiaries included: Ashden Sustainable solutions (£300,000); Sustainable Restaurant Association (£125,000); The Social Innovation Partnership (£18,000); Centre for Sustainable Energy (£10,000); Food works (£5,800); Kent Refugee Action Network (£2,600), Environmental Funders Network (£1,600).

Exclusions

Grants are not normally made to individuals.

Applications

The trustees do not accept unsolicited proposals. Instead they prefer to focus their grant-making on a small portfolio of charities which receive sustained support over an extended period.

Sources of information

Accounts; annual report; Charity Commission record; funder's website.

Leri Charitable Trust

 General charitable purposes

UK, with a preference for Manchester and the London borough of Brent

(£) £8.4 million (2016/17)

CC number: 1075107

Trustees: Alison Lesley Caroline Broadberry; Geoffrey Justin Hellings; Leon Rosselson; Ruth Rosselson; Rina Rosselson.

Correspondent: Michael Reynolds, Administrator, Edwin Coe LLP, 2 Stone Buildings, Lincoln's Inn, London WC2A 3TH (tel: 020 7691 4048; email: michael.reynolds@edwincoe.com)

The Leri Charitable Trust's 2016/17 annual report states that the charity supports the following causes:

- Empowering and facilitating the independence of those in need by reason of poverty, youth, age, ill health, disability, financial hardship or other disadvantage
- Advancing human rights, conflict resolution or reconciliation or the promotion of religious or racial harmony or equality and diversity
- Advancing education, the arts, culture, heritage and science
- Advancing of community development and environmental protection and improvement
- Advancing and promoting health and the care of older people
- Supporting refugees and asylum seekers and raising awareness of issues affecting refugees and asylum seekers
- Promoting justice to Palestinians
- Promoting economic justice
- Supporting the projects of charitable organisations meeting these aims in the London borough of Brent, Manchester and their immediate surrounds

In 2016/17 the trust received a large donation of £15.8 million. The trustees agreed that this income would be used to make one-off payments to certain charities which had been supported in the past. The trustees also agreed that a sum be set aside to make contributions to community foundations in order to support projects combating loneliness in later life.

The charity does not respond to direct appeals for funding from individuals or organisations.

Financial information

In 2016/17 the trust had assets of £12.2 million and an income of £16.1 million. Due to the higher than normal income for the year, grants worth a total of £8.4 million were provided. Historically the trust has usually provided grants totalling around £500,000 per annum.

No list of beneficiaries was available.

Applications

The trust does not accept unsolicited applications.

Sources of information

Accounts; annual report; Charity Commission record.

The Leverhulme Trade Charities Trust

 Charities supporting: commercial travellers, grocers or chemists and their dependants; social welfare; education and training

UK

(£) £639,000 to organisations (2017)

CC number: 1159171

Trustees: Niall Fitzgerald; Patrick Cescau; Steve Williams; Paul Polman; Prof. Keith Gull; Clive Butler; Rudy Markham; Christopher Saul; Doug Baillie; Amanda Sourry; Leena Nair.

Correspondent: Paul Read, Secretary, 1 Pemberton Row, London EC4A 3BG (tel: 020 7042 9881; email: pdread@ leverhulme.ac.uk)

 www.leverhulme-trade.org.uk

The Leverhulme Trade Charities Trust derives from the will of the first Viscount Leverhulme, who died in 1925. He left a proportion of his shares in Lever Brothers Ltd on trust for specified beneficiaries, including certain trade charities. In 1983 the Leverhulme Trade Charities Trust itself was established, with its own shareholding in Unilever, and with grant-making to be restricted to charities connected with commercial travellers, grocers or chemists, their wives, widows or children. The trust also provides scholarships and bursaries to higher education students, including fellowships for pharmacists; however, no awards are given to individuals directly.

Financial information

In 2017 the trust had assets of £94.8 million and an income of £2.85 million. Grants totalled £2.56 million and were distributed as follows:

Undergraduate bursaries	£1.56 million
Grants to institutions	£639,000
Postgraduate bursaries	£368,000

Beneficiaries included: The Salespeople's Charity (£400,000).

Exclusions

The trust does not fund: capital grants and general appeals. Individual grants are only made through charitable organisations.

Applications

Applications for bursaries need to be made using an online application system on the trust's website (deadlines are in November and March for undergraduate and October for postgraduate funding). Applications from eligible institutions on behalf of qualifying individuals need to be made in writing to the correspondent. The trustees meet quarterly.

Sources of information

Accounts; annual report; Charity Commission record; funder's website.

The Leverhulme Trust

 Academic research

UK

£78.9 million (2017)

CC number: 1159154

Trustees: Niall Fitzgerald; Patrick Cescau; Steve Williams; Paul Polman; Keith Gull; Clive Butler; Rudy Markham; Christopher Saul; Doug Baillie; Amanda Sourry; Leena Nair.

Correspondent: Paul Read, Director of Finance, 1 Pemberton Row, London EC4A 3BG (tel: 020 7042 9881; email: grants@leverhulme.ac.uk)

www.leverhulme.ac.uk

This trust derives from the will of William Hesketh Lever, who left a proportion of his interest in Lever Brothers to benefit specific beneficiaries. A redefinition of the trust's objectives in 1983 led to the trust concentrating its attention solely on research and education.

Types of awards

The following guidelines on grant programmes are taken from the trust's website. For full details, refer to the website.

1. Research grants

(a) Research project grants
Provision of financial support for innovative and original research projects of high quality and potential. The grants provide support for the salaries of research staff involved with the project, plus associated costs directly related to the research. Up to £500,000 over five years is available.

2. Fellowships and studentships

(a) Early Career Fellowships – provides 50% (up to £25,000) of the salary costs of a three-year academic appointment for researchers with a proven record but who have not yet held an academic post.

(b) Research Fellowships – up to £55,000 over three to 24 months to experienced researchers.

(c) Major Research Fellowships – supporting academics in the humanities and social sciences.

(d) Emeritus Fellowships – research expenses of up to £22,000 for senior researchers who have retired from an academic post to complete a research project.

(e) Visiting Professorships – maintenance, travel expenses and research costs to UK institutions that wish to invite a

researcher from overseas to enhance the knowledge and skills of staff and students within the host institution.

(d) Study Abroad Studentships – supporting an extended period of advanced study or research at a centre of learning in any overseas country, with the exception of the USA.

(e) International Academic Fellowships – up to £40,000 available for three to 12 months to enable established researchers to spend a period of time in overseas research centres.

3. Philip Leverhulme Prizes

Philip Leverhulme Prizes recognise the achievement of outstanding researchers whose work has already attracted international recognition and whose future career is exceptionally promising. The prize scheme makes up to thirty awards of £100,000 a year, across a range of academic disciplines.

4. Major research initiatives

(a) Leverhulme Doctoral Scholarships – ten awards of over £1 million each to UK universities, allowing each institution to fund 15 Leverhulme Doctoral Scholarships in a research area of their choice, with five scholarships to be offered in each year of the three-year award.

(b) Leverhulme Research Centres – the scheme supports high quality, innovative research that encourages new approaches and 'disruptive thinking capable of establishing or reshaping areas of study important to modern society'. Each research centre will receive up to £1 million for up to ten years.

(c) Research Leadership Awards – funding of £800,000 to £1 million over four to five years for established researchers who want to build a team to address a distinct research problem.

(d) Arts Scholarships – funding for specialist arts training organisations to develop innovative teaching and to provide bursaries for individuals of exceptional talent to develop their skills in the fine and performing arts. The Arts Scholarships scheme runs every three years.

Financial information

In 2016 the trust had assets of £2.6 billion and an income of £86.7 million. There were 496 grants made to organisations totalling £78.6 million, broken down as follows:

Responsive Mode Projects	£34.9 million
Research Awards Advisory Committee	£18.2 million
Doctoral Scholarships	£12.6 million
Major Research Fellowships	£4.9 million
Academy Fellowships/ Scholarships	£3.8 million
Prizes	£3 million
Visiting Professors	£1.6 million

Beneficiaries included: University College London (£6 million in 38 grants); University of Birmingham (£2.7 million in 15 grants); University of Liverpool (£1.6 million in 14 grants); University of Nottingham (£688,000 in ten grants); University of Southampton (£536,000 in seven grants).

Exclusions

When submitting an application to the trust, applicants are advised that the trust does not offer funding for the following costs, and hence none of these items may be included in any budget submitted to the trust:

- Core funding or overheads for institutions
- Individual items of equipment over £1,000
- Sites, buildings or other capital expenditure
- Support for the organisation of conferences or workshops, which are not directly associated with International Networks, Early Career Fellowships; Visiting Fellowships or Philip Leverhulme Prizes
- Contributions to appeals
- Endowments
- A shortfall resulting from a withdrawal of or deficiency in public finance
- UK student fees where these are not associated with a Research Project Grant bid or Arts Scholarships

The trust also does not accept research applications for:

- Medicine and related clinical activities in humans or animals
- Policy-driven research where the principal objective is to assemble an evidence base for immediate policy initiatives
- Projects where advocacy is an explicit component
- Research that is aimed at immediate commercial application
- Applications in which the balance between assembling a data bank or database and the related subsequent research is heavily inclined to the former

Applications

Each programme, scholarship and award has its own individual application deadlines and procedures. Full details and guidelines for each scheme are available from the trust directly or via its website. Consult the full contact details on the trust's website to determine which person is the most suitable to approach. The trust welcomes contact from applicants who are uncertain about their eligibility.

In assessing appeals, the trustees evaluate the project's originality, importance, significance and merit. Cross-disciplinary projects may be favoured.

For all applications, the trustees particularly favour those that:

- Reflect an individual's personal vision, aspiration, or intellectual curiosity
- Take appropriate risks in setting and pursuing research objectives
- Enable a refreshing departure from established patterns of working – either for the individual, or for the discipline
- Transcend disciplinary boundaries

Sources of information

Accounts; annual report; Charity Commission record; funder's website.

Lord Leverhulme's Charitable Trust

General charitable purposes, environment and animal welfare, education, the arts, health and disability, young people, religious causes, community purposes

UK, especially Cheshire, Merseyside and Lancashire

£708,500 (2016/17)

CC number: 212431

Trustees: Sir Algernon Heber-Percy; Anthony Hannay; Henry Wilson.

Correspondent: Lynne Loxley, Leverhulme Estate Office, Hesketh Grange, Manor Road, Thornton Hough CH63 1JD (tel: 0151 336 4828; email: lynne.loxley@leverhulmeestates.co.uk)

The trust was established in 1957 by the late Lord Leverhulme and supports general charitable purposes, in particular those organisations that have been chosen by the children and grandchildren of the settlor and other members of the Leverhulme family.

The restricted fund (The Lady Lever Art Gallery Annuity Fund) has now expired but the trustees have continued to fund the gallery and intend to do so in the foreseeable future.

Financial information

In 2016/17 the trust had assets of £38.3 million, an income of £681,000 and made grants totalling £708,500, categorised as follows:

Health	£339,500
Community	£164,000
Animal welfare	£73,000
Education	£51,500
Arts	£47,500
Religious establishments	£20,500
Environmental	£12,500

Beneficiaries included: Psychic Research Trust (£101,000); Animal Health Trust £62,500); Royal College of Surgeons (£50,000); Liverpool University (£20,000).

Exclusions

Grants are not made to non-charitable organisations.

Applications

The trust states in its 2016/17 annual report:

> Priority is given [...] to applications from Cheshire, Merseyside and South Lancashire and the charities supported by the settlor in his lifetime. Others who do not meet those criteria should not apply without prior invitation but should, on a single sheet, state briefly their aims and apply fully only on being asked to do so. A handful of charities have heeded this warning and telephoned our administrator but the continuing volume of applications from charities which plainly do not meet the stated criteria suggests that many applicants do not concern themselves with their target's policies. Generally, the trustees do not acknowledge receipt of applications or notify unsuccessful applicants in order to minimise management expense.

Sources of information

Accounts; annual report; Charity Commission record.

Joseph Levy Foundation

General charitable purposes including: arts, culture and sport, education and training, health and community care, social welfare, children and young people, older people, people with disabilities

UK and Israel

£467,000 (2016/17)

CC number: 1165225

Trustees: Jane Jason; Peter Levy; Melanie Levy; Claudia Giat; James Jason; Kate Ellison.

Correspondent: Maria Zava, Grants Administrator, 1st Floor, 1 Bell Street, London NW1 5BY (tel: 020 7616 1200; email: info@jlf.org.uk)

 www.jlf.org.uk

The Joseph Levy Foundation was established in January 2016 to take forward the work of the Joseph Levy Charitable Foundation (Charity Commission no. 245592). The Joseph Levy Charitable Foundation was established by the late Joseph Levy C.B.E. B.E.M. under a trust deed dated 5 April 1965. In March 2016 the two charities merged, with the merger being registered with the Charity Commission.

According to the foundation's website, the objects of the charity are to support general charitable purposes. The board of trustees consists primarily of children and grandchildren of the original benefactor and awards grants only to officially registered charities and not to individuals.

The amount committed each year varies considerably and is given to a wide range of causes; although traditionally support has been given 'to charities serving the elderly, young people, people with disabilities and people with ill health' as well as 'community care and social welfare causes'.

Financial information

In 2016/17 the foundation had assets of £21 million and an income of £827,000. Grants were awarded to 16 organisations and broken down as follows:

Social welfare	5	£232,000
Arts, culture, and sport	4	£135,500
Education and training	3	£49,500
Health and community care	2	£35,000
Other	2	£15,000

Beneficiaries included: Cystic Fibrosis Holiday Fund (£94,500); Cystic Fibrosis Trust (£54,500); England and Wales Blind Golf (£40,000); Creative Future (£15,000); Chickenshed Theatre Company (£10,000); Institute for Jewish Policy Research (£5,000).

Applications

The foundation's website states: 'The Trustees wish to inform you that due to current commitments, the Foundation is no longer able to accept unsolicited applications.'

Any change in this policy will be announced on the foundation's website.

Sources of information

Accounts; annual report; Charity Commission record; funder's website.

Bernard Lewis Family Charitable Trust

Child welfare, medical, general charitable purposes, medical research, older people, education, Jewish religious support

UK

£1.9 million (2016/17)

CC number: 1125035

Trustees: Clive Lewis; Bernard Lewis; Caroline Grange; Leonard Lewis.

Correspondent: Mark Woodruff, c/o The Giving Department, Sky Light City Tower, 50 Basinghall Street EC2V 5DE

The trust was established in 2008 and makes grants for child welfare, medical, general charitable purposes, medical research, older people, education and Jewish religious support throughout the UK.

Financial information

In 2015 the trust had assets of £7.2 million and an income of

£3.4 million. Grants awarded to organisations totalled £1.9 million and were broken down as follows:

Child welfare	£1.2 million
Medical	£370,000
Jewish religious support	£167,500
Education	£70,500
Older people	£55,000
General	£44,000

Beneficiaries included: Place2Be (£677,500); Newlife Foundation for Disabled Children (£250,000); Sightsavers (£40,000); Westminster Synagogue (£18,000); Brainwave (£10,000); The Disability Centre (£5,000); Jewish Heritage (£2,500); Dog Trust (£2,000); Rainbow Trust (£1,500); Sudbury Neighbourhood Centre (£1,000).

Applications
Apply in writing to the correspondent.

Sources of information
Accounts; annual report; Charity Commission record.

David and Ruth Lewis Family Charitable Trust

 A wide range of charitable purposes, particularly Jewish causes

UK and Israel

£856,000 (2016/17)

CC number: 259892

Trustees: Julian Lewis; Deborah Lewis; Benjamin Lewis; Simon Lewis; Rachel Lewis.

Correspondent: The Trustees., Chelsea House, West Gate, Ealing, London W5 1DR (tel: 020 8991 4502)

The trust was established in 1969 and originally aimed to serve for the charitable intentions of members of the families of David, Bernard, Geoffrey and Godfrey Lewis and certain companies which they control.

Areas of giving
The trust's legally permitted objectives are very wide and 'cover virtually every generally accepted charitable object'. In practice, charitable causes supported by the trust in recent years have been:

- Child and social care
- Medical research
- Support for older people
- General charitable purposes

Jewish charities are prominent throughout the categories of giving.

Types of grant
Most grants are awarded as a single payment, although a few are committed over a period of two to three years. The annual report for 2016/17 states that 'certain medical research grants normally run for a period of three years'.

Financial information
In 2016/17 the trust had assets of £18.5 million and had an income of £3.5 million. During the year, the trust gave a total of £856,000 in grants to organisations. Grants were distributed as follows:

General medical support	£382,500
Child and social care	£263,000
General charitable funding	£122,000
Support for older people	£87,500

Although a number of beneficiaries had a Jewish connection, support was also given to non-Jewish organisations.

Beneficiaries included: The Anna Freud Centre (£150,000); Orr Shalom (£136,500); Jewish Care (£87,500); Brain Tumour Research (£61,500); Diabetes UK (£25,000); Meningitis Research Foundation (£20,000).

Exclusions
Grants are not made to individuals (apart from in exceptional circumstances).

Applications
Applications may be made in writing to the correspondent.

Sources of information
Accounts; annual report; Charity Commission record.

John Lewis Partnership General Community Fund

 Welfare, music, arts, education, environment, community causes, young people, relief of poverty

UK

£762,500 (2016/17)

CC number: 209128

Trustee: John Lewis Partnership Trust Ltd.

Correspondent: The Secretary to the Trustee, Partnership House, Carlisle Place, London SW1P 1BX (tel: 020 7592 5957)

 www.johnlewispartnership.co.uk

The charity was set up in 1961 and supports UK and supports charities and good causes that are beneficial to the community including those for: children and young adults, at risk groups, people who are sick or who have disabilities, people disadvantaged by poverty and socially isolated individuals. Medical professionals and research workers may also be considered for funding. The charity's objectives include the advancement of education, the relief of poverty and religious causes, generally

awards are given in the areas of welfare, music, environment and education.

The website states: 'The Partnership favours charities local to the communities where we operate or in which Partners are personally involved.'

Financial information
In 2016/17 the charity had an income of £766,000 and made grants totalling £762,500 to 167 organisations. Awards were broken down into the following categories:

Welfare	21	£374,000
Music	136	£262,500
Learning	7	£103,500
Environment	3	£22,000

The charity's record on the Charity Commission's website notes that it 'allocates approximately £1 million per annum for charitable purposes'.

Beneficiaries included: British Red Cross (£100,000); Retail Trust (£50,000); Royal College of Music and The Voices Foundation (£20,000 each); The Trust for Sing for Pleasure (£15,000); Samaritans (£13,000); Royal Academy of Music (£10,500); Pro Corda Trust and Bumblebee Conservation Trust (£10,000 each); Environmental Vision and Chilterns MS Centre Ltd (£5,000 each); Backworth Colliery Band (£750).

Exclusions
The charity does not support the following: loans; sponsorship; religious, ethnic or political groups; advertising; individuals; third-party fundraising.

Applications
The John Lewis Partnership website notes the following information:

> If you have a cause you think we could support, contact the Waitrose champion for community giving at your local branch (www.waitrose.com) or the John Lewis Community Liaison Coordinator at your local branch (www.johnlewis.com). As we are contacted by so many organisations throughout the year, we cannot always give you a swift reply, but we will reply as soon as possible if we can help.

Sources of information
Accounts; annual report; Charity Commission record.

Life Changes Trust

 Care experienced young people, people with dementia

Scotland

£4.12 million (2016/17)

OSCR number: SC043816

Trustees: Alexis Jay; Nigel Fairhead; Harriet Dempster; Isobel Grigor; Shona Munro; Collete Gallagher; Claire Lightowler; Gillian Brown; Shona Hill.

Correspondent: The Trustees, Edward House, 2nd Floor, 283 West Campbell Street, Glasgow G2 4TT (tel: 0141 212 9600; email: enquiries@lifechangestrust. org.uk)

 www.lifechangestrust.org.uk

 facebook.com/LifeChangesTrust

 @LifeChangesTrst

The Life Changes Trust was set up in 2013 with a grant of £50 million from The Big Lottery Fund. The aim of the trust is to improve the quality of life, well-being, empowerment, and social inclusion of care experienced young people and people affected by dementia.

The following information has been taken from the trust's website:

Care experienced young people

At the heart of our work is a commitment to giving young people with care experience a voice, so that they themselves can shape our work and influence change. As such, our work will fall into five priority areas.

These are:

- Care experienced young people are loved, respected, valued, listened to
- Care experienced young people are in safe and settled accommodation
- Care experienced young people have access to support and guidance when and where they need it
- Care experienced young people have increased access to education, training and employment
- Care experienced young people lead healthy lives

People affected by dementia

We want to drive change so that that people affected by dementia are empowered to exercise choice and control over their own lives and become active citizens in their communities. We are committed to seeing the whole person and ensuring that he or she is central to decisions that affect their life, empowered and included in their own community.

As such, our work will fall into five priority areas.

- Enable people affected by dementia to live in a place that suits them and their needs
- Protect and promote the independence of people affected by dementia
- Support work that will guarantee that people affected by dementia get the help they need when they need it
- Create a culture in Scotland where people affected by dementia feel safe, listened to, valued and respected
- Empower people affected by dementia so that they can do the things that are important to them

Financial information

In 2016/17 the trust held assets of £43.7 million and had an income of £2 million. Grants awarded to organisations totalled £4.12 million.

Previous beneficiaries have included: Care and Repair Scotland (£1 million); East Renfrewshire Council (£406,500); North West Carers Centre (£105,000); Outside the Box (£94,000); Haven Centre (£93,000); The Eric Liddle Centre (£84,000); Aberdeen Council of Voluntary Organisations (£20,000); Studio LR (£17,500).

Applications

Refer to the trust's website for details of grant programmes and application deadlines.

Sources of information

Accounts; annual report; Charity Commission record; funder's website.

The Linbury Trust

 General charitable purposes, arts and culture, museums and galleries, heritage, education, social welfare, medical research, humanitarian aid overseas

 Worldwide

£ £8.6 million (2016/17)

CC number: 287077

Trustees: Richard Adams; Sarah Butler-Sloss; James Barnard; John Sainsbury; Lady Anya Sainsbury; Sir Martin Jacomb; Lord Sainsbury of Preston Candover; Hon. Mark Sainsbury.

Correspondent: Robert Bell, Director, The Peak, 5 Wilton Road, London SW1V 1AP (tel: 020 7410 0330; email: info@sfct.org.uk)

 www.linburytrust.org.uk

This is one of the Sainsbury Family Charitable Trusts, which share a joint administration but work autonomously as independent legal entities. They have a common approach to grant-making and generally discourage applications from organisations not already in contact with the trust concerned, although some are open to unsolicited approaches.

The Linbury Trust was established in 1973 and has traditionally been associated with arts. Nevertheless, in recent years about 65% of support has been allocated to other causes. The trust, as a rule, does not consider unsolicited appeals and the trustees take a proactive approach and award grants selectively. Priority is given to charitable causes where the trustees have particular knowledge and experience. In past years, the trust has supported major capital projects such as the Royal National Theatre and the Royal Opera House, as well as other museums and galleries. It

also has a special interest in dance and dance education, Lady Sainsbury being the well known ballerina Anya Linden.

Causes supported include:

- **Arts:** particularly visual and performing arts. Grants are normally awarded to cultural institutions carrying out major capital projects.
- **Education:** support for organisations that work with those suffering from poor literacy skills and children who are disadvantaged.
- **Museums and heritage:** generally large museums with major development projects.
- **Environment:** supporting the Ashden Awards, promoting the use of renewable energy in the UK and developing countries.
- **Medical:** historically the trust tended to support research into chronic fatigue syndrome/ME and has in recent years supported studies into paediatric issues with this condition. Recently the trust has funded mental health care projects.
- **Social welfare:** organisations that work with people who are socially excluded and disadvantaged, particularly work with young people to reduce or prevent offending. The trustees also support charities working to improve the quality of life of older people and those living with dementia.
- **Overseas countries and humanitarian aid:** organisations (particularly medical) working in Palestine and organisations working with refugees in the Mediterranean.

Financial information

In 2016/17 the trust had assets of £136.5 million and an income of £6.2 million. There were 80 grants paid in the year, totalling £8.6 million, broken down into the following categories:

Arts	£4.7 million
Museums and heritage	£1.6 million
Social welfare/medical	£1 million
Education	£900,000
Developing countries/ humanitarian aid	£200,000

Beneficiaries included: Royal Opera House Foundation (£3.3 million); Royal National Theatre (£500,000); Art Fund (£250,000); Royal Botanic Gardens (£100,000); Gingerbread and Grange Festival (£50,000 each).

Exclusions

Individuals; educational fees; expeditions.

Applications

The trust's website states: 'The Trustees generally do not make grants in response to unsolicited applications and they do not make grants to individuals.'

Sources of information

Accounts; annual report; Charity Commission record; funder's website.

The Lind Trust

 Young people, community development, Christianity

 UK, particularly Norwich and Norfolk

£ £423,500 (2016/17)

CC number: 803174

Trustees: Leslie Brown; Dr Graham Dacre; Gavin Wilcock; Julia Dacre; Samuel Dacre.

Correspondent: Gavin Wilcock, Trustee, Drayton Hall, Hall Lane, Drayton, Norwich, Norfolk NR8 6DP (tel: 01603 262626)

This Lind Trust was established in 1990 and makes grants to individuals and organisations. The trust funds general charitable activities, with a particular interest in the promotion of the Christian faith in Norfolk and Norwich.

Financial information

In 2016/17 the trust had assets of £22.5 million and an income of £1.37 million. The trust awarded £423,500 million in grants. A list of beneficiaries was not available.

Previous beneficiaries have included: Today's Lifestyle Church (£124,000); The Open Youth Trust (£100,000).

Applications

Applications can be made in writing to the correspondent at any time. However, the trust commits most of its funds in advance, giving the remainder to eligible applicants as received.

Sources of information

Accounts; annual report; Charity Commission record.

The Enid Linder Foundation

 General charitable purposes, medical research and education, the arts

 UK

£ £619,000 to organisations (2016/17)

CC number: 267509

Trustees: Jack Ladeveze; Audrey Ladeveze; Michael Butler; Carole Cook; Jonathan Fountain.

Correspondent: Martin Pollock, 150 Aldersgate Street, London EC1A 4AB (tel: 020 7334 9191; email: enidlinderfoundation@moorestephens.com)

 www.enidlinderfoundation.com

The foundation was registered in 1974 and benefitted from the fortune of the Linder family, who ran a marine chandler business for many years.

According to the foundation's website, the aims of the foundation are:

> - To continue funding chosen general charitable causes which are of particular interest or concern to the Trustees
> - To distribute in full, in accordance with the governing Trust Deed, all the income available each year
> - To maintain resources at a reasonable level in order to continue to provide general charitable assistance in the foreseeable future

Grant-making policy

The foundation's website states:

> The Enid Linder Foundation has established its grant-making policy to achieve its objectives for the public benefit to improve the lives of sufferers of a wide range of disease and illnesses and promoting illustrative and musical talent. The Foundation carries out these objectives by awarding grants in the following categories:
>
> **Medicine:** To fund research, education and capital projects related to all areas of medicine through grants to selected medical universities, institutions and charities.
>
> **The Arts:** To fund projects which aim to develop and encourage individual and group talent in musical, theatre and illustrative art.
>
> **General:** To make donations to projects through other registered UK charities which support and care for the benefit of the public as a whole.

Note: The trustees prefer to invite applications from charities that are already known to them.

Financial information

In 2016/17 the foundation had assets of £16.4 million and an income of £561,500. During the year, the foundation awarded a total of £621,500 in grants. Of this amount, £2,500 was given to one individual, with the remainder given to organisations. Grants to organisations were distributed as follows:

General charitable causes	21	£508,000
Electives and hardship grants	9	£111,000

Beneficiaries included: Royal College of Surgeons – Fellowships (£120,000); National Children's Orchestra – Special Capital Project (£96,000); University of Bristol (£50,000); Imperial College (£35,000); Cherry Trees Respite Home (£20,000); DEBRA (£10,000); Cystic Fibrosis (£7,000); SkillForce (£6,000); the egg – Theatre Royal Bath (£5,000).

Exclusions

> - The foundation only considers applications from UK-registered charities (unless you have exempt

status such as a church, educational establishment, hospital or housing corporation)

> - The foundation does not typically fund projects outside the UK, even if the organisation is registered within Britain
> - The foundation is not able to accept applications from individuals or for individual research or study. This includes gap year activities, study trips, fundraising expeditions and sponsorship

Applications

Apply using the online form on the foundation's website.

The annual report for 2016/17 states: 'Unsolicited applications are accepted, but the Trustees do receive a very high number of grant applications which, in line with their grant making policy, are mostly unsuccessful.'

Sources of information

Accounts; annual report; Charity Commission record; funder's website.

The Charles Littlewood Hill Trust

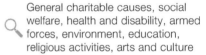 General charitable causes, social welfare, health and disability, armed forces, environment, education, religious activities, arts and culture

 UK, with a preference for Nottinghamshire and Norfolk

£ £190,000 (2016)

CC number: 286350

Trustees: Charles Barratt; Tim Farr; Nigel Savory; John Pears.

Correspondent: John Thompson, Trust Administrator, PO Box 10454, Nottingham NG5 0HQ (tel: 01476 552429; email: charles.hill@btinternet.com)

 www.charleshill.org.uk

The trust was established in 1978 and supports a wide range of charitable causes. It can give in the UK but there is a particular preference to applications from Norfolk and Nottinghamshire.

Areas of work

While the trustees have wide discretion, the areas that they have historically supported, as stated on the trust's website, are as follows:

> - Charitable projects and activities in or benefiting the people of Nottinghamshire or Norfolk
> - Activities relating to community healthcare services including home care, after care, sufferers of long-term medical conditions and the continuing care of disabled people

- Health education and prevention – promoting knowledge and awareness of specific diseases or medical conditions
- Lifelong learning projects helping people of any age to achieve their educational potential through supplementary schools, literacy and numeracy projects, community education, vocational/restart education for the unemployed, and alternative education for excluded school pupils
- Community development by helping groups to organise and respond to problems and needs in their communities
- Personal social services including organisations assisting individuals or families to overcome social deprivation, e.g. people who are homeless or who have disabilities and their carers, single parent and childcare groups and other family support groups
- Social preventive schemes covering activities which prevent crime, 'dropping out' and general delinquency, provide social care outreach services, deliver social health and safety awareness schemes
- Community social activities which promote social engagement for vulnerable people, mitigating against isolation and loneliness

Grants are made only to registered charities and or other organisations that can demonstrate their charitable purpose.

Financial information

In 2016 the trust had assets of £4.8 million and an income of £214,500. Grants to organisations totalled £190,000. These were distributed in the following categories:

Medical/disability	23	£57,500
Welfare	29	£45,000
Other	3	£30,000
Education	4	£15,000
Churches	3	£10,500
Services	5	£6,000
Environment	1	£5,000
Groups/clubs	2	£2,700
Accommodation	1	£2,500
Arts	1	£2,500

Beneficiaries included: The Norfolk Hospice – Tapping House (£20,000); Nottinghamshire Community Foundation (£10,000); Norfolk Churches Trust (£7,500); Nottinghamshire Wildlife Trust (£5,000); ABF The Soldiers' Charity – Nottinghamshire (£3,000); The Prince's Trust – Norfolk (£2,500); Nottingham Play Forum Ltd (£1,700); Young Norfolk Arts Trust (£1,500); Asthma UK and Carewatch in Nottingham (£1,000 each).

Exclusions

Grants are not awarded to individuals or for any activities which are the responsibility of local authorities or similar bodies.

Applications

Applications should be made in writing to the correspondent, by post and not email, and should include the latest set of audited accounts. The website has the following guidance on what to include:

1. Clearly identify the name of the organisation which is making the application and its status as a registered charity or a community interest company (CIC) or provide other evidence of the organisation's charitable purpose
2. Explain the project or activity for which the grant is requested and how it meets the Trust's policy as described in The Trust's Grant Policy
3. Explain who will benefit from the project or activity and show that the benefit is sustainable
4. Identify the likely costs of the project/ activity and explain what other finance is sought or is available. The Trustees need to understand if and when the project/activity will actually go ahead
5. Explain if the project/activity will be managed or organised by paid staff and/or volunteers and the numbers involved
6. Include a copy of the organisation's last audited accounts

Applications are reviewed by every trustee and discussed at meetings in March, July and November but must be received by 20 January, 20 May and 20 September respectively for consideration at each meeting. To limit costs on the trust's resources, unsuccessful applicants are not informed of the outcome. Note that both the Charles Littlewood Hill Trust and the Lady Hind Trust are jointly administered, and applicants should only apply to one.

Sources of information

Accounts; annual report; Charity Commission record; funder's website.

The Second Joseph Aaron Littman Foundation

 General charitable purposes including social welfare, education, Jewish causes, academic and medical research

UK

£268,000 (2016/17)

CC number: 201892

Trustees: Glenn Hurstfield; Colette Littman; Joanna Littman; Thomas Salamon.

Correspondent: Joanna Littman, Trustee, Manor Farm, Mill Lane, Charlton Mackrell, Somerton TA11 7BQ (tel: 01458 223650)

The foundation's objects are: to relieve poverty anywhere in the world; to advance knowledge anywhere in the world; and for general charitable purposes. The foundation provides regular support to The Littman Library of Jewish Civilisation (£220,000 in 2016/17).

Financial information

In 2016/17 the foundation held assets of £5.5 million and had an income of £318,000. Grants were made to 17 organisations, totalling £268,000.

Beneficiaries included: Wolfson College (£10,000); Leo Baeck College UK and The Spiro Ark (£5,000 each); Fight for Sight (£2,500); Great Ormond Street Hospital, London Village Network and Hadassah UK (£1,000 each).

Exclusions

Applications from individuals are not considered.

Applications

Apply in writing to the correspondent.

Sources of information

Accounts; annual report; Charity Commission record.

The George John and Sheilah Livanos Charitable Trust

 General charitable purposes, health, social welfare

UK

£375,500 (2016)

CC number: 1002279

Trustees: Philip Harris; Timothy Cripps; Anthony Holmes.

Correspondent: The Trustees, Gordon Dadds LLP, 6 Agar Street, London WC2N 4HN (tel: 020 7759 1682)

The trust was established in 1985 to support general charitable purposes in the UK. The organisations that the trust awards grants to are varied, and in recent years there has been a focus on health and welfare.

Financial information

In 2016 the trust held assets of £1.1 million and had an income of £43,500. Grants totalling £375,500 were made to 25 organisations.

Beneficiaries included: Burrswood (£150,000); Gainsborough House (£100,000); Sparks (£20,000); Dystonia Society (£5,000); Alzheimer's Society (£2,500); Macmillan Cancer Support (£2,000).

Exclusions

Individuals; non-registered charities.

Applications

The annual report for 2016 states:

Unsolicited applications are accepted, but the Trustees do receive a very high number of grant applications which, in line with the Trustees' grant-making policy, are mostly unsuccessful. The Trustees prefer to make donations to charities whose work they have researched and which is in accordance with the aims and objectives of the Charity for the year.

Sources of information

Accounts; annual report; Charity Commission record.

The Ian and Natalie Livingstone Charitable Trust

 Children and young people, disadvantaged people

 UK

£565,000 (2016/17)

CC number: 1149025

Trustees: Ian Livingstone; Natalie Livingstone; Mark Levitt.

Correspondent: The Trustees, Hazlems Fenton LLP, Palladium House, 1–4 Argyll Street, London W1F 7LD (tel: 020 7437 7666; email: info@ hazlemsfenton.com)

Registered in September 2012, this trust supports charities working with children and other disadvantaged groups.

Financial information

In 2016/17 the trust held assets of £111,000 and had an income of £573,500. Grants awarded to organisations totalled £565,000.

Beneficiaries included: Great Ormond Street Children's Charity and The Mayor's Fund for London (£200,000 each); Dalaid (£50,000); Christ's College (£33,500); NSPCC (£25,000); British Fashion Council (£10,000); Target Ovarian Cancer (£10,000).

Applications

Apply in writing to the correspondent.

Sources of information

Accounts; annual report; Charity Commission record.

The Andrew Lloyd Webber Foundation

Arts, culture, heritage

England and Wales

£2.8 million (2017)

CC number: 1015648

Trustees: Louise Fennell; Mark Wordsworth; Philip Freedman;

Madeleine Lloyd Webber; Dr Simon Thurley.

Correspondent: Sarah Miller, Sydmonton Court Estate, Burghclere, Newbury, Berkshire RG20 9NJ (tel: 01635 278594; email: sarah@ andrewlloydwebberfoundation.com)

 www.andrewlloydwebber foundation.com
facebook.com/The-Andrew-Lloyd-Webber-Foundation-112831905467918

 @ALWFoundation

The Andrew Lloyd Webber Foundation was registered with the Charity Commission in December 1992. Since 2010, the foundation has awarded £19 million to projects that focus on the enhancement of arts education and participation, improving access and increasing diversity across the arts, culture and heritage sector.

According to its website:

The Foundation believes that in order to maintain vibrancy in the arts, it is critical that the new generation of potential artists are nurtured and encouraged. Recognising that these are difficult economic times to get a start in life, the Trustees will prioritise projects that enable people to develop their abilities and careers, by providing professional training, apprenticeships and work place experience in all areas of the arts, from stone masonry to stage electricians.

In addition to its grant programmes, the foundation also works in partnership with a number of selected schools to offer performing arts scholarships. A list of schools and colleges can be found on the foundation's website.

Full details of all the foundation's current grants programmes are available on the website.

Financial information

In 2017 the foundation had assets of £38.6 million and an income of £642,000. Grants awarded to organisations totalled £2.8 million including £329,500 in performing arts scholarships.

Beneficiaries included: Scottish Civic Trust (£175,000); Royal Shakespeare Company (£122,000); Historic Wales, Gainsborough House (£50,000 each); Urdang Academy (£36,500); Rose Bruford College of Theatre Performance (£18,500); Liverpool Institute for Performing Arts (£9,300).

Exclusions

The trustees are unlikely to support projects that:

- Are for a pilot project
- Are for a one-off event, such as an arts festival or production of a play

- Ultimately profit a commercial organisation
- Are for the building of a new venue where other funding has not been obtained. Are for the funding of a theatrical tour
- Are from an individual

Applications

At the time of writing (July 2018) the foundation was working on a new application process and was not accepting applications. See the website for more information.

Sources of information

Accounts; annual report; Charity Commission record; funder's website.

Lloyd's Charities Trust

 Disasters and emergencies, social welfare

Worldwide, with a preference for UK and East London

£728,000 (2016)

CC number: 207232

Trustees: Graham Clarke; Chris Harman; Neil Smith; Victoria Carter; David Ibeson; Simon Beale; Karen Green; Andrew Brooks.

Correspondent: Michaele Hawkins, Global Corporate Social Responsibility Manager, Lloyd's Building, 1 Lime Street, London EC3M 7HA (email: communityaffairs@lloyds.com)

 www.lloyds.com/lct

The charity was set up in 1953, and is the charitable arm of Lloyd's insurance market in London. The trust makes grants on behalf of the Society of Lloyd's through three main programmes:

General fund

The trust makes its grants through the general fund. The trust has a policy of working with a small number of selected charities over a three-year period. Current partner charities will be supported until 2019. The following information on the fund's priorities has been taken from its website:

Insurance plays a valuable role in creating a more confident and secure world and we believe that our charitable funding should extend this role in relevant ways.

Mindful of Lloyd's position as the world's leading specialist insurance market, and given its role in covering global risks including natural disasters, Lloyd's Charities Trust aims to help the global communities most at risk from disasters and emergencies in the following ways:

- We give to charities responding to disasters and emergencies, to help relieve suffering and rebuild lives
- In areas prone to natural disasters, we fund disaster risk reduction initiatives

aiming to build resilience into these communities

Mindful of Lloyd's position as one of the UK's leading financial institutions and a major employer and contributor to the economy, Lloyd's Charities Trust focuses some of its giving:

- To spread the economic and social benefits of the Lloyd's market by supporting projects that tackle disadvantage and foster opportunity
- To support the individual and collective charitable efforts of those working in the Lloyd's market and the City of London

Around the world our offices also support their local communities through the Lloyd's Together programme.

Smaller donations are available through the Lloyd's Charity Awards. The trust's website states:

Donations of £2,000 are given to charities supported by individuals working in the market in recognition of their fundraising and voluntary work. Awards are also made to charities that have given invaluable support to those in the market whose lives have been affected by difficult circumstances.

Since the initiative was launched in 2007, over £650,000 has been donated to 300 charities.

To apply, you must be a permanent employee working in the Lloyd's market (employed by managing or members' agents, brokers, coverholders, the Corporation, LMA or LIIBA) on the date the application is made and when the award is announced.

Education fund
The education fund is used to benefit young people in London communities. The fund currently supports students from low-income backgrounds from Cambridge Heath Sixth Form Partnership schools in Tower Hamlets, to study at universities outside London.

Lloyd's Community Programme
Lloyd's Community Programme (LCP) is a sub-fund of the trust. Lloyd's Community Programme encourages volunteering and acts as a catalyst for the Lloyd's market to empower people in its neighbouring London communities to achieve their potential.

Financial information
In 2016 the trust had assets of £3 million and an income of £716,500. Grants awarded to organisations totalled £728,000, with an additional £60,000 given in bursaries. Grants were broken down as follows:

General Fund grants	£349,500
Lloyd's community programmes	£278,500
Lloyd's market charity awards	£64,000
Lloyd's Educational Fund – bursaries	£60,000
Other donations	£36,000

Beneficiaries included: Ready to Respond (£150,000); Build Change

(£100,000); Whizz-Kidz (£50,000); Children's Air Ambulance (£49,500).

Applications
Lloyd's Charities Trust makes ad hoc donations and the majority of funds are committed to supporting the partner charities the trust works with. Current partner charities are being supported until October 2019.

Check the trust's website for further information on Lloyd's Charity Awards or contact Sarah Chamberlain at sarah. chamberlain@lloyds.com.

Sources of information
Accounts; annual report; Charity Commission record; funder's website.

Lloyds Bank Foundation for England and Wales

🔍 Domestic and sexual abuse, sexual exploitation, mental health, homelessness/vulnerably housed, offending, prison or community service, care leavers, learning disabilities, addiction and dependency on alcohol, drugs, substances and/or gambling, trafficking and modern slavery, sex work, young parents, asylum seekers and refugees

📍 England and Wales

£ £16.6 million (2016)

CC number: 327114

Trustees: Paul Farmer; Dr Neil Wooding; James Garvey; Hilary Armstrong; Prof. Patricia Broadfoot; Helen Edwards; Rennie Fritchie; Catharine Cheetham; Joanna Harris; Lesley King-Lewis; Dame Gillian Morgan; Sara Weller.

Correspondent: Paul Streets, Chief Executive, Pentagon House, 52–54 Southwark Street, London SE1 1UN (tel: 0370 411 1223; email: enquiries@lloydsbankfoundation.org.uk)

🌐 www.lloydsbankfoundation.org.uk

📘 facebook.com/ lloydsbankfoundation

🐦 @LBFEW

The foundation receives the majority of its income from Lloyds Bank plc. There is an agreement with Lloyds Bank that until 2020 the foundation will receive 0.3616% of the group's adjusted pre-tax profits/loss, averaged over three years.

Areas of work
The foundation funds charities working on the following social issues:

 Domestic and sexual abuse
 Sexual exploitation
 Mental health

- Homelessness/vulnerably housed people
- Offending, prison or community service
- Care leavers
- Learning disabilities
- Addiction and dependency on alcohol, drugs, substances and/or gambling
- Trafficking and modern slavery
- Sex work
- Young parents
- Asylum seekers and refugees

Grant programmes
The foundation runs three main funding schemes, details of which have been taken from the website:

Invest
Our Invest Grants provide long-term funding for the day-to-day running of your charity (core costs), and/or the direct delivery of your charity's work.

We can provide a minimum of £30,000 to a maximum of £100,000, delivered across three years. There is also the opportunity for continuation funding, so your charity could be funded by our Invest grant for up to six years in total.

You can apply for either a core costs grant or a project costs grant.

If you are applying for a core costs grant then you will be able to use the funding to cover any of your charity's core or delivery costs. Please be aware that if you are applying for core cost funding, we'll ask you to demonstrate that the majority of your charity's work (more than 50% of your work and expenditure) meets our eligibility criteria.

If you are applying for project costs you will be able to apply for the direct delivery costs of the project. You will only be able to apply for the core costs associated directly with delivering the project.

Enable
Enable Grants are awarded to charities which have identified clear development needs, and provide a great opportunity to strengthen charities to deliver more effectively.

Through Enable Grants we fund opportunities for your charity to develop, or trial new approaches to service delivery, so you can become more effective in your work. You may want to improve your charity's capability in areas such as business development and planning, monitoring, leadership and governance and communications; an Enable grant could put your charity in a stronger position to deliver services and attract more volunteers, funding and support.

We can provide up to a total of £15,000 across one or two years.

What Enable Grants Fund

- Enable grants fund activities related to the development and improvement of your charity's capability. Examples include:

- Pilot initiatives, to trial new ways of delivering your programmes
- Strengthening your monitoring systems
- Creating stronger business plans and service development plans
- Improving your charity's marketing and communications
- Investigating mergers, partnerships, shared services and contracts
- Developing new streams of income and enterprise for your charity
- Expanding your charity's capacity to reach new audiences and recruit volunteers
- Improving your structures and systems, for example, in finance, HR, risk management and volunteer management
- Quality standards (please note that if you already hold a quality mark, you cannot apply for renewal costs under the Enable programme)

Enable Grants are awarded to charities that meet our eligibility criteria and have identified clear development areas which will support their growth. The costs covered by Enable grants must be additional to those you would already incur through your charity's regular activities; they are not awarded for core costs or direct delivery costs. If this is what you are looking for, please consider applying to our Invest programme instead.

Enhance

Our Enhance programme provides a range of non-financial, tailored support to help charities we fund thrive.

We help charities that we fund identify what (if any) support might help them work more effectively. When they've agreed on a specific area for development, have a clear plan of activities in mind to address this, and a clear idea of what they hope to achieve, they'll be offered support in one or more of the following ways:

- Service development and improvement
- Improved leadership and governance
- Strategic planning and policy development
- Improved structures and systems
- Improved communication

Financial information

In 2016 the foundation had assets of £20.8 million and an income of £13.8 million. During the year, the foundation awarded £16.6 million in grants.

Grants were approved in the following categories:

Invest and Enable	£12 million
Matched giving	£3.2 million
Enhance	£686,500
National Programmes	£666,000

New Invest and Enable grants in 2016

Invest	172	£10.6 million
Enable	109	£1.5 million

Exclusions

According to the foundation's website, the following work cannot be funded:

- Organisations not registered with the Charity Commission
- Community interest companies
- Second or third-tier organisations (unless there is evidence of direct services to individuals with multiple disadvantage). By 'second or third-tier' we mean organisations whose main purpose is to support other organisations. These are also known as infrastructure or umbrella organisations. We would consider requests from these organisations only for any direct delivery of support to disadvantaged people
- Organisations whose primary purpose is to give funds to individuals or other organisations. By this we mean organisations using more than 50% of annual expenditure as grants
- Hospitals, health authorities or hospices
- Rescue services
- Nurseries, pre-schools or playgroups
- Schools, colleges or universities
- Animal charities
- Charities working outside England and Wales

Grants are not given for:

- Medical care or medical research
- Online or telephone advice services
- Events and short-term interventions including holidays, expeditions and trips
- Activities for which a statutory body is responsible
- Capital purchases or building work. This includes IT, building work, purchase of vehicles/equipment etc
- Environmental, arts based or sports activities. However, we would consider requests from charities who use these activities as part of the transition process – the final outcomes and destination must meet all other guidance – for example we may fund a food growing project for people with mental health problems
- The promotion of religion. This does not exclude organisations that may have a religious element to them as long as their charitable objectives show a wider benefit other than just religion and they are working with the identified groups through transition points – we do not fund charities where the Trustees, staff or volunteers are required to be of a particular faith unless there is a Genuine Occupational Requirement – see ACAS for further guidance on GORs
- Loan repayments
- Sponsorship or funding towards an appeal
- Work that has already taken place
- Evaluation which is not related to the funded work
- Professional qualifications such as ACCA
- Professional fundraisers or bid writers – we will invest in up skilling your staff or volunteers in fundraising skills to make your charity more sustainable
- Redundancy payments

Applications

Applications can be made through the foundation's website. The following information on the application procedure was taken from the foundation's website:

Decide which grant to apply for

We offer two grant programmes, one for core costs and one for developing your charity. You can apply for either programme, but not both.

Our Invest grants provide long-term funding for the day-to-day running of your charity (core costs), and/or the direct delivery of your charity's work. Invest is open for applications twice a year, please check the funding timetable to find out when we are open for new applications.

Enable grants are awarded to charities which have identified clear development needs, and provide a great opportunity to strengthen charities to deliver more effectively.

Before you apply, take a look at our Funding Timetable to check if the programme is accepting applications.

If you are not sure which programme to apply for, get in touch with us to talk about which one is right for you.

Check your eligibility

Before you apply, please read our detailed eligibility criteria to make sure you are the right fit for our grants programmes. You will also need to ensure you can meet our reporting requirements.

Prepare your application

If you meet all our eligibility criteria, congratulations! You can now apply for a grant.

Check below which programme is right for you and follow the guidelines to create the best possible application.

Submit your application

Once you are familiar with the guidelines and have drafted your application, fill in the Application Form. You will be able to save and return to your saved application if you need to.

What happens next?

If you are applying for our Enable Grants, you can expect to hear if you are successful within four months of submitting your application.

If you are applying for our Invest grants, you can expect to hear if your Stage One application has been successful within three months. Successful Stage One applicants will then be invited to submit a more detailed Stage Two application. Once your Stage Two application has been received, you can expect to hear back within three months.

We are happy to offer feedback if your application is unsuccessful.

Sources of information

Accounts; annual report; Charity Commission record; funder's website.

Lloyds Bank Foundation for the Channel Islands

 General charitable purposes

 Channel Islands

£ £704,000 (2016)

CC number: 327113

Trustees: Sarah Bamford; Michael Starkey; Timothy Cooke; Katheryn Le Quesne; David Hodgetts; Alison Le Feuvre; John Henwood; Gavin Ferguson; Heather MacCallum.

Correspondent: Jo Le Poidevin, Executive Director, Sarnia House, Le Truchot, St Peter Port, Guernsey GY1 4EF (tel: 01481 706360; email: jlepoidevin@lloydsbankfoundation.org. uk)

 www.lloydsbankfoundationci.org. uk

 @lloydsbfci

The foundation was set up by Lloyds Bank in 1986. The foundation derives its income almost entirely from Lloyds Banking Group but is an independent entity with policies determined by a board of trustees, which meets three times each year, agrees on strategic priorities and distributes funding. According to the foundation's website, grants are made 'to support charitable organisations which help people, especially those who are disadvantaged or disabled, to play a fuller role in communities throughout the Channel Islands'.

Areas of work

According to the foundation's grant guidelines, it likes to fund the following areas:

People with health issues or a disability – We support charities which create opportunities for people with health issues or a disability to live and work independently.

People experiencing homelessness – We help charities which provide accommodation and support for people who are homeless, and support their return into society.

People with dependency on alcohol or drugs – We support charities providing education and rehabilitation for people who misuse alcohol and drugs.

Carers – We help charities providing support, training, and respite care.

Challenging disadvantage and discrimination – We help charities who challenge discrimination and stigma, and promote equality of opportunity for all.

People with literacy problems – We support learning programmes for people disadvantaged by poor education and literacy.

People affected by domestic violence – We support charities [that] help prevent and protect people from abusive relationships.

People leaving institutional care to live independently – We help charities providing support and accommodation for people who are getting back into society, maybe after leaving care or prison.

Financial information

In 2016 the foundation had assets of £818,000 and an income of £545,700. Grants to 30 organisations totalled £704,000. Grants were distributed as follows:

Children and young people	9	£207,000
Disability	5	£148,000
Health, including mental health	5	£123,500
Relationships, including caring	2	£52,500
Victim support	1	£52,000
Advice and advocacy	2	£38,000
Training, employment and lifelong learning	1	£35,000
Community support	2	£20,000
Older people	2	£17,800
Offenders/ex-offenders	1	£10,000

Beneficiaries included: Jersey Action Against Rape (£52,000); Guernsey Association for Mental Health (£46,000); Guernsey Alcohol Advisory (£40,000); Giving Opportunities to Guernsey Young People (£35,000); Jersey Child Care Trust (£24,000); St Peter's Youth Club (£15,500); Guernsey Bereavement Service (£15,000); Creative Learning in Prison and St Saviours Community Centre (£10,000 each); Little Oaks Nursery (£5,000).

Exclusions

According to the application guidelines, the following fall outside the funding criteria:

- Organisations which are not registered charities.
- Individual requests.
- Sponsorship request.
- International appeals.
- Animal welfare.
- Environmental charities.
- Expeditions or overseas travel.
- The promotion of religion. We might not exclude charities which have a religious element, if their objectives demonstrate a wider benefit to people experiencing disadvantage.
- Schools and colleges (except for projects that will benefit disadvantaged students and are clearly additional to statutory responsibilities).
- Activities which are the responsibility of a statutory body or the islands' governments.
- Activities which duplicate or overlap a service already provided.
- Applications for salaries which would apply to the applicant.
- Charities which have received one of our grants in the previous 12 months, or have received three years continuous funding

Applications

Application forms, along with guidelines, are available to download from the website. Forms should be submitted together with:

- A copy of a recent bank statement
- An income tax letter of exemption
- Your organisation's latest audited accounts
- If you are applying for funding for a post(s), the job description
- If you are applying for funding over multiple years, a business plan

Applications can be returned to the foundation at any time and must be submitted by post. The foundation does not accept forms that have been emailed or faxed.

Applications are assessed on a continual basis. The trustees meet three times a year to approve grants. Deadline dates for these meetings may vary but generally fall in mid-February, mid-June and mid-October. The process of making a decision can, therefore, take up to four months. All applicants are informed of the outcome of their application.

Applicants are encouraged to discuss their project with the Executive Director before completing an application form. This will help to ensure that their project is within the criteria and that they are applying for an appropriate amount.

Sources of information

Accounts; annual report; Charity Commission record; funder's website.

Lloyd's Patriotic Fund

 Armed forces, social welfare, health and disability, education and training

 England and Wales

£ £345,000 (2016/17)

CC number: 210173

Trustees: Sir David Manning; Tim Coles; James Kininmonth; Alexander Findlay; Bruce Carnegie-Brown; Henry Dyson; Richard Williams; Simon Beale; Gp Capt. Wendy Rothery; William Roscoe; Mark Drummond Brady; Duncan Welham.

Correspondent: Jo Taylor, Corporate Social Responsibility Manager, c/o Lloyd's, One Lime Street, London EC3M 7HA (tel: 020 7327 6208; email: jo.taylor@lloyds.com)

 www.lloyds.com/lpf

Established in 1803 following the Napoleonic Wars, the Lloyd's Patriotic Fund (LPF) supports the armed forces community and their dependants, particularly those with disabilities, facing poverty, or experiencing other forms of hardship. It provides long-term support to a number of partner organisations and in recent years has made additional grants for special projects to respond to the need arising from recent past conflicts. Its current long-term partners are SSAFA, Gurkha Welfare Trust, The Royal Navy and Royal Marines Children's Fund, and The Royal Navy Officers' Charity.

The LPF has an annual grants programme that charities can apply to. Grants of up to £200,000 are available, to be spent within a 12-month period. Only UK-registered charities are eligible and the project must support UK beneficiaries. Grants should be for a specific one-off project or the startup of a new, innovative project for an as yet unmet need. The LPF requires successful applicants to provide a detailed mid-project and end-of-project report which demonstrates the impact that the project will have. Examples of grants awarded in the past can be found on the fund's website.

Financial information

In 2016/17 the fund held assets of £3.5 million and had an income of £469,500. Grants awarded to organisations totalled £345,000.

Previous beneficiaries have included: Stoll (£101,500); The Royal British Legion Industries (£100,000); SSAFA (£75,500); Gurkha Welfare Trust (£21,500); University Hospital of Coventry and Warwickshire (£12,900); Combat Stress and Walking with the Wounded (£1,300 each).

Other donations totalled £31,500.

Exclusions

Applications for general ongoing core services, unrestricted funding, running costs, contributions directly towards individual beneficiaries, sponsorship, and payment of expenses are not eligible. War memorials will not be funded by the LPF.

The LPF notes that it is unable to consider requests from charities that only support a specific sector of society based on ethnicity, faith, sexual orientation or political beliefs.

Applications

Application forms are available from the correspondent and should be submitted along with your accounts and any other additional supporting information. The application window is only open once a year and applications should be received by the end of March. All shortlisted applicants will be notified by the end of April.

Unsuccessful applicants will be given feedback on their applications and the fund welcomes potential applicants to make contact to request further guidance.

Sources of information

Accounts; annual report; Charity Commission record; guidelines for applicants; further information provided by the funder.

Lloyd's Register Foundation

Engineering-related education, research, science and technology, safety

Worldwide

£20.6 million (2016/17)

CC number: 1145988

Trustees: Carol Sergeant; Sir Brian Bender; Lambros Varnavides; Thomas Thune Andersen; Rosemary Martin; Ron Henderson.

Correspondent: Michelle Davies, Company Secretary, 71 Fenchurch Street, London EC3M 4BS (tel: 020 7709 9166; email: michelle.davies@lr.org)

 www.lrfoundation.org.uk

Lloyd's Register Foundation was registered with the Charity Commission in 2012. It is funded by the profits of its trading arm, Lloyd's Register Group Ltd, a professional services organisation working mainly in the transportation and energy sectors.

According to the 2015/16 annual report, the foundation's mission is:

- To secure for the benefit of the community high technical standards of design, manufacture, construction, maintenance, operation and performance for the purpose of enhancing the safety of life and property at sea and on land and in the air
- The advancement of public education including within the transportation industries and any other engineering and technological disciplines

Funding priorities

According to the foundation's 2014–2020 Strategy Map, its priorities are:

- Supporting safety organisations
- Communication and public debate of scientific research
- Developing the Lloyd's Register Foundation Heritage & Education Centre library and archive
- Pre-university education
- University education
- Vocational training and professional development
- Structural integrity and systems performance
- Resilience engineering
- Human and social factors
- Emergent technologies

Financial information

In 2016/17 the foundation had assets of £306.7 million and an income of £908.2 million. Grants made to organisations totalled £20.6 million. Grants were broken down as follows:

Accelerating the application of research	£10.7 million
Supporting excellent scientific research	£8.5 million
Advancement of skills and education	£1.3 million
Promoting safety and public understanding of risk	£190,000

Beneficiaries included: Health and Safety Executive and University of York (£10 million each); University of Southampton (£600,000); University College London (£250,000); Nesta (£90,000); Plymouth Marine Laboratory (£75,000); Tolani Maritime Institute (£10,000).

Applications

Applications can be made through the foundation's grants portal. Applications for over £500,000 are considered at quarterly board meetings; all other applications are considered monthly.

Sources of information

Accounts; annual report; Charity Commission record; funder's website.

The Locker Foundation

Jewish causes, illness, disability

UK and overseas

£949,000 (2016/17)

CC number: 264180

Trustees: Susanna Segal; Irving Carter; Malcolm Carter.

Correspondent: Irving Carter, Trustee, 9 Neville Drive, London N2 0QS (tel: 020 8455 9280; email: brian@ levyscharteredaccountants.co.uk)

The trust was established in 1972 and mainly supports Jewish organisations. Its objects are for general charitable purposes with a preference for the welfare of individuals in poor health and the teaching of the Jewish religion. The annual report and accounts for 2015/16 state that grants are given 'to projects that are targeted in providing facilities for the sick and injured both in the UK and overseas and to a teaching organisation targeted in providing religious education to members of the public'.

Financial information

In 2016/17 the foundation had assets of £7.8 million and an income of £1 million. During the year, the foundation gave a total of £949,000 in grants to 27 organisations.

Beneficiaries included: Magen David Adom UK (£164,000); Kehal Chassidim Bovov (£80,000); Chai Cancer Care (£50,000); Wizo UK (£40,000); Supporters of Israel's Dependants (£20,000); Shalva (£10,000); Chana Fertility (£5,000); Tikva Children's Home (£150).

Applications

Applications may be made in writing to the correspondent. Decisions must be agreed unanimously by the trustees.

Sources of information

Accounts; annual report; Charity Commission record.

The Lockwood Charitable Foundation

 General charitable purposes, including: medical research, education, culture and heritage, museums, libraries, art galleries, Christianity

UK

£727,000 (2016/17)

CC number: 1123272

Trustees: Lesley Lockwood; Dr Rebecca Lockwood; Richard Lockwood.

Correspondent: Richard Lockwood, Trustee, The Tithe Barn, The Avenue, Compton, Guildford, Surrey GU3 1JW

The foundation was registered in 2008 and provides support to registered organisations in the UK. It particularly focuses on:

- Helping to preserve public health by funding research projects to benefit the sick and terminally ill
- Advancement of education by providing equipment for schools, colleges and universities
- Financial support for the charitable divisions of museums, libraries and art galleries
- Organisations which seek to advance the Christian religion for the benefit of the public
- Other charitable purposes not provided by local authorities

Financial information

In 2016/17 the foundation held assets of £5.8 million and an income of £498,000. Grants to 19 organisations totalled £727,000.

Beneficiaries included: The Children's Trust (£100,000); Missing People (£86,000); Embrace (£75,000); Carers UK (£65,000); Sense (£59,000); The Encephalitis Society (£25,000); Help to Read (£7,200); Research Autism (£5,000).

Exclusions

Organisations that receive funding from local authorities.

Applications

Applications in writing to the correspondent.

Sources of information

Accounts; annual report; Charity Commission record.

Loftus Charitable Trust

Jewish causes, relief of poverty, health and disability, education, religion

UK and overseas

£1.3 million (2016/17)

CC number: 297664

Trustees: Andrew Loftus; Anthony Loftus; Richard Loftus.

Correspondent: Anthony Loftus, Trustee, 55 Blandford Street, Marylebone, London W1U 7HW (tel: 020 7604 5900; email: post@ rhodesandrhodes.com)

The trust was established in 1987 by Richard Ian Loftus. Its objects, as stated on the Charity Commission record, are the following:

- Advancement of the Jewish religion
- Advancement of Jewish education and the education of Jewish people
- Relief of the Jewish poor

Financial information

In 2016/17 the trust had assets of £5.5 million and an income of £6.7 million. Grants totalled £1.3 million.

Beneficiaries included: South Hampstead Charitable Trust (£950,000); Kisharon (£30,000); United Synagogue (£22,000); Henry Jackson Society (£12,500); Chai Cancer Care (£5,400); Bicom (£2,500); Chamah (£1,800); Wizo UK (£1,100).

Applications

The trustees prefer to invite applications rather than considering unsolicited applications.

The annual report for 2016/17 states:

The trustees meet regularly to consider what grants they will make and to review any feedback they have received. Nominations for grants are elicited by formal and informal means. The trustees travel widely in the UK and abroad and use knowledge gained to support the objects of the Trust and to inform grant making. Though the trustees make some grants with no formal application, they normally ask invited organisations to submit a formal application saying how the funds would be used and what would be achieved. The trustees have a policy, which is communicated to all beneficiaries, that they make grants with no guarantees of future funding.

Sources of information

Accounts; annual report; Charity Commission record.

The Lolev Charitable Trust

Orthodox Jewish causes, education, religion, health and disability

UK, Hackney and the surrounding area

£378,000 to organisations (2016)

CC number: 326249

Trustees: Abraham Tager; Eve Tager; Michael Tager.

Correspondent: Abraham Tager, Trustee, 14A Gilda Crescent, London N16 6JP (tel: 020 8806 3457)

The trust was established in 1982 and its objects are to assist people in need or those in ill health and to support Orthodox Jewish religious education. Both organisations and individuals can be assisted.

Financial information

In 2016 the trust had negative assets of −£35,000 and an income of £8.7 million. It distributed £8.8 million in grants, which includes £378,000 made to organisations and £8.4 million given to individuals. Grants to organisations were broken down as follows:

Religious education	£122,000
Poor and needy	£112,500
Schools (including repairs)	£55,500
Medical	£35,000

Previous beneficiaries have included: Chasdei Shalom (£8,100); Birkat Naftoli Shmuel (£7,600); Netivot Hora'ah (£7,300); Tikvah Layeled (£7,100).

Applications

Applications may be made in writing to the correspondent. The annual report for 2016 states:

Applications by individuals must be accompanied by a letter of recommendation by the applicant's minister or other known religious leader. In the case of applications by charities the collecting agent's references are verified by special agency, unless known to the trustees. Assistance is given according to circumstances and available finance.

Sources of information

Accounts; annual report; Charity Commission record.

Trust for London

 Relief and prevention of poverty, social welfare

 London.

£ £11.3 million (2016)

CC number: 205629

Trustee: Trust for London Trustee.

Correspondent: The Grants Team, 6–9 Middle Street, London, EC1A 7PH (tel: 020 7606 6145; email: info@ trustforlondon.org.uk)

 www.trustforlondon.org.uk

 facebook.com/trustforlondon

 @trustforlondon

Trust for London is the largest independent charitable foundation funding work which tackles poverty and inequality in the capital. It does this by funding local and charity groups, funding indpendent research and providing information and expertise on London's social issues to policymakers and the media.

Grant programmes

The trust has seven funding programmes, details of which have been taken from its website:

Good homes and neighbourhoods – Funding for advocacy work on housing issues and housing legal advice at a specialist level.

Better work – Progression routes out of low-paid work; specialist employment legal advice; advocacy on employment issues and capacity-building.

Decent living standards – Welfare reform; the cost of living, and public attitudes to poverty. Representation and strategic legal action in social welfare law.

Shared wealth – Advocacy work on understanding and reducing income and wealth inequality in London.

Pathways to settlement – Specialist immigration legal advice and advocacy work on the immigration system and pathways to leadership.

Stronger voices – Funding for second-tier and specialist organisations to help other organisations develop their skills.

Connected communities – Small grants for small groups with an annual income under £100,000. Funding for campaigning, advice and community activities in isolated areas.

What is funded

The trustees fund voluntary and community organisations undertaking charitable activities. You do not need to be a registered charity. This may be for a specific project or on-going costs. This includes staff salaries and overheads. Applicants are encouraged to include a reasonable amount of core costs to cover their overheads when they apply for funding. The majority of funding is for revenue costs, though small capital items can also be funded.

There is no minimum or maximum size of grant. However, the average grant is around £80,000 and the trust rarely makes grants over £150,000. Grants can be spread over one, two or three years.

Financial information

In 2016 the trust held assets of £316 million and had an income of £8.4 million. A total of £11.3 million was awarded in grants.

Beneficiaries included: Child Poverty Action Group (£200,000); Asylum Aid (£90,000); Africa Advocacy Foundation (£60,000); Beyond Youth (£50,000); Mind in Haringey (£40,000); People First Lambeth (£20,000); Legal Services Agency (£8,600).

A full list of beneficiaries can be found on the trust's website.

The following information is taken from the trust's application guidelines:

The charity will not support proposals:

- Which do not benefit Londoners
- That directly replace or subsidise statutory funding (including contracts)
- That are the primary responsibility of statutory funders such as local and central government and health authorities
- From individuals, or which are for the benefit of one individual
- For mainstream educational activity including schools
- For medical purposes including hospitals and hospices
- For the promotion of religion
- For umbrella bodies seeking to distribute grants on our behalf
- For work that has already taken place
- For general appeals
- For large capital appeals (including buildings and minibuses)
- From applicants who have been rejected by us in the last six months

The charity is unlikely to support proposals:

- From large national charities which enjoy widespread support
- For work that takes place in schools during school hours
- Where organisations have significant unrestricted reserves (including those that are designated), generally up to six months expenditure is normally acceptable
- Where organisations are in serious financial deficit

Applications

Applications can be made via the trust's website. Application deadlines and funding guidelines for 2018–22 can be found on the trust's website. If, after reading these funding guidelines, you are in doubt as to whether your work fits then please telephone to discuss your application. It is strongly recommended that potential applicants read the guidelines before making an application. The guidelines for applicants state the following:

We aim to contact you within six weeks of the relevant closing date to let you know whether you have been rejected or shortlisted. Please avoid contacting us during this period to find out about your application as this takes up our time and resources. If you are unsuccessful we will give you feedback. However, please understand our funding decisions are final.

Sources of information

Accounts; annual report; Charity Commission record; guidelines for applicants; funder's website.

London Catalyst

 Health and disability, social welfare

 Greater London, within the boundaries of the M25

£ £270,000 (2016)

CC number: 1066739

Trustees: Mark Palframan; Philippe Granger; Zoe Camp; Revd Adrian McKenna-Whyte; Margaret Elliott; Dr Muhammad Bari; Dr Ruth Kosmin; Andrew Davidson; Dr Sarah Divall; Emma Whitby.

Correspondent: Alison Beck, Grants Administrator, 45 Westminster Bridge Road, London SE1 7JB (tel: 020 3828 4204; email: london.catalyst@peabody. org.uk)

 www.londoncatalyst.org.uk

London Catalyst (formerly the Metropolitan Hospital Sunday Fund) was established in 1873. Among its founders were Florence Nightingale, Elizabeth Garrett Anderson, Baroness Burdett-Coutts and William Henry Smith MP.

Since its creation, the charity has held an annual 'Hospital-Sunday' appeal to 'raise funds to provide food, clothing and other basic items to people leaving hospital and those living in the community who are destitute and coping with chronic ill-health'.

Today, the charity makes grants to assist the work of charities, voluntary and community organisations, social work and health agencies operating in Greater London (within the M25). It particularly targets health inequalities and poverty in areas of social deprivation. Each year around £300,000 is available in grants.

Grant programmes

The charity currently runs two grant programmes:

Project grants

Project grants support new initiatives and service developments targeted at people disadvantaged as a result of long-term ill health, disability and poverty. Grants range from £1,000 to £5,000; the average in 2015 was £3,900. Occasionally larger grants are considered if the trustees take a special interest in a project as determined by merit, impact and how closely it matches the charity's current priorities. The trustees will also consider collaborations with other funders.

Samaritan grants

Samaritan grants are made available to front line health, social work and advice agencies to provide immediate assistance to people in an emergency. Samaritan grants normally range from £100 to £2,000 and can be repeated annually subject to available resources, evidence of need and satisfactory reporting.

The charity notes that 'any reasonable and appropriate project cost', including salaries, training, volunteer expenses, management, supervision and evaluation costs are available. The trustees prefer 'time-limited 'catalytic' project-related grants'.

Partners for Health grants

This year, the charity partnered with the Hospital Saturday fund to offer the 'Partners for Health' grants. Grants fund projects which work in partnership with expert health agencies/providers to support people with long-term health conditions. Grants of up to £10,000 are awarded, with priority given to charities with an annual income of less than £250,000 which have not previously received a 'Partners for Health' grant.

Financial information

In 2016 the charity had assets of £13 million and an income of £321,000. There were 138 awards to organisations and projects, which totalled £270,000.

Beneficiaries included: Age Exchange Theatre Trust Ltd, Bell Farm Christian Centre, Forced Migration Trauma Service and Mental Fight Club (£4,000 each); 13 Rivers Trust, Enfield Mind and Waterloo Community Counselling

(£3,000 each); In Touch Kids Ltd (£1,000); Enfield Judo Club (£750).

Exclusions

The charity does not respond to general appeals and does not normally fund charities with an income of over £500,000. Nor does it fund the following: hospitals and homes within the NHS (except Samaritan Grants); hospital leagues of friends for NHS and independent hospitals; government departments; profitable organisations.

Applications

The charity has recently launched a new online application procedure, accessible via the charity's website. All applications are recorded and reviewed by the staff against eligibility criteria before consideration by the Grants Scrutiny Committee and the board. Full guidance for each of the charity's grants programmes is also available to download from the charity's website. The trustees meet four times a year in February, May, September, and November. Full and complete applications must be received at least four weeks in advance of meetings. Applicants are advised to call the office if they have any questions regarding their application prior to submission.

Sources of information

Accounts; annual report; Charity Commission record; funder's website.

London Housing Foundation Ltd (LHF)

Homelessness

London

£351,000 (2016/17)

CC number: 270178

Trustees: Simon Dow, Chair; Ian Brady; Donald Wood; John Stebbing; Jeremy Swain; Derek Joseph; Clare Miller; Eleanor Stringer; Victoria Rayner.

Correspondent: Derek Joseph, 57A Great Suffolk Street, London SE1 0BB (tel: 020 7934 0177; fax: 020 7934 0179; email: jane.woolley@lhf.org.uk)

 lhf.org.uk/programmes-and-grants

The London Housing Foundation was set up to help ease the problems of single

people in London who are either homeless or vulnerable to homelessness. It achieves this in two ways:

- Targeted grant-making, supporting agencies with good ideas that want to make a difference
- Direct training, educational and development support to strengthen the capacity of voluntary agencies tackling 'single homelessness' in the capital

The foundation prefers to concentrate its funding on a couple of specialist areas at any one time. Recent examples include increasing access to private rented sector accommodation for young single people and promoting access to health and dental treatment. The accounts note:

A constant theme over much of the Foundation's existence has been assisting agencies who are wanting to consider mergers, usually with the aim of increasing efficiency or preserving services. In these situations we fund professional advice, usually to smaller agencies who have insufficient resources. Such support covers diverse aspects of mergers such as seeking a partner and ensuring staff and boards work together effectively once a merger is embarked upon. This comes under the heading 'Sector Support'.

The foundation is also the largest funder of the London Homelessness Awards for homelessness charities.

The foundation also offers grants and bursaries to enable those working in the homelessness sector, particularly young leaders, to expand their knowledge of work being carried out elsewhere. See the website for further information.

Criteria

The following is taken from the website and information shared by the foundation:

We will consider your idea if it meets three criteria:

1) Your idea must help people who are, have been, or are at risk of becoming homeless

2) Within [these] broad criteria, the LHF Board [has] agreed themes that [it wants] to prioritise

- The top priority will be given to projects dealing with criminal justice or health
- The second priority will be given to projects looking at migration and destitution, or employment
- The board would also welcome proposals dealing with the use of

volunteering, or the prevention of homelessness

You can find more information about projects that we have worked with in these areas on our case studies page. Note that we will still consider homelessness projects that do not deal with these areas.

3) Your idea must have the potential to improve the way that homelessness services are delivered in future.

We are always interested in finding new and better ways to tackle the problems of homeless people.

We like to fund risky or radical ideas, rather than tried-and-tested approaches, however effective they may be!

Financial information

In 2016/17 the foundation had assets of £16.4 million and an income of £634,000. A total of 11 grants were made, totalling £351,000. They are shown in the table opposite.

Beneficiaries included: De Paul International (£100,000); Safer London (£50,000); PACT (£42,000); Lambeth Law Centre (£38,700); Cambridge House (£18,000); Hope (£15,000); Union Chapel (£7,500).

Applications

Applicants are asked to first complete the short application form on the foundation's website detailing their project idea. The foundation will then follow this up with the applicant.

Sources of information

Accounts; annual report; Charity Commission record; funder's website.

London Legal Support Trust (LLST)

 Voluntary legal services

London and South East England

£840,500 (2016)

CC number: 1101906

Trustees: Richard Dyton; Marc Sosnow; Peter Gardner; Graham Huntley; Steve Hynes; Joy Julien; Jeremy Thomas; Emma Turnbull; Amanda Illing; Rodger Pressland.

Correspondent: Nezahat Cihan, National Pro Bono Centre, 48 Chancery Lane, London WC2A 1JF (tel: 020 3088 3656; email: ceo@llst.org.uk)

 www.londonlegalsupporttrust.org. uk/grants

 facebook.com/ LondonLegalSupportTrust

 @londonlegal

The London Legal Support Trust (LLST) is an independent charity fund and supports the provision of free specialist legal advice services through law centres, advice agencies and Citizens Advice. The trust raises funds from fundraising events, including the London Legal Walk as well as ad hoc donations from law firms and chambers.

Grants programmes

Small grants – awards of up to £5,000 are given for: pro bono surgeries; one-off capital costs, especially to improve sustainability; and development of legal agencies where none currently exist. These awards form about 10 to 15% of the trust's grant expenditure. Any charity that provides free legal advice in London and the South East can apply.

Centres of Excellence – about 80 to 85% of the trust's funding goes to this project providing finance, in-kind help and other support to organisations which 'have been providing free specialist legal advice (through employed staff providing casework and/or representation) for at least one year' and whose service is 'based in and provided wholly or mostly to residents of London and the home counties'. Giving consists of core grants and additional support to maintain and develop the organisation.

In addition to financial support, the trust also offers any charity that provides free legal advice (including pro bono services) the opportunity to take part in LLST's events in order to raise funds for themselves. See the website for more details.

Financial information

In 2016 the trust had assets of £245,500 and had an income of around £1.16 million. During the year, the trust awarded around £840,500 in grants to 176 organisations.

Beneficiaries included: Islington Law Centre (£30,000); St Hilda's East Community Centre (£6,900); Citizens Advice Richmond (£5,500); Hillingdon Law Centre (£4,600); Age UK Reading (£1,700); Child Poverty Action Group (£950); Family Rights Group (£710); REDRESS (£570); Salvation Army Merton (£460).

Exclusions

The trust does not fund non-charitable activity or applications for general advice as opposed to specialist legal advice.

Applications

Application forms for small grants can be downloaded from the trust's website together with criteria and guidelines. Grants are normally awarded three times a year, check the trust's website for the latest deadlines dates.

Applicants who wish to participate in the Centres of Excellence scheme should contact the trust and ask to be added to the waiting list. The process is explained in detail on the trust's website.

Sources of information

Accounts; annual report; Charity Commission record; funder's website.

The London Marathon Charitable Trust Ltd

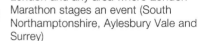

 Sports, recreation and leisure activities

London and any area where London Marathon stages an event (South Northamptonshire, Aylesbury Vale and Surrey)

£4.65 million (2016/17)

CC number: 283813

Trustees: John Austin; Sir Rodney Walker; Dawn Austwick; Simon Cooper; Sir John Spurling; Lee Mason; Rosie Chapman; Charles Maddock Johnston; Charles Patterson Reed; Robert Rigby; Alan Pascoe; Claire Shepherd; Danna Fraser; Gillian McKay; Terry O'Neill.

Correspondent: Sarah Ridley, Chief Grants Officer, Marathon House, 190 Great Dover Street, London SE1 4YB (tel: 020 7902 0200; email: info@lmct. org.uk)

www.lmct.org.uk

The trust was formed to distribute the surplus income donated to the charity by its subsidiary, the London Marathon Ltd, which organises the annual London Marathon and other such events each year. Funds are given for much-needed recreational facilities across the city, as well as in areas where London Marathon Ltd stages an event. Areas of benefit also include South Northamptonshire, Aylesbury Vale and Surrey.

The trust's website states that it welcomes applications for:

- Capital expenses of projects that have realistic plans to increase the number of physically inactive people participating regularly in sport and physical activity
- Projects that have realistic plans for their long-term sustainability without additional funding from us once you have completed your capital project
- Projects that will be open to the local community for a significant proportion of each year

Note: The trust has no connection to the fundraising efforts of the individuals involved in the race, who raise over £40 million each year for their chosen good causes.

Grant programmes

The trust currently has two open grant programmes:

Small Capital Project Grants

The Small Capital Project Grants Programme provides awards of between £5,000 and £19,999 to small projects which aim to help improve existing amenities or to build new facilities that will enable organisations to encourage and support more people to become involved in sport and physical activity, particularly those who are currently physically inactive.

The trust has a simple, one-stage online application process for its Small Capital Project Grants. This is a rolling grant programme and applications are considered on a quarterly basis.

Major Capital Project Grants

The Major Capital Projects Grants Programme provides funds of between £20,000 and £150,000 for the renovation, modernisation or creation of significant facilities for organisations that have already shown a commitment to encouraging and supporting people who are not physically active to participate in sporting activities. The trust expects successful applicants to have in place robust business plans as well as strategies for increasing participation into the future along with plans for monitoring and evaluating their impact.

Financial information

In 2016/17 the trust had assets of £10.8 million and an income of £7.1 million. Grants awarded to organisations totalled £4.65 million.

Beneficiaries included: YMCA East Surrey (£350,000); The Royal Parks (£300,000 in two grants); The National Trust (£150,000); Bankside Open Spaces Trust (£145,000); Peabody (£100,000); Abbey Rangers Football Club (£75,000); London Borough of Harrow (£30,000); Lea Rowing Club and Stonebridge Boxing Club (£10,000 each).

Exclusions

According to the trust's website it will not fund:

- Personal sports equipment and clothing (e.g. bats, balls, gloves)
- Living quarters for grounds staff or club employees
- Projects intended primarily for private gain
- Projects that contribute direct to a company's distributable profits
- Funds to build up reserves or surplus and loan repayments
- Retrospective payments we will not reimburse costs already incurred
- Activities that promote religious beliefs
- If your project is applying for a school or educational establishment, it should ensure it opens opportunities for the community as we will not fund projects used solely for delivering curriculum activity
- Support for individuals, including student grants or bursaries
- General and round-robin appeals
- Campaigns

- One-off events, such as conferences, trips, seminars, masterclasses, summer schools, single commissions, productions or festivals

Applications

Applications can be made online through the trust's website. Full details of application process can be found on the 'How to apply' page of the website.

Applications can be submitted regularly throughout the year and the trustees meet quarterly to make funding decisions. Check the website for the latest deadline dates. Note that this is a two-stage application process.

The trust has a very helpful FAQs page on its website and welcomes queries from potential applicants.

Sources of information

Accounts; annual report; Charity Commission record; funder's website.

The William and Katherine Longman Trust

🔍 General charitable purposes

📍 UK

£ £415,000 (2016/17)

CC number: 800785

Trustees: William Harriman; Alan Bell.

Correspondent: Karen Wall, Administrator, 28 Julian Road, Orpington, Kent BR6 6HU (email: karen@walltrustsupport.co.uk)

Established in 1988, the trust supports general charitable purposes by making grants to any registered charities in England and Wales.

Financial information

In 2016/17 the charity held assets of £2.34 million and had an income of £56,000. Grants totalled £415,000. A full list of beneficiaries was not included in the accounts.

Previous beneficiaries have included: Mizpah Trust (£125,000); The Kel Trust (£80,000); Vanessa Grant Trust (£30,000); Chelsea Arts Club Trust (£25,000); Chelsea Festival and World Child Cancer Fund (£20,000 each); Care (£12,000); Hope Education Trust and RADA (£10,000 each); Action for ME (£5,000); The Children's Society (£4,500); Age Concern – Kensington and Chelsea (£3,500); RSPCA – Harmsworth Hospital (£3,000); St Mungo's (£2,500); Prisoners Abroad (£1,000).

Exclusions

Grants are only made to registered charities.

Applications

The 2016/17 annual report states:

> The trustees' current policy is to consider all written appeals received but only successful applicants are notified of the trustees' decision. The trustees' current policy is to fully distribute the annual income of the Trust to certain selected Charities although no commitment is given to the recipients. The trustees review the selected charities and consider new appeals received at their annual meeting. It is unusual for the trustees to respond favourably to unsolicited appeals.

Sources of information

Accounts; annual report; Charity Commission record.

The Lord's Taverners

🔍 Youth cricket, increasing participation, equipment and facilities, disability, disadvantage

📍 Unrestricted, in practice, UK

£ £2.2 million (2016/17)

CC number: 306054

Trustees: David Collier; Richard White; Ruth Fitzsimons; John Taylor; Samantha Gladwell; Tim Graveney; Ian Martin; Alistair Subba Row; Angela Rippon; Suzy Christopher.

Correspondent: Nicky Pemberton, Charitable Programmes Director, 90 Chancery Lane, London WC2A 1EU (tel: 020 7025 0015; email: nicky. pemberton@lordstaverners.org)

🌐 www.lordstaverners.org

f facebook.com/thelordstaverners

@lordstaverners

@lordstaverners

The Lord's Taverners was founded in 1950 at the Tavern pub at Lord's Cricket Ground. At first, the money raised each year was given to the National Playing Fields Association (now the Fields in Trust) to fund artificial cricket pitches.

There are now three fundraising groups: Lord's Taverners, Lady Taverners (established in 1987) and Young Lord's Taverners. The trust has 28 regional groupings (all volunteer) throughout the UK and Northern Ireland. The Lady Taverners has 24 Regions.

The charity's principal activities and charitable mission are to enhance the prospects of marginalised young people (up to the age of 25) – particularly those with disabilities, special needs or otherwise disadvantaged – through cricket and other forms of sport.

Grant programmes

The charity's mission is carried out by using specially adapted forms of cricket and other sports, including rugby, tennis, squash, basketball and boccia, as well as providing specialist equipment. According to the website, support programmes include:

- Disability and disadvantaged cricket programmes – 'opportunities for young people with a range of abilities and disabilities to engage in cricket and other sporting activities within their local communities'
- Disability programmes and play spaces – 'sporting and recreational activities for young people with disabilities and special needs'
- Fun days – for pupils with disabilities and their carers' at venues across the UK
- Provision of minibuses – 'specially adapted transport to special schools catering for young people with learning and physical disabilities'
- Sporting equipment – specially adapted sports wheelchairs, sensory and soft play and outdoor play equipment, high-quality sports kit for socially deprived communities
- Fields in Trust – a long-standing relationship supporting the organisation in securing access to outdoor spaces for sport and recreation
- Delivery, management and support of inner city, disability and other youth sports activities and competitions
- Supporting the installation of non-turf pitches to increase the opportunities for young people to play and donation of hundreds of cricket equipment bags to communities, clubs and school teams across the UK
- Pathways for young people into employment, education and training and other positive activities including mainstream cricket

Note: The charity has refocused its cricket giving 'from grant provision to expansion of its community cricket programmes, targeting young people in socially deprived areas of the UK and those with disabilities'.

The Lord's Taverners has been recognised by the England and Wales Cricket Board (ECB) as the official national charity for recreational cricket. Most cricket grants are distributed in association with the ECB. An annual grant is also made to the English Schools Cricket Association.

See the website for more details of specific programmes.

Financial information

In 2016/17 the charity held assets of £9.3 million and had an income of £6.3 million. Charitable activities totalled almost £2.9 million, with 175 specific beneficiaries or organisations receiving £2.2 million. The following breakdown was included in the accounts:

Minibuses	£1.6 million
Cricket – disadvantage or disability	£671,000
Wheelchair and disability sports	£513,000
Brian Johnston Memorial Fund	£44,500

A list of beneficiaries was not included in the annual report and accounts.

Exclusions

See specific details for each of the programmes.

Applications

The trustees meet at least four times a year. All applications must be presented on the appropriate application forms – see the grant-making section for further information on separate programmes. Application forms with detailed application instructions are available from the charity's website or the correspondent.

Sources of information

Accounts; annual report; Charity Commission record; funder's website.

LPW Ltd

🔍 Jewish causes

📍 UK

💷 £638,500 (2016)

CC number: 1148784

Trustees: Irwin Weiler; Paula Weiler; Riki Greenberg; Alexander Weiler; Daniela Rosenthal; Monica Rosenthal; Nicholas Rosenthal; Talia Cohen.

Correspondent: The Trustees, c/o Cohen Arnold, New Burlington House, 1075 Finchley Road, London NW11 0PU (tel: 020 8731 0777)

The charity was registered in September 2012 and, according to its annual report for 2016, it makes grants to 'established Jewish Orthodox institutions providing religious education and relief for the poor'. It is further stated that 'Grants are considered for both capital projects and revenue funding'.

Financial information

In 2016 the charity held assets of £10.8 million and an income of £1.2 million. Grants awarded to organisations totalled £638,500 and were broken down as follows:

Relief of poverty	£262,500
Advancement of the Jewish religion	£194,000
Advancement of education	£171,000
Other	£10,300

Beneficiaries included: The Lolev Charitable Trust (£140,000); Before Trust (£100,000); Care All Ltd (£50,000); Viznitz (£30,000); Inspiration (£15,000);

Mercaz Hatorah Netzach Yisroel (£10,000).

Grants under £10,000 totalled £32,500.

Applications

Apply in writing to the correspondent.

Sources of information

Accounts; annual report; Charity Commission record.

Robert Luff Foundation Ltd

🔍 Medical research

📍 UK

💷 £878,000 (2015/16)

CC number: 273810

Trustees: Sir Robert Johnson; Melanie Condon; Brian Nicholson; Richard Price; Jean Tomlinson; Revd Matthew Tomlinson; Lady Ruth Bodley; Paul Coleridge.

Correspondent: Richard Price, Secretary, Waters Edge, Ferry Lane, Moulsford, Wallingford, Oxfordshire OX10 9JF (tel: 01491 652204; email: rpjprice@gmail.com)

The foundation supports medical research based upon its trustees' knowledge, rather than in response to applications. Where extra funding is left, one-off awards are made.

Financial information

In 2015/16 the foundation had assets of almost £33 million and an income of £431,000. During the year, the charity awarded around £878,000 in grants to organisations.

Beneficiaries included: Cystic Fibrosis Trust (£154,000); Rosetrees Trust (£150,000); ESPA Research (£100,000); Bowel Disease Research Foundation (£80,000); Asthma UK and Sheffield Teaching Hospital (£50,000 each); Royal Brompton Hospital (£40,000); International Spinal Research Trust (£30,000); Myotubular Trust (£20,000); St Augustine's Church (£5,000); Trinity Hospice (£4,000).

Applications

The foundation has previously stated that 'outside applications are not considered, or replied to'.

Sources of information

Accounts; annual report; Charity Commission record.

The Lyndal Tree Foundation

 Children and young people, older people, health, social welfare, medical research

UK, with a preference for Yorkshire and Scotland

£375,500 (2016/17)

CC number: 1125024

Trustees: Antony Duttine; Lynda Duttine; Steven Duttine; Susan Fidler; Jennifer Brodie.

Correspondent: The Trustees, PO Box 330, Ilkley LS29 1GD

@LyndalTree

Established in 2008, the foundation makes grants to organisations working with children and young people and medical research charities. The foundation generally makes one-off grants of up to £10,000 but will also consider providing longer-term support for up to three years.

Financial information
In 2016/17 the foundation held assets of £1.7 million and had an income of £262,500. Grants totalled £375,500 and were awarded to nine organisations.

Beneficiaries included: Alzheimer's Research (£300,000); Motivation (£25,000); The Beamsley Centre and Perth and Kinross Association (£10,000 each); Action for Kids (£8,600); Cancer Support Yorkshire (£8,000); Beacon (£6,000); Maggie's Yorkshire (£5,000); Lifelites (£3,000).

Applications
Apply in writing to the correspondent.

Sources of information
Accounts; annual report; Charity Commission record.

The Lynn Foundation

General charitable purposes, especially: people with disabilities, music and other arts, sponsorship of young people, medical research and hospices

UK and overseas

£284,500 (2016/17)

CC number: 326944

Trustees: Guy Parsons; Ian Fair; John Emmott; Philip Parsons; John Sykes.

Correspondent: Guy Parsons, Trustee, 17 Lewes Road, Haywards Heath, West Sussex RH17 7SP (tel: 01444 454773; email: thelynnfoundation@yahoo.com)

The foundation was established in 1985 for general charitable purposes and has previously stated that it supports a very wide range of organisations, including those in the areas of music, the arts, Masonic charities, people with disabilities, older people and children.

Financial information
In 2016/17 the foundation had assets of £6.8 million, an income of £302,000. There were 499 grants made to organisations, totalling £284,500, however, details of individual beneficiary organisations were not available. The average grant awarded was £570. The grants were broken down as follows:

Children with disabilities	196	£98,000
Adults with disabilities	189	£95,000
Arts	7	£27,000
Youth sponsorship	33	£16,500
Medical research	32	£16,500
Hospices	31	£16,000
Music	10	£15,000
Sundry	1	£500

A list of beneficiaries was unavailable.

Applications
Applications can be made in writing to the correspondent.

Sources of information
Accounts; annual report; Charity Commission record.

John Lyon's Charity

 Children and young people (up to the age of 25), there is a preference for education in its broadest sense

The London boroughs of Barnet, Brent, Camden, City of London, City of Westminster, Ealing, Hammersmith and Fulham, Harrow and Kensington and Chelsea

£10.5 million (2016/17)

CC number: 237725

Trustee: The Governors of the John Lyon School, Harrow.

Correspondent: Cathryn Pender, Grants Director, The Grants Office, Griffin Lodge, 45A Cadogan Gardens, London SW3 2TB (tel: 020 7259 1700; fax: 020 7591 3412; email: info@jlc.london)

www.jlc.london

@JohnLyonCharity

The history of John Lyon's Charity dates back to the 16th century when John Lyon donated his 48-acre Maida Vale farm as an endowment for the upkeep of two roads from London to Harrow and Kenton. In 1991 the charity was given discretion to use the revenue from the endowment to benefit the inhabitants of the London boroughs through which these roads passed. The charity is an independent branch of the larger Harrow Foundation which also governs Harrow and the John Lyon schools.

The charity is now one of the largest local educational charities in the country, making grants to benefit children and young people up to the age of 25 (sometimes up to 30 for young people who have disabilities) who live in Barnet, Brent, Camden, Ealing, Hammersmith and Fulham, Harrow, Kensington and Chelsea, the City of London and the City of Westminster. Its budgets vary greatly from year to year for historical reasons, and from one part of its beneficial area to another. There are, however, significant cross-borough grants. All of the charity's grants are given in line with its mission, which is 'to promote the life-chances of children and young people through education'.

Grant-making policy
Education is the priority of the charity's grant-making, reflecting the interests of its founder, John Lyon. However, the charity considers education in its broadest sense and supports a variety of projects which provide children and young people with opportunities to take part in a wide range of activities.

As described on its website, John Lyon's Charity makes grants to: registered charities; state schools; independent schools with charitable status; local authorities; exempt charities; and 'national organisations with a track record and reputation in the charity's beneficial area'.

The charity's grant-making is informed by a set of 'Grant-giving principles'. These principles are described on the website and should be considered by organisations before an application is submitted.

Programme areas
Grant-making by the charity is split into nine programme areas and each application is considered on its own merits using this framework. The website explains that these programme areas 'reflect the variety of ways in which organisations seek to help children and young people either by providing them with opportunities or seeking to address specific needs directly'.

The following details are taken from the website, where full information on each programme area is available:

Arts and science
'Projects that provide opportunities for children and young people to participate in Arts activities are always high on the Charity's agenda. These should be of high quality and seek to engage under-represented groups.' The charity supports projects that:

'Seek to engage the hardest to reach in effective programmes'

'Help to increase the confidence and skills of teachers and headteachers to deliver Arts and Science projects and leave a legacy in the school'

'Provide opportunities for children to leave their classrooms and get into Arts and Science venues'

Children and families

'We seek to help parents give their children the best start in life by supporting a variety of projects that help develop parenting skills, support to those in need and prevent families from reaching crisis point.' The charity considers applications for:

'Activities for children aged 0 to 10 years outside the formal school setting'

'Services that provide support to families'

Education and learning

'As an educational foundation, Education & Learning is always at the heart of what we do. We seek to support organisations that help raise the attainment of children and young people and encourage parental engagement in children's learning.' Applications are accepted for:

'Projects that happen within state schools in the Charity's beneficial area including colleges of Further Education'

'Supplementary schools'

'Structured learning activities outside the school day'

Emotional well-being

'The emotional health of young people is vitally important but often neglected by statutory providers. We seek to support projects that help young people most in need of support, frequently delivered in school settings.' The charity 'will consider applications from specialist mental health organisations or from schools seeking to engage these services'. It is further explained:

'Interventions must be delivered by qualified practitioners'

'Delivery must happen in a dedicated setting or within a school'

On its website the charity has guidelines for psychotherapeutic work in schools with children and families.

Special needs and disability

'We support projects that provide opportunities for children and young people with disabilities to have the same experiences as their peers and to help them become more independent and have the ability to make their own decisions.' The charity accepts applications for:

'Family support'

'Education and learning'

'Activities that take place within special and mainstream schools'

'Activities that take place outside special and mainstream schools'

Sports

'We aim to support organisations that encourage participation in sport, nurture talent and provide access to high quality services and equipment. We also support projects that enable young people to gain coaching qualifications.' Applications for the following are encouraged:

'Mass participation in sport'

'Focused work with specific target groups'

'Nurturing talent and creating realistic pathways to elite status'

Training

'Frequently young people leave school without the necessary skills to enter the world of work. We seek to provide training opportunities and apprenticeships to enhance the employability of young people.' Applications for projects providing the following are considered:

'Employment related training'

'Apprenticeships'

'ESOL (English for Speakers of Other Languages)'

Youth clubs and activities for young people

'We are one of the main supporters of youth clubs and young activities in our beneficial area. We are committed to supporting high quality, open access provision and keeping the lights on in youth clubs around north west London.' The charity considers applications for:

'Activities for young people aged 11+ outside the school setting (except educational activities)'

'Universal access to youth clubs and youth activities'

Issues affecting young people

'The pressures on young people today are varied and constantly evolving. Young people continue to be affected by homelessness, teenage pregnancy and health and body image, but the threat from online sources is now equally as worrying.' The charity considers applications for projects that raise awareness among young people about issues that may affect them. These issues could include, but are not limited to:

'E-safety'

'Equality issues (e.g. race, sexuality, gender, religion)'

'Homelessness'

'Sexual exploitation and domestic abuse'

'Youth Offending'

Types of support

The website describes John Lyon's Charity as a flexible funder as its grants can be used in a range of ways. Both new and well established projects can be supported with the following types of support: core costs; some salary costs; direct project costs; apprenticeships in voluntary sector organisations; costs of specialist pieces of equipment; capital costs (buildings and refurbishments); and capacity building. There are specific restrictions depending on the type of funding applied for, which are detailed on the website.

Grant funds

The charity has a number of different funds to which organisations can apply, these are: the Main Grants Fund; Schools in Partnership Fund; Bursary Fund; the Small Grants Fund; the School Holiday Activity Fund; and the School Explorer Fund. The following brief outline was taken from the website:

> The most popular is the Main Grants Fund, and the majority of grants are awarded under this Fund. The Small Grant Fund can be used as a useful introduction to the Charity and often grants awarded under this Fund can lead into larger grants under the Main Grants Fund. Both the Schools in Partnership Fund and School Explorer Fund are open to state schools in the Charity's Beneficial Area and the Bursary Fund supports young people to attend The John Lyon School, Harrow School and selected girls' schools in the Charity's Beneficial Area.

Guidelines, grants limits and application processes differ depending on the fund applied to.

Financial information

In 2016/17 the charity had assets of £364.3 million and an income of £7.8 million. Grants totalled £10.5 million and 479 grants were awarded during the year. They were detailed in the annual report as follows:

Arts and science	£1.68 million
Youth clubs and activities for young people	£1.6 million
Education and learning	£1.3 million
Youth Issues	£1.1 million
Bursaries	£1 million
Children and families	£940,000
Emotional well-being	£876,000
Sport	£583,000
Training	£558,000
Special needs and disability	£397,000
Other	£7,000

Also contained in the annual report is a helpful breakdown of grants given according to funding programmes:

Main Grants	£8.2 million
Bursaries	£1 million
Schools in Partnership	£652,000
SHAF	£518,000
Small Grants	£101,000
School Explorer	£2,000

Previous beneficiaries have included: Barnet and Southgate College (£200,000); Young Barnet Foundation (£100,000); The Media Trust (£72,000); Friends of Mapledown School (£70,000);

National Resource Centre for Supplementary Education (£60,000); Lyric Theatre Hammersmith (£50,000); Brentford Football Club Community Sports Trust and StreetGames (£45,000 each); Paddington Arts, Prisoners' Education Trust, Refugee Youth and Samuel Lithgow Youth Centre (£40,000 each).

Exclusions

Grants are restricted to the London boroughs of Harrow, Barnet, Brent, Ealing, Camden, City of London, City of Westminster, Hammersmith and Fulham and Kensington and Chelsea.

The charity's website specifies that grants are not made to:

- Individuals
- Organisations that do not have charitable status or those acting as a conduit
- National organisations with no track record of delivery in the Charity's Beneficial Area
- Grant-giving organisations
- Not-for-profit organisations that are not registered charities
- Registered social landlords
- Schools that have not yet been inspected by Ofsted
- Hospitals, hospices or Clinical Commissioning Groups
- Registered charities that have applied on behalf of organisations that are not registered with the Charity Commission
- Statutory obligations
- General charitable appeals
- Lobbying and campaigning
- Endowment funds
- Mother tongue teaching
- Promotion of religion or politics
- Feasibility studies
- Research
- Medical care (including rehab) and resources
- Telephone helplines
- Overnight school journeys or trips abroad
- Capital for mainstream secondary schools and mainstream FE colleges
- IT equipment for mainstream providers (primary, secondary, FE colleges)
- Bursaries for higher education (including postgraduate)
- Projects that aim to teach healthy eating and reduce obesity
- Gardening, conservation, environmental projects and therapeutic gardens
- Core costs for umbrella bodies or second tier organisations
- Salaries of posts employed by statutory bodies

Applications

In the first instance, potential applicants should visit the charity's website where they will find extensive details of the charity's programme areas and grant funds, as well as full application guidelines.

In brief, the charity operates a two-stage application process for requests to the Main Grants Fund, the Schools in Partnership Fund and for Small Grants of more than £2,000. Stage One requires an initial proposal letter. These letters are accepted at any time and are considered by the trustees at meetings held three times a year, in March, June and November. The website notes that the application process takes approximately six months to complete and that proposals received less than four months before a particular trustees' meeting may not be considered until the following meeting. Applicants who are successful with their initial proposal will be invited to complete the Second Stage Application Form.

For Small Grants of less than £2,000, applications are made through an initial proposal letter and there is no application form. A member of the Grants Team will request more information should it be required.

Applications to the School Holiday Activity Fund and the School Explorer Fund should be made using the appropriate application forms, which are available to download from the website.

For further information, including regarding the Bursary Fund, the Grants Team can be contacted by email, telephone or via the contact form on the website.

Sources of information

Accounts; annual report; Charity Commission record; guidelines for applicants; funder's website.

Sylvanus Lysons Charity

🔍 Religious and charitable work of the Church of England, particularly involving: young people, children and family, disadvantaged individuals

📍 Diocese of Gloucester

£ £285,500 to organisations (2015/16)

CC number: 202939

Trustees: Graham Doswell; The Ven. Robert Springett; Ian Templeton; Ven. Philip Andrew; Revd Ruth Fitter.

Correspondent: Mr A. Holloway, 8–12 Clarence Street, Gloucester GL1 1DZ (tel: 01452 522047)

The trust supports the religious and charitable work of the Church of England in the diocese of Gloucester. The trustees award grants to organisations and individuals, particularly clergy and widows.

Grants are given to parishes and other Christian organisations for Christian causes. The 2015/16 annual report states:

The Trustees' policy is to give assistance to establishing projects and to support

them through the initial years before they can become self-funding.

Grants have been given in the past to assist with the following types of projects:- working with disadvantaged/ disabled young persons and adults, youth workers and support in the local community.

Grants are normally paid as a single initial payment or in quarterly instalments over a specific time.

Financial information

In 2015/16 the trust had assets of £11.4 million and an income of £353,500. Grants were made to 27 organisations, totalling £285,500. A further 72 grants were given to individuals totalling £31,000. All grants were broken down as follows:

Youth work	£179,500
Children and family work	£43,000
Courses and training	£42,500
Work with disadvantaged children and individuals	£36,000
Grants to clergy, widows and other individuals	£31,000
Other	£29,000

Beneficiaries included: Viney Hill Christian Adventure Centre (£36,000); Discover DeCrypt (£30,000); Cirencester PCC (£25,000); The Door (£6,000); Innervation Trust (£4,800); Kick Off – Stroud (£2,000); Ashchurch PCC St Nicholas (£200).

Exclusions

Grants are not given for repair or maintenance and improvement of churches or other buildings, other than in very exceptional circumstances.

Applications

Apply in writing to the correspondent.

Sources of information

Accounts; annual report; Charity Commission record.

M and C Trust

🔍 General charitable purposes, Jewish causes, social welfare, health and disability

📍 UK

£ £210,000 (2016/17)

CC number: 265391

Trustees: Rachel Lebus; Matthew Bernstein; Elizabeth Marks; Victoria Fairley.

Correspondent: Helen Price, c/o Mercer & Hole Trustees Ltd, 72 London Road, St Albans AL1 1NS (tel: 01727 869141; email: helenprice@mercerhole.co.uk)

Established in 1973, the trust supports general charitable purposes, with a preference for social welfare, health and disability and Jewish causes. One-off grants typically range from £3,000 to

£10,000, although occasionally larger multi-year grants are awarded.

Financial information

In 2016/17 the trust held assets of £4.8 million and had an income of £140,500. Grants were made to 24 organisations and totalled £210,000.

Beneficiaries included: Jewish Care (£20,000); Jerusalem Foundation (£16,000); UK Friends of The Abraham Foundation (£10,000); Freedom from Torture and MQ Mental Health (£8,000 each); Carers Trust (£8,000); Ambitious About Autism, Changing Faces, Chickenshed Theatre Company and Refugee Resource (£5,000 each); Kids N'Action (£3,000).

Exclusions

Grants are not made to individuals.

Applications

Apply in writing to the correspondent. The trustees meet once a year to approve applications. Unsuccessful applicants are not responded to.

Sources of information

Accounts; annual report; Charity Commission record.

M B Foundation

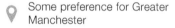 Jewish causes, social welfare, religion and education

Some preference for Greater Manchester

£1 million (2016/17)

CC number: 222104

Trustees: Rabbi Wolf Kaufman; Rabbi Mordechai Bamberger.

Correspondent: Isaac Dov Bamberger, Trustee, Fairways House, George Street, Prestwich, Manchester M25 9WS (tel: 0161 787 7898)

The foundation was registered with the Charity Commission in March 1965.

The charity's aim is to promote religion and education and the relief of poverty with a focus on people of a particular ethnic or racial origin.

Financial information

In 2016/17 the foundation had assets of £6.2 million, an income of £1.26 million. Grants totalled £1 million and were broken down as follows:

Relief of poverty in the Jewish community	£489,000
Advancement of Jewish education	£483,000
Advancement of the Jewish faith	£90,500

A list of beneficiaries was unavailable.

Applications

Apply in writing to the correspondent.

Sources of information

Accounts; annual report; Charity Commission record.

The MK Charitable Trust

 Orthodox Jewish charities, education, religion, health and disability, relief of poverty

Unrestricted, in practice mainly UK

£990,500 (2016/17)

CC number: 260439

Trustees: A. Piller; D. Katz; S. Kaufman.

Correspondent: Simon Kaufman, Trustee, 50 Keswick Street, Gateshead, Tyne and Wear NE8 1TQ (tel: 0191 490 0140)

This trust was established in 1966 for general charitable purposes and applies its income for 'the provision and distribution of grants and donations to Orthodox Jewish charities'. Support is given to educational and religious causes, health and disability and other needs. Grants were awarded to organisations in support of the following:

- Financial support to the poor
- Provision of basic necessities to the poor
- Relief of sickness and disabilities
- Jewish education and places of worship for the Jewish community

Financial information

In 2016/17 the trust had assets of £10.9 million and had an income of £783,000. During the year, the trust gave a total of £990,500 in grants to organisations.

The annual report and accounts did not list any further details of grant recipients.

Applications

Applications can be made in writing to the correspondent. The trust accepts applications for grants from representatives of Orthodox Jewish charities, which are reviewed by the trustees on a regular basis.

Sources of information

Accounts; annual report; Charity Commission record.

The RS Macdonald Charitable Trust

 Neurological conditions, visual impairment, child welfare, animal welfare, medical research, RNLI lifeboats

Scotland

£2 million (2016/17)

OSCR number: SC012710

Trustees: Bruce Rigby; Moira McCaig; Dr Patricia Donald; Fiona Patrick; John Paterson.

Correspondent: Katie Winwick, Grants Administrator, 21 Rutland Square, Edinburgh EH1 2BB (tel: 0131 228 4681; email: office@rsmacdonald.com)

 www.rsmacdonald.com

 @rsmacdonaldct

@rsmacdonaldct

Established in 1978, this is the trust of the late RS Macdonald, whose family founded the famous whisky distiller Glenmorangie plc in 1893. The trust sold its shares in Glenmorangie plc in 2004 and then reinvested the proceeds, with a view to making more money available to charities.

Areas of work

The trust supports charities concerned with the following:

- Neurological conditions
- Visual impairment
- Child welfare
- Animal welfare
- Medical research into neurological conditions, visual impairment or sight loss
- RNLI lifeboats

Types of grant

The trust's website states:

We provide around £3 million in grants every year to charities working in Scotland. The Trust will consider applications for:

- revenue or capital costs
- project funding or core funding
- one-off awards (small and main grants)
- multi-year awards for up to 3 years (main grants only)

The trust provides the following types of grants:

Small grants – grants of up to £15,000 can be applied for at any time of year. Multi-year applications are not considered under this programme.

Main grants – grants of over £15,000 with an average award of around £30,000. Multi-year grants are considered under this programme.

Medical research grants – research into neurological conditions, visual impairment or sight loss. Universities can apply for seedcorn or unrestricted funding for specific academics, research groups or centres. Charities can apply for specific research projects that have completed a peer review process. The trust's website suggests contacting the director before applying for a medical research grant.

Strategic grants – a small number of grants are provided to charities that have previously received funding from the trust. Proposals should fit with the trust's funding themes and meet one or more of the following criteria:

▶ Involves a collaboration with partners
▶ Supports innovation of a new programme or concept that requires pump priming
▶ Enables a programme to be taken to scale by replicating it in one or more new areas

Applicants should contact the director before applying.

Financial information

In 2016/17 the trust had an income of £2 million and held assets of £78.2 million. Grants to 91 organisations totalled £2 million and were broken down as follows:

Purpose	Appli-cations	Grants	Amount
Neurological conditions	79	47	£770,500
Child welfare	60	25	£627,500
Medical research	11	8	£377,500
Visual impairment/ sight loss	13	7	£163,000
Animal welfare	7	3	£52,000
RNLI	1	1	£50,500

Beneficiaries included: Scottish Huntington's Association (£76,500); University of St Andrews (£60,000); Children 1st (£58,500); Sight Action Ltd (£42,000); Revive MS Support (£30,000); Dr Bells Family Centre (£10,000); Drake Music Scotland (£7,500); Granton Youth Centre (£6,000); Macrobert Arts Centre (£5,000).

Applications

Applications can be made through the trust's website. Small grant applications can be submitted anytime. The main grants programme has specific deadlines for each area of work. Check the website for the latest deadlines.

Sources of information

Annual report; accounts; OSCR record; funder's website.

The Mackintosh Foundation

🔍 Theatre and the performing arts, medical aid particularly research into cancer and HIV/AIDS, community projects, homelessness, environment

📍 Worldwide, in practice, mainly UK

£ £606,500 (2016/17)

CC number: 327751

Trustees: Nicholas Allott; Sir Cameron MacKintosh; Nicholas MacKintosh; Robert Noble; Bart Peerless; Thomas Schonberg; Richard Pappas; Alan Finch; Paule Constable.

Correspondent: Richard Knibb, 1 Bedford Square, London WC1B 3RB (tel: 020 7637 8866; email: info@camack. co.uk)

The foundation was established in 1998 by the settlor, Sir Cameron Mackintosh. It awards grants for a variety of purposes with a preference for the theatre and performing arts.

The foundation has provided financial support to a number of projects in the United States, most recently The Actors Fund for the Lillian Booth Actors Home for US $1 million to be paid in equal instalments.

Grant-making information

According to the 2016/17 annual report, the foundation particularly awards grants under the following categories:

▶ Financing education in the United Kingdom and abroad by making grants to schools' core costs and assisting the disadvantaged
▶ Funding the relief of poverty and those in hardship or distress In the United Kingdom and abroad
▶ Promoting and developing theatrical, musical and dramatic arts by a variety of means including education, theatre refurbishment/restoration programmes and the support of a broad range of theatre productions for the enjoyment and education of the public at large
▶ Funding medical research and the relief of sickness generally
▶ Providing grants to environmental projects aimed at the conservation, protection and enhancement of nature in the United Kingdom and elsewhere
▶ Funding community-based projects where often a relatively small grant can make a big impact to many people both immediately and into the future

The annual report notes that the foundation also supports relief for the homeless and poverty stricken, the relief of refugees and to provide funds for any other objects which are exclusively charitable.

Financial information

In 2016/17 the foundation had assets of £6.3 million and an income of £501,000.

There were 169 grants made, totalling over £606,500. Grants awarded were broken down as follows:

Theatre and performing arts	£281,000
Children and education	£147,000
Medical	£68,500
Community projects	£50,000
Homelessness	£50,000
Environment	£10,000

The value of grants awarded in this year is broken down as follows:

More than £75,000	1
£50,000 to £75,000	2
£20,000 to £49,999	2
£10,000 to £19,999	5
£5,000 to £9,999	13
£1,000 to £4,999	101
Less than £1,000	45

Beneficiaries included: Save the Children Fund (£100,500); The Actors Fund (£73,500); Centrepoint – Soho (£50,000); The Royal Theatrical Fund (£20,000); Royal Academy of Music (£10,000); Denville Hall, Good Chance Theatre and Roundhouse Trust (£5,000 each).

Donations of less than £5,000 totalled £202,500.

Applications

Apply in writing to the correspondent, outlining details of the organisation, details of the project for which funding is required and a breakdown of the costs involved. Supporting documentation should be kept to a minimum and an sae enclosed if materials are to be returned. The trustees meet in May and October in plenary session, but a grants committee meets weekly to consider grants of up to £10,000.

Sources of information

Accounts; annual report; Charity Commission record.

The MacRobert Trust

🔍 Armed forces and merchant sailors, children and young people, science engineering and technology, education and training, agriculture and horticulture, local charities

📍 UK, mainly Scotland

£ £798,000 (2016/17)

OSCR number: SC031346

Trustees: Mr K. Davis; Mrs S. Campbell; Mr C. Crole; Mr J. Fowlie; Mr D. Noble; Mr C. Richardson; Commodore C. B. H. Stevenson; Mr J. Strickland; Mrs J. Swan; Gp Capt. W. Gibson; Dr J. Smithson.

Correspondent: EA to Chief Executive Officer, Cromar, Tarland, Aberdeenshire AB34 4UD (tel: 01339 881444; email: alison@themacroberttrust.org.uk)

www.themacroberttrust.org.uk

The MacRobert Trust is an amalgamation of four trusts established by Lady MacRobert in memory of her three sons who were all killed as aviators, the eldest in a civil air accident in 1938 and the middle and youngest as officer pilots in the Royal Air Force on operational sorties in 1941.

This trust was established on 6 April 2001 when the assets of the no longer operating MacRobert Trusts, a collection of four charitable trusts and two holding companies were merged into the new, single MacRobert Trust. The merging of these trusts has led to a decrease in management and administration costs and a general increase in grant-making.

The trust has assets comprising of Douneside House and an estate of 1,800 acres of woodland and 5,100 acres of farmland and associated residential properties let by the trust. The surplus income generated from these assets, following management and administration costs, is donated in grants.

Grant-making information
There are three levels of grants available: small (up to £10,000); medium (between £10,000 and £50,000); and large (£50,000 or more). The website notes that trustees rarely make grants under the large category. Applications for grants are welcomed from across the UK but preference is usually given to Scotland. The current grant-making themes are:

- Services and sea – support for the armed forces and mercantile marine, particularly accommodation and leisure facilities at Douneside House. Other charitable support is given to the single-Service charities and other charitable organisations providing training, welfare, rehabilitation and medical treatment for serving and retired members of the armed forces community
- Education and training – educational grants to individuals and grants to schools, colleges, universities and other training institutions. Support is also given to pupils at independent Scottish secondary schools whose families encounter difficulties with paying fees as a result of unexpected circumstances
- Children and young people – health, welfare and well-being of young people in particular charities addressing addiction, crime, homelessness, disadvantage and disability
- Science, engineering and technology – awards for engineering, grants for research and to support the study and practice of science engineering and

technology. Support is also given to encourage young people to take up engineering as a profession
- Agriculture and horticulture – farming scholarships, horticultural and agricultural charities and sustainability research
- Tarland and the local area – environmental protection, public access to the countryside and the promotion of sport and health, as well as education, citizenship and community development and youth movements

The trust offers a very detailed breakdown of these categories on its website.

Financial information
In 2016/17 the trust had assets of £90.8 million and an income of £2.7 million. There were 80 grants made to organisations in the year, totalling £798,000 broken down as follows:

Services and sea	15	£235,500
Children and youth	26	£200,500
Science, engineering and technology	5	£180,500
Education and training	10	£84,500
Agriculture and horticulture	8	£50,500
Tarland and the local area	14	£38,500
Awards and prizes	2	£8,600

Beneficiaries included: University of Strathclyde (£133,500); Poppy Scotland (£66,500); Wing Warriors (£30,000); The National Piping Centre (£10,000); Tornaveen Community Hall (£7,800); Smallpiece Trust (£4,000); Youthbank Scotland (£500); Stonehaven (£250); Game and Wildlife Conservation Trust (£100).

Exclusions
According to the trust's website, the following applications are not accepted:
- Organisations based outside the United Kingdom
- Beneficiaries resident outside the United Kingdom
- Individuals, except through The Trust's own training schemes
- General or mailshot appeals
- Political organisations
- Religious organisations
- Retrospective applications
- Student bodies as opposed to universities
- Departments within a university unless the appeal gains the support of, and is channelled through, the Principal
- Expeditions, except through the auspices of recognised bodies
- Community and village halls other than those in the local area
- Pre-school groups, after-school clubs or school PTA's other than those in the local area
- Organisations with multiple branches should only apply through their headquarters other than those in the local area

Applications
The application form and full guidelines can be downloaded from the website. Application forms must be emailed along with a cover letter and a full set of audited accounts.

Time bars:
- Unsuccessful applicants must wait for at least one year from the time of being notified before reapplying
- Successful applicants must wait for at least two years from the time of receiving a donation before re-applying
- When a multi-year donation has been awarded, the time bar applies from the date of the final instalment
- Withdrawn applications do not normally face a time bar

Applications for small grants
Applications under this category can be made at any time as the trustees meet every two months to review small grants. Small grants of under £1,000 will be considered on merit at the time of receipt and may receive a quicker response. For grants under £1,000, a letter to the Chief Executive Officer will suffice but it must cover as much detail in the formal application as possible.

Applications for medium and large grants
The trustees meet to consider applications twice a year. Applications for the autumn meeting should be submitted by 31 May and applications for the spring meeting should be submitted by 31 December.

Sources of information
Accounts; annual report; OSCR record; guidelines for applicants; funder's website.

The Mactaggart Third Fund

Q General charitable purposes

♀ UK and overseas

£ £485,000 (2016/17)

OSCR number: SC014285

Trustees: Alastair Mactaggart; Robert Gore; Fiona Mactaggart; Andrew Mactaggart; Sir John Mactaggart.

Correspondent: The Trustees, 7th Floor, 80 St Vincent Street, Glasgow G2 5UB

 www.mactaggartthirdfund.org

The Mactaggart Third Fund is a grant-making charity, established in 1968 by Deed of Trust granted by Western Heritable Investment Company Ltd. The objectives of the fund are to distribute funds by way of charitable donations to suitable charities in the UK and abroad.

The trustees' present policy is to make grants to those charities which have aims they support and who they believe have demonstrated excellence in their achievements. The fund aims to make grants of circa £250,000 each year and since its inauguration it has made grants of over £6 million to a range of charitable organisations.

Note: The fund does not accept unsolicited applications.

Financial information

In 2016/17 the charity had assets of £19.2 million and an income of £825,000. Grants awarded to organisations totalled £485,000.

Beneficiaries included: Lyford Cay Foundation Ltd (£60,000); Amazon Conservation Team (£21,000); The Ranfurley Home for Children (£15,000); Cancer Society of the Bahamas (£6,500); Angling for Youth Development (£5,000); Islay Arts Association (£4,900); Migratory Salmon Foundation (£2,000); Strongbones Children's Charitable Trust (£500); The Banff Centre (£80).

Applications

The fund's website states: 'The trustees are solely responsible for the choice of charitable organisations to be supported. Trustees are proactive in seeking out charities to support and all projects are chosen on the initiative of the trustees. Unsolicited applications are not supported.'

Sources of information

Accounts; annual report; OSCR record; funder's website.

The Ian Mactaggart Trust (The Mactaggart Second Fund)

 General charitable purposes, culture, social welfare, disability

UK, with a preference for Scotland

£420,500 (2016/17)

OSCR number: SC012502

Trustees: Sir John Mactaggart; Fiona Mactaggart; Jane Mactaggart; Robert Gore; Philip Mactaggart; Leora Armstrong.

Correspondent: The Trustees, 7th Floor, 80 St Vincent Street, Glasgow G2 5UB

 www.ianmactaggarttrust.org

The Ian Mactaggart Trust is a grant-making charity, established in 1984. The objectives of the trust are to distribute funds by way of charitable donations to suitable charities in the UK and abroad. The trustees have decided to take a proactive approach to their grant-making. Their present policy is to make grants to those charities which have aims

they support and have demonstrated excellence in their achievements.

Financial information

In 2016/17 the trust had assets of £17.2 million and an income of £630,000. There were 97 grants made to organisations, totalling £420,500.

Beneficiaries included: Islay Heritage (£51,000); Eagle Hill Foundation (£41,000); Battersea Arts Centre (£35,000); Robin Hood Foundation (£2,000); Penny Brohn Centre (£1,000); Sense (£750); The Phoenix Trust for Deaf People (£600); Switchback (£300).

Applications

The trust does not accept unsolicited applications.

Sources of information

Accounts; annual report; OSCR record; funder's website.

Man Group plc Charitable Trust

 Literacy and numeracy

UK

around £397,500 (2016)

CC number: 275386

Trustees: Keith Haydon; Carol Ward; Teun Johnston; Lydia Bosworth; Antoine Forterre; Steven Desmyter.

Correspondent: Bayo Adeyeye, Man Group plc, Riverbank House, 2 Swan Lane, London EC4R 3AD (email: charitable.trust@man.com)

 www.man.com/responsibility

This trust, which was registered in 1978, is the corporate charity of the investment management firm Man Group plc. The trust is the vehicle for most of the company's charitable donations and operates as an independent charity.

The trust has two main aims: firstly, it looks to support organisations working to raise literacy and numeracy levels in the UK and, secondly, it looks to facilitate opportunities for Man Group employees to share their time and expertise for charitable causes. It works to achieve these aims by carrying out the following activities, which are outlined on the trust's webpage:

- Providing grants via a two-stage application process, or through negotiated partnerships with selected charities
- Tracking success by measuring impact, carefully monitoring all grants to ensure progress against agreed objectives

- Providing volunteering opportunities to Man Group UK employees via the Trust's community volunteering programme, ManKind
- Supporting Man Group UK employees' fundraising activity and charitable donations via the Trust's Sponsorship Matching and Give As You Earn schemes

Funding criteria

The trust supports small to medium-sized charities registered in the UK whose work is focused on the promotion of literacy and/or numeracy. There is a document available to download from the website which sets out full criteria and guidelines for applying for support. It states that, in order to be eligible, a charity must:

- Have an annual income greater than £1 million and less than £10 million
- Raise levels of literacy and/or numeracy with evidence of an increase in attainment in one or both of these areas
- Have a significant impact; changing wider policy and practice or having the potential to be mainstreamed or replicated
- Have clear and measurable outcomes and benefits and use evidence of results to improve performance
- Lead to leverage of additional funding wherever possible

The document further explains that applicants must be able to show that they are 'well run, with good governance and financial management' and that they 'have an ambitious approach to tackling social issues'. The trustees prefer to support activities that provide assistance directly to individuals, families and communities and also those that increase the capacity of organisations and individuals.

The trustees also consider the interest and involvement of Man Group employees and hold an interest in finding out about volunteering opportunities, however no preference is given to organisations or projects that can offer such opportunities.

Grant-making

The document from the Man Group website explains that the trust is 'currently funding one-year grants of up to £50,000, but will consider longer-term support for applications that are deemed by trustees to have particular merit'. Grants are typically given to fund core costs (including salaries and overheads) and project costs.

Financial information

In 2016 the trust had an income of £3,100 and a total expenditure of £475,000. Due to its low income, the trust was not required to submit its accounts to the Charity Commission, however the following information was available from Man Group plc's 2016 corporate annual report: 'The Trust spent $592,219 [approx. £447,500 at the time of writing – June 2018] in charitable donations and employee engagement programmes over 2016.' Based on this information and financial information available for previous years, we estimate that grants totalled around £397,500.

Beneficiaries included: Discover Children's Story; Mayor's Fund for London; National Literacy Trust; Vision for Literacy Business Pledge.

Exclusions

The guidelines state that the trust does not as a rule support:

- Large national charities
- Charities which use external fundraising agencies
- Charities primarily devoted to promoting religious beliefs
- Endowment funds
- Requests to directly replace statutory funding
- Individual beneficiaries
- General media campaigns or campaigning or advocacy work to influence policy debates
- Applicants which have been successful during the last twelve months
- Work which has already been completed
- Capital projects and appeals
- Sponsorship or funding towards marketing appeals or fundraising events
- Organisations or projects whose primary purpose is political

Furthermore, the trust will not consider charities with 'high administration costs relative to the services provided'.

Applications

In the first instance, see the trust's page on the Man Group website, where a document detailing eligibility criteria and guidelines on how to apply is available.

The document states that the trust has a two-stage application process. After reading the trust's eligibility criteria and exclusions, a brief expression of interest (not exceeding one side of A4) should be sent by email, including the following: a brief summary of your organisation's aims and activities and, if relevant, the project for which the funding is intended (including the work you hope to carry out, what the need for this work is, who the beneficiaries are, when the project will be undertaken and where it will be based); details of how your organisation meets the trust's focus; the amount of funding being requested; how funds will be used if the application is successful; and contact details.

If your expression of interest is successful, you will be invited to submit a stage two application form for consideration by the trustees, who usually meet twice a year. Successful applicants will be notified by telephone or email. All unsuccessful applicants will be notified and will usually receive an outline explanation for the rejection.

The guidelines also note that 'meeting all of the criteria does not guarantee you will be invited to complete a full application form or that if you are invited to do so, you will receive funding'.

Sources of information

Accounts; annual report; Charity Commission record; funder's website.

The W M Mann Foundation

 General charitable purposes, the arts, education, music, sports, medical causes, disadvantaged individuals

Mainly Scotland but UK-wide organisations may be assisted

£ £184,000 (2016/17)

OSCR number: SC010111

Correspondent: The Trustees, 201 Bath Street, Glasgow G2 4HZ (tel: 0141 248 4936; fax: 0141 221 2976; email: mail@ wmmanngroup.co.uk)

Grants are generally given to organisations based in Scotland or serving the Scottish community, in support of general charitable purposes, including arts, education, music, medical causes and sports, to help disadvantaged individuals. In 2012 the foundation registered as a SCIO. During that financial year, the former W M Mann Trust transferred nearly £4.4 million in assets to the new foundation.

Financial information

In 2016/17 the foundation had assets of over £6.7 million and an income of £227,500. Grants to 94 organisations totalled £184,000.

Beneficiaries included: Glasgow School of Art and University of Glasgow Trust (£50,000 each); Barrwood Trust and Glasgow Phoenix Choir (£5,000 each); Glasgow Old People's Welfare Association (£3,000); Maggie's Centre (£2,000); Little Art School Trust (£500); Glasgow City Mission (£375).

Exclusions

The foundation does not make grants to individuals.

Applications

Applications may be made in writing to the correspondent providing your organisation's latest set of annual report and accounts.

Sources of information

Accounts; annual report; OSCR record.

The Manoukian Charitable Foundation

 General charitable purposes with a preference for: Armenian causes, medical research, arts and culture, education

Worldwide

£ £475,500 to organisations (2015)

CC number: 1084065

Trustees: Tamar Manoukian; Anthony Bunker; Steven Press; Armen Sarkissian.

Correspondent: Steven Press, Trustee, St Yeghiche Armenian Church, 13B Cranley Gardens, London SW7 3BB

According to the 2015 annual report:

> The objects of the charity are the promotion of general charitable purposes; the trustees give particular emphasis to projects with medical, educational or cultural aspects and those that relate to Armenian matters, although they consider applications for other charitable purposes.

In previous years, funding has typically been given in the following areas:

- Social services and relief
- Education and training
- Medical research and care
- Culture and the arts

The foundation will also consider providing assistance to projects that may be partly funded by others if this will enable the project to proceed.

The foundation has received donations from sources associated with the Manoukian family.

Financial information

At the time of writing (June 2018), the most recent set of accounts available to view were from 2015. In 2015 the foundation has assets of £228,500 and an income of £768,000 from donations. Grants made to organisations totalled £475,500.

Beneficiaries included: Action Innocence (£199,500); NSPCC (£98,500); St Yeghiche Armenian Church Parish (£79,000); Holy Etchmiadzin Library (£70,000); Looys Charitable Trust (£20,000); British Lebanese Association (£8,500).

Applications

According to the 2015 annual report, the foundation receives applications from the general public and charitable and other organisations through 'knowledge of the activities of the foundation and through personal contacts of the settlor and the trustees'. The trustees meet at least once per year.

Sources of information

Accounts; annual report; Charity Commission record.

The Marchig Animal Welfare Trust

 Animal welfare

Worldwide with the exception of the USA and Canada

(£) £2.4 million (2016)

CC number: 802133/SCO38057

Trustees: Colin Moor; Les Ward; Dr Jerzy Mlotkiewicz; Janice McLoughlin.

Correspondent: Les Ward, Trustee, Caledonian Exchange, 19A Canning Street, Edinburgh EH3 8HE (tel: 01383 737084; email: info@marchigtrust.org)

 www.marchigtrust.org

The Marchig Animal Welfare Trust was established in 1989 by the late Madam Jeanne Marchig of Geneva for nature and animals and in memory of her husband, the painter Giannino Marchig.

The objects of the trust are:

> To encourage initiatives designed to improve animal welfare, promote alternative methods to the use of animals in experiments and their practical implications and encourage practical work in alleviating suffering, preventing cruelty and improving conditions for animals.

The trust's website states the following:

> There are no restrictions on the geographical area of the work (with the exception of the USA and Canada), the type of grant, or the applicant. All applications meeting the following criteria will be considered by the Trust

> ▹ Those encouraging initiatives designed to improve animal welfare
> ▹ Those promoting alternative methods to animal experimentation and their practical implementation
> ▹ Those promoting and encouraging practical work in alleviating suffering and preventing cruelty to animals
> ▹ Those groups who are registered charities

In addition to making grants, the trust also makes The Jeanne Marchig Awards. These awards, which take the form of a financial donation in support of the winner's animal welfare work, are given in either of the following two categories:

▹ The development of an alternative method to the use of animals in experimental procedures and the practical implementation of such an alternative resulting in a significant reduction in the number of animals used in experimental procedures
▹ Practical work in the field of animal welfare resulting in significant improvements for animals either nationally or internationally

Financial information

In 2016 the trust had assets of £18.2 million and an income of £2.7 million. Grants were made totalling almost £2.4 million. The annual report did not include a list of beneficiaries; however, some information on award recipients are available on the website.

Previous beneficiaries have included: Animals Asia Foundation – Hong Kong; Bedfordshire Wildlife Rescue, UK; Blue Cross of India; Free the Bears – Australia; Frendicoes Society for the Eradication of Cruelty to Animals – India; Help in Suffering – India; Tanzania Animal Protection Organisation; University of Edinburgh; VIDAS International Veterinarians Dedicated to Animal Health – Mexico; Worldwide Veterinary Service – UK.

Exclusions

Expeditions; activities that are not totally animal welfare-related; educational studies or other courses; salaries; support of conferences and meetings.

Applications

Application forms are available from the trust's website or the correspondent and should be returned by post or email along with the most recent accounts and annual report. Applications are accepted throughout the year and all of them are acknowledged. Applicants can reapply after one year following the initial application.

Note: Applicants are expected to also have applied to other organisations for financial support for the project. Application queries should be sent to: applications@marchigtrust.org.

Sources of information

Accounts; annual report; Charity Commission record; funder's website; guidelines for applicants.

The Michael Marsh Charitable Trust

General charitable purposes, education/training, disabilities, children/young people, the relief of poverty, older people

Birmingham, Staffordshire, Worcestershire, Warwickshire, Coventry, Wolverhampton and associated towns in the Black Country

(£) £404,000 (2016/17)

CC number: 220473

Trustees: Peter Barber; Susan Bennett; Lee Nuttall.

Correspondent: The Michael Marsh Charitable Trust, Pear Tree Cottage, Yarrington Road, Alfrick, Worcester WR6 5EX (tel: 07812 743485; email: louise.ruane@michaelmarsh.org.uk)

Registered in 1964, this trust makes grants in support of charities in Birmingham, Staffordshire, Worcestershire, Warwickshire, Coventry, Wolverhampton and associated towns in the Black Country.

Grants are made for a wide range of purposes and the trust's annual report for 2016/17 states that the trustees seek to make a roughly equal division of funds between charities concerned with older people, children, people who have disabilities, people who are poor, and educational needs.

Financial information

In 2016/17 the trust had assets of £3.6 million and an income of £151,500. Grants to 69 organisations totalled £404,000, and were distributed as follows:

Children/young people	21	£223,500
General charitable purposes	17	£121,500
Education/training	10	£21,300
People who have disabilities	12	£18,600
Relief of poverty	5	£12,000
Older people	4	£7,000

Beneficiaries included: Free@Last (£100,000); The Ikon Gallery (£90,000); S4E Ltd (£75,000); Barnardo's, Castle Vale Tenants and Residents Alliance, Ladywood Community Project and Trinity Methodist Church (£5,000 each); Prisoners' Education Trust (£3,400); Birmingham Jewish Community Care (£3,000); Douglas Bader Foundation (£2,000); Bipolar UK and Enrych Warwickshire (£1,000 each); Deafblind UK (£900).

Exclusions

Animals; entertainment charities; replacement of statutory funding; running costs.

Grants to individuals are only given through charitable institutions on their behalf.

Applications

Applications may be made in writing to the correspondent. The trustees meet on a half-yearly basis, normally in June and December, to consider applications. However, our research suggests that they may also consider on an ad hoc basis any requests that they consider should not be retained until their next scheduled meeting.

Sources of information

Accounts; annual report; Charity Commission record.

The Marsh Christian Trust

 Social welfare, environmental and animal welfare, health care, education and training, literature, arts and heritage

UK

 £275,000 (2016/17)

CC number: 284470

Trustees: Brian Marsh; Natalie Collins; Antonia Marsh; Camilla Kenyon; Charles Micklewright; Nicholas Carter.

Correspondent: Brian Marsh, Trustee, 4 Matthew Parker Street, London SW1H 9NL (tel: 020 7233 3112; email: mccarthy@bpmarsh.co.uk)

www.marshchristiantrust.org

@marshawards

The following was published on the trust's website:

> The Trust is a grant-making body, established in 1981 with the sum of £75,000. Having grown through investments and additional donations by the founder and current Chairman, Mr Brian Marsh OBE, the Trust's funds currently stand at just over £8 million. Since its establishment in 1981, the number of organisations supported each year has grown from just 8 to over 300 today.

Grants programme

The trust funds the following areas:

- Social welfare
- Environmental causes and animal welfare
- Health care
- Education and training
- Literature, arts and heritage

The trust's website states:

> The Trust focuses on providing funding which could help small organisations pay for various running costs, such as volunteer expenses, training days, equipment maintenance and other core outgoings.
>
> Our funding strategy is to provide long-term core funding for such costs, as we understand that many of the organisations we support depend on unrestricted income in order to meet their operating needs.
>
> Grants are unrestricted and range from £250 to £4,000, with new applications at the lower end of this scale.
>
> Applications are considered on the basis of the organisation's financial position, performance against charitable aims and objectives and the ratio of voluntary income against fundraising expenses

The Trust aims to build long-standing relationships with successful applicants and, subject to an annual review, continue its support over time.

Awards scheme

The trust also maintains the Marsh Awards Scheme to recognise individual and group achievements in the charity sector. The 2016/17 annual report notes that there are over 80 different programmes for this scheme and that details can be found on the trust's website.

Financial information

In 2016/17 the trust held assets of £11.8 million and had an income of £1.4 million. There were about 340 grants and awards made, including over 55 to new charities, totalling £275,000. Grants and awards were broken down as follows:

Purpose	Awards	Grants
Social and welfare	£24,500	£105,000
Literature, arts and heritage	£40,000	£43,000
Environmental causes and animal welfare	£39,000	£13,400
Education and training	-	£6,100
Health care and medical research	-	£4,000

Beneficiaries included: The Refugee Council (£2,000); Military Ministries International and The Tate Foundation (£1,500 each); Magdalene Group (£1,000); Matthew Trust (£900); Action on Poverty (£850); British Hen Welfare Trust (£500); Maytree Respite Centre (£300); The Lin Berwick Trust (£250); The National Liberal Club (£110).

Exclusions

Individuals; individual/group sponsorship proposals; individual churches; hospices or hospitals; start-up costs.

Applications

Apply in writing to the correspondent. The trust requires a cover letter and a full copy of the applicant's annual report and accounts. Applicants should demonstrate that they have understood the type of funding which the trust provides and illustrate how this would benefit their charity on a long-term basis.

Sources of information

Accounts; annual report; Charity Commission record; funder's website.

Charity of John Marshall

 Support for parsonage buildings throughout England and Wales, help with the upkeep of Anglican churches and cathedrals in Kent, Surrey and Lincolnshire (as the counties were defined in 1855), support for the parish of Christ Church in Southwark, awards for educational purposes to Marshall's Educational Foundation (4% of the expenditure)

England and Wales (for parsonage grants), Kent, Surrey and Lincolnshire only (for church grants)

£732,000 (2016)

CC number: 206780

Trustees: Adrian Smallwood; Eleanor Lang; Anthony Guthrie; Colin Bird; Stephen Clark; Bill Eason; Anthea Nicholson; Georgina Farquhar Isaac; John Heawood; Revd Jonathan Rust; Surbhi Malhotra-Trenkel; Lesley Bosman; Charles Ledsam; Alastair Moss.

Correspondent: Catherine de Cintra, Clerk to the Trustees, 66 Newcomen Street, London SE1 1YT (tel: 020 7407 2979; email: grantoffice@marshalls.org.uk)

www.marshalls.org.uk

This charity has a history dating back to 1631, when John Marshall, a baker in Southwark, left money in his will to be used for charitable purposes. Over the centuries, the charity's purposes have been adapted to suit changing needs and according to the 2016 annual report it now has four primary purposes:

- To support as patrons the parish church of Christ Church, Southwark
- To make grants for the support of personages to dioceses of the Church of England and the Church in Wales
- To make restoration and repair grants to Anglican churches in the three counties of Kent, Surrey and Lincolnshire as those counties were defined in 1855
- To make 4% of net income available to Marshafi's Educational Foundation which makes grants for educational purposes in Stamford and Southwark

The annual report for 2016 describes how the charity's annual budget for grants is allocated:

> Each year, when approving the budget, the Trustees first decide how much to make available for the costs associated with Christ Church, Southwark. Then, after making adequate provision for the grant to Marshall's Educational Foundation, the Trustees decide how to split the available balance between grants for the Support of Parsonages and those for Restoration of Churches. This is

considered carefully as the claims of both areas are strong. In recent years the Trustees have directed approximately 75% of the balance to Parsonages and 25% to Churches and have maintained this pattern in the current year.

Parsonages

The majority of the charity's funds are used to make grants to support parsonages of the Church of England and the Church in Wales. All grants are made through applications from the relevant diocesan parsonage board.

The website specifies:

We only support Parsonages of Rectors, Team Rectors, Vicars, Team vicars and Priests-in-Charge resident or becoming resident in the Parsonage House owned by the Diocese and subject to the Repair of Benefice Measure 1972 (but including the Diocese of Sodor and Man which is not covered by this Act).

According to the charity's website, there are three types of grant available:

- Grants for the purchase or improvement of a parsonage: 'These grants are allocated as a block amount at the commencement of each financial year, and each Diocesan Property Board indicates how they intend to allocate the grants to individual parsonages.'
- Grants for the installation of burglar alarms in a parsonage: 'In 1991, as a result of the rising levels of violence which were experienced by parish clergy, the Trustees offered to support the purchase and installation of burglar alarms in parsonages. Each grant is for a maximum of £250.'
- Grants for the installation of CCTV systems at a parsonage: 'In 2001, the Trustees agreed to extend the above scheme to support the installation of CCTV systems in parsonages which were particularly at risk. Each grant is for up to £1,000 with a maximum of 50% of the cost of installation.'

Churches

Grants, typically in the range of £3,000 to £10,000, are made towards the repair or improvement of parish churches or cathedrals of the Church of England in Kent, Surrey and Lincolnshire as constituted in 1855. It is explained on the website that 'the main effect of this is that all of Greater London south of the Thames is within the qualifying area because, in 1855, it formed part of either Kent or Surrey'.

In the past, grants have been given to help with: roof repairs; tower repairs; stonework; church floors; new heating and lighting; new toilets; adaptations for disability access; reordering including kitchen facilities, as long as they are within the footprint of the church; sound systems; and rewiring. The guidelines note that 'it would be unusual

for the Trustees to agree to fund the full cost of a project'.

Financial information

In 2016 the charity had assets of £20.1 million and an income of £1.4 million. Charitable expenditure amounted to £821,500 and was broken down in the accounts as follows:

Support of parsonage grants	£557,500
Restoration of churches grants	£174,500
Christ Church, Southwark	£56,000
Marshall's Educational Scholarship	£33,500
Stamford Lectureship	£115

We have taken the sum of parsonage grants and church restoration grants as our grant total for the year as we feel this makes the best indicator of the amount of funding that was available to apply for.

Beneficiaries included: Christ Church – Camberwell (£15,000); All Saints – Saxby and St Luke – Whyteleafe (£10,000 each); St John the Evangelist – Ickham (£5,000); Holy Trinity - West End (£3,000).

Exclusions

Churches: Applicants who have received a grant from the charity within the past three years; churches outside the counties of Kent, Surrey and Lincolnshire, as defined in 1855; churches of denominations other than Anglican; professional fees; works outside the footprint of the church, such as church halls, external meeting rooms and facilities, church grounds and boundary walls and fences; redecoration; bells; organs; clock; monuments; brasses; stained glass.

Parsonages: Applications from individual clergy or other denominations (appeals should be made by applications from the relevant diocesan parsonage board).

Applications

Application forms for church grants can be downloaded, along with full guidelines, from the charity's website and can be returned by post or email to the correspondent at any time. The Grants Committee meets three times a year (for exact dates see the website). Applications for parsonages must be made through the relevant diocesan parsonage board.

The website also has a helpful page dedicated to other funding sources for church improvements.

Sources of information

Accounts; annual report; Charity Commission record; guidelines for applicants; funder's website.

The Kristina Martin Charitable Trust

General charitable purposes, health, medical research, environment/ conservation, overseas development, Christian charities

UK and overseas, with some interest in local causes in Suffolk

(£) £2.4 million (2016/17)

CC number: 249913

Trustees: Peter Tompkins; Andrew Parry; Kirsty Cunningham; Lara Barton.

Correspondent: Andrew Parry, Trustee, Irwin Mitchell LLP, Mercantile House, 18 London Road, Newbury RG14 1JX (tel: 01635 571022; email: andrew.parry@ irwinmitchell.com)

This trust was registered in 1967 with general charitable purposes by Thomas and Jacqueline Martin in honour of their daughter, Kristina. The trustees have shown an interest in areas including medical research and health care, environment/conservation, and overseas development. Christian charities, churches and schools have also been supported. In addition to supporting UK-registered charities operating nationally and internationally, the trust has supported local causes in Suffolk.

Financial information

In 2016/17 the trust had assets of £8.4 million and an income of £315,000. Grants to 53 organisations totalled more than £2.4 million.

Beneficiaries included: British Eye Research Foundation, Bury St Edmunds Women's Aid Centre, CAFOD, Combat Stress, Compassion in World Farming, St Christopher's Hospice and Suffolk Wildlife Fund (£50,000 each); The National Trust (£40,000); Patna Jesuit Society (£15,000); St Anthony's School (£400).

Applications

The annual report for 2016/17 explains that the trustees: 'are seldom able to make grants in response to unsolicited applications. In order to minimise administrative costs, the trustees regret that they are not able to reply to any printed or electronic correspondence or return material supplied in support of unsolicited applications.'

Sources of information

Accounts; annual report; Charity Commission record.

Sir George Martin Trust

 Children and young people, environment, health, including mental health, heritage, music and the arts, older people, disability, education, sports, social welfare

 West and North Yorkshire

£ £228,000 (2016/17)

CC number: 223554

Trustees: David Coates, Chair; Martin Bethel; Roger Marshall; Paul Taylor; Marjorie Martin; Morven Whyte; Sarah Blenkinsop; Sir George Martin Trust Company Ltd.

Correspondent: Carla Marshall, Trust Manager, 6 Firs Avenue, Harrogate, North Yorkshire HG2 9HA (tel: 01423 810222; email: info@ sirgeorgemartintrust.org.uk)

🌐 www.sirgeorgemartintrust.org.uk

The trust was formed in 1956 from endowments from Sir George Martin for general charitable purposes, mainly small or medium-sized local organisations in North and West Yorkshire, particularly the cities of Leeds and Bradford.

The trust's website states that grants will be made for the following:

▷ Children and young people
▷ Church appeals – connected with community outreach only
▷ Countryside, environment, green issues
▷ Hospices
▷ Mental well-being
▷ Museums and historic buildings
▷ Music and the arts
▷ Older people
▷ Physical and learning disabilities
▷ Schools, education, universities – must be outreach work
▷ Social welfare
▷ Sports for disadvantaged communities

The website states that the trust prefers to make one-off grants available for capital rather than revenue projects, generally between £500 and £5,000, with most between £1,000 to £2,000.

Financial information

In 2016/17 the trust held assets of £8.3 million and had an income of £245,500. The trust made 144 grants totalling £228,000.

Beneficiaries included: Methodist Homes for the Aged (£15,000); Craven Trust, Older People's Action in the Locality and Sea Cadet Corps Leeds (£5,000 each); Bradford Deaf Community Association (£2,500); Ryedale Festival (£2,000); Kettlewell Village Hall, Parents4Parents North Yorkshire, Sikh Sport UK and Trees for Cities (£1,000 each); Bangladeshi Playscheme (£750); Buglife (£500).

Exclusions

Support is not available for:

▷ Appeals that are not focused on West and/or North Yorkshire
▷ Appeals from individuals seeking grants
▷ Applications from overseas
▷ Overseas seminars or exchange visits by individuals or groups
▷ Medical appeals of a capital or revenue nature
▷ Medical research projects
▷ Restoration schemes of church roofs, spires, etc
▷ Playgroups

Applications

Application forms can be requested by email or phone from the correspondent. It should be returned by post along with a statement of no more than two pages outlining your proposal and a copy of your latest set of accounts. You should also specify the amount required and whether any other funding has been secured. The trustees meet in March, July and November each year to consider applications. The website notes:

> If an application meets the Trust's initial criteria, our Trust Manager will be in touch to arrange a telephone call or visit in order for her to find out further information on the project. Each application and the Trust Manager's report will then be reviewed by our six Trustees. Applications that are relevant will be acknowledged and successful applicants will be told following the meeting. Unsuccessful applicants are generally informed by email.

Sources of information

Accounts; annual report; Charity Commission record; funder's website.

John Martin's Charity

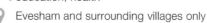 Religious activities, social welfare, education, health

 Evesham and surrounding villages only

£ £253,500 to organisations (2016/17)

CC number: 527473

Trustees: Nigel Lamb; John Smith; Richard Emson; Cyril Scorse; Diana Raphael; Frances Smith; Julie Westlake; John Wilson; Revd Mark Binney; Catherine Evans; Gabrielle Falkiner; Stuart Allerton; Valerie Butler.

Correspondent: John Daniels, Clerk to the Trustees, 16 Queen's Road, Evesham, Worcestershire WR11 4JN (tel: 01386 765440; email: enquiries@johnmartins. org.uk)

🌐 www.johnmartins.org.uk

The charity was created following the death of John Martin of Hampton, Worcestershire in 1714. His property was left for the benefit of local residents and over the years some of this property has been sold to generate income to enable the charity to carry out its objectives in accordance with his wishes. It was formally registered with the Charity Commission in 1981.

Aims and objectives

The overall aim of the charity is to benefit the residents of the town and neighbourhood of Evesham, Worcestershire. This is achieved through four specific aims, outlined within the annual report for 2016/17:

▷ **Religious support:** To assist the vicars in Hampton and Bengeworth and the three parochial church councils within the town of Evesham
▷ **Relief in need:** To assist generally or individually, people living within the town of Evesham who are in conditions of need, hardship and distress
▷ **Promotion of education:** To promote education to people living within the town of Evesham and to provide benefits to schools in the town
▷ **Health and other charitable purposes:** To assist beneficiaries within the town of Evesham or within the immediate neighbourhood. The trustees mainly use this ability to support people with chronic health problems and other related health issues across a wider beneficial area

A great proportion of support is given to individuals directly, including the provision of winter heating grants to pensioners and grants to assist people in education or training.

With regard to organisations, the website states that 'the trustees will consider requests for both capital items and general expenditure, including project costs'. The website also notes that 'it is unusual for the charity to provide the majority of the funds', therefore organisations which show self-help or those which give valid reasons why alternative sources of finance are not available are given preference.

Financial information

In 2016/17 the charity held assets of almost £24 million and had an income of £808,500. Grants totalled £650,000 of which £396,000 was awarded to 834 individuals. A total of 32 grants were made to organisations and schools amounting to £253,500. They were distributed as follows:

Relief in need	11	£79,000
Religious support	3	£67,000
Education	12	£65,000
Health and other charitable purposes	6	£42,500

Previous beneficiaries have included: Evesham Volunteer Centre (£36,000); All Saints PCC Evesham (£30,500); St Richard's Hospice (£24,000); Prince

Henry's High School (£12,200); South Worcestershire Citizens Advice (£10,000); Breast Cancer Haven and Garage Art Group (£5,000 each); Yellow Scarf CIC (£4,000); Life Education Centre (£3,000); Evesham Festival of Music (£1,100); Hampton Flower Show (£200).

Exclusions

The charity will not assist with the payment of rates or taxes, replacement of statutory benefits or retrospective funding.

Applications

Application forms are available on the charity's website. Informal contact prior to submitting an application is welcome. Grant applications are considered quarterly, approximately four weeks after the following application closing dates: 1 June, 1 September, 20 November and 1 March. The trustees will check that the applicant's filing is up-to-date on the applicable regulator's website.

Note: The charity receives more requests than it can support.

Sources of information

Accounts; annual report; Charity Commission record; funder's website.

Masonic Charitable Foundation

 Social welfare, health, disability, education, young people, medical and social research, hospices

Mainly England and Wales

£7.66 million to non-Masonic organisations (2016/17)

CC number: 1164703

Trustees: John Codd; David Watson; John Boyington; Andrew Campbell Ross; Dr Charles Akle; Christopher White; Dr Michael Woodcock; James Newman; Antony Harvey; Michael Heenan; Andrew Wauchope; John D'Olier Duckworth; Timothy Dallas-Chapman; Jean-Paul da Costa; Hon. Richard Hone; John Hornblow; Howard Sabin; Charles Cunnington; Sir Paul Williams; Adrian Flook; Christopher Head; Nigel Vaughan; Howard Wilson.

Correspondent: Charity Grants Dept., Freemasons' Hall, 60 Great Queen Street, London WC2B 5AZ (tel: 020 3146 3337; email: charitygrants@mcf.org.uk)

 mcf.org.uk

The Masonic Charitable Foundation was registered with the Charity Commission in December 2015 to bring together the work of four national Masonic charities: The Freemasons' Grand Charity; the Royal Masonic Trust for Girls and Boys;

the Masonic Samaritan Fund; and the Royal Masonic Benevolent Institution.

The foundation provides support for Freemasons and their dependants and to a range of non-Masonic registered charities benefitting people in England, Wales and areas affected by natural disasters, both in the UK and overseas. The foundation's non-Masonic grant-making activities are outlined below.

Community support

The foundation makes grants to charities working with people affected by poverty and disadvantage, sickness or disability, or barriers to education and employment. Grants have been given to charities within the following categories: financial hardship; well-being; education; and social exclusion and disadvantage.

At the time of writing (June 2018) the programmes for large and small grants were under review and the foundation was considering ways to target its funding to make the 'greatest possible impact'. See the foundation's website for updates.

Medical and social research grants

The foundation funds research into a broad range of disabilities, diseases and conditions. Examples include:

▷ Age-related degenerative diseases (e.g. Alzheimer's)
▷ Childhood illnesses (e.g. cystic fibrosis)
▷ Chronic illnesses (e.g. cancer and heart disease)

It also supports social research studies which address and improve understanding of social or cultural factors which impact health, well-being or active participation in society. Examples include:

▷ The impact of providing end-of-life or palliative care for a family member
▷ Social deprivation and poverty
▷ Education and barriers to employment

Other charitable causes

Hospices

Grants for core operating costs are made to adult and children's hospices that receive less than 60% of their funding from the NHS.

Through a partnership with Hospice UK, grants of up to £20,000 are also available to allow hospices to develop and extend their bereavement support services.

Air ambulances and disaster relief

Grants are made for air ambulances and for disaster relief; however, these categories are not open to applicants.

Further information about each of the foundation's funding programmes is provided on the website.

Financial information

In 2016/17 the foundation had assets of £416.7 million and an income of £67 million. Grants to organisations and individuals totalled £18.75 million. Those to non-Masonic organisations amounted to £7.66 million.

Beneficiaries of non-Masonic grants included: Achievement for All (£240,000); Kidney Research UK (£144,500); British Red Cross – Hurricane Matthew (£50,000); Norfolk Carers Support (£10,000); Back on Track Manchester Ltd and Disability Law Service (£5,000 each); Devon Air Ambulance (£4,000); Wirral Hospice St John's (£3,300); Second Chance Furniture (£1,000 each).

Applications

See the foundation's website for full details of funding programmes and how to apply for a grant. The foundation can be contacted by email (charitygrants@mcf.org.uk) or telephone (020 3146 3337) for further information or to discuss a potential application.

Sources of information

Accounts; annual report; Charity Commission record; funder's website.

The Nancie Massey Charitable Trust

Medical research and care, the arts, education, the young, older people

Scotland, particularly Edinburgh and Leith

£265,500 (2016/17)

OSCR number: SC008977

Correspondent: The Trustees, c/o Chiene and Tait LLP, 61 Dublin Street, Edinburgh EH3 6NL

The trust was established in 1989 to help organisations in Scotland, primarily in the Edinburgh and Leith areas. The trust's 2016/17 accounts state that the trustees mainly assist in the areas of medical research and care, the arts, education, young people and older people.

Awards generally range from £1,000 to £2,000, although larger donations may be made.

Financial information

In 2016/17 the trust held assets of £7.3 million and had an income of £298,000. Grants were made to 88 organisations and totalled £265,500.

Beneficiaries included: National Museum of Scotland Charitable Trust (£50,000); Fettlor Youth Club (£25,000); St Columba's Hospice (£8,000); Hearts and Minds (£6,000); Bliss Scotland (£3,000); Leith School of Art (£2,000);

National Deaf Children's Society (£1,800); The PBC Foundation and Penumbra (£1,000 each).

Exclusions
Individuals are excluded.

Applications
Apply in writing to the correspondent.

Sources of information
Accounts; annual report; OSCR record.

The Master Charitable Trust

General charitable purposes, education and training, disadvantage, poverty, community development, environment, animal care, arts, sport, religion

UK and overseas

£8 million (2015/16)

CC number: 1139904

Trustee: Hoare Trustees.

Correspondent: Messrs Hoare Trustees, 37 Fleet Street, London EC4P 4DQ (tel: 020 7353 4522)

www.hoaresbank.co.uk/master-charitable-trust

The Master Charitable Trust was launched in 2011 and supports a wide variety of charitable activities undertaken by UK-registered charities both at home and abroad. It is a donor-advised fund, to encourage customers of C. Hoare banking in philanthropic activities.

Donors can name their own Giving Fund and make an initial lump sum contribution through cash shares or assets. Donors can also recommend UK charities and worldwide causes to the trust.

Financial information
In 2015/16 the trust had assets of £30.6 million and a total income of £16.1 million. Grants to charitable organisations totalled £8 million and were broken down as follows:

Education	£5.1 million
Health	£1 million
Welfare	£522,000
Citizenship/community	£428,000
Arts, culture, heritage, science	£289,500
Relief of poverty	£234,500
Human rights	£96,500
Sport	£67,000
Religion	£65,500
Animal welfare	£44,500
Crown forces/services	£11,600

Beneficiaries included: University of Toronto (£989,500); School Governors' One-Stop Shop (£620,000); UK Stem Cell Foundation (£400,000); Barnabus Fund (£140,000); Buttle UK, National Society for the Prevention of Cruelty to Children, The Malala Fund (£100,000 each); The Friends of the Strays of

Greece, The Hilary Craft Charitable Foundation and University of Exeter (£10,000 each).

Applications
Charities and organisations are usually chosen at the donor's request.

Sources of information
Accounts; annual report; Charity Commission record; funder's website.

The Mathew Trust

Adult education, vocational and professional training, employment

City of Dundee, Angus, Perth and Kinross, and Fife

£300,500 to organisations (2016/17)

OSCR number: SC016284

Correspondent: The Trustees, c/o Henderson Loggie, The Vision Building, 20 Greenmarket, Dundee DD1 4QB (tel: 01382 200055; email: shg@hlca.co.uk)

The trust was set up in 1935 and makes grants and loans for the following:

▶ Adult education in Dundee, Angus, Perth and Kinross, and Fife
▶ Vocational and professional training of adults
▶ The relief of poverty by providing assistance in the recruitment of such people who are unemployed, or who are likely to become unemployed in the near future

Financial information
In 2016/17 the trust held assets of £9.2 million and had an income of £302,500. Grants were awarded to 20 organisations and totalled £300,500, and £3,200 was paid in grants to eight individuals.

Beneficiaries included: Design Dundee Ltd (£89,000); Dundee Museum of Transport (£44,000); Dundee Heritage Trust (£29,500); University of Abertay (£16,500); Showcase the Street (£13,800); The Unicorn Preservation Society (£6,200); Autism Initiatives, Dundee Science Centre and Hope Gartden SCIO (£5,000 each); Tayside Deaf Hub (£3,000); Faith in Community (£820); Tall Ships Youth Trust (£600).

Applications
Apply in writing to the correspondent. Appeals are generally considered every two months.

Sources of information
Accounts; annual report; OSCR record.

The Matliwala Family Charitable Trust

Advancement of Islam, education, social welfare, health

UK and India

£284,000 (2016/17)

CC number: 1012756

Trustees: Ayub Bux; Yousuf Bux; Hasina Bux; Usman Salya; Fatima Ismail.

Correspondent: Ayub Bux, Trustee, 9 Brookview, Fulwood, Preston PR2 8FG (tel: 01772 706501)

The trust was established in 1992. Its charitable objectives are as follows:

▶ The advancement of education for pupils at Matliwala School of Bharuch in Gujarat – India, including assisting with the provision of equipment and facilities
▶ The advancement of the Islamic religion
▶ The relief of sickness and poverty
▶ The advancement of education

Our research indicates the trust tends to award the larger grants to charities with which it has trustees in common.

Financial information
In 2016/17 the trust had assets of £5.8 million and an income of £459,500. Grants totalled £284,000, the majority of which was given to various projects in Bharuch, Gujarat – India. The grants were broken down as follows:

Relief of poverty (overseas)	£127,500
Education (overseas)	£95,000
Relief of sickness (UK)	£20,000
Education (UK)	£17,500
Religion (UK)	£5,500
Relief of sickness (overseas)	£5,000

A list of beneficiaries was not included within the annual report and accounts.

Applications
Applications may be made in writing to the correspondent. The trustees meet monthly to assess grant applications and approve awards. The annual report for 2016/17 states: 'The charity welcomes applications for grants from all quarters and these are assessed by the trustees on their individual merits. Awards are given according to the individual needs of the applicant, depending on the funds available.'

Sources of information
Accounts; annual report; Charity Commission record.

Maudsley Charity

 Mental health care and well-being

Croydon, Lambeth, Lewisham and Southwark

(£) £2.8 million to organisations (2016/17)

CC number: 1055440

Trustees: Roger Paffard; Alan Downey; Duncan Hames; Dr Julie Hollyman; June Mulroy; Mike Franklin; Anna Walker; Professor Matthew Hotopf; Dr Matthew Patrick; Gus Heafield; Kristin Dominy; Dr Neil Brimblecombe; Dr Michael Holland.

Correspondent: David Blazey, Head of Grants, ORTUS, 82–96 Grove Lane, London SE5 8SN (tel: 07825 629469; email: david.blazey@maudsleycharity. org)

 maudsleycharity.com

 facebook.com/slamnhs

 @MaudsleyNHS

Tracing its origins back to a charitable deed of gift in 1247, the Maudsley Charity today awards funds for hospital and community-based projects and activities that promote mental health care and well-being, research and service improvement.

The charity's funds are administered within South London and Maudsley NHS Foundation Trust (SLaM), separately from the exchequer funds, by the full Board of the NHS Foundation Trust which acts as a Corporate Trustee. As a result, the charity works closely with SLaM which provides the UK's widest range of mental health services.

In 2016/7 the charity implemented a new strategy in line with recommendations from strategic and governance reviews carried out in 2015. The strategy builds on the legacy of the Maudsley charity and confirms its core purpose as an NHS charitable foundation focused on mental health, with funding provision focused on the following priorities:

- Recovery from mental ill health and support to stay well
- Improved experience of care – primarily in services provided by South London and Maudsley NHS Foundation Trust
- Growth and spread of knowledge and understanding which will impact future care and prevention

As part of its new strategy the charity has also taken a new approach to grant-funding, concentrating on five funding streams outlined in the 2016/17 annual report:

- A micro-grants programme intended to maximise the benefit of small amounts of funding which can have an immediate positive benefit
- A dynamic open grants programme intended to provide small to medium-sized funds (up to £50k in value). Funded projects are likely to involve the initiation and evaluation of new approaches to care, education and support or may deliver discreet improvements to the hospital environment and facilities
- Ongoing commitment to support the continued success and positive impact of the Bethlem Gallery and Museum of the Mind
- A partnership programme with South London and Maudsley NHS Foundation Trust established to support ongoing and programmes of work, appropriate for charitable funding
- A commitment to regular though infrequent large contributions to major programmes of work. These will be projects that can make a 'step change' to improved mental health and will often involve partnerships across the trust and the Institute of Psychiatry, Psychology and Neuroscience, King's College London

The main beneficiaries of funded projects should be people with mental health problems. Projects will not normally be funded for more than three years although exceptions may be made if the charity is one of several funders for the project and at least one of those funders will support the project for a longer period.

Financial information

In 2016/17 the charity had assets of £136.8 million and an income of £5.47 million. During the year, the charity awarded 55 grants to organisations totalling £2.8 million. In addition, the charity also awarded £20,000 in grants to 63 individuals.

Beneficiaries included: South London and Maudsley NHS Foundation Trust (£1.4 million in 27 grants); King's College London (£448,000 in ten grants); Bethlem Gallery (£109,000); Bethlem Art and History Museum (£70,000 in two grants); Mind and Soul Community Choir (£26,000); South East London Arts Network (£25,000).

Applications

Before submitting a formal application, applicants are requested to contact the charity by phone or email to arrange a time to discuss their project idea. According to the charity's website, 'applications will only be accepted from those who have had a preliminary discussion with the charity and who have been advised that their proposal is suitable for consideration'.

Sources of information

Accounts; annual report; Charity Commission record; funder's website.

Mayfair Charities Ltd

Orthodox Jewish religion and education, the relief of poverty

UK and overseas (especially Israel)

(£) £12.56 million (2016/17)

CC number: 255281

Trustees: Benzion Freshwater; D. Davis; Solomon Freshwater; Richard Fischer.

Correspondent: Benzion Freshwater, Trustee, Freshwater Group of Companies, Freshwater House, 158–162 Shaftesbury Avenue, London WC2H 8HR (tel: 020 7836 1555)

The charity was established in 1968 and makes grants to 'organisations and institutions engaged in the provision of education and promotion of religious observance within the tenets of Orthodox Judaism and for the relief of poverty' in the UK and overseas, especially Israel.

It appears to be a vehicle for the philanthropic activities of property investor Benzion Freshwater, who is closely connected with the management of some of the major beneficiary organisations.

There are no set amounts for sizes of grants – several substantial donations are made and many organisations receive small grants of a few hundred pounds. The annual report for 2016/17 notes that 'In recent years, the Trustees have continued to support certain major projects which, during previous years, have received substantial financial grants from the Company.' Our research suggests that support for core or capital expenditure is usually given on a one-off basis.

Financial information

In 2016/17 the charity had assets of £105.5 million and an income of £4.6 million. Grants were made to over 380 organisations and totalled £12.56 million. A further £150,000 was given in 'non-monetary donations' (i.e. the provision of facilities). Grants were awarded in the following categories: the advancement of religion and education (£11.1 million) and the relief of poverty (£1.6 million).

Beneficiaries included: The Raphael Freshwater Memorial Association Ltd (£6 million); Society of Friends of the Torah Ltd (£1.73 million); Beth Jacob Grammar School for Girls (£1.1 million); Chevras Mo'oz Ladol (£258,000); The Jewish Learning Exchange (£146,000); Friends of Bobov (£46,000); Orthodox Council of Jerusalem (£26,000); Glasgow Rabbinical College (£25,000); Chazon Ish Kollel (£21,000).

Applications

Apply in writing to the correspondent.

Sources of information

Accounts; annual Report; Charity Commission record.

Mayheights Ltd

 Orthodox Jewish religion, general charitable purposes

 Barnet, Hackney and Israel

 £1.37 million (2016/17)

CC number: 1112291

Trustees: Menashe Eichenstein; Rachel Low; Oscar Low.

Correspondent: Oscar Low, Trustee, 36 Gilda Crescent, London N16 6JP (tel: 020 8806 1234 or 020 8800 8058)

Mayheights Ltd was registered with the Charity Commission in 2005. It is constituted as a limited company and is governed by its Memorandum and Articles of Association dated 3 October 1983. According to the charity's 2016/17 annual report 'the objects of the charity are, the advancement of religion in accordance with the Orthodox Jewish Faith, the relief of poverty and for such other purposes as are recognised by English Law as charitable'.

Financial information

In 2016/17 the charity had assets of around £14.4 million and an income of £7.8 million. Grants worth a total of £1.37 million were awarded. Grants were distributed as follows:

Religious education	£668,500
Advancement of religion	£585,000
Relief of poverty	£83,000
General purposes	£29,500
Medical	£5,000

Beneficiaries included: Ezer V'hatzlah Ltd (£400,000); Hadras Kodesh Trust (£207,500); Chasidei Yerusholayim (£136,000); Mifal Torah (£102,000); Shaykel Esuh (£70,000); Cosmon Belz (£55,000); Yeitev Lev (£53,000); United Talmudical Associates (£45,000); Mifal Tedoko (£38,500).

Applications

Apply in writing to the correspondent. The charity's 2016/17 accounts note that 'the trustees consider all requests received' and that 'in making grants the trustees use their personal knowledge of the institutions, its trustees and reputation'.

Sources of information

Accounts; annual report; Charity Commission record.

Mazars Charitable Trust

 General charitable purposes

 UK and Ireland

£401,000 (2016/17)

CC number: 1150459

Trustees: Alan Edwards; David Evans; Bob Neate; Philip Verity; Kim Hurst.

Correspondent: Bryan Rogers, 1 Cranleigh Gardens, South Croydon, Surrey CR2 9LD (tel: 020 8657 3053)

The firm Mazars LLP specialises in audit, tax and advisory services across a range of markets and sectors. This associated charitable trust was registered with the Charity Commission in January 2013 and makes grants to charitable organisations in the UK and Ireland. In 2016/17 the majority of the trust's income was received from Mazars LLP. It does not respond to unsolicited applications; however, applications can be made through a team member of Mazars LLP.

The trust's 2016/17 annual report states:

The Trustees have determined that all grants are to be based on nominations by team members of Mazars LLP, the donor firm, and reflect criteria developed by the Trustees.

The major part of these grants are determined nationally by the Management Committee, with the remainder being allocated to each Mazars LLP office pro-rata to its income.

Financial information

In 2016/17 the trust had assets of £446,000 and an income of £439,500. Grants awarded to organisations totalled £401,000.

Beneficiaries included: Midlands Air Ambulance Charity (£26,000); WellChild (£12,000); The Elizabeth Foundation (£10,000); Licketyspit Ltd (£5,500); Cancer Research (£3,300); Heads On and Motor Neurone Disease Association (£1,500 each).

Exclusions

National grants are not generally repeated within three years and they are rarely given for core costs.

Applications

The trust does not respond to unsolicited applications. All nominations for grants have to be proposed by staff members of Mazars LLP and no grant applications should be submitted directly to the trust.

Sources of information

Accounts; annual report; Charity Commission record; funder's website.

MBNA General Foundation

General charitable purposes, children and young people, older people, people with disabilities

Within a 30-mile radius of the company's Chester campus

£454,000 (2016)

CC number: 1065515

Trustees: Mr Stables; Ian Doherty; Sean Humphreys; Ellyn Corfield; Mark Elliot.

Correspondent: Sean Humphreys, Trustee, Stansfield House, Chester Business Park, Chester CH4 9QQ (tel: 01244 673333)

The charity was established in 1997 and is the charitable foundation of MBNA Ltd, a large credit card provider based in Chester. Grants are made for general charitable purposes to charities and organisations based within 30 miles of the company's Chester campus. Applicants should have an associate connection or a historic relationship/connection with the company.

The foundation's 2016 annual accounts state: 'The trustees consider the levels of donations to be satisfactory and in line with their set goals. They are happy to have been able to support, in particular, Charities working with children and young people, the elderly and disabled, as well as local schools and clubs which are not registered as Charities.'

Financial information

In 2016 the foundation held assets of £2.6 million and had an income of £221,000. Grants to 43 organisations totalled £454,000.

Financial information: Sale Sharks Trust (£288,500); Chester Football Club (£90,000); Hadlow Field Scouts (£10,000); Neuromuscular Centre and Chester Boxing Club (£5,000 each); Park Run (£3,000); Head Injured People Cheshire (£2,000); Happy Days Animal Rescue (£500); Countess of Chester Hospitals (£200).

Applications

Apply in writing to the correspondent. Applicants should have an associate connection or a historic relationship/connection with the company.

Sources of information

Accounts; annual report; Charity Commission record.

The Robert McAlpine Foundation

 Children and young people, social welfare, older people, medical research

UK

£600,000 (2016/17)

CC number: 226646

Trustees: Adrian McAlpine; Cullum McAlpine; The Hon David McAlpine; Gavin McAlpine.

Correspondent: Gillian Bush, Secretary, Eaton Court, Maylands Avenue, Hemel Hempstead, Hertfordshire HP2 7TR (email: foundation@srm.com)

www.robertmcalpinefoundation.org

Sir Robert McAlpine Ltd is a family-owned UK construction and civil engineering company. The foundation was established by the family of Sir Robert McAlpine and gives grants to support small charities situated throughout the UK that fall within specific categories, namely:

- Children
- Social welfare
- Older people
- Young people
- Medical research

The foundation's 2016/17 accounts state that 'The policy of the Trustees is to make grants to charitable institutions of amounts from £5,000 upwards in the specific categories of objectives which they support.'

The foundation's website states that it will only support registered charities which meet the following criteria:

- Total income should be less than £1 million per annum
- The funds must be used for a UK-based project
- We do not fund fundraising activities
- We do not support fundraising by established charities for a target sum

Financial information

In 2016/17 the foundation had assets of £18.5 million and an income of £707,000. During the year, the foundation gave a total of £600,000 in grants to organisations.

A list of beneficiaries was not available.

Previous beneficiaries have included: Age Concern; Community Self Build Agency; DENS Action Against Homelessness; Downside Fisher Youth Club; Ewing Foundation; the Golden Oldies; Grateful Society; James Hopkins Trust; Merchants Academy Withywood; National Benevolent Fund for the Aged; National Eye Research Centre; Prostate UK; Royal Marsden NHS Trust; St Johns Youth Centre; the Towers School and 6th Form Centre.

Applications

Apply in writing or by email to the correspondent. The foundation's website states that appeals should be no more than two A4 pages and outline:

- Who you are
- Your charity number
- What work your charity does
- Details of the specific project for which you require funding
- The amount of funding you are looking for
- Your contact details, together with website address if you have one

The foundation also asks that applicants enclose a copy of their most recent accounts. The trustees meet annually in November to approve grants – applications must be received no later than 31 August for to be considered in the next meeting.

The foundation is unable to accept any appeal requests by telephone.

Sources of information

Accounts; annual report; Charity Commission record.

D D McPhail Charitable Settlement

 Medical research, health care, disability, causes, children and young people, older people

UK

£212,000 (2016/17)

CC number: 267588

Trustees: Julia Noble; Christopher Yates; Michael Craig; Mary Meeks; Olivia Hancock; Drew McNeil.

Correspondent: Katharine Moss, Executive Director, PO BOX 432, Bicester, Oxfordshire OX26 9JL (tel: 07523 440550; email: director. ddmcphail@gmail.com)

 www. ddmcphailcharitablesettlement. co.uk

The D D McPhail Charitable Settlement was established in 1973 for general charitable purposes. The annual report for 2016/17 clarifies that the trustees will prefer the following:

- The advancement of medical research
- The care of people with disabilities, particularly children
- The care of the older people and those in weak health

According to the 2016/17 annual report, the charity prefers 'to make a relatively small number of substantial grants to charities to fund a major change or a significant piece of medical research'. Awards can be made to small and medium-sized charities 'to make an investment and/or step change in their activities by making a relatively large grant award, usually over a period of two to three years'. The charity will support pilot projects; however, it expects projects to factor in how they will become self-sustaining following the conclusion of the grant.

Financial information

In 2016/17 the charity held assets of £10.7 million and had an income of £359,000. During the year, the charity gave £212,000 in grants to nine organisations.

Beneficiaries included: Carer's Trust (£150,000); Pancreatic Cancer Action (£50,000); The Cure Parkinson's Trust and The Dinosaur Trust (£2,000 each); Dandelion Time and The Maytree Respite Care (£1,000 each).

Applications

Apply in writing to the correspondent. The 2016/17 annual report states the following: 'Trustees identify potential projects for assessment by the Executive Director. The Trust makes no commitment to respond to unsolicited applications. There have also been ongoing smaller grants to causes supported by the Trustees.'

Sources of information

Accounts; annual report; Charity Commission record; funder's website.

Medical Research Foundation

 Medical research

UK and Africa

£4.06 million (2016/17)

CC number: 1138223

Trustees: David Zahn; Prof. Nicholas Lemoine; Stephen Visscher; Prof. Daniel Altmann; Prof. Bobbie Farsides; Susan Wilkinson; Russell Delew.

Correspondent: The Trustees, 49–51 East Road, London N1 6AH (tel: 020 7250 8200; email: research@ medicalresearchfoundation.org.uk)

 www.medicalresearchfoundation. org.uk

 @medresfdn

This is the foundation of the Medical Research Council (MRC) which has been accepting charitable donations and bequests since its inception in 1923. It was launched in 2011 when the funds previously held by the MRC's various medical research charities were transferred to the new charity.

According to the foundation's 2016/17 annual report, support is provided across four strategic research themes:

- **Increasing understanding** – The fundamental research that increases understanding of the biological processes underpinning all human health and disease
- **High need, low research investment** – Research on the conditions and diseases that devastate lives where there is an unmet need for new research but a low research investment
- **Emerging research leaders** – Opportunities for the emerging research leaders who will address the biomedical research questions of the future and support for their cutting-edge research today
- **Disseminating findings** – Disseminating research results beyond the scientific press to people and places that will ensure that the findings change health care policy and practice as well as personal life-choices

The foundation's website states:

> We provide support for research grants, infrastructure and equipment grants, fellowships and studentships, skill-sharing and collaborations, and the dissemination of research results. Unlike many other funding bodies, we are not restricted in having to support a particular disease area or institution.

Financial information

In 2016/17 the foundation held assets of £57.4 million and had an income of £4.5 million. Grants awarded to organisations totalled £4.06 million.

Beneficiaries included: University of Bristol (£2.7 million); King's College London (£558,000); Keele University (£30,000); The Francis Crick Institute, (£62,000); University of Nottingham (£40,000); Cardiff University (£11,000).

Applications

Application procedures and requirements vary between funding programmes. See the foundation's website for full details.

Sources of information

Accounts; annual report; Charity Commission; funder's website.

Medical Research Scotland

 Medical research

Scotland

£1.56 million (2016/17)

OSCR number: SC014959

Trustees: Prof. John Brown; Prof. Bernard Conway; Brian Duffin; Alasdair Gill; Scott Johnstone; Prof. Andrea Nolan; Graham Paterson; Barry Rose; Prof. Jenny Rose.

Correspondent: Trust Secretaries, Turcan Connell, Princes Exchange,

1 Earl Grey Street, Edinburgh EH3 9EE (tel: 0131 659 8800; email: applications@medicalresearchscotland.net)

 www.medicalresearchscotland.org.uk

Formerly known as the Scottish Hospital Endowments Research Trust, the charity's website states the following:

> Medical Research Scotland is one of the largest and most comprehensive independent research charities in Scotland. We aim to invest in the future of Scotland's biomedical research and help to maintain its well-deserved international reputation for pioneering medical research. We do this by supporting young scientists in the early stages of the establishment of careers in health-related fields.

> Unlike most medical research charities, our funding isn't restricted to any one disease or condition, we simply support high-quality research that aims, ultimately, to improve the understanding, diagnosis, treatment and prevention of all diseases and disease mechanisms.

Funding is awarded to universities in Scotland for the following purposes:

- Undergraduate Vacation Scholarships (up to 50), 'offering a 6 to 8-week period of hands-on research experience in a Scottish University, recognised Research Institution or company trading in medically relevant research during the summer vacation'
- PhD Studentships (up to ten, fully funded), which 'require close working between universities and companies trading in medically relevant biomedical research and offering bespoke training on how to develop careers in biomedical science in an increasingly difficult and competitive market to complement universities' own doctoral training programmes'
- Medical Research Scotland Daphne Jackson Fellowships (up to three). 'Unique and unlike any other academic fellowships, these awards are intended for those wishing to return to an area of biomedical research after a career break of two years or more. Fellowships are normally for two years, half time and involve a challenging research project and an individually tailored retraining programme. Awarded in conjunction with the Daphne Jackson Trust, applications for these Fellowships must be made direct to the Daphne Jackson Trust and NOT to Medical Research Scotland'

Financial information

In 2016/17 the charity had assets of £41.8 million and an income of £1.77 million. The total amount of funding awarded to institutions was £1.56 million. A total of 11 PhD Studentships and 75 Undergraduate

Vacation Research Scholarships were awarded.

Exclusions

Grants are only for projects carried out in Scotland.

Applications

Detailed information regarding the foundation's grant programmes, guidance notes, deadlines for applications and more is available from the charity's website. Application forms can also be downloaded from the website.

Sources of information

OSCR record; funder's website.

The Medlock Charitable Trust

Education, health and medicine, research, social welfare

UK

£1.2 million (2016/17)

CC number: 326927

Trustees: Leonard Medlock; Jacqueline Medlock; David Medlock; Mark Goodman.

Correspondent: David Medlock, Trustee, St Georges Lodge, 33 Oldfield Road, Bath BA2 3NE (tel: 01225 428221)

The trust was established in 1985 for general charitable purposes, to provide funding to other charitable trusts, to make donations to universities, and to provide funding for local community charities in any part of the country.

The annual report 2016/17 states:

> To date the charity has supported and funded a number of projects in these areas by making substantial amounts of grants. These grants have been made to fund projects in the areas of education, medicine, research and social services all for the benefit of the local community. The trustees also receive many applications for assistance from many diverse areas in the United Kingdom. These are all considered sympathetically.

Financial information

In 2016/17 the trust had assets of £35 million and an income of £508,500. Grants to 140 organisations totalled £1.2 million.

Beneficiaries included: The Boshier-Hinton Foundation (£180,000); Forever Friends Appeal (£56,000); Quartet Community Foundation (£50,000); Sixty-One (£30,000); Beanstalk (£15,000); Genesis Trust (£10,600); Life Cycle UK (£10,000); Aldbourne Recreation Centre (£5,000); Canal and River Trust (£2,500); South Somerset Mind (£2,000).

Exclusions

Applications from individuals or students will not be considered.

Applications

Applications can be made in writing to the correspondent.

Sources of information

Accounts; annual report; Charity Commission record.

The Melow Charitable Trust

 Jewish causes

UK and overseas

£640,000 (2015)

CC number: 275454

Trustees: Miriam Spitz; Esther Weiser.

Correspondent: Miriam Spitz, Trustee, 21 Warwick Grove, London E5 9HX (tel: 020 8806 1549)

The trust was established in 1978 and makes grants to Jewish charities, both in the UK and overseas.

At the time of writing (April 2018) the charity's 2015 annual report and accounts was the most recent available. In 2015 grants were made totalling £640,000 and were broken down as follows:

General	£250,500
Publication of religious books	£168,000
Education	£126,500
People in need	£63,000
Synagogues	£20,000
Talmudical colleges	£3,000
Community organisation	£500
Religious institutions	£500
Medical assistance and research	£10

The largest grants were listed in the accounts: Ezer V'Hatzalah (£205,000); Hadres Kodesh Trust (£168,000); The Bais Rochel D'Satmar Charitable Trust (£101,000).

Applications

Apply in writing to the correspondent.

Sources of information

Accounts; annual report; Charity Commission record.

Meningitis Research Foundation

 Meningitis and septicaemia research and treatment

UK

£485,000 (2016/17)

CC number: 1091105

Trustees: Mathew Gilbert; Stephen Trump; Prof. George Griffin; Dr Nick Manson; Dr Jane Cope; Deborah

Warman; Martin Vaggers; Dr Brian Scott; Prof. Ray Borrow. David Daniel.

Correspondent: Liz Rodgers, Research Officer, Newminster House, 27–29 Baldwin Street, Bristol BS1 1LT (tel: 0333 405 6262; email: info@meningitis.org)

 www.meningitis.org

 facebook.com/meningitisresearch

 @M_R_F

 @meningitis_research

The Meningitis Foundation was registered with the Charity Commission in 2002. Its goals are 'to see fewer people get meningitis and septicaemia; to see more people survive with a better quality of life and reduced disability; to have more engaged, informed and supported patients and communities'. The foundation seeks to achieve these goals by funding vital research, advocating for change, and taking action that benefits people, including running awareness campaigns, training health professionals and providing support and information.

Research programmes

Since the charity was founded in 1989, it has awarded £19.1 million for vital scientific research.

Grant rounds and calls for proposals are advertised on the foundation's website and are usually themed around certain priority topics. In the 2016/17 grant round, the foundation invited proposals dealing with all forms of meningitis and associated infections, improving prevention, treatment and outlook for patients, and improving the speed and accuracy of diagnosis.

The foundation will consider funding basic science, but this 'must increase understanding of the disease area and have a clearly defined potential for early translation into alleviation of the diseases'. Furthermore, the foundation's website notes that 'research funded must be of the highest scientific merit, in terms of the importance of the investigation, excellence of the study, ability of the research team, and probability of success'.

Research grants may be held in any country and must meet UK standards of research ethics, scientific integrity and animal welfare.

Financial information

In 2016/17 the foundation had assets of £1.95 million and an income of £2.95 million. During the year, the foundation awarded around £485,000 in research grants to institutions.

A list of beneficiaries was not available.

Exclusions

Eligibility criteria may vary depending on the specific funding programme. Check the guidelines on the foundation's website for full details.

Applications

Calls for funding proposals are periodically posted on the foundation's website. Preliminary proposals will be assessed by the foundation's research staff and advisory panel, after which successful applicants will be invited to submit full applications. The foundation's website states the application process typically takes around six months.

Sources of information

Accounts; annual report; Charity Commission record; funder's website.

Menuchar Ltd

 Orthodox Jewish faith, relief in need

UK

£546,000 (2016/17)

CC number: 262782

Trustees: Norman Bude; Gail Bude.

Correspondent: Helena Bude, Secretary, c/o Barry Flack & Co. Ltd, The Brentano Suite, Prospect House, 2 Athenaeum Road, London N20 9AE (tel: 020 8369 5170)

The charity was set up in 1971 and its main objective is the advancement of religion in accordance with the Orthodox Jewish faith. Support may also be given for the relief of people in need.

Financial information

In 2016/17 the charity had assets of £206,000 and an income of £521,000. During the year, the charity gave around £546,000 in grants. A list of beneficiaries was not included in the accounts; however, it was stated that grants went to religious organisations.

Applications

Applications can be made in writing to the correspondent.

Sources of information

Accounts; annual report; Charity Commission record.

Mercaz Torah Vechesed Ltd

 Orthodox Jewish faith, religious education and relief in need among the Orthodox Jewish community

Worldwide, with a preference for Barnet, Hackney and Israel

£ £2.06 million (2016/17)

CC number: 1109212

Trustees: Joseph Ostreicher; Mordche Rand.

Correspondent: Joseph Ostreicher, Secretary, 28 Braydon Road, London N16 6QB (tel: 020 8880 5366; email: umarpeh@gmail.com)

The charity was formed in 2005 for 'the advancement of the orthodox Jewish faith, orthodox Jewish religious education, and the relief of poverty and infirmity amongst members of the orthodox Jewish community'.

Financial information

In 2016/17 the charity had assets of £3,800 and an income of £2.1 million. During the year, grants totalling £2.06 million were awarded to organisations.

A list of beneficiaries was not available in the annual report and accounts.

Applications

Apply in writing to the correspondent.

Sources of information

Accounts; annual report; Charity Commission record.

The Brian Mercer Charitable Trust

 Social welfare, health, visual arts

Worldwide

£ £1.1 million (2016/17)

CC number: 1076925

Trustees: Roger Duckworth; John Merrill; Ann Clitheroe; Jane Clancy.

Correspondent: J. M. Adams, Secretary, c/o Beever and Struthers, Central Buildings, Richmond Terrace, Blackburn BB1 7AP (tel: 01254 686600; fax: 01254 682483; email: info@ brianmercercharitabletrust.org)

 www.brianmercercharitabletrust.org

The trust was established in 1999 by Brian Mercer, an inventor and industrialist who invented a revolutionary process for the manufacture of plastic nets that became known as Netlon. The trust awards grants in the following areas:

▪ **Prevention and relief of human suffering** – to support interventions directed towards reducing suffering caused by poverty and ill health whether in the UK or overseas. Such interventions must be of proven best value or demonstrate the potential to become so. Both direct interventions (e.g. provision of medical treatment) and indirect interventions (e.g. medical or technological research) will be considered

▪ **Art** – to encourage and support the development of promising young artists (working broadly in the field of visual arts), especially within the north west of the UK

▪ **Causes local to Blackburn, Lancashire** – to provide funding for well designed, evidence-based interventions benefitting those living in the area of Blackburn, Lancashire

The Trust welcomes applications for evaluation of previously unevaluated initiatives provided that these are consistent with one of the three funding categories, methodologically robust and accompanied by an explanation of how the results will be used and disseminated.

The total value of all grants awarded annually is approximately £800,000. The proportion of funds allocated to the three causes is:

75% – Prevention and Relief of Human Suffering

15% – Art

10% – Causes Local to Blackburn Lancashire

Financial information

In 2016/17 the trust had assets of £29.8 million and an income of over £1.1 million. Grants were made totalling £1.1 million to 30 organisations.

Beneficiaries included: Moorfields Eye Clinic (£180,000); Sightsavers, Médecins Sans Frontières (£140,000 each); Royal British Society of Sculptors (£13,100); British Art Medal Society (£4,000); Blackburn College, Blackpool Sixth Form College, Lancaster Royal Grammar School, North Cumbria University Hospital (£2,500 each).

Applications

The trust encourages grant applications by email. They should be received at least four weeks before the trustees' meeting, the exact dates of which are listed online. The trustees meet three times a year, currently in January, May and October.

Sources of information

Accounts; annual report; Charity Commission record; funder's website.

The Mercers' Charitable Foundation

 General welfare, education, Christianity, heritage and the arts

UK, with a preference for London, the east and north east of England

£ £4.6 million (2016/17)

CC number: 326340

Trustee: The Mercers' Company.

Correspondent: The Clerk, The Mercers' Company, Becket House, 36 Old Jewry, London EC2R 8DD (tel: 020 7776 7250; email: grants@mercers.co.uk)

 mercersphilanthropy.co.uk

The Mercers' Company has several trusts, the main one being the Mercers' Charitable Foundation. The foundation was established in 1983 to make grants and donations for the benefit of a wide range of charitable purposes including welfare, education, the arts, heritage and religion.

The foundation seeks to support a range of organisations with the common theme of providing effective services and facilities to those in need and to strengthen communities. While continuing to support small grassroots organisations, the foundation has developed relationships with some much larger organisations, complementing work that is funded by statutory bodies. Grants can be awarded on a one-off or multi-year basis. Capital and core costs are supported.

Grant-making guidelines

At the time of writing (June 2018) the foundation was undertaking a major strategic review of its grant-making strategy. Historically, the following purposes have been supported:

▪ **General welfare** – support for inclusive grassroots and front-line charities that work to improve the lives of disadvantaged and marginalised people within the M25.

▪ **Education** – grants to improve the availability and quality of education for children and young adults. These grants are focused on young people from the ages of 3 to 19, particularly in London, and in the West Midlands areas of Walsall, Sandwell and Telford and Wrekin.

▪ **Advancement of the Christian religion** – support for the Christian faith in one of the following areas: people working in the church, churches in the City of London or churches with a Mercer connection, cathedrals and sacred music.

⟩ **Heritage and the arts** – grants to preserve and promote the cultural and artistic heritage of the UK. Wildlife and environmental conservation is also supported.

Financial information

In 2017/18 the foundation held assets of £18.2 million and had an income of £4.9 million. Grants were made to 237 organisations and totalled £4.6 million. The majority of grants (139) were for less than £10,000, primarily to small, London-based charities. During the year, grants were made to 24 individuals and totalled £20,300.

Education	41	£1.6 million
Religion	67	£1.1 million
Heritage and the arts	55	£727,000
Other	21	£556,000
Family and social welfare	42	£521,000
Older people	11	£63,000

Beneficiaries included: Westminster Abbey Foundation (£250,000); Abingdon School (£175,000); The Cinnamon Network (£89,000); Buttle UK (£45,000); St Luke's Healthcare for the Clergy (£20,000); Beyond the Streets (£15,000); Afghan Association Paiwand (£12,900); Almshouse Association, Arts 4 Dementia, British Library, Sir John Soane's Museum and Young Classical Artists Trust (£10,000 each).

Exclusions

Generally the foundation does not fund the following:

⟩ Animal welfare charities
⟩ Endowment appeals
⟩ Campaigning work and projects that are primarily political
⟩ Activities that are the responsibility of the local, health or education authority or other similar body
⟩ Activities that have already taken place
⟩ Other grant-making trusts
⟩ Sponsorship or marketing appeals and fundraising events
⟩ Loans or business finance
⟩ General or mailshot appeals
⟩ Uniformed groups unless there is a link to the Mercers' Company
⟩ Organisations that have made an application in the last three years
⟩ Independent schools (except for specific outreach programmes)
⟩ Overseas projects

Applications

At the time of writing (June 2018) the foundation's website noted the following:

> We are currently undergoing a major strategic review of the Company's grant making, and are not currently accepting applications. We look forward to launching the new strategy in autumn 2017 and encourage you to check the website then for more details.

Sources of information

Accounts; annual report; Charity Commission record; funder's website.

Merchant Navy Welfare Board

 Seafarers, merchant navy, sailors, social welfare, medical care

 UK and Gibraltar

 £223,000 (2016)

CC number: 212799, SC039669

Trustees: Anthony Dickinson; Cmdre Barry Bryant; Timothy Springett; Stephen Todd; Graham Lane; Martin Foley; Robert Jones; Alison Godfrey; Deanne Thomas; Capt. Andrew Cassels; Mark Carden; David Colclough; Cdre Malcolm Williams; Alexander Campbell; David Appleton.

Correspondent: Port Welfare Committee, 8 Cumberland Place, Southampton SO15 2BH (tel: 023 8033 7799; email: enquiries@mnwb.org.uk)

🌐 www.mnwb.org

f facebook.com/TheMNWB

This is an umbrella charity for the maritime charity sector. It makes grants to over 40 constituent charities and maintains 15 Port Welfare Committees in the UK and Gibraltar. The charity's aim is to promote and support the welfare of merchant seafarers, fishers and their dependants. The charity also holds a number of restricted funds, including the Emergency Grant Fund and the Merchant Navy Medal Fund.

Awards are made towards capital expenditure, evaluation studies and start-up costs. Grants of up to £5,000 for small projects are considered throughout the year. The board will normally allocate a maximum of £50,000 each year for grants in this category. Grants in excess of £10,000 will normally be decided towards the end of each calendar year and applications should be submitted no later than 1 September. In the case of larger projects, the trustees may consider partnership funding with other charities. All grants for local purposes must be reviewed by the appropriate Port Welfare Committee and its view will be taken into account.

Emergency Capital Grants can be applied for at any time and will be considered throughout the year. In exceptional circumstances, the board will endeavour to make a prompt decision.

The board does not provide grants to individuals but a number of the constituent member charities do. The board has dedicated staff trained to assist

by accessing guidance and practical financial support for serving or retired seafarers, their dependants or those acting on their behalf. Further details can be found on the website.

Financial information

In 2016 the charity held assets totalling £15.3 million and had an income of £709,000. Grants totalled £233,000 and were distributed among 17 organisations and the Port Welfare Committees.

Beneficiaries included: International Seafarers Welfare and Assistance Network (£50,000); Nautilus Welfare Fund (£26,500); Queen Victoria's Seamen's Rest (£24,000 in two grants); Lighthouse Seamen's Mission (£20,000); Tyne Mariners Benevolent Institute (£13,000); Liverpool Seafarers' Centre (£12,000); Maritime Charities Group (£5,000); Fishermen's Mission – Lowestoft (£1,900).

Exclusions

Funding is not available retrospectively. Although grants are not made to individuals, other than in emergency, the charity acts as a 'clearing house' for those seeking assistance from other maritime charities.

Applications

Application forms are available to download from the charity's website and once completed, should be emailed to the board. It is recommended that applicants contact the Chief Executive at an early stage, outlining the purpose of the application. This will help to ensure that it meets the criteria and that all the requirements are met.

Applicants seeking amounts over £5,000 should submit their latest annual report and accounts. Those applying for amounts over £25,000 may also be asked to submit a five-year business plan. The trustees meet to consider applications in March, July and November (requests for larger grants of over £10,000 must be submitted by 1 September).

Applications should contain the following information:

⟩ A demonstration of need which highlights the direct benefit to seafarers
⟩ A summary of the organisation's reserves policy, stating whether the policy is to reduce, maintain or increase reserves and why that policy is appropriate
⟩ Whether or not the organisation is able to reclaim VAT

Capital grants will only be paid on proof of expenditure or the submission of a valid invoice.

Sources of information

Accounts; annual report; Charity Commission record; funder's website.

Merchant Taylors' Consolidated Charities for the Infirm

Older people, disability, people with health issues (mental or physical), relief of need

Lewisham, Southwark, Tower Hamlets, Hackney and their bordering boroughs, occasionally Greater London

£106,500 (2016)

CC number: 214266

Trustees: Duncan MacDonald Eggar; Rupert Bull; Richard Sullivan; Richard Charlton; Lady Patricia Harding.

Correspondent: Giles Hutchinson, Charities Officer, Merchant Taylors' Hall, 30 Threadneedle Street, London EC2R 8JB (tel: 020 7450 4447; email: charities@merchant-taylors.co.uk)

 www.merchant-taylors.co.uk/charities

This charity is one of a number of grant-making charities administered by the Merchant Taylors' Company, one of the 'Great Twelve' City of London livery companies. It was established under a Charity Commission scheme in 1960.

Grant-making policy
The charity makes grants to registered charities working in the following categories:

- Category 1: activities benefitting older people
- Category 2: activities benefitting people who are in financial hardship who also have either physical or mental health issues or have a disability and/or a developmental condition (e.g. autism)

The charity's strongest preference is to support work which mainly or exclusively benefits the London boroughs of Tower Hamlets, Hackney, Lewisham and Southwark. Support can also be considered for work mainly or exclusively benefitting (in order of preference): London boroughs sharing a border with those listed; Greater London; a part of Greater London outside the boroughs listed and their bordering boroughs.

The trustees prioritise helping charities with an annual income of less than £100,000 and have a second preference for charities with an annual income between £100,000 and £500,000. National charities can only be supported with applications for projects within Tower Hamlets, Hackney, Lewisham and Southwark and their neighbouring boroughs.

Grants are typically in the range of £5,000 to £20,000, although larger amounts may be considered. According to the website, the trustees prefer to award them towards projects which have a clear outcome, or proposals which significantly improve a charity's resilience, efficiency, ability to achieve its charitable purposes, or will have a positive, broader impact beyond its beneficiaries. However, core costs can be considered. Where the trustees feel it is appropriate, funding for up to three years may also be considered.

See the website for full guidelines.

Financial information
In 2016 the charity held assets of £13.5 million and an income of £262,000. Grants totalling £106,500 were awarded to 19 organisations.

Beneficiaries included: Deptford Reach (£10,000); Time and Talents Association (£8,000); Blind in Business and The Wheelchair Sport Foundation (£5,000 each); Rheumatoid Arthritis (£1,500); Combat Stress (£1,000).

Exclusions
According to the guidelines on the charity's website, the following are never funded: bricks and mortar appeals; charities that mainly make grants or loans to individuals; medical research; individuals.

Applications
In the first instance, applicants should refer to the charity's website for full guidelines.

All applications for funding should be made using the online application form, which can be accessed via the website. Any applications received by post or email will not be considered.

Applications can be made at any time but will be considered according to this annual timetable published on the website:

- Applications made between 10 September and 8 January will be considered at the trustees' February meeting, with the decision notified on 16 March
- Applications made between 9 January and 9 March will be considered at the trustees' April meeting, with the decision notified on 18 May
- Applications made between 10 March and 9 May will be considered at the trustees' June meeting, with the decision notified on 6 July
- Applications made between 10 May to 9 September will be considered at the trustees' October/November meeting, with the decision notified on 30 November

Sources of information
Accounts; annual report; Charity Commission record; funder's website.

The Merchants' House of Glasgow

General charitable purposes, relief of poverty, health and disability, older people, young people, the arts, education

Glasgow area and the west of Scotland

£251,500 (2016)

OSCR number: SC008900

Correspondent: The Trustees, 7 West George Street, Glasgow G2 1BA (tel: 0141 221 8272; email: info@merchantshouse.org.uk)

 www.merchantshouse.org.uk

The charity's main activities include paying 'pensions to pensioners, who may or may not have membership qualifications', and 'providing assistance in the form of grants to charitable institutions within and around Glasgow'. Awards are made to charities registered in Scotland. The website notes:

The Merchants House is now a major charitable institution and donations of more than £700,000 are awarded each year to deserving charities and individuals in Glasgow and beyond. For over four hundred years after its foundation, it is part of the fabric of Glasgow and the city is richer for it.

Benevolence is available on application from other organisations active in charitable fields in Glasgow and the local West of Scotland area. The House also makes grants and provides bursaries from its funds to various educational institutions.

The House will normally consider, favourably, applications for grants from the central administrative body of (but not from individual units of) and in the following order of preference:-

- Organisations providing care and assistance to groups of or concerned with disabled, elderly or terminally ill, and the socially deprived
- Organisations providing for the care, advancement and rehabilitation of youth
- Universities, Colleges of Further Education and Schools
- Organisations connected with the Arts – Music, Theatre and the visual arts
- Such organisations of which the Dean of Guild is an honorary President or vice-President or other honorary office-bearer, or on which the Merchants House is officially represented

Financial information
In 2016 the charity held assets of £10.4 million and had an income of £513,500. Grants awarded to organisations totalled £251,500.

Previous beneficiaries have included: Erskine; East Park Home; Guide Dogs

285

for the Blind; Citizens Theatre; Greater Glasgow Scout Council; Princess Royal Maternity Unit; Scottish Opera; The Boys' Brigade Glasgow Battalion.

Exclusions

The website notes:

The House will not, except in exceptional circumstances, make grants to:-

▶ Individuals
▶ Charities which have their principal sphere of operation outwith the Glasgow and West of Scotland area
▶ Charities, the objects of which are identical to those of the House (i.e. the award of pensions and/or precepts to individuals)
▶ Charities to which a grant has been made by the House in the two years preceding any application
▶ Churches other than Glasgow Cathedral
▶ The Directors of the Merchants House reserve the right to decline any application for assistance without specifying any reason.

Applications

Applications can be made through the charity's website. All applications must be accompanied by details of the applicant's charitable status, a copy of their last financial statement and details of their activities.

Sources of information

OSCR record; funder's website.

T. & J. Meyer Family Foundation Ltd

🔍 Education, health, environment, overseas aid

📍 Worldwide

£ Approx. £689,000 (2016)

CC number: 1087507

Trustees: Jane Meyer; Annabelle Ahouiyek; Miranda Spackman; Edwin Falkman; Della Drees.

Correspondent: Timothy Meyer, Company Secretary, 3 Kendrick Mews, London SW7 3HG (tel: 020 7581 9900; email: info@tjmff.org)

The foundation was set up in 2000 and is administered by the Meyer family. It focuses primarily on education, health care and the environment. Support can be given to organisations that:

▶ Alleviate the suffering of humanity through health, education and environment
▶ Have extremely high correlation between what is gifted and what the beneficiary receives
▶ Struggle to raise funds either because either they are new, their size or their access to funds is constrained
▶ Promote long-term effective sustainable solutions

Financial information

All figures have been converted from US Dollars at the rate of $1 = £0.77.

In 2016 the foundation had assets of $24.6 million (approx. £19 million) and an income of $588,500 (approx. £454,000). It gave 18 grants totalling $892,000 (approx. £689,000) to organisations in a range of different countries across the world, broken down in the accounts into the following categories:

Health	$614,500	(approx. £474,000)
Education	$142,000	(approx. £109,500)
Environment	$120,500	(approx. £92,500)
Membership	$16,100	(approx. £12,400)

Beneficiaries included: Last Mile Health ($150,000 – approx. £116,000); CREES Foundation ($120,000 – approx. £92,500); Angkor Hospital for Children (£100,000 – approx. £77,000); Sisters of Sacred Heart of Jesus and Mary ($91,500 – approx. £70,500); Room to Read (£10,200 – approx. £7,900); Royal Marsden Cancer Charity ($3,800 – approx. £2,900); The Philanthropy Workshop ($270 – approx. £210).

Applications

The foundation does not accept unsolicited applications.

Sources of information

Accounts; annual report; Charity Commission record.

The Gerald Micklem Charitable Trust

🔍 General charitable purposes, disability in adults, including learning disabilities and blindness, health causes, medical conditions and hospices, carers, environment and wildlife, support for older people, including those living with dementia

📍 UK, East Hampshire and West Sussex

£ £323,500 (2016)

CC number: 802583

Trustees: Susan Shone; Joanna Scott-Dalgleish; Helen Ratcliffe.

Correspondent: Susan Shone, Trustee, Bolinge Hill Farm, Buriton, Petersfield, Hampshire GU31 4NN (tel: 01730 264207; email: mail@geraldmicklemct.org.uk)

🌐 www.geraldmicklemct.org.uk

The trust was established in November 1989 with a bequest left in the will of Gerald Micklem. The trust's annual report for 2016 states that the trustees 'are prepared to fund core costs as well as capital projects, but are unlikely to provide initial funding for new established organisations'. Occasionally appeals from charities working in East

Hampshire outside the preferred fields can also be considered.

According to the trust's website, the organisations in which the trust is most interested are UK charities working either on a national basis or specifically in Hampshire or West Sussex and in one of the fields listed below:

▶ Adults and children with physical disabilities
▶ Adults and children with learning disabilities
▶ Carers for older people and people with disabilities, especially young carers
▶ Environment and wildlife
▶ Hospices for adults and children
▶ Medical conditions affecting both adults and children
▶ Support for older people, including those with Alzheimer's or dementia

Financial information

In 2016 the trust held assets of £2.5 million and had an income of about £281,500. There were 36 grants made to organisations totalling £323,500.

Previous beneficiaries have included: Home Farm Trust (£72,500); The Golf Foundation (£23,000); Maggie's (£20,000); Penny Brohn Cancer Care (£18,000); SeeAbility (£10,000); The Rowans Hospice (£7,000); Dogs for Good, Fundatia Adept Ltd, Marine Conservation Society and Off The Record (£5,000 each); Action Aid UK (£3,000).

Exclusions

The trust does not make grants to, or enter into sponsorship arrangements with, individuals. Grants are not made to organisations that are not UK-registered charities. The annual report for 2016 notes that 'the trustees have not formally excluded any category of charitable activity, but they have established some funding priorities'. The trust is 'unlikely to support the regional work of such charities in locations outside Hampshire and West Sussex or charities working only in other areas of the UK'.

The website notes that the following areas fall outside the trust's current funding priorities:

▶ Drug/alcohol abuse and counselling
▶ Disadvantaged children and young people
▶ Educations/schools (except for those for children with disabilities)
▶ Homelessness and housing
▶ Local community groups
▶ Medical research
▶ Mental health
▶ Museums, galleries and heritage
▶ Performing arts and cultural organisations
▶ Churches
▶ Overseas aid

Applications

There is no formal application form and applications should be made in writing to the correspondent by letter – *not by email*. Applicants also have to provide a copy of their latest annual report and accounts. Enquiries prior to any application may be made by email. The trustees usually consider awards in January/February; therefore, they ask to submit requests 'towards the end of a calendar year so that the information they contain is most up to date when considered', preferably as late as possible. However, appeals are not carried forward and should be with the trustees by 31 December.

Sources of information

Accounts; annual report; Charity Commission record; funder's website.

Millennium Stadium Charitable Trust (Ymddiriedaeth Elusennol Stadiwm Y. Mileniwm)

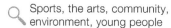 Sports, the arts, community, environment, young people

 Wales

£350,500 (2016/17)

CC number: 1086596

Trustees: Ian Davies; Martin Davies; John Lloyd-Jones; Gerallt Hughes; Russell Goodway; Linda Pepper; Andrew Walker; John Hardy Rawlins; William Jones; Cllr Peter Bradbury; David Hammond.

Correspondent: Sarah Fox, Trust Administrator, 4 Bessemer Road, Cardiff CF11 8BA (tel: 02920022 143; email: info@millenniumstadiumtrust.org.uk)

 www.millenniumstadiumtrust.co.uk

The trust was established by an agreement between the Millennium Commission and the Millennium Stadium plc. Its income is generated through a levy on every ticket purchased for public events at the stadium.

Local and regional grants

Grants for both programmes are made in four categories – arts, community, environment and sports. Refer to the trust's website for its priorities in these areas.

The maximum grant for regional projects is £7,500 and £2,500 for local grants.

The following information has been taken from the trust's website:

A regional project is where the organisations usually have a remit to serve a region of Wales or a local authority area. This means that they are the only organisation providing that service within the county borough. Successful applicants in this category must demonstrate that their project is regional or local-authority wide.

Applicants are asked to note that bids must be classified by the organisation's geographical remit. It is the applicant's responsibility to determine and prove their classification.

A local project is where the organisations usually have a remit to serve their local community or town. If there is more than one organisation providing a similar service in the local authority, the group should be considered local (i.e. if there is more than one tennis club in the local authority, then the tennis club will be considered a local organisation).

Applicants are asked to note that bids must be classified by the organisation's geographical remit. It is the applicant's responsibility to determine and prove their classification.

Youth grant fund

The Trustees have chosen to provide a one-off grants scheme of £5,000 for 2018 focusing on young people. Applications must be for projects engaging with disadvantaged young people who live or work in Wales. (capital, salaries and overheads will not be entertained), Funding must be for equipment, volunteer costs, training and may include but cannot solely be for project delivery costs.

The organisation applying does not necessarily need to be a youth organisation, but the project must be working with young people to age 19.

Financial information

In 2016/17 the trust held assets of £131,500 and had an income of £285,500. Grants were made to 94 organisations totalling £350,500 and distributed as follows:

Sport	£252,500
Community	£62,000
Environment	£21,500
Art	£15,000

A list of beneficiaries was not available.

Exclusions

The trust does not support:

- Projects outside Wales
- Day-to-day running costs
- Projects that seek to redistribute grant funds for the benefit of third party organisations
- Payments of debts/overdrafts
- Retrospective requests
- Requests from individuals
- Payment to profit-making organisations
- Applications made solely in the name of a local authority

Applications

The trust holds three rounds a year; one for each type of application – national, regional and local. Deadline dates can be found on the trust's website, along with full guidelines and application forms.

Unsuccessful applicants may re-apply after one year.

Sources of information

Accounts; annual report; Charity Commission record; guidelines for applicants; funder's website.

The Millfield House Foundation

 Social disadvantage, social policy

 North east England, particularly Tyne and Wear

£ Around £200,000 (2016/17)

CC number: 1158914

Trustees: Jane Streather; Sheila Spencer; Laura Seebohm; Toby Lowe; Michael Hill; Peter Deans; Rhiannon Bearne; Evelyn Cole; David Handyside.

Correspondent: Cullagh Warnock, 7 Lesbury Road, Newcastle Upon Tyne NE6 5LB (tel: 07595 280401; email: cullagh@mhfdn.org.uk)

 www.mhfdn.org.uk

@MillfieldHouseF

Millfield House Foundation (MHF) was founded in 1976 and helps to tackle poverty, disadvantage and exclusion and to promote social change in the North East, particularly Tyne and Wear. The current priority is to promote social change by funding projects that inform discussion and influence public policy and attitudes, with the aim of diminishing social deprivation and empowering communities.

The foundation seeks to tackle the causes of poverty and other social issues rather than alleviate the symptoms, to create a more equal society.

The foundation runs a Fellowship Scheme which helps to develop skills in North East-based policy workers, and the trustees retain the right to make occasional one-off grants to help organisations develop ideas that contribute to their overall aims.

Financial information

In 2016/17 the foundation had an income of £169,000 and a total expenditure of £230,000. Full accounts were not available to view on the Charity Commission website at the time of writing. We estimate that grants awarded to organisations totalled around £170,000.

Previous beneficiaries have included: Institute for Public Policy Research North (£134,500); Regional Refugee Forum North East (£120,000); North

East Child Poverty Commission (£72,500); Newcastle Citizens Advice (£60,000).

Applications

The foundation's website states that it funds in three ways:

- We invite a limited number of policy-focused organisations to become our strategic partners
- We are developing the capacity and policy skills of the North East voluntary sector through placements we are setting up with accomplished policy-focused organisations
- The Trustees will make occasional one-off grants to help organisations develop interesting or potentially powerful ideas that contribute to their overall aims. We do not accept unsolicited applications

Sources of information

Accounts; annual report; Charity Commission record; funder's website.

The Millichope Foundation

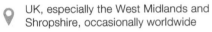 Arts and culture, conservation projects and the environment, heritage, disaster relief, general charitable purposes

UK, especially the West Midlands and Shropshire, occasionally worldwide

£ £431,000 (2016/17)

CC number: 282357

Trustees: Bridget Marshall; Sarah Bury; Lindsay Bury; Frank Bury; H. Horne.

Correspondent: Sarah Bury, Trustee, The Old Rectory, Tugford, Craven Arms, Shropshire SY7 9HS (tel: 01584 841234; email: sarah@millichope.com)

The foundation makes donations in the UK to arts, culture, conservation and heritage. Grants are made specifically within Shropshire for general charitable purposes. Worldwide conservation projects and disaster funds are also occasionally supported.

Financial information

In 2016/17 the foundation held assets of £8.6 million and had an income of £466,000. There were 131 grants made totalling £431,000.

Previous beneficiaries have included: Brazilian Atlantic Rainforest Trust (£75,000); Global Canopy Foundation (£55,000); Fauna and Flora International (£20,000); Shropshire Historic Churches Trust (£10,000); Syria Relief (£5,000); Corvedale C of E Aided Primary School (£3,500); Prisoners' Education Trust (£2,000); South Shropshire Domestic Violence Service (£1,000); Music in Hospitals (£750); Arts for Health (£500).

Exclusions

Individuals and non-registered charities are not supported.

Applications

Applications can be made in writing to the correspondent. The trustees meet several times a year to consider grants.

Sources of information

Accounts; annual report; Charity Commission record.

The Clare Milne Trust

 Disability causes

South West England, with a preference for Devon and Cornwall

£ £740,000 (2016/17)

CC number: 1084733

Trustees: Margaret Rogers; Nigel Urwin; Christine Kirk; Robert Spencer.

Correspondent: Emma Houlding, Claypitts, Ladram Road, Otterton, Devon EX9 7HT (tel: 01395 270418; email: emma@claremilnetrust.com)

www.claremilnetrust.com

The trust was established in 2002 by the granddaughter of the author A. A. Milne, Clare Milne, with funds derived from the sale of the copyright royalties from her grandfather's books.

The trust supports people, especially adults living with disabilities in Devon and Cornwall. The trustees prefer to support charities which are small and well run, have strong support from volunteers and only a modest expenditure on fundraising and administration. Typically grants are between £1,000 and £25,000 and often make up a partial contribution towards the total project cost.

The trust's record on the Charity Commission's website notes that it 'prefers to make a small number of carefully researched one-off grants towards capital projects or core funding'. Help can be given to organisations providing services, facilities or equipment to people with disabilities, and in some exceptional cases grants can be made to cover salaries.

Financial information

In 2016/17 the trust had assets of £35.45 million and an income of £1.67 million. Grants were made to 75 organisations totalling £740,000.

Beneficiaries included: Rainbow Living (£25,000); Somerset Sight (£15,000); Age UK Mid Devon, Children's Hospice South West, iSight Cornwall (£10,000 each); Brain Tumour support (£6,000); Access Theatre, Home-Start Kernow, Mid Devon Alliance for Special

Children, Torbay Advice Network (£5,000 each).

Exclusions

Individuals and national charities are not normally supported.

Applications

Application forms can be downloaded from the trust's website or requested from the correspondent. Forms should be submitted either by post or by email to the correspondent, along with a covering letter (on letterheaded paper), details regarding your proposal (up to two sides of A4) and a budget for the project. Detailed application guidance is available on the trust's website.

Applications are considered at trustee meetings, held four times a year. The trustees aim to contact applicants within two weeks from the date of the meeting.

Sources of information

Accounts; annual report; Charity Commission record; further information provided by the funder; funder's website.

The Laurence Misener Charitable Trust

 General charitable purposes, health, seafarers, people with disabilities, Jewish causes

UK

£ £303,000 (2016/17)

CC number: 283460

Trustees: Jillian Legane; Capt. George Swaine.

Correspondent: David Lyons, 1 Printing Yard House, London E2 7PR (tel: 020 7739 8790; email: enquiries@ leonardjones.co.uk)

The trust was established in 1981 for general charitable purposes with a preference for supporting medical charities, organisations working with people with disabilities or seafarers, and Jewish causes. The trustees tend to make grants to the same organisations each year, in accordance with the settlor's wishes.

Financial information

In 2016/17 the trust held assets of £2.6 million and had an income of £109,000. Grants were made totalling £303,000 and were distributed to 15 organisations.

Previous beneficiaries have included: Multiple Sclerosis Society, Royal Marsden Hospital and Seafarers UK (£40,000 each); Great Ormond Street Hospital (£30,000); Fight for Sight and RNLI (£25,000 each); Imperial War Museum Development Trust (£15,000); St Peter and St James Home and

Hospice (£13,000); Sussex Stroke and Circulation Fund (£10,000).

Applications

Applications can be made in writing to the correspondent. Note the following taken from the annual report for 2016/17:

> The Trustees receive a considerable number of requests for donations and grants each year but have a policy to restrict donations approved to those charities which in their view would have been approved by the Settlor himself, or fall under the heading of approved charitable purposes.

Sources of information

Accounts; annual report; Charity Commission record.

The Brian Mitchell Charitable Settlement

 General charitable purposes, especially arts and education, medical care and research, social welfare

UK

£226,000 (2015/16)

CC number: 1003817

Trustees: Brian Mitchell; Andy Buss; John Andrews; Michael Conlon; Fraser Moore Reavell.

Correspondent: Brian Mitchell, Trustee, Round Oak, Old Station Road, Wadhurst, East Sussex TN5 6TZ (tel: 01892 782072)

The charity provides grants to a range of charitable organisations. According to the annual report for 2015/16, 'approximately sixty percent of the total grants were directed to supporting arts and education while the remaining grants were allocated to a wide field of other activities including medical care and research, social welfare and international support'.

Financial information

In 2015/16 the charity had assets of £2.4 million and an income of £290,500. There were 51 grants made to organisations totalling £226,000.

Beneficiaries included: Glyndebourne Festival Society (£25,000); British Red Cross and Shakespeare's Globe Theatre (£15,000 each); Myeloma UK (£10,000); Hospice on the Weald, Macmillan Nurses and Orchestra of the Age of Enlightenment (£7,500 each); Temple Music Foundation (£7,000); Canterbury Cathedral, Child Hope and The Rose Theatre Trust (£5,000).

Applications

Applications may be made in writing to the correspondent, although be aware

that the charity has already identified several regular beneficiaries.

Sources of information

Accounts; annual report; Charity Commission record.

The Alexander Moncur Trust

 Cultural, health, educational and social projects

Dundee and surrounding areas

£251,000 to organisations (2017)

OSCR number: SC008863

Trustee: The Trustees.

Correspondent: Ernest Boath, Administrator, Miller Hendry Solicitors, 13 Ward Road, Dundee DD1 1LU (tel: 01382 200000; email: info@moncurtrust. org)

www.moncurtrust.org

The trust provides funding to cultural, educational, health and social projects in Dundee and its surrounding areas. Grants of up to £5,000 are awarded twice a year. Grants of over £10,000 may be made in exceptional circumstances.

The following information has been taken from the trust's website:

Who can apply?

In almost all circumstances only applications from registered charities will be considered.

In exceptional circumstances, applications on behalf of an individual or non-charitable body will be considered, if there is a unique and significant common good to be gained in the Dundee area.

The Alexander Moncur Trust has in the past entered into multi-year arrangements to support specific projects. In these exceptional cases, grants in the range of £10,000 per year for three years have been awarded. Past recipients include, Sense Scotland and Maggie Cancer Care, for projects based in Dundee.

Geographical area

Whilst most successful applications come from Dundee and the surrounding area, applications will be considered from charities based furth of Dundee and area, if a clear link can be shown that will support and benefit the Dundee area and its residents.

As a rough geographic guide, almost all grants are awarded to charities or their projects that fall within an area stretching around Dundee, through north Fife, Perth and Angus.

Financial information

In 2017 the trust held assets of £8.6 million and had an income of £293,000. Grants were made to 86 organisations and totalled £251,000, with

a further £1,000 awarded to two individuals.

Beneficiaries included: Leisure and Culture Dundee (£18,000); Cancer Research UK (£15,000); Dundee Industrial Heritage Ltd, The Food Train and Women's Rape and Sexual Abuse Centre (£5,000 each); Hearing Voices Network Dundee (£4,000); Drugs Initiative Group (£3,000); Dundee Association for Mental Health, Edinburgh Science Festival, Ninewells Community Garden (£2,000 each); Scottish Chamber Orchestra and Ye Amphibious Ancients Bathing Association (£1,000 each).

Applications

Application forms are available to download from the trust's website and should be returned to Miller Hendry Solicitors. Forms can also be requested from Miller Hendry Solicitors on 01382 200000. Application deadlines are 31 March and 30 September each year.

Sources of information

Accounts; annual report; OSCR record; funder's website.

Money Advice Trust

 Debt and money advice, social welfare

UK

£355,500 (2016/17)

CC number: 1099506

Trustees: Claire Whyley; Simon Crine; Merrick Willis; Sian Williams; Adam Sharples; Gail Scott-Spicer; Paul Smee; Ade Keasey; Anna Bennett; Lawrence Slade.

Correspondent: Ian Witcombe, Company Secretary, Money Advice Trust, 21–26 Garlick Hill, London EC4V 2AU (tel: 020 7653 9721; email: info@moneyadvicetrust.org)

www.moneyadvicetrust.org

Money Advice Trust was established in 2003 to help people across the UK tackle their debts and manage their money with confidence. The trust's main activities are: providing free advice through National Debtline and Business Debtline; supporting advisers through Wiseradviser; and improving the UK's money and debt environment through policy, research and campaigns.

Grant programmes

Since 2011, the trust has funded innovative debt advice projects, aiming to improve the quality and range of money advice in the UK, through its Innovation Grants programme.

The trust funds projects that demonstrate innovative practice in terms of:

- How they deliver debt/money advice – these can be different models of delivery, products or materials produced; and/or
- Who they deliver debt/money advice to – these can be groups and/or individuals whose specific needs are not currently catered for

Financial information

In 2016/17 the trust had assets of £3.5 million and an income of £9 million. During the year, the trust awarded grants of £355,500.

A list of beneficiaries was not available.

Applications

Apply in writing to the correspondent. At the time of writing (June 2018) the Innovation Grants programme was closed for applications. Check the website for the latest updates.

Sources of information

Accounts; annual report; Charity Commission record; funder's website.

The Monument Trust

General charitable purposes, arts and heritage, health and community care, particularly HIV/AIDS, sexual health and hospices, social development, criminal justice, particularly rehabilitation of offenders and homelessness

Unrestricted, in practice the UK, South Africa, USA

£35.2 million (2016/17)

CC number: 242575

Trustees: Stewart Grimshaw; Linda Heathcoat-Amory; Charles Cator; Dominic Flynn.

Correspondent: Robert Bell, Director, The Peak, 5 Wilton Road, London SW1V 1AP (tel: 020 7410 0330; fax: 020 7410 0332; email: info@sfct.org.uk)

 www.sfct.org.uk

The Monument Trust was established in 1965 and, according to its website, makes grants under the following categories:

- Health and community care – 'substantial HIV/AIDS projects in the UK and Africa, social exclusion, community care, and hospices'
- Arts and heritage – 'arts, architectural and environmental projects of national or regional importance, including galleries, museums, and historic houses and gardens. Proposals are particularly welcome for cultural projects which will make a major contribution to improving economically depressed areas'
- Criminal justice – 'including prisoners' resettlement and

alternatives to custody'. The trustees also have an interest in homelessness 'especially projects which encourage homeless people to take an active role in the services designed to assist them'

This is one of the Sainsbury Family Charitable Trusts, which share a joint administration but work autonomously as independent legal entities. The website states that 'the trustees have almost completed their plan to spend the trust's endowment and close down, so in their final period of operation they will only be considering new grants to charities with which they already have a close association'.

Financial information

In 2016/17 the trust had assets of £35.2 million and an income of £3.1 million. During the year, the trust paid a total of £35.2 million in grants to organisations, broken down as follows:

Arts and heritage	24	£29.25 million
Health and hommunity care	12	£2.6 million
Other grants payable	-	£1.4 million
Social development	12	£1.3 million
General causes	3	£546,500

Beneficiaries included: The Woolbeding Charity (£8 million); Garden Bridge (£5 million); Glasgow School of Art (£3.5 million); University of Cambridge – Judge's Business School (£3 million); Parkinson's UK (£1.2 million); National Gallery (£786,000); Inspiring Scotland (£250,000); Diagrama Foundation (£50,000).

Exclusions

Grants are not normally awarded for individuals, educational fees, or expeditions.

Applications

The trust will consider suitable proposals so long as they closely match the areas in which the trustees are interested. Generally, the trustees tend to invite or initiate proposals from organisations themselves, so a large number of unsolicited applications will be unsuccessful.

Eligible proposals can be sent by post to the correspondent including the following:

- Details of your organisation – charitable aims and objectives, most recent annual income and expenditure, current financial position (do not send a full set of accounts)
- Information on the project requiring funding – why it is needed, who will benefit and in what way
- Breakdown of costs – any money that has been raised so far and how the balance will be achieved

Refrain from sending any other supporting materials. All applications are acknowledged and candidates for support are informed within eight weeks of the acknowledgement. If you have not heard from the trust by then, then assume you have been unsuccessful. **Note:** A single application will be considered for support by all the trusts in the group.

Sources of information

Accounts; annual report; Charity Commission record; funder's website.

Moondance Foundation

Education, children, social welfare, health, arts and humanities

UK, with a preference for Wales, and overseas

£7.6 million (2015/16)

CC number: 1139224

Trustees: Louisa Scadden; Henry Engelhardt; Diane Briere de L'Isle Engelhardt; Damien Englehardt; Adrian Engelhardt; Shanna Briere de L'Isle Engelhardt; Tara Briere de L'Isle Engelhardt.

Correspondent: The Trustees, c/o KPMG LLP, 3 Assembly Square, Britannia Quay, Cardiff Bay CF10 4AX (email: moondancefoundation@gmail. com)

The foundation was established in 2010 by Henry Engelhardt, founder of Admiral Group, and his wife Diane Briere de l'Isle.

The foundation's 2015/16 accounts state:

The objectives of the Foundation are to allocate funds for general charitable purposes. The charity uses its investment income to donate to a variety of good causes which benefit the public in a number of different areas. The Foundation focuses its donations in the following key areas, but are not limited to:

- Causes in Wales
- Children
- Education
- Poverty
- Care and research for crippling diseases
- Arts and humanities

Financial information

In 2015/16 the charity had assets of £203 million and an income of £34 million. Grants awarded to organisations totalled £7.6 million and were broken down as follows:

Causes in Wales	£2.2 million
Education	£1.8 million
Children	£1.5 million
Other	£1.2 million
Care and research for crippling diseases	£801,500
Arts and humanities	£125,000

Beneficiaries included: Techniquest (£1 million); Plan UK (£625,000); NSPCC (£500,000); Safer Wales (£125,000); Teach First (£100,000); Ty Hapus (£80,000); Caerphilly Miners Centre (£55,000); Elton John AIDS Foundation (£50,000); College Bound (£34,000); Surfers Against Sewage (£30,000); Chapter Cardiff (£25,000); Tenovus Cancer (£20,000).

Applications
Apply in writing to the correspondent.

Sources of information
Accounts; annual report; Charity Commission record.

The George A. Moore Foundation

 General charitable purposes

Yorkshire and the Isle of Man

£371,500 (2016/17)

CC number: 262107

Trustees: Elizabeth Moore; Jonathan Moore; Paul Turner.

Correspondent: Angela James, Chief Administrator, The George A. Moore Foundation, 4th Floor, 10 South Parade, Leeds LS1 5QS (tel: 0113 386 3393; email: info@gamf.org.uk)

 www.gamf.org.uk

The trustees of the foundation select causes and projects from applications received during the year, as well as using independent research to identify specific objectives where they wish to direct assistance. Education, community activities, disability, health and the armed forces have all been supported.

Financial information
In 2016/17 the foundation held assets of £6.6 million and had an income of £303,500. During the year, the foundation awarded 158 grants to organisations totalling £371,500. Grants awarded ranged from £30 up to £70,000.

Beneficiaries included: King James School (£77,000); Boston Charitable Foundation (£30,000); Bridge Community Church, Harrogate Neighbours Association and The Jorvik Group (£10,000 each); Breast Cancer Now, Disability Action Yorkshire and Girlguiding (£5,000 each); Arthritis Research UK (£3,000); CatZero and D:Side (£2,000 each); Asthma UK and Mind (£1,000 each); Sir George Martin Trust (£30).

Exclusions
Assistance is not given to/for:

▪ Individuals
▪ Courses of study
▪ Overseas travel
▪ Holidays
▪ Activities outside the UK

Local appeals for UK charities will only be considered if in the area of interest. Because of present long-term commitments, the foundation is not prepared to consider appeals for religious property or institutions.

Applications
Apply in writing to the correspondent. The foundation's website states:

> Please include with your application all relevant details for the funding requested, a contact email address and, if applying for funding for a specific project, include details of the total funding required, funds raised to date and the charity's proposals to raise any shortfall.

It is not necessary to enclose annual accounts with your application, but these may be requested at a later stage.

There are no formal guidelines or application forms issued, and accounts are not required. Applications should be received by the middle of the month prior to the meeting. The meetings are held four times a year and dates of upcoming meetings are posted on the foundation's website. All applicants are notified of the outcome following the meeting.

The annual report for 2016/17 notes that:

> For the most significant grants provided, greater than £5,000, the Chief Administrator will hold a meeting with the applicant to determine how the funds will be used to ensure that ultimately the users of the organisation benefit from the grant and to prevent mis-management of funds by the applicant.

Sources of information
Accounts; annual report; Charity Commission record; funder's website.

The Henry Moore Foundation

 Fine arts, in particular sculpture, research and development, projects and exhibitions which expand the definition of sculpture, such as film, photography and performance

UK and overseas

£468,000 (2016/17)

CC number: 271370

Trustees: Nigel Carrington; Charles Asprey; Henry Channon; Celia Clear; William Edgerley; Antony Griffiths; Anne Wagner; Peter Wienand; Pamela Raynor; Martin Barden.

Correspondent: Lesley Wake, Chief Operating Officer, Dane Tree House, Perry Green, Much Hadham, Hertfordshire SG10 6EE (tel: 01279 843333; email: admin@henry-moore.org)

 www.henry-moore.org

 @HenryMooreFDN

The foundation was established in 1977 to promote the public's appreciation of the visual arts and in particular the works of Henry Moore. It concentrates most of its support on sculpture. The aims of the foundation are achieved through specific projects initiated within the foundation both at Perry Green and in Leeds, particularly exhibitions and publications, and by giving grant aid to other suitable enterprises.

The foundation's grant-making programme has been revised to provide additional financial resources to support the work of living artists and contemporary art practice. Special consideration is given to projects outside London and to venues with limited opportunities to show contemporary art. The foundation is willing to support projects in the UK which involve artists from another country but overseas projects must include a British component.

The foundation owns a trading subsidiary company, HMF Enterprises Ltd, and the majority of its profits are paid annually to the foundation.

Grant-making information
The foundation awards grants under the following five categories:

New projects and commissions
This includes exhibitions, exhibition catalogues and commissions. The maximum grant is £20,000 but most grants are for less.

Acquisitions and collections
This is designed to provide minor capital grants and includes acquisitions, conservation, cataloguing and display. The maximum grant is £20,000 but most grants are for less.

Research and development
Long-term research: for projects that require funding for more than one year, e.g. a permanent collection catalogue. The maximum grant is £20,000 but most grants are for less.

Research and travel grants: for research on history and interpretation of sculpture. Academics, curators and independent scholars may apply for research costs, e.g. travel, photographs, archival access. The maximum grant is £2,500.

Research fellowships
This programme supports up to three two-year postdoctoral research

fellowships in the field of sculpture studies.

Conferences, lectures and publications

Grants of up to £5,000 are available. **Note:** A publication can be a book or a journal but not an exhibition catalogue or a permanent collection catalogue. If applying for a publication, specify within the application, how and where the publication will be distributed.

Financial information

In 2016/17 the foundation held assets of around £120.3 million and had an income of £3.6 million. During the year, the foundation awarded a total of 89 grants totalling £468,000. Grants were distributed as follows:

Exhibitions and new projects	53	£341,500
Fellowships	9	£48,500
Collections	5	£33,000
Conferences, publications and workshops	14	£31,500
Research	8	£13,500

Previous beneficiaries have included:

The Public Catalogue Foundation, London (£20,000 per annum over four years); Bodleian Weston Library University of Oxford, Lady Lever Art Gallery and Worcestershire County Council Archive and Archaeology Service (WAAS) (£10,000 each); GI – Glasgow International (£7,000); Museum of Modern Art Warsaw, Northern Gallery for Contemporary Art and University of Winchester (£2,000 each); Frontier Publishing Norwich (£1,000).

Exclusions

No grants are given for revenue expenditure. No grant (or any part of a grant) may be used to pay any fee or to provide any other benefit to any individual who is a trustee of the foundation. Applications from individuals are only accepted when applying for a small research grant.

Applications

Applicants should complete an application form, which is available on the trust's website. Applications must be posted to the grants administrator. Applications will be acknowledged by letter.

The grants committee meets quarterly; consult the trust's website for exact dates as the trust advises that applications received late will not be considered until the next meeting. It is advised to leave six months between the grants committee meeting and the project start date as funds cannot be paid for retrospective projects.

Applicants should also advise the foundation whether it is envisaged that any trustee will have an interest in the project for which a grant is sought.

Sources of information

Accounts; annual report; Charity Commission record; guidelines for applicants; funder's website.

John Moores Foundation

 Social, educational, cultural, geographical and other disadvantage, community cohesion and development

Merseyside (including Skelmersdale, Ellesmere Port and Halton), and Northern Ireland

£666,500 (2016/17)

CC number: 253481

Trustees: Barnaby Moores; Kevin Moores; Nicola Eastwood; Christina Mee.

Correspondent: Phil Godfrey, Grants Director, John Moores Foundation, 1st Floor Front Office, 96 Bold Street, Liverpool L1 4HY (tel: 0151 707 6077; email: info@johnmooresfoundation.com)

 www.jmf.org.uk

 @JMF1964

John Moores Foundation was established in 1964 with aims and objectives that were widely drawn at the beginning to allow for changing patterns of need.

The foundation primarily supports projects based in the Merseyside area (including Skelmersdale, Ellesmere Port and Halton) and Northern Ireland. Its website states that, through its work, it aims 'to enable people who face barriers, as a result of social, educational, physical, economic, cultural, geographical or other disadvantage, to improve their social conditions and quality of life'. It does this by making grants to local groups. Priority is given to small, grassroots and volunteer-driven organisations that find it difficult to attract money from other sources.

The 2016/17 trustees' report outlines how the foundation's giving is allocated:

▶ **Merseyside:** is the primary concern of the trustees, receiving around 60% to 75% of the annual grant total
▶ **Northern Ireland:** receives, on average, around 25% of the annual grant total
▶ **One-off exceptional grants:** are 'rare and unspecific' and are given to causes that interest the trustees. **Note:** Unsolicited applications are not accepted for grants in this category

The foundation describes itself as an 'enabling funder' and organisations that receive a grant may also receive additional support through the foundation's Community Groups

Development Worker in areas such as fundraising, strategic planning or trustee development, and through the Monitoring and Evaluation Worker to help establish 'systems that best meet their needs, capacity, etc'.

What the foundation funds

Grants are made to organisations working with disadvantaged or marginalised people, with preference given to projects which fall within the foundation's priority areas:

▶ Local community groups
▶ Black and minority ethnic organisations
▶ Women, including girls
▶ Second-chance learning
▶ Advice and information to alleviate poverty
▶ Grassroots social health initiatives
▶ Training for voluntary organisations
▶ Joint working and trust-building initiatives
▶ Equality and diversity

And, in Merseyside only:

▶ Refugees
▶ Children and young people
▶ Family support
▶ Homeless people
▶ Carers

Further details of each of these areas are available on the foundation's website.

Grants can be given towards running costs, volunteers' out-of-pocket expenses, one-off projects, equipment and salaries.

Financial information

In 2016/17 the foundation had assets of £27 million and an income of £1 million. A total of 147 grants were paid, amounting to £666,500.

A list of beneficiaries was not included in the 2016/17 annual report and accounts.

Previous beneficiaries in Merseyside have included: Family Tree – Wirral, Homebaked Co-operative Anfield Ltd, Sahir House and Vauxhall Community Law and Information Centre (£10,000 each); Asylum Link Merseyside (£7,000 each); Pakistan Association Liverpool (£5,000); Merseyside Welfare Rights (£2,000); HALDS – Halton Adults with Learning Disabilities Support (£600).

Previous beneficiaries in Northern Ireland have included: Jigsaw Community Counselling Centre (£4,500); Polish Saturday School Ballymena and Strabane Community Unemployed Group (£3,000 each); Banbridge Arthritis Care (£1,200); Tullygarley and District Residents' Association (£750).

Exclusions

According to the website, as a general rule the foundation does not fund:

- Individuals
- Projects that are not substantially influenced by their target beneficiaries
- National organisations or groups based outside the Merseyside region even where some of the service users come from the area
- Statutory bodies or work previously done by them
- Education (schools, colleges, universities, supplementary schools)
- Faith-based projects exclusively for members of that faith, or for the promotion of religion
- Capital building costs
- Festivals, carnivals and fêtes
- Medicine or medical equipment
- Holidays and expeditions
- Gifts, parties, etc
- Organising conferences
- Sport
- Vehicles
- Animal charities
- The creative industries
- Heritage or local history projects
- Employability and enterprise schemes
- Academic or medical research
- Credit Unions – except for the training of management committee members or the development of a new business plan
- Veterans
- Uniformed groups (e.g. scouts, cadets, majorettes)
- Sponsorship, advertising or fundraising events
- Counsellors not registered with the BACP, UKCP or IACP

Furthermore, 'Unsolicited applications which fall outside the policy criteria are not considered, nor are applications for one-off exceptional grants.'

Applications

In the first instance, refer to the foundation's website and make sure your project falls within the funding criteria.

Applications should be made by letter and be no longer than four A4 sides. They must be accompanied by a completed organisational details form, which is only available from the foundation's offices and can be requested by letter, telephone, email or via the link on the website. The website's helpful FAQs section explains: 'We don't want you wasting your time putting together an application that is unlikely to succeed, so we like to check that your proposal is something our trustees might consider before sending an application pack.'

Organisations based in Merseyside can get in touch with the Merseyside office to request an application form using the contact details above. Organisations in Northern Ireland should contact the foundation's Northern Ireland office (PO Box 4, Carnlough BT44 0WZ; tel:

028 2888 6161; email: jmfni@btinternet. com).

The trustees meet to consider applications five to six times a year. Applicants should generally allow three to five months for a decision to be made.

Sources of information

Accounts; annual report; Charity Commission record; funder's website.

The Steve Morgan Foundation

 Children and young people, older people, health and disability, social welfare

North Wales, Merseyside, Cheshire and North Shropshire

£2.8 million (2016/17)

CC number: 1087056

Trustees: Vincent Fairclough; Ashley Lewis; Sally Morgan; Jonathan Masters; Steve Morgan; Rhiannon Walker.

Correspondent: Jane Harris, Administrator, PO Box 3517, Chester CH1 9ET (tel: 01829 782808; fax: 01829 782223; email: contact@ morganfoundation.co.uk)

 www.morganfoundation.co.uk

 facebook.com/Steve-Morgan-Foundation-106137272803911

 @stevemorganfdn

The Steve Morgan Foundation was established in 2001 with an endowment of over £2 million from Stephen Morgan CBE, founder of Redrow plc and Chair of Wolverhampton Wanders FC. The foundation supports projects that help children and families, people with physical or learning disabilities, older people, or those who are socially disadvantaged or isolated.

The foundation typically provides funding for small to medium-sized organisations working to address a specific need and is particularly keen to support organisations 'who have already begun to make an impact, but need a helping hand to expand their work and increase their effectiveness'. Although the majority of grant recipients are registered charities, the foundation will also consider applications from other types of organisations which are pursuing charitable causes and where aims and objectives are 'not for profit'.

Grants programmes

Funding provided by the foundation typically falls into one of the following four categories:

- **Project grant funding:** Multi-year revenue grants for core funding,

salaries and ongoing running costs for projects
- **Enable:** Funding for specialist disability equipment for people of all ages
- **Capital:** One-off capital funding for projects of all sizes
- **Smiley Bus:** Funding for both standard and wheelchair accessible minibuses

Financial information

In 2016/17 the foundation had assets of around £229 million and an income of £204 million, the majority of which was as the result of a gift of 42,000,000 shares in Redrow plc resulting in an in-kind donation of almost £203 million. During the year, 82 grants were made totalling £2.8 million.

Beneficiaries included: Neuro Therapy Centre (£75,000); Bridge Community Farm CIC (£65,000); Designs in Mind (£57,500); Chester Sexual Abuse Support Service (£21,500); ADHD Foundation (£20,000); Birkenhead Youth Club Minibus (£15,000); Children's Trust (£10,000); Handicapped Children's Action Group (£2,000); Cancer Research (£250).

Exclusions

The foundation will not give grants for the following:

- Animal welfare
- Arts/heritage
- Conservation/environment
- Expeditions and overseas travel
- General fundraising appeals
- Individual and sports sponsorship
- National charities and large organisations
- Mainstream education
- Mainstream sport
- Promotion of specific religions

Note: Local branches of national charities which are based within the remit area, or programmes delivered locally by organisations working on a national basis, are not generally supported.

Applications

For project and capital grants, applicants are requested to first check their eligibility against the criteria listed on the foundation's website. Eligible organisations are then asked to call the foundation for an informal conversation about their application. There are no specific deadlines for applications and the trustees hold regular meetings throughout the year. As part of the process applicants may be visited by representatives of the foundation. The process from initial application to completion can take up to six months.

Applications for 'Enable funding' can be completed using the downloadable form available on the foundation's website.

Applicants for funding for accessible minibuses are asked to call the foundation for a conversation about their needs.

Sources of information

Accounts; annual report; Charity Commission record; funder's website.

Morgan Stanley International Foundation

 Children's health, education

 Tower Hamlets, Glasgow, Europe, Middle East and Africa

£1.3 million (2016)

CC number: 1042671

Trustees: Clare Woodman; Hanns Seibold; Maryann McMahon; Stephen Mavin; Fergus O'Sullivan; Sue Watts; Oliver Stuart; Jon Bendall; Simon Evenson; William Chalmers; Mandy DeFilippo.

Correspondent: Anish Shah, Morgan Stanley & Co. International plc, 20 Bank Street, London E14 4AD (tel: 020 7425 1302; email: communityaffairslondon@ morganstanley.com)

 www.morganstanley.com/ globalcitizen/msif_guidelines. html

The Morgan Stanley International Foundation (MSIF) was registered with the Charity Commission in 1994 and is the corporate charity of Morgan Stanley and Co. International plc, the financial services corporation. The foundation's trustees are all present employees of the company. The foundation focuses on supporting organisations in the London borough of Tower Hamlets, Glasgow and overseas.

According to the foundation's website, funding is typically given to organisations working in the following areas:

- **Children's Health:** The Foundation looks to invest in innovations and development in children's health care. Working with charitable organisations, hospitals and community-based initiatives, the MSIF focuses on supporting young people. The MSIF strives to ensure that more children have access to quality health care to enable them to have a more meaningful life
- **Education:** The MSIF aims to work with registered charities and state-funded schools which provide benefit to communities across EMEA. The MSIF works with organisations that increase access and opportunity for young people, supporting programmes that address academic achievement and employability skills, by inspiring talented but underserved young people

Funding types

Funding types

According to the its 2016 accounts, the foundation currently gives grants through three different channels: direct charitable grants, employee-nominated charity partnerships and employee matching grants:

- Direct charitable grant applications are invited for the funding of projects in the EMEA region, and are reviewed at the Trustees' meetings against specific grant objectives. Multi-year grants are monitored on an annual basis to ensure the grant criteria continue to be met.
- Employee nominated charity partnerships are voted for by Morgan Stanley employees, and the Foundation matches employee fundraising and donations up to a set target.
- Employee matching grants focus on creating incentives for Morgan Stanley's employees' fundraising and volunteering efforts in their local communities. The Foundation currently matches fundraising efforts by an employee for a charitable organisation to a maximum of £500 per employee in one given year. In addition, grants in recognition of employees' time volunteering are awarded of £500 per employee in one given year.

Financial information

In 2016 the foundation had assets of almost £2.1 million and an income of almost £1.9 million, of which £1.2 million was a donation from Morgan Stanley and Co. International plc. Grants made during the year totalled nearly £1.3 million, with the employee-nominated charity partner, Great Ormond Street Hospital, receiving over £631,500. Grants to organisations from the unrestricted fund totalled £671,000.

Beneficiaries included: The Prince's Trust (£100,00); Play Association Tower Hamlets (£65,000); Bromley by Bow Centre (£55,000); Glasgow Children's Hospital Charity (£51,000); Magic Breakfast (£50,000); MyTime Active (£37,000); Children 1st (£30,000); Die Arche – Frankfurt (£21,500).

Exclusions

According to its website, the foundation does not provide grants for any of the following:

- Organisations which are not registered as a non-profit organisation with the appropriate regulatory agencies in their country (unless a state funded school)
- National or International charities which do not operate in the regions we are located
- Grants will not be made to either political or religious organisations, pressure groups or individuals outside the Firm who are seeking sponsorship either for themselves (e.g. to help pay for education) or for onward transmission to a charitable organisation

- Programmes that do not include opportunities for Morgan Stanley employee volunteer engagement

Applications

The foundation's website gives the following details on making an initial approach for funding:

The Morgan Stanley International Foundation takes a proactive approach to grant making and therefore does not accept unsolicited proposals. If you think your organisation is a match for the criteria set out below, please send an email to communityaffairslondon@ morganstanley.com with the following information:

- Program description, including mission, goals and numbers served
- Measurement strategies
- Geographic scope

Please note that due to the large number of quality proposals we receive, only applications that have been reviewed and are considered to fit within the MSIF priorities will be contacted directly.

Sources of information

Accounts; annual report; Charity Commission record; funder's website.

The Miles Morland Foundation

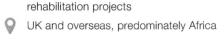 General charitable purposes including: African writing and literature, human rights, theatre, literacy, drug rehabilitation projects

 UK and overseas, predominately Africa

£713,500 (2016/17)

CC number: 1150755

Trustees: The Hon. Alice Bragg; Cornelie Ferguson; Kate Gozzi; Miles Morland.

Correspondent: Miles Morland, Trustee, 2nd Floor, Jubilee House, 2 Jubilee Place, London SW3 3TQ (tel: 020 7349 1245; email: mmf@blakman.com)

www.milesmorlandfoundation.com

The Miles Morland Foundation was registered with the Charity Commission in February 2013. According to the foundation's website, Miles Morland set up the foundation after a career investing in Africa via two companies he created, Blakeney Management and SPI (Development Partners International). The foundation has general charitable purposes but states that its main aim is to support entities in Africa which allow Africans to have their voices better heard, with a particular interest in supporting African writing and literature.

The foundation has previously supported literary festivals and cultural initiatives across Africa and also runs an annual

African writing scholarship scheme. According to the website, the foundation has also previously supported human rights organisations, London theatres, sports, projects in Haiti and Palestine and schemes that support recovering addicts and detained prisoners in the UK.

Financial information

In 2016/17 the foundation had assets of £307,000 and an income of £1.2 million. There were 40 grants made totalling £713,500:

- £395,000 was donated to UK-based organisations
- £319,000 was donated to overseas based organisations

Beneficiaries included: The Longford Trust (£47,500); Give a Future (£25,000); Book Buzz Foundation (£20,000); Inside Out (£15,000); London Library (£20,000); Young Vic (£7,000); Oxfam (£5,000); Reprieve (£4,000); Nelson Mandela Children's Fund (£1,000).

Applications

Complete the application form available on the foundation's website and send it by email to the correspondent. The website states the following:

The organisation's minimal infrastructure means glossy brochures, unsolicited letters and mass-mailed appeals for money are automatically filed in the bin. If you would like the foundation to consider funding a project, fill in and send the Application Form on this website.

We know there are a million good causes in the world which deserve support. Please only seek that support from the MMF if it falls within the areas noted.

Sources of information

Accounts; annual report; Charity Commission record, funder's website.

G M Morrison Charitable Trust

Medicine and health, social welfare, education and training, general charitable purposes

UK

£266,500 (2016/17)

CC number: 261380

Trustees: Elizabeth Morrison; Jane Hunt; Edward Perks.

Correspondent: Edward Perks, Trustee, c/o Currey & Co. LLP, 33 Queen Anne Street, London W1G 9HY (tel: 020 7802 2700; email: gen@curreyandco.co.uk)

Grants are given to support a wide variety of UK-registered charities but mainly those working in the areas of medicine and health, social welfare, and education and training. Recipients of grants are usually selected based on the

personal knowledge or recommendation of a trustee and the trust has a core list of charities which receive grants on an annual basis.

Financial information

In 2016/17 the trust had assets of £13.9 million and an income of £402,500. A total of £266,500 was given in 224 grants to organisations, distributed as follows:

Medical and health total	**98**	**£107,000**
Medical research and support	60	£66,000
Disability (mental and physical)	25	£25,000
Hospitals/hospices	9	£9,600
Medical professional bodies	2	£3,900
Respite care	2	£2,600
Social welfare total	**70**	**£76,500**
Young people (homes and support)	19	£22,000
General welfare	11	£10,600
Homelessness	9	£10,100
Older people	7	£9,000
Families	5	£5,600
Counselling and advice (social)	4	£4,700
Residential and nursing homes	3	£3,000
Crime prevention/victim support	3	£2,600
Holidays	2	£2,100
Benevolent associations	2	£1,900
Prisoners	2	£1,800
Drugs and alcohol	1	£1,400
Refugees and immigrants	1	£1,400
Housing trusts	1	£1,100
Other total	**41**	**£64,000**
Overseas aid/UK aid	18	£37,500
Churches	10	£11,000
Conservation/nature	9	£9,600
Research (non-medical)	2	£3,700
Sports and recreation	2	£2,500
Education and training total	**15**	**£18,600**
Music and arts	5	£7,000
Universities, colleges and adult education	5	£6,300
Spiritual and religious education	5	£5,300

Beneficiaries included: British Red Cross – Syria Crisis Appeal (£5,000, one-off); International Medical Corps UK (£2,600); Northwick Park Institute of Medical Research, SSAFA and University of Liverpool (£1,500 each); Asylum Aid and Autism Initiative UK (£1,400 each); St Christopher's Hospice (£1,100); Seafarers UK, Woodland Trust and YMCA Norfolk (£850 each).

Exclusions

Support is not given for:

- Individuals
- Charities not registered in the UK
- Retrospective applications
- Schemes or activities which are generally regarded as the responsibility of statutory authorities
- Short-term projects
- Commercial or business activities
- One-off capital grants (except for emergency appeals)

Applications

The trust's annual report for 2016/17 explains:

Beneficiaries of grants are normally selected on the basis of the personal

knowledge and recommendation of a trustee. The Trust's grant-making policy is however to support the recipient of grants on a long-term recurring basis. The trustees have decided that for the present, new applications for grants will only be considered in the most exceptional circumstances, any spare income will be allocated to increasing the grants made to charities currently receiving support. In the future this policy will of course be subject to periodic review. Applicants understanding this policy who nevertheless wish to apply for a grant should write to the [correspondent].

Sources of information

Accounts; annual report; Charity Commission record.

The Ken and Lynne Morrison Charitable Trust

General charitable purposes including: people with disabilities, education and training

Yorkshire

£333,000 (2016/17)

CC number: 1125586

Trustees: Andrea Shelley; Lady Lynne Morrison.

Correspondent: Lady Morrison, Trustee, Myton Hall, Myton-on-Swale, Helperby, York YO61 2QX

The trust was established in 2008 by former life president and Chair of Morrisons, Sir Kenneth Morrison and his wife Lady Lynne Morrison.

The trust makes grants for general charitable purposes including people with disabilities, education and training.

Financial information

In 2016/17 the trust held assets of £14.4 million and had an income of £459,500. Grants to 16 organisations totalled £333,000.

Beneficiaries included: Marie Curie and Macmillan Cancer Support (£40,000 each); Henshaw's Society for Blind People, The Acorn Committee and Yorkshire Air Ambulance (£30,000 each); Hollybank Trust, Samaritans and The Sick Children's Trust (£20,000); Pendragon Community Trust (£15,000); Otley Sailing Club (£10,000); The Bradford Toy Library (£2,200); Simon on the Streets (£1,000).

Applications

The trust's 2016/17 annual report states:

The trustees identify projects and organisations they wish to support. Requests from people or organisations who apply speculatively will be considered if they are pertinent to the Trust's objectives. The trustees also have a policy that they make only one-off grants with no guarantees of future funding.

Sources of information

Accounts; annual report; Charity Commission record.

The Morrisons Foundation

 General charitable purposes

 Areas of company presence in the UK

 £8 million (2016/17)

CC number: 1160224

Trustees: Charles Jones; Guy Mason; John Holden; Jonathan Burke; Kathryn Tunstall; Sharon Mawhinney; David Scott; Andrew Clappen.

Correspondent: Sam Burden, Hilmore House, Gain Lane, Bradford, West Yorkshire BD3 7DL (tel: 0845 611 5364; email: foundation.enquiries@ morrisonsplc.co.uk)

 www.morrisonsfoundation.com

The Morrisons Foundation, registered January 2015, was established by the supermarket chain Morrisons to make a difference to the lives of people living in the UK communities in which it has a presence.

The foundation makes charitable contributions in two ways: firstly, by match funding employee fundraising efforts; and secondly, by making grants.

Funding is given only to registered charities for particular projects which aim to improve people's lives.

Financial information

In 2016/17 the foundation had assets of £4.1 million and an income of almost £9.16 million, which largely came from the sale of carrier bags in Morrisons stores. There were 655 grants made totalling £8 million and the foundation donated over £255,000 by match funding employees fundraising. Grants were broken down as follows:

Health	42%
Social investment	33%
Education	15%
Other	6%
Arts and culture	4%

Previous beneficiaries have included: W.O.T.S. Project (£16,500); Willow Wood Hospice (£10,000); Hey Smile Foundation (£9,300); MedEquip4Kids (£6,900); Carers' Support Bexley (£6,600); Couple Counselling Lothian (£5,900); Theodora Children's Charity (£5,000); Mansfield Play Forum (£4,700); The Comedy Trust (£2,000); Deaf Children North West (£500).

Applications

Applications can be made through the foundation's website. Match funding applications are normally processed within six weeks and grant applications can take up to three months to review.

Sources of information

Accounts; annual report; Charity Commission record; funder's website.

The Morton Charitable Trust (Dundee)

 General charitable purposes

UK, with a preference for Scotland

£202,000 (2016/17)

OSCR number: SC004507

Trustee: The Trustees.

Correspondent: Ms M. McLaren, c/o Walker Dunnett & Co. Solicitors, 29 Commercial Street, Dundee DD1 3DG (tel: 01382 204242)

The trust was established in 1987 to make grants to organisations that have the following purposes:

- The prevention or relief of poverty
- The advancement of education
- The advancement of health and the saving of lives
- The advancement of public participation in sport
- The provision of recreational facilities
- The relief of those in need by reason of age, ill health, disability, financial hardship or other disadvantage

Financial information

In 2016/17 the trust held assets of almost £1.4 million and had an income of £64,000. Grants totalled £202,000.

A list of beneficiaries was not available.

Applications

Apply in writing to the correspondent.

Sources of information

Annual report; accounts; OSCR record.

The Alexander Mosley Charitable Trust

 General charitable purposes including: armed forces, international development, heritage, animal welfare, medical research

UK, overseas

£3.7 million (2016/17)

CC number: 1142898

Trustees: Max Mosley; Emma Maitland Mosley; Horatio Mortimer; Max Mosley.

Correspondent: Payne Beach, 10 New Square, Lincoln's Inn, London WC2A 3QG (tel: 020 7465 4300)

The trust was established in 2011 and makes grants throughout the UK and overseas. The trust has previously supported the armed forces, international development, heritage, animal welfare and medical research.

The trust's 2016/17 accounts state:

> The Charity will not normally support applications from large national charities, i.e. those with an annual income in excess of £10 million or with £100 million assets or charities dedicated to issues deemed by the Trustees to be already well funded within the UK.

Financial information

In 2016/17 the trust held assets of £4.2 million and had an income of £4.8 million. Grants awarded to organisations totalled £3.7 million.

Beneficiaries included: St Peter's College Development (£1.1 million); The 353 Trust (£150,000); Airborne Assault (£135,000); The Children's Radio Foundation (£10,000); Sreepur Village Charity, Stand By Me and Willow Foundation (£5,000 each).

Applications

Apply in writing to the correspondent.

Sources of information

Accounts; annual report; Charity Commission record.

Moto in the Community

 General charitable purposes, community development, education

UK

£740,000 (2016)

CC number: 1111147

Trustees: Brian Lotts; Christopher Rogers; Brian Larkin; Ashleigh Lewis; Jon Shore; Nicholas Brookes; Gene Macdonald; Julie Sturgess; Coral Brodie; Guy Latchem; Brynn Hewitt; Louise Hughes; Fiona Stevenson; Daniel Horsley; Linda Parslow; Timothy Gittins.

Correspondent: Fiona Falle, Moto Hospitality Ltd, Toddington Service Area, Junction 12 M1 Southbound, Toddington, Bedfordshire LU5 6HR (tel: 01525 878500; email: motocharity@ moto-way.co.uk)

 www.motointhecommunity.co.uk

Moto in the Community is the charitable arm of Moto Hospitality, the UK's leading motorway service area provider. The charity uses funds raised at Moto locations nationwide to support local community groups and schools as well as national charities.

Each Moto branch can adopt a local community partner in their area, which can be a charity or a local school.

Community partners are eligible to apply for grants.

The trustees accept applications under the following conditions:

- You are a charity or community school within a 25-mile radius of a Moto site
- You have opportunities for Moto staff to be involved with your group/school
- You are happy to support your Moto site with their fundraising events

Moto employees regularly volunteer with local partner organisations and partners are given the opportunity to hold collection days at their local Moto site.

In addition to working with local partners, the charity also runs a national Charity of the Year scheme.

Financial information

In 2016 the charity had assets of £487,000 and an income of £702,000. In total, £740,000 was awarded in grants, including one major grant to Moto's Charity of the Year, Help for Heroes (£400,000). A further £15,800 was paid in benevolent grants in support of Moto employees and their dependants facing hardship.

Previous beneficiaries have included: Brain Tumour Charity (£2,700); Toddington Scouts (£2,500); St Sebastian School (£1,000); The Youth Association (£930); The Children's Farm Trust (£900); Darton College (£680); Prostate Cancer and The Stroke Association (£500 each); Walton Hall Special School (£490); Moon Walk (£100).

Exclusions

The trust does not consider applications for religious, political or overseas projects.

Applications

Charities or schools interested in becoming a local community partner should email motocharity@moto-way.co.uk, stating:

- Which Moto site you wish to apply to
- The charity's long and short-term objectives
- Ideas about how the Moto staff could work with you

Applications are invited throughout the year, and partnerships run from January to December. Applicants may be requested to visit their local Moto station. If the local Moto site already has a community partner, it may be able to take on an additional partner, or it may carry over applications for consideration in the next year. Phone calls from potential community partners are also welcomed by the charity.

Grant applications can be made using a form on the charity's website. Guidance notes are also available to download from the website. It may take around six weeks for an application to be approved. Applications can also be made by a

manager or Charity Champion from a Moto site on behalf of a community partner.

Sources of information

Accounts; annual report; Charity Commission record; funder's website.

Motor Neurone Disease Association

 Scientific and medical research into motor neurone disease

UK and overseas

£3.7 million (2016)

CC number: 294354

Trustees: Wendy Balmain; Alun Owen; Richard Owen; Dr Heather Smith; Janice Parks; Susan Edwards; Charlotte Layton; Steven Parry – Hearn; Dr Nikil Sharma; Janet Warren; Timothy Kidd; Lyndsay Lonsborough; Siobhan Rooney; Katy Styles; Emma Adams.

Correspondent: Research Grants Team, 10–15 Notre Dame Mews, Northampton NN1 2BG (tel: 01604 611873; email: research.grants@mndassociation.org)

 www.mndassociation.org/research

Motor Neurone Disease Association (MNDA) works to support care, research and campaigning for people affected by motor neurone disease (MND) in the UK. Its vision is 'a world free from MND'.

Research grants

The MNDA website explains that it only funds and supports 'scientific and medical research of the highest quality and relevance to MND' in the UK and overseas. Through its research strategy the association looks to support research into the causes and treatments of MND and, ultimately, into finding a cure for the disease.

There are a number of types of grants funded by MND Association, which are outlined on the website:

- PhD studentships
- Biomedical research projects
- Clinical research fellowships
- Non-clinical research fellowships
- Healthcare research projects

Eligibility information and guidelines for each of these grant types can be found on the website.

Financial information

In 2016 the charity had assets of £10.3 million and an income of £17.4 million. Grants and donations totalled £3.7 million.

The annual report 2016 states: 'The value of our whole research grant portfolio on 1 January 2017 was £14.6m, and we are currently funding 88 projects. In 2016,

the Board of Trustees approved 29 grants with a total value of £2.4m.'

Beneficiaries included: University of Sheffield (£636,000); University College London (£513,000); University of Sussex (£101,000); Leeds General Infirmary (£47,000); Newcastle General Hospital (£27,000); Cardiff University (£7,000).

Applications

In the first instance, we recommend visiting the website, where full information on research funding, including how to make an application and deadline dates is available.

Sources of information

Accounts; annual report; Charity Commission record; funder's website.

J P Moulton Charitable Foundation

Education and training, health care, medical research, counselling, social welfare

UK

£567,500 (2016)

CC number: 1109891

Trustees: Jon Moulton; Spencer Moulton; Sara Everett.

Correspondent: Jon Moulton, Trustee, c/o Perscitus LLP, 10 Buckingham Street, London WC2N 6DF (tel: 020 3727 6601; email: jon.moulton@jonmoulton.gg)

Registered in 2005, this is the foundation of venture capitalist, Jon Moulton. The foundation's Charity Commission record explains that, 'the charity receives donations, particularly from [high-net-worth] individuals, and supports valid research plus funds appropriate charitable institutions'.

The 2016 annual report states that the primary purposes of the charity are:

- to fund non-commercial clinical trials with the aim to make clinical advances and promote the relief of suffering
- to provide charitable donations for community service projects of any kind to promote education, training and counselling of disadvantaged persons
- to provide donations to hospitals, medical and care projects of any kind to assist with the general welfare of patients

Financial information

In 2016 the foundation held assets of £224,500 and had an income of £844,000. Grants totalled £567,500.

Beneficiaries included: University College London (£202,000); University of Leeds (£84,000); Great Ormond Street Hospital (£77,500); Muscular Dystrophy Campaign (£37,500); King's College London (£28,500).

Applications

The foundation advertises opportunities to encourage institutions and community projects to apply for available funding. The trustees award grants on the perceived merits of applications, which can be made to the foundation in writing. According to the 2016 annual report, approximately 30% of applications receive full or partial funding.

Sources of information

Accounts; annual report; Charity Commission record.

The Frederick Mulder Foundation

Philanthropy, climate change, global poverty

Worldwide

£449,500 (2016/17)

CC number: 296019

Trustees: Dr Frederick Mulder; Hannah Mulder; Robin Bowman.

Correspondent: Eugenie Harvey, Director, 83 Belsize Park Gardens, London NW3 4NJ (tel: 020 7722 9628; email: eugenie@ frederickmulderfoundation.org.uk)

www.frederickmulderfoundation. org.uk

Based in London and formerly known as the Prairie Trust, this foundation was founded in 1986 and takes the name of its settlor, Dr Frederick Mulder. Dr Mulder is a director of Frederick Mulder Ltd, a company specialising in European printmaking from 1470 to 1970, and is also founder of The Funding Network, a 'giving-circle' of individuals who join together to fund social change projects.

The foundation's website states that it envisions 'a world which is fair, secure and environmentally sustainable, and in which the rights of future generations are respected in decisions taken today'.

Areas of support

Support is primarily directed towards organisations working in three main areas:

▶ The development of social change philanthropy
▶ The threat of climate change
▶ The persistence of global poverty

The trustees' report for 2016/17 states:

Most of the grants to small-scale projects are made through The Funding Network (TFN), to projects which present at TFN events held in London, in UK cities outside London, and in other countries.

The Trust also helps to support the operational costs of The Funding Network, both in the UK and internationally, and some of the travel costs incurred in Frederick Mulder's (unpaid) role as the Global Ambassador of TFN, which involves helping to set up TFN groups both in the UK outside London and outside the UK itself.

Larger grants are made directly to the organisations supported by the Trust.

Financial information

In 2016/17 the foundation held assets of almost £6.7 million and had an income of over £1 million. Grants awarded to organisations totalled £449,500.

Previous beneficiaries have included: Client Earth (£50,000); The Funding Network UK (£47,500); Greenpeace Environmental Trust (£20,000); Write to Freedom (£18,000); Centre for Effective Altruism (£15,000); Incentives for Global Health (£10,800); Peace Brigades International UK (£10,000); War on Want (£6,000); People and Planet (£5,000); Sheila McKechnie Foundation (£3,000).

Applications

The foundation does not accept unsolicited applications or enquiries but rather is proactive in identifying organisations and individuals within its areas of interest.

Sources of information

Accounts; annual report; Charity Commission record; funder's website.

Multiple Sclerosis Society

Multiple sclerosis research

UK

£4.67 million to organisations (2016)

CC number: 1139257

Trustees: Sarah Schol; Stuart Secker; Christine Gibbons; Esther Foreman; Ruth Hasnip; Nicholas Winser; John Grosvenor; Ceri Smith; Karen Jones; Anne Shinkwin; Jason Atkinson; Marion King; Dowsham Humzah.

Correspondent: Grants Team, 372 Edgware Road, London NW2 6ND (tel: 0300 500 8084; email: grants@ mssociety.org.uk)

www.mssociety.org.uk

 facebook.com/MSSociety

 @mssocietyuk

 @mssocietyuk

Multiple sclerosis (MS) is a neurological condition which affects around 100,000 people in the UK. Most people are diagnosed between the ages of 20 and 40, but it can affect younger and older people too. Roughly three times as many women have MS as men.

The MS Society is the UK's leading MS charity and has been providing information and support, funding research and campaigning for change since 1953. The MS Society is the biggest charitable funder of MS research in the UK.

Types of grant

The society will consider any research grant application that is relevant to MS. Applications are judged on scientific merit and relevance the society's research strategy which is available to view on its website. It offers four types of grant, which are outlined on the website:

Project grant

The essential purpose of a project grant is to provide support for a time-limited research project designed to answer a single question or a small group of related questions. Project grants provide support for a maximum of three years.

Innovative award

The essential purpose of an innovative award is to provide support for a short-term, small-scale pilot or proof of concept research project. It is hoped that these awards will encourage established researchers from both within and outside the MS field to explore ideas in MS research that, if merited, may lead to further support through the society or other funding sources.

PhD studentship

PhD studentships are designed to encourage the best graduates to embark on a research career in MS. These awards provide practical research training leading to a doctorate, through a time-limited research project related to MS, under the direct supervision of a senior and experienced researcher.

Application should be made by the prospective supervisor, who should be associated with an established multidisciplinary research group in a UK university department or similar research environment in the UK. The award will provide a competitive tax-free stipend for the candidate student, tuition fees at home/EU student rates and the running costs of the project over a three-year period.

Junior fellowship

Junior fellowships are aimed at attracting and retaining talented postdoctoral researchers who are early in their career in MS research. These grants are intended to provide a staged career structure and an opportunity to progress towards higher-level appointments.

Support grants

Support grants are also made to individuals with MS to help pay for items such as such as scooters, wheelchairs, specially adapted beds, respite stays and communication equipment.

Financial information

In 2016 the society had assets of £17.4 million and a total income of £29 million. Grants awarded to organisations totalled £4.67 million with a further £1.48 million given to individuals.

Beneficiaries included: Swansea University (£732,000 in three grants); University of Edinburgh (£556,000 in four grants); Medical Research Council (£168,000 in two grants); Walton Centre NHS Trust (£67,000).

Applications

Refer to the society's website for full details.

Sources of information

Accounts; annual report; Charity Commission record; funder's website.

The Edith Murphy Foundation

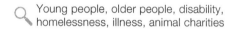 Young people, older people, disability, homelessness, illness, animal charities

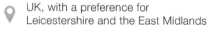 UK, with a preference for Leicestershire and the East Midlands

£ £1.48 million (2015/16)

CC number: 1026062

Trustees: David Tams; Christopher Blakesley; Richard Adkinson; Charlotte Blakesley; Julian Tams.

Correspondent: Richard Adkinson, Trustee, c/o Crane and Walton, 113–117 London Road, Leicester LE2 0RG (tel: 0116 255 1901; email: richard.adkinson@btinternet.com)

 www.edithmurphy.co.uk

The Edith Murphy Foundation was established in 1993 by the late Edith Murphy in memory of her husband, Mr Hugh Murphy.

Following the death of Mrs Murphy in 2005, her will provided for the foundation to receive certain benefits including a proportion of the residue of her estate. The value of the benefits received the following year amounted to £28.2 million. A further £1.8 million was added in 2007. This has resulted in the level of grant-giving increasing substantially in recent years.

Since its inception in 1993 the charity has supported over 650 organisations with grants of around £17.5 million

The foundation's website states that while it operates with a broad remit, grants are predominantly made to registered charities. There is a focus on national charities and smaller causes

based in Leicestershire and the East Midlands. The foundation has supported organisations working to help unwanted animals, people who are young, older, homeless or sick or who have disabilities. In addition, the foundation also funds research.

The value of grants made is normally between £500 and £5,000 although larger grants are made in some circumstances.

Financial information

In 2016/17 the foundation held assets of £35.7 million and had an income of £785,500. Grants were made to 177 organisations and totalled £930,000. The annual report for 2016/17 provided the following breakdown:

Welfare	£472,000
Education	£119,500
Children	£118,500
Heritage	£92,000
Disability	£64,500
Animals	£46,500
Research	£40,000

Beneficiaries included: Age UK (£75,000); Leicestershire Cares (£70,000); De Montfort University, Healing Little Hearts, Stroke Association (£20,000 each); Motor Neurone Disease Association (£15,000); Barnardo's, DEBRA, Leicester Animal Aid Ltd and Leicester Charity Link (£10,000 each).

Exclusions

The foundation does not make grants to individuals.

Applications

Applications should be submitted by post to the correspondent (email applications are not accepted).

The foundation requests that applicants provide the following information:

▶ The charity name
▶ The charity registration number provided by the Charity Commission
▶ What the grant will be used for
▶ Who will benefit
▶ The amount being requested with a breakdown of the costs being incurred
▶ Other fundraising activities and the amount raised to date
▶ A set of accounts is desirable but not essential
▶ Non-registered charities will additionally be asked to complete a form to clarify their tax residency

The foundation's trustees meet four times a year to consider grant applications, usually in January, April, July and October.

Sources of information

Accounts; annual report; Charity Commission record; further information provided by the funder; funder's website.

The John R. Murray Charitable Trust

 General charitable purposes, arts and culture

UK

£ £752,000 (2016)

CC number: 1100199

Trustees: John Murray; Virginia Murray; Hallam Murray; John Grey Murray; Charles Grey Murray.

Correspondent: John Murray, Trustee, 50 Albemarle Street, London W1S 4BD (tel: 020 7493 4361)

The John R Murray Charitable Trust primarily awards grants to UK-registered charities which support arts and literature. The trust also awards some grants for general charitable purposes and provides ongoing support to the National Library of Scotland. In the trust's 2016 accounts the trustees state that the scope of 'giving is determined only by the extent of [the charity's] resources; it is not otherwise restricted either geographically or by the type of activity carried on by prospective beneficiaries or applicants'.

Financial information

In 2016 the trust had assets of £28.3 million and an income of £879,500. The trust made 40 grants to organisations totalling £752,000.

Beneficiaries included: Abbotsford Trust (£300,000): Trailblazers Mentoring (£20,000); Finding Rhythms (£15,000); Hall School Charitable Trust (£12,500); John Stuart Mill Library Project (£7,500); Dream Makers Children's Charity, Friends of Lancashire Gardens, River and Rowing Museum and St Mungo's Broadway (£5,000 each).

Applications

The trustees do not consider unsolicited applications for grants.

Sources of information

Accounts; annual report; Charity Commission record.

MW (RH) Foundation

Education, relief of poverty, advancement of the Orthodox Jewish faith

Worldwide, with a preference for the UK

£ £411,000 (2015/16)

CC number: 1134918

Trustees: Rosalind Halpern; Jacob Halpern; Abraham Halpern.

Correspondent: Jacob Halpern, Trustee, 29 Waterpark Road, Salford M7 4FT

The foundation was registered with the Charity Commission in March 2010. It was initially known as the Deborah Weisz Foundation and is closely linked with the MW (CL) Foundation, MW (GK) Foundation and MW (HO) Foundation and shares the same charitable objectives (as stated in the 2015/16 annual report):

- To promote the education of people of all ages around the world in such ways as the charity trustees think fit, including awarding to such persons scholarships, maintenance allowances or g rants, or by grants to charities or other organisations worldwide that provide education
- The prevention or relief of poverty or financial hardship anywhere in the world by providing grants or loans to individuals in need and/or charities, or other organisations working to prevent or relieve poverty or financial hardship
- To advance the Orthodox Jewish religion worldwide for the benefit of the public in accordance with the principles of the Code of Jewish Law (Shulchan Aruch)

Financial information
In 2015/16 the foundation had assets of £2.6 million and an income of £392,500. Grants awarded to organisations totalled £411,000.

A list of beneficiaries was not available.

Applications
Apply in writing to the correspondent.

Sources of information
Accounts; annual report; Charity Commission record.

National Art Collections Fund

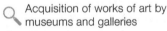 Acquisition of works of art by museums and galleries

 UK

(£) £4.5 million (2016)

CC number: 209174

Trustees: Prof. Antony Griffiths; Jeremy Palmer; Michael Wilson; Richard Calvocoressi; James Lingwood; Philippa Glanville; Chris Smith; Prof. Chris Gosden; Caroline Butler; Prof. Lisa Tickner; Dame Liz Forgan; Alastair Laing; Prof. Richard Deacon; Axel Rüger; Prof. Marcia Pointon; Isaac Julien; Monisha Shah.

Correspondent: Eleanor McGrath, Senior Programmes Manager (Acquisitions), 2 Granary Square, King's Cross, London N1C 4BH (tel: 020 7225 4815; email: emcgrath@artfund.org)

 www.artfund.org

 @artfund

 @artfund

Known simply as The Art Fund, this fundraising and membership charity believes that everyone should have the opportunity to experience great art at first hand and it works to achieve this:

- By giving grants to museums to buy works of art and develop new collections;
- Supporting the showing of art through tours and exhibitions;
- Seeking to influence government policy and stimulating debate

The trustees also campaign to make it easier for museums to add to their collections, from pressing for new tax incentives to encourage giving, to campaigning for reforms to the export control system for art.

Grant-making guidelines
It is essential for all applicants to contact the Programmes office to discuss any potential application as soon as possible to receive advice on eligibility, application deadlines and any specific application requirements. The detailed criteria published on the charity's website should be read before making contact.

The fund has two grants programmes:

Art Fund Acquisitions Programme
For the purchase of works of art and other objects of aesthetic interest, dating from antiquity to the present day. UK public museums, galleries, historic houses, libraries and archives that are accredited under the Arts Council Scheme and are open for at least half the week for at least six months of the year. Under this programme there are three grants schemes:

- Main grants: grants of £7,500 or more and/or where the total cost of work is more than £15,000
- Small grants: of less than £7,500 where the total cost of work is £15,000 or less
- Auctions: applications can be fast-tracked for items at auctions (see applications information below)

The fund sometimes operates time-limited programmes with their own criteria which aim to address specific collecting needs within the museum sector. These will be advertised on the fund's website.

The Jonathan Ruffer Curatorial Grants
For individual UK curators, scholars and researchers to undertake travel or other activities to extend and develop their curatorial expertise, collections-based knowledge and art history interests. There are two categories:

- Grants of £200 to £1,500
- Grants of more than £1,500

Costs that may be supported include: travel and accommodation; training courses/programmes of study; books and subscriptions to add to a museum's research resources or library; translation and transcription; temporary administrative cover to enable time away from work to undertake research. The fund welcomes adventurous applications and will not always expect material outcomes to be an immediate consequence of the support.

Financial information
In 2016 the fund had assets of almost £52 million and an income of almost £15.1 million. During the year, the charity awarded grants totalling £4.48 million to organisations.

Beneficiaries included: National Maritime Museum (£2.4 million); The Bowes Museum (£2 million); Ashmolean (£261,000); British Museum (£180,000); Museum of London (£40,000); University of Salford (£25,000); V&A Museum of Childhood (£15,000); Wiltshire Museum (£8,500).

Exclusions
The following are excluded:

- Objects that are primarily of social-historical interest; scientific or technological material; letters, manuscripts or archival material with limited artistic or decorative inscription
- Applications where the applicant has already purchased or made a commitment to purchase the object, or made a financial commitment
- Other costs associated with acquisitions such as the conservation and restoration of works, transport and storage costs, temporary or permanent exhibitions and digitisation projects
- Applications from individuals, artist groups, commercial organisations, hospitals, places of worship, schools or higher education institutions
- Funding towards professional development, travel or research

Applications
Firstly, discuss the application with a member of the programmes office then register on the website to access the online application form.

Note: The fund will not accept applications that have not been discussed in advance and approved for submission by the Programmes office. There are extensive guidelines available to download from the website.

There are six deadlines a year for the main grants scheme; these can be requested by telephone. Small grants applications can be submitted at any time. Potential applicants for auctions grants should contact the fund at the earliest opportunity. There needs to be a minimum of seven working days' notice for an auction in London or ten working days' notice for an auction outside London.

Applications for the small curatorial grants can be submitted at any time. There are three deadlines a year for curatorial grants of more than £1,500; these can be obtained by telephoning the fund.

Application forms and deadlines can be downloaded from the website.

Sources of information
Accounts; annual report; annual review; Charity Commission record; funder's website.

The National Churches Trust

 Preservation of historic churches

England and Wales → UK

£ £1.4 million (2016)

CC number: 1119845

Trustees: Alastair Hunter; Richard Archer; Dr Julie Banham; Revd Lucy Winkett; John Drew; Jennifer Page; Luke March; Sir Paul Britton; Dr Stephen Skalroff; Nicholas Warns.

Correspondent: Clare Wand, 7 Tufton Street, London SW1P 3QB (tel: 020 7222 0605; fax: 020 7796 2442; email: info@ natinalchurchestrust.org.)

 www.nationalchurchestrust.org/ our-grants

The National Churches Trust was launched in 2007 and promotes and supports buildings of historic, architectural and community value across the UK.

According to the trust's website, its aims are:

- To help maintain the UK's heritage of church buildings and to enhance their ability to serve local communities
- To promote the benefit to communities of church buildings and to inspire everyone to value and enjoy them

The website outlines the trust's key areas of work as:

- Providing grants for the repair, restoration and modernisation of places of worship
- Supporting projects that enable places of worship to engage with their local communities and keep their buildings open
- Collaborating closely with other heritage organisations, local churches trusts and volunteer networks across the UK in their support for places of worship
- Encouraging good management and regular maintenance of places of worship by providing practical advice, support and information

- Providing new ways of promoting visits to places of worship and bringing a new generation of people into contact with church history and architecture
- Working to increase awareness among the public and decision makers of the value of places of worship

Grant programmes
The following grants programmes open and close throughout the year; check the website for deadline dates.

Community grants – grants usually of between £5,000 and £25,000 towards the costs of projects introducing facilities (kitchens and accessible toilets) to enable increased community use of places of worship.

Maintenance grants – a pilot programme offering awards of between £500 and £3,000 to encourage churches to act on small, urgent maintenance issues and repairs to church buildings.

Partnership grants – grants of £2,500 to £10,000 for urgent repair projects with estimated costs of between £10,000 and £100,000 (including VAT and fees). The installation of kitchens and toilets under £25,000 (including VAT and fees) can also be considered in some areas.

Repair grants – grants usually of between £5,000 and £40,000 towards the cost of urgent and essential structural repair projects.

Project development grants – grants from this pilot programme are outlined on the website:

Offering awards up to £10,000 to support churches to develop high-quality, well researched, sustainable projects through the diagnosis of issues affecting the church, by testing the viability of proposed solutions, and through developing plans up to RIBA stage 1, in advance of applying to a major church heritage funder such as the Heritage Lottery Fund.

Financial information
In 2016 the trust had assets of £5 million and an income of £1.6 million. Grants totalled £1.4 million and were broken down as follows:

Repair grants	£487,000
Partnership grants	£337,500
Conerstone grants	£320,000
Community grants	£175,000
Project viability and development grants	£66,000
Cinnamon grants	£14,000

Beneficiaries included: Cubert Church – Cornwall (£40,000); All Saints – Staffordshire (£20,000); St Philip and St James – Worcestershire (£17,000); Sacred Heart – East Riding of Yorkshire (£14,000); Holy Trinity – Merseyside (£10,000).

Applications
Applications can be made through the trust's website.

Sources of information
Accounts; annual report; Charity Commission record; funder's website.

The National Gardens Scheme

 Nursing, health care, gardening and horticulture

England and Wales → England and Wales

£ £3.1 million (2016)

CC number: 1112664

Trustees: Miranda Allhusen; Peter Clay; Susan Copeland; Rosamund Davies; Colin Olle; Sue Phipps; Patrick Ramsay; Richard Thompson; Rupert Tyler; Martin Macmillan; Heather Skinner; Andrew Ratcliffe; Mark Porter.

Correspondent: George Plumptre, Chief Executive, The National Gardens Scheme, 1 Courtyard Cottage, Hatchlands, East Clandon, Guildford GU4 7RT (tel: 01483 211535; email: gplumptre@ngs.org.uk)

www.ngs.org.uk

The National Gardens Scheme (NGS) was registered with the Charity Commission in 2005 but dates back to 1927, when it was founded by the Queen's Nursing Institute. The charity opens gardens to public visitors, through a network of volunteers, in order to raise money for charities – in particular, supporting charities that are focused on nursing and caring.

The charity has a list of beneficiary charities that it supports, which are nominated by the trustees and include:

- Macmillan Cancer Support
- Marie Curie
- Hospice UK
- Carers Trust
- The Queen's Nursing Institute
- Perennial
- Parkinson's UK

Guest charities
The charity also supports a guest charity for between two and three years, which may be chosen from the following criteria:

- Charities focusing on nursing and caring are preferred, although wider community benefit may be considered
- Charities involved in research, as long as they deliver value to local communities
- Organisations that are not charities but are constituted in some legal form as a social enterprise, and which are involved in nursing and caring

Elspeth Thompson Bursary
The charity also offers a bursary in memory of Elspeth Thompson, a

supporter of the NGS and a well known gardener. Grants are available to amateur gardeners within community groups in England and Wales, to 'enable them to create a garden or horticultural based project for the benefit of the community, or to enable them to acquire horticultural knowledge and skills and to develop and share their love of gardening'.

Grants are usually between £1,000 and £5,000, although no fixed amount is set. Guidance notes are provided on the website, along with a list of previous beneficiaries.

Grants are administered by the Royal Horticultural Society.

Partners

The charity also works in partnership with the National Trust, the Royal Horticultural Society and the Garden Museum. The partners provide support for the NGS, promoting its gardens, and the NGS provides annual funding to its partners to support training for young gardeners.

Financial information

In 2016 the charity had assets of £856,000 and an income of £4.2 million. Grants were made totalling £3.1 million.

Beneficiaries included: Hospice UK, Macmillan Cancer Support and Marie Curie (£500,000 each); Carers Trust (£400,000); The Queen's Nursing Institute (£375,000); Parkinson's UK (£172,000); Perennial, National Autistic Society (£130,000 each); The National Trust Gardening Careership Scheme (£30,000); Garden History Museum (£10,000).

Exclusions

For the Elspeth Thompson Bursary, funding will not be provided for the following:

- Promotional costs (e.g. leaflets)
- Hire tools (e.g. JCB, rotavators, etc.)
- Transport to visit gardens
- Insurance cover
- Educational course fees or training costs
- Volunteer expenses
- Salaries

Applications

Apply in writing to the correspondent. For the Elspeth Thompson Bursary, an application form and guidance notes are provided on the website, along with deadlines. Queries should be submitted to: ngsbursary@rhs.org.uk or 01483 479719.

Sources of information

Accounts; annual report; Charity Commission record; funder's website.

The Nationwide Foundation

 Community development, housing, legal assistance, social welfare

UK

£781,000 (2016/17)

CC number: 1065552

Trustees: Martin Coppack; Benedict Stimson; Ian Williams; Juliet Cockram; John Taylor; Antonia Bance; Sarah Mitchell; Tony Prestedge; Clara Govier; Sara Bennison.

Correspondent: Jonathan Lewis, The Nationwide Foundation, Nationwide House, Pipers Way, Swindon SN38 2SN (tel: 01793 655113; email: enquiries@ nationwidefoundation.org.uk)

 www.nationwidefoundation.org.uk

Registered with the Charity Commission in 1997, the Nationwide Foundation is principally funded by Nationwide Building Society, which makes annual lump sum donation of 0.25% of its pre-tax profit. Its aims and objectives are to improve the lives of people who are disadvantaged because of housing circumstances by increasing the number of decent affordable homes available to them.

Grants programmes

At the time of writing (March 2018) the foundation operates three separate grant programmes:

Nurturing ideas to Change the Housing System

This programme supports ideas 'for protecting and creating decent, affordable homes and creating changes that lead to an increased number of homes for people in need'.

On its website the foundation states that it would be willing to fund the researching, testing, developing, or piloting of new ideas as well as the evaluation of existing ideas. It is noted that ideas should seek to address the root causes of the UK's housing crisis rather than mitigate its effects.

The foundation is willing to consider applications from a wide range of grantees, from academics and think-tanks through to small community groups. Furthermore, projects which are part-funded or delivered in collaboration with other stakeholders in the housing sector, be that other charities, local authorities or funders are strongly encouraged.

The foundation does not set a minimum or maximum grant limit; however, it is unlikely that the foundation would fund a project with less than £5,000.

Backing Community-Led Housing

This programme supports and champions the growth of community-led housing, so that more people who are in need will benefit. At the time of writing (March 2018) the foundation was not accepting applications for this programme but stated on its website that it hoped to reopen the fund in late 2018.

Transforming the Private Rented Sector

This programme helps to 'transform the private rented sector so that it provides homes for people in need that are more affordable, secure, accessible and are better quality'. At the time of writing (March 2018) the foundation was not accepting applications for this programme.

Financial information

In 2016/17 the foundation had assets of £2.77 million and an income of almost £2.64 million of which £2.5 million came from a donation from the Nationwide Building Society. There were nine grants made totalling £781,000, all under the 'Decent Affordable Homes' grant-making strategy.

Beneficiaries included: University of York (£202,000); Wales Cooperative Centre (£130,000); The National Custom and Self Build Association (£110,000); New Economics Foundation, Young Foundation (£83,500 each); DAH Added Value (£4,400).

Exclusions

The foundation will not consider funding for the following:

- Promotion of religion or politics
- Applications which do not comply with the foundation's funding criteria/guidelines

Applications

Proposals should be no more than 500 words and should be sent to applications@nationwidefoundation.org. uk. Your proposal should tell the foundation about the following:

- Your organisation and the work you already do
- The idea you want it to fund and why it will contribute to the foundation's strategy
- The estimated amount of funding you are looking for and proposed timescales

The foundation aims to respond to proposals within ten working days, at which point successful applicants will be invited to submit a full bid for funding.

Nurturing Ideas enquiries should be directed to programme manager, Jonathan Lewis, by email (jonathan. lewis@nationwidefoundation.org.uk) or phone (01793 652618).

There is no deadline for applications.

Sources of information

Accounts; annual report; Charity Commission record; funder's website.

Near Neighbours

Community development and inter-community understanding

Birmingham, the Black Country, East London, East Midlands, Greater Manchester, Lancashire, Luton, West London and West Yorkshire

£1.45 million (2016)

CC number: 1142426

Trustees: Baroness Eaton; Revd Canon Denise Poole; The Rt Revd Richard Atkinson; The Rt Revd Dr Toby Howarth; The Rt Revd Mark Davies; Revd Sarah Schofield; Brian Carroll; Revd Mark Poulson; The Rt Revd Dr Michael Ipgrave; Matthew Girt; Revd Canon Eve Pitts; Francis Davis.

Correspondent: Local Near Neighbours Co-ordinator, Church House, 27 Great Smith Street, London SW1P 3AZ (tel: 020 7898 1647; email: hello@ nearneighbours.org.uk)

www.near-neighbours.org.uk

facebook.com/nearneighbours

@nearneighbours

@nearneighbours

Near Neighbours offers small grants between £250 and £5,000, as seed funding for local groups and organisations working to bring together neighbours and develop relationships across diverse faiths and ethnicities in order to improve their communities.

According to the application guidelines, eligible projects should:

- **Bring together peoples of two or more different faiths and/or ethnicities**, to build friendships and develop relationships of trust.
- **Work locally**. We want to see people who are living very locally (i.e. in the same street, estate or neighbourhood) come together.
- **Work sustainably**. We want to see long-term and natural relationships grow, that will last beyond the period of funding.
- **Work to improve the community**. We want to see people working to make their communities a better place to live.
- **Involve a diverse group of people in planning and implementation**. People from more than one faith group and/or ethnicity are involved in running the project

In the past, the Ministry of Housing, Communities and Local Government (formerly the Department for Communities and Local Government or DCLG) has provided funding for larger grant programmes but at the time of writing (June 2018) these programmes had ended.

Financial information

In 2016 the charity held assets of £173,000 and had an income of £1.9 million, which represents a grant from the DCLG and another grant from the Church Urban Fund. Grants totalled £1.45 million and were awarded through three programmes (two of which are no longer active). During the year, £838,000 was awarded through the small grants programme.

Exclusions

Consult the application guidelines for a full list of exclusions.

Applications

Full application details can be found on the charity's helpful website, which potential applicants should read before starting an application. Near Neighbours runs local support hubs and contact information for the local co-ordinators can be found in the application guidance and on the website. Application forms, additional documents and the optional equal opportunities form should be submitted to the local Near Neighbours Co-ordinator who will offer feedback and recommendations. The co-ordinator will forward applications to the Church Urban Fund, which is acting as administrator for the programme. The charity aims to make a decision on all grant applications within 14 days. Applications are accepted on a rolling basis until all funds are spent.

Sources of information

Accounts; annual report; Charity Commission record; funder's website.

Nesta

Social innovation, health, education, arts and culture

UK

£11.1 million (2016/17)

CC number: 1144091

Trustees: Simon Linnett; Sir John Gieve; Natalie Tydeman; David Pitt-Watson; Kim Shillinglaw; Imran Khan; Judy Gibbons; Kersten Gibbons; Edward Wray; Piers Linney; Moira Wallace; Prof. Anthony Lilley.

Correspondent: Corinna Theuma, Company Secretary, 1 Plough Place, London EC4A 1DE (tel: 020 7438 2500; email: info@nesta.org.uk)

 www.nesta.org.uk

Nesta is 'an innovation charity with a mission to help people and organisations bring great ideas to life', as described on its website. It was originally formed as a non-departmental public body, funded by a £250 million endowment form the National Lottery and has been an independent charity since 2011.

Nesta's priority areas of work for 2017 to 2020 are:

- Health
- Education
- The creative economy, arts and culture
- Government innovation
- Innovation policy

Funding

Nesta awards funding, often in partnership with other organisations, through a mix of grants, direct investment and challenge prizes.

Challenge prizes

Challenge prizes, as stated on the Nesta website, are used 'to stimulate innovative solutions to some of the biggest challenges we face'. Nesta's Challenge Prize Centre was established in 2012 to 'increase practical evidence and understanding about challenge prizes so that they can be used effectively by governments, charities and businesses to have a tangible positive impact on society'.

Nesta is currently funding the Longitude Prize, a £10 million prize fund to help solve the issue of antibiotic resistance. This issue was chosen from six challenges by public vote in 2014. This prize will run until 2019 and is open to all ages and organisations. For more information, including application deadlines, refer to the website.

Impact investment

The following information is provided on the Nesta website:

Impact investment aims to bring about positive outcomes for people, communities and society as a whole, as well as providing financial returns for investors.

We want to support the development of the impact investment market. In particular we want to see more investment focused on:

- Inclusive, accessible, affordable innovations that address major social needs
- Delivering positive social outcomes regardless of legal form
- The standard of evidence of a venture's impact
- Profitable, sustainable and resilient business models capable of scaling their impact

As well as running a number of open impact investment programmes, the website states 'if you have a social venture that has the potential for social impact and has a sound business model, please get in contact'. More information can be found on the dedicated nest impact investments website (nestainvestments.org.uk).

Grants

Nesta provides grants through a number of funding programmes, often in partnership with other organisations. For example, the Centre for Social Action Innovation Fund is funded in partnership with the Cabinet Office. Grants from Nesta are provided alongside non-financial support, such as advice, mentoring and coaching. When a grants programme is opened, the criteria are made available on the Nesta website.

Within each of the above categories, Nesta operates a number of funding programmes which open and close on a regular basis, so for up-to-date information on the funding currently available, refer to the website.

Financial information

In 2016/17 Nesta had assets of £435.5 million and an income of £14.5 million. Grants to 88 organisations totalled £11.1 million.

Beneficiaries of grants of £50,000 and above included: British Lung Foundation (£958,000); The Stroke Association (£832,000); Carers UK (£420,000); Family Action (£250,000); Whole Education (£113,000); Behavioural Insights (£55,000); Leicester City Council (£50,000).

Grants of less than £50,000 to 45 organisations totalled £812,000.

Exclusions

Refer to the website for exclusions from each funding programme.

Applications

Information on current funding programmes is provided on the Nesta website, including details of how to apply.

Sources of information

Accounts; annual report; Charity Commission record; funder's website.

Network for Social Change Charitable Trust

 Environment, peace, human rights, economic justice, health, arts and education

 UK and overseas

 £1.24 million (2016/17)

CC number: 295237

Trustees: Chris Marks; Imran Tyabji; Giles Wright; Carolyn Hayman; Marian Tucker; Jessica Paget.

Correspondent: Tish McCorry, BM 2063, London WC1N 3XX (tel: 01647 61106; email: thenetwork@gn.apc.org)

 thenetworkforsocialchange.org.uk

Network for Social Change, formerly the Network Foundation, is a group of philanthropic individuals who have come together to support progressive social and ecological change. Grants typically go to organisations addressing such issues as environmental sustainability and economic and social justice.

The network is unusual in its organisation and offers the following information about how it operates:

> Network members are each personally active in sponsoring, assessing, selecting and commending projects to fellow members. Our funding processes are designed to encourage members to find worthwhile projects, assess their potential and evaluate their achievements. Those without previous experience of such an undertaking work alongside more experienced members.

Funding

Funding is given in the UK and overseas to projects which are likely to affect social change, either through research, public education, innovatory services and other charitable activities. The network tends to favour structural change rather than relief work, but there is no set policy on the specific types of organisations it will fund.

The website states that:

> We look for projects that promote social change (broadly defined) and tend to favour projects which are innovative, highly leveraged, and/or difficult to fund (a category which may include core funding for an organisation). We like addressing the root causes of a problem, not the symptoms.

Grants are usually for up to £20,000 but major and longer-term projects can also be funded with much higher donations.

There are three funding streams:

 Pools – members sponsor projects from one of six pools, currently: Green Planet; Human Rights; Economic Justice; Health and Wellbeing; Peace; Arts and Education. Around half of the funding is given through pools. Grants of up to £20,000 are available per project

▷ Major projects – initiated and driven by a small group of members, these typically focus on a neglected area of social change. Funding is normally provided for three to six years with £50,000 to £100,000 given per year per project

▷ FastTrack – grants of up to £6,000

Refer to the website for further details on each stream.

Financial information

In 2016/17 the trust had assets of £302,000 and an income of over £1.35 million. Grants awarded to organisations totalled £1.24 million.

Beneficiaries included: Oxford Research Group (£150,000); Campaign Academy Ltd (£119,000); City of Sanctuary (£65,000); Platform and Sustain (£20,000 each); Prism the Gift Fund (£18,000); Cocoon Family Support (£15,000); Peace Direct (£13,400); The Civil Liberties Trust (£10,000).

Applications

All applications to the trust must be sponsored by a member. Unsolicited applications are not accepted. However, project summaries can be posted on the trust's project noticeboard. If a member is interested, they will get in touch. Last year only one to two per cent of project noticeboard entries resulted in funding.

Sources of information

Annual report; accounts; Charity Commission record; funder's website.

Newby Trust Ltd

 Health, social welfare, education

Q UK, with a preference for England

£ £372,000 to organisations (2016/17)

CC number: 227151

Trustees: David Charlton; Duncan Reed; Ben Gooder; Anna Foxell; Evelyn Montgomery; Nigel Callaghan; Dr Stephen Gooder.

Correspondent: Annabel Grout, Company Secretary, PO Box 87, Petworth GU28 8BH (email: info@ newby-trust.org.uk)

www.newby-trust.org.uk

The aims of the trust are to promote medical welfare, training and education and the relief of poverty. The following is taken from the trust's annual report:

> The principal focus of the company's grant-giving has been on education, training and research and medical welfare and the company also makes small social welfare grants.

The trust has stated on its website that it 'is more likely to fund smaller or medium-sized charities with an annual income of less than £1 million although the trust will sometimes make grants to larger charities for a specific project'.

Grant-making criteria

The following information was taken from the trust's website:

Health

The broad objectives of the health category are to fund:

1 Equipment and activities in hospitals, residential and nursing homes, day care centres and hospices

2   Patient support services to improve the mental and physical health of adults or children

3   Medical research

Education

The broad objectives of the trust's education programme are:

1   To fund postgraduate study

2   To provide financial support to enable disadvantaged people to access and stay in education and training

For postgraduate study, funds are distributed to selected UK educational establishments for the support of research at postgraduate or post-doctoral level. The Trustees will from time to time agree the appropriate institutions to receive these funds. Education grants are not given to individuals.

Other educational grants will be made from time to time to charities recommended by the Trustees and members of the Trust and may include:

▷ Education and training at all levels of arts and crafts

▷ Life skills and vocational training

▷ Activities and training for people with physical or learning disabilities and

▷ Educational opportunities for disadvantaged children and young people

Social Welfare

The broad objectives of the welfare category are:

1   To provide small grants of up to £250 for short-term emergency relief

2   To fund support and activities for vulnerable and disadvantaged people

The Newby Trust supports a wide range of charities that benefit disadvantaged people and communities.

Annual Special Category

This category is selected by the directors each year under one of the main headings of education, health and welfare and provides a focus for grant-giving in that year.

In 2016/17 the special category was 'smaller charities providing counselling, support and vocational opportunities for people with mental health issues' and in 2017/18 it will be 'smaller charities using sport or dance to encourage healthy and active lifestyles for disadvantaged young people'. Further information is provided on the trust's website.

Financial information

In 2016/17 the trust held assets of over £20 million and had an income of £483,500. During the year, the charity gave around £372,000 in grants. Of this amount, 272 grants were directly awarded to organisations for individuals.

Grants to organisations were broken down as follows:

Health (including 'special category')	20	£150,000
Welfare	279	£119,000
Education	8	£103,000

Beneficiaries included: Motor Neurone Disease Association (£32,000); University of Durham (£30,000); Angel Community Canal Boat Trust (£18,000); Blue Smile, Dolphin Society and Penny Brohn Cancer Cure (£10,000 each).

Exclusions

The trust's website states that it does not fund the following:

▷ Statutory bodies

▷ Large national charities enjoying widespread support

▷ Organisations not registered with the Charity Commission

▷ Exhibitions, conferences or events

▷ Individuals volunteering overseas

▷ Promotion of religion

▷ Work outside of the UK

▷ Large capital appeals

▷ Endowment appeals.

Applications

In general, unsolicited applications are not accepted. If you would like to discuss making an application, you can email info@newby-trust.org.uk. The trust does not have an application form but if you are invited to apply, you will receive a list of points to consider when making an application.

The application procedure differs for the special category and individuals.

The website provides the following information on special category applications:

> Most special category applications will be considered at a Trustees meeting in November. The Trust may contact charities that have applied previously. Charities that fit within the special category may send an introductory email to the Company Secretary at info@newby-trust.org.uk describing their activities and their specific funding needs for the relevant year. Thereafter, only charities that are specifically invited to apply will be considered.

For individuals, refer to the website for details of whether applications are currently being accepted and how to apply. Applications must be made through an eligible organisation, not directly by the individual.

Sources of information

Accounts; annual report; Charity Commission record; funder's website.

The Frances and Augustus Newman Foundation

🔍 Medical research projects and other medical charitable causes

📍 UK

💷 £476,000 (2016/17)

CC number: 277964

Trustees: David Sweetnam; Lord Hugh Rathcavan; John Williams; Stephen Cannon.

Correspondent: Hazel Palfreyman, c/o Baker Tilly Chartered Accountants, Hartwell House, 55–61 Victoria Street, Bristol BS1 6AD (tel: 0117 945 2000; email: hazel.palfreyman@rsmuk.com)

The foundation aims to advance the work of medical professionals working in teaching hospitals and academic units, mostly (but not exclusively) by funding medical research projects and equipment, including fellowships of the Royal College of Surgeons. Grants range from £1,000 to £110,000 a year and can be given for up to three years.

Financial information

In 2016/17 the foundation held assets of £15 million and had an income of £563,000. During the year, the charity awarded eight grants to organisations, totalling £476,000. Grants were distributed as follows:

Building and equipment	£360,000
Research costs	£307,000
Other charitable endeavours	£5,000

Beneficiaries included: University of Cambridge, Sir Rodney Sweetnam Laboratory (£250,000); UCL Cancer Research Trust (£110,000); St Wilfrid's Hospital (£50,000).

A grant relating to 'other charitable endeavours' was given to Head Talks Productions CIC, a charitable organisation set up to provide online resources which support the mental health needs of the public.

Exclusions

Applications are not normally accepted from overseas. Requests from other charities seeking funds to supplement their own general funds to support medical research in a particular field are seldom supported.

Applications

Applications should include a detailed protocol and costing and be sent to the correspondent. They may then be peer-reviewed. The trustees meet in June and December each year and applications must be received at the latest by the end of April or October respectively. The foundation awards for surgical research fellowships should be addressed to the Royal College of Surgeons of England at 35–43 Lincoln's Inn Fields, London WC2A 3PE.

Sources of information

Accounts; annual report; Charity Commission record.

Newpier Charity Ltd

Jewish causes, social welfare, education

UK and Israel

£717,500 (2016/17)

CC number: 293686

Trustees: Charles Margulies; Helen Knopfler; Rachel Margulies.

Correspondent: Charles Margulies, Trustee, 186 Lordship Road, London N16 5ES (tel: 020 8802 4449)

The main objectives of the charity are the advancement of the Orthodox Jewish faith and the relief of poverty. The 2016/17 annual report states:

> The charity was set up to support the activities of religious Jewish organisations especially in the field of education. The trustees identify institutions and organisations which meet its criteria and regularly support a number of these institutions and organisations, which themselves are growing not only in England but also worldwide.
>
> The charity is also supportive of organisations which are solely committed to the relief of poverty. Such organisations assist needy Jewish families financially and also through the distribution of basic necessities.

Financial information

In 2016/17 the charity held assets of over £2 million and had an income of almost £1.5 million. Grants totalling £717,500 were made during the year. A list of beneficiaries was not included in the accounts.

Previous beneficiaries have included: BML Benityashvut, Friends of Biala, Gateshead Yeshiva, KID, Mesdos Wiznitz and SOFT for redistribution to other charities.

Applications

Apply in writing to the correspondent. The trustees meet on a regular basis to consider applications.

Sources of information

Accounts; annual report; Charity Commission record.

The NFU Mutual Charitable Trust

Community development, education, the relief of poverty, social welfare, research focusing on initiatives that will have a significant impact on rural communities

UK, with a preference for rural areas

£256,500 (2016)

CC number: 1073064

Trustees: Stephen James; Lindsay Sinclair; Richard Percy; Meurig Raymond; Stanley Bell; Dr Harriet Kennedy; Andrew McCornick.

Correspondent: James Creechan, Tiddington Road, Stratford-upon-Avon, Warwickshire CV37 7BJ (tel: 01789 204211; email: nfu_mutual_charitable_trust@nfumutual.co.uk)

 www.nfumutual.co.uk/about-us/charitable-trust

Registered with the Charity Commission in 1998, the NFU Mutual Charitable Trust is the corporate charity of the National Farmers Union Mutual Insurance Society Ltd (NFU Mutual), one of the UK's leading insurers. Notable trustees include Richard Percy, chair of NFU Mutual, and Lindsay Sinclair, its chief executive.

The website states that 'the objectives of The NFU Mutual Charitable Trust are to promote, facilitate and support such purposes as are exclusively charitable according to the laws of England and Wales in the areas of agriculture, rural development and insurance in the United Kingdom', in particular:

- To advance the education of the public by means of research and dissemination of information in relation to agriculture
- To advance the education of young people within rural areas
- To relieve poverty within rural areas
- To promote the benefit and social welfare of inhabitants of rural communities by associating together with the inhabitants and local authorities, voluntary and other organisations to advance education and leisure
- To promote research into agriculture-associated activities
- To advance the education of the public by means of research and dissemination of information in relation to insurance

Grants range from £1,000 to £50,000. Larger grants are used to support organisations which have a significant impact on rural communities at a national level. The trustees do not normally consider multi-year funding.

Financial information

In 2016 the trust had assets of £241,500 and an income of £258,000. Grants totalling £256,500 were made to 15 charitable organisations.

Beneficiaries included: Farming and Countryside Education (£55,000); The National Federation of Young Farmers Clubs (£30,000); Royal Agricultural Benevolent Institution (£26,000); Rural Support (£20,000); Royal Scottish Agricultural Benevolent Institution (£17,500); Wales Federation of Young Farmers Clubs, The Prince's Countryside Fund (£10,000 each); Open Farm Weekend Northern Islands (£5,000); Farms for City Children (£4,000); Gareth raw Rees Memorial Scholarship (£1,000).

Applications

Apply in writing to the correspondent either by post or email. The application form is available from the trust's website.

Applications should include:

- Details of the project, initiative or organisation for which funding is sought
- An indication of the amount of the donation requested
- Details of any business plans
- Details of any other funding sought and or obtained
- Details of any recognition which would be given to the trust in recognition of its support
- Confirmation of whether or not the applicant is a registered charity

Following a recent strategic review, the trustees have indicated that in future, the trust will focus on providing funding to larger initiatives, which would have a significant impact on the rural community. The trustees are particularly interested in initiatives in the areas of education of young people in rural areas and relief of poverty within rural areas. The trustees meet twice a year to consider applications received. These meetings are currently held in June and November.

Sources of information

Accounts; annual report; Charity Commission record; funder's website.

The Nineveh Charitable Trust

Environmental understanding, access, education and research

UK

£194,000 (2016/17)

CC number: 256025

Trustees: Robert G. H. Lewis; Dr Michael James; John MacGregor.

Correspondent: R. G. H. Lewis, Trustee, Park Farm, Frittenden Road, Biddenden, Ashford TN27 8LG (tel: 01580 291531; email: robert@ninevehtrust.org.uk)

 www.ninevehtrust.org.uk

The trust was established in 1968 by Marjorie and Thomas James, both of whom had strong interests in farming and the environment.

The trust supports a wide range of projects and activities with a strong focus on environmental understanding, access, education and research.

According to the trust's website its objects are:

- The health, welfare and education of the general public
- The study and appreciation of agriculture, horticulture, silviculture and land and estate management
- The study and appreciation of ecology & land conservation, and
- The study and appreciation of forms of agricultural practice or land management that would encourage the preservation of the countryside

Grants are made to UK-registered charities and community interest companies. Individual applicants may be considered if the outcome benefits are clearly defined

Financial information

In 2016/17 the trust held assets of £10 million and had an income of £298,000. Grants to 46 organisations totalled £194,000.

Beneficiaries included: The Garden Classroom (£15,000); Future Roots (£10,000); Friends of the Sedgwick Museum (£7,000); Trees for Cities (£5,000); Sustrans (£4,000); The Country Trust (£2,300); Bosavern Community Farm and Caring for Life (£2,000 each); Tywi Gateway Trust (£1,000); Penumbra (£500).

A full list of beneficiaries is available on the trust's website.

Exclusions

The trust's website states that it is unlikely to provide funding for the following:

- Expeditions or personal educational needs without a wider benefit
- Animal sanctuaries and care
- Projects unrelated to the Trust's objects
- Organisations based outside the UK
- General appeals or mailshots

Applications

Apply in writing to the correspondent. Three copies of the proposal should be sent to the correspondent along with an sae. Applications should be no longer than two sides. The trust suggests using a Situation-Target-Proposal structure for proposals.

The trust's website states that proposals should include the following information:

- How much you want
- What the money is going to be used for (e.g. provide a breakdown)
- Methodologies (e.g. of a field study; how the data will be measured)
- Successful outcome indicators (e.g. please specify up to 3 measures that will demonstrate the success of your project)
- What the benefit will be, not only to your organisation but thinking about the wider world
- How your target will support [the trust's] aims

Background information such as websites and annual accounts should also be included.

Sources of information

Accounts; annual report; Charity Commission record; funder's website.

The Nisbet Trust

Children and young people, arts, sport and recreation, homelessness, education and training

Bristol, North Somerset and South Gloucestershire

£704,000 (2016/17)

CC number: 1143496

Trustees: Andrew Nisbet; Anne Nisbet; Joseph Nisbet; Emily Nisbet; Zoe Joyner; Henry Bothamley.

Correspondent: Anna Gillies, Trust Administrator, 22 Clifton Road, Bristol BS8 1AQ (email: admin@nisbettrust.co.uk)

 www.nisbettrust.co.uk

Established in 2012 by the Nisbet family, this trust supports social welfare, education and training and the arts in Bristol. The trustees have a particular interest in projects supporting disadvantaged young people and projects which tackle homelessness. There are three levels of grant:

- Small: up to £5,000
- Medium: £5,001 to £30,000
- Large: over £30,000

Single and multi-year grants for up to three years can be requested. Applicants must be a registered charity, exempt charity, not-for-profit social enterprise or CIC benefitting communities in the Greater Bristol area. CICs must have been established for at least three years, with an annual income of more than £50,000 which should include at least 25% from trading.

Financial information

In 2016/17 the trust held assets of £366,000 and had an income of £750,000. Grants totalling £704,000 were made to 71 organisations.

Beneficiaries included: Bristol Music Trust (£102,500); Bristol Old Vic (£100,000); Access Sport CIO (£30,000); YMCA Bath (£25,000); Network Counselling and Training (£20,000); St Mungo's (£15,000); Bristol Drugs Project and Teach First (£10,000 each); Urban Pursuit CIC (£6,000); Colston's Girls School (£5,000).

Grants of less than £5,000 totalled £18,900.

Exclusions

The following are not eligible for support:

- Medical research
- Single condition medical charities
- Grants for individuals
- Animal welfare charities
- Sponsorship

CICs which have a core business model that is substantially grant-reliant are unlikely to be successful.

Applications

Application forms are available from the trust's website. The trustees meet quarterly to consider applications. Deadlines for applications are posted on the trust's website.

Sources of information

Accounts; annual report; Charity Commission record; funder's website.

Educational Foundation of Alderman John Norman

Education

Norwich and Old Catton

£192,000 to organisations (2016/17)

CC number: 313105

Trustees: Revd Philip Butcher; Revd Jonathan Boston; Roger Sandall; Julia Leach; Tracey Hughes; Christopher Brown; Francis Whymark; Roy Hughes; Nicholas Bevington.

Correspondent: Nick Saffell, Clerk, The Atrium, St George's Street, Norwich NR3 1AB (tel: 01603 629871; email: nick.saffell@brown-co.com)

 wp.normanfoundation.org.uk

The original aims of the foundation were laid out in the will of the late Alderman John Norman who died in 1724. According to the trustees' report for 2016/17, the income of the foundation is applied mainly to assist the education of:

- Young persons descended from Alderman John Norman
- Young persons resident in the parish of Old Catton
- Young persons resident in the city of Norwich and for the benefit of schools established for charitable purposes only or for the benefit of local authority schools for benefits not provided by the local authority

Financial information

In 2016/17 the foundation held assets of £8 million and had an income of £273,000. Grants totalled £304,500, of which £192,000 was given in special awards to 40 organisations. In addition, grants totalling £85,500 were made to 306 individuals descended from

Alderman John Norman and grants totalling £26,500 were made to residents of Old Catton.

Previous beneficiaries have included: How Hill Trust (£36,000); Connects and Co. (£8,000); Mile Cross Primary School (£6,900); BUILD, Leeway Domestic Violence and Abuse Services, Norwich Cathedral and Teens and Toddlers (£5,000 each); Norfolk Fire Service (£3,000); The Prince's Trust (£2,000); East Anglian Air Ambulance (£1,000).

Exclusions

No applications from outside Norwich and Old Catton will be considered.

Applications

Apply in writing to the correspondent. All applications should be made through the Clerk.

Sources of information

Accounts; annual report; Charity Commission record.

The Norman Family Charitable Trust

 General charitable purposes

Primarily Cornwall, Devon and Somerset

£410,000 (2016/17)

CC number: 277616

Trustees: Roger Dawe; Margaret Evans; Michael Saunders; Margaret Webb; Catherine Houghton; Sarah Gillingham; William Tee.

Correspondent: The Trustees, 14 Fore Street, Budleigh Salterton, Devon EX9 6NG (tel: 01395 446699; email: info@nfct.org)

 www.nfct.org

The trust was established in 1979 due to the success of a chain of cash and carries owned by the Norman family. Ken and Pat Norman, who started the cash and carries, used some of the proceeds from the business to start the Normal Family Charitable Trust. The aim of the trust is to support worthy causes in South West England with the intention of repaying loyal customers who helped to make the Norman's business a success.

Grant-making

The trust's primary objective is to provide funding for registered charities, non-profit and voluntary organisations working in Somerset, Devon and Cornwall. The trust does consider applications from national charities but only if the proposed project with specifically benefit the South West.

For 2017/18, the trust has reviewed their grant-making policy and will now be

funding schools in the Devon area, to benefit pupils and parents, as a result of government cuts and financial hardship being faced in the community. Details are available on the trust's website.

Financial information

In 2016/17 the trust had assets of £9.4 million and an income of £442,000. There were 343 grants made to organisations; they totalled £410,000 and were broken down as follows:

Children	£82,000
Medical, including medical research	£62,000
Community projects	£61,000
Blind, deaf, and physical disabilities	£52,500
Homelessness and social welfare	£31,000
Youth	£25,500
Mental health and learning disabilities	£21,000
Sport and leisure	£21,000
Senior welfare	£17,000
Animals, environment and conservation	£11,500
Employment, skills and training	£10,000
Forces, ex-forces, and emergency services	£6,500
Crime prevention, rehabilitation and addictions	£6,000

Beneficiaries (receiving over £2,500) included: University of Exeter Medical School (£15,000); East Budleigh Village Green, Exmouth and District Community Transport Group (£10,000 each); Hospiscare Exeter, Mid and East Devon (£9,000); Action on Hearing Loss, Lord Lieutenant's Fund for Youth in Cornwall and St Peter's Primary Budleigh Salterton PTA (£5,000 each); Budleigh Salterton Carnival (£3,000); Force Cancer Charity (£2,700).

Exclusions

Individuals are not supported directly. Grants are not made to/for: organisations which use live animals for experimental or research purposes; the maintenance or repair of religious buildings; projects outside the UK. National charities will only be supported for projects which will help the area of benefit.

Applications

Application forms are available to download from the trust's website and must be submitted by post. Once an initial application has been submitted, the trust will communicate with the applicant via email.

Include in all applications:

▶ The legal status of your organisation
▶ Your organisation's latest accounts
▶ A brief explanation of what your organisation is set up to do, the main activities it carries out, how many people your organisation assists, and if you rely on volunteers
▶ A clear and concise summary of the purpose of your application (no more than 35 words)
▶ The total amount you are bidding for

▶ Grant payment details – if payment is to be made by BACS, include your organisation's bank details

Applicants seeking grants of less than £5,000 will be considered by a sub-committee which meets every six to eight weeks. Applications for grants of more than £5,000 are considered by the trustees at quarterly meetings in March, June, September and December.

Sources of information

Accounts; annual report; Charity Commission record; funder's website.

Normanby Charitable Trust

 Arts and culture, heritage, social welfare, disability, general charitable purposes

Mainly North Yorkshire and the North East

£353,500 (2016/17)

CC number: 252102

Trustees: The Marquis of Normanby; Lady Lepel Kornicki; Lady Evelyn Buchan; Lady Peronel Cruz; Lady Henrietta Burridge.

Correspondent: The Marquis of Normanby, Trustee, 52 Tite Street, London SW3 4JA (email: nct@normanby.org)

The Normanby Charitable Trust has general charitable purposes and in recent years has supported organisations working in areas including arts and culture, heritage, social welfare and disability. The trust has also occasionally given grants for the preservation of religious and secular buildings of historical or architectural interest. Grants are mainly given in North Yorkshire and the North East.

Financial information

In 2016/17 the trust had assets of £13.1 million and an income of £354,000. Grants to 35 organisations totalled £353,500.

Beneficiaries included: Caedmon College Whitby (£25,000); Cued Speech Association UK (£11,400); St Mary's Restoration Appeal (£10,000); Alcohol and Drugs Service and Joseph Banks Archive Project (£1,000 each); Tall Ships Youth Trust (£600); Whitby Literary Writers Group (£275).

Exclusions

Grants are not made to non-UK charities. Grants to individuals are only made in exceptional circumstances.

Applications

Apply in writing to the correspondent. The trustees meet two to three times a year to award grants, although there are no regular dates. Only successful applications are acknowledged.

Sources of information
Accounts; annual report; Charity Commission record.

North West Cancer Research

 Cancer research

North West England and North Wales

£4.1 million (2016/17)

CC number: 519357

Trustees: Catherine Jones; Nigel Lanceley; Stephen Claus; Francis Street; Moira Owen; Mark Haig; Catherine Bond; Hilary Atherton; Philip Robertshaw; Prof. David Sibson; Steven Smith.

Correspondent: Maureen Catton, Trust Officer, North West Cancer Research Centre, 200 London Road, Liverpool L3 9TA (tel: 0151 709 2919; email: maureen@nwcr.org)

 www.nwcr.org

North West Cancer Research is an independent research charity funding research for local people in North West England and North Wales. The charity prioritises research that has a direct impact on the people in the region and targets the cancers that are most prevalent. The charity invests in studies from 'bench to bedside'.

Two main types of grant are available, details of which have been taken from the charity's website:

Project grants
Researchers within the North West of England and North Wales are invited to apply for project grants twice a year. We provide funding for three main research areas:

- Basic
- Translational
- Preventative

The research we fund **must** have a demonstrable impact on people within North West England and North Wales and principal investigators **must** be based within our regional footprint. We will invest in researchers at every stage of their career to develop the cancer researchers of the future.

Projects should be up to three years in length

Equipment grants
North West Cancer Research accepts applications for equipment grants to fund new, multi-use equipment for cancer research. We will accept proposals up to £50,000 including match funding. Equipment grants are for the benefit of cancer research at our funded universities:

- University of Liverpool
- Lancaster University
- Bangor University
- Chester University

Once a grant application is received, Trust Officer, Maureen Catton, will then send an application out to relevant trusts to acquire funds. Please provide as much information regarding the equipment in lay terms as you can. We cannot guarantee funding for any application submitted.

Financial information
In 2016/17 the charity had assets of £5.7 million and an income of £1.3 million. Grants to institutions totalled £4.1 million.

A list of beneficiaries was not available.

Applications
Application forms and guidelines are available to download from the charity's website. Check the website for details of application deadlines.

The charity's website states: 'If you are interested in funding for fellowships, studentships, PhDs or Centre funding within our area, please contact the Chief Executive Officer, Alastair Richards for further information.'

Sources of information
Accounts; annual report; Charity Commission record; funder's website.

The Northwick Trust

 General charitable purposes

UK and overseas

£395,000 (2016/17)

CC number: 285197

Trustees: Peter McCarthy; Lady Rachel Gordon Willcocks; Mary Penoyne Morgan; Kate Willcocks; Anne Willcocks; Xanthe Vaughan Williams; Andrew Laurie.

Correspondent: Peter McCarthy, Trustee, 13 Queensway, Wellingborough NN8 3RA (tel: 01933 222986; email: petermc1711@btinternet.com)

The Northwick Trust was registered with the Charity Commission in 1982 and supports general charitable purposes, including environmental sustainability and conservation, culture and heritage, social welfare, projects for people with mental and physical disabilities, and projects encouraging young people to become more involved in their community. The trust supports registered charities in the UK and those operating overseas.

Financial information
In 2016/17 the trust held assets of £11.5 million and had an income of £336,500. Grants were made to 48 organisations and totalled £395,000.

Previous beneficiaries have included:
WaterAid (£30,000); Practical Action (£25,000); Environmental Justice Foundation (£20,000); Asylum Welcome, Citizens UK and Sightsavers (£10,000 each); Helping the Burmese Delta (£8,000); Community Action Nepal, Médecins Sans Frontières and Northamptonshire Carers (£5,000 each); Equal Arts, Home-Start – Wellingborough and Twins and Multiple Births Trust (£2,000 each).

Applications
Apply in writing to the correspondent.

Sources of information
Accounts; annual report; Charity Commission record.

Northwood Charitable Trust

 General charitable purposes

Dundee and Tayside

£1.8 million (2016/17)

OSCR number: SC014487

Correspondent: The Trustees, 22 Meadowside, Dundee DD1 1LN

The Northwood Trust is connected to the D C Thomson Charitable Trust, D C Thomson and Company and the Thomson family. It was established by Eric V Thomson in 1972 and has received additional funding from other members of the family. The trust gives for general charitable purposes in Dundee and Tayside.

Financial information
In 2016/17 the trust had assets of £95.8 million and an income of £3 million. During the year, the charity gave around £1.8 million in grants to 120 organisations.

Beneficiaries included: Tenovus Major Projects (£362,000); DC Thomson Charitable Trust (£150,000); Dundee Heritage Trust (£60,000); Dundee Dance Theatre (£15,000); Age Concern Dundee and Dundee Women's Aid (£10,000 each); Whitehall Theatre Trust (£8,500); Howe of Fife Rugby Club (£7,000).

Applications
The trust's 2016/17 accounts state: 'Unsolicited applications for donations are not encouraged and will not normally be acknowledged.'

Sources of information
Accounts; annual report; OSCR record.

The Norton Rose Fulbright Charitable Foundation

 Education, social welfare, medical, disaster relief

 Worldwide

 £644,500 (2015/16)

CC number: 1102142

Trustees: Simon Cox; Patrick Farrell; Ffion Flockhart.

Correspondent: Patrick Farrell, Trustee, 3 More London Riverside, London SE1 2AQ (tel: 020 7283 6000)

www.nortonrosefulbright.com/corporate-responsibility

The foundation was set up in 2004 and is funded by donations from partners of the Norton Rose Group, an international legal practice.

The foundation supports a wide range of charitable purposes, including education, medical causes and social welfare. The foundation does this through fundraising, volunteering and grant-making. Many of the charities supported are nominated by the partners and staff of Norton Rose Group. Grants may be made for one-off purchases or given as longer-term support.

Financial information

In 2015/16 the foundation had assets of £249,000 and an income of £559,500, mostly from donations. There were 74 grants made, which totalled £644,500 and were distributed for the following purposes:

Social welfare	29	£332,000
Medical	33	£229,000
Educational	12	£83,000

Beneficiaries included: Barretstown (£100,000); Action for Children (£40,000); South West London Law Centres (£25,000); MS Society (£20,500); Special Olympics (£35,000).

Applications

Apply in writing to the correspondent. The 2015/16 annual report states:

> In many cases, the charities we support are those we have supported in the past, but new charities are considered at Trustee meetings. The Trustees also meet on an ad hoc basis to consider specific urgent requests such as the support of major disaster relief appeals.

The foundation also prefers to 'maintain a regular dialogue' with the charities it supports.

Sources of information

Accounts; annual report; Charity Commission record; funder's website.

Norwich Town Close Estate Charity

 Education

 Within a 20-mile radius of the Guildhall of the city of Norwich

 £483,000 to organisations (2016/17)

CC number: 235678

Trustees: John Rushmer; David Fullman; Brenda Ferris; Geoffrey Loades; Pamela Scutter; Philip Blanchflower; Nigel Back; Jeanne Southgate; Brenda Arthur; Robert Wellesley Self; Heather Tyrrell; Michael Quinton; James Symonds; David Barber; Stuart Lamb; Owen Gibbs.

Correspondent: Vanessa Soer, Grants Officer, 1 Woolgate Court, St Benedict's Street, Norwich NR2 4AP (tel: 01603 621023; email: info@norwichcharitabletrusts.org.uk)

www.norwichtowncloseestatecharity.org.uk

@Norwich_Freemen

The charity has the following objects:

> To provide relief in need and pensions to Freemen or their widows or daughters where required

> The promotion of education of those in need of financial assistance who are Freemen or the sons or daughters of Freemen

> To make grants for educational purposes to bodies which benefit people living within the 20-mile radius of the Norwich Guildhall

The trust has close links with Norwich Consolidated Charities and Anguish's Educational Foundation. They share their administration processes and collaborate on grant-making.

Grants to individuals are prioritised, particularly for pensions and education.

Financial information

In 2016/17 the charity had assets of £25.4 million and an income of £938,000. There were grants made to individuals and organisations totalling £705,500, which included 43 grants to organisations totalling £483,000 and 116 grants made to individuals totalling around £222,500 (mostly for educational purposes and pensions).

Beneficiaries included: Norfolk Museums Development Foundation (£100,000); Erpingham PCC (£50,000); Norwich Eagle Canoe Club (£25,000); Young Norfolk Arts Trust (£10,000); Mile Cross Primary School (£8,200); Total Ensemble Theatre (£3,000); Break (£2,500); Home Education group (£840).

Exclusions

No grants are given to: individuals who are not Freemen (or dependants of Freemen) of the city of Norwich; charities more than 20 miles from Norwich; or charities which are not educational. Revenue funding for educational charities is not generally given.

Applications

After a preliminary enquiry, apply in writing to the Grants Officer.

When submitting an application, the following points should be considered:

> Brevity is a virtue. If too much written material is submitted, there is a risk that it may not all be assimilated

> The trustees like to have details of any other financial support secured

> An indication should be given of the amount that is being sought and also how that figure is arrived at

> The trustees will not reimburse expenditure already incurred

> Generally, the trustees will not pay running costs, e.g. salaries

Sources of information

Accounts; annual report; Charity Commission record; funder's website.

The Nuffield Foundation

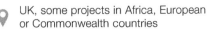 Science and social science research and capacity development, particularly in the fields of: law and justice, children and families, education

UK, some projects in Africa, European or Commonwealth countries

£4.7 million (2016)

CC number: 206601

Trustees: Prof. Lord Krebbs; Prof. Sir David Rhind; Prof. Terrie Moffitt; Dame Colette Bowe; Prof. James Banks; Prof. Rt Hon. Lord Justice Ernest Ryder; Prof. Anna Vignoles; Sir Keith Burnett.

Correspondent: Grants Team, 28 Bedford Square, London WC1B 3JS (tel: 020 7681 9610; email: info@nuffieldfoundation.org)

 www.nuffieldfoundation.org

The Nuffield Foundation is an independent charity established in 1943 by William Morris, Lord Nuffield, the founder of Morris Motors.

The following information is taken from the very detailed and informative 'Guidance for Applicants' which can be found on the foundation's website and should be read by potential applicants:

> Its [the foundation's] aim is to advance educational opportunity and social well-

being across the United Kingdom. We do this by funding research, development and analysis in education, welfare and justice, and by equipping young people with skills and confidence in quantitative and scientific methods through our student programmes.

In June 2017, the Foundation published a five-year strategy setting out its funding priorities, and we have updated our Guide for applicants to reflect these priorities. Our primary objective is to improve people's lives through better understanding of the issues affecting their life chances. We are also keen to engage with, and to understand the significance of, new and emerging trends and disruptive forces – social, demographic, technological and economic – that are changing the structures and context of people's lives. Our work is also concerned with securing social inclusion in an increasingly diverse and fragmented society; with the implications of a data-enabled digital culture (for example, for trust, evidence and authority); and with safeguarding, through the justice system, the rights of the individual in relation to the State.

The Foundation seeks to be an open, collaborative and engaged funder that offers more than money. We are not simply an academic funding body, though the research we fund must stand up to rigorous academic scrutiny. We want the policies and institutions that affect people's well-being to be influenced by robust evidence. We will work with the research, policy and practice communities to foster an environment where that is possible.

This guide is for those who are considering applying for funding from the Foundation for research, development and analysis projects through our responsive application rounds, of which there are two a year. It describes our funding priorities, which have been updated in light of the new strategy, explains our application process, and sets out our expectations for successful proposals.

Financial information

In 2016 the foundation had assets of £369 million and an income of £7.3 million. A total of £4.7 million was awarded in grants, broken down as follows:

Open Door	£4 million
Early years education and childcare	£1.2 million
Law in society	£897,000
Nuffield Research Placements	£738,000
Economic Advantage and Disadvantage	£591,000
Education grants	£376,000
Q-Step	£305,000
Children and families	£304,000

Beneficiaries included: All Souls College University of Oxford (£500,000); School of Psychology and Clinical Language Sciences University of Reading (£333,000); Solent NHS Trust (£315,000); Institutional Research

Information Service (£247,000); Department of Psychology University of Sheffield (£179,000); Department of Education University of Oxford (£171,500); Centre for Justice Innovation (£155,500); Social and Economic Research University of Essex (£72,000); Royal College of Physicians (£30,000); The Association of Lawyers for Children (£17,000).

Exclusions

The website lists the following areas which are not funded:

- Individuals without a formal employment or other relationship with the institution hosting the grant
- Projects led by individuals unaffiliated to any particular organisation
- Projects led by schools or further education colleges
- Projects led by undergraduates or master's students
- PhD fees or projects where the main purpose is to support a PhD
- The establishment of academic posts
- Ongoing costs or the costs of rolling out existing work or services
- Dissemination-only projects, including campaigning work, which are not connected to the foundation's funded work
- Local charities, replacement of statutory funding, or local social services or social welfare provision
- Requests for financial help or educational fees from or on behalf of individuals
- Projects from individuals and institutions outside the UK, unless they are collaborative projects with a UK institution

Note: The above is general guidance and different programmes may have specific exclusions.

Applications

Refer to the detailed 'Guidance for Applicants' document before making an application.

Sources of information

Accounts; annual report; Charity Commission record; guidelines for applicants; funder's website.

The Sir Peter O'Sullevan Charitable Trust

🔍 Animal welfare, especially horses

📍 Worldwide

💷 £1.6 million (2016/17)

CC number: 1078889

Trustees: Nigel Payne; Geoffrey Hughes; Michael Dillon; John McManus; Michael Kerr-Dineen; Anthony McCoy; Dierdre Flood.

Correspondent: Nigel Payne, Trustee, The Old School, Bolventor, Launceston, Cornwall PL15 7TS (tel: 01566 880292; email: nigel@earthsummit.demon.co.uk)

 www.thevoiceofracing.com

This trust was established in 2000 by horse racing commentator Peter O'Sullevan, in order to improve the welfare of retired, injured or ill-treated animals. The trust regularly supports six horse and animal welfare charities: Blue Cross, Brooke Hospital for Animals, Compassion in World Farming, World Horse Welfare, the Racing Welfare Charities and the Thoroughbred Rehabilitation Centre. The trust occasionally supports other specific projects and causes, mainly (but not exclusively) related to horses or the racing industry.

Financial information

In 2016/17 the trust had assets of £7.2 million and an income of £611,000. In total, the trust awarded grants worth £1.6 million. This total included £240,000 distributed equally between the six animal welfare charities named above as well as £1.35 million to other specific projects and good causes.

Beneficiaries included: Home of Horseracing Trust – Palace House Project (£350,000); Blue Cross, Brooke Hospital for Animals, Compassion in World Farming, the Racing Welfare Charities, the Thoroughbred Rehabilitation Centre and World Horse Welfare (£40,000 each); Jockey Club Racecourses – Aintree Community programme (£30,000); World Veterinary Service (£8,000).

Applications

Apply in writing to the correspondent.

Sources of information

Accounts; annual report; Charity Commission record; funder's website.

The Oakdale Trust

🔍 Community and social welfare, medical support and research, environmental conservation, the arts, overseas aid, penal reform

📍 UK, mainly Wales, and overseas

💷 £228,000 (2016/17)

CC number: 218827

Trustees: Rupert Cadbury; Bruce Cadbury; Olivia Tatton-Brown; Dr Rebecca Cadbury.

Correspondent: Rupert Cadbury, Trustee, Tansor House, Main Street, Tansor, Peterborough PE8 5HS (tel: 01832 226386; email: oakdale@tanh.co.uk)

www.oakdaletrust.org.uk

This trust was founded in 1946 by Brandon Cadbury, who initially administered it alongside his wife, Flavia. Originally, the trust supported small charities in the West Midlands but following their relocation to mid-Wales in 1990, the couple found the Welsh voluntary sector to be poorly served by grant-makers and shifted the emphasis of the trust's funding to support charities throughout Wales. The trust is now administered by members of Brandon and Flavia's family.

Grant-making information

The trust distributes grants, ranging from £250 to £2,000 (with the average grant being about £1,000), to charities and community organisations in Wales. Funding can be given for both project and core costs.

According to its website, the trust's main areas of interest for its grant-making include:

- Wales-based social and community projects
- Medical support groups operating in Wales and UK-based medical research projects
- Environmental conservation projects in Wales
- Some support, where there is a Welsh connection, is given to the arts
- UK-based and registered charities working in the developing world
- Penal reform

Applications are accepted from registered and exempt charities, community interest companies and community groups (with a constitution, an elected committee and bank account controlled by two or more committee members).

Financial information

In 2016/17 the trust had assets of £14.6 million and an income of £353,500. Grants to 219 organisations totalled £228,000.

Beneficiaries included: Community Arts Rhayader and District – CARAD (£15,000); Money for Madagascar (£8,000); Diabetes UK and The Organic Research Centre (£1,000 each); Global Justice Now and Glyndwr Women's Aid (£750 each); Global Greengrants Fund UK (£500); The Fishermen's Mission (£250).

Exclusions

Grants are not awarded to/for: individuals; holiday schemes; sports; or expeditions. Repeat applications are not normally accepted within a two-year period.

Applications

Applications can be made using the online form on the website (this the trustees' preferred format) or by post. Applications are no longer accepted by email. An official application form is available to download from the website, although applicants can submit applications in any format as long as they are 'clear and concise, covering – aims and achievements, plans and needs supported by a budget for the project in question'. Applicants applying for grants of more than £1,500 should include a recent set of audited accounts, but only if these are not available to view on the Charity Commission's website. Where supporting information is available online, applicants should include a web address.

The trustees meet twice a year to consider applications, in April and October. The application deadline for the April meeting is usually the first week in March, and for the October meeting, it is usually the first week in September. Full guidelines are published on the website.

Note: The trust's website states that telephone calls are accepted; however, messages should not be left on the answerphone as this is for private use only.

Sources of information

Accounts; annual report; Charity Commission record; funder's website.

Odin Charitable Trust

 General charitable purposes

 UK

£ £219,000 (2016/17)

CC number: 1027521

Trustees: Susan Scotford; A. H. Palmer; Donna Kelly; Pia Cherry.

Correspondent: Susan Scotford, Trustee, PO Box 1898, Bradford-on-Avon, Wiltshire BA15 1YS (tel: 020 7465 4300)

The Odin Charitable Trust was established in 1993 for general charitable purposes. Although the objects of the charity are wide, the trust has a preference for: the arts; care for people who have disabilities or are disadvantaged people; hospices; homeless people; prisoners' families; refugees; gypsies and 'tribal groups'; and research into false memories and dyslexia.

Our research indicates that the trustees are more likely to support small organisations and those who, by the nature of their work, find it difficult to attract funding. Grants range from one-off donations to three-year awards.

Grants usually range from £1,000 to £5,000.

Financial information

In 2016/17 the trust had assets of £8.2 million and an income of £466,500. During the year, the charity awarded around £219,000 in grants to organisations.

Beneficiaries included: Bath Recital Artists Trust (£3,500); Bag Books, Hearts and Minds, St Peter's Hospice and Wiltshire Music Centre (£3,000 each); Anjali Dance Company Ltd, Asylum Welcome and Firebird Theatre (£2,000 each).

Exclusions

Applications from individuals are not considered.

Applications

Applications should be submitted in the form of a letter or email and contain the following information:

- Aims and objectives of the charity
- Nature of the appeal
- Total target, if for a specific project
- Registered charity number
- Any other relevant factors

Letters should be accompanied by a set of the charitable organisation's latest report and full accounts and should be addressed to the correspondent.

Sources of information

Accounts; annual report; Charity Commission record.

The Ofenheim Charitable Trust

 General charitable purposes, health, social welfare, the arts, animals and the environment

 Worldwide but in practice UK with some preference for East Sussex

£ £437,500 (2016/17)

CC number: 286525

Trustees: Roger Clark; Rory McLeod; Alexander Clark; Fiona Byrd.

Correspondent: The Trustees, c/o RSM UK Tax and Accounting Ltd, The Pinnacle, 170 Midsummer Boulevard, Milton Keynes MK9 1BP (tel: 01908 687800)

Established in 1983 by Dr Angela Ofenheim, the trust provides regular support for a number of charities in East Sussex because of the founder's association with that area. Support is given for health, welfare, arts, animals and the environment, with many of the same large national organisations benefitting each year. One-off appeals may be considered if the trustees have some prior knowledge of the charity's work.

Financial information

In 2016/17 the trust held assets of £16.1 million and had an income of £485,000. There were 73 grants made to organisations totalling £437,500.

Previous beneficiaries have included: Trinity-Laban Conservatoire of Music and Dance (£28,000); Royal Trinity Hospice (£13,000); Friends of the Elderly, Help Musicians UK and St Mungo's (£11,000 each); Glyndebourne Arts Trust, Motor Neurone Disease Association, National Trust and The Hepworth Wakefield (£6,000 each); Game and Wildlife Conservation Trust (£4,000); British Wheelchair Sports Foundation (£3,000); Red Squirrel Survival Trust (£2,500).

Exclusions

No grants are given to individuals.

Applications

Apply in writing to the correspondent.

Note: The trust tends to support the same organisations each year and prefers to support organisations that the trustees have prior knowledge of.

Sources of information

Accounts; annual report; Charity Commission record.

The Ogle Christian Trust

 Evangelical Christianity, the relief of poverty, famine relief

 Worldwide

£ £241,500 to organisations (2016)

CC number: 1061458

Trustees: Ronald Goodenough; Stephen Procter; Fiona Putley; Lynne Quanrud; Dr David Harley; Dr Carol Walker.

Correspondent: Fiona Putley, Secretary, 43 Woolstone Road, London SE23 2TR

The trust was established in 1996 and supports the promotion of evangelical Christianity throughout the world, including missionary enterprises, Bible training and assistance for retired missionary workers. The trust also supports charities and organisations working towards the relief of poverty and distress, including famine relief.

Financial information

At the time of writing (June 2018) the trust's 2016 annual report and accounts were the latest available to view at the Charity Commission.

In 2016 the trust had assets of £2.3 million and an income of £109,500. Grants to 61 organisations and

individuals totalled £244,000, of which £241,500 was given to organisations.

Beneficiaries included: Operation Mobilisation (£101,000); iNet Trust (£10,500); Global Care and Redcliffe College (£4,000 each); France Mission Trust and Make Jesus Known (£2,000 each).

Exclusions

Previous research indicates that applications from individuals are discouraged and those granted require accreditation by a sponsoring organisation. Grants are rarely made for building projects. Funding will not be offered in response to general appeals from large national organisations.

Applications

Applications can be made in writing to the correspondent, and should be accompanied by documentary support and an sae. Our research suggests that the trustees usually meet in May and November, but applications can be made at any time.

Sources of information

Accounts; annual report; Charity Commission record.

Oglesby Charitable Trust

 General charitable purposes, particularly: arts, education, environment, social welfare, and medical aid and research

 North west of England

£ £2.6 million (2015/16)

CC number: 1026669

Trustees: Jean Oglesby; Michael Oglesby; Bob Kitson; Katharine Vokes; Jane Oglesby; Chris Oglesby; Peter Renshaw.

Correspondent: Louise Magill, Lowry House, 17 Marble Street, Manchester M2 3AW (email: welcome@ oglesbycharitabletrust.org.uk)

🌍 www.oglesbycharitabletrust.co.uk

The Oglesby Charitable Trust was established in 1992 and has been active since the early 2000s. The funding of the trust comes from annual contributions from Bruntwood Ltd, part of a group of North West-based property investment companies owned by the founding trustees.

The following information is taken from the trust's website:

> The Trust was set up to support activities in the North West of England to further the well-being of the Region and its people through a very wide range of activities which include the Arts, Education, Environment, Medical Research and tackling Social Inequality. Since its

inception the principal activities of the OCT have remained focused in the North of England, although the Trustees have supported a limited number of projects outside both the North West and the UK.

The Trustees take both a grassroots and a strategic approach to their giving, understanding that local approaches tend to reach those most in need, whilst broader initiatives and collaborations are sometimes necessary to drive meaningful change. The Trustees have therefore taken the decision to become focused on root causes, rather than consequences.

Eligibility

Who we help

According to the website, the trust primarily supports the following

- ▶ Registered charities whose activities are based in the north west of England
- ▶ Organisations who can demonstrate that the funds are making a real difference, rather than being absorbed into a large anonymous pool, no matter how significant the end result may be
- ▶ Organisations that demonstrate both the highest standards of propriety and sound business sense in their activities. This does not mean high overheads but it does mean focused use of funds, directly to where they are needed
- ▶ Projects that can be ring-fenced

Types of activity

The trust supports the following:

- ▶ Artistic development, both on an individual and group level
- ▶ Educational – revenue grants, bursaries and building projects
- ▶ Environmental projects
- ▶ Tackling social inequality, especially projects in which individuals and communities can be enabled to become self-supporting
- ▶ Medical aid and research

Financial information

At the time of writing (June 2018) the most recent accounts available were from 2015/16. In that year, the trust had assets of £9 million and an income of £1.05 million. Grants were awarded totalling £2.6 million and were distributed as follows:

Social welfare	29%	£774,000
Artistic development	24%	£613,000
Education	23%	£595,000
Medical aid and research	15%	£383,000
Environmental improvement	9%	£231,000

Beneficiaries included: Bloodwise (£100,000); Manchester Cathedral (£34,000); Mango Tree (£30,000); Salford Heart Care (£26,000) Charles Halle Foundation and Mustard Tree (£25,000 each); Royal Exchange Theatre (£18,400); Outward Bound Trust/Factory Youth (£6,500).

Exclusions

The trust does not support:

- Non-registered charities
- Activities which are for the purpose of collecting funds for redistribution to other charities
- Animal charities
- Charities mainly operating outside the UK
- Church and all building fabric materials
- Conferences
- Continuing running costs of an organisation
- Costs of employing fundraisers
- Expeditions
- General sports, unless there is a strong association with a disadvantaged group
- Holidays
- Individuals
- Loans or business finance
- Charities promoting religion
- Routine staff training
- Sponsorship and marketing appeals

Applications

Unsolicited applications are not acknowledged. The trust's website states the following:

> The Trustees are generating, through existing and new relationships, a level of giving that more than matches the Trust's income. This is despite planned growth in the future income over the next few years. The Trustees have taken the decision to develop further this proactive stance to their giving, and only give to charities that they themselves select.
>
> Please do not, therefore, make unsolicited approaches, either by email, letter or in any other form, as they will not be considered or acknowledged.

Sources of information

Accounts; annual report; Charity Commission record; funder's website.

Oizer Charitable Trust

 Jewish causes

 UK, with a preference for Greater Manchester

£ £698,000 (2016/17)

CC number: 1014399

Trustees: Joshua Halpern; Cindy Halpern.

Correspondent: Joshua Halpern, Trustee, c/o Lopian Gross Barnett & Co., 6th Floor, Cardinal House, 20 St Mary's Parsonage, Manchester M3 2LG (tel: 0161 832 8721)

According to the 2016/17 annual report, the trust awards donations 'to a wide variety of charities within the Jewish community'.

Financial information

In 2016/17 the trust had assets of almost £3.8 million and an income of £1.2 million. During the year, the trust awarded almost £698,000 in grants to organisations.

Beneficiaries included: Yesemach Levav Trust (£90,000); Friend of Boyan Trust (£76,000); Chaim Charitable Trust (£62,500).

Applications

Apply in writing to the correspondent. According to the 2016/17 annual report:

> The trustees have identified a number of Orthodox Jewish charities which profess and teach the principles of traditional Judaism or which carry out activities which advance religion in accordance with the Orthodox Jewish faith. Grants are given on application to the trustees by these or similar charities.

Sources of information

Accounts; annual report; Charity Commission record.

Old Possum's Practical Trust

 Literary, artistic, musical and theatrical projects; historical conservation

 UK

£ £1.15 million (2016/17)

CC number: 328558

Trustees: Judith Hooper; Deidre Simpson; Clare Reihill.

Correspondent: The Trustees, c/o RSM, The Pinnacle, 170 Midsummer Boulevard, Milton Keynes MK9 1BP (tel: 01908 687800; email: generalenquiry@ old-possums-practical-trust.org.uk)

 www.old-possums-practical-trust. org.uk

The trust's website states that it supports literary, artistic, musical and theatrical projects, with priority given to those which will have an impact on future literary work and that 'display enterprise in their artistic endeavour'. It was established in 1990 by Valerie Eliot, the widow of T S Eliot, from funds derived from the success of the musical Cats.

The trust's website states:

> Grants are more likely to be given for projects which fall within artistic, aesthetic, literary, musical and theatrical criteria. All applications must demonstrate a high level of sustainability and contextual impact. Priority will be given to those which have an impact on future literary work and display enterprise in their artistic endeavour.

Grants typically fall within the range of £500 to £5,000.

Financial information

In 2016/17 the trust had assets of £9.9 million and an income of £175,000. Grants were made totalling £1.15 million and were distributed to 22 organisations for the following purposes:

The arts and historical conservation	16	£1.07 million
Educational support	4	£62,000
Support for people affected by disability or disadvantage	2	£20,000

Beneficiaries included: The TS Elliot Foundation (£900,500); Shoreditch Town Hall (£50,000); Friends of the National Libraries (£30,000); Edlumino Educational Aid and First Story (£25,000); The National Theatre (£20,000); Fitzwilliam Museum (£5,000); The Little Angel Theatre (£1,500).

Exclusions

The trust does not support the following:

- Activities or projects already completed
- Capital building projects
- Personal training and education, e.g. tuition or living costs for college or university
- Projects outside the UK
- Medical care or resources
- Feasibility studies
- National charities having substantial amounts of potential funding likely from other sources

Applications

Applications can only be made online through the trust's website. The trustees meet regularly to consider applications but state in the latest accounts that:

> The emphasis will be on continued support of those institutions and individuals who have received support in the past. Unfortunately, we have to disappoint the great majority of applicants who nevertheless continue to send appeal letters. The Trustees do not welcome telephone calls or emails from applicants soliciting funds.

To keep administration costs to a minimum the trust does not give reasons for unsuccessful applications or allow applicants to appeal a decision.

Sources of information

Accounts; annual report; Charity Commission record; funder's website.

The John Oldacre Foundation

Research and education in agricultural sciences

UK

£202,000 (2015/16)

CC number: 284960

Trustees: Henry Bonner Shouler; Harvey Grove; Jill Sinnott.

Correspondent: Henry Bonner Shouler, Trustee, Hazleton House, Hazleton, Cheltenham, Gloucestershire GL54 4EB (tel: 01451 860752; email: h.shouler@ btinternet.com)

Grants are made to universities and agricultural colleges towards the advancement and promotion of research and education in agricultural sciences for the public benefit. The majority of grants are made to undergraduate and postgraduate students, and research must be published.

Financial information
In 2015/16 the trust had assets of £10 million and an income of £157,500. Grants totalling £202,000 were made to seven organisations.

Beneficiaries included: Harper Adams (£55,000); University of Bristol (£52,000); Royal Agricultural College (£40,000); Oxford University (£25,000); Nuffield Farming Trust (£22,000); University of Exeter (£21,500); National Institute of Agricultural Botany (£15,000).

Exclusions
Grants are not made towards tuition fees, general maintenance allowances, or living expenses.

Applications
Organisations, or individuals on behalf of an organisation, can apply by writing to the trust, stating how the funds would be used and what would be achieved.

Sources of information
Accounts; annual report; Charity Commission record.

The Oldfield Charitable Trust

Promotion of entrepreneurship, homelessness and addiction, programmes which reduce offending and reoffending

Kent

£1.3 million (2016/17)

CC number: 1156496

Trustees: Richard Oldfield; Leonara Philipps; Amicia Oldfield; Christopher Oldfield; Edward Oldfield.

Correspondent: Richard Oldfield, Trustee, Dodington Place, Church Lane, Doddington, Sittingbourne ME0 0BB (tel: 01795 886385)

The trust was established in 2014 and according to its Charity Commission record aims to support: 'programmes which reduce offending and reoffending, promote entrepreneurship amongst the young and disadvantaged, and tackle other challenges such as homelessness and addiction'.

Financial information
In 2016/17 the trust held assets of £8.9 million and had an income of £2.9 million. Grants to 29 organisations totalled £1.3 million.

Beneficiaries included: Royal Marsden Cancer Charity (£500,000); The Prince's Trust (£439,000); Ark Schools (£83,500); Demelza (£5,000); Mike Campbell Foundation (£2,900); Beanstalk (£1,000); Ashaka UK (£350).

Applications
Apply in writing to the correspondent.

Sources of information
Accounts; annual report; Charity Commission record.

OneFamily Foundation

General charitable purposes

UK

£300,000 (2017)

Correspondent: Foundation Team, 16–17 West Street, Brighton BN1 2RL (tel: 0800 373010; email: foundation@ onefamily.com)

 www.onefamily.com/your-foundation

 facebook.com/OneFamilyMutual

 @OneFamilySocial

Formally known as the Engage Foundation, the OneFamily Foundation was launched in January 2014 with the aim of helping communities and families in the areas where OneFamily (previously known as Engage Mutual Assurance) – a UK-based provider of financial products including life insurance, savings and health cash plans – operates. The foundation awards grants to charitable projects through its community awards scheme as well as personal grants of up to £1,000 to help customers in need.

Community grants
The foundation offers community awards of £5,000, £10,000 and £25,000 for community projects nominated by customers. Customers must nominate local projects and improvements which they would like to be funded. Community projects will be voted for by members of the public. The projects with the most votes will be awarded the funding.

Community Awards are made to projects in the following categories:

- Active living
- Community groups
- Health, disability and social care
- Lifelong learning

Grants are awarded to not-for-profit organisations and community groups that have been in existence for at least six months to run a discrete project that will benefit the community and will be wholly funded by the foundation.

Further detailed guidance is given on the foundation's website.

Financial information
The foundation is not a registered charity and so there were no accounts or annual report to view.

During the year, community awards were granted to 32 organisations totalling £300,000.

Beneficiaries included: Hove Park School Outdoor Gym, Red Admiral (£25,000 each); Growing Together, Surbiton Royal British Legion Youth Marching Band and Wansbeck Gymnastics and Trampolining Club (£10,000 each); Athena Sports Academy, Holistic Cancer Support (£5,000).

Exclusions
The website states the following about what will not be considered:

- Support for commercial or profit-making ventures
- Funding toward property bills (rent/mortgage payments, utility bills, maintenance costs, etc.) although projects which require funding toward room/facility hire may be considered
- Financial contribution directly towards salaries (we may consider staffing costs on an hourly basis, but only if this is necessary to achieve the project objectives e.g. a music teacher to lead a music therapy group, or a builder to construct a sensory room)
- Funding for 'paid for advertising
- General contributions towards large appeals or fundraising (we may consider funding of standalone items, providing the use of these is not reliant on additional funds being raised e.g. replacing a kitchen as part of a hospice renovation project)
- The promotion of political parties/groups/factions
- The advancement of religion/faith, including projects that promote religious advocacy, attempt to convert people to another religion, or attempt to expand membership
- Projects that involve any form of mandatory religious study or discriminate against any faith or group (although groups may be eligible for secular and inclusive community-based

activities e.g. a food bank run by a local church)

▶ Refreshments for attendees of a project

▶ Groups where membership or other participation costs are considered by The Foundation to be prohibitive (e.g. a golf club with high membership costs that would prohibit certain members of the community from joining)

▶ Overseas travel or activities outside the UK

▶ Transport or entry fees for sites or attractions

▶ Regional or local offices of a national organisation (we will only support local community groups that are affiliated to a national organisation if they are not eligible for, or receiving, funding for the project from the parent organisation)

▶ Improvements to land or buildings that are generally not open or accessible for use by members of the community

▶ Contingency amounts provided for in any project budget

▶ Deficit or retrospective funding (e.g. grants for activities or purchases that have already taken place)

▶ Organisations that are for the sole relief or benefit of animals and plants

▶ Projects that have received substantial funding from another grant provider within 12 months prior to the date of the nomination

▶ Projects that are connected to for-profit business ventures or that financially compensate an idea creator beyond fair wage

▶ Use of the award amount as or part of a raffle, chance or lottery prize

Applications

Nominations for a project to support can be made by OneFamily customers on the foundation's website. Once your project suggestion has been accepted, you will receive a confirmation. There is at least one round of awards during the year – check the website for upcoming deadlines. Community projects are voted for by members of the public and those with the most votes are awarded grants.

Sources of information

Funder's website.

Open Gate

 Grassroots environmental, technological and educational projects to benefit small communities; social equality; disadvantage; disability

UK and overseas. In the UK, support is concentrated on the North Midlands area

£221,500 (2016/17)

CC number: 1081701

Trustees: Mary Wiltshire; Ned Wiltshire; John Wiltshire; Jane Methuen; Tom Wiltshire; Alice Taylor; Lesley Williamson.

Correspondent: Mary Wiltshire, Trustee, Brown House Cottage, Ashleyhay,

Matlock, Derbyshire DE4 4AH (tel: 01629 822018; email: opengate@w3z.co.uk)

 www.opengatetrust.org.uk

Established in 2000, the charity has stated on its website that its objectives are 'to support grassroots environmental, technological and educational projects to benefit small communities, both in the UK and abroad'. Schemes that look to advance social equality and become self-sufficient are viewed favourably.

The charity's website states that its work in the UK 'is concentrated around the North Midlands area where the charity is based, although the trustees may consider requests from suitable projects outside this area'. The trust has a focus on supporting people who are disadvantaged or who have a disability and draws on the experience of trustees in these fields.

Open Gate's overseas work is not confined to a particular area and it has supported projects in Asia, Africa and South and Central America. Applications must come from charities registered in the UK.

Grants from the trust are usually in the range of £500 to £2,500.

Financial information

In 2016/17 the charity had assets of more than £1 million and an income of £54,000. Grants totalled £221,500.

Previous beneficiaries have included: WaterAid (£5,000); Children of the Andes and Traidcraft (£3,000 each); Clean Rivers Trust, Plant Aid UK and Tools For Self Reliance (£2,500 each); Fish Aid, Wells for India and Youth Hostel Association (£2,000 each); Seeds for Africa (£1,800); Clifton Scout Group (£1,400); Derbyshire Association of the Blind (£1,300); Caring for Life (£500).

Exclusions

No grants are given to individuals or overseas-based charities. According to the website, the trustees 'have not supported purely medical charities'.

Applications

The charity's website notes that 'Applications should be submitted by **both** post and email'. The trustees meet to consider requests quarterly, usually in January, April, July and October. Applications need to be received six weeks in advance to be considered at a particular meeting.

Sources of information

Accounts; annual report; Charity Commission record; funder's website.

Orthopaedic Research UK

Medical research

UK

£496,500 (2016/17)

CC number: 1111657

Trustees: David Martin; Robert Vallings; Patrick Latham; John Edge; Dr Kate Allen.

Correspondent: Dr Arash Angadji, Furlong House, 10A Chandos Street, London W1G 9DQ (tel: 020 7637 5789; email: info@oruk.org)

www.oruk.org

Orthopaedic Research UK (formerly known as the Furlong Research Charitable Foundation) was established in 1989 by the orthopaedic surgeon Mr Ronald Furlong FRCS. The charity is dedicated to advancing orthopaedic knowledge by funding and publicising research and also by organising training and events which promote collaboration between orthopaedic surgeons, scientists and engineers. Today the charity is one of the most significant funders of orthopaedic research in the UK, working alongside many of the UK's leading academic institutions.

The scope of the research funded by the charity is broad, some projects aim to widen general scientific knowledge while others target specific disorders. Where appropriate, the charity also supports work into controversial areas of research.

Since 2004, the charity has supported 130 research project with grants totalling more than £9 million. Grants vary in size and duration, dependent upon the nature of the research and the stream involved.

Financial information

In 2016/17 the charity had assets of £21.5 million and an income of £723,500. During the year, the charity awarded seven grants totalling £496,500.

Beneficiaries included: University College London (£225,000 in three grants); University of East Anglia, University of Edinburgh and University of Liverpool (£75,000 each); Northumbria NHS Foundation Trust (£48,000).

Exclusions

The charity does not accept applications not submitted by a UK research institution.

Applications

Applications can be submitted through the charity's online portal. There is a four-stage process which requires applicants to submit a succession of forms electronically. See the charity's website for full details. Applications are considered by trustees as well as the charity's scientific advisory committee and an independent review panel, both of which are comprised of eminent figures in their respective fields of expertise. Applicants are invited to contact the charity by phone or email to discuss their proposal prior to submission.

Sources of information
Accounts; annual report; Charity commission record; funder's website.

Oxfam (GB)

Humanitarian work, development, tackling inequality

Africa, Asia, the Caribbean, Central America, Eastern Europe, countries of the former Soviet Union, Great Britain, the Middle East and South America

£63.1 million (2016/17)

CC number: 202918

Trustees: Caroline Thomson; Katy Steward; Gavin MacNeill Stewart; Stephen Walton; Kul Gautam; Mohammed Khan; Lois Jacobs; Lydinyda Nacpil; Kenneth Mathieson Caldwell; Angela Cluff; Babatunde Olanrewaju; Nicholas Cheeseman.

Correspondent: Joss Saunders, General Counsel and Company Secretary, 2700 John Smith Drive, Oxford Business Park South, Oxford OX4 2JY (tel: 0870 333 2444; email: enquiries@oxfam.org.uk)

www.oxfam.org.uk

Oxfam (GB)'s work supports people of all ages who are disadvantaged by poverty or disability or are victims of famine, disasters or war. Its website states:

> Whether we are running life-saving emergency responses, life-changing development projects or campaigning at the grassroots to tackle poverty, Oxfam's work is always rooted in a vision of a world where women and men are valued and treated equally, able to influence the decisions that affect their lives and meet their responsibilities as full citizens.

The charity works with partner organisations across the world to help achieve shared goals of combating poverty and injustice, focusing on six goals:

- Active citizens
- Advancing gender justice
- Saving lives, now and in the future
- Sustainable food
- Fair sharing of natural resources
- Financing for development and universal essential services

Grant-making policy
In the 2016/17 annual report, Oxfam states the following about its grant-making policy:

> Oxfam works with and through others to take action to achieve common goals for overcoming poverty and injustice based on complementarity and respect for the contribution that each party brings. Oxfam's partner relations are informed by, and managed to, a set of clear principles. These five principles underpin our programme and partnership decisions in development, humanitarian and campaigns work at every level of activity. We hold ourselves accountable to these principles and seek to be held accountable by partners, communities and other stakeholders with whom we and our partners work. The five principles are:
> - Complementary purpose and added value
> - Mutual respect for values and beliefs
> - Clarity on roles, responsibilities and decision-making
> - Transparency and accountability
> - Commitment and flexibility
>
> Before making a grant, Oxfam completes appraisals of the project and the proposed partner organisation. These ensure that there is a good strategic fit between Oxfam and the partner organisation, and that the project objectives are consistent with the principles listed above and reflect a coherent and well-designed project that will be a cost-effective way of bringing about the intended impact.
>
> Grants are managed through specific agreements with partners, which set out the conditions of the grant, including reporting requirements, and when and how disbursement will happen. The agreement also outlines Oxfam's responsibilities in the partnership to ensure that it can be held to account by partners and other stakeholders. Grants are usually disbursed in instalments to ensure that agreed timings and results are being met and managed.

Note: Oxfam GB has been permanently banned from operating in Haiti after failing to inform the authorities about sexual misconduct allegations made against some employees. In a statement shared with Civil Society News, Oxfam GB apologised again to the Haitian people and their government. It also confirmed that the charity remained committed to its statement to 'strengthen our safeguarding globally' following the sexual misconduct allegations in February.

Financial information
In 2016/17 Oxfam (GB) had assets of £76.6 million and an income of £408.6 million. During the year, Oxfam awarded a total of £63.1 million in grants to international, national and local partner organisations. A total of 965 grants were made to 589 organisations. The average grant per

project was £65,000 and per partner was £107,000.

The grants were broken down as follows:

Development	£38 million
Humanitarian	£22.9 million
Campaigning and advocacy	£2.2 million

Major beneficiaries included: Kachin Baptist Convention (£952,000); Concern Worldwide UK (£901,000); Tearfund (£574,000); Save the Children UK (£500,000); Caritas, Germany (£536,000); Unification Nepal (£352,000); Lumanti Support Group for Shelter (£305,000); Utopia (£257,000); International Rescue Committee (£232,000).

Exclusions
Oxfam will not consider:

- Partnership for work that falls outside Oxfam's charitable or geographical remit
- Partnership through governments or government agencies
- Projects that include the teaching of religion in their proposal
- Individuals
- Requests submitted by a second party on behalf of another
- Requests from UK-based organisations for projects overseas

Applications
A brief project proposal should be sent to the Oxfam team in the appropriate country, the details of which are given on the website which states: 'Oxfam receives many requests for partnership and unfortunately we are unable to support or reply to every request. If you don't hear from us within three months, please assume that we are unable to offer support.'

Sources of information
Accounts; annual report; Charity Commission record; funder's website.

P F Charitable Trust

General charitable purposes

UK, with local interests in Oxfordshire and Scotland

£2.69 million (2016/17)

CC number: 220124

Trustees: Robert Fleming; Philip Fleming; Rory Fleming; Matthew Fleming.

Correspondent: The Secretary, P F Charitable Trust, c/o RF Trustee Co. Ltd, 15 Suffolk Street, London SW1Y 4HG (tel: 020 3696 6721; email: charities@rftrustee.com)

The trust was established in 1951 to assist religious and educational charities and for general charitable purposes. The trust makes grants to a wide range of causes and states that its policy is to continue to make a substantial number of small grants to charitable organisations, both on a one-off and recurring basis.

Financial information

In 2016/17 the trust had assets of almost £124.3 million and an income of £3.28 million. During the year, grants were made to organisations totalling £2.69 million.

Beneficiaries included: Great Ormond Street Children Hospital Charity Scar Free Foundation (£100,000 each); Alzheimer's Research UK (£75,000); Helen and Douglas House, Oxfordshire Community Foundation, Prior's Court Foundation and Tudor Hall (£50,000 each).

Other donations equal to or individually less than £50,000 totalled £2.2 million.

Exclusions

No grants are made to individuals or non-registered charities.

Applications

Apply in writing to the correspondent. The trustees usually meet monthly to consider applications and approve grants.

Scottish organisations working in the areas of disability, health, youth work, older people, children, families and homelessness may also apply through Foundation Scotland's 'Express Grants' programme. More information is available from the website: www. foundationscotland.org.uk/programmes/ pf-charitable-trust.

Sources of information

Accounts; annual report; Charity Commission record.

The Doris Pacey Charitable Foundation

 Jewish causes, education, medical, social welfare and the arts

Worldwide

£ £655,500 (2016/2017)

CC number: 1101724

Trustees: Ray Locke; Leslie Powell; Linda Courtney.

Correspondent: Michael Theodorou, c/o Charities Aid Foundation, 25 Kings Hill Avenue, Kings Hill, West Mailing, Kent ME19 4TA (tel: 0300 012 3187; email: paceyandbrynbergfoundations@ cafonline.org)

The Doris Pacey Charitable Foundation was established in 2003 to make grants to organisations worldwide. The foundation has a preference for working with Jewish organisations and 'major

charitable institutions', particularly those focused on alleviating poverty, ill health and educational disadvantage among children and young people. The foundation also supports the arts.

Financial information

In 2016/17 the foundation had assets of £5 million and an income of £109,000. During the year, the foundation awarded grants to 11 organisations totalling £696,000.

Beneficiaries included: World Jewish Relief (£250,000); Magen David Adom (£90,000); ORT (£48,500); Jewish Child's Day (£35,000); Jewish Care Scotland (£31,000); Carers Trust (£30,000); Clapton Common Boys Club (£17,500); The London Library (£4,000).

Applications

Apply in writing to the correspondent.

Sources of information

Accounts; annual report; Charity Commission record.

The Panacea Charitable Trust

 Christian religion, social welfare

UK, with a strong preference for Bedford and its immediate region

£ £371,000 (2016)

CC number: 227530

Trustees: Prof. Christopher Rowland; Charles Monsell; Dr Justin Meggitt; Dr Naomi Hilton; Evan Jones.

Correspondent: David McLynn, Executive Officer, 14 Albany Road, Bedford MK40 3PH (tel: 01234 359737; email: admin@panaceatrust.org)

 panaceatrust.org

The Panacea Charitable Trust is a UK-registered charity, first registered with the Charity Commission in 1926. The trust provides grants to the local community, supports academic research, seminars, conferences and activities and operates The Panacea Museum while maintaining the trust's archive of books, manuscripts and papers.

Up to 2012 the charity was known as The Panacea Society, at which point it changed its name to The Panacea Charitable Trust to mark the end of the Panacea Society as a religious community.

Objectives

The trust's website states it has the following two objectives:

> Educating and disseminating information to the public about the Christian religion particularly the history, beliefs and practices of the Panacea Society its

antecedents and similar Christian religious groups which is achieved by:

1   funding, supporting and co-ordinating academic research, seminars and conferences and their outputs
2   operating a museum on the site of the former community and maintaining in perpetuity the collection displayed in the museum
3   maintaining and making available the Charity's archive of books, manuscripts and papers
4   supporting any other activities which the Trustees consider will help the Charity to achieve this objective

Furtherance of Christian principles making grants for the relief of poverty and sickness and to advance education generally, primarily in Bedford and the surrounding area.

Grant-making information

Education grants

The trust seeks to provide education and information to the public about the Christian religion, particularly the history, beliefs and practices of the Panacea Society. This is achieved by:

▶ Funding, supporting, and co-ordinating academic research, seminars and conferences

▶ Operating a museum on the site of the former community, and maintaining the collection in the museum

▶ Maintaining and making available the charity's archive of books, manuscripts and papers

Grants in this area are mainly for the field of historical theology, in particular: Prophecy; the Book of Revelation; The Second Coming of Christ; Jewish Apocalyptic literature and Christian Theology; and Millennialism and Christian millenarian movements.

Poverty, sickness and social related grants

The trust seeks to further Christian principles by making grants for the relief of poverty and sickness and to advance education, primarily in the area of Bedford. Applications for these grants are not considered as the charity administers this grant through the Bedford and Luton Community Foundation.

Financial information

In 2016 the trust had assets of £32.6 million and an income of £704,500 from investments. There were grants made totalling £371,000, which were awarded as follows:

Museum and archives	£281,500
Health and social	£50,000
Educational and publishing	£40,000

Beneficiaries included: Bedford and Luton Community Foundation (£100,000); Bristol University Downing Research Project (£50,000); IB Tauris

Publishing Report (£7,500); M. Niblett Blockley Research and Bunyan Meeting Museum (£5,000 each).

Exclusions

The trust will not consider funding:

- Political parties or political lobbying
- Pressure groups
- Commercial ventures
- Non-charitable activities
- Replacement of statutory funding

Applications

Applications should be made in writing to the correspondent.

Grants for purposes relating to poverty, sickness and social purposes are administered through the Bedfordshire and Luton Community Foundation (www.blcf.org.uk).

Sources of information

Accounts; annual report; Charity Commission record; funder's website.

The James Pantyfedwen Foundation

 Religion, education, the arts, general charitable purposes

Wales

£449,000 (2016/17)

CC number: 1069598

Trustees: Ken Richards; Gwerfyl Jones; Roy Sharp; Dr Rhidian Griffiths; Geraint Jones; Revd Alun Evans; Prof. Derec Morgan; David Lewis; Dr Eryn White; Wyn Jones; Enid Lewis; Prof. Jane Aaron; Alun Charles.

Correspondent: Gwenan Creunant, Executive Secretary, Pantyfedwen, 9 Market Street, Aberystwyth, Ceredigion SY23 1DL (tel: 01970 612806; email: post@jamespantyfedwen.cymru)

 www.jamespantyfedwenfoundation. org.uk

The foundation resulted from a merger of the John and Rhys Thomas James Foundation and the Catherine and Lady Grace James Foundation in April 1998. The original foundations were set-up by Sir D J James who established the first 'super' cinema in London (the Palladium in Palmers Green) and owned 13 other pre-war cinemas.

Grant-making

The foundation's website states its objects as 'the advancement, encouragement and promotion of religion, education, the arts and agriculture and other charitable purposes for the benefit of Welsh persons primarily in Wales'. Only the following three categories of application will be considered:

- **Educational:** 50% of the grant total – postgraduate students, particularly for research work, grants can be for up to £7,000
- **Religious buildings:** 28% of the grant total – particularly for the repair of the fabric, with priority being given to improvements linked to local mission and outreach projects
- **Eisteddfodau:** 22% of the grant total – up to £18,000 but usually for less than £1,000

Financial information

In 2016/17 the foundation held assets of almost £17 million and had an income of £1.3 million. There were 159 grants paid in the year; they totalled £449,000 and were distributed for the following purposes:

Educational purposes – tuition fees for postgraduate students	54	£263,000
Religious buildings	30	£148,000
Eisteddfodau	67	£75,000
Urdd Gobaith Cymru	2	£13,200
Morlan-Pantyfedwen Lecture	6	£480

Previous beneficiaries have included: National Eisteddfod of Wales (£18,000); Tabernacle St Dingat's Church – New Tredegar (£8,000); Eton Road Methodist Church – Swansea (£5,000); Talaith a Chadair Powys Eisteddfod (£1,100); Upper Chapel Eisteddfod (£500); Mynydd y Garreg Eisteddfod (£60).

Exclusions

Salaries and general revenue costs. Exclusions vary according to the type of grant being applied for. See the appropriate guidelines document on the website for details.

Applications

Guidelines for student, local eisteddfodau and churches applications can be found on the website and should be carefully considered before an application is made. Application forms for grants to local eisteddfodau and students may be downloaded from the website; however, churches wishing to make an application must contact the foundation to obtain a form. The trustees meet three times a year to consider applications.

Sources of information

Accounts; annual report; Charity Commission record; further information provided by the funder; funder's website.

Parabola Foundation

 General charitable purposes, with a particular focus on poverty, arts, culture, and music

England

£770,000 (2016/17)

CC number: 1156008

Trustees: Deborah Jude; Anne Millican; Peter Millican.

Correspondent: Deborah Jude, Trustee, Broadgate Tower, 20 Primrose Street, London EC2A 2EW (tel: 07980 769561)

This foundation, registered in March 2014, shares its name with Parabola Land Ltd and its associated companies, which specialise in real estate and property development. Trustee Peter Millican serves as a director of the company.

Peter Millican has had a well-publicised involvement in the arts and was responsible for the development of Kings Place, a London concert venue and office space.

Parabola Foundation operates with general charitable purposes, although there is a particular focus on: education; poverty; arts, culture, heritage and science; and environment, conservation and heritage. The annual report states:

> The objects of the charity are to further charitable and cultural projects that will bring benefit to the public. It has been particularly keen to support music and the arts in a way that benefits the community. The charity carefully evaluates all applications for funds based on merit.

Financial information

In 2016/17 the foundation had an income of £11,100 and a total expenditure of £774,500. We estimate that grants totalled around £770,000. Full accounts were not available to view on the Charity Commission website due to the foundation's low expenditure.

Previous beneficiaries have included: Kings Place Music Foundation (£391,000); Aurora Orchestra (£305,000); Poverty Relief Foundation (£56,500); Bowes Museum (£50,000).

Applications

Apply in writing to the correspondent.

Sources of information

Accounts; annual report; Charity Commission record.

Paradigm Foundation

General charitable purposes; community; education, training and employability; financial inclusion

Areas in which Paradigm Housing has homes, mainly the South East and East Midlands (a map of the areas covered is available on the foundation's website)

£190,000 to organisations (2016/17)

CC number: 1156204

Trustees: Bob Marshall; Ewan Wallace; Alfred Dench; Jane Harrison; Revd Timothy Yates; Patricia Buckland.

Correspondent: Manjit Nanglu, Paradigm Housing Group, Glory Park Avenue, Wooburn Green, High Wycombe, Buckinghamshire HP10 ODF (tel: 01628 811835; email: enquiries@paradigmfoundation.org.uk)

 www.paradigmfoundation.org.uk

This trust was registered with the Charity Commission in March 2014 as a new charity designed to help individuals and communities in the area in which Paradigm Housing Group operates (the South East and the East Midlands). The foundation receives between 2% and 10% of the surplus from the group's non-social housing activities.

Projects should benefit Paradigm residents and the local community. According to its 2016/17 accounts, the objects of the charity are:

To further projects and initiatives within the geographical areas in which Paradigm Homes Charitable Housing Association Ltd or any other entity in the Paradigm Housing Group operates:

- The prevention or relief of financial hardship
- The relief of unemployment
- The advancement of education
- The maintenance or improvement of public amenities
- The provision of recreational facilities for the public or those who by reason of their youth, age, infirmity or disablement, financial hardship or social and economic circumstances, have need of such facilities
- The protection or conservation of the environment
- The promotion of public safety and prevention of crime
- And to carry out such other charitable purposes as the Charity may think fit from time to time

The foundation has two grant streams: small-scale community projects up to £3,000 and larger projects over £3,000. For grants of over £5,000 applicants should not submit a form. Instead they may submit an expression of interest to the trustees. Individual grants are also made to Paradigm residents for up to £1,500. The Paradigm Housing website has a map which shows where Paradigm manages housing stock.

Financial information
In 2016/17 the foundation held assets of £260,500 and had an income of £350,500. Grants awarded to organisations totalled £190,000 with a further £8,100 given to individuals.

Beneficiaries included: Citizens Advice – Welwyn Hatfield (£61,000); The Oasis Partnership (£25,000); The Chesham and Community Association (£14,500); Chesham Rugby Club (£10,000); Sudbury Neighbourhood Centre (£9,000).

Applications
Applicants to the small and large community project schemes can apply online or download application forms available from the foundation's website. Those applying for £5,000 or more should not complete an application form but should send the trustees an expression of interest form. This should outline the purpose of your bid and how you consider it will support one or more of the foundation's priorities. The foundation will let you know if a full application is then required. Applications may be submitted by post or by email, but if applicants are successful, a signed version of the application will be required before funds can be released.

All applications will be acknowledged within seven working days of receipt. Decisions on larger grants will normally be made within ten weeks of the application being received. Applications for smaller grants are usually decided within eight weeks. Successful and unsuccessful applicants will be notified of the outcome. The trust conducts monitoring and evaluation of all grants.

Sources of information
Accounts; annual report; Charity Commission record; guidelines for applicants; funder's website.

The Park House Charitable Trust

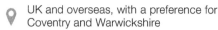

Ecclesiastical, education, medical and social welfare

UK and overseas, with a preference for Coventry and Warwickshire

£750,000 (2016)

CC number: 1077677

Trustees: Margaret Bailey; Niall Bailey; Paul Bailey.

Correspondent: Paul Varney, c/o Dafferns LLP, 1 Eastwood Business Village, Harry Weston Road, Binley, Coventry CV3 2UB (tel: 024 7622 1046)

The trust was registered with the Charity Commission in 1999 to support general charitable purposes in the UK. Today, the trust primarily supports ecclesiastical causes, education, and social welfare organisations, particularly in Coventry, Warwickshire and overseas.

Financial information
In 2016 the trust had assets of £2 million and an income of £797,000. A total of £750,000 was donated in grants to 52 organisations. Grants were distributed as follows:

Social welfare	38	£560,000
Ecclesiastical	7	£130,000
Medical	4	£30,000
Education	3	£30,000

Beneficiaries included: Friends of the Holy Land and Scottish International Relief (£100,000 each); The St Barnabas Society (£25,000); African Mission, Calcutta Rescue Fund, National Shrine of St Jude, Salvation Army and St Augustine's Catholic Primary School (£10,000 each); Bible Alive, Coventry Cathedral and Tiny Tim's Children's Centre (£5,000 each).

Exclusions
No grants are made to individuals.

Applications
Apply in writing to the correspondent.

Sources of information
Accounts; annual report; Charity Commission record.

Parkinson's UK

Parkinson's disease research

UK

£5.1 million (2016)

CC number: 258197

Trustees: Nadra Ahmed; Richard Raine; Mary Whyham; Tim Tamblyn; Mark Goodridge; Margaret Chamberlain; Freda Lewis; Anne MacColl Turpin; Paul Warner; David Burn.

Correspondent: Parkinson's UK, 215 Vauxhall Bridge Road, London SW1V 1EJ (tel: 020 7931 8080; email: researchapplications@parkinsons.org.uk)

www.parkinsons.org.uk

facebook.com/parkinsonsuk

@ParkinsonsUK

@parkinsons.uk

The aim of Parkinson's UK is to find a cure for Parkinson's disease as well as improving the lives of everyone affected by it.

Grant programmes
According to information on the Parkinson's UK website, the charity offers funding in the form of the following grants:

- Research grants: according to guidelines available from the website, grants are made to support research into Parkinson's disease which will have 'the greatest chance of improving the lives of people with Parkinson's'. A wide range of support is available for researchers at every stage of their careers, from major project and pilot study grants, to fellowships and support for clinical trials and cohort studies

- Take Control grants: grants of up to £1,500 are made to individuals affected by Parkinson's who are in financial need to buy things that will improve their quality of life or help them to access activities and services which will improve their well-being

The charity also provides grants to pump prime the employment of specialist nurses in response to recognised local need, often with Parkinson's UK local group support. Awards are granted after negotiation with the relevant NHS commissioning authority.

Financial information
In 2016 the charity held assets of £18 million and an income of £32.9 million. During the year, the charity awarded almost £5.1 million in grants, the vast majority of which was awarded to organisations. The charity awarded 22 research grants totalling more than £4.7 million and nine Parkinson's nurse grants amounting to £331,000. Grants totalling £3,000 were made to individuals through the Take Control programme.

Beneficiaries included: University of Oxford (£1.25 million in two grants); School of Pharmacy and Biomedical Science – Portsmouth (£225,000); NHS North Manchester CCG (£129,000); NHS Brent CCG (£114,000); Cardiff University (£46,000).

Applications
Details of how to apply for research and Take Control grants are available from the Parkinson's UK website.

Sources of information
Accounts; annual report; Charity Commission record; funder's website.

The JGW Patterson Foundation

 Medical research

 North East of England

£ £1.04 million (2016/17)

CC number: 1094086

Trustees: David Gold; Jim Dias; Philip Robson; Prof. Alan Craft; Prof. Tim Cawston; Stephen Gilroy; Pippa Aitken.

Correspondent: Pippa Aitken, Secretary, The Cube, Arngrove Court, Barrack Road, Newcastle Upon Tyne NE4 6DB (tel: 0191 226 7878)

 jgwpattersonfoundation.co.uk

The Patterson Foundation registered with the Charity Commission in 2002 and has since supported both clinical and laboratory research to further the understanding of disease, improve treatment and promote best practice. Applicants may be clinicians, laboratory scientists or allied health professionals involved in the study of cancer or rheumatic disease.

Grant programmes
At the time of writing (April 2018) the foundation offered the following types of funding:

- **Pump priming:** Grants of up to £50,000 for between six months and two years. Pump priming will typically be awarded to a specific individual undertaking a specific project with a view to acquiring sufficient data to subsequently apply for either a project grant or fellowship funding from national grant awarding bodies
- **Fellowships:** Grants of £30,000 per annum awarded for a period of up to two years to supports scientists or allied health professionals who wish to undertake a defined period of research into a specific area with a view to obtaining a higher qualification
- **PhD studentships:** Awarded to support young science graduates in university departments who wish to embark on a research career. The projects should have relevance to the aims of the JGW Patterson Foundation. Awards are normally for three years, include tuition fees, and are in line with current national PhD remuneration rates
- **Bridging funding:** Project grants of senior academics (lecturer or above) who require financial support between grant applications so that they may retain essential laboratory staff. Such individuals would normally have 'an established research track record and be considered critical members of a particular academic team'. Bridge funding is usually provided for no longer than six months
- **Special purpose grants:** Small grants of less than £10,000, awarded for purposes which do not fit into any other category of funding. Such grants would be subject to approval by the trustees and be seen as one-off awards. In the past, such grants have been made to hospices for specific requirements relating to the relief of cancer patients

No intellectual property created or acquired in connection with a foundation funded activity may be exploited in any way without the foundation's prior written consent. As a condition of granting such consent, the foundation will require agreement to its terms of exploitation including the sharing of the benefits arising from such exploitation.

Financial information
In 2016/17 the foundation had assets of £19.78 million and an income of £1.07 million. During the year, the charity awarded around £1.04 million in grants. Grants were distributed as follows:

Cancer research	15	61%	£633,000
Rheumatology and arthritis research	9	31%	£332,000
Equipment, hospice and patient care	4	7%	£71,000

Beneficiaries included: Newcastle University (£940,500 in 24 grants); Northumbria University (£46,500); St Oswald's Hospice (£29,000); National Rheumatoid Arthritis Society (£10,000); Fighting All Cancers Together (FACT) (£9,200).

Applications
Initial expressions of interest should be made by completing an online form on the foundation's website. All applications will be considered at the trustees' quarterly meetings which are usually held on the first Tuesday in February, May, September and November. Completed applications for funding must be received at least one month prior to a quarterly meeting. Applications are usually then sent out for peer review and discussed again at the subsequent quarterly meeting of the trustees.

Sources of information
Accounts; annual report; Charity Commission record; funder's website.

Payne-Gallwey 1989 Charitable Trust

 General charitable purposes

 Berkshire, Dorset, Oxfordshire, Wiltshire

£ £295,500 (2016/17)

CC number: 1016286

Trustees: Tom Luckock; Emma Nutt; Caroline Todhunter; John Ritchie; Charles Leigh-Pemberton; Edward Leigh-Pemberton.

Correspondent: The Trustees, Estate Office, Manor Farm, Little Coxwell, Faringdon SN7 7LW

 www.pgct.co.uk

Payne-Gallwey Charitable Trust (PGCT) was originally created by Sir Philip Payne-Gallwey in 1987 and is established for general charitable purposes. The information provided here is taken from the trust's helpful and informative website.

Support is most likely to be given to charities with a connection to:

- Berkshire, in particular the environs of Newbury
- Horse racing
- The Services
- Rural life and field sports
- Enabling young people particularly from poorer or deprived backgrounds to travel in order to teach or better the lives of others. (However, in the main, the trustees do not support sponsored activities involving travel, e.g. mountain climbs and car or motor bike rallies)
- Medical research
- The Church of England
- Care of the terminally ill and hospices within Berkshire
- People who are deaf
- People who are blind

It is exceptionally rare for the trustees to make a donation of more than £10,000.

The trust's annual income is redistributed evenly between the following types of grants: high donations (from £7,500 to £10,000); medium donations (from £4,000 to £6,000); and small donations (between £100 and £2,000, usually £2,000).

Whether a recipient receives a high, medium or small donation the trustees stipulate that they give no guarantee whatsoever that recipients will receive further donations from the trust in future years.

Financial information
In 2016/17 the trust had assets of £8 million and an income of £182,000. The trustees awarded grants totalling £295,500.

Beneficiaries included: National Horse Racing Museum (£50,000); Thames Valley Air Ambulance (£10,000); Game and Wildlife Conservancy (£7,500); Combat Stress and Waterloo Uncovered (£5,000 each); Watermill Theatre Trust (£4,000); Moorfields Eye Hospital (£3,000).

Exclusions
Unless a connection can be shown to Sir Philip's interests and/or the Payne-Gallwey family, it is unlikely that the trustees will support:

- Any appeal with a target of more than £10 million
- Capital projects outside the county of Berkshire
- Schools, hospitals and community centres outside Berkshire
- Church restoration or maintenance projects outside Berkshire
- Any charity which is primarily administered by or primarily funded by, the government, a local authority or a quango or has been established by one of those

It is highly unlikely that the trustees will support any charity with policies or activities which conflict with the interests of The National Farmers Union or The Country Land Business Group.

It should also be noted that the trustees are unable to support organisations (or individuals) which do not have charitable objectives. They will also not support charities that in their view are ambivalent about, or actively campaign for the abolition of, field sports.

Applications
If having read the criteria for funding given on the trust's website you wish to make an application to PGCT, complete the application form, which is available as a download. The trustees are unable to consider requests for support from PGCT unless the application form has been completed. If there is insufficient space, provide supplementary information (preferably max four pages of A4). Do not send bulky annual reports, etc.

PGCT does not have an email address and does not deal with telephone requests.

Sources of information
Accounts; annual report; Charity Commission record; funder's website.

Peacock Charitable Trust

🔍 Education of young people, relief of poverty, general charitable purposes, medical research

📍 UK, with a possible preference for London and the south of England

£ £1.47 million (2016/17)

CC number: 257655

Trustees: Charles Peacock; Bettine Bond; Dr Clare Sellors.

Correspondent: The Trustees, c/o Charities Aid Foundation, Kings Hill, West Malling, Kent ME19 4TA (tel: 0300 012 3334; email: mtheodorou@cafonline.org)

This family trust is administered by the Charities Aid Foundation (CAF). Its main objects are 'to advance the education of poor and deserving boys and girls' and 'to relieve poverty, hardship, suffering and distress', and it can also support general charitable purposes.

The trust has previously stated that many of its repeated grants go towards the running costs of organisations (in recognition of the fact that charities need, and sometimes lack, continuity), whereas newer grants are often for capital purposes. Some of its more recent grants have also helped organisations to pay off their debts.

The trustees rely on CAF to present charities requiring grants to them, although the majority of current beneficiaries have been supported for a number of years. As such, the potential for new applicants to be successful appears to be limited.

Financial information
In 2016/17 the trust had assets of £47 million and an income of £320,500. During the year, a total of £1.47 million was awarded in grants to organisations.

Beneficiaries included: The Prince's Youth Business Trust (£103,000); The Neuro-Disability Research Trust (£63,000); Royal Trinity Hospice (£25,000); Volunteering Matters (£13,000); Prisoners' Education Trust (£6,000); Royal National Lifeboat Institution (£2,000).

Exclusions
No donations are made to individuals and only in rare cases are additions made to the list of charities already being supported.

Applications
Apply in writing to the correspondent. The trustees meet three times a year with representatives from CAF to decide on grants to be made. The trust makes a lot of recurring grants and as such, new applications are unlikely to be successful.

Sources of information
Accounts; annual report; Charity Commission record.

The David Pearlman Charitable Foundation

🔍 Social welfare, education, health, arts, culture and heritage, citizenship and community development, Jewish causes, general charitable purposes

📍 UK

£ £547,000 (2015/16)

CC number: 287009

Trustees: Michael Goldberger; Stuart Appleman; David Pearlman; Jonathan Hager.

Correspondent: Mr D. Goldberg, Secretary, New Burlington House, 1075 Finchley Road, London NW11 0PU (tel: 020 8731 0777)

Set up in 1983, the foundation makes grants to charitable institutions and organisations for the following purposes:

- Social welfare
- Education
- Health
- Citizenship and community development

- Arts and culture
- General charitable purposes

There is some preference for supporting Jewish organisations and causes.

Financial information
In 2015/16 the foundation held assets of £4.2 million and had an income of £943,500. Grants were made totalling £547,000.

Previous beneficiaries have included:
Rehabilitation Trust (£65,000); National Youth Theatre (£51,000); The English Heritage Trust (£40,000); St Paul's Cathedral Foundation (£34,500); Merkaz Chasidei Wiznitz Trust (£20,000); Sir Roger Cholmeley's School (£15,000); Museum of London (£11,200); Gateshead Talmudical College (£5,500); Friends of Beis Chinuch Lebonos (£5,000).

Grants of less than £5,000 totalled £46,000 during the year.

Applications
Apply in writing to the correspondent.

Sources of information
Accounts; annual report; Charity Commission record.

The Pears Family Charitable Foundation

 General charitable purposes, education and research, social change

 Worldwide

£ £14.6 million (2016/17)

CC number: 1009195

Trustees: Trevor Pears; Mark Pears; David Pears.

Correspondent: Ian Shaw, Finance Director, 2 Old Brewery Mews, Hampstead, London NW3 1PZ (tel: 020 7433 3333; email: contact@pearsfoundation.org.uk)

 www.pearsfoundation.org.uk

 @PearsFoundation

The Pears Foundation is an independent family foundation rooted in Jewish values and registered with the Charity Commission in 1992. According to its website, the foundation aims to:

> Promote understanding of key issues through research and education programmes; drive engagement in social progress across the UK and globally, particularly in young people, and support organisations focused on well-being for everyone, especially those with a tough challenge to face.

The foundation typically awards £15 million to £20 million in grants per year. The foundation's website notes that there are no restrictions on what it will fund and that it is 'not afraid to fund things that others might shy away from, including core operating costs and experimental ideas that may not work'. In 2016/17 the foundation awarded grants under the following categories:

- Special educational needs, disability and social welfare
- Holocaust education
- Mental health and well-being
- Youth social action
- Shared society
- International development
- Higher education
- Encouraging philanthropy

Financial information
In 2016/17 the foundation had assets of £23 million and an income of £18.3 million. There were grants made totalling £14.6 million.

Beneficiaries included: Jewish Care (£4 million); The Hebrew University of Jerusalem (£1 million); University College London (£500,000); Carers Trust (£400,000); The Duke of Edinburgh's Award (£400,000); Marie Curie, (£200,000); Step Up To Serve (£75,000); Royal Holloway, University of London (£65,000); Samaritans and Scope (£50,000 each).

Applications
The foundation's annual report for 2016/17 states the following about its grant-making policy:

> Pears Foundation does not accept external applications (except in limited circumstances for restricted initiatives such as the National Youth Social Action Fund) and draws on its experience, networks and external and internal research to identify suitable partners. The Foundation proactively undertakes research to establish the wider context and strategy for its funding and assesses the impact of grants and projects against this research and Foundation staff keep up to date with relevant social policy including joining wider networks, receiving advice and presentations from external experts and attending conferences where appropriate.

Sources of information
Accounts; annual report; Charity Commission record; funder's website.

The Pebble Trust

 General charitable purposes including community work, education, care, the arts

 Brighton and Hove

£ £662,000 (2016/17)

CC number: 1129132

Trustees: James Arnell; Louise Arnell; Louise Stoten.

Correspondent: Charlotte Jackson, New Quadrant Partners Ltd, 22 Chancery Lane, London WC2A 1LS (tel: 020 7430 7159; email: charities@nqpltd.com)

 www.pebbletrust.org

The trust was established in 2009 and supports organisations and talented young people in Brighton and Hove. Its website states:

> We particularly invite applications for funding from local organisations involved in community work, education, care or the arts.
>
> Donations are generally in the region of £500 to £5,000 although, occasionally, larger donations may be considered. A detailed breakdown of how any money would be spent is extremely helpful. It is important to demonstrate in your application that the money for which you are applying would have a direct and positive impact on people living in Brighton and Hove.
>
> We do not give funding to businesses or for-profit organisations.

Financial information
In 2016/17 the trust held assets of £111,500 and had an income of £149,000. Grants to 24 organisations totalled £662,000. In previous years, grants have normally totalled around £100,000.

Beneficiaries included: Brighton Festival (£500,000); Brighton Festival Fringe (£37,500); Martlets Hospice (£25,000); Bridge Community Centre (£10,000); Sussex Nightstop (£4,500); Brighton Youth Orchestra (£3,700); Hove Park School (£1,000); Waterloo Street Community Garden (£500).

Applications
Applications can be made through the trust's website. Check the website for application deadlines.

Sources of information
Accounts; annual report; Charity Commission record; funder's website.

The Dowager Countess Eleanor Peel Trust

 Medical research, older people, socially disadvantaged people, general charitable purposes

 Worldwide, in practice UK, with a preference for Lancashire (especially Lancaster and district), Cumbria, Greater Manchester, Cheshire and Merseyside

£ £518,000 to organisations (2016/17)

CC number: 214684

Trustees: Michael Parkinson; John Parkinson; Prof. Richard Ramsden; Prof. Sir Robert Boyd; Prof. Margaret Pearson; Julius Manduell.

Correspondent: Michelle Bertenshaw, c/o Hill Dickson, 50 Fountain Street, Manchester M2 2AS (tel: 0161 838 4977; email: secretary@peeltrust.com)

 www.peeltrust.com

The Dowager Countess Eleanor Peel Trust was established by trust deed in 1951 and mainly supports medical charities and charities working with people who are older or disadvantaged. The trust also supports a group of charities specified in its trust deed. The trustees have a clear preference for supporting charities and projects in the north west of England, from where the trust fund monies originally emanated.

Grants are made to:

▶ Medical charities (specifically relating to conditions which affect older people, e.g. Alzheimer's, macular disease, prostate cancer and Parkinson's disease)
▶ Charities in connection with older people
▶ Charities assisting people who have fallen upon hard times (disability, hospices and hospitals, ex-services, relief after natural or man-made disasters, mental health, addiction and homelessness)
▶ Various charitable bodies specified in the trust deed

The trust also has two grant programmes for medical research projects: the major programme gives grants of up to £50,000 per year for a defined project of between one and three years; and the minor programme awards grants of up to £15,000 for pilot studies or equipment. The trust also supports individuals pursuing research, advanced study or the acquisition of a new clinical skill through The Peel and Rothwell Jackson Postgraduate Travelling Fellowship.

Financial information

In 2016/17 the trust held assets of £18.8 million and had an income of £640,000. Grants were made to 51 organisations, including the Travelling Fellowship awards (£61,200), totalling £579,500.

Beneficiaries included: Bolton Carers Support (£15,000); Asylum Link Merseyside and Council for Assisting Refugee Academics (£10,000 each); University of Dundee (£6,250); New Bridge and The Progressive Supranuclear Palsy Association (£5,000 each); Fatima Women's Association (£2,500); Family Tree Wirral (£1,500).

Exclusions

Grants are not made to

▶ Charities substantially under the control of central or local government
▶ Charities primarily devoted to children

▶ Unregistered organisations
▶ Projects outside the preferred geographical location (unless for a medical grant)

The trust does not consider applications from individuals, except for medical research grants and the annual travelling fellowship awards. Charities with an income above £2.5 million should refer to the guidelines on the website.

Applications

Details of deadlines and how to apply are available from the trust's website, which includes notice if the programmes are closed. The trustees meet three times a year in March, July and November to approve applications for general and medical research grants and in December to consider grants for the travelling scholarships. Unsuccessful applications will not receive feedback.

Sources of information

Accounts; annual report; Charity Commission record; guidelines for applicants; funder's website.

People's Health Trust

🔍 Health and well-being, communities, social welfare

📍 Great Britain

£ £14.9 million (2015/16)

CC number: 1125537

Trustees: Barbara Simmonds; Sue Hawkett; Nigel Turner; Dr Eva Elliott; Alan Francis; Sue Cohen; Paul Ballantyne; Prof. Elizabeth Dowler; Duncan Stephenson.

Correspondent: John Hume, 3rd Floor, 64 Great Eastern Street, London EC2A 3QR (tel: 020 7749 9100; email: enquiries@peopleshealthtrust.org.uk)

🌐 www.peopleshealthtrust.org.uk

📘 facebook.com/peopleshealthtrust

🐦 @Peoples_health

📷 @peopleshealthtrust

This trust was established to distribute the charitable proceeds of the 51 local society lotteries and the good causes money they raise through the health lottery. Since the organisation launched in 2011, it has raised £100 million and funded over 2,700 projects. The trust takes a wide view of the word health. The trust's aims for this financial year, as stated in the annual report for 2015/16, are as follows:

▶ To work with and invest in people to create fairer places to grow, live, work and age

▶ To contribute to a clear and strong evidence base for addressing the wider social determinants of health
▶ To deliver our work in a timely, knowledgeable, flexible and rigorous way;
▶ To raise awareness of the wider social determinants of health
▶ To develop and maintain diverse income streams

Funding Programmes

The trust has three main funding programmes, which are described on the website as follows:

▶ **Active Communities** – for great local ideas of between £5,000 to £25,000 each year for up to two years. The programme is open in different parts of the country at different times
▶ **Local Conversations** - an approach which involves working together with the residents of a neighbourhood to determine how they would like to use the money raised through their local society lottery
▶ **Local People** – a programme through which we fund several larger charities, all of whom work very locally

Schemes open and close at different times for different areas – for information on what funding is currently available in your area, refer to the website.

Financial information

In 2015/16 the trust had assets of £7.2 million and an income of £12.1 million. During the year, the trust gave around £14.9 million in grants to organisations.

Beneficiaries included: West Itchen Community Trust (£369,500); Penparcau Community Forum (£300,500); Community Action MK (£242,000); Cymunedau'n Gyntaf Mon Communities (£235,000); Home on the Range (£50,000); Hart Gables (£37,000); Asha Neighbourhood Project and Lightburn Elderly Association Project (£35,000 each); The Buzz Project (£30,500); SPARC (£28,000); Bristol Reggae Orchestra (£25,500); Greenhill Tenants Association (£14,000).

Exclusions

Refer to the website for the restrictions on each funding programme.

Applications

Applications can be submitted online. The trust funds in areas in which the Health Lottery operates. However, grant rounds are divided into regional schemes. Check the website to see if a grant scheme is open in your area. Note that schemes open and close throughout the year.

Sources of information

Accounts; annual report; Charity Commission record; funder's website.

People's Postcode Trust

Employability and skills development, the promotion of human rights through combatting discrimination, poverty prevention

Scotland, Wales and England

£2.05 million (2016)

OSCR number: SC040387

Trustees: Aidan Connolly; Michael Pratt; Judith Hills; Robert Flett.

Correspondent: People's Postcode Trust, 28 Charlotte Square, Edinburgh EH2 4ET (tel: 0131 322 9377; email: info@postcodetrust.org.uk)

www.postcodetrust.org.uk

@PostcodeTrust

This trust is funded by the income from the People's Postcode Lottery with at least 32% of each ticket sale going to charities and good causes.

Areas of support

The themes of the trust are:

- Employability and skills development
- The promotion of human rights through combatting discrimination
- Poverty prevention

Only registered charities can apply for grants of over £2,000.

Financial information

In 2016 the trust held assets of £313,500 and had an income of £8.5 million. Grants to 222 projects totalled £2.05 million and were broken down as follows:

England	169	£1.6 million
Scotland	29	£294,500
Wales	24	£163,500

Health	99	£872,000
Poverty	100	£839,500
Human rights	23	£340,000

Previous beneficiaries have included: Thistle Foundation (£17,500); Magic Me (£16,800); Emmaus Merseyside (£16,700); G39 & Warp (£1,700).

Exclusions

According to the trust's funding guide, it will not fund:

- Organisations currently in receipt of funding from players of the People's Postcode Lottery, including previous
- Grant recipients who have not submitted a project evaluation form
- Existing projects (unless significant expansion)
- Bodies seeking to distribute grants/ funds to others
- Organisations with restricted or exclusive memberships

- Applications where our funding would be less than 10% of the overall project cost
- Organisations that have previously breached their funding agreement with People's Postcode Trust
- Political parties or party-political activities
- Projects that promote religion
- schools (except for special schools), PTAs, nurseries, and universities/ colleges
- Lunch clubs, mother and toddler and after-school groups
- Individuals
- Feasibility studies
- Foreign travel
- General marketing appeals or sponsorship
- Medical research, advice and equipment
- End-of-life or palliative care
- Short-term projects such as events, conferences, day trips, seminars, galas or festivals
- Training or educational workshops that do not result in a tangible outcome for participants
- Building renovations/general refurbishment
- Installations of toilets, showers, lifts or changing rooms
- Organisations that appear to have excessive unrestricted or free reserves and no policy to reflect the
- Rationale behind this
- Projects or activities that the state has a legal obligation to provide

Applications

There are two funding rounds per year, with a two-stage application process.

Stage one: a very short expression of interest (EOI) which requires only some basic details about your organisation, as well as a very short summary of the project you are proposing. Successful applicants will be invited to stage two, while unsuccessful groups are welcome to re-apply for new projects in future rounds.

Stage two: those invited will complete a full application form, with more in-depth detail on both their organisation and the project. Decisions will be made within ten weeks of a stage two submission.

Note: Forms are only accessible through the trust's website on the dates specified. More details, including guidance notes and deadlines, are available from the website.

Sources of information

Accounts; annual report; OSCR record; funder's website.

The Performing Right Society Foundation

Music

UK

£1.86 million to organisations (2016)

CC number: 1080837

Trustees: Simon Platz; Royce Bell; Ameet Shah; Vanessa Swann; John Reid; Richard King; Julian Nott; Mark Poole; Caroline Norbury; Hannah Kendall; Susannah Simons; Chris Butler.

Correspondent: Fiona Harvey, Secretary, 2 Pancras Square, London N1C 4AG (tel: 020 3741 4233; email: info@ prsformusicfoundation.com)

www.rsfoundation.com

facebook.com/PRSforMusic

@PRSFoundation

@prsfoundation

The PRS for Music Foundation (PRSMF) is the UK's largest independent funder purely for new music of any genre. The principle objectives of the foundation are to support, sustain and further the creation and performance of new music and to educate the public in order to augment its appreciation in the UK. The foundation awards grants and works in strategic partnerships with like-minded organisations.

Grant-making policy

The foundation awards grants under a variety of themes, which are currently listed on the website. Only two are available for charities and not-for-profit organisations:

The Open Fund

- Funding for organisations and music creators. This fund is suitable for a wide range of new music projects across all genres
- Supports new music projects led by promoters, talent development organisations, venues, curators and large performance groups (which includes orchestras, choirs, jazz bands or folk groups with 12 or more performers)
- Projects must involve the creation, performance and promotion of new music and enable songwriters, composers, solo artists, bands and performers of all backgrounds to develop creatively and professionally
- Grants are available for up to £10,000 and include support of touring, recording, promotion and marketing, commissions of new music by UK-based creators, community projects, residencies and live programmes

Beyond Borders

- Grants of up to £15,000 to organisations working with at least two other partners based in the UK or Ireland that want to co-commission or tour new music across the UK
- Funding is available for projects that include new commissions, recordings and repeat performances of music written in the past five years

Full details of the foundation's activities are available on the website, including grant-making policies, priorities for each scheme and application forms.

Financial information

In 2016 the foundation had assets of £1 million and an income of £3.8 million. A total of £2.83 million was awarded in grants, including £1.86 million in 244 grants to organisations and £931,000 in 203 grants to individuals.

A list of beneficiaries was not available; however, details of previous beneficiaries are available on the foundation's website.

Previous beneficiaries have included: Birmingham Contemporary Music Group; Birmingham Royal Ballet; FACT; Halle; London Sinfonietta; Merseyside Arts Foundation; Parr Street Studios; Small Green Shoots; Unity Theatre Liverpool.

Exclusions

The foundation will not offer funding for:

- Companies limited by shares
- Technological development if it does not contain a significant aspect of new music creation
- Projects that contain no element of live performance (unless applying for recording costs only)
- The purchase of vans and cars
- Bursaries, tuition/education costs, or scholarships
- Capital projects (e.g. building work)
- Any project raising funds for another charity
- Buying equipment/building a studio
- Organisations or projects that have been running for less than 18 months and musicians that have not been active for 18 months
- Retrospective activity
- Activity that falls before the grant decision date
- Organisations based outside the UK
- Artists and music creators based outside the UK
- British artists no longer permanently resident in the UK
- International tours/recording internationally (see the foundation's International Showcase Fund scheme)
- Radio stations/broadcasting costs
- Start-up companies or labels
- A roster of artists on a record label

- Editing, mastering or distribution of work
- Salary and living costs
- Core organisational costs
- Individuals in full-time education or who are under 18, unless represented by an adult with a valid DBS check

Note: Companies limited by shares applying for funds will be considered on a case-by-case basis.

Applications

Apply via the foundation's website. The application forms for each programme also include full guidelines for applicants. Deadlines for applications vary from programme to programme. Contact the foundation or go to the website for further information.

Note: The foundation's website states: 'Due to high levels of demand for our funding schemes, we can only accept one application per calendar year to The Open Fund. Please contact the team if you are unsure which funding scheme is most appropriate.'

Sources of information

Accounts; annual report; Charity Commission record; funder's website.

The Persula Foundation

🔍 Homelessness, people with disabilities, human rights, animal welfare

📍 Worldwide

💷 1.3 million (2016/17)

CC number: 1044174

Trustees: Hanna Oppenheim; Julian Richer; David Robinson; Rosie Richer; Robert Rosenthal; Jonathan Levy.

Correspondent: Teresa Chapman, Secretary, Gallery Court, Hankey Place, London SE1 4BB (tel: 020 7551 5343; email: info@persula.org)

The Persula Foundation was established in 1994 by Richer Sounds plc, the UK home entertainment retailer. Trustees include Julian Richer, founder of the company, and David Robinson, the Managing Director. The foundation supports general charitable purposes, but its main aim is to relieve and prevent poverty. At present, the foundation is focusing on providing funding for charities supporting the following causes:

- Homelessness
- People with disabilities
- Human rights
- Animal welfare

The Persula Foundation also manages three projects: Storytelling Tour, which annually provides 100 free sessions of storytelling and music to visually impaired people, older people and children and adults with disabilities; ACTS 435, a website that allows people

to give money directly to those struggling financially; and ASB Help, which provides advice and support to victims of anti-social behaviour.

Financial information

In 2016/17 the foundation had assets of £97,500 and an income of £1.4 million, mostly from donations from Richer Sounds plc (5% of the yearly profit is donated to the foundation). There were grants made to a variety of organisations totalling £1.3 million, which were distributed as follows:

Human welfare	166	£557,500
Human rights	37	£339,500
Animal welfare	59	£236,500
People with disabilities	39	£123,000
Homelessness	16	£37,000

Beneficiaries included: Civil Liberties Trust (£60,000); Amnesty International (£50,000); Prison Reform Trust (£34,000); Changing Faces (£30,000); Hope and Homes for Children and Christians against Poverty (£25,000 each); Israel Palestine Teaching Initiative (£24,000); Soil Association (£20,000); PETA (£17,500).

Applications

Apply in writing to the correspondent.

Sources of information

Accounts; annual report; Charity Commission record.

The Jack Petchey Foundation

🔍 Young people aged 11 to 25

📍 London and Essex

💷 £6.7 million (2016)

CC number: 1076886

Trustee: Jack Petchey Foundation Company.

Correspondent: Gemma Dunbar, Head of Grants, Dockmaster's House, 1 Hertsmere Road, London E14 8JJ (tel: 020 8252 8000; email: mail@ jackpetcheyfoundation.org.uk)

🌐 www.jackpetcheyfoundation.org.uk

📘 facebook.com/ JackPetcheyFoundation

🐦 @JPFoundation

This foundation was established in 1999 by Jack Petchey and gives grants to programmes and projects that benefit young people aged 11 to 25 by enabling them to achieve their potential by inspiring, investing in and developing activities that increase their personal, social, emotional and physical development. In the UK, the foundation benefits all London boroughs and Essex.

Grant programmes

Internship programme

Grants are available to ten youth organisations to help them fund a one-year internship. It will aim to support dynamic young individuals in their first steps towards being the sector's future leaders.

18th Birthday Open Grants Programme

To celebrate the 18th birthday of the foundation it has launched an open grants programme focusing on supporting young people aged 18 to 25 years as they transition into adulthood. Projects funded through this programme will identify a clear area of need for this age group as well as a well-thought-out way to support young people, to build on their strengths and address the need.

Achievement Award Scheme

The Achievement Award Scheme is run in over 2,000 schools, colleges and clubs throughout London and Essex and contributes over £2 million annually to youth organisations. The scheme is a reward and recognition initiative which enables schools and clubs to celebrate the achievements of young people and receive additional funding for the organisation.

Each month, participating youth clubs, schools, colleges and registered charities select one young person to receive an achievement award. The month's winner receives a framed certificate and a cheque for £250 (payable to the organisation) to be spent on a school, club or community project of the recipient's choice.

Leader Award

Young people in organisations that are participating on the Achievement Award scheme can nominate an adult to honour the dedication of exemplary staff and volunteers. The winning organisations will then be offered the opportunity to apply for a small grant once a year.

Small Grants Fund

Organisations that are running the achievement awards effectively can apply for up to £750 to enhance their work with young people once a year. The total project cost must not be more than £5,000 and the project must be completed within nine months of the funding being awarded. The project must benefit groups of young people who are most in need of support and must not promote religious or political beliefs.

Educational visits

Organisations participating in the Achievement Award Scheme can apply for two small grants of up to £600 per year to facilitate educational trips.

Individual grants for volunteering

The foundation will consider sponsoring young people (11 to 25 years old) living in London and Essex who are undertaking voluntary projects with UK-based organisations. The normal support from the foundation will be £300 (maximum of 50% of the costs). An application form is available from the foundation's website.

Partnership programmes (major grants)

The foundation funds and works in partnership with several organisations to deliver programmes. These include:

- First Give: students can compete for a grant of £1,500 by advocating for a local charity in a school competition
- School planners: Up to £500 is available for recipients of the Achievement Award towards the costs of producing school planners for the coming academic year. Schools should contact the School Planner Company directly, visit www.school-planners.co.uk

Further details of all partnerships can be found on the website.

These funds may change and others may be added so potential applicants should regularly check the foundation's website.

Financial information

In 2016 the foundation had assets of £10.7 million and an income of £7.5 million. During the year, 3,092 grants were made totalling £6.7 million.

Beneficiaries included: Speakers Trust (£589,000); Table Tennis England (£171,000); Media Trust (£142,000); London Youth (£50,000); Essex Boys and Girls Clubs (£41,500); City YMCA (£26,000); Army Cadet Force (£22,000); Stepney City Farm (£15,000); St Christopher's Hospice (£6,000); Archway Project (£4,000).

Exclusions

Check the website for each grant programme's specific eligibility criteria.

Applications

Application forms for each of the grant schemes can be downloaded from the foundation's website.

Sources of information

Accounts; annual report; Charity Commission record; funder's website.

Petplan Charitable Trust

 The welfare of dogs, cats, horses and rabbits; veterinary research and education

UK

£538,500 (2016/17)

CC number: 1032907

Trustees: John Bower; Clarissa Baldwin; David Simpson; Patsy Bloom; Ted Chandler; Peter Laurie; Kathryn Willis; Jamie Crittall; Gary Davess; Prof. The Lord Trees.

Correspondent: Catherine Bourg, Trust Administrator, Great West House (GW2), Great West Road, Brentford, Middlesex TW8 9EG (tel: 020 8580 8013; email: catherine.bourg@allianz.co.uk)

 www.petplantrust.org

The trust was established in 1994 by pet insurance company Petplan Ltd which is a subsidiary company of Allianz Insurance plc. Petplan gives its policy holders the option of making a small annual donation to the trust, which they are able to increase from the suggested £2 per year should they wish to do so. The trust aims to promote the welfare of dogs, cats, horses and rabbits by funding clinical veterinary investigation, education and welfare projects. Since its creation, the trust has awarded almost £10 million in grants.

Grant programmes

Scientific grants

The trust awards two types of scientific grant:

- Full grants for in-depth research for up to three years
- Pump priming/pilot grants of up to £10,000 over a period of no more than one year to fund initial research which should ideally lead to further research

Support is given for clinical research that will potentially help vets in practice to treat and care for animals. Only work which involves the study of companion animals will be funded. Applications for these grants are invited from the major veterinary schools.

Welfare grants

According to the trust's terms and conditions document, the trust awards:

- One major welfare grant of up to £20,000 towards an innovative project which will improve animal care and welfare
- Up to £40,000 in general grants of between £5,000 and £7,500
- Up to £40,000 in general grants of up to £5,000
- Grants to assist with vehicle purchase

General grants can include items such as neutering, kennelling and veterinary costs but not general overheads. Projects involving pet therapy have previously been supported.

Capital grants

When funds permit, grants for major projects may be awarded to veterinary schools.

Financial information

In 2016 the trust had assets of £714,000 and an income of £790,500. Grants were paid totalling £538,500 and were distributed as follows:

Scientific grants	£337,000
Welfare grants	£201,500

Beneficiaries included: Animal Health Trust (£181,000 in five grants); Royal Veterinary College (£105,000 in three grants); Lincolnshire Trust for Cats (£20,000); Headway Suffolk – Brainy Dogs (£12,000); Dogs for Good (£9,000); Canine Partners, Carla Lane Animals in Need, Dogs Trust and Yorkshire Cat Rescue (£5,000 each); Blue Cross (£1,500).

Exclusions

Grants are not made for individuals, non-registered charities or studies involving invasive procedures. The trust cannot consider applications for funding for overheads such as rent, general staff costs, etc.

Applications

Application forms, eligibility criteria, full terms and conditions, and the dates for application rounds for each grant programme are available from the trust's website.

Sources of information

Accounts; annual report; Charity Commission record; guidelines for applicants; funder's website.

The Pilgrim Trust

Social welfare, the preservation of buildings and heritage

 UK

£ £3 million (2016)

CC number: 206602

Trustees: David Barrie; Lady Sarah Riddell; Prof. Sir Colin Blakemore; Sir Mark Jones; Michael Baughan; James Fergusson; Caroline Butler; Sarah Staniforth; Kevin Pakenham; Simon Antrobus.

Correspondent: Georgina Nayler, Director, 23 Lower Belgrave St, London SW1W 0NR (tel: 020 7834 6510; email: info@thepilgrimtrust.org.uk)

 www.thepilgrimtrust.org.uk

The Pilgrim Trust was founded in 1930 by the wealthy American philanthropist Edward Stephen Harkness. It was Harkness's wish that his gift be given in grants for some of Britain's 'more urgent needs' and to 'promote her future well-being'. The first trustees decided that the trust should assist with social welfare projects, preservation (of buildings and countryside) and the promotion of art and learning. This has remained the focus of The Pilgrim Trust and the current board of trustees follow Harkness's guidelines. The trustees review these objectives every three years.

Grant programmes

The trust aims to distribute £2 million a year with 60% directed towards preservation and conservation and 40% towards social welfare.

There are two grant schemes:

- **Main Grant Fund:** 90% of the annual grant budget is allocated to this scheme, for grants of over £5,000
- **Small Grant Fund:** the remainder of the grants budget is distributed through this scheme in grants of £5,000 or less

These grants are available to UK-registered charities including exempt charities, recognised public bodies and registered friendly societies for revenue costs, project costs, costs of initial exploratory work for organisations seeking to rescue important buildings and monuments and capital costs.

The following is taken from a funding guideline document available in full on the trust's website, with the main points reproduced here:

Preservation and scholarship

- Preservation of and repairs to historic buildings and architectural features. Special consideration is given to projects that give new use to buildings which are at risk and of outstanding importance
- Conservation of works of art, books, significant ephemera, museum objects and records held in museums, galleries, specialist archives and repositories
- Promotion of knowledge through academic research and its dissemination, including cataloguing within museums, galleries and libraries and institutions where historic, scientific or archaeological records are preserved
- Cataloguing of archives and manuscripts
- Conservation of manuscripts is funded through the National Manuscripts Conservation Trust. Visit www.nmct.co.uk for more information

- Places of worship. To apply under the block grant allocation scheme, contact the relevant administering organisation directly

Social welfare

Projects that have a positive impact on the lives of women and girls facing severe and multiple disadvantage, particularly where their vulnerabilities put them at risk of offending.

- Projects that seek to reduce the use of custody for women, including diversion and alternatives to custody
- Interventions at an earlier stage in a woman's life to prevent multiple and severe disadvantage and negative outcomes

Applications regarding the above will be considered for:

- Revenue costs such as staff salaries but, generally, not equipment costs
- Project costs
- Costs of initial exploratory work for organisations seeking to rescue important buildings, monuments, etc.
- Capital costs

For full information on grant-making visit the trust's website.

Financial information

In 2016 the trust held assets of £69 million and had an income of £1.8 million. Grants awarded to organisations totalled £3 million:

- £1.1 million was paid to social welfare organisations
- £1.9 million was paid to preservation and scholarship organisations

Beneficiaries included: Queen Elizabeth Scholarship Trust (£38,000); Fitzwilliam Museum (£30,000); Glasgow Building Preservation Trust, Heckington Windmill Trust and Hay Castle Trust (£25,000 each); Bournemouth University Higher Education Corporation and Edinburgh World Heritage Trust (£15,000 each); The Horniman Public Museum and Public Park Trust (£10,000); The Families in British India Society (£5,000).

Exclusions

According to the trust's website grants are not made to:

- Individuals
- Non-UK-registered charities or charities registered in the Channel Islands or the Isle of Man
- Projects based outside the UK
- Projects where the work has already been completed or where contracts have already been awarded
- Organisations that have had a grant awarded by the trust within the past two years. **Note:** This does not refer to payments made within that timeframe

- Projects with a capital cost of over £5 million pounds where partnership funding is required
- Projects where the activities are considered to be primarily the responsibility of central or local government
- General appeals or circulars
- Projects for the commissioning of new works of art
- Organisations seeking publishing production costs
- Projects seeking to develop new facilities within a church or the reordering of churches or places of worship for wider community use
- Any social welfare project that falls outside the trustees' current priorities
- Arts and drama projects, unless they can demonstrate that they are linked to clear educational goals for prisoners
- Drop-in centres, unless the specific work within the centre falls within one of the trustees' current priority areas
- Youth or sports clubs, travel or adventure projects, community centres or children's play groups
- Organisations seeking funding for trips abroad
- Organisations seeking educational funding, e.g. assistance to individuals for degree or post-degree work, or school, university or college development programmes
- One-off events such as exhibitions, festivals, seminars, conferences or theatrical and musical productions

Note: The trust no longer considers applications from projects aimed at people who misuse drugs and alcohol.

Applications
Applications for both small and main grants can be made using the trust's online form. Applicants should read the application guidelines available on the website in full before applying. There is also a very useful FAQ section. There are no deadlines; applications are considered at quarterly trustees' meetings. The trust welcomes informal contact prior to an application by phone or email.

Sources of information
Annual report; accounts; Charity Commission record; guidelines for applicants; funder's website.

Cecil Pilkington Charitable Trust

Environmental conservation, medical research, general charitable purposes

UK, particularly Sunningwell in Oxfordshire and St Helens

£175,000 (2016/17)

CC number: 249997

Trustees: Arnold Pilkington; Mark Feeny; Vanessa Pilkington; Heloise Pilkington.

Correspondent: Anthony Bayliss, Duncan Sheard Glass, Castle Chambers, 43 Castle Street, Liverpool L2 9TL

Cecil Pilkington Charitable Trust supports a wide range of charitable causes including organisations which support environmental conservation and medical research.

Financial information
In 2016/17 the trust had an income of £268,000 and a total expenditure of £238,500. Based upon the information provided in previous years' accounts, we estimate that the trust provided grants totalling around £175,000.

Beneficiaries have previously included: Psychiatry Research Trust (£50,000); Prostate Cancer Research Centre (£33,000); Peninsular Medical School Foundation (£24,000); Allergy UK, Epilepsy Research, Oxford Preservation Trust and Beating Bowel Cancer (£2,000 each); British Horse Loggers Charitable Trust and Gordon Russell Trust (£1,000 each).

Applications
Apply in writing to the correspondent.

Sources of information
Accounts; annual report; Charity Commission record.

Pilkington Charities Fund

Social welfare, older people, health

Merseyside

£226,000 (2016/17)

CC number: 225911

Trustees: Neil Pilkington Jones; Arnold Pilkington; Eleanor Jones.

Correspondent: Lynsey Lewis, Rathbones, Port of Liverpool Building, Pier Head, Liverpool L3 1NW (tel: 0151 236 6666; email: lynsey.lewis@rathbones.com)

 pilkingtoncharitiesfund.org.uk

This fund was established in 1950 to assist employees or former employees of Pilkington's or any associated companies. It now mainly supports registered charities in the areas of welfare, older people and health. A small proportion of its support is reserved for the benefit of present or former employees of the Pilkington Glass Company.

The fund's website states:

> We only award grants to charities working to help people affected by poverty, old age or ill health and particularly welcome applications from organisations based in Merseyside.

> We will also consider applications from national charities working in these fields – but priority will be given to those with specific projects in Merseyside and the surrounding region.

> Only in exceptional circumstances will applications for work outside the UK be considered.

Most grants range from £1,000 to £6,000. Grants are made for core costs, capital costs and project costs.

Financial information
In 2015/16 the fund had assets of £25 million and an income of £662,000. Grants were awarded to 65 organisations totalling £226,000.

Beneficiaries included: ARC (£10,000); Bradbury Fields and Liverpool Lighthouse (£5,000 each); React (£3,000); Strongbones (£2,800); Deafblind UK (£2,000); Lullaby Trust (£1,500); Butterflies (£1,000).

Exclusions
Grants are only made to registered charities. No grants are given to individuals.

Applications
Apply in writing to the correspondent. The fund's website states:

> Charities can apply for a grant at any time. The Trustees meet twice a year, with deadlines for applications on 1 May and 1 October. Urgent applications may be considered separately: please highlight and explain the need for urgency in your covering letter.

> Applications should be made in writing or by email.

> Please explain concisely the reasons for your request and the expected outcomes.

> For national charities care should be taken, wherever possible, to explain how your work will specifically benefit the people of Merseyside and the surrounding region.

> Where possible, please ask for a specific sum, rather than simply asking for a contribution.

> Please enclose with your application any details relating to budgets or costs and, where relevant, details of any funding already received from other sources.

Sources of information
Accounts; annual report; Charity Commission record; further information provided by the funder; funder's website.

The Austin and Hope Pilkington Trust

 Categories of funding repeated in a three-year rotation (see the entry for further information)

 Great Britain

£ £312,500 (2016)

CC number: 255274

Trustees: Debbie Nelson; Penny Badowska; Eleanor Stride.

Correspondent: Karen Frank, Administrator, c/o Rathbone Trust Company, Port of Liverpool Building, Pier Head, Liverpool L3 1NW (tel: 0151 236 6666; email: admin@austin-hope-pilkington.org.uk)

www.austin-hope-pilkington.org.uk

Each year, the trust focuses on supporting projects in particular areas, which are repeated on a three-year cycle. At the time of writing (June 2018), the trust's website states the following are the focus over the next three years:

▷ 2018: medical; community
▷ 2019: children and young people
▷ 2020: music and the arts; older people

In all cases, priority is given to projects focusing on homelessness, domestic abuse, prisoners/offenders, refugees and asylum seekers. The trust particularly welcomes applications that address rehabilitation and mental health needs.

Only registered charities are eligible for support. National projects are preferred, rather than those with a local remit, and grants are rarely awarded to local projects unknown to the trustees. Grants are generally either of £1,000 or £5,000. The majority of grants are of £1,000. Exceptionally, grants of up to £10,000 are made for medical research projects. Grants are usually awarded for one year only and unsuccessful applicants may not reapply in the same year. The trust's website provides further clarification on what is and is not supported.

Financial information

In 2016 the trust held assets of £11 million and had an income of £301,000. The grant priority for 2016 was children and young people. Grants were made to 196 organisations totalling £260,000. The trust made two additional grants in memory of a former trustee – the British Red Cross received £16,000 and the British Refugee Council received £5,000. The trust also provides a scholarship to Purcell School, which totalled £32,500 in 2016.

Beneficiaries included: Freedom from Torture, Missing People, St Giles Trust, Stonewall and Victim Support (£3,000 each); East Sussex Foster Care

Association, Incest and Sexual Abuse Survivors, Outside Chance, Refugee Therapy Centre, Southern Domestic Abuse Service and The Lowry Centre (£1,000 each).

Exclusions

Overseas projects; capital appeals; schools; village halls; minibuses; shopmobility; charities involved with religion (including the repair of church fabric); churches (even those used by community groups); charities involved with animals; individuals (including individuals going overseas for a charitable organisation); students; scouts, guides, cubs, brownies; sea cadets; holidays; individual hospices (although national organisations may apply).

Applications

The trust prefers to receive applications through the online form on its website; however, hard copies of the application form are available for anyone who is unable to complete it online. Postal applications are not accepted. Grants are made four times a year and applications are subject to closing dates, the details of which can be seen on the website.

Sources of information

Accounts; annual report; Charity Commission record; funder's website.

Pink Ribbon Foundation

 Breast cancer

 UK

£ £220,000 (2016/17)

CC number: 1080839

Trustees: Angela Brignall; Errol McBean; Jonathan Prince.

Correspondent: Jonathan Prince, Trustee, Crofton House, 5 Morley Close, Orpington, Kent BR6 8JR (tel: 01689 858877; email: enquiries@ pinkribbonfoundation.org.uk)

 www.pinkribbonfoundation.org.uk

 facebook.com/ PinkRibbonFoundation

 @pinkribbonfound

 @pinkribbonfoundation

The following information was taken from the foundation's website:

The Pink Ribbon Foundation is a grant-making trust with a mission to fund projects and provide financial support to UK charities which relieve the needs of people who are suffering from, or who have been affected by breast cancer or who work to advance the understanding of breast cancer, its early detection and

treatment. There are a large number of such charities in the UK, each as deserving as the next. Many of the charities supported are the smaller ones, which operate on a shoestring.

The Pink Ribbon Foundation has very little infrastructure. It relies on the hard work given by Trustees, interested parties and its Patrons. This is done in order to maximise the amount, which goes to the charities that benefit from the funds raised.

Every year the Foundation invites charities in the UK to apply for a grant in order to help them continue their vital work or to fund one-off projects.

Financial information

In 2016/17 the foundation held assets of £279,500 and had an income of £237,500. During the year, the charity awarded £220,000 in grants to more than 44 organisations.

Beneficiaries included: Cavendish Cancer Care (£10,000); Bosom Buddies and Cancer Active (£7,500 each); Keep Abreast, Mulberry Centre and St John's Hospice (£5,000 each); Sara Lee Trust (£1,000).

Applications

Application forms can be downloaded from the foundation's website or requested by email.

Sources of information

Accounts; annual report; Charity Commission record; funder's website.

Thomas Pocklington Trust

 Research into sight loss, support for people with sight loss

 UK

£ £1.8 million (2016/17)

CC number: 1113729

Trustees: Jenny Pearce; Rodney Powell; Mervyn Williamson; Alastair Chapman; Philip Longworth; Graham Findlay; Fadeia Hossian; John Thompson; Matt Wadsworth; Marsha Chantol de Cordova.

Correspondent: Deborah Brown, Tavistock House South (Entrance D), Tavistock Square, London WC1H 9LG (tel: 020 8995 0880; email: info@ pocklington-trust.org.uk)

 www.pocklington-trust.org.uk

 facebook.com/ thomaspocklingtontrust

 @TPTgeneral

The trust was established in 1958 with a bequest from Thomas Pocklington, a jeweller turned property developer who suffered a period of temporary sight loss.

The aim of the trust is to increase awareness and understanding of the needs of people with sight loss and to develop and implement services which meet their needs and improve lives.

The charity splits its activities into two areas, details of which have been taken from its 2016/17 accounts:

Understanding needs

▸ Identify priority needs across the sector and ensure that these are communicated and disseminated widely

▸ Undertake research and pilot interventions into priority needs and the effectiveness of interventions

▸ Influence change in the sector using our knowledge and expertise, and the outcomes of our research

Meeting needs

▸ Using our knowledge and resources we will seek to ensure needs are met by:

▸ Direct service provision

▸ Supporting service providers in the sector

▸ Working with other sector bodies (charities, umbrella bodies and government) to develop frameworks for the provision of future services

Research funding

The trust provides funding for research into sight loss, details of which have been taken from the trust's website:

Pocklington welcomes proposals for research and related development work in line with our priority themes. We also periodically issue calls for research proposals to address particular topics within these areas.

The priority themes sit within Pocklington's overarching strategic goals of understanding and meeting the needs of people with sight loss.

Our research themes include:

▸ Support for independent living – employment, technology, lighting and design, housing and locality, social life and leisure

▸ Prevention, detection and awareness of sight loss

▸ Early intervention, rehabilitation and continuing advice and support

▸ Social and economic factors and circumstances

▸ Health and well-being – sight loss and ageing; sight loss and dementia, mental health and other concurrent health conditions

Financial information

In 2016/17 the trust held assets of £174,500 and had an income of £6.15 million. Grants awarded to organisations totalled £1.8 million.

Beneficiaries included: Visionary (£488,000); South East London Vision (£286,000); Birmingham Vision (£261,000); Visually Impaired (£61,000).

Applications

Research funding: The trust's website states: 'Prospective applicants for project funding should first send an email to research@pocklington-trust.org.uk, outlining their idea or topic and their approach in two or three brief paragraphs. We may then ask for a draft proposal, either in short or full version.'

Other funding: The trust's 2016/17 accounts state: 'Other funding or provision of support to other Charities in the sight loss sector is provided on a case by case basis based on an assessment of need and an organisation's current position and strategy by members of the Senior Leadership Team.'

Sources of information

Accounts; annual report; Charity Commission record; funder's website.

Polden-Puckham Charitable Foundation

 Peace and security, environmental sustainability

UK and overseas

£546,500 (2016/17)

CC number: 1003024

Trustees: Stephen Pittam; Angela Seay; Jonathan Gillett; Dorothy Ball; Simon Fisher.

Correspondent: C. Oliver, Secretary, BM PPCF, London WC1N 3XX (tel: 020 7193 7364; email: ppcf@polden-puckham.org.uk)

 www.polden-puckham.org.uk

Polden-Puckham Charitable Foundation is a grant-making charity with Quaker family roots in the UK. The charity's aim is to contribute to the development of a just society based on its commitment to non-violence and environmental sustainability.

The foundation works to address 'systemic threats by seeking to change policy and attitudes at a national or European level'. In order to achieve this goal, the foundation provides grants to organisations working to achieve change in the following areas:

▸ **Peace and sustainable security:** supporting the development of ways of resolving violent conflicts peacefully, and of addressing their underlying causes

▸ **Environmental sustainability:** supporting work that addresses the pressures and conditions that risk global environmental breakdown

The foundation supports UK-registered charitable organisations, although it also considers supporting organisations which are not UK-registered charities if they can demonstrate that a UK-registered charity is able to receive funds on their behalf. Beneficiary organisations may be single-issue groups working to achieve a particular change, or organisations with a broader remit. Furthermore, the trustees note that they will give particular consideration to small headquarters organisations and that they will only support projects 'when they are clearly of a pioneering nature, with potential for influencing UK national policy'.

Grants are usually between £5,000 and £15,000 per year and are typically awarded for up to three years. The trustees note that they usually support organisations for which this would represent between 3% and 50% of their annual income or organisations with an annual income of between £10,000 and £500,000 approximately.

Financial information

In 2016/17 the foundation had assets of £17.3 million and an income of £478,000. During the year, the foundation awarded grants to 46 organisations, totalling £546,500. Grants were distributed as follows:

Environmental sustainability	32	£374,000
Peace and security	14	£172,500

Beneficiaries included: British American Security Information Council and Oxford Research Group (£15,000 each); Campaign Against the Arms Trade (£12,000); Biofuelwatch, Compass, Rethinking Economics and Trade Justice Movement (£10,000 each); Centre for Human Ecology (£8,000); UK Youth Climate Coalition (£2,000).

Exclusions

The foundation does not fund:

▸ Large organisations (see general information)

▸ Organisations outside the UK (unless they are linked with a UK-registered charity and doing work of international focus)

▸ Work outside the UK (unless it is of international focus)

▸ Grants to individuals

▸ Travel bursaries (including overseas placements and expeditions)

▸ Study

▸ Academic research

▸ Capital projects (e.g. building projects or purchase of nature reserves)

▸ Community or local practical projects (except innovative projects for widespread application)

▸ Youth work, youth training and youth camps

▸ Environmental/ecological conservation

▸ International agencies and overseas appeals

▸ General appeals

▶ Human rights work (except where it relates to peace and environmental sustainability)

▶ Community mediation and crime-related work

Applications

Applicants should first read the foundation's guidelines and check their eligibility using the foundation's online survey. Applications may then be made using a form available to download from the foundation's website. This should be submitted along with copies of the applicant's latest audited accounts and annual report. Note that the foundation no longer accepts applications by post. All applications should be submitted by email. If you are not able to send your application electronically, contact the foundation by phone or email to discuss this.

Applications are generally acknowledged by email within two weeks of receipt or one week after the deadline – if an acknowledgement is not received within this timeframe, applicants should contact the foundation to check that their application has been received.

The trustees usually meet to discuss applications twice a year, in the spring and in the autumn. Deadlines for applications are posted on the foundation's website.

Organisations that have had an application turned down by the foundation are ineligible to reapply within twelve months of that application.

Sources of information

Accounts; annual report; Charity Commission record; funder's website.

The Institute for Policy Research

🔍 Social science, policy and research

📍 Throughout England and Wales

£ £578,000 (2016/17)

CC number: 285143

Trustees: Nicholas Finney; Eric Koops; Simon Webley; Richard Hamilton.

Correspondent: Peter Orbell-Jones, Secretary, Flat 38, Charleston Court, 61 West Cliff Road, Broadstairs, Kent CT10 1RY (tel: 01843 866423; email: peter.orbelljones@yahoo.com)

The institute was registered with the Charity Commission in 1982 and funds research studies, conferences and seminars which promote the education of the public in major social sciences, management studies and economic policy studies.

Grants are made to organisations to fund specific policy studies, conferences and lectures. The purpose of these studies must be to enhance public discussion of issues in the economic, industrial, social and foreign policy fields. The institute expects any findings to be published and made publicly available.

Financial information

In 2016/17 the institute held assets of £278,500 and had an income of £508,000. Grants were awarded to nine organisations and totalled £578,000. The amount awarded in each area of work is summarised in the table below:

Research projects	£485,000
Conferences/seminars	£90,000
Publications	£3,000

Previous beneficiaries have included: Centre for Policy Studies (£223,000); Open Europe (£208,500); TaxPayers' Alliance (£75,000); News-Watch (£35,000); Migration Watch (£11,100); New Culture Forum (£10,000); Parents and Teachers (£9,500); Eurofacts and Politeia (£3,000 each).

Applications

Apply in writing to the correspondent.

Sources of information

Accounts; annual report; Charity Commission record.

The Polonsky Foundation

🔍 Higher education (humanities and social sciences), medical research, the arts, conflict resolution

📍 UK, Israel and the USA

£ £4.4 million (2016/17)

CC number: 291143

Trustees: Dr Georgette Bennett; Dr Leonard Polonsky; Marc Polonsky; Hannah Polonsky Whitney; Joshua-Marc Tanenbaum.

Correspondent: The Trustees, 8 Park Crescent, London W1B 1PG (tel: 020 7436 1997)

Established in 1985, this is the foundation of Dr Leonard Polonsky, executive chair of Hansard Global plc, a global financial services company based in the Isle of Man and listed on the London Stock Exchange.

The foundation supports preserving, promoting access to and dissemination of culture and heritage. It achieves its objectives through supporting major institutions, funding scholarships and advanced studies in humanities and social science, and supporting innovation through higher education and the arts.

Financial information

In 2016/17 the foundation held assets of £30.2 million and had an income of £834,000. Grants were made to organisations totalling £4.4 million.

Beneficiaries included: Theatre for a New Audience (£1.5 million); The Van Leer Jerusalem Institute (£530,000); University of Oxford (£274,500); British Library (£241,000); The Metropolitan Museum (£109,500); Aspen Music Festival and School (£93,000); Oxford Centre of Hebrew and Jewish Studies (£80,000); British Friends of Haifa University (£74,500); Royal Academy of Arts (£70,000).

Grants of less than £50,000 totalled £453,500.

Applications

Apply in writing to the correspondent.

Sources of information

Accounts; annual report; Charity Commission record.

Postcode Community Trust

🔍 Grassroots sports, arts and recreation, health and well-being

📍 England, Scotland and Wales

£ £1.8 million (2016)

OSCR number: SC044772

Trustees: Aidan Connolly; Robert Flett; Judith Hills; Michael Pratt.

Correspondent: Postcode Community Trust, 28 Charlotte Square, Edinburgh EH2 4ET (tel: 0131 322 9399; email: info@postcodecommunitytrust.org.uk)

🌐 www.postcodecommunitytrust.org.uk

f facebook.com/postcodecommunitytrust

🐦 @pcommunitytrust

Postcode Community Trust is a grant-giving body funded by players of People's Postcode Lottery. Postcode Community Trust provides funding opportunities to community groups and charities in Scotland, England and Wales, through grants ranging from £500 to £20,000.

Areas of support

The following information has been taken from the trust's website:

Postcode Community Trust funds new projects, or significant expansions of existing projects, in Great Britain. These projects can be up to 12 months in length. Postcode Community Trust will consider projects which improve health and wellbeing through:

- Grassroots sports arts and recreation projects that improve health and wellbeing
- Projects that improve the health of communities through, for example, first aid courses, befriending, counselling or reducing isolation

Financial information

In 2016 the trust held assets of £298,500 and had an income of £8.6 million. There were 226 grants made, totalling £1.8 million. Grants were geographically distributed as follows:

England	173	£1.4 million
Wales	30	£272,000
Scotland	23	£119,500

Previous beneficiaries have included:

Taming the Floods Somerset Levels (£750,000); Amnesty International, Jamie Oliver Foundation and Music in Hospitals (£100,000 each); St John Ambulance (£20,000); Glasgow East Women's Aid (£17,700); South Birmingham Young Homeless Project (£17,300); Bumblebee Conservation Trust (£14,000); Blantyre Soccer Academy (£13,100); Llety Shenkin Tenants Association (£1,400).

Exclusions

According to its website, the trust will not fund:

- Organisations that are not based in or do not bring a benefit to Scotland, England or Wales
- Hospices or end-of-life care
- Statutory bodies that the state has an obligation to fund (inc. schools/PTAs, councils and local authorities)
- Colleges or universities
- Parish councils
- Medical equipment or research
- Any type of feasibility or research studies
- Building renovations that are purely for cosmetic purposes
- Groups with exclusive membership policies

Applications

There are two funding rounds per year, with a two-stage application process:

Stage one: submit a very short expression of interest (EOI), which requires only some basic details about your organisation, as well as a very short summary of the project you are proposing. Successful applicants will be invited to stage two, while unsuccessful groups are welcome to re-apply for new projects in future rounds.

Stage two: those invited will complete a full application form, with more in-depth detail on both their organisation and the project. Decisions will be made within ten weeks of a stage two submission.

Note: Forms are only accessible through the trust's website on the dates specified there. More details, including guidance notes and deadlines, are available from the website.

Sources of information

Accounts; annual report; OSCR record; funder's website.

Postcode Dream Trust

 Health and well-being, education, loneliness and social isolation, biodiversity, sustainability, sport

 England, Scotland and Wales

£ £1.6 million (2016)

OSCR number: SC044911

Trustees: Aidan Connolly; Michael Pratt; Judith Hills; Robert Flett.

Correspondent: Postcode Dream Trust, 28 Charlotte Square, Edinburgh EH2 4ET (tel: 0131 603 8611; email: info@postcodedreamtrust.org.uk)

🌐 www.postcodedreamtrust.org.uk/ dream-fund.htm

🐦 @DreamFundPPL

The People's Postcode Lottery's Dream Fund 'gives organisations the chance to deliver the project they have always dreamed of, but never had the opportunity to bring to life'.

Dream Fund

The Dream Fund has a total award fund of £3 million for charitable organisations in Great Britain to deliver their dream project in 2019–2021. Grants of between £500,000 and £1 million each are available for collaborative projects lasting 24 months.

Areas of support

The fund's priorities for 2018 are:

- Changing lives through early intervention
- Ending loneliness and social isolation
- Protecting Britain's biodiversity
- Sustainable systems change
- Transforming society through sport

Applications should be submitted jointly between at least two organisations. The lead organisation must be a registered charity; other partners may include charities, voluntary groups, community interest companies, universities or other not-for-profit organisations. The trust states:

> The Dream Fund supports charities to develop innovative solutions to society's most challenging problems. Applications that can score highly in their originality, ambition and collaborative nature stand the highest chances of being successful.

Full guidance is given on the trust's website.

Financial information

In 2016 the trust held assets of £3.5 million and had an income of £9.8 million. Grants were made to four organisations and totalled £1.6 million.

Beneficiaries included: Valley Kids (£583,000); Canal and River Trust and Ellen McArthur Foundation (£500,000 each); Prince of Wales Charitable Foundation (£25,000).

Exclusions

The trust's website states that it does not support projects that:

- Take place overseas
- Are not innovative and do not represent a 'dream
- Do not demonstrate a long-term impact beyond the duration of funding
- Are applied for by local authorities and statutory bodies
- Will not spend the funding within 24 months
- Request less than £500,000
- Request more than £1 million

Applications

There are two funding rounds per year, with a two-stage application process:

Stage one: submit a very short expression of interest (EOI), which requires only some basic details about your organisation, as well as a very short summary of the project you are proposing. Successful applicants will be invited to stage two, while unsuccessful groups are welcome to re-apply for new projects in future rounds.

Stage two: those invited will complete a full application form, with more in-depth detail on both their organisation and the project. Decisions will be made within ten weeks of a stage two submission.

Note: Forms are only accessible through the trust's website on the dates specified there. More details, including guidance notes and deadlines, are available from the website.

Sources of information

Accounts; annual report; OSCR record; further information provided by the funder; funder's website.

Postcode Local Trust

 Outdoor spaces, biodiversity

England, Wales and Scotland

£ £3.9 million (2016)

OSCR number: SC045504

Trustees: Aidan Connolly; Michael Pratt; Judith Hills; Robert Flett.

Correspondent: Postcode Local Trust, 28 Charlotte Square, Edinburgh EH2 4ET (tel: 0131 322 9388; email: info@postcodelocaltrust.org.uk)

🌐 www.postcodelocaltrust.org.uk

The trust was established in 2015 to help communities enhance their natural environment. It funds new projects or significant expansions of existing projects which can be up to 12 months in length.

Areas of support

The trust's funding guidelines state that it:

Will consider projects that improve biodiversity and outdoor spaces such as:

- Community gardens and play areas using sustainable materials
- Outdoor education and heritage
- Green Energy projects and flood prevention

Financial information

In 2016 the trust held assets of £1 million and had an income of £9.2 million. Grants awarded to organisations totalled £3.9 million.

The trust made 385 small grants totalling £3.62 million. These were broken down as follows:

England	271	£2.3 million
Scotland	73	£783,500
Wales	41	£272,500
Community environments	368	£3.19 million
Sustainable energy	17	£172,000

Exclusions

According to the trust's funding guide, it will not fund:

- Organisations currently in receipt of funding from players of the People's Postcode Lottery, including previous grant recipients who have not submitted a project evaluation form
- Existing projects (unless significant expansion)
- Bodies seeking to distribute grants/funds to others
- Organisations with restricted or exclusive memberships
- Applications where our funding would be less than 10% of the overall project cost
- Organisations that have previously breached their funding agreement with Postcode Local Trust
- Political parties or party-political activities
- Projects that promote religion
- Schools (except for special schools), PTAs, nurseries, and universities/colleges
- Lunch clubs, mother and toddler and after-school groups
- Individuals
- Feasibility studies
- Foreign travel
- General marketing appeals or sponsorship
- Medical research, advice and equipment
- End-of-life or palliative care
- Short-term projects such as events, conferences, day trips, seminars, galas or festivals
- Training or educational workshops that do not result in a tangible outcome for participants
- Building renovations/general refurbishment
- Installations of toilets, showers, lifts or changing rooms
- Organisations that appear to have excessive unrestricted or free reserves and no policy to reflect the rationale behind this
- Projects or activities that the state has a legal obligation to provide

Applications

There are two funding rounds per year, with a two-stage application process:

Stage one: submit a very short expression of interest (EOI), which requires only some basic details about your organisation, as well as a very short summary of the project you are proposing. Successful applicants will be invited to stage two, while unsuccessful groups are welcome to re-apply for new projects in future rounds.

Stage two: those invited will complete a full application form, with more in-depth detail on both their organisation and the project. Decisions will be made within ten weeks of a stage two submission.

Note: Forms are only accessible through the trust's website on the dates specified there. More details, including guidance notes and deadlines, are available from the website.

Sources of information

Accounts; annual report; OSCR record; funder's website.

David and Elaine Potter Foundation

Education, civil society, social research, the arts

UK and overseas, particularly sub-Saharan Africa

£885,000 (2016)

CC number: 1078217

Trustees: Michael Polonsky; Michael Langley; Dr David Potter; Elaine Potter; Samuel Potter.

Correspondent: Ben Stewart, Director, 5 Welbeck Street, London W1G 9YQ, United Kingdom (tel: 020 3915 9283; email: info@potterfoundation.com)

 www.potterfoundation.com

Established in 1999, the foundation has general charitable purposes but focuses primarily on supporting education, civil society and the arts. On its website, the foundation describes its activities as follows:

Our initial aim was to improve education and access to education in Africa, but our experience was that the improvement of education was often hampered by failures of governance – of inequality and corruption. Hence, we also provided grants to help the growth of civil society and governance to create a platform upon which education could flourish and be effective. In 2015 our focus was revised to two main areas: Education and Civil Society.

Grant-making priorities

Education

The foundation funds projects that work on 'improving policy, improved practices and techniques and sustainability' and favours 'grants directed at education in support of economic and social well-being in low and middle-income countries, especially in southern Africa'. Projects can be in the following countries: the UK, South Africa, Malawi, Zambia, Zimbabwe, Lesotho, Namibia or Mozambique. Grants made to UK organisations should focus on providing young people with life skills and enhancing their employability. Projects in southern Africa should focus on STEM subjects, school governance, leadership and teacher training as well as the development of young people. The foundation will fund pilot projects, especially those that could influence policy.

Civil Society

The foundation believes that 'in order for education to flourish it needs to be underpinned by a strong civil society'. Its primary focus is on transparency, accountability, anti-corruption and good governance. However, the foundation has also expressed an interest in human rights, drones, investigative journalism, the rule of law, democracy, equality, and the misuse of natural resources. Grants are made to UK-based organisations that undertake cross-border or non-geographic work. There is a smaller secondary focus on non-governmental organisations or civil society organisations in Africa.

Arts and non-strategic

Outside of the core grants to organisations working in the above fields, the foundation also supports causes that are of a personal interest to the Potter family. This includes grants to London-based theatres and Performa, an arts organisation based in New York City.

Grants can be made for up to a maximum of three years and the foundation is willing to enter into joint funding agreements with other grant-makers.

Financial information

In 2016 the foundation had assets of £19.4 million and an income of £357,000. Grants totalling £885,500 were made to 30 organisations and were distributed for the following purposes:

Education	£495,000
Civil Society	£276,000
Arts	£106,500
Other	£7,500

Beneficiaries included: University of Cape Town Trust (£90,000); Philharmonic Orchestra (£60,000); Transparency International UK (£45,000); Centre for Evaluation and Monitoring and University of Durham (£40,000); Performa and Global Leadership Foundation (£30,000 each); CHIVA Africa (£25,000); Involve Foundation (£15,000); Almeida Theatre (£6,000).

Exclusions

The foundation does not support the following:

- Individuals
- CICs
- Retrospective costs
- Full economic costs for universities
- Political organisations
- Clinical trials
- Religious organisations that only work for the benefit of members of their own religion
- Building or rebuilding of schools
- School equipment
- Scaling-up projects
- Bursaries for individual schoolchildren/undergraduate education
- Civic education/citizenship education programmes
- Local issues

Applications

Applications are by invitation only, unsolicited applications are not accepted. The website states: 'If you think your work may fit our remit you should email us to discuss your potential eligibility and whether it is something that we may potentially fund. Please do not send written correspondence.'

Sources of information

Accounts; annual report; Charity Commission record; funder's website.

Power to Change Trust

Community businesses

England

£11.7 million (2016)

CC number: 1159982

Trustee: Power to Change Trustee Ltd.

Correspondent: The Grants Team, The Clarence Centre, 6 St Georges Circus, London SE1 6FE (tel: 020 3857 7270; email: info@thepowertochange.org.uk)

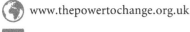 www.thepowertochange.org.uk

 facebook.com/communitybiz

 @peoplesbiz

The trust was established in 2015 and has received £150 million from the Big Lottery Fund to support community businesses across England. The following was taken from the trust's website:

> Over ten years, with a £150 million endowment from Big Lottery Fund, Power to Change is supporting community businesses to create better places across England.
>
> We want to support people to take action to address local challenges, enabling them to control vital assets and services that might otherwise disappear, or start new businesses themselves in response to local needs.
>
> At the heart of our vision is the devolution of power to local communities. We believe that putting business in community hands makes places better.

Community Business Fund

The Community Business Fund is the trust's main grant programme. Grants of between £50,000 and £300,000 are available to make community businesses more sustainable. Grants are available for both capital and revenue funding.

Bright Ideas Fund

The Bright Ideas Fund aims to gives community groups the tools and support they need to start a community business, by providing finance for feasibility studies and seed funding.

Eligibility

To be considered for funding, you will need to show that your organisation meets the trust's definition of a community business. In previous funding rounds around two thirds of applications were rejected for not meeting the trust's four criteria of what makes a community business. The following criteria were taken from the trust's website:

Locally rooted
We only fund businesses that are based in their community

- Typically that local area will be smaller in size than a local authority. It will be well defined and may include a number of postcodes or villages
- People must self-identify with that area
- A majority of staff, volunteers and other stakeholders must be drawn from the local community and reflect its diversity

Accountable to the local community
The business must be locally controlled

- The local community must have a genuine say in how the business is run, e.g. through regular consultation, membership or ownership
- There are formal structures to engage a large number of local people on a frequent and ongoing basis
- A large majority of the management and trustees are drawn from the community

Trading for the benefit of the local community
Profits must stay in the area

- The organisation must have a clear trading model
- A majority of its profits should be distributed locally and used to deliver local benefit
- The project we are funding must have charitable purpose. Any private benefit must be incidental

Broad community impact
You must address challenges in your community

- A community business should contribute to a broader sense of confidence and pride in a place
- It must be able to articulate how it is tackling the specific issues that exist in its community
- A community business must be able to show the impact it is making

Financial information

In 2016 the trust held assets of £131.6 million and had an income of £4.5 million. There were 167 grants awarded totalling £11.7 million.

Beneficiaries included: Holborn Community Association (£300,000); Brixton Green (£231,000); Ideal for All (£215,500); Real Farming Trust (£88,500); Cuckmere Community Bus (£75,000); Calico Homes (£10,000); Grimsby Community Energy Ltd (£6,000); Kirkgare Arts (£3,000).

Applications

Applications can be made through the trust's website. Deadlines, guidance and eligibility criteria can all be found on the trust's website.

Sources of information

Accounts; annual report; Charity Commission record; funder's website.

Pret Foundation Trust

Homelessness

UK (but projects should be local to a branch of Pret)

£782,000 (2016)

CC number: 1050195

Trustees: Clive Schlee; Andrea Wareham.

Correspondent: Giovanna Passini, Financial Donations Manager, Verde Building, 10 Bressenden Place, London SW1E 5DH (tel: 020 8827 8814; email: giovanna.passini@pret.com)

 www.pret.co.uk/en-gb/pret-foundation-trust

The trust, which is the corporate charity of the sandwich shop chain Pret A Manger, was founded in 1995. The charity delivers surplus food throughout the night, runs the Rising Stars Initiative which helps vulnerable people off the streets and into work, and supports charities working with homeless people.

The trust's website states:

> In order for charities to receive funding from the Pret Foundation Trust they must be:
>
> - A registered charity
> - Set up to support the homeless in some way
> - Local to a Pret shop
> - Receiving no more than 20% of income via statutory funding
> - Solving a real problem in a practical way

Financial information

In 2016 the trust had assets of £336,500 and an income of £1.8 million. Grants to 52 organisations totalled £782,000. The foundation also made food and equipment donations totalling £58,000.

Beneficiaries included: Cardboard Citizens (£50,000); FareShare (£33,000); Nottingham Winter Shelter (£30,000); Restart (£20,000); Glass Door (£16,900); St Stephen's Church – Canonbury and This Is Growth Ltd (£15,000 each); The 999 Club (£13,100); Bethany Christian Trust (£13,000); Vision Care for Homeless People (£7,400); Action Homeless – Leicester (£6,300); Bridges Project (£6,000); The Simon Community (£5,000).

Applications

Contact the correspondent for further information.

Sources of information

Accounts; annual report; Charity Commission record; funder's website.

Sir John Priestman Charity Trust

General charitable purposes, older people, churches, clergy, social welfare

Counties of Sunderland, Durham and York (in relation to churches)

£385,500 (2016)

CC number: 209397

Trustees: Peter Taylor; Timothy Norton; Anthony Coates; Thomas Greenwell; Jean Majer.

Correspondent: The Trustees, c/o McKenzie Bell, 19 John Street, Sunderland, Tyne and Wear SR1 1JG (tel: 0191 567 4857)

The trust was established in 1931. The main aims of the trust, as stated by the trustees in their 2016 annual report, are:

- The feeding of poor in the county borough of Sunderland in times of distress
- The payment of annuities to older and infirm people residing in the county of Durham
- The provision of education at any English university of young men as candidates for holy orders in the Church of England who are resident in the county of Durham at the time of their assistance
- The establishment of maintenance of any hospital or convalescent home in the county of Durham for the benefit of the poor in the county
- The employment and payment of nurses for the sick and infirm in the county of Durham
- The making of donations to any charitable institution for the benefit of people in the beneficial area
- For the benefit of members of the church of England – building, maintaining and furnishing (including provision of organs) churches, mission halls and schools in the counties of Durham and York; the relief, if in necessitous circumstances, of ministers of the church of England who have worked or may be working in the counties of Durham or York and the relief of widows or families of any such persons who may be in necessitous circumstances

Grant-making

The following information about the trust's grant-making was taken from the 2016 annual report:

> The trustees support a number of charities by way of regular annual grants, but otherwise the trustees aim where possible to award grants for specific projects as opposed to general running costs. In this way the trustees aim to assist charities to achieve particular objectives such as acquiring or replacing essential equipment or extending the scope of the benefits which they provide. In making grants the trustees are particularly concerned to establish that projects are viable. Accordingly grants are awarded subject to such conditions as to funding or otherwise as the trustees consider appropriate and payment is deferred until the conditions are satisfied. If these cannot be fulfilled the grant is cancelled.

Grants are awarded to churches in the Church of England for 'building, restoring, altering, enlarging, maintaining and furnishing (including provision of organs)' and the trustees 'recognise the challenges faced by parishes, often in deprived areas, in maintaining historic church buildings which often fulfil a vital role in the wider community. Where necessary, the Trustees seek information from the diocese in relation to such applications.'

The trustees generally award a relatively large number of modest grants, rather than a few large grants, and they support a range of causes.

Financial information

In 2016 the trust had assets of £13.2 million and an income of £466,000. A total of £385,500 was awarded in grants to 118 organisations including churches. Only in special circumstances are grants awarded outside the specified geographical area or to individuals. A number of charities are supported by way of recurring annual grants.

Beneficiaries included: Outward Bound Trust (£13,000); Durham School (£12,000); St Nicholas Church, Ganton (£9,000); Stockton Parish Church (£8,000); Independence at Home (£4,000); Motor Neurone Disease Association (£3,000); Sunderland Victim Support Scheme (£2,500); Macular Society (£2,000); Young Asian Voices (£1,100).

Exclusions

Organisations operating outside charity's beneficial area.

Applications

Apply in writing to the correspondent. The trustees meet on a quarterly basis to consider applications and award grants.

Sources of information

Accounts; annual report; Charity Commission record.

The Prince of Wales's Charitable Foundation

Built environment, responsible business and enterprise, young people and education, global sustainability

UK

£3.07 million (2016/17)

CC number: 1127255

Trustees: Clive Alderton; Dame Julie Moore; Dr Kenneth Brockington Wilson; Sir Ian Cheshire.

Correspondent: The Trustees, Clarence House, St James's, London SW1A 1BA (email: contactpwcf@royal.gsx.gov.uk)

www.princeofwalescharitable foundation.org.uk

The Prince of Wales's Charitable Foundation was established by trust deed in 1979 and has the aim of transforming lives and building sustainable communities. It is funded through profits from sales of Waitrose Duchy Organic and Highgrove products, as well as from tours of the gardens at Highgrove.

The foundation supports a wide range of causes with a particular interest in funding projects centred around the built environment, responsible business and enterprise, young people and education, and global sustainability.

Grant programmes

The foundation states that, in view of its aim of making a difference to people and their communities, it particularly welcomes small grants applications from UK-based grassroots community projects. It operates two grants programmes:

Major grants

This programme awards grants of £5,000 upwards. Unsolicited applications are not accepted.

Small grants

Grants of up to £5,000 are awarded through this programme. Awards average £1,500 and are awarded for a single financial year. Applications are considered from UK-registered charities that have been active for at least two years and are able to submit accounts.

Financial information

In 2016/17 the foundation had assets of £10.9 million and an income of £8.1 million. Grants totalling £3.07 million were made to 134 organisations.

Previous beneficiaries have included: The Great Steward of Scotland Dumfries House Trust (£3 million); The Soil Association (£500,000); The Prince's Regeneration Trust (£250,000); The Prince's Trust and Prince's Trust International (£150,000 each); Turquoise Mountain (£80,000); Step Up To Serve (£50,000); AMREF, St Catherine's Foundation and Royal Deeside Railway Preservation Society (£10,000 each).

Exclusions

According to the foundation's website, grants will not be made to:

- Individuals
- Public bodies
- Organisations that mainly distribute grants to other organisations
- Organisations that are looking to deliver similar projects to any of The Prince's Charities (please visit The Prince's Charities page for further project details at www.princeofwales.gov.uk/prince-waless-charities)
- Organisations with an income of £1m or more
- Organisations with political associations or interests
- Cover capital expenditure with the exception of community-based, religion-related and heritage restoration projects

Applications

Fill out the online eligibility form in the first instance. If you are eligible, you will be given access to the full online application form. The major grants programme is not open to unsolicited applications.

Sources of information

Accounts; annual report; Charity Commission record; funder's website.

The Prince's Countryside Fund

 Service provision in rural areas, rural enterprise, education and training in farming

UK

£1.2 million (2016/17)

CC number: 1136077

Trustees: Lord Curry of Kirkdale; Elizabeth Buchanan; Edwin Booth; Mark Allen; Paul Murphy; Andrew Wright; Steven McLean; Sara Bennison; Mat Roberts; Mark Duddrige; John Wilkinson; Mark Pendington; Rob Collins; Lord Lindsay.

Correspondent: Helen Aldis, Senior Manager, 137 Shepherdess Walk, London N1 7RQ (email: helen.aldis@bitc.org.uk)

www.princescountrysidefund.org.uk

facebook.com/princescountrysidefund

@countrysidefund

The fund was set up in 2010 as 'a response to concerns expressed by HRH The Prince of Wales and by Business in the Community's Rural Action Leadership Team regarding the future of farming and rural communities in the United Kingdom'. The fund is supported by 'a unique collaboration of businesses working together to secure a sustainable future for British agriculture and the wider rural economy'.

According to its 2016/17 annual report, the three goals of the charity are:
- To improve the prospects of viability for family farm businesses
- To support aid delivery in emergencies and build resilience
- To sustain rural communities and drive economic vibrancy

Grant-giving programme

The following information has been taken from the charity's website:

The Prince's Countryside Fund provides more than £1m in grants each year to projects across the UK. We have grants of up to £50,000 available for innovative projects that will provide a lasting legacy to the individuals and communities they seek to benefit.

We recognise that rural communities face a range of challenges. One way in which we help grassroots organisations overcome these is through our grant programme.

We seek applications to support activity that results in a long-term positive impact on rural communities by helping the people that live and work in the countryside. Our grant programme currently aims to tackle the following key rural issues:

- Developing thriving rural communities by improving service provision in rural areas
- Transforming rural livelihoods by supporting rural enterprise and farming businesses
- Creating the farmers of the future by providing training opportunities for young people and unemployed people

The charity also provides emergency grants and free business skills training to family dairy and livestock farms across the UK.

Financial information

In 2016/17 the charity held assets of £831,000 and had and an income of £2.4 million. Grants awarded to organisations totalled £1.2 million.

Beneficiaries included: Friends of Nidderdale Area of Outstanding Beauty and Yorkshire Dales Rivers Trust (£50,000 each); Herefordshire Rural Hub (£46,500); Wereham Village Hall (£31,500); The St Tudy Community Shop (£25,000); National Sheep Association (£14,700); Trawden Forest (£7,000); The Farmer Network (£3,000).

Exclusions

According to the charity's website, it will not fund:

- Statutory bodies, such as local authorities, NHS bodies, or work where there is statutory responsibility to provide funding
- Religious bodies where the funding will be for religious purposes
- Political organisations where the funding will be used for political purposes Projects where the work has begun and money has been spent in anticipation of receiving funding
- Projects where the funding would displace existing funding streams, such as agri-environment schemes
- Projects which do not demonstrate sufficient public benefit and in which private benefit is more than incidental
- Applications for feasibility studies where the outcome is unknown cannot be funded
- Applications from support organisations that do not provide direct service delivery to clients will be accepted, however applications will have to be for specific projects with tangible and deliverable outcomes

Applications

All applications have to be made online on the charity's website (registration is required). Check the charity's website for information on application deadlines.

Sources of information

Accounts; annual report; Charity Commission record; guidelines for applicants; funder's website.

The Professional Footballers' Association Charity

 Community participation, community relations, recreation, education, general charitable purposes

England and Wales

£16.43 million to organisations (2016/17)

CC number: 1150458

Trustees: David Weir; Garth Crooks; Gordon Taylor; Darren Wilson; Gareth Griffiths; Christopher Powell; Brendon Batson; Paul Elliot; Simon Morgan.

Correspondent: Darren Wilson, Trustee, 20 Oxford Court, Bishopsgate, Manchester M2 3WQ (tel: 0161 236 0575; email: info@thepfa.co.uk)

www.thepfa.com

The Professional Footballers' Association was originally founded in 1907 as a sportspeople's union, aiming to protect, improve and negotiate the conditions, rights and status of all professional players. In 2013 the charity was registered with the Charity Commission to make grants to organisations, as well as sportspeople and ex-sportspeople in need. The charity is particularly interested in supporting the education of young people, promoting good health, increasing community partnership and encouraging healthy recreation.

According to the charity's 2016/17 annual report, its objects relating to the public are:

▶ To advance the education of the public
▶ To support and promote community participation and healthy recreation by providing facilities for the playing of football and other sports
▶ To provide and assist in providing facilities for sport, recreation and other leisure time occupations of people who have a need for such facilities by reason of age, illness or disability

The charity states that its beneficiaries are:

▶ Trainee professional footballers
▶ Young people registered with professional football academies associated with a club or centre of excellence
▶ Former trainee professional footballers
▶ Professional footballers
▶ Former professional footballers

In all cases, beneficiaries should play or have played or trained with a club in any football league.

Financial information

In 2016/17 the charity held assets of £53.4 million and had an income of £27.9 million. Grants totalled £16.96 million, with £16.43 million given to organisations and £530,000 given to individuals.

Beneficiaries included: English Football League Community Fund (£3.5 million); Football League Youth Development Programme (£3 million); PFA Educational and Vocational Grants (£1.8 million); National Football Museum (£20,000); Heart4More Foundation (£11,000).

Applications

Apply in writing to the correspondent.

Sources of information

Accounts; annual report; Charity Commission record; funder's website.

Prostate Cancer UK

Prostate cancer research and treatment

UK

£7.2 million (2016/17)

CC number: 1005541

Trustees: Prof. Jonathan Waxman; Steve Ford; Andrew Mitchell; Martin Roland; Robert Humphreys; Charles Packshaw; Michael Tye; Tom Shropshire; Prof. Sara Faithfull; Simon Hammett; Marion Leslie; David Neal; Lynne Robb.

Correspondent: The Research Team, Fourth Floor, The Counting House, 53 Tooley Street, London SE1 2QN (tel: 020 3310 7037; email: research@prostatecanceruk.org)

www.prostatecanceruk.org

facebook.com/prostatecanceruk

@prostateuk

Prostate Cancer UK was established in 1991 with the aim of improving the care and welfare of those affected by prostate cancer, increasing investment in research, and raising public and political awareness of the disease.

From 2012 to 2020 all of the foundation's research funding is targeted at three priority areas:

▶ Identifying men at highest risk of developing aggressive prostate cancer
▶ Better tests to distinguish indolent from aggressive tumours
▶ New targeted treatments for advanced prostate cancer

Grant programmes

At the time of writing (May 2018) all of the charity's funding opportunities fall within one of the following three categories:

▶ **Research Innovation Awards:** Funding for innovative research that has the potential to impact the way prostate cancer is diagnosed, treated or prevented. All proposals must align with the foundation's research strategy. Projects should be one to five years in duration. Shorter projects may also be eligible but applicants should first contact the research team. The programme will fund both fundamental and clinical research and there are no financial restrictions on the amount that can be requested
▶ **Training Learning and Development Awards:** Bursaries are available for professional development activities that have a clear focus on prostate cancer or benign prostate disease
▶ **Major Awards and Themed Calls:** Periodically, the charity advertises themed calls on its website. Previous themed calls have included research into 'accelerating precision medicine trials in prostate cancer' as well as 'more accurate methods for diagnosing prostate cancer'

Full details of all current open programmes and funding calls can be found on the charity's website.

Financial information

In 2016/17 the charity had assets of £15.8 million and an income of £20.7 million. During the year, the charity awarded £7.2 million in research grants.

Beneficiaries included: Queen's University Belfast (£2.1 million); The Institute of Cancer Research (£1.9 million); University of Manchester (£1.3 million); University of York (£536,000); University College London (£300,000); University of Essex (£256,000); University of Cardiff (£280,000); University of East Anglia (£209,000); University of Nottingham (£183,000).

Applications

The following information is given in the charity's annual report 2016/17:

The charity awards grants for research funding in line with the standards and guidelines set out by the Association of Medical Research Charities. Calls for applications are advertised through our website, researcher newsletter and appropriate specialist media. All applications for funding are sent to a minimum of three external independent expert reviewers who provide a written assessment of the quality, novelty, importance and relevance of the proposal. We also seek input from men affected by prostate cancer, and/or their families, to ensure that the research proposed has been explained well for a lay audience and that it has the potential to make a difference from their experience. Once all peer reviews are received a final funding recommendation is made by our Research Advisory Committee.

Sources of information

Accounts; annual report; Charity Commission record; guidelines for applicants; further information provided by the funder; funder's website.

The PwC Foundation

 Employability, health care, education

UK

£1.76 million (2016/17)

CC number: 1144124

Trustees: Neil Sherlock; Kevin Ellis; David Adair; Zelf Hussain; Kalee Talvitie-Brown; David Walters; Emma Cox.

Correspondent: Sean Good, PricewaterhouseCoopers, 1 Embankment Place, London WC2N 6RH (tel: 07764 902846; email: sean.good@uk.pwc.com)

 www.pwc.co.uk/who-we-are/ corporate-sustainability/ community-involvement/ pwcfoundation.html

The PwC Foundation was established in 2011 and is the corporate charity of PricewaterhouseCoopers LLP (PwC), which was formed by a merger between Coopers and Lybrand and Price Waterhouse in 1998.

The objectives of the PwC Foundation are to promote sustainable development and social inclusion and environmental awareness for public benefit. The foundation is also the company's vehicle for providing matched funding to the charity sector.

Financial information

In 2016/17 the foundation had assets of £378,000 and an income of £1.8 million, all of which was donated. There were 440 grants made totalling £1.76 million. Grants were broken down as follows:

Employability	74	£609,500
Health care	199	£488,500
Education	44	£278,500
Other	123	£189,000

Beneficiaries included: Wellbeing of Women (£222,500); School for Social Entrepreneurs (£154,500); Teach First (£112,500); Beyond Food CIC (£109,500); Southbank Centre (£60,000); Alzheimer's Scotland (£20,000); Enabling Enterprise (£15,000).

Exclusions

The foundation will not fund political organisations, lobbying groups, animal rights groups or religious bodies.

Applications

The foundation's 2016/17 accounts state: 'Currently there is no formal open grant application process. The Steering Committee and Trustees can independently identify recipients for funding who meet the charitable objectives of the Foundation. Recipients are approved by the trustees.'

Sources of information

Accounts; annual report; Charity Commission record; funder's website.

Mr and Mrs J A Pye's Charitable Settlement

 General charitable purposes, environment, adults' health and care, children's health and care, youth organisations, education, heritage and the arts

Mainly Oxfordshire and the surrounding areas

£598,000 (2016)

CC number: 242677

Trustees: Simon Stubbings; David Tallon; Patrick Mulcare.

Correspondent: The Trustees, Leander College, 30 East Street, Oxford OX2 0AU (tel: 01865 721269; email: pyecharitablesettlement@gmail.com)

 www.pyecharitablesettlement.org

The charity was endowed in 1965 by the Pye family of Oxford for general charitable purposes. The charity emphasises that it is mainly concentrating its funding in the Oxfordshire region.

The following information – obtained from the charity's website – is not exhaustive but gives guidance as to the areas where the charity looks to direct its funding:

- Environment: 'this subject particularly deals with organic farming matters, conservation generally and health-related matters such as pollution research and some wildlife protection'
- Adult health and care: 'especially causes supporting the following: post-natal depression, schizophrenia, mental health generally and research into the main causes of early death'
- Children's health and care: 'for physical, mental and learning disabilities, respite breaks, etc.'
- Youth organisations: 'particularly projects encouraging self-reliance or dealing with social deprivation'
- Education: nursery, primary, secondary or higher education institutions (but not individuals)
- Heritage and the arts: 'under this category, the trustees will consider applications relating to heritage and the arts generally'

The trustees prefer to support under-funded charities working in the areas stated above in order to enable them to 'play a fuller role in their communities'. Due to high demand, the charity cannot support every eligible application, although the website states that the trustees 'recognise the difficulty many smaller charities experience in obtaining core funding in order to operate efficiently in today's demanding environment'.

Financial information

In 2016 the charity had assets of £13.6 million and an income of £1.3 million. During the year, the charity gave around £598,000 in grants to 125 organisations.

Beneficiaries included: Magdalen College School (£80,000); Music @ Oxford (£55,000); Reinvigorating the Ridgeway (£25,000); Association for Post-Natal Illness (£20,000); Banbury Museum Trust (£15,000); Artist in Residence (£10,000); Falcon Rowing and Canoeing Club (£5,000).

Exclusions

Grants are not made for:

- Individuals
- Organisations that are not registered charities
- Animal welfare
- The promotion of religion

Applications

All applications should be sent to the administrative office (and not to individual trustees). They are reviewed on a continual basis and are considered at quarterly trustees' meetings; therefore, it may be four months before a decision is made. All applications are acknowledged and all candidates are notified of the outcome. The charity notes that telephone calls are usually counterproductive.

While there is no application form, the following essential requirements are listed on the website:

- The registered charity number or evidence of an organisations tax exempt status
- Brief description of the activities of the charity
- The names of the trustees and chief officers [NB more important than patrons]
- Details of the purpose of the application and where funds will be put to use
- Details of the funds already raised and the proposals for how remaining funds are to be raised
- The latest trustees' report and full audited or independently examined accounts (which must comply with Charity Commission guidelines and requirements)

▶ Details of full name of the bank account, sort code, and number into which any grant should be paid
▶ The charity's email address

Applicants are invited to apply by email.

Sources of information
Accounts; annual report; Charity Commission record; funder's website.

The Queen Anne's Gate Foundation

🔍 Educational, medical and rehabilitative charities and those that work with underprivileged areas of society

📍 UK and Asia

💷 £204,000 (2016/17)

CC number: 1108903

Trustees: Nicholas Allan; Jonathan Boyer; Deborah Fisher.

Correspondent: Deborah Fisher, Trustee, The Old Coach House, Sunnyside, Bergh Apton, Norwich NR15 1DD (tel: 01508 480100; email: info@fisherlegal.co.uk)

The following information was taken from the 2016/17 annual report:

The foundation seeks to support projects and charities within the following broad criteria. It seeks to make a contribution that is meaningful in the context of the project/charity with which it is working. It tries to focus in particular on projects which might be said to make potentially unproductive lives productive. This tends to mean a bias towards educational and rehabilitative charities and those that work with underprivileged areas of society. There is an attempt to focus a significant proportion of donations in the UK and Asia. In principle there is a willingness to commit or soft commit funding for three years if it enables the chosen charity or project to plan more effectively. The Foundation also supports one-off appropriate causes, as they become available.

Financial information
In 2016/17 the foundation held assets of £1.6 million and had an income of £45,500. Grants totalling £204,000 were made to 11 organisations and were broken down as follows:

Education	£107,000
Children's welfare	£50,000
General welfare	£47,000

Beneficiaries included: English National Opera, Families for Children, Trail Blazers and The Citizen Foundation (£25,000 each); Horatio's Garden and Safe Lives (£20,000 each); The Hong Kong Polytechnic University (£17,000); Christian Friends of Korea (£16,100); Sri Aurobindo Society (£11,000); City of Exeter YMCA Community Projects and The Two Moors Festival (£10,000 each).

Applications
Apply in writing to the correspondent. The trustees meet twice a year.

Sources of information
Accounts; annual report; Charity Commission record.

Queen Mary's Roehampton Trust

🔍 Ex-Service support

📍 UK

💷 £544,000 (2016/17)

CC number: 211715

Trustees: James Macnamara; Col. Paul Cummings; Cdr Stephen Farringdon; Colin Green; Debbie Bowles; Stephen Coltman; Sir Barry Thornton; Anne Child; Ed Tytherleigh; Dr Rakesh Bhabutta.

Correspondent: Col. Stephen Rowland-Jones, Clerk to the Trustees, 2 Sovereign Close, Quidhampton, Salisbury, Wiltshire SP2 9ES (tel: 01722 501413; email: qmrt@hotmail.co.uk)

The trust was established for the benefit of people who served in the armed forces or in mercantile marine or other services established under the Civil Defence Acts 1937 and 1939 who have suffered a disability in that service and their widows/widowers or dependants.

The trust's objectives are met by making grants to any charities or organisations whose objects include the reception, accommodation, treatment or aftercare of people who come within the charity's objects. Grants may also be made in aid of medical or surgical research having particular regard to the needs of people with disabilities who served in the armed forces.

Financial information
In 2016/17 the trust had assets of £14.7 million and an income of £552,500. Grants totalling £544,000 were awarded to 36 organisations.

Beneficiaries included: Combat Stress, Erskine Hospital and Haig Homes (£30,000 each); Broughton House (£25,000); The Not Forgotten Association (£22,000); Bournemouth War Memorial Homes (£20,000); Scottish Veterans Residences (£15,000); Canine Partners (£10,000); Deafblind UK (£5,000); Association of Jewish Ex-Service Men and Women (£2,000).

Exclusions
No grants are made to individuals.

Applications
Apply on a standard application form available from the correspondent.

Representatives of the trust may visit beneficiary organisations.

Sources of information
Accounts; annual report; Charity Commission record.

Quintessentially Foundation

🔍 Education, health and welfare of disadvantaged children and young people worldwide

📍 Worldwide

💷 £1.6 million (2016)

CC number: 1144584

Trustees: Caroline Hurley; Aaron Simpson; Kevin Burke; Dr Peter Crowther; Benjamin Elliot; Ian Ewart; Sebastian Lee; Joyce Hytner.

Correspondent: The Trustees, 29 Portland Place, London W1B 1QB (tel: 0845 388 7985; email: info@quintessentiallyfoundation.org)

 www.quintessentiallyfoundation.org

The foundation was established in 2008 and is the grant-making arm of the Quintessentially Group. The aim of the foundation is to improve the education, health and welfare of disadvantaged children and young people worldwide to allow them to fulfil their potential and realise their dreams.

The foundation partners with eight to ten charities per year, hosting events solely for their benefit. The foundation also works with other charities, promoting their own events to members and creating unique opportunities through charitable ventures.

Financial information
In 2016 the foundation had assets of £125,500 and an income of £2 million. Grants to 12 organisations totalled £1.6 million.

Beneficiaries included: Sentebale (£300,000); British Heart Foundation and Greenhouse Foundation (£217,000 each); Wellchild and Macmillan Cancer Support (£125,000 each); The Prince's Trust (£123,000); Good Chance (£54,000); Anthony Nolan and Prostate Cancer UK (£36,000 each); Royal Parks Foundation (£15,300).

Exclusions
The foundation's website states: 'Your Charity must be registered in the UK. The Charity must be independent of state, political party or religion. The Service provided must be independently audited.'

Applications

Applications to partner with the foundation can be made through its website.

Sources of information

Accounts; annual report; Charity Commission record; funder's website.

Rachel Charitable Trust

 General charitable purposes, in practice, mainly Jewish charities for religion and religious education and the relief of poverty

 Worldwide

£ £5.45 million (2015/16)

CC number: 276441

Trustees: Leopold Noe; Susan Noe; Simon Kanter.

Correspondent: Robert Chalk, 30 Market Place, London W1W 8AP

This trust was established in 1978 for general charitable purposes and focuses on the relief of poverty and the advancement of religion and religious education. Our research indicates that, in practice, the trust gives mainly to Jewish organisations.

Financial information

In 2015/16 the trust had assets of almost £7 million and an income of £8.5 million. Grants were made totalling £5.45 million. A list of beneficiary organisations was not included in the annual report and accounts, although this information can be purchased from the correspondent.

Previous beneficiaries have included: British Friends of Shuut Ami; Children's Hospital Trust Fund; Cometville Ltd; Encounter – Jewish Outreach Network; Choshen Mishpat Centre; Gertner Charitable Trust; Hertsmere Jewish Primary School; Jewish Learning Exchange; London Millennium Bikeathon; Manchester Jewish Grammar School; Project Seed; Shaarei Zedek Hospital; Shomrei Hachomot Jerusalem; Yeshiva Ohel Shimon Trust; Yeshiva Shaarei Torah Manchester.

Applications

Apply in writing to the correspondent.

Sources of information

Accounts; annual report; Charity Commission record.

The Racing Foundation

 Welfare of members of the horseracing industry, education and training connected with the horseracing industry, racehorse welfare, equine science research

 UK

 £2 million (2016)

CC number: 1145297

Trustees: Ian Barlow; William Rucker; Katherine Keir; Mark Johnston; Susannah Gill; Mark Johnston; Linda Bowles.

Correspondent: Robert Hezel, Chief Executive, 75 High Holborn, London WC1V 6LS (tel: 01763 852790)

🌐 www.racingfoundation.co.uk

🐦 @rfoundation01

The foundation was established in 2012. The Racing Foundation has received an endowment of £78 million from the net proceeds of the UK government's sale of the Horserace Totalisator Board ('Tote') and aims to use these funds to achieve a lasting legacy for the sport of horseracing.

Areas of support

The foundation's website states:

We will support work on the people agenda that directly supports the stated aims of the industry's strategy and in the following areas:

Social Welfare

▪ The improvement in the health or the rehabilitation from injury of current or former members of the horseracing industry

▪ The prevention or relief of poverty among current or former members of the horseracing industry and their dependents

▪ Community development work in areas particularly connected with the horseracing industry (provided it is clear how such grant will benefit current or former members of the horseracing industry)

Education, Training & Participation

▪ The promotion of education and training connected with the horseracing and Thoroughbred breeding industry

Thoroughbred Horse Welfare

▪ The improvement of the welfare of current or former Thoroughbred racehorses

Equine Science Research (Thoroughbred horses)

▪ Veterinary research into the Thoroughbred horse that will benefit both the breed and the sport

Financial information

In 2016 the foundation had £88 million in assets and an income of £1.9 million. The foundation gave grants totalling £2 million.

Beneficiaries included: Northern Racing College (£846,000); Retraining of Racehorses (£252,000); Liverpool John Moores University (£208,000); Racing Centre (£114,000); British Racing School (£32,000); New Beginnings (£35,000); Racehorse Sanctuary (£10,000); Racing Welfare (£4,000).

Exclusions

No grants are made for:

▪ Work that does not deliver benefits associated with the UK horseracing and thoroughbred breeding industry

▪ Grants to individuals or to causes that will benefit one person

▪ Grants towards staffing costs primarily associated with fundraising

▪ The promotion of religion

▪ Work that addresses gambling addiction (unless specifically focused on participants within the horseracing and thoroughbred breeding industry)

▪ Retrospective funding, meaning support for work that has already taken place

▪ Work that is not legally charitable

Applications

Apply online using the foundation's standard form. The Racing Foundation operates a three-month application process, three times a year.

Sources of information

Accounts; annual report; Charity Commission record; funder's website.

The Radcliffe Trust

 Music, crafts, conservation

📍 UK

£ £399,000 (2016/17)

CC number: 209212

Trustees: Felix Warnock; Sir Henry Aubrey-Fletcher; Christopher Butcher; Margaret Casely-Hayford; Timothy Wilson; Ellen Schroder; Richard Morrison.

Correspondent: Bianca Myers, 6 Trull Farm Buildings, Tetbury, Gloucestershire GL8 8SQ (tel: 01285 841900; email: radcliffe@thetrustpartnership.com)

🌐 www.theradcliffetrust.org

The Radcliffe Trust was established in 1714 as a charitable trust under the will of Dr John Radcliffe, the most eminent physician of his day. The will provided for a permanent endowment, the income from which is used exclusively for charitable purposes.

The following information is taken from the trust's website:

> By his will, Dr Radcliffe directed his trustees to spend £40,000 on building a library, and today the Radcliffe Camera is one of Oxford's architectural glories. The trustees subsequently built two other important Oxford landmarks, the Radcliffe Observatory and the Radcliffe Infirmary, precursor of the modern John Radcliffe Hospital. In 1970 the agricultural holdings which Dr Radcliffe had bought in 1713 were acquired to become the new town of Milton Keynes, leaving the trustees with a substantial endowment and increased income.
>
> Today the trust has a policy of making grants principally in two sectors: Music; and Heritage and Crafts.

Music

The Radcliffe Trust supports classical music performance and training especially chamber music, composition and music education. Particular interests within music education are music for children and adults with special needs, youth orchestras and projects at secondary and higher levels, including academic research. The Trustees respond to applications and also initiate their own projects.

Heritage and crafts

The Radcliffe Trust supports the development of the skills, knowledge and experience that underpin the UK's traditional cultural heritage and crafts sectors. This includes support for craft and conservation training, for practical projects and for strategic projects which demonstrate clear benefits to individuals and to the sector. However, the Trust remains committed to flexible, open and inclusive grant-giving and will consider other projects, should they fall broadly within its remit. The Radcliffe Trust wishes to promote standards of excellence through all its support.

Financial information

In 2016/17 the trust had assets of £20.5 million and an income of £692,000. Grants were made totalling £399,000, broken down as follows:

Heritage and crafts	£180,500
Music	£165,500
Tercentenary	£51,000
Miscellaneous	£2,100

Beneficiaries included: Ashmolean Museum (£48,000); Church Building Council (£15,000); University of Cambridge (£8,000); Little Angel Theatre (£5,000); Historic Royal Palaces (£5,000); Target Housing Ltd (£4,000); SNAPS Yorkshire (£3,000); Greenwich Foundation (£2,000); The Open Door Choir (£1,500); St Barts (£600).

Exclusions

General exclusions

▶ No retrospective grants
▶ No general appeals or endowment funds

▶ The trust does not accept applications from individuals, only from organisations

Music scheme

The music scheme does not support:

▶ Operating costs
▶ Competitions
▶ Capital projects
▶ Applications from individual mainstream primary or secondary schools

Refer to the FAQs on the website, which provide very helpful information.

Applications

Applications may now only be submitted through the online application form. Visit the trust's website for further details of its schemes. The trustees meet twice yearly to oversee the trust's activities and to make decisions on grants.

▶ **For consideration by the trustees in June:** the deadline is 31 January for applications to both the music and the heritage and crafts schemes
▶ **For consideration by the trustees in December:** the heritage and crafts scheme deadline is 31 July and the music scheme deadline is 31 August

Sources of information

Accounts; annual report; Charity Commission record; funder's website.

The Bishop Radford Trust

 Christian activities

Worldwide

£ £482,000 (2016/17)

CC number: 1113562

Trustees: Stephen Green; Janian Green; Suzannah O'Brien; Dr Ruth Dare.

Correspondent: Mr D. Marks, Devonshire House, 1 Devonshire Street, London W1W 5DR (tel: 020 7304 2000; email: enquiries@bishopradfordtrust.org.uk)

 bishopradfordtrust.org.uk

The trust was set up in 2006 to help 'promote the work of the Christian church in a manner consistent with the doctrines and principles of the Church of England', according to the 2016/17 annual report, in particular:

▶ Church-related projects promoting charitable purposes
▶ Education of priests, future priests and church workers
▶ Other support for church ministry

Grants are only made to churches and UK-registered charities. Most grants are between £1,000 and £10,000.

Financial information

In 2016/17 the trust had assets of £13.1 million and an income of £811,500. Grants totalled £482,000 and were distributed as follows:

Church-related projects	£343,000
Support of church ministry	£129,000
Education of priests and other church workers	£10,000

Beneficiaries included: Anglican Communion Fund (£130,000); Bible Reading Fellowship (£50,000); Freedom Declared (£10,000); Indochina Starfish Foundation (£5,000); Queen Alexandra Hospital Home (£1,000).

Exclusions

According to the trust's website, it will not support:

▶ Non-UK-registered charities
▶ Individuals
▶ Core funding requests
▶ Building projects (unless the request is not more than £1,000 and the impact is significant)
▶ Campaigns/lobbying
▶ Research studies
▶ Activities that have already taken place, i.e. retro-funding

Applications

Apply online or download an application form from the trust's website.

Sources of information

Accounts; annual report; Charity Commission record.

The Rank Foundation Ltd

 Christian communication, young people, education, older people, general charitable purposes

UK

£ £5.2 million (2016)

CC number: 276976

Trustees: Joey Newton; Mark Davies; Andrew Cowen; The Hon Caroline Twiston Davies; Lucinda Onslow; Lord St Aldwyn; Johanna Ropner; Rose Fitzpatrick; Daniel Simon; Nicholas Buxton; Jason Chaffer; William Wyatt; Andrew Fleming; Lindsey Clay.

Correspondent: Wendy Matthews, 12 Warwick Square, London SW1V 2AA

 www.rankfoundation.com

facebook.com/TheRankFoundation

 @RankFoundation

---

The foundation was established in 1953 by the late Lord and Lady Rank (the founders). It was one of a number of charities established by the founders at that time and to which they gifted their controlling interest in The Rank Group plc (formerly The Rank Organisation plc), best known as a film production company, although this was but one of its commercial interests. The Rank trusts and foundations all share a Christian ethos.

This is a heavily proactive foundation, with offices around the country. It concentrates on:

- Encouraging and developing leadership among young people
- Promoting enterprise and innovation
- Supporting disadvantaged young people and those frail or lonely through old age or disability
- Promoting the understanding of Christianity from a perspective that respects those of all faiths and those of none

Grant-making

The foundation's executive directors actively seek out projects that support its focus areas. However, they continue to run the Pebble grants programme for unsolicited appeals. The following information was taken from the foundation's website:

This is our small funding stream for only UK-registered charities and recognised churches which are raising money for projects where the total cost is less than £1 million. If you are raising money for a particular project for which the mainstay is capital costs (building work, refurbishment or the purchase of long-term equipment) or a one-off short-term activity (such as an annual respite break or holiday for disadvantaged young people) and have already raised a third of the total costs, you may be eligible for this.

Eligibility

Applicants for Pebble grants must meet the following criteria:

- UK-registered charity
- Annual income of less than £500,000
- Funding to be spent in the UK only
- For the benefit of UK residents
- Inclusive use by the wider community

Financial information

In 2016 the foundation had assets of £232.7 million and an income of £2.9 million. Grants totalled £5.2 million. A list of current beneficiaries was unavailable.

Previous beneficiaries have included: Help the Hospices (£100,000); Winston Churchill Memorial Trust (£82,000); Youth Work in Sport (£66,000); City Year London (£50,000); Oban Youth Cafe (£36,500); Banbury Youth Housing (£31,000); Mersey Youth Support Trust, The Royal British Legion Industries and Women's Aid – Berks and Bucks (£30,000 each); Belfast Activity Centre (£28,500); Wellingborough Youth Project (£28,000); Deaf Hill Ward,

Greenbank Community Church and Prisoners Abroad (£25,000 each).

Exclusions

Overseas applications are not accepted. Running costs and salaries are not funded. Pebble grants are not given in areas supported elsewhere by the foundation or for things which are the responsibility of the state.

Applications

Applications for Pebbles grants can be made through the foundation's website.

The foundation has two application forms for Pebble grants, each of which can be accessed through the website. The capital costs application form is for fixed, one-time expenses incurred on the purchase of land, buildings, construction and equipment. The short break application form is targeted towards respite breaks for children or adults and short-term activities or programmes.

Note: The foundation does not publish deadlines or maximum amounts as this is dependent on the number of applications received. The most commonly donated amount is £1,000, according to the website. The Rank Foundation will also only consider applications once per year. Regardless of the outcome of an application, organisations may only reapply 12 months after the original date of submission.

Sources of information

Annual report; accounts; Charity Commission record; funder's website.

The Joseph Rank Trust

 The Methodist Church, Christian social work

 UK and Ireland

£2.67 million (2016)

CC number: 1093844

Trustees: Revd David Cruise; Revd Darren Holland; Revd Carole Holmes; The Very Revd John Irvine; Gay Moon; Tony Reddall; Mike Shortt; Sue Warner; Colin Rank; Joseph Jennings.

Correspondent: Dr John Higgs, Secretary, Worth Corner, Turners Hill Road, Crawley RH10 7SL (tel: 01293 873947; email: secretary@ranktrust.org)

www.ranktrust.org

The Joseph Rank Trust is an independent Christian grant-maker which works with all Christian denominations in the UK. The trust was established in 2002 for the advancement of the Christian faith and represents an amalgamation of a number of charities established by the late Joseph Rank, or

members of his family, during the period from 1918 to 1942.

The trust's two main areas of interest are:

- Projects that demonstrate a Christian approach to the practical, educational and spiritual needs of people of all ages
- The adaptation of church properties with a view to providing improved facilities for use by the church and its work in the community in which it is based

After distributing funds to support the trust's primary objectives, the trustees note that they are 'prepared to consider other unsolicited appeals, although resources remaining to support such appeals are limited'. On the trust's website it is stated that 'unsolicited appeals are selected for consideration by the Trustees that demonstrate, in their view, a Christian approach to the practical, educational and spiritual needs of people'. The trust will consider funding one-off grants for capital expenditure and three-year grants for project/salary funding.

Financial information

In 2016 the trust had assets of £73.7 million and an income of £378,000. Grants were made totalling £2.67 million, with the grants being distributed to the following areas:

South West	£411,500
North West	£353,000
Anglia	£320,000
London	£311,000
Midlands	£299,000
Scotland	£265,000
South East and Central	£184,000
Northern Ireland	£183,000
North East	£140,000
Wales	£95,000
Channel Islands	£75,000
Republic of Ireland	£36,000

Beneficiaries included: Methodist Evangelicals Together (£45,000); Upper Thames Methodist Church (£39,000); St Cyngar's Church (£35,000); Bishop's Stortford Youth Project (£30,000); London Community Church (£25,000); St Helen's Church (£20,000); Sandy Row Methodist Church (£18,000).

Exclusions

The trust does not consider applications for:

- Heritage projects
- Delayed church maintenance (e.g. roof repairs)
- Purchase or restoration of stained glass or church bells
- Overseas projects
- Church organ appeals
- Completed capital projects
- IT projects
- Book publishing
- Provision of lighting or audio equipment

- Loan repayments
- Individuals
- Educational bursaries
- Medical research
- Gap years
- Intern placements
- Hospices
- Social enterprises that have no charitable status
- Musical instruments
- Community interest companies
- Organisations registered under the Industrial and Provident Societies Act 1965
- Registered charities for the benefit of named individuals

Applications

Due to ongoing commitments, combined with the fact that the trustees are taking an increasingly active role in identifying projects to support, the trustees note that it may not always be possible to make grants in response to unsolicited appeals.

Nevertheless, if prospective applicants consider that their project falls within the trust's areas of interest, the trust recommends that they include the following information in their application:

- Charity name and charity registration number
- A detailed description of the project for which funding is sought
- Details of the amount already raised towards the target
- Details of grant applications made to other external funders
- Details of the amount committed from your own resources
- Contact person, with postal address, email address and telephone number

There are no application forms, instead applications should be submitted on no more than two-sides of A4 paper. In addition to the application itself, a summary of the budget and the costings of the project, monthly management accounts and a copy of the applicant's most recent audited annual report and accounts should be attached as appendices. In addition, the trust also requests that applicants accompany their submissions with a covering letter (not a compliment slip).

Note: Applications must be sent in hard copy and not by email.

Further information about the trust's application requirements can be found on the website. Methodist churches are advised to read the guidance on the trust's website before submitting an application.

There are no deadlines for applications. Instead, applications will be considered on a first-come, first-served basis. All appeals are acknowledged and applicants are advised that if they do not receive a reply by a specified date, it has not been possible for the trustees to make a grant.

Sources of information

Accounts; annual report; Charity Commission record; funder's website.

Rashbass Family Trust

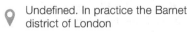

Education/training, health, disability, welfare, religion

Undefined. In practice the Barnet district of London

(£) £240,000 (2016/17)

CC number: 1135961

Trustees: Jacqueline Rashbass; Andrew Rashbass.

Correspondent: Jacqueline Rashbass, Trustee, 17 Wykeham Road, London NW4 2TB (tel: 07974 151494; email: jacqueline@rashbass.com)

This grant-making trust was established in May 2010 with general charitable purposes, with a focus on poverty, education, religion, health and the relief of people who are disadvantaged. The trust makes grants to both organisations and individuals.

Financial information

In 2016/17 the trust had assets of £59,000 and an income of £329,500. Grants totalling £240,000 were made to organisations, broken down as follows:

The advancement of education	£92,500
The advancement of religion	£92,000
The advancement of health or the saving of lives	£25,000
The relief of poverty	£15,500
The relief of those in need	£14,000
Other	£470

A list of beneficiaries was not included in the trust's annual report or accounts.

Applications

Apply in writing to the correspondent.

Sources of information

Accounts; annual report; Charity Commission record.

The Ratcliff Foundation

General charitable purposes

UK, with a preference for local charities in the Midlands and North Wales

(£) £210,000 (2016/17)

CC number: 222441

Trustees: David Ratcliff; Edward Ratcliff; Carolyn Ratcliff; Gillian Thorpe; Michael Fea; Christopher Gupwell.

Correspondent: Christopher Gupwell, Secretary, Woodlands, Earls Common Road, Stock Green, Redditch B96 6TB (tel: 01386 792116; email: chris.gupwell@ btinternet.com)

This foundation was established in 1961 by Martin Rawlinson Ratcliff. Grants are made for a wide range of charitable purposes. There is preference for local charities based in the Midlands and North Wales.

Financial information

In 2016/17 the foundation had assets of £4.05 million and an income of £239,000. A total of 90 grants were made to organisations, amounting to £210,000.

Beneficiaries included: Cancer Research UK – Kemerton (£10,000); Royal National Lifeboat Institution (£5,000); Multiple Births Foundation (£4,700); Worcester Animal Rescue Shelter (£3,500); Orchestra of the Swan, Progressive Farming Trust Ltd and Walsall Cardiac Rehabilitation Centre (£3,000 each); Sandwell Young Carers (£2,500).

Exclusions

No grants are made to individuals.

Applications

Apply in writing to the correspondent.

Sources of information

Accounts; annual report; Charity Commission record.

The Eleanor Rathbone Charitable Trust

Women, deprivation, social exclusion, unpopular causes

UK, with the major allocation for Merseyside, also international projects (Africa, the Indian subcontinent, plus Afghanistan and Palestine)

(£) £324,000 (2016/17)

CC number: 233241

Trustees: William Rathbone; Jenny Rathbone; Andrew Rathbone; Lady Angela Morgan; Mark Rathbone.

Correspondent: Lieselottie van Alwon, Administrator, 546 Warrington Road, Rainhill, Prescot, Merseyside L35 4LZ (tel: 0151 430 7914 or 07837 656314; email: eleanorrathbonetrust@gmail.com)

 www.eleanorrathbonetrust.org.uk

Eleanor Rathbone was the first woman to be elected to Liverpool City Council, representing Granby from 1909 to 1934. In 1929 she was elected as an independent MP and campaigned for social reform, particularly on issues affecting women, human rights and refugees. This charitable trust was established in 1947 with money left by Eleanor following her death in 1946.

The trust's website states that it concentrates its support on the following causes:

- Charities and charitable projects focused on Merseyside
- Charities benefiting women and unpopular and neglected causes but avoiding those with a sectarian interest

Most donations are one-off, although requests for two or three-year grants will be considered. Applications are only considered from small to medium-sized charities.

Areas of funding

The current funding areas are:

- **Merseyside**: charities and projects which are based in or delivered in Merseyside (particularly more deprived areas) and meet the funding priorities (grants in Merseyside accounted for 53% of total grants in 2016/17)
- **Holiday Fund**: small grants for holidays and outings provided by charities helping disadvantaged children and adults from Merseyside
- **National**: charities and projects which meet the priorities and have a nationwide reach
- **International**: projects in Sub-Saharan Africa, the Indian subcontinent and, exceptionally, Iran, Palestine and Haiti. Projects must be sponsored and monitored by a UK-registered charity and do one or more of the following:
  - Benefit women or orphaned children
  - Demonstrate local involvement in scoping and delivery
  - Aim to repair the damage in countries recently ravaged by international or civil war
  - Deliver clean water and sanitation

Grants made to Merseyside-based charities range from £100 to £5,000. For national and international grants, awards range between £1,000 and £3,000. In exceptional cases, grants may be higher. Successful applicants are asked to wait two years before re-applying for a grant.

Financial information

In 2016/17 the trust had assets of £10.4 million and an income of £367,000. During the year, the trust gave a total of £324,000 in grants to organisations. Grants were distributed as follows:

Merseyside	71	£171,500
National	30	£75,500
International	55	£69,000
Holidays (Merseyside)	4	£7,800

Beneficiaries included: Liverpool Community Advice and Merseyside Holiday Service (£5,000 each); Action on Addiction, Bluecoat and Centre 63 (£3,000 each); Africa Educational Trust, Cameroon Catalyst and Find your Feet

(£2,000 each); A Second Chance, All We Can and Motivation (£1,000 each).

Exclusions

The trust does not support:

- Any activity which relieves a statutory authority from its obligations
- Individuals
- Medical research
- Gap year projects
- Lobbying or campaigning organisations
- Organisations which have a primary purpose of promoting a religion, church or sect

Applications

Apply using the online form. Additional supporting documents are listed on the website and should be sent by post. Applications are accepted at any time and are considered at trustees' meetings held three times a year.

Sources of information

Accounts; annual report; Charity Commission record; funder's website.

The Sigrid Rausing Trust

 Human rights and social justice

 Worldwide

£ £19.9 million (2016)

CC number: 1046769

Trustees: Sigrid Rausing; Andrew Puddephatt; Jonathan Cooper; Margo Picken.

Correspondent: Sheetal Patel, 12 Penzance Place, London W11 4PA (tel: 020 7313 7727; email: info@srtrust.org)

 www.sigrid-rausing-trust.org

The Sigrid Rausing Trust was set up in 1995 by Swedish philanthropist, anthropologist and publisher Sigrid Rausing and takes as its guiding framework the United Nations' Universal Declaration of Human Rights. Its vision is 'A world where the principles of the Universal Declaration of Human Rights are implemented and respected and where all people can enjoy their rights in harmony with each other and with the environment.'

The trust made its first grants in 1996 and, from the beginning, has taken a keen interest in work that promotes international human rights. It was originally called the Ruben and Elisabeth Rausing Trust after Sigrid's grandparents. In 2003 the trust was renamed the Sigrid Rausing Trust to identify its work more closely with the aims and ideals of Sigrid Rausing herself.

Areas of support

The trust currently has nine grants programmes:

- Advocacy, research and litigation
- Detention, torture and death penalty
- Human rights defenders
- Free expression
- Transitional justice
- Women's rights
- LGBTI rights
- Xenophobia and intolerance
- Transparency and accountability

In addition, a Miscellaneous Fund enables trustees to fund charitable projects and organisations which may be outside the current remit of the nine thematic programmes. There is also a small grants fund which allows individual trustees to nominate organisations for support.

The trust has five main principles which guide its grant-making:

- The essential role of core funding
- Good and effective leadership
- Flexibility and responsiveness to needs and opportunities
- The value of clarity and brevity in applications and reports
- Long-term relationships with grantees

Types of grant

The trust's grants are mostly for core costs, rather than funding specific projects. The trust typically makes a one-year initial grant followed by up to three grants of three years each. There is no minimum or maximum level for a grant but the trust will not normally support more than 25% of the budget of an organisation or a project.

Financial information

In 2016 the trust had assets of £3.1 million and an income of £20.2 million. Grants totalling £19.9 million were awarded.

Previous beneficiaries have included: Arab Human Rights Fund (£200,000); International Federation of Human Rights (£160,000); Center for Legal and Social Studies (£125,000); Zimbabwe Lawyers for Human Rights (£100,000); International Consortium of Investigative Journalists (£80,000); Mesoamerican Initiative of Women Human Rights Defenders (£75,000); Greek Council for Refugees (£70,000); World Organisation Against Torture (£60,000); Civil Society Prison Reform Initiative (£50,000); Crude Accountability (£45,000); GENDERDOC-M (£40,000).

Exclusions

No grants are made to individuals or faith-based groups. Funds are not normally given for building projects.

Applications

The trust does not accept unsolicited applications for funding but rather invites applications from organisations that it has proactively identified.

Sources of information

Accounts; annual report; Charity Commission record; funder's website.

The Rayne Foundation

 Arts, education, health and well-being, social welfare

UK

£1.6 million (2015/16)

CC number: 216291

Trustees: Lady Jane Rayne; Rabbi Baroness Julia Neuberger; Robert Rayne; Lady Browne-Wilkinson; Prof. Sir Anthony Newman Taylor; Natasha Rayne; Nicholas Rayne; Sir Emyr Jones Parry.

Correspondent: The Trustees, Office 107, 239 Kensington High Street, London W8 6SN (email: info@ raynefoundation.org.uk)

 www.raynefoundation.org.uk

The Rayne Foundation was founded in 1962 by Lord Rayne who chaired or was on the board of numerous arts, education, medical and social welfare organisations.

The Rayne Foundation makes grants to charitable and not-for-profit organisations across the UK tackling a variety of issues. The foundation supports work which is untried and which may have uncertain outcomes but which has clear objectives. The overall theme underpinning the foundation's work is social cohesion. The foundation is particularly interested in the arts, health and well-being, education in its widest sense, and social issues.

Guidelines

Applications from organisations working in the arts, health and well-being or education in its widest sense, and those that cover social issues are considered. The trustees favour work which could change the way issues are tackled in society and which could have lessons for others beyond the funded organisation.

Within the broad criteria, there are three areas of special interest:

- Arts as a tool to achieve social change
- Improved quality of life for carers and for older people
- Young people's improved mental health

Organisations and projects that are considered for funding

The foundation looks for all of the following characteristics in the organisations and projects that it funds:

- Wider than local application and awareness of the bigger picture
- Real expertise and sector knowledge
- Commitment to demonstrating results and sharing learning
- Strong leadership, management and track record
- Direct benefits to vulnerable and disadvantaged people

The trustees fund charities and not-for-profit organisations, targeting their funding towards unpopular issues and organisations. 'Household name' charities are unlikely to receive support. Hospitals, local authorities, government departments and schools are not funded.

Types of grant

Salaries and project costs (including a reasonable contribution to overheads or oncosts) for up to three years will be considered. The trustees will consider grants towards an organisation's core costs but only tend to award these when an organisation is making a step-change in the way that it works or tackles a particular issue, and where a core grant will provide greater flexibility during the transition period.

Grants typically fall between £10,000 and £20,000 per year for up to three years. The foundation prefers to fund alongside others as it is unlikely to fund a project in full.

Financial information

In 2015/16 the foundation held assets of £83.5 million and had an income of over £1.7 million. Grants to 57 organisations totalled over £1.6 million.

Beneficiaries included: Bosence Community Farm Ltd (£58,000); Music in Detention (£45,000); Society for Mucopolysaccharide Diseases, The Maytree Respite Centre and The West London Mission (£40,000 each); The Choir With No Name, World Jewish Relief and NEPACS (£30,000 each); Early Break (£24,000); Link Age Southwark (£15,000).

Exclusions

Grants are not made:

- For medical research, including cancer research
- For retrospective funding
- For capital appeals
- For campaigning and lobbying work
- For endowments
- For one-off events (including performances, festivals, conferences, holidays, respite breaks and residential trips)
- For community transport schemes and vehicle purchases
- For church halls and community centres
- For running costs of local organisations
- For feasibility studies or scoping work
- To individuals
- To organisations working or based outside the UK
- To brand new organisations
- To organisations which have applied and been rejected within the last 12 months
- To charities supporting servicemen/women's organisations working outside the UK
- For work that has already taken place
- Towards repayment of debts
- Towards endowments
- Towards general appeals
- To organisations that have applied in the last twelve months

Organisations with more than nine months' running costs in unrestricted reserves are less likely to receive support.

Organisations with tiny reserves or an overall deficit will need to convince the trustees that their organisation is viable and they are taking action to increase reserves.

Applications

The foundation has a two-stage application process which is designed to minimise the time and effort spent by applicants. Stage one involves a short outline application which the foundation uses to assess the quality of a proposal and whether it fits with their objectives. Stage two provides an opportunity to provide a more fully developed and formal proposal.

Stage one application forms and guidance can be downloaded from the foundation's website. Completed applications should be sent to applications@raynefoundation.org.uk. The foundation prefers to receive applications by email but, if this not possible, they can be posted to the correspondent's address. For specific queries about grants or monitoring, email Morin Carew – mcarew@ raynefoundation.org.uk or telephone 020 7487 9656.

Sources of information

Annual report; accounts; Charity Commission record; funder's website.

The Rayne Trust

 Jewish organisations, older and young people and people disadvantaged by poverty or social isolation, intercultural understanding

 Israel and UK

£536,000 (2016/17)

CC number: 207392

Correspondent: The Trustees, Office 107, 239 Kensington High Street, London W8 6SN (tel: 020 7487 9650; email: info@raynefoundation.org.uk)

www.raynefoundation.org.uk/our-work/grant-making-israel

The Rayne Trust is the sister organisation of the Rayne Foundation, founded by Lord Rayne. The overarching theme of the two organisations is social cohesion; however, the Rayne Trust is particularly focused on Jewish causes in the UK and Israel. We have taken our general information from the trust's website.

The trustees are interested in funding work which is 'untried, tests new approaches, but has clear objectives, which could eventually change the way social issues are tackled in our society'. The work of the trust is primarily focused on strengthening relationships between Jews and Arabs and improving mental health.

Organisations and projects that are considered

The trustees look for all of the following characteristics in the organisations and projects that they fund:

- Wider than local application and awareness of the bigger picture
- Real expertise and sector knowledge
- Commitment to demonstrating results and sharing learning
- Strong leadership, management, and track record

See the website for full and very helpful detailed information.

Further information

The trustees fund charitable and not-for-profit organisations, targeting funding towards unpopular issues and organisations. Large, national organisations are unlikely to receive support unless they are the only organisation in a position to tackle a particular problem. Salaries and other core funding costs for up to three years can be considered.

Grants typically fall between £10,000 and £20,000 per year for up to three years. The trustees prefer to contribute alongside other funders as they will not donate more than 50% of the funding required.

All financial information should be submitted in pound sterling. Hebrew Audited Accounts need to be included with the application.

Financial information

In 2016/17 the trust had assets of £30.3 million and an income of £492,000. Grants totalling £536,000 were made to 58 organisations. Grants amounted to £226,000 in the UK and £310,000 in Israel.

Beneficiaries included: King's College London (£45,000); Chicken Shed Theatre Trust (£25,000); Harris and Trotter Clients Charitable Trust and World Jewish Relief (£20,000 each); New Entrepreneurs Foundation and Teenage Cancer Trust (£10,000 each).

Exclusions

No grants are given to:

- Individuals
- Retrospective applications
- Repayment of debts
- Organisations which have had a grant in the last year
- General appeals
- Endowments

Organisations with more than nine months' running costs in unrestricted reserves are less likely to receive support.

Organisations with tiny reserves or an overall deficit will need to convince the trustees that their organisation is viable and they are taking action to increase reserves. This is used as a measure of financial health.

Applications

Stage one application forms can be downloaded from the trust's website and should be returned to israelapplications@raynetrust.org.

Sources of information

Accounts; annual report; Charity Commission record; funder's website.

The Sir James Reckitt Charity

 General charitable purposes, Quaker

Hull and the East Riding of Yorkshire, UK and occasional support for Red Cross or Quaker work overseas

£1 million (2016)

CC number: 225356

Trustees: William Upton; James Holt; Robert Gibson; Ondine Upton; Caroline Jennings; Philip Holt; Robin Upton; Sarah Craven; Charles Maxted; Simon James Upton; Simon Edward Upton; Oliver Jennings; Edward Upton; Rebecca Holt; Andrew Palfreman; James Atherton.

Correspondent: The Administrator, 7 Derrymore Road, Willerby, Hull, East

Yorkshire HU10 6ES (tel: 01482 655861; email: charity@thesirjamesreckittcharity. org.uk)

 www.thesirjamesreckittcharity.org. uk

The charity was founded by Sir James Reckitt in 1921 and was registered with the Charity Commission in 1964. The charity gives for a wide range of charitable purposes and particularly favours organisations that provide benefit in Hull and East Riding of Yorkshire, as well as Quaker causes.

Support is given to:

- Community-based groups and projects in the city of Hull and the county of East Yorkshire
- Quaker causes and organisations wherever they are
- National and regional charities focused on social welfare, medicine, education or the environment, particularly if their work brings benefit to Hull and East Yorkshire
- Individuals or groups from Hull or East Yorkshire

Support is also given to individuals and families in need who reside in Hull or East Yorkshire and have the support of an agency such as social services or of a local charitable organisation. Such cases are dealt with by the Consortium of Grant Giving Trusts (Hull and East Yorkshire) of which the Sir James Reckitt Charity is a member. Aid is usually given in the form of household goods and equipment.

Grants are made for:

- Start-up and core costs
- Purchase of equipment and materials
- Building improvements
- Training costs
- Project development costs

The majority of grant applications are for funding of between £500 and £5,000, although larger grants can be considered. Small grants can be made outside the scheduled meetings, particularly if there is an element of urgency involved.

Financial information

In 2016 the charity had assets of £44 million, an income of £1.5 million and made grants totalling £1 million, broken down as follows:

Social work	£457,000
Education	£272,000
Religion	£100,000
Medical	£76,500
Young people	£47,000
Children	£44,000
Older people	£16,900
Environment	£11,000

Beneficiaries included: Walden School (£35,000); The Retreat (£30,000); Leighton Park Trust (£25,000); Woodbrooke Quaker Study Centre (£15,000); Barnardo's Farm Africa

(£5,000); Yorkshire Friends Holiday School and Multiple Sclerosis Society (£4,000 each); Abbeyfield UK (£2,500); Labour Ward Hull and East Riding NHS (£2,000).

Exclusions

Grants are normally made only to registered charities. Local organisations outside the Hull area are not supported unless their work has regional implications. Grants are not normally made to individuals other than Quakers and residents of Hull and the East Riding of Yorkshire. Support is not given to causes of a warlike or political nature.

Grants are not made for replacement of statutory funding or activities which collect funds to be passed on to other organisations, charities or individuals.

Applications

There is no application form. Apply in writing to the correspondent. The charity's website states that applications should include the following key points:

- The name and address of your organisation; telephone number and email address
- The nature of your organisation; its structure, aims and who it serves; and its links with other agencies and networks
- The project or funding need. What is the grant to be used for and who will benefit from it
- When is the funding required; the date of the project or event
- The bank account payee name of your organisation
- Any links to the Hull and East Yorkshire region, or the Quakers (which together are our funding priorities)
- A copy of your latest Annual Report and Accounts or equivalent

Applications are measured against the charity's guidelines and decisions are taken at a twice-yearly meeting of trustees in May and November. Applications should be submitted well in advance of these meetings as late submissions are likely to be carried forward to the following meeting.

Applications to the Consortium of Grant Giving Trusts (Hull and East Yorkshire) should only be made by the agency working with the individual or family. The Consortium application form, which may be downloaded from the 'Links' page on the charity's website, is not to be used for any other purpose.

Sources of information

Accounts; annual report; Charity Commission record; guidelines for applicants; funder's website.

The Reece Foundation

 Development of maths, science and engineering skills, employment opportunities

UK, with a strong preference for the North East

£ £740,000 (2016)

CC number: 1121325

Trustees: Eric Morgan; Simon Gilroy; John Reece; Anne Reece.

Correspondent: Faye Dent, Armstrong Works, Scotswood Road, Newcastle upon Tyne NE15 6UX (tel: 0191 234 8700; email: enquiries@reece-foundation. org)

The foundation was established in 2007 by businessman John Reece. The aim of the foundation is to improve the long-term and sustainable prosperity of North East England, primarily through the promotion of engineering and manufacturing. There is a particular focus on the improvement of education in engineering and related scientific and mathematical subjects, training in engineering skills and the development of employment opportunities. The foundation may occasionally support other causes which the trustees feel are beneficial to the area or the country.

Funding is currently focused on projects and groups based in North East England, including Northumberland, Tyne and Wear and County Durham.

Financial information

In 2016 the foundation held assets of £24.8 million and had an income of £360,000. Grants to 30 organisations totalled £740,000.

Beneficiaries included: John Muir (£200,000); Villiers Park (£101,000); The North of England Institute of Mining and Mechanical Engineers (£100,000); Centre for Life (£85,000); Greenpower (£30,000); Bee Smart and North Durham Academy (£10,000 each); Durham University (£4,000); Harton Primary School (£1,500); Discovery School (£100).

Applications

Application forms are available to download from the foundation's website. Applications can be made at any time.

Sources of information

Accounts; annual report; Charity Commission record; funder's website.

Richard Reeve's Foundation

Education for children and young people

Camden, City of London and Islington

£ £658,000 to organisations (2016/17)

CC number: 1136337

Trustees: John Tickle; Michael Bennett; Michael Hudson; Mark Jessett; Shannon Farrington; Gerald Rothwell; Revd David Ingall; Lorna Russell; Jo Emmerson; Dr Sotonye Odugbemi.

Correspondent: Andrew Fuller, Clerk to the Governors, 13 Elliott's Place, London N1 8HX (tel: 020 7726 4230; email: enquiries@richardreevesfoundation.org. uk)

 www.richardreevesfoundation.org. uk

Richard Reeve's Foundation was first established in 1706 following the death of Richard Reeve, a Merchant Taylor who had no immediate family and left his estate in trust to help educate children in the parish of St Sepulchre's. The foundation now makes grants to local organisations, charities and schools towards the education and training of disadvantaged children and young people (up to the age of 25) who live in the City of London, Camden or Islington.

The foundation's website states:

Projects are usually funded for up to three years to increase their impact. We are flexible in our approach to these issues. We look for projects that are exciting, innovative and attractive to the people we most want to help.

The Foundation's current focus is:

- Raising Literacy and Numeracy among early years and primary school students
- Aiding young people's progression into work through:

i) supporting improved Careers Education and Guidance in secondary schools

ii) enabling increased opportunities for young people, aged 16–24, to 'earn while they learn.

Sometimes we fund other work related to our general aims of education and care of young people under 25. Please ask the Clerk for advice if you would like to submit an application that does not meet the above priorities.

In addition to our 2 main areas of strategic focus, the Foundation provides:

- Support to projects which assist young people under 25 from disadvantaged backgrounds who wish to study music
- Maintenance grants to college students aged 16 – 24 attending colleges within our area of benefit
- Maintenance grants to City University NHS students under the age of 40

⬤ An annual grant to Christ's Hospital school in Horsham, West Sussex

Financial information
In 2016/17 the foundation had assets of £42.5 million and an income of £1.1 million. Grants totalled £703,000, with £658,000 awarded to organisation and £45,000 awarded to individuals.

Beneficiaries included: Partners in Learning (£231,000 in two grants); Islington Giving (£100,000); BIG Alliance (£50,000); Christ's Hospital (£21,000); Ampersand Learning (£12,000); Camden Music Trust (£11,800).

Exclusions
No grants are made individuals.

Applications
Application forms and details of the application procedure can be found on the foundation's website.

Sources of information
Accounts; annual report; Charity Commission record; funder's website.

The Resolution Trust

 Research/education in economic and social sciences with a particular focus on the causes, prevention or relief of poverty

📍 UK

💷 £1.6 million (2015/16)

CC number: 1123128

Trustee: The Resolution Trust (Trustee) Ltd.

Correspondent: Christina Alexandrou, 2 Queen Annes Gate, London SW1H 9AA (tel: 020 3372 2960; email: info@resolutiontrust.org)

The trust makes grants to charitable organisations/projects involving research/education in economic and social sciences with a particular focus on the causes, prevention or relief of poverty.

The trust's 2015/16 accounts state:

> The Trust acts as catalyst, convenor and sponsor of work with a range of partners to promote shared growth and reforms that distribute power more widely across society. The Trust takes a specific interest in long-term problems that are often viewed as intractable due to the short-term nature of the political cycle. The approach taken is non-partisan, evidence-based and draws on international experience.

Financial information
In 2015/16 the trust had assets of £50.2 million and an income of £1.8 million. Grants to six organisations totalled £1.6 million.

Beneficiaries included: Ark Swift (£1 million); Prospect Magazine (£278,000); Institute for New Economic Thinking Oxford (£183,500); Open Reason (£100,000); Living Wage Commission (£10,000); Clore Social Leadership Programme Collaboration on Leadership Administration Fund (£5,000).

Applications
Apply in writing to the correspondent.

Sources of information
Accounts; annual report; Charity Commission record.

Responsible Gambling Trust (GambleAware)

 Gambling education, prevention and treatment services, research aimed at minimising the impact of gambling

📍 UK

💷 £5.3 million (2016/17)

CC number: 1093910

Trustees: Alan Jamieson; Christopher Pond; Annette Dale-Perera; Prof. Patrick Sturgis; Prof. Sian Griffiths; Brigid Simmonds; Henry Birch; Katheryn Lampard; James Mullen; Prof. Anthony Kessel.

Correspondent: Natalie Simpson, Operations Manager, 7 Henrietta St, London WC2E 8PS (tel: 020 7287 1994; email: info@gambleaware.org)

 about.gambleaware.org

Responsible Gambling Trust (RGT) is dedicated to minimising the negative impact gambling has on individuals and societies. The trust's income is derived principally from donations from the gambling industry and is used to fund related education, prevention and treatment services as well as to commission research to promote awareness and understanding of the harm caused by gambling.

Commissioning
RGT commissions research and education, prevention and treatment services with the purpose of minimising gambling-related harm. The website notes that the trust interprets the word 'commissioning' as 'the commitment of financial resources by funders to relevant organisations (not limited to health and social care providers) with the aim of improving health and social outcomes by responding to local need, reducing inequalities and providing high-quality services'. It is further explained that the trust is a grant-maker which aims to use 'best-practice aspects of commissioning, such as needs assessment, service planning and outcome reporting to

support its ongoing role as a grant-funder of effective, evidence-informed, high-quality gambling-related harm support services'. Furthermore, the trust monitors and evaluates services 'to ensure ongoing and continuous quality improvement of the grant-funding process'.

Financial information
In 2016/17 the trust had assets of £5.9 million and an income of £8.26 million. During the year, grants were made amounting to £5.3 million, £425,000 of this amount was spent on research.

Beneficiaries included: GamCare (£3.9 million); The Gordon Moody Association (£640,000); Central and North West London NHS Foundation Trust – Problem Gambling (£360,000).

Applications
The trust does not respond to unsolicited applications received. However, it does annually invite tenders for funding in relation to innovative applied research intended to support original and creative projects that help deliver or extend the National Responsible Gambling Strategy, within the bounds of the trust's charitable objectives. See the website for more details.

Sources of information
Accounts; annual report; Charity Commission record; funder's website.

Reuben Foundation

 Health care, education, general charitable purposes

📍 UK and overseas, with a focus on Israel and the United States

💷 £2.48 million to organisations (2016)

CC number: 1094130

Trustees: Richard Stone; Simon Reuben; Malcolm Turner; Annie Benjamin; Patrick O'Driscoll; James Reuben; Dana Reuben.

Correspondent: Patrick O'Driscoll, Trustee, 4th Floor, Millbank Tower, 21–24 Millbank, London SW1P 4PQ (tel: 020 7802 5000; email: contact@reubenfoundation.com)

 www.reubenfoundation.com

This foundation was established in 2002 as an outlet for the charitable giving of billionaire property investors David and Simon Reuben. The foundation was endowed by the brothers with a donation of $100 million (£54.1 million), with the income generated to be given to a range of charitable causes. The foundation's annual report and accounts list its objects as:

- To promote and further the education of persons but in particular young persons;
- To relieve persons who are in need, hardship or distress as a result of or by reason of their social or economic circumstances, their infirmity or age
- To relieve persons who are in need, hardship or distress as a result of local, national or international unrest or disorder
- To facilitate medical research and the development of medical facilities worldwide
- To support, procure or further such objects, which are exclusively charitable according to the law

Grants are mainly made for educational and healthcare purposes. The foundation supports a number of scholarship initiatives including the Reuben Scholarship Programme, which was launched in 2012 in partnership with the University of Oxford, University College London and Ark Schools, and has recently extended to include the University of Cambridge.

Financial information
In 2016 the foundation had assets of £87.85 million and an income of £5.09 million. Grants paid during the year totalled £2.51 million, of which £2.48 million was given in grants to organisations. Individuals were paid a further £25,500.

Beneficiaries included: Oxford University (£1.38 million); Centrepoint (£147,500); Nancy Reuben Primary School (£101,000); Ark Schools (£80,000); Carers Trust (£20,000); Holocaust Educational Trust (£12,000); Design Museum (£10,000); Yorkshire Air Ambulance (£7,100); NSPCC (£5,000).

Applications
The foundation's website states that applications for grants are made by invitation only.

Sources of information
Accounts; annual report; Charity Commission record; funder's website.

The Revere Charitable Trust

🔍 Medical research, environment, arts and culture, animal welfare, older people, young people, people with disabilities

📍 UK and overseas

💷 £406,000 (2016/17)

CC number: 1117369

Trustees: John Saner; Peter Willmott; Richard Willmott; Teifion Evans.

Correspondent: Teifion Evans, 9 Hillside Close, Heddington, Calne SN11 0PZ (tel:

01380 859198; email: teifion@tevans. plus.com)

The trust was registered in 2006 and, according to its Charity Commission record, supports:

- National and international medical organisations
- Environmental and cultural projects
- Animal welfare
- Young people
- Older people
- People with disabilities

Financial information
In 2016/17 the trust held assets of £6 million and had an income of £780,500. Grants awarded to organisations totalled £406,000.

Beneficiaries included: Médecins Sans Frontières and Tadworth Children's Trust (£50,000 each); Woodland Trust (£30,000); Arthritis Research (£15,000); Christie Hospital Proton Beam (£10,000); Hitchin Band (£5,000); Hitchin Thespians (£4,500); Yemen Crisis Appeal (£1,500).

Applications
Apply in writing to the correspondent.

Sources of information
Accounts; annual report; Charity Commission record.

Rhodi Charitable Trust

🔍 Social welfare, education, health, emergency relief

📍 UK, with a preference for Preston, and India

💷 £213,500 to organisations and individuals (2016)

CC number: 1082915

Trustees: Hamida Bux; Ibrahim Bux.

Correspondent: Ibrahim Bux, Trustee, 1 Fishwick Park, Mercer Street, Preston PR1 4LZ (tel: 01772 562288)

The trust's main objective is the relief of poverty. The trust seeks to make immediate and lasting improvement to the lives of people affected by poverty and disaster.

Financial information
In 2016 the trust held assets of £1.3 million and had an income of £211,000. Grants to both organisations and individuals totalled £213,500. A complete list of beneficiaries was not available.

Previous beneficiaries have included: Masjid e Salaam – Preston (£158,500); Matiwala Darul Uloom Charitable Trust and Preston Muslim Girls High School (£10,000 each).

Applications
Apply in writing to the correspondent.

Sources of information
Accounts; annual report; Charity Commission record.

Rhondda Cynon Taff Welsh Church Acts Fund

🔍 General charitable purposes

📍 Rhondda Cynon Taff, Bridgend and Merthyr Tydfil County Borough Councils

💷 £627,500 (2016/17)

CC number: 506658

Trustee: Rhondda Cynon Taff County Borough Council.

Correspondent: The Trustees, Rhondda Cynon Taff County Borough Council, Council Offices, Bronwydd, Porth CF39 9DL (tel: 01443 680734; email: treasurymanagement@rctcbc.gov.uk)

Lloyd George, under the provisions of the 1914 and 1919 Welsh Churches Acts, established the Welsh Church Act Fund. These two acts transferred certain categories of secularised property to a Welsh Church Act Fund to be administered by county councils. However, these funds were not activated until 1942–47, when property to the value of almost £2.5 million was handed over to the county councils. The Welsh Churches Acts state that income of the funds should be devoted to charitable or alms-giving purposes and that each council is required to prepare a scheme for the use of the fund.

This fund was established in 1976 to make grants for projects in the areas of Bridgend, Merthyr Tydfil and Rhondda Cynon Taff. Applications may be considered from organisations based outside the beneficial area providing the work has a local significance (to the beneficial area). The charitable purposes to which the fund may be applied are:

- Education
- Social welfare
- Libraries, museums and art galleries
- Social and recreation projects
- Protection of historical buildings and heritage
- Medical and social research and treatment
- Probation and projects involving ex-offenders
- Blind people
- Older people
- Places of worship and burial grounds
- Emergencies or disasters
- Other general charitable purposes

According to the 2016/17 annual report, grant limits during the year were as follows:

> Grants under £2,000 did not require match funding, grants exceeding £2,000 required a minimum of 10% match funding and grants exceeding £10,000 required a minimum of 20% match funding from non-Welsh Church Fund sources. Maximum grant available was £50,000.

Those grants which are structural in nature are only considered where a professional assessment for the necessary works has been made. Organisations providing hobby activities for their members should provide their facilities to the public at large. Any assistance given will be towards project expenditure of a capital nature. Normal running expenses will not be supported.

Financial information

In 2016/17 the fund held assets of £12.3 million and had an income of £319,000. During the year, 46 organisations were awarded grants totalling £627,500. Of these, 40 grants were for over £2,000 and 16 grants were for less than £2,000 and represented £23,000 of the grant total. The following breakdown is taken from the 2016/17 accounts:

Social and recreational purposes	21	£292,500
Places of worship and burial grounds	28	£150,500
General charitable purposes	4	£98,000
Libraries, museums and art galleries	2	£77,500
Protection of historic buildings	1	£9,000

Previous beneficiaries have included:

Citizens Advice Merthyr Tydfil (£50,000); Cambrian Village Trust (£48,000); Beddau and Tynant Community Library (£41,000); Llantrisant Guildhall CIO (£36,500); Friends of Tonteg Community Park (£23,000); Darren Las Community Building (£17,200); Welsh Religious Building Trust (£9,000); Arts Factory Ltd (£8,400); Bethel Baptist Church – Laleston (£5,100); Avon Street Gardening and Allotment Society (£2,000).

Exclusions

The following are not supported:

- Students
- Individuals
- Clubs with a liquor licence
- Projects operating outside the area of benefit
- Normal running expenses

Applications

Apply in writing to the correspondent, submitting your application together with estimates, accounts and constitutions. The 2016/17 annual report states: 'Recommendations for grant awards are made by officers in an

Assessment Round Report, which is considered at special meetings regularly throughout the year on approximately a monthly basis.'

Sources of information

Accounts; annual report; Charity Commission record.

Edmund Rice Bicentennial Trust Ltd

 Advancement of the Christian faith, education and training, children and young people

UK and overseas

£1.35 million (2016)

CC number: 1098358

Trustees: Mark Holland; Kieran Gordon; Br Julian McDonald; Br Clement Mukuka; Br George Gordon; Paul Griffiths.

Correspondent: The Trustees, Woodeaves, Wicker Lane, Hale Barns, Altrincham, Cheshire WA15 OHF (tel: +353 633 3800; email: LP-cosec@cantor.com)

The Edmund Rice Bicentennial Trust Ltd was registered with the Charity Commission in 2003. Its main objects are to 'advance the Christian faith, promote Christian ideals and provide for the education and training of children and other persons according to the spirit and ideals of Blessed Edmund Rice'.

According to its 2016 annual report, the trust intends to meet these objectives by:

- Providing assistance to children or other persons especially those who are poor by the provision of accommodation, training, instruction, or pastoral care in order to develop their physical, mental, emotional and spiritual capacities.
- Providing assistance as the Trustees may from time to time think fit for the provision of educational facilities.
- Assisting in the provision of education of any child or person in keeping with the precepts of Christian faith and Christian ideals.
- Providing assistance for the training or teachers, parents, youth leaders or other persons engaged or to be engaged in provision of education, leadership, development, or instruction of children and other person.
- Providing assistance for the furtherance or development of education or youth leadership, religious and moral development especially of the young and disadvantaged as well as for the relevant educational research.
- Providing assistance of those who have served the main objects of the charity and to provide them with the necessary resources required in the performance of their duty in keeping with the main objects of the Charity

provided always that no part of the capital or income of the Charity may be distributed to any person by way of profit of dividend.

- Advancing the Christian faith in any part of the world.
- Assisting in the relief of poverty in any part of the world.
- Providing assistance to other bodies involved in charitable works having main objects similar to those of the Charity.

Financial information

In 2016 the trust had assets of £29.3 million and an income of £641,500. During the year, the trust awarded grants of around £1.35 million.

Beneficiaries included: The Christian Brothers (£822,000); Edmund Rice Development (£299,500).

Applications

Apply in writing to the correspondent.

Sources of information

Accounts; annual report; Charity Commission record.

The Clive and Sylvia Richards Charity Ltd

 Education, health care, heritage, the arts, religious institutions, overseas educational and religious institutions

 Mainly UK, with some preference for Herefordshire

£1.1 million (2016/17)

CC number: 327155

Trustees: Peter Henry; Clive Richards; Sylvia Richards; Peter Dines; Peregrine Banbury; David Iddon; Gareth Davies; Liz Deutsch.

Correspondent: Rob Woolf, Lower Hope Farm, Ullingswick, Hereford HR1 3JF (tel: 01432 820557; email: admin@csrcharity.com)

 csrcharity.com

This charity was established in May, 1986 by Sylvia Richards and her husband Clive. The couple donate the vast majority of the charity's income, which is used to make grants to a wide range of organisations.

Grant-making

The charity focuses its support on education, health care, heritage, the arts, religious institutions and overseas educational and religious institutions. The website explains that the charity 'will provide support to charity organisations where [it seeks] to be a catalyst to unlock other funding sources for good causes and ensure sustainability and transformational change'. The trustees prefer to focus on smaller charities or projects that probably would not happen if not for the charity's help.

The charity's website states that, while historically the emphasis of funding has centred on the West Midlands with a focus on Herefordshire, in recent years grants have been given within a broader geographic region – a 100-mile radius from the centre of Hereford now comprises the beneficial area. There is an upper limit of £250,000 in any one year to any one charity.

Individuals who are seeking to further their education, primarily in the areas of music and arts, can also be supported, as can young people who are carrying out charity work overseas.

Financial information

In 2016/17 the charity held assets of £731,500 and had an income of £498,500. Grants awarded to organisations totalled £1.1 million and were broken down as follows:

Health care	£408,500
Arts	£378,000
Religious	£133,500
Heritage	£102,000
Education	£78,000
Other	£21,500

Grants of over £50,000 included: Cobalt Unit Appeal Fund (£275,000); City of Birmingham Symphony Orchestra (£255,000); Premananda Orphanage (£110,000) Canine Partners (£89,500) Hanley Castle High School, Ironbridge Gorge Museum Trust and Wales Millennium Centre (£50,000 each).

Grants of less than £50,000 totalled £243,000.

Exclusions

The charity does not usually fund the following:

- National charities
- Operating costs
- Salaries
- Activities that are/were the responsibility of a statutory body

Overseas applications must have a UK sponsor, preferably one that is known to the trustees.

Applications

The website stresses that it is important to ensure that your organisation is eligible to apply for funding before making an application. Around half of applications received by the charity are ineligible. In the first instance, we would recommend that applicants visit the charity's website for full information, including the detailed 'Guidance for Applicants' document. Application forms are available to download from the charity's website and may be submitted at any time.

Sources of information

Accounts; annual report; Charity Commission record; funder's website.

Richmond Parish Lands Charity

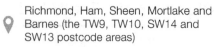 General charitable purposes, education, community

Richmond, Ham, Sheen, Mortlake and Barnes (the TW9, TW10, SW14 and SW13 postcode areas)

£1.3 million to organisations (2016/17)

CC number: 200069

Trustees: Paul Velluet; Ian Durant; Paul Cole; Ros Sweeting; Rosie Dalzell; Tim Sketchley; Ashley Casson; Kate Ellis; Lisa Blakemore; Gill Moffett; Roger Clark; Peter Buckwell; Owen Carew-Jones; Rachel Holmes; Paul Lawrence.

Correspondent: Sharon La Ronde, Grants Director, Vestry House, 21 Paradise Road, Richmond, Surrey TW9 1SA (tel: 020 8948 5701; email: grants@rplc.org.uk)

 www.rplc.org.uk

 @RPLC1786

Established in 1786, the charity supports a wide range of causes in specified parts of the borough of Richmond upon Thames. A map of the beneficial area is available on the charity's website. The charity describes its objectives as: to further all or any of the following purposes within the area of benefit – the London postcode districts of TW9, TW10, SW13 and SW14:

- The support of older people and those in need
- The care of those suffering ill health or hardship
- The provision of recreational facilities and support for leisure activities
- The promotion of education and helping people to undertake courses and training
- Any other charitable purposes for the benefit of the local community

The trustees carry out these objectives through the provision of charitable housing, educational support and grant-making. Some organisations are supported on a regular basis through grants for their core administration costs, others are offered funds to assist with project-related activities or salaries. Individuals are given assistance with education courses and costs, winter fuel payments or help in times of crisis.

Types of grant

The charity makes the following types of grant:

- Grants of more than £1,000
- Grants of less than £1,000
- Grants to regularly funded organisations
- Small grants (for fast response to crisis situations where statutory funding is not accessible)
- Educational grants to individuals, schools and organisations within the charity's catchment area (TW9, TW10, SW13, SW14) to further the learning and development of those in the community

There is some crossover within these types. As well as grant-giving to organisations, the charity also gives crisis grants, fuel grants and educational grants to individuals within the beneficial area. The charity also maintains some 90 properties available for affordable rented housing.

Financial information

In 2016/17 the charity had assets of £98.8 million and an income of £2 million. During the year, the charity awarded around £1.5 million in grants. Of this amount, £1.3 million was given in 109 awards to organisations. The figure for grants to organisations includes £68,000 given to schools in child support grants. During the year, grants were made to individuals totalling £209,000.

Beneficiaries included: Integrated Neuro Services (£72,000); Vineyard Community Centre (£54,000); Richmond Borough Mind £45,000); SPEAR (£30,000); Kew Neighbourhood Association (£25,000); Holly Lodge (£10,000); Lowther Primary School (£6,000); UK Creative (£2,000); Walnut Tree MAS (£500).

Exclusions

Projects and organisations located outside the benefit area, unless it can be demonstrated that a substantial number of residents from the benefit area will gain from their work. National charities (even if based in the benefit area), except for that part of their work which caters specifically for the area.

Applications

There are separate application forms and guidelines available on the website for the various types of grant. Be sure that you fill in each section and provide the required documents.

Regularly funded organisations must apply by specific deadlines which are available on the website.

Sources of information

Accounts; annual report; Charity Commission record; funder's website.

The River Farm Foundation

 Children, homeless people, disadvantaged groups

UK, overseas

(£) £2.3 million (2016/17)

CC number: 1113109

Trustees: Mark Haworth; Nigel Langstaff; Deborah Fisher.

Correspondent: Deborah Fisher, Trustee, The Old Coach House, Bergh Apton, Norwich, Norfolk NR15 1DD (tel: 01508 480100; email: info@ fisherlegal.co.uk)

The foundation was established in 2006 with an initial donation from Sloane Robinson Investment Services Ltd. The foundation's 2016/17 accounts state:

> The Trustees intend to continue making grants to other charities, using funds they are holding. In particular, they continue to develop and forge new links with previous recipients, academic institutions, museums and charities providing support to children, the homeless and other disadvantaged groups. Over a period of time and as these links evolve, the Trustees intend to increase the number and level of grants to enable those recipient organisations to provide better and ever more appropriate levels of support.

Financial information

In 2016/17 the foundation had assets of £43.9 million and an income of £2.3. Grants to nine organisations totalled £2.3 million.

Beneficiaries included: River Farm America Foundation (£2 million); St Edmund Hall Development (£115,000); Busoga Trust (£74,000); Centrepoint Soho (£22,000); Helen and Douglas House (£14,800); Shelter (£13,500); The Woodland Trust (£12,300); The Royal British Legion (£4,900).

Applications

Apply in writing to the correspondent.

Sources of information

Accounts; annual report; Charity Commission record.

The Roan Charitable Trust

 General charitable purposes including: social welfare, medical research, overseas aid, education

 UK

(£) £506,500 (2016/17)

CC number: 1122851

Trustees: Amelia Harris; Susan Swete; Lady Margaret Jarvis; Trevor Swete.

Correspondent: The Trustees, Solid Management Ltd, First Floor, 95 Mortimer Street, London W1W 7ST (tel: 020 7580 8084; email: jeff@ solidmanagement.co.uk)

The trust was established in 2008 and supports a wide range of charitable purposes, including social welfare, medical research, overseas aid and education.

Financial information

In 2016/17 the trust held assets of £9.4 million and had an income of £268,000. Grants to 28 organisations totalled £506,500.

Beneficiaries included: Cancer Research and The Royal National Institute of Blind People (£100,000 each); The Royal Opera House Foundation (£57,000); The Stroke Association (£25,000); Peace Hospice Care and The Disability Foundation Ltd (£5,000 each); Battersea Dogs and Cats Home and Women's Interfaith Network (£1,000 each).

Applications

Apply in writing to the correspondent. The trust's 2016/17 accounts state: 'There is no formal grant application procedure. The trustees retain the services of a charitable grants advisor and take account of the advice when deciding on grants.'

Sources of information

Accounts; annual report; Charity Commission record.

The Robertson Trust

 Care and well-being, community development, young people

Scotland

(£) £18.5 million (2016/17)

OSCR number: SC002970

Trustees: Shonaig Macpherson; Judy Cromarty; Mark Laing; Heather Lamont; Andrew Walls; Lorne Crerar; Mark Batho; Garry Coutts.

Correspondent: The Trustees, Robertson House, 152 Bath Street, Glasgow G2 4TB (tel: 0141 353 7300; email: funding@ therobertsontrust.org.uk)

 www.therobertsontrust.org.uk

 @robertsontrust

The trust was established in 1961 by the Robertson sisters, who inherited a controlling interest in companies in the Scotch Whiskey Industry (now the Edrington Group) from their father and wished to ensure the dividend income

from the shares would be given to charitable purposes.

The trust makes grants to registered charities and CICs working in Scotland whose work falls within one of its three funding strands.

The following information on areas of work and funding strands has been taken from the trust's website:

Funding strands

Care and Wellbeing

This Strand focuses on improving people's physical and mental health. It recognises the need to address the significant health inequalities which exist in Scotland and reduce the levels of exclusion faced by some of the most vulnerable members of our society.

In addition to encouraging preventative approaches to improve health and wellbeing, this Strand will also incorporate responsive approaches which support those with mental or physical ill-health to live independently.

Applications under this strand must directly address one of themes listed below. We have provided examples within each of the themes of some activities which may be relevant. However, this is not an exhaustive list.

- Ensuring the best quality of life for Scotland's vulnerable adults, including those directly or indirectly affected by Dementia
- Improving the health and wellbeing of children & young people affected by mental and/or physical ill health
- Supporting adults with life limiting, long-term health conditions or disability to overcome barriers and remain involved with their communities

Strengthening Communities

This Strand has been developed in response to the social inequalities in Scotland. Within Strengthening Communities we hope to support work which benefits those who have been disproportionately affected either economically, or due to the marginalised nature of their peer group.

We also recognise the value of building on local assets and wish to support organisations and communities which come together to create meaningful, sustainable solutions to address local need.

Applications under this strand must directly address one of themes listed below. We have provided examples within each of the themes of some activities which may be relevant. However, this is not an exhaustive list.

- Reducing health and social equalities in Scotland's communities
- Supporting people and communities to find routes out of poverty
- Empowering communities

Realising Potential

This Strand is based on recognition that there are social and educational inequalities in Scotland which emerge from a very young age. By supporting activities, projects and organisations that seek to address these inequalities The Robertson Trust aims to support more young people to reach positive destinations.

This Strand will also capture work which identifies and nurtures talent in young people across a wide range of disciplines, helping to create a body of young people who are confident and resilient with the potential to become future leaders within their field.

Applications under this strand must directly address one of themes listed below. We have provided examples within each of the themes of some activities which may be relevant. However, this is not an exhaustive list.

- Enabling young people to realise their potential
- Supporting 'at risk' young people to make positive choices
- Broadening horizons and nurturing talents among Scotland's young people

Types of funding

Revenue

These range from £500 upwards but rarely exceed £20,000 per annum. Revenue grants may be for core or project funding for a maximum initial period of 3 years. Please note as a general rule we do not make donations which exceed 50% of the salary cost of one member of staff. For a smaller project with no salary costs the Trust is unlikely to make a donation in excess of 50% of the total project costs. As the Robertson Trust is extremely unlikely to fully fund your request you should provide details of potential match funding at the point of application.

Capital

These start from £500 upwards and can be considered for up to a maximum of 25% of total project costs. Capital may relate to the upgrading of buildings, refurbishment costs or equipment. As a general rule, we would expect applicants to have around 30% to 40% of income secured before progressing applications.

Check the trust's website for community facility and transport funding requirements.

Financial information

In 2016/17 the trust held assets of £314 million and had an income of £23.8 million. Grants totalling £18.5 million were made to 718 organisations and were broken down as follows:

Realising Potential	145	£8 million
Strengthening Communities	213	£5.8 million
Care and Well-being	164	£4.5 million
Other awards	196	£316,000

Beneficiaries included: Glasgow Kelvin College (£132,000); Border College (£79,000); SportAid Scotland (£75,000); Glasgow Academy (£35,000); Scottish Rugby Union (£30,000); Citizens Theatre (£20,000); Borders College (£5,000).

Further information on the trust's grant-making can be found in the trustees' report and on the trust's website.

Exclusions

The trust's website states:

Types of activities which we do not fund:

- Funding for individuals, including travel/personal training costs/uniforms
- Projects and activities which incorporate the promotion of political or religious beliefs, or requests for salaried posts where there is a requirement for the post holder to be of a particular faith or none
- Work which takes place outside Scotland
- Research or feasibility studies
- The provision of information and advice (e.g. Helplines) with no associated, longer term support
- Replacement of statutory revenue funding for mainstream playgroups and nurseries
- Capital costs of Memorials/Statues/Universities/Colleges
- One-off events/festivals which have no associated educational activities or where these do not address disadvantage, in line with our funding strands
- The standalone purchase costs of buildings and/or land
- Capital work on buildings not owned by the applicant or on which the applicant does not have a long-term lease
- Any retrospective costs already incurred by the applicant
- Work which does not address one of our funding themes

Types of organisations which we do not fund:

- Housing Associations
- ALEOs
- Charities which seek funding for onward distribution to third parties
- Umbrella groups which do not provide direct services
- CICs limited by shares
- Organisations operating as a collective

Applications

Applications can be made through the trust's website.

Sources of information

Accounts; annual report; Charity Commission record; funder's website.

The Roddick Foundation

 Arts and culture, environment, human rights, medical/health, social justice

UK and overseas

£902,000 (2016/17)

CC number: 1061372

Trustees: Justine Roddick; Samantha Roddick; Gordon Roddick; Tina Schlieske.

Correspondent: Karen Smith, Unit H, The Old Bakery, Golden Square, Petworth, West Sussex GU28 0AP (tel: 01798 344362; email: karen@ theroddickfoundation.org)

www.theroddickfoundation.org

The Roddick Foundation was established in 1997 by the late Dame Anita Roddick, founder of the Body Shop. On its website, the foundation describes itself as a 'family-run, independent and progressive organisation dedicated to the support of visionary organisations and individuals who show leadership and results in making this a more just and kind world'.

The foundation states that it favours applications from 'people and groups who show exceptional creativity, entrepreneurial spirit, and courage' as well as those who can 'affect social change on a measurable scale'. The foundation generally provides funds for arts and culture, protecting the environment, securing human rights, medicine and health, and social rights. The foundation notes that it is open to collaborations with other charities and philanthropic organisations.

Financial information

In 2016/17 the foundation had assets of £18.5 million and an income of £398,000. The foundation made 35 grants to organisations totalling £902,000. Grants were distributed as follows:

Human rights	£388,000
Social justice	£290,000
Arts and culture	£177,500
Medical/health	£34,500
Environment	£11,000

Beneficiaries included: Institute of Global Labour and Human Rights (£80,000); Actors' Gang (£61,000); AHA! (£56,000); Belarus Free Theatre (£20,000); Article 39 (£12,500); Forgiveness Project (£11,000); Community Environmental Council (£6,900); Children on the Edge (£600).

Exclusions

The foundation has previously stated that it would not consider funding any of the following:

- Projects related to sport
- Fundraising events or conferences
- Sponsorship of any kind

Applications

The foundation does not accept unsolicited applications.

Sources of information

Accounts; annual report; Charity Commission record; funder's website.

The Romeera Foundation

General charitable purposes

Worldwide

£1 million (2016/17)

CC number: 1076325

Trustees: Madhoo Mehta; Meenal Mehta.

Correspondent: Madhoo Mehta, Trustee, 8 Temple Gardens, London NW11 0LL (tel: 020 8458 5864; email: romeerafoundation@gmail.com)

The foundation was established in June 1999 with general charitable purposes.

Financial information

In 2016/17 the foundation had an income of £3,600 and a total expenditure of £1 million. Due to its low income, the foundation was not obliged to submit accounts to the Charity Commission. Based on an analysis of the foundation's previous grant-making activity, we estimate that the foundation awarded grants of approximately £1 million.

Previous beneficiaries have included: Global Giving UK (£245,000); Cleft Lip and Palate Association, Find Your Feet, State of Ambition Ltd and UNLTD India (£10,000 each); Africa Prisons Project and Karuna Trust (£5,000 each); Jersey 2 Africa 4 Football Foundation (£2,500).

Applications

Apply in writing to the correspondent.

Sources of information

Accounts; annual report; Charity Commission record.

The Gerald Ronson Family Foundation

General charitable purposes

UK and overseas

£1.4 million (2016)

CC number: 1111728

Trustees: Gerald Ronson; Dame Gail Ronson; Alan Goldman; Jonathan Goldstein; Lisa Althasen; Nicole Ronson Allalouf; Hayley Ronson; Jeffrey Shear; Marc Zilkha; Ian Rosenblatt; Amanda Ronson.

Correspondent: Jeremy Trent, Secretary, H. W. Fisher & Company, Acre House, 11–15 William Road, London NW1 3ER (tel: 020 7388 7000; email: jtrent@ hwfisher.co.uk)

The foundation was registered with the Charity Commission in September 2005. It is the foundation of businessman and philanthropist Gerald Ronson, chief executive of Heron International, a UK-based property developer. The trustees make donations to registered charitable organisations undertaking a wide range of charitable activities, although there is some preference for Jewish causes; children and young people; health and disability; and arts and culture.

Financial information

In 2016 the foundation held assets of £91.6 million and had an income of £602,500. Grants were made totalling £1.4 million and were distributed for the following purposes:

Community and welfare	£765,000
Medical and disability	£307,000
Education	£168,000
General	£61,000
Arts and culture	£47,500
Religion	£41,000
Overseas aid	£33,500

Previous beneficiaries have included: Jewish Community Secondary School (£200,000); Community Security Trust (£83,000); Race Against Dementia (£50,000); Royal Opera House Covent Garden Foundation (£40,000); Police Arboretum Memorial Trust (£20,000); Refugee Council (£3,000); Jewish Women's Aid (£2,000); Chiltern Centre for Disabled Children (£1,000); British Friends of Israeli War Disabled (£500); Jewish Music Institute (£260).

Applications

Apply in writing to the correspondent. According to the foundation's 2016/17 accounts, it 'generally makes donations on a quarterly basis in March, June, September and December. In the interim periods, the Chairman's Action Committee deals with urgent requests for donations which are approved by the trustees at the quarterly meetings.'

Sources of information

Accounts; annual report; Charity Commission record.

Mrs L D Rope's Third Charitable Settlement

 Education, religion, relief of poverty, general charitable purposes

 UK and overseas, with a particular interest in East Suffolk

£647,000 to organisations (2016/17)

CC number: 290533

Trustees: Crispin Rope; Jeremy Winteringham Heal; Ellen Jolly; Catherine Scott; Paul Jolly.

Correspondent: Crispin Rope, Trustee, Lucy House, St William Court, Kesgrave, Ipswich, Suffolk IP5 2QP (tel: 01473 333288; email: ropetrust@lucyhouse.org. uk)

The charity takes the name of Lucy Rope, who died in 2003, aged 96. Mrs Rope engaged in many charitable endeavours throughout her life. The charity, administered by Mrs Rope's son Crispin, is based near Ipswich and takes a keen interest in helping people from its local area, working closely with local organisations.

Guidelines

The charity offers the following distinction between projects initiated by itself and unsolicited applications in its very detailed and informative 2016/17 accounts and annual report:

> In practice, the work of the Charity may be divided into two distinct categories. Firstly, it initiates, supports and pursues certain specific charitable projects selected by the Founder or known to be generally in accordance with her wishes. Secondly, it approves grants to unsolicited applications that fall within the Founder's stated objectives and that comply with the grant-making policies outlined below, specifically for this second element of its work.

Funding is aimed at making a direct impact and therefore the trustees have:

> An in-built presumption against funding major national charities or other charities which clearly already have the support of 'the great and the good' and are able to employ paid fundraisers, since these are much more likely to be able to raise the funds they need without our help.

The charity's main aim is the relief of poverty, but the trustees may also support educational or religious causes and other charitable purposes. Grants are rarely awarded for capital expenditure.

Successful unsolicited applications to the charity usually display a combination of the following features, as outlined in the charity's 2016/17 accounts:

Size

> The Trustees very much prefer to encourage charities that work at 'grass-roots' level within their community. Such charities are unlikely to have benefited greatly from grant funding from local, national (including funds from the National Lottery) or European authorities. They are also less likely to be as wealthy in comparison with other charities that attract popular support on a national basis. The charities assisted usually cannot afford to pay for the professional help other charities may use to raise funds.

Volunteers

> The Trustees prefer applications from charities that are able to show they have a committed and proportionately large volunteer force.

Administration

> The less a charity spends on paying for its own administration, particularly as far as staff salaries are concerned, the more it is likely to be considered by the Trustees.

Areas of interest

Charities with the above characteristics that work in any of the following areas:

a) Helping people who struggle to live on very little income, including the homeless

b) Helping charities in our immediate local area of East Suffolk

c) Helping people who live in deprived inner city and rural areas of the UK, particularly young people who lack the opportunities that may be available elsewhere

d) Helping to support family life

e) Helping disabled people

f) Helping certain types of Roman Catholic charities and ecumenical projects

Grants made to charities outside the primary beneficial area of East Suffolk are usually one-off and small in scale (in the range between £100–£2,000).

In addition to making grants to organisations, the charity also makes grants to individuals for welfare purposes, with a preference for those living in East Sussex.

Financial information

In 2016/17 the charity had assets of £66 million and an income of almost £1.6 million. Grants to 187 organisations totalled almost £647,000 and a further £514,000 was given to 2,141 individuals. The annual report notes that of the £647,000 awarded to organisations, £514,000 was awarded in unsolicited grants and £132,500 in grants initiated by the charity.

Beneficiaries of major grants included:
FIND – Ipswich (£50,000); Disability Information and Advice – Lowestoft (£35,000); St Alban's Catholic School – Ipswich (£32,500); L'Arche (£30,000); Ipswich Furniture Project (£27,000); Catholic Agency For Overseas Development and Felixstowe and District Citizens Advice (£20,000 each); Thetford Foodbank (£12,000); Médecins Sans Frontières (£10,000); Books Beyond Words (£9,200); Talitha Koum (£8,000).

Exclusions

The following categories of unsolicited applications will not be successful:

- Overseas projects
- National charities
- Requests for core funding
- Buildings
- Medical research/health care (outside the beneficial area)
- Schools (outside the beneficial area)
- Environmental charities and animal welfare
- The arts
- Matched funding
- Repayment of debts for individuals

Applications

Send a concise letter (preferably one side of A4) explaining the main details of your request. Always send your most recent accounts and a budgeted breakdown of the sum you are looking to raise. The charity will also need to know whether you have applied to other funding sources and whether you have been successful elsewhere. Your application should say who your trustees are and include a daytime telephone number.

Sources of information

Accounts; annual report; Charity Commission record.

Rosa Fund

 Initiatives that benefit women and girls in the UK

UK

£601,500 (2016/17)

CC number: 1124856

Trustees: Marilyn List; David Aeron-Thomas; Prof. Ruth Pearson; Sheila Malley; Sharon Mahli; Linda McDowell; Kay Ali; Niamh Grogan; Catherine Dovey.

Correspondent: Samantha Rennie, c/o WRC United House, 4th Floor, North Road, London N7 9DP (tel: 020 7697 3466; email: info@rosauk.org)

 www.rosauk.org

 facebook.com/RosaUK

 @RosaForWomen

Rosa was established in 2008 and supports initiatives that benefit women and girls in the UK. It has a vision of equality and justice for all women and girls in the UK.

Rosa's work is underpinned by four pillars:

- Leadership and representation
- Safety
- Health and well-being
- Economic justice

The fund's flagship grant programme is Voices from the Front Line. Its previous grant programmes include the Woman to Woman Fund, which funded work to increase women's representation, skills building and civic engagement, and Supporting Survivors, which provided funding for mental health service for female genital mutilation survivors in Birmingham.

Voices from the Frontline

Grants of £300 to £5,000 are available under this programme.

The following information has been taken from the fund's website:

The programme aims to:

- Support campaigning, advocacy and activists working across any one of Rosa's four pillars
- Amplify the voices of individual women at the Frontline of grassroots work in the UK
- Support work which can, long-term, tackle the underlying causes of a problem women face
- Nurture talent. Activism driven by inspiring, committed leaders can achieve remarkable results

What do we mean by advocacy and campaigning?

We want to support work that has an impact beyond the direct beneficiaries of an organisation, and is based on a clear understanding of how change happens. We envisage supporting a range of organisations, from those who are just beginning to make their voices heard, to those looking to catalyse change at a higher level. We hope to support projects which:

- Stimulates debate and amplifies women's voices
- Raises awareness of one or more of Rosa's four pillars*
- Influences the public, policy makers, media and/or government
- Changes behaviours, attitudes or policies

What sort of work will be supported?

The money can be used to pay for increasing the skills, capacity, credibility and effectiveness of women who wish to challenge gender inequality, promote awareness and change. Creative approaches are encouraged. Examples of work we will fund include:

- Travel costs for a service user to speak at an event or national conference
- Presentation, media or lobbying training to support organisational advocacy strategies
- Costs of creating campaign materials, such as posters, infographics or videos
- Articulating the story of a woman to champion an organisation's work
- Making a case to local commissioners for the value of a service
- Meeting costs with local/national government representatives or for planning a campaign

Financial information

In 2016/17 the charity held assets of £1.8 million and had an income of £422,500. Grants to organisations totalled £601,500.

Beneficiaries under the Woman to Woman programme included: Granby Somali Women's Group and Hull Sisters (£25,000 each); Open Gate (£20,000); Women of Worth (£18,000); Footsteps Counselling and Care (£10,300); Halo Project (£8,700); Rainbow Muslim Women's Group (£7,500); Sisters of Frida (£5,500).

Applications

Applications can be made through the fund's website.

Sources of information

Accounts; annual report; Charity Commission record; funder's website.

The Rose Foundation

 Building projects

London

£ £828,500 (2015/16)

CC number: 274875

Trustees: Martin Rose; Alan Rose; John Rose; Paul Rose.

Correspondent: The Trustees, 28 Crawford Street, London W1H 1LN (tel: 020 7262 1155; email: martin@ rosefoundation.co.uk)

 www.rosefoundation.co.uk

The foundation registered with the Charity Commission in 1978 and supports charities requiring assistance for their building projects. It gives small grants to benefit as large a number of people as possible rather than large grants to small, specific groups.

To a lesser extent, when extra funding is available, the foundation will also support general charitable purposes.

What is funded?

The foundation provides assistance to registered charities and exempt bodies undertaking building projects that cost less than £200,000 in the London area. Donations are usually between £5,000 and £10,000.

What is a building project?

Anything involving the use of builders – it can be general refurbishment or a specific scheme. For example: a repair to a roof or windows; or the creation of disability access; or the provision of new toilets. Redecoration and fulfilment of health and safety requirements are also included.

Financial information

In 2015/16 the foundation had assets of £28.3 million and an income of £1 million. During the year, the foundation awarded 64 grants to organisations totalling around £828,500.

Beneficiaries included: St John Ambulance (£470,000); Fred Hollows Foundation (£50,000); Al-Huda Marble Arch Association, London Maccabi Recreational Trust and St Paul's Church Covent Garden (£10,000 each); Jewish Care (£8,000); BFI Development (£7,500); English National Ballet, Hampstead Theatre, Shepherd's Bush Families Project and Children's Centre

(£5,000 each); Mayhew Animal Home (£2,500).

Exclusions

The foundation will not fund the purchase of equipment (although equipment might be an integral part of an overall refurbishment scheme and so could be partially funded), or the purchase of a building or a site. It will not provide the seed money needed to draw up plans, or cover general fees.

Applications

Apply in writing to the correspondent including details of the organisation and the registered charity number, together with the nature and approximate cost of the scheme and its anticipated start and completion dates. Applications can be submitted anytime between 1 July and 31 March. The foundation hopes to inform applicants of its decision by the second week in July (the following year).

Further information can be found on the foundation's website.

Sources of information

Accounts; annual report; Charity Commission record; funder's website.

The Cecil Rosen Foundation

 Jewish causes, people with disabilities, social welfare, health and medical research, education

UK and Israel

£ £355,500 (2015/16)

CC number: 247425

Trustees: Malcolm Ozin; John Hart; Peter Silverman.

Correspondent: Malcolm Ozin, Trustee, 35 Langstone Way, Mill Hill East, London NW7 1GT (tel: 020 8346 8940; email: contact@cecilrosenfoundation. org)

Established in 1966, this foundation's Charity Commission record states that it supports a number of Jewish organisations and organisations working with people who are blind or who have disabilities. The 2015/16 annual report states that the foundation supports causes in the following areas: health; education; medical research; religion; social welfare.

The foundation makes long-term commitments to a small number of charities but also considers applications. It also responds to international disasters.

Financial information

In 2015/16 the foundation had assets of £8 million and an income of £502,500. At the time of writing (March 2018) these were the latest accounts available.

Grants totalling £355,500 were made during the year, distributed in the following categories:

Welfare	56.84%	£190,000
Health	15.82%	£53,000
Medical research	10.64%	£35,500
Education	10.36%	£34,500
Religion	6.34%	£21,000

The accounts state that around 9% of the total grants were given to Israeli charities.

A list of beneficiaries was not provided in the accounts.

Exclusions

No grants are given to individuals.

Applications

Apply in writing to the correspondent. The 2015/16 annual report states: 'The Trustees consider all applications received and give special attention to those which were originally chosen by the Settlor, Cecil Rosen.'

Sources of information

Accounts; annual report; Charity Commission record.

Rosetrees Trust

 Medical research

 UK

£ £4.25 million (2016/17)

CC number: 298582

Trustees: Richard Ross; Clive Winkler; Sam Howard; Lee Mesnick.

Correspondent: The Trustees, Russell House, 140 High Street, Edgware, Middlesex HA8 7LW (tel: 020 8952 1414; email: info@rosetreetrust.co.uk)

 www.rosetreetrust.co.uk

Registered as the Teresa Rosenbaum Golden Charitable Trust, the trust was established in 1987 to support medical research leading to early improved treatments or new therapies covering many medical conditions. In 2009/10 a transfer of assets from the settlors' estate to the trust amounted to around £30 million. Richard Ross is the settlors' son and a well-known philanthropist.

Grants programmes

The following information on grants programmes has been taken from the trust's website:

> Our funding supports the brightest minds in medical research to hasten discoveries that will provide cures or improve medical treatment. We support research into all aspects of biomedical science, by researchers with the most innovative and exciting ideas.
>
> Rosetrees Trust will help with the cost of salaries and consumables (but not equipment, overheads or tuition fees), and

typically funds, but does not limit itself to, projects based in the United Kingdom that are covered by the following categories:

▶ **Early career scientists:** part-funded PhD studentships, MBPhDs, Clinical Fellows

▶ **Pilot studies:** Seed corn funding to obtain data to apply for major grants from larger funders

▶ **Project grants:** part funding of projects, postdoctoral fellowships and cross discipline research

▶ **Continuation funding and PhD extension grants:** (by prior agreement only)

Financial information

In 2016/17 the trust had assets of £35.4 million and an income of £3.8 million. Grants awarded to organisations totalled £4.25 million.

Beneficiaries Included: University College London and Royal Free (£1.2 million each); University of Cambridge (£452,500); University of Oxford (£194,000); Barts and Queen Mary (£167,000); The Royal College of Surgeons (£114,000); University of Manchester (£47,000).

Applications

Application forms and guidelines are available to download from the website. Refer to the website for the dates of application rounds.

Sources of information

Accounts; annual report; Charity Commission record; funder's website.

The David Ross Foundation

 General charitable purposes including: education, sport, arts, heritage, community

 UK

 £1.65 million (2016/17)

CC number: 1121871

Trustees: Mark Bolland; David Ross; Anita Bott; Marcia Mercier; Lady Caroline Ryder.

Correspondent: Joanne Hoareau, 10 St James's Place, London SW1A 1NP (tel: 020 7534 1551; email: joanne@ davidrossfoundation.com)

 www.davidrossfoundation.co.uk

 facebook.com/davidpeterjohnross

 @davidrosspr

The David Ross Foundation was registered with the Charity Commission in 2007. The foundation's belief is that every child and young person has passion and talent and so it offers a range of educational opportunities to explore these talents.

Areas of support

The foundation has four key areas of interest, details of which have been taken from its website:

Education – The David Ross Foundation is the sponsor of the David Ross Education Trust. The David Ross Education Trust is developing a network of unique and diverse schools and academies. There are currently 33 within the Trust group.

Sport - Key priorities are to increase the number of students participating in quality sport, to encourage and deliver quality sports competition opportunities and to provide pathways and support for talented individuals to participate and succeed in elite sport.

Arts - The David Ross Foundation is a passionate supporter of projects that work towards providing greater access to the arts. The Foundation supports a number of organisations and schemes across a range of artistic fields, from music to theatre and the visual arts and is the major sponsor of Nevill Holt Opera.

Heritage – Though a national charity, many of the Foundation's activities are concentrated on the areas that David cares deeply about; areas where he is from and now lives. That is why every decision made and project supported must have a lasting impact and make a real difference to the communities that they serve.

Financial information

In 2016/17 the foundation had assets of £6.1 million and a total income of £4 million. The foundation awarded grants during the year which totalled £1.65 million.

Beneficiaries included: David Ross Educational Trust (£609,000); Grimsby Regeneration Project (£196,500); Life Cycle (£20,000); National Youth Orchestra (£10,000); British Shooting (£6,100); Wellbeing in Women (£2,000); RNLI (£1,800); Ambitious About Autism (£500); Breast Cancer Now (£200); Shooting Star (£50).

Applications

Apply in writing to the correspondent. The foundation's website states:

In assessing applications we are looking for:

▶ An outline of your project – its purpose and activities

▶ Financials – total budget, fundraising strategy and the level of funding you are seeking from DRF

▶ Who will benefit?

▶ Community support, sustainability and legacy of your project

Sources of information

Accounts; annual review; funder's website; Charity Commission record.

The Rothermere Foundation

 General charitable purposes, education, medical research, the arts, religious organisations

 UK

 £553,500 (2016/17)

CC number: 314125

Trustees: Rt Hon. Viscount Jonathan Rothermere; The Viscountess Claudia Rothermere; Vyvyan Harmsworth.

Correspondent: Vyvyan Harmsworth, Trustee, Beech Court, Canterbury Road, Challock, Ashford TN25 4DJ (tel: 01233 740641)

This foundation was registered with the Charity Commission in 1956 for the establishment and maintenance of Rothermere Scholarships to be awarded to graduates of the Memorial University of Newfoundland, to enable them to undertake further periods of study in the UK. The foundation also funds general charitable purposes, including the arts, culture and heritage; children and young people; sport; education and medical research. The trustees have decided to designate £150,000 a year until further notice to make grants to Rothermere Fellows and support other such long-term projects.

Financial information

In 2016/17 the foundation held assets of £35.4 million and had an income of £1.1 million. Grants to organisations were made totalling £553,500. Grants to organisations were broken down as follows:

Educational/children's charities	10	£248,000
General charitable purposes	18	£197,500
Medical research	8	£56,000
Arts	2	£38,500
Religious organisations	3	£13,400

Beneficiaries included: The Black Stork Charity (£50,000); RAI – Northcliffe First World War Project (£45,000); Action Against Cancer, Chelsea and Westminster Hospital and The Weidenfeld Fund (£25,000 each); The Rugby Portobello Trust and Live Music Now (£10,000 each); Learning Skills Research (£5,000); Hunt Staff Benevolent Society (£3,000); On Course Foundation (£500).

Applications

Apply in writing to the correspondent. The trustees meet twice a year to consider grant applications.

Sources of information

Accounts; annual report; Charity Commission record.

The Rothley Trust

General charitable purposes

North East England

£265,000 to organisations (2016/17)

CC number: 219849

Trustees: Alice Brunton; Julia Brown; Anne Galbraith; Mark Bridgeman; Gerard Salvin; David Holborn.

Correspondent: Gillian Allsopp, MEA House, Ellison Place, Newcastle upon Tyne NE1 8XS (tel: 0191 232 7783; email: mail@rothleytrust.co.uk)

www.rothleytrust.org.uk

The trust has been in operation since 1959 and was registered with the Charity Commission in 1966. The trust supports general charitable purposes with a preference for the following:

- Children and young people
- Community
- Energy saving projects
- Education
- Disability
- Medical charities
- Ex-services
- World in need

Apart from a few charities with which the trust has been associated for many years, its activities are now directed almost exclusively towards North East England – Northumberland, Tyne and Wear, Durham and Cleveland. The annual report for 2016/17 notes that the trustees are now considering appeals from older age groups, providing they fall within the existing grant criteria.

Grants are generally made for specific projects such as the purchase of equipment or the provision, refurbishment or repair of premises. This can include energy saving devices, IT equipment, website start-up and development costs. Wherever possible and where it is financially viable, the Rothley Trust encourages charities to choose energy-efficient electrical items with an energy rating of A or above. Registered charities, CICs and voluntary groups are all eligible for support.

Financial information

In 2016/17 the trust held assets of £8.2 million and had an income of £237,500. Grants were made to 226 organisations and totalled £265,000. The following breakdown was provided in the accounts:

Community	61	£71,500
Children and young people	65	£71,500
Disability	44	£48,500
Medical	19	£32,000
Education	21	£20,500
Energy	7	£7,900
Ex-Service	3	£6,000
World in need	2	£5,700
Older people	1	£1,200

Beneficiaries of grants exceeding £2,000 included: St Oswald's Hospice Ltd (£14,000); Durham Association of Boys and Girls Clubs (£5,500); Citizens Advice – County Durham and Unicorn Centre (£5,000 each) Combat Stress (£3,800); Community Action Northumberland and Consett Churches Detached Youth Project (£3,500 each); Maggie's – Newcastle and North East (£2,000).

Grants for less than £2,000 totalled £183,000.

Exclusions

No grants are given for the following:

- Further education
- The repair of buildings solely used for worship
- Religious purposes
- Arts, heritage or science
- Amateur sport
- Human rights, conflict resolution or reconciliation (except family mediation)
- Environmental protection or improvement
- Animal welfare
- Residents associations
- Parish councils
- University of the Third Age

Applications

The trustees prefer to receive applications by email, although they will also accept applications by post. There is an eligibility checklist on the website that should be completed and included with the application along with the following information:

- Your group's details including a brief history, your current activities, charitable status, a copy of the most recent annual report and accounts, and a copy of your governing document, e.g. constitution
- Further information about your funding request such as project costs, other funders you have approached and a list of items with estimated costs

All grants are paid by bank transfer; therefore, provide bank details with your application. If you are a newly constituted group, you must include a list of your trustees and/or management committee.

Further information is available on the trust's website, including examples of successful projects.

Sources of information

Accounts; annual report; Charity Commission record; funder's website.

The Rothschild Foundation

Arts and humanities, education, environment, social welfare

UK, with a preference for Buckinghamshire

£7.48 million (2016/17)

CC number: 1138145

Trustees: The Marquess Of Cholmondeley; Lord David John Ogilvy; Francesco Goedhuis; The Hon. Janet De Botton CBE; The Hon. Emily Magda Freeman-Attwood; The Hon. Hannah Rothschild; Lord Rothschild OM GBE; The Hon. Beth Matilda Rothschild.

Correspondent: Simon Fourmy, Head of Grants, The Dairy, Queen Street, Waddesdon HP18 0JW (tel: 020 7647 8577; email: grants@ rothschildfoundation.org.uk)

www.therothschildfoundation.com

The Rothschild Foundation was established by Lord (Jacob) Rothschild to maintain and promote Waddesdon Manor and to further the Rothschild family's charitable aims. Assets are derived from a number of charitable trusts inherited or created by Lord Rothschild, which were merged in 2010. The foundation's grant-making work focuses on several key policy areas, including: arts and heritage; the environment; education; and social welfare.

Although much of the foundation's funding is proactive and closed to unsolicited applications, the charity also operates two grants programmes 'Impact Grants' and Local and Community Grants' which are open to applications from charities which meet the eligibility criteria.

These programmes are largely focused on Buckinghamshire, this being the foundation's home county.

Impact Grants programme

The foundation's flagship grants programme, Impact Grants, aims to make a difference to Buckinghamshire through addressing a number of priority areas within three broad funding themes:

- Art with social impact
- Opportunities and life chances
- Resource sustainability

The maximum grant size is £150,000 over three years, although applications for lower levels of funding or for single-year projects will also be considered.

Local and Community Grants programme

The Local and Community Grants programme provides small grants of up to £5,000 to organisations in the area around Waddesdon working in the broad field of social welfare. Small and medium-sized charities are generally prioritised for funding and grants are usually made for specific programme-related costs or, in the case of smaller charities, core costs. The trustees are 'keen to engage with small organisations where unique local knowledge and a nimble approach can often best meet community needs'.

Further details on each grant programme are available via the foundation's website.

Financial information

In 2016/17 the foundation had assets of £633.5 million and an income of £37.8 million. In total the foundation provided 140 grants to organisations worth £7.48 million. These funds were distributed as follows:

Arts and humanities	£6.02 million
Education and social welfare	£1.03 million
Energy and environment	£432,500

Beneficiaries included: Illuminated River Foundation (£5 million); Cambridge Conservation Institute (£250,000); Factum Foundation JW3 (£150,000); Louisa Cottages (£93,000); Teach First (£90,000); Botanic Gardens Conservation International (£73,500); South Bank Centre (£60,500); Art UK, Give a Book (£60,000 each); Berks Bucks and Oxon Wildlife Trust, Institute of Historical Research, Modern Art Oxford and Norden Farm Centre for the Arts (£50,000 each).

Exclusions

Individuals; major capital projects; medical causes; academic research and bursaries; animal charities; projects outside the UK.

Applications

Impact Grants programme

Applications for Impact Grants are made through a three-stage process:

- Initial approach (informal eligibility conversation with a grants manager)
- Expression of interest (EOI)
- Full application

Applicants wishing to make an initial approach, are asked to include 'EOI request' in the subject heading of their email. Emails should be sent to: grants@rothschildfoundation.org.uk.

Deadlines for EOIs are in January and June each year.

Local and Community Grants programme

Applications to the Local and Community Grants programme can be submitted via an application form on the foundation's website. The programme has submission periods in the spring and the autumn. Further information

regarding deadlines and eligibility criteria are available on the foundation's website.

Should applicants require support or advice, enquiries should be submitted to: grants@rothschildfoundation.org.uk with either 'Local Grants programme' or 'Impact Grants programme' in the subject heading.

Sources of information

Accounts; annual report; Charity Commission record; funder's website.

Rothschild Foundation (Hanadiv) Europe

🔍 Jewish causes, religious education and research, heritage

📍 Europe

£ £3.2 million (2016)

CC number: 1083262

Trustees: Dr David Landau; Michael Kay; Lord Rothschild; Beatrice Rosenberg; Adam Cohen; Sir Maurice Victor; Beth Rothschild.

Correspondent: Trace Rice, Grants Administrator, Spencer House, 27 St James's Place, London SW1A 1NR (tel: 01296 658778; email: info@ rothschildfoundation.eu)

🌐 www.rothschildfoundation.eu

The foundation is one of the three philanthropic charities supported by the Rothschild family, the other two being The Rothschild Foundation (CC no. 1138145), which supports a range of charitable causes in the UK and Yad Hanadiv, which is based in Israel.

Rothschild Foundation (Hanadiv) Europe's website states that the foundation is 'committed to protecting European Jewish heritage, fostering scholarship and enhancing Jewish life in Europe'. The foundation's various grant programmes aim to 'assist universities, museums, libraries, archives and Jewish organisations that understand and appreciate that Jewish culture and heritage have a dynamic role to play in contemporary society'.

Applications to any of the foundation's grants programmes should:

- Support and develop skilled, trained professionals to ensure that the Jewish heritage found in the archives, libraries and museums of Europe is protected, conserved and accessible to a wide range of people
- Encourage and nurture the field of academic Jewish studies across Europe by funding individual scholars, university departments and academic and research conferences

- Enable community groups to explore their own Jewish heritage and disseminate their own research to a wider audience

Applications are welcomed from any organisation or institution active in Europe (including Russia, Ukraine, Moldova and Belarus), where activities qualify as charitable under UK charity law.

Grant programmes

Academic Jewish studies

Grants are available in this programme for the teaching of and research into Jewish studies. Three kinds of grant are available:

- Doctoral and postdoctoral fellowships
- Language studies
- Regional Jewish studies hubs

Detailed information on each of these categories is provided on the website, along with information about what support is currently available.

Archives and libraries

A number of different grants are available for archives and libraries relating to Jewish studies and Jewish history:

- Conservation and protection
- Inventories and cataloguing
- Professional training
- Yerusha
- Endangered Jewish archives

In all categories, the foundation has a preference for applications which 'adhere to internationally accepted methodological standards'. For more information on each of these grant areas, refer to the website.

Museums

Grants are available to European museums for projects relating to 'the preservation, study and dissemination of Jewish history, culture and religion'. Grants are available for the following purposes:

- Exhibition support
- Collections management
- Professional development
- Technology support

Detailed information about support available in each of these categories is provided on the website.

Jewish education

Grants are available to support a small number of organisations 'to enhance the level of Jewish literacy within their own programmes and encourages the use of local heritage resources, including museums and libraries, as an effective tool for creative educational programmes'.

Financial information

In 2016 the foundation had assets of almost £128 million and an income of £406,000. During the year, the charity awarded 91 grants totalling around £3.2 million.

Beneficiaries included: Jewish Theological Seminary (£158,000); London Metropolitan Archives (£152,000); Pillar Foundation (£104,500); University of Sussex (£81,000); Jewish Museum Hohenems (£80,000); Department of History, Ludwig Maximilians University and Menasseh Ben Israel Institute for Jewish Social and Cultural Studies (£65,000 each); Jewish Museum London (£60,000).

Exclusions

The foundation does not fund any of the following:

- On-going costs of schools, synagogues or welfare organisations
- The building of new museums or communal institutions
- Requests for artistic projects in the fine arts, the performing arts, film production, creative writing or for book publication

Further programme-specific restrictions may also apply. Check the website for full details.

Applications

Refer to the website for application forms, deadlines and guidance for each programme. Contact details for the grant managers of specific programmes are also provided on the website. Applications can only be submitted via the online application process, unless specifically requested by the foundation. The foundation does not accept applications by mail or email.

Sources of information

Accounts; annual report; Charity Commission record; funder's website.

The Roughley Charitable Trust

 Community projects, young people, older people, social welfare, disability, health and well-being, education, arts and leisure, heritage, environment

Birmingham

£231,000 to organisations (2016/17)

CC number: 264037

Trustees: John Smith; Martin Smith; Verity Owen; Victor Thomas; Rebecca McIntyre; Rachel Richards; Benjamin Newton.

Correspondent: J.R.L Smith, Trustee, 90 Somerset Road, Edgbaston, Birmingham B15 2PP (email: correspondent@roughleytrust.org.uk)

 www.roughleytrust.org.uk

This trust makes grants to support a wide range of causes in the Birmingham area. Its website explains that the trustees are 'as concerned about addressing special needs, deprivation and disadvantage as [they] are in fostering health and wellbeing and a greater engagement with the arts, heritage and environment' and use their local knowledge to select applicants who can 'use modest grants for the greatest benefit'.

Main grants programme

The trust supports a wide range of registered local charities working inside the Birmingham city boundary. In some cases, applications will be accepted from charities working near to the Birmingham city boundary provided the majority of their beneficiaries live within the city.

Applications are accepted from charities with an annual income of less than £1 million – with priority given to applications from smaller and medium-sized organisations – working in the following areas:

- Area-based community work such as church-based community projects
- Work with special needs including the following: childhood and youth; old age; death and bereavement; homelessness; disability; prison; addiction; victim support; other special needs
- Health and well-being, including syndrome support groups, counselling, bereavement support, complementary health and mental health initiatives
- Education
- Arts and leisure, including theatre in education groups, museums and arts centres
- Heritage
- Environment, particularly environmental improvement projects and green projects

Other grants

A small number of larger grants are awarded each year to charities in Birmingham known by one or more of the trustees. Regular support is also given to some overseas charities, or to national charities where one or more of the trustees has a personal involvement. Since November 2015, the trust has also awarded grants from funds gifted by the AW60 Trust. The trust supports up to five student gap year travel grants each year.

Financial information

In 2016/17 the trust had assets of £7.15 million and an income of £298,500. Grants to 41 organisations totalled £231,000 and a further £900 was awarded to two students through gap year awards. Grants to organisations were distributed as follows:

Birmingham larger grants	10	£107,000
International	3	£60,000
Birmingham smaller grants	25	£50,000
AW60 grants	3	£14,000

Birmingham smaller grants can be broken down further, into the following categories:

Church-based community projects	5	£13,000
Arts	6	£11,000
Community and youth work	6	£11,000
Special needs	4	£9,000
Environment	2	£3,000
Disability	1	£2,000
Refugees and asylum seekers	1	£1,000

Beneficiaries included: Hope Projects West Midlands (£40,000); Appropriate Technology Asia (£25,000); Restore Birmingham Churches Together (£5,000); Big Brum, Carrs Lane Counselling and West Midlands Quaker Peace Project (£3,000 each); Disability Resource Centre (£2,000); Birmingham Civic Society Awards, South Sudanese East Bank Community Association and Trees for Life (£1,000 each).

Exclusions

Applications are not considered from:

- Birmingham-based medical charities
- Church fabric appeals
- Community interest companies
- Social enterprises
- Church-based projects which are essentially about the teaching of religion
- Animal charities

A Birmingham branch of a national charity cannot be funded unless the branch has its own charity number and accounts.

Applications for projects in Sandwell, Solihull, Wolverhampton and Walsall are not normally accepted.

Applications

Applications should be made using the form available to download on the trust's website, where the criteria and guidelines are also available. Application forms should be returned to the trust by email, along with a signed letter on headed paper, two or three photographs which give a good idea of what the project is about, and any other supporting material (in moderation). Latest accounts should only be sent if they are not available to view on the Charity Commission website. For more information, including details of key dates for applications, refer to the trust's website.

Sources of information

Accounts; annual report; Charity Commission record; funder's website.

Rowanville Ltd

The advancement of the Orthodox Jewish faith

UK and Israel

£1.2 million (2016/17)

CC number: 267278

Trustees: Joseph Pearlman; Ruth Pearlman; Allan Becker.

Correspondent: Joseph Pearlman, Trustee, 8 Highfield Gardens, London NW11 9HB (tel: 020 8458 9266)

The object of this charity is to advance religion in accordance with the Orthodox Jewish faith. The charity provides grants to charitable institutions and its charitable subsidiary provides a Jewish faith school with accommodation free of charge, in addition to providing budgetary assistance to the school.

Financial information

In 2016/17 the charity had assets of £10.7 million and an income of almost £1.2 million. During the year, the charity gave a total of £1.2 million in grants to organisations.

Beneficiaries included: Achisomoch Aid Company Ltd (£100,000); MGS/ Menorah Grammar School (£85,500); Gevurath Ari Academy Trust (£72,500); Chovovei Torah Synagogue (£60,000); Friends of Beis Yisroel Trust (£50,000); Yesamach Levav (£40,000); Chevras Maos Ladol (£25,000); Sunderland Talmudical College (£21,500).

Grants of less than £20,000 each totalled £596,500.

Applications

The trustees have previously stated that applications are unlikely to be successful unless one of the trustees has prior personal knowledge of the cause, as this charity's funds are already very heavily committed.

Sources of information

Accounts; annual report; Charity Commission record.

The Rowlands Trust

General charitable purposes

Birmingham, Gloucestershire, Herefordshire, Shropshire, Warwickshire and Worcestershire

£719,000 (2016)

CC number: 1062148

Trustees: Felicity Burman; Gary Barber; Timothy Jessop; Diana Crabtree; Ian Crockatt Smith.

Correspondent: Louise Ruane, Bishop Fleming Rabjohns LLP, 1–4 College Yard, Worcester WR1 2LB (tel: 07812 743485; email: louise.ruane@ therowlandstrust.org.uk)

The Rowlands Trust was created in 1997 by the Will of Herbert Roy Rowlands and was registered with the Charity Commission the same year. The trust primarily supports projects in the West Midlands and the South Midlands, including Hereford and Worcester, Gloucester, Shropshire and Birmingham. Grants are given for general charitable purposes, particularly in the following areas:

- Research, education, and training in the broadest sense with special regard to medical and scientific research
- People who are sick or poor, those with disabilities and older people
- Music and the arts
- The environment

Financial information

In 2016 the trust had assets of £3.7 million and an income of £175,000. Grants totalling £719,000 were provided and were distributed as follows:

Social welfare, disability and older people	94	£310,000
Research, education and training	22	£211,000
Church buildings	22	£99,000
Music and the arts	29	£85,000
The environment	6	£12,000

Beneficiaries included: Islet Research (£120,000); Suckley SPACE (£30,000); Young Enterprise (£25,000); Midlands Air Ambulance Charity (£18,000); Titley Village Hall (£10,000); Elmhurst Ballet School (£9,000); Herefordshire Cathedral Perpetual Trust (£6,000); Martineau Gardens (£5,000); NMC Midlands (£2,500); Plantlife International (£1,500).

Exclusions

The trust does not fund core costs or projects which are eligible for state funding.

Applications

Application forms are available from the correspondent and are the preferred means by which to apply. Completed forms should be returned with a copy of the most recent accounts. The trustees meet to consider grants four times a year.

Sources of information

Accounts; annual report; Charity Commission record.

The Joseph Rowntree Charitable Trust

Equalities, rights and justice, power and accountability, peace and security, Northern Ireland, sustainable future

Unrestricted, in practice mainly UK

£5.5 million (2016)

CC number: 210037

Trustees: Linda Batten; Margaret Bryan; Susan Seymour; Helen Carmichael; Imran Tyabi; John Fitzgerald; Michael Eccles; Hannah Torkington; Jenny Amery; Huw Davies; David Newton; Janet Slade.

Correspondent: Nick Perks, Trust Secretary, The Garden House, Water End, York YO30 6WQ (tel: 01904 627810; email: enquiries@jrct.org.uk)

 www.jrct.org.uk

 @jrctinfo

The Joseph Rowntree Charitable Trust (JRCT) was established in 1904 for general charitable purposes and benefits people and organisations mainly within Britain. Outside Britain, the trust makes grants for work towards peace, justice and reconciliation in both jurisdictions in the island of Ireland and, increasingly, in relation to influencing the policies of the European Union.

This is a Quaker trust and the value base of the trustees, as of the founder Joseph Rowntree (1836–1925), reflects the religious convictions of the Society of Friends. In the original founding trust deed of 1904 (from which the present deed is derived) Joseph Rowntree gave the trustees power to spend the trust fund and its income on any object which is legally charitable. In a memorandum written at the same time, which is not part of the trust deed and therefore not binding, he expressed a clear vision of how he hoped the fund would be used, while urging that 'none of the objects which [he has] enumerated, and which under present social conditions appear to [him] to be of paramount importance, should be pursued after it has ceased to be vital and pressing'.

Regular reviews are undertaken to reassess how it is appropriate to interpret the founder's vision in today's conditions. The trust continues to operate an ethical investment policy, aiming to ensure that, as far as possible, the trust's income is earned in ways which are compatible with its Quaker values and its grant-making policy. In line with Quaker ethos, the trust shares a belief in the equal worth of all members of the human race, together with a recognition and appreciation of diversity.

Grant-making programmes

The trust's current programme areas are:

- **Peace and security**, particularly:
  1. Challenging militarism
  2. Scrutiny of counter-terrorism measures in the context of human rights and peacebuilding
  3. Building support for alternative approaches to defence and security
- **Power and accountability,** particularly:
  1. Strengthening corporate accountability
  2. Strengthening democratic accountability
  3. Encouraging responsible media
- **Rights and justice**, particularly:
  1. Protection and promotion of equality and human rights and their enforcement in the UK
  2. Promoting rights and justice for minorities who face the most severe forms of racism and discrimination
  3. Promotion of rights and justice for refugees and other migrants
- **Sustainability**, particularly:
  1. Better economies
  2. Beyond consumerism
  3. New voices, empowering marginalised groups and young activists
- **Northern Ireland**, particularly:
  1. Strengthening human rights and equality
  2. Supporting inclusive, non-sectarian and participatory politics
  3. Supporting processes of demilitarisation
  4. Dealing with the past

Detailed guidelines for each of these funding priorities can be found on the website.

The trust is interested in funding projects which:

- Are about tackling problems through radical solutions and not simply about making problems easier to live with
- Have a clear sense of objectives and how to achieve them
- Are innovative and imaginative
- Clearly demonstrate that the grant has a good chance of making a difference

Financial information

In 2016 the trust had assets of £13 million and an income of £1.7 million. A total of £5.5 million was awarded in grants to 93 organisations.

Beneficiaries included: Nuclear Information Service (£159,000); Verification, Research, Training and Information Centre (£135,000); City of Sanctuary (£120,000); Conflict Resolution Services (Ireland) (£120,000);

Climate Outreach and Information Network (£90,000); CORE Coalition (£90,000); Transparency International (UK) (£90,000); Friends of the Earth Scotland (£66,000); JUST West Yorkshire (£60,000); Northern Ireland Council for Ethnic Minorities (£50,000).

Exclusions

Generally, the trust does not make grants for:

Organisations

- Larger, older national charities with an established group of supporters and substantial levels of reserves
- Statutory bodies
- For-profit organisations

Individuals

- The personal support of individuals in need
- Educational bursaries
- Travel or adventure projects

Projects

- Medical research
- Academic research, except as an integral part of the trust's policy and campaigning work
- Building, buying or repairing buildings
- Business development or job creation schemes
- Service provision
- Housing and homelessness
- The arts, except for projects specifically concerned with issues of interest to the trust

Types of funding

- General appeals
- Work the trustees believe should be funded by statutory sources, or which has been funded in this way in the recent past
- Work that has been already undertaken

Place

- Local or national work anywhere outside the UK; however, it does 'make a small number of grants for work at a pan-European level, in relation to international institutions, or to replicate or amplify local work in the UK with wider significance'.

Individual programme areas have their own specific exclusions. Organisations with a political stance cannot be funded. A full list of exclusions is available on the website.

Applications

Only online applications are accepted. Those sent by post, email or fax are not considered. The online form must be submitted and you should have the following information ready: a narrative proposal; budgets; accounts; your organisation's governing document (for

non-registered charities); and information on your organisation's policies (equal opportunities and sustainability), should you have any. Guidelines can be found on the website, along with application deadlines.

The trust accepts 'cross-cutting' applications for projects that relate to more than one of its programme areas. It is recommended that anybody considering a 'cross-cutting' proposal telephones the trust in the first instance for a discussion.

Sources of information

Accounts; annual report; Charity Commission record; funder's website.

The Joseph Rowntree Foundation

🔍 Research and development in social policy and practice

📍 UK

💷 £5.7 million (2016)

CC number: 210169

Trustees: Maureen Lloffil; Graham Millar; Prof. Dianne Willcocks; Steven Burkeman; Deborah Cadman; Saphieh Ashtiany; Gillian Ashmore; William Haire; Carol Tannahill; David Lunts; Paul Jenkins; Helen Evans.

Correspondent: Campbell Robb, Chief Executive, The Homestead, 40 Water End, York YO30 6WP (tel: 01904 629241; email: info@jrf.org.uk)

 www.jrf.org.uk

 facebook.com/ JosephRowntreeFoundation

 @jrf_uk

The Joseph Rowntree Foundation is an independent social organisation which, through research, policy, collaboration and practical solutions, aims to inspire action and change that will create a prosperous UK without poverty.

The foundation supports research usually carried out in universities or research institutes and issues 'calls for proposals' inviting submissions. It is not a grant-making charity and the trustees do not generally accept speculative enquiries for funding. The foundation does have a wide range of activities not necessarily involving grants of any kind. It works in partnership with private, public and voluntary sectors, as well as with individuals and communities.

The Joseph Rowntree Foundation also works in collaboration with the Joseph Rowntree Housing Trust to understand the root causes of social problems, identify ways of overcoming them and show how social needs can be met in practice.

Current Work

During 2015–17, the foundation's focus has been on: individuals and relationships; the places where people live; and work and worth. The 2016 annual report states that the new chief executive will be working alongside trustees and staff to develop JRF's future strategy.

Where people live

This area of work includes: cities; climate change; devolution; economic development and local growth; flooding; loneliness; neighbourhoods; planning; public spaces; regeneration; services and local government; transport.

Housing

This area of work includes: affordable housing; care homes; home ownership; homelessness; housing market; housing providers; private rented sector; regeneration; social housing; tenant participation; tenants.

Income and benefits

This area of work includes: debt; food; living standards; living wage; minimum income standards; pay; pensions; personal finance; tax; unemployment; universal credit.

People

This area of work includes: ageing society; carers; child poverty; children; civic participation; dementia; people with disabilities; divorce/family breakdown; drugs/alcohol; ethnicity; gender; immigration; independent living; lone parents; loneliness; mental health; older people; sexuality; social care; young people.

The trust aims to:

▶ Achieve a better understanding of how individual and collective actions prevent or reduce poverty
▶ Develop evidence about the role of relationships in reducing poverty in local communities
▶ Empower the places and communities we work with to be rich in positive relationships, building on our work on dementia and loneliness

Society

This area of work includes: ageing society; austerity; care homes; civic participation; crime/anti-social behaviour; faith and religion; government; immigration; local government; localism; riots; slavery; social care; social exclusion; voluntary sector.

Work

This area of work includes: employment; equality; forced labour; labour markets; pay; retirement; skills; unemployment; volunteering; working with employers.

The trust aims to achieve:

▶ Recognition among businesses and employers that there is a strong business and social case for better pay and jobs
▶ A measurable increase in the number of JRHT residents who are in employment, education or training or involved in enterprise, along with consistent reduction of debt and increase in savings for JRHT residents
▶ Changes in public policy that draw solutions from our evidence base on the future and nature of work, and the value of contributions beyond paid work

The annual report for 2016 states:

Looking ahead to the final year of the current strategic plan, the Board and Executive agreed three themes as priorities for JRF's delivery and external profile during 2017, building on the launch (in September 2016) of our strategy We can solve UK poverty. The priorities are:

▶ In-work poverty, with a focus on low-wage sectors
▶ Inclusive growth, with a focus on cities and city regions
▶ Costs and living standards, with a focus on housing and on the poverty premium linked to JRF social investment

Financial information

In 2016 the foundation had assets of £369 million and an income of £6.9 million. A total of £5.7 million was awarded in grant commitments.

Beneficiaries included: Economic and Social Research Council (£1 million); Loughborough University (£688,000); Crisis and Housing Associations Charitable Trust (£100,000 each); Centre for Sustainable Energy and Sheffield Hallam University (£75,000 each); Newcastle University (£50,000); RSA (£30,000).

Grants under £25,000 totalled £670,000.

Exclusions

The foundation does not generally support:

▶ Projects outside the topics within its current priorities
▶ Development projects which are not innovative
▶ Development projects from which no general lessons can be drawn
▶ General appeals, for example from national charities
▶ Conferences and other events, websites or publications, unless they are linked with work which the foundation is already supporting
▶ Grants to replace withdrawn or expired statutory funding, or to make up deficits already incurred
▶ Educational bursaries or sponsorship for individuals for research or further education and training courses
▶ Grants or sponsorship for individuals in need

Full details can be found on the trust's website.

Applications

The foundation initiates, manages and pays for an extensive social research programme. It does not normally respond to unsolicited applications and many of its programmes issue formal and detailed requests for proposals. However, modest proposals for minor gap-filling pieces of work in the foundation's fields of interest may sometimes be handled less formally and more rapidly.

Full application details and guidelines are available on the website.

Sources of information

Accounts; annual report; Charity Commission record; funder's website.

Joseph Rowntree Reform Trust Ltd

 Political causes promoting democratic reform, civil liberties and social justice

UK

£903,000 for non-political purposes (2016)

Trustees: Lisa Smart; Andrew Neal; Prof. Susan Mendus; Dr Julian Huppert; Sir Nicholas Harvey; Dr Christopher Greenfield; Alison Goldsworthy; Amy Dalrymple; Baroness Sarah Brinton; James Wallace.

Correspondent: Tina Walker, Trust Secretary., The Garden House, Water End, York YO30 6WQ (tel: 01904 625744; fax: 01904 651502; email: info@jrrt.org.uk)

 www.jrrt.org.uk

 @jrrt1904

Joseph Rowntree was a Quaker businessman with a lifelong concern for the alleviation of poverty and the other great social ills of his day. He made a considerable fortune from the chocolate company which bore his name, and in 1904 transferred a large part of this wealth to three charities, each designed to reflect and develop different aspects of his thinking about contemporary social problems. Known today as The Joseph Rowntree Foundation, The Joseph Rowntree Charitable Trust and the Joseph Rowntree Reform Trust (JRRT), all three continue to build upon the founder's original vision, applying the charitable funds in different ways to the problems of present-day society. Note that the three organisations have always been separately administered and are totally independent of each other.

JRRT differs from the Rowntree charities, and from almost every other charity in the UK, in that it is not, in fact, a charity. Charities must not have political objectives and while they may engage in political activity in pursuit of their charitable aims, those aims must not in themselves be political. By contrast, JRRT is a limited company which pays tax on its income. It is, therefore, free to give grants for political purposes; to promote political and democratic reform and defend civil liberties.

Aims

JRRT's main aims are set out on its website as the following:

- Correct imbalances of power, supporting the voice of the individual, the small and weak where that voice is stifled by the group, the big and strong
- Strengthen the hand of individuals, groups and organisations who are striving for reform, speaking truth to power and challenging the systems that hinder justice
- Address the underlying causes of weakness and injustice in the body politic rather than remedying its superficial manifestations
- Foster creative intervention by anticipating and brokering change within the body politic
- Support a politically plural society by helping to correct the financial imbalance between the major parties
- Assist political liberals from all the major parties in the UK to promote new liberal ideas and policies

What the trust funds

The trust's strategic review in 2017 decided that the priority for grant-making in the coming years will be campaigning on democratic and political reform.

The website informs us that:

> When the Trust was founded in 1904, Joseph Rowntree, our founder, underlined the importance of working on underlying causes – rather than the manifestations of societal evils. In its political work, the Trust was urged to be mindful of the greatest danger to national life, the power of 'selfish and unscrupulous' wealth which influences public opinion – at that time largely through the press – as well as to work for the purity of elections.

> Today the need for wholesale democratic and political reform is urgent; without this many of the social and economic challenges the UK faces will fester.

Applications are particularly welcome for work on:

Electoral reform: ensuring that citizens' votes count, that turnout is high and elections are fair.

Examples could include: campaigning for proportional representation, improved voter turnout, votes at 16, and reforms to election party funding.

An open and responsive democracy: in which executive power is checked by an effective parliament, and power is devolved to the nations, regions and communities.

Examples could include: work to ensure that the Brexit process returns power to parliament rather than the executive, or measures to promote further devolution and related mechanisms for accountability. It could also include measures to enhance 'taking back control', making both parliament and government more accountable and responsive to citizens.

Democratic culture: making sure it is thriving, with respect for diversity, collaboration and informed public debate, encouraging participation.

Examples could include: supporting effective cross-party collaboration; media and social media influence on elections and political trust; and threats to key democratic rights to protest, speak out and campaign.

Other work JRRT will fund

While the trust will allocate the majority of funding to its work on democratic and political reform, funds will be available for a small number of grants for fast-response capacity for significant new political developments (where such development could be considered 'exceptional') and JRRT legacy issues.

Limited funding is available for taking work the trust has previously invested in to fruition, where the applicant can demonstrate that one further grant would 'take the issue over the line' to achieve a policy or legislative change.

Type of grants

Applications can be made:

- To quarterly application rounds for larger grants
- At any time for small grants of up to £7,500

Note: Applications should be for campaign activity to achieve a specific change within the period of the grant.

Spending power

The website states: 'The Trust's assets are invested in equity investments and a limited amount of property. From the Trust's present capital of about £50m, Directors allocate a potential grant budget of around £1.25m each year, excluding administrative expenses and tax.'

In 2016 the trust awarded £1.27 million in grants of which, £903,000 was awarded for non-political purposes.

Beneficiaries included: The Constitution Reform Group (£60,000); Open Rights Group (£47,000); Campaign for Nuclear Disarmament (£27,500); Open Democracy (£25,000); Forces Watch (£15,500); Index on Censorship (£7,500);

Greater Manchester and District CND (£2,000).

Exclusions

JRRT is not a charitable funder and will not make grants for the following, as stated on its website:

- Unsolicited applications from registered charities
- Unsolicited applications for work which may be funded from charitable sources
- Campaigns outside the UK
- Local campaigns without national impact
- General appeals
- Academic research
- Work which we believe should be funded from statutory sources, or which has been in the recent past
- Legal fees
- Administrative or other core costs of party organisations
- Personal support of individuals in need
- Educational bursaries
- Travel & adventure projects
- Building, buying or repairing properties
- Business development or job creation

Applications

Applicants should visit the trust's website where the four-stage application process is detailed in full. In brief, the stages are as follows:

- **Stage one – preparation:** all of the information available from the trust's website should be considered, including details of what the trust does and doesn't fund, important dates for applications (requests for amounts of more than £7,500 are subject to deadlines), and the stages of the application process
- **Stage two – outline proposal:** the trust's pre-application process requires applicants to submit a one or two page outline of their proposal. The trust then provides an initial response as to whether the proposal fits with its criteria and the board's current concerns
- **Stage three – writing your application:** applicants whose outline proposals are 'given the go-ahead' are invited to draft a full application. The trust's Grants and Projects Adviser can provide feedback on the draft and raise any issues that may exist
- **Stage four – online application:** applicants can submit the final version of their application via the trust's online application system where they will be asked to provide some basic information about their organisation

Sources of information

Funder's website.

Royal Artillery Charitable Fund

 Armed forces

 UK and overseas

£ £290,000 to organisations (2016)

CC number: 210202

Trustees: Col. Clive Fletcher-Wood; Maj. Andrew Dines; Col. Christopher Comport; Maj. General David Cullen; Maj. Jame Leighton; Col. William Prior; Col. Michael Kelly; Col. John Musgrave; Brig. Mark Pountain; Col. Michael Relph; Col. Hugh Baker; Col. Giles Malec.

Correspondent: Lt Col. Ian Vere Nicoll, General Secretary, Artillery House, Royal Artillery House, Larkhill, Salisbury, Wiltshire SP4 8QT (tel: 01980 845698; email: rarhq-racf-welfaremailbox@mod.uk)

🌐 www.theraa.co.uk

🐦 @gunner_net

The fund, established in 1839, promotes the efficiency and welfare of all ranks of the Royal Artillery and gives relief and assistance to any past or present members, living or deceased, their dependants and families who are in need of such assistance by way of poverty, illness or disability. The charity achieves this in part by making grants to institutions which serve such beneficiaries.

Financial information

In 2016 the fund had assets of almost £30.7 million and an income of over £1.5 million. Throughout the year, the charity awarded around £1.1 million in grants. Of this amount, £631,000 was given in welfare grants to individuals and £290,000 to organisations (this figure includes permanent endowment of £36,467 and excludes donations made from the Royal Artillery Benevelont Fund (RABF)). Further detailed information is contained within the charity's 2016 annual report and accounts.

Beneficiaries included: Regiments and Batteries (£77,000); Royal Artillery Sports (£65,000); Army Benevolent Fund (£60,000); Gunner Magazine (£18,000); King Edward VII Hospital and Veterans Aid (£3,000 each); Not Forgotten Association (£500); Army Widows' Association (£400).

Applications

Apply in writing to the correspondent.

Sources of information

Accounts; annual report; Charity Commission record; funder's website.

The Royal British Legion

 Armed forces

 England, Wales, Northern Ireland

£ £108.8 million (2015/16)

CC number: 219279

Trustees: Terry Whittles; Catherine Quinn; Adrian Burn; Una Cleminson; Denise Edgar; Rod Bedford; Anthony Macaulay; Maj. General David Jolliffe; Lt Col. Joe Falzon; Jason Coward; Colin Kemp; Philip Moore; Pat Chrimes; Lt Col. David Whimpenny; Roger Garratt; Anny Reid.

Correspondent: Luke Joannou, Haig House, 199 Borough High Street, London SE1 1AA (tel: 020 3207 2100; email: info@britishlegion.org.uk)

🌐 www.britishlegion.org.uk

f facebook.com/OfficialPoppyLegion

🐦 @PoppyLegion

📷 @royalbritishlegion

The Royal British Legion was formed in 1921 as a caring organisation for people in need from the Service and ex-Service community. It aims to safeguard the welfare, interests and memory of those who have served in the armed forces. In June 2011 The Royal British Legion merged with Poppyscotland, which continues to operate a distinct charity and which makes grants in Scotland.

The charity makes grants to organisations through its External Grants Scheme. The website states: 'It is intended to fund specialised projects or services for serving and/or ex service personnel and/or their families that are not already being provided by The Royal British Legion (the Legion) and that are in line with our programme's Funding Priorities.'

The funding priorities for the scheme are:

▷ Employment and training
▷ Support for families
▷ Homelessness and outreach
▷ Supporting older people

The maximum grant for any single award is £50,000 and applications for smaller grants are encouraged. At the moment, the charity is only providing one-off payments rather than multi-year funding.

Grants may be awarded for purposes including capital costs, projects, services and salaries. The charity is also able to part-fund projects. Applications for funding exceeding £50,000 for any form of building work are not normally considered unless there are exceptional circumstances. Furthermore, applications of less than £50,000 for building work will only be considered if the amount requested from the charity will complete the total amount needed for the project, allowing building work to begin.

Grants are made to charities that have been operating for at least two years. The guidance on the charity's website states that applicants must share its aims and objectives as well as being able to:

▷ Demonstrate that the money we give you will directly benefit serving and/or ex-Service personnel and/or their families
▷ Demonstrate that you have attempted to secure funding from other sources (whether you were successful or not)
▷ Demonstrate that your charitable organisation is run efficiently
▷ Provide evidence to show that there is demand for the project or service and how your project fits with our aims and objectives
▷ Describe the impact (project outcomes) your project will achieve for serving and/or ex-Service personnel and/or their families, providing evidence

The charity also makes grants to individuals.

Financial information

In 2015/16 the charity had assets of £295.6 million and an income of £151.2 million. Total direct charitable expenditure was £108.8 million, across the following areas:

Community welfare	£48 million
Care	£26 million
Communications and campaigning	£12 million
Remembrance and ceremonial	£10 million
Membership	£10 million
Personnel recovery centres	£1.5 million
Comradeship	£854,000

Beneficiaries included: The Officer's Association (£2 million); Imperial College of Science, Technology and Medicine (£1.5 million); Combat Stress (£851,000); Services Sound and Vision Corporation (£810,000); STOLL Housing for Veterans (£693,000); Fields Trust (£600,000); Somme Nursing Home (£385,000); Mission Motorsport (£191,000); The Royal British Legion Industries (£135,000).

Grants of less than £100,000 were awarded to 95 other charities, totalling £2.6 million. Additionally, Poppyscotland awarded a total of £10 million to organisations.

Exclusions

Funding is not awarded to:

▷ Commercial ventures (social clubs, for example)
▷ Statutory services

- Commemoration, memorials, monuments or war cemeteries
- Projects that duplicate services already provided by The Royal British Legion

Applications

The application process has two stages. Stage one involves the completion of a brief expression of interest form, which should be returned to the external grants officer (externalgrants@britishlegion.org.uk). Applicants that are successful at the first stage will be invited to complete a stage two application form to be considered by the grants panel. The stage one application form is available to download from the website along with guidelines.

Sources of information

Accounts; annual report; Charity Commission record; funder's website.

Royal Docks Trust (London)

Community development, social welfare, education, recreation and sport, arts, environment, disability, heritage, religious charitable work

Parts of the London borough of Newham (south of the Newham Way (A13) – Beckton, Canning Town (part), Custom House, North Woolwich, West Silvertown, Silvertown – see the map on the trust's website)

£204,500 (2016/17)

CC number: 1045057

Trustees: Eric Sorensen; Stephen Nicholas; Sid Keys; Amanda Williams; Kayar Raghavan; Katie Carter; James Kenworth; Belinda Vecchio; Gary Quashie; Giovanna Grandoni; Shani Thomas; Sandra Erskine.

Correspondent: John Parker, Trust Secretary, Olive Cottage, Station Road, St Margarets-at-Cliffe, Dover CT15 6AY (tel: 01304 853465; fax: 0871 522 7008; email: jb.parker@tiscali.co.uk)

 www.royaldockstrust.org.uk

The trust works to provide community benefits to Newham's Docklands – that part of Newham which lies between the A13 trunk road and the River Thames. In the decade up to its demise in 1998, the London Docklands Development Corporation (LDDC) worked in partnership with the London Borough of Newham (LBN) and Newham's voluntary sector to run a joint funding programme which offered financial support to community projects and the voluntary sector. To maintain this support into the future the LDDC and LBN, in partnership with representatives of the local community and senior

business leaders, established the Royal Docks Trust (London). The LDDC provided the trust with a core endowment of £2.7 million. The income generated is added to year on year by the London Borough of Newham. This has allowed the trust and the council to develop and sustain a grants programme approaching some £200,000 a year.

Grants programmes

Grants can be made in the following fields:

- Educational and vocational training
- Recreational and leisure-time pursuits
- Advancement of public education in the arts
- Improvement of the physical and social environment
- Relief of poverty and sickness
- Housing for people who have disabilities or are otherwise in need
- Preservation, repair and maintenance of buildings of historical or architectural significance
- General support of any religious order solely and specifically of its charitable work

There is also a minor grants programme with slightly different guidelines, which deals with grants of up to £2,000 (grants for social events must not exceed £500). Specific priorities of this programme are to:

- Assist projects to meet the social and economic needs of the community, encourage community development and assist community integration
- Enable projects to secure additional funding from other sources
- Enable projects to continue to undertake activities by meeting the cost of minor repairs to premises or equipment
- Assist new projects to establish themselves, such as hiring meeting venues, provision of stationery and meeting the costs of charity registration
- Provide an opportunity for the trust to demonstrate its purpose and promote its activities (therefore there needs to be an opportunity for the grant to be appropriately and sensitively publicly acknowledged)

Financial information

In 2016/17 the trust held assets of £9.4 million and had an income of £1.5 million. Grants were made totalling £204,500.

Beneficiaries included: Royal Docks Learning and Activity Centre (£30,000); Caramel Rock (£20,500); Middlesex University (£15,000); Care in Mind (£8,600).

Exclusions

The trust cannot support:

- Activities outside the area of benefit, or that do not directly benefit communities within the area
- General appeals for funds
- Individuals

The following cannot be supported through the minor grant programme:

- Revenue funding (except to assist with the start-up costs of a project)
- Top-up funding for projects which have a deficit
- Retrospective appeals

Applications

Major grants

Applications should be made on a form available to download from the trust's website. The annual grants programme timetable, described on the website, broadly follows a similar pattern every year:

- September – October: Agree priorities/ criteria and an indicative level of funding for the forthcoming year
- November – February: Invite applications via open advertisement and contact with existing recipients of grant aid and voluntary organisations known to the Trust
- February – March: Assessment of applications received, liaison with other funding bodies as necessary and discussions with applicants
- February – March: Determination of funding for the forthcoming year and approval of applications

The website also informs us that the trustees 'will not normally enter into correspondence in respect of unsolicited applications for funds' or, apart from minor grants, consider applications outside the annual grants programme.

Minor grants

Application forms are available to download from the website. Local organisations can apply for these grants throughout the year.

Further information can be obtained from the trust's website. The correspondent should not be contacted for matters relating to the grant programmes.

Sources of information

Accounts; annual report; Charity Commission record; funder's website.

The Royal Navy And Royal Marines Charity

 Organisations supporting Service or ex-Service personnel from the Royal Navy and the Royal Marines, and their dependants

UK

£7 million (2016)

CC number: 1117794

Trustees: William Stocks; Jennifer Rowe; Commodore Annette Picton; WO1 Gary Nicholson; The Hon. Stephen Watson; James Parkin; James Pitt; Oona Muirhead; William Thomas; Roderic Birkett; Michael Tanner; Mark Lewthwaite; Jamie Webb; Mark Dowie; Sub Lieutenant Harriet Delbridge.

Correspondent: Mike Burningham, HMS Excellent, Whale Island, Portsmouth, Hampshire PO2 8ER (email: theteam@rnrmc.org.uk)

 www.rnrmc.org.uk

 facebook.com/RNRMC

 @RNRMC

 @rnrmcharity

The Royal Navy and Royal Marines Charity supports sailors, marines and their dependants. The charity's objectives are:

- The relief in need, hardship or distress of beneficiaries
- Assistance with the education and training of children
- The promotion of efficiency of the Royal Navy and Royal Marines by way of the enhancement of morale and the improvement of recruitment and selection
- The relief and encouragement of serving men and women

The charity achieves these objectives through making grants to:

- Other naval charities
- Military charities
- Other charities with naval beneficiaries
- Ships, units and personnel of the Royal Navy, Royal Marines and Auxiliary Services
- Individual serving personnel and veterans, through the other funds in its group (Royal Navy Officers' Charity and Royal Marines Charity Trust Fund)

Support to individuals

The charity supports serving members of the armed forces, veterans and their families by providing large block grants to military welfare organisations. A list of these organisations can be found in the charity's Impact Report.

Amenities grants

As well as providing grants to organisations for benevolence support, the charity also provides grants directly for amenities, in two categories:

Amenities under £5,000

Grants of up to £5,000 are provided for a wide range of purposes, such as 'families' days, ship's company dances, team building events, recreational and entertainment items, and Mess refurbishment or enhancements'.

Amenities over £5,000

Grants of over £5,000 are provided for a range of causes, such as 'recreational and entertainment items, mess refurbishment or enhancement of facilities which improve the conditions of service for serving personnel and where applicable the quality of life of their dependants'.

Financial information

In 2016 the charity had assets of £61.6 million and an income of over £11.6 million. Grants were made totalling £7 million. Grants were broken down as follows:

Benevolence	£3.8 million
Amenities	£1.9 million
Sports	£837,000
Dependants grants	£240,000

Beneficiaries included: Royal Naval Benevolent Trust (£1 million); Royal Navy and Royal Marines Children's Fund (£629,500); Royal Marines Association (£186,500); HMS Queen Elizabeth (£183,000); Relate (£104,000); Globe and Laurel Magazine (£97,000); Combat Stress (£93,500); HMS Drake (£58,000); Queen Alexandra Hospital Home (£40,000); Royal Marines Band Service (£25,500).

Applications

Application forms are available to download from the website, where further guidance and deadlines are also provided.

Sources of information

Accounts; annual report; Charity Commission record; funder's website.

Royal Society of Wildlife Trusts

 Conservation, heritage and the environment

England, Wales, Northern Ireland and Scotland

£9.27 million (2016/17)

CC number: 207238

Trustees: Jonathan Hughes; Jennifer Fulton; Peta Foxall; Carole Nicholson; Stewart Goshawk; Ian Brown; Michael Power; Bill Stow; Ruth Sutherland; Rod Aspinwall; Peter Young; Anne Selby.

Correspondent: RSWT, The Wildlife Trusts, The Kiln, Waterside, Mather Road, Newark, Nottinghamshire NG24 1WT (tel: 01636 677711; email: enquiry@wildlifetrusts.org)

 www.wildlifetrusts.org

 facebook.com/wildlifetrusts

 @WildlifeTrusts

@thewildlifetrusts

Royal Society of Wildlife Trusts (RSWT), also known as The Wildlife Trusts (TWT), was registered with the Charity Commission in 1962 and its charitable objects are: to promote the conservation and study of nature; to further the research into conservation; and to educate the public in understanding and appreciating nature.

According to the trust's website:

> The Wildlife Trusts is a movement made up of 46 Wildlife Trusts: independent charities who all share a mission to create living landscapes and living seas and a society where nature matters.

> Each Wildlife Trust is a member of a central charity – the Royal Society of Wildlife Trusts (RSWT). The central charity's role is to ensure a strong voice for wildlife at a UK and England level and, internally, to lead the development of the movement.

Grant-making policy

Biffa Award

Grants are made subject to the terms and conditions placed upon RSWT by the relevant funding bodies. Biffa Award grants are subject to the approval of a board comprising nominees of Biffa and RSWT. Detailed criteria and procedures for applying for grants from Biffa Award can be found on www.biffa-award.org. The 2016/17 annual report states:

> A major part of RSWT's turnover relates to the administration and distribution of Landfill Communities Funds through the Biffa Award programme. Our work in this area seeks to distribute these funds to achieve the maximum benefit for the environment, local communities and UK biodiversity.

Our Bright Future

Eight key partners oversee Our Bright Future, a major programme of youth and environment work funded by £33 million from the Big Lottery Fund.

Grants from RSWT's own unrestricted funds are made at the discretion of TWT Council.

Financial information

In 2016/17 the trust had assets of £7.69 million and an income of

£14.9 million. Total grant expenditure amounted to £9.27 million.

Beneficiaries included: Freshwater Biological Association (£1 million); Harwell Village Hall (£41,000); Avon Wildlife Trust (£30,000); Gloucestershire Wildlife Trust (£18,000); York Citizens' Theatre Trust (£8,000); WAVE (£1,000).

Applications

Apply in writing to the correspondent. For the Biffa Award Scheme, go to www. biffa-award.org for full details of how to apply.

Sources of information

Accounts; annual report; Charity Commission record; funder's website.

The Ruddock Foundation for the Arts

 Art conservation, research into medieval art, theatre and playwriting

UK

£1.4 million (2016/17)

CC number: 1134994

Trustees: Sir Paul Ruddock; Lady Jill Ruddock; Michael Fullerlove; Sophie Ruddock; Isabella Ruddock.

Correspondent: Sir Paul Ruddock, 7 Lansdowne Walk, London W11 3LN (tel: 020 7313 9350; email: nikita@ ruddockfamily.com)

The foundation was established in 2010 by businessman and philanthropist Sir Paul Ruddock. He is Chair of the University of Oxford Endowment and former Chair of the Victoria and Albert Museum.

According to its 2016/17 annual report, the objects of the charity are:

- To advance, promote and educate for the benefit of the public generally all branches of the arts with particular, but not exclusive reference to the performing, literary and decorative arts
- To advance the preservation, protection and improvement of pictures, historic records, books, manuscripts, monuments, armour, porcelain, silver and gold objects d'art and other chattels or items of artistic, historic, or national interest
- To establish and maintain a museum and/or art gallery for the display and promotion of the arts with particular, but not exclusive, reference to the decorative and medieval arts for the benefit of the public
- Notwithstanding the above, to support or carry out such other objects or purposes as are exclusively charitable in accordance with the laws of England and Wales

The foundation's current grant-making policy focuses on three main areas:

- Institutions which look after and conserve paintings and works of art
- Research projects with a focus on medieval art
- Theatre and playwriting

Financial information

In 2016/17 the foundation held assets of £21.4 million and had an income of £136,500. Grants awarded to organisations totalled £1.4 million.

Beneficiaries included: The Victoria and Albert Museum (£568,000); Metropolitan Museum of Art (£474,000); The British Museum (£60,000); Oxford University Development Trust and The Art Fund (£50,000 each); The John Paul Getty Trust (£38,500); Bard Graduate Center (£11,000); The Savitri Waney Charitable Trust (£1,000).

Applications

Apply in writing to the correspondent. The trustees meet twice a year to discuss applications.

Sources of information

Accounts; annual report; Charity Commission record; funder's website.

Rugby Football Foundation

 Amateur rugby

England

£402,500 (2016/17)

CC number: 1100277

Trustees: Malcolm Wharton; Philip Johnson; Peter Grace; Sheila Pancholi; Neil Hagerty; Richard Daniel.

Correspondent: Angus Bujalski, Secretary, Rugby House, Twickenham Stadium, 200 Whitton Road, Twickenham TW2 7BA (tel: 020 8831 7985; email: foundation@therfu.com)

rugbyfootballfoundation.org

The Rugby Football Foundation is a charitable trust established by the Rugby Football Union in 2003. The purpose of the foundation is to promote and develop community amateur rugby in England.

Grants programmes

The foundation runs two grant programmes:

Groundmatch Grants

The Groundmatch scheme provides grants of between £1,500 and £5,000 on a matched basis for the recruitment and retention of rugby players, for clubs at level 5 and below.

Helping Hand Grants

Helping Hand Grants of between £500 and £1,500 are awarded for eligible capital projects, and must also be matched by the club. Grants are available for clubs at level 5 and below.

Under both schemes, clubs can apply for funds to carry out capital improvements to their facilities which will support the retention and recruitment of players. These can include:

- pitches (land purchase, pitch construction, drainage and levelling)
- changing rooms and clubhouses (all areas apart from bars)
- floodlights and equipment which supports the playing of the game (grounds maintenance, goalposts and perimeter fencing)

A club can apply for a maximum of £5,000 over a 24-month period, including both Helping Hand and Groundsmatch grants.

The foundation also runs two loan schemes:

Interest-free loans

Interest-free loans of up to £100,000 are available to clubs at level 3 and below for capital projects which contribute to the recruitment and retention of players. The website states that 'the maximum loan period is 15 years. Loans are available on a 'stand-alone' basis, but projects are considered stronger if they include additional funding (internally or externally generated).'

Green Deal Loans

Loans of up to £20,000 are available to clubs at level 3 or below for the installation of facility solutions that reduce utility costs. The website states:

Green Deal Loan repayments are structured to be the equivalent of the projected savings over the agreed payback period. Applications must be underpinned by independent, accredited energy surveys and clubs must evidence the no cost/low cost improvements that they have already implemented and the impact of those improvements.

For more details visit the website.

Financial information

In 2016/17 the foundation had assets of £1.9 million and an income of £30.8 million. Grants were made totalling £402,500.

A list of beneficiaries was not included in the accounts.

Exclusions

The foundation will not fund works that can be classified as annual maintenance, such as end of season pitch renovations.

Applications

Application forms can be downloaded from the foundation's website. Completed forms can be submitted by post or by email. The panel generally meets bi-monthly.

The website notes that:

The Rugby Football Foundation operates a series of minimum standards and best practice guides in the planning, development and construction of club facilities. Clubs should consult the Technical Advice section and download the relevant guide to their project before submitting an application.

The foundation states that it aims to turn around Helping Hand Grants in six weeks and Groundmatch grants in eight weeks from receipt of a completed application. For any further support or information, applicants can contact their area facilities manager. Contact details are listed on the foundation's website.

Sources of information

Accounts; annual report; Charity Commission; funder's website.

The Rugby Group Benevolent Fund Ltd

 Community projects in specific geographical areas where employees and ex-employees of Rugby Group Ltd live

Barrington (Cambridgeshire), Chinnor (Oxfordshire), Kensworth (Bedfordshire), Lewes (Sussex), Rochester (Kent), Rugby and Southam (Warwickshire), South Ferriby (North Lincolnshire) and Tilbury (Essex)

£440,000 to organisations (2017)

CC number: 265669

Trustees: Graeme Fuller; Norman Jones; Jim Wootten; Ian Southcott; Geoff Thomas; Nigel Appleyard; John Brooks; David Holton; Kevin Murch.

Correspondent: Daphne Murray, Secretary, Cemex House, Coldharbour Lane, Thorpe, Egham, Surrey TW20 8TD (tel: 01932 583181; email: info@ rugbygroupbenevolentfund.org.uk)

www.rugbygroupbenevolentfund.org.uk

This fund was established in 1955 with the aim of supporting employees and former employees of Rugby Group Ltd, and their dependants. The Rugby Group is now a part of CEMEX UK, a global cement manufacturer but the fund has kept its independence and is managed by a group of employees and former employees.

Today, the fund maintains the same objectives by which it was established but has broadened its scope to include charitable causes in communities where employees, former employees and their dependants live. These are: Barrington (Cambridgeshire); Chinnor (Oxfordshire); Kensworth

(Bedfordshire); Lewes (Sussex); Rochester (Kent); Rugby and Southam (Warwickshire); South Ferriby (North Lincolnshire); and Tilbury (Essex). Grants are made to provide capital for specific projects.

Financial information

In 2017 the fund had assets of almost £2.1 million and an income of £69,500. Grants totalled £468,000. Of this amount, £440,000 was given in 52 grants to organisations. Grants to individuals amounted to a further £28,000.

Beneficiaries included: Thomley Activity Centre (£50,000); East Anglia Air Ambulance (£30,000); Hill Street Youth and Community Centre (£15,000); Harston Village Hall (£10,000); War Memorial Long Itchington (£5,000); Barton and District Athletic Club (£3,000); Rugby Christmas Cracker (£2,000); Cambridge Cancer Help Centre (£1,000).

Exclusions

Organisations operating outside the areas of benefit; support is not normally given for day-to-day revenue costs.

Applications

At the time of writing (June 2018) the 'applying' section of the fund's website stated that an initial expression of interest form and full application form would be available shortly.

Sources of information

Accounts; annual report; Charity Commission record; funder's website.

The RVW Trust

 Music education and appreciation

 UK

£200,000 to organisations (2016)

CC number: 1066977

Trustees: Hugh Cobbe; Lord Armstrong; Anthony Burton; Andrew Hunter Johnston; Helen Faulkner; Prof. Nicola LeFanu; Sally Groves; Richard Causton; Musicians Benevolent Fund.

Correspondent: Hannah Vlček, Secretary and Administrator, 13 Calico Row, Plantation Wharf, London SW11 3YH (tel: 020 7223 3385; email: info@ rvwtrust.org.uk)

www.rvwtrust.org.uk

@RVW_Trust

The trust was established in 1997 and supports music education and appreciation. According to the 2016 annual accounts, the policies of the trust are:

- To give assistance to British composers who have not yet achieved a national reputation
- To give assistance towards the performance and recording of music by neglected or currently unfashionable 20th and 21st century British composers, including performances by societies and at festivals which include works by such composers in their programmes
- To assist national organisations which promote public knowledge and appreciation of 20th and 21st century British music
- To assist education projects in the field of music
- To support post-graduate students of composition taking first masters degrees at British universities and conservatoires

Financial information

In 2016 the trust had assets of £2.3 million and an income of £440,500. During the year, the trust awarded 139 grants totalling £220,000. The following breakdown was provided in the accounts:

Public performance	90	£121,500
Music festival	21	£53,000
Public education (including recordings)	23	£26,000
Postgraduate education	5	£20,000

Previous beneficiaries have included: Park Lane Group (£10,000); Huddersfield Contemporary Music Festival (£9,000); Cheltenham Music Festival (£5,000); Ikon Arts (£3,500); Scottish Opera (£3,000); Scottish Chamber Orchestra (£2,500); London Ear and Spitalfields Festival (£2,000 each); City of Cambridge Brass Band and London Chorus (£1,500 each); Nash Ensemble (£1,000).

Exclusions

According to the trust's website, it will not support the following:

- concerts, concert series or concert tours which do not include music by 20th and 21st century British composers
- concerts for which income from box office receipts, together with support from other organisations, is forecast to amount to less than half of the estimated expenditure
- commissions purely for youth or children's ensembles
- grants for musicals, rock or pop music, ethnic music, jazz or dance music or multi-media and theatrical events in which music is not the primary art form
- 'workshops' with no planned public performance
- grants to organisations directly administered by local or other public authorities
- grants to managing agents and commercial promoters
- vocal or instrumental tuition
- the making, purchase or repair of musical instruments, computer or multi-media equipment

▶ the construction or restoration of buildings

Applications

Apply in writing to the correspondent. Detailed guidelines are available from the website and should be read before an application is started. If you have any doubts as to the eligibility of your application, contact the trust in the first instance.

Sources of information

Accounts; annual report; Charity Commission record; funder's website.

SF Foundation

🔍 Jewish organisations
📍 Worldwide
💷 £2.7 million (2016/17)

CC number: 1105843

Trustees: Hannah Jacob; Rivka Niederman; Miriam Schrieber.

Correspondent: Rivka Niederman, Secretary, 143 Upper Clapton Road, London E5 9DB (tel: 020 8802 5492; email: sffoundation143@gmail.com)

Set up in 2004, this foundation gives grants towards the 'advancement and furtherance of the Jewish religion and Jewish religious education and the alleviation of poverty amongst the Jewish community throughout the world'. The 2016/17 annual report states:

> The charity was set up to support the activities of religious Jewish organisations especially in the field of education. The trustees identify institutions and organisations which meet its criteria and regularly support a number of these institutions and organisations, both in England and abroad. The charity is also supportive of organisations which are solely committed to the relief of poverty. Such organisations assist needy Jewish families financially and through the distribution of basic necessities.

Financial information

In 2016/17 the foundation had assets of almost £39 million and an income of nearly £5.7 million. Grants were made totalling £2.7 million.

Beneficiaries included: Gevurath Ari Academy Trust (£300,000); Rentrust Foundation Ltd (£82,000); Beit Medresh Yetev Lev (£72,000); United Talmudical Associates (£42,000).

Applications

The foundation's annual report states: 'The charity accepts applications for grants from representatives of various charities, which are reviewed by the trustees on a regular basis.'

Sources of information

Accounts; annual report; Charity Commission record.

The Sackler Trust

🔍 Education, art, science, medical research
📍 UK
💷 £21.1 million (2016)

CC number: 1132097

Trustees: Dame Theresa Sackler; Peter Darling; Christopher Mitchell; Marissa Sackler; Sophia Dalrymple; Michael Sackler; Marianne Mitchell; Anthony Collins.

Correspondent: Christopher Mitchell, Trustee, 9th Floor, New Zealand House, 80 Haymarket, London SW1Y 4TQ (tel: 020 7930 4944)

The trust was set up in 2009 to support the advancement of research and education in England and Wales and elsewhere, in the fields of art, science and medical research. It would appear that, in the main, the trust supports larger institutions.

Financial information

In 2016 the trust held assets of £47.5 million and had an income of £2.5 million. There were 68 grants made to organisations totalling £21.1 million.

Beneficiaries included: University of Sussex (£6 million); Moorfields Eye Hospital (£3 million); Siftung Les Arts (£2.9 million); Royal College of Art (£2 million); Universities of Edinburgh and Glasgow (£1.5 million); The Ashmolean Museum (£1.1 million); The National Portrait Gallery (£1 million); The Prince's Trust (£750,000).

Grants of under £500,000 totalled £2.9 million.

Applications

Apply in writing to the correspondent.

Sources of information

Accounts; annual report; Charity Commission record.

The Saddlers' Company Charitable Fund

🔍 General charitable purposes, education, equestrianism, disadvantaged young people, social welfare, churches, armed forces, saddlery and leathercraft
📍 UK
💷 £313,500 to organisations (2016/17)

CC number: 261962

Trustees: Campbell Pulley; David Hardy; David Snowden; Hugh Dyson-Laurie; Iain Pulley; Jonathan Godrich; Michael Laurie; Peter Laurie; Peter Lewis; Tim Satchell; Mark Farmar; Paul Farmar; Petronella Jameson; Nicholas Mason; Charles Barclay; John Robinson; Hugh

Thomas; James Welch; William Dyson-Laurie; The Hon Mark Maffey; Lucy Atherton; Benjamin Laurie; Hugh Medley Taylor.

Correspondent: Clerk to the Company, Saddlers' Company, Saddlers' Hall, 40 Gutter Lane, London EC2V 6BR (tel: 020 7726 8661; email: clerk@saddlers.co.uk)

🌐 www.saddlersco.co.uk

🐦 @fishmongershall

The Saddlers' Company has a long tradition of charitable activity. Since the earliest days of the company quarterly membership subscriptions have been used to support members' widows and children. The company also still continues the ancient tradition of Bounty Day each December when Court of Assistants can nominate a charity to receive a Christmas grant from the Company's Charitable Fund.

The Saddlers' Company Charitable Fund was formed in 1970. Over time, the objects of the fund have been refined to provide support for education, the British saddlery trade, the equestrian world, the City of London and general charitable activities.

The R. M. Sturdy Charitable Trust and the Mollie Priestly Fund are both part of the Saddlers' Company Charitable Fund. The Kaye's and Labourne's Charity is a linked charity that has been incorporated into the Saddlers' Company Charitable Fund's 2016/17 accounts.

R. M. Sturdy Charitable Trust

A past master of the Worshipful Company of Saddlers and former trustee of the fund, Mr R. M. Sturdy, died in 2006. By a letter of wishes, he expressed the desire that the R. M. Sturdy Charitable Trust, of which he was the benefactor, be administered by the Worshipful Company of Saddlers after his death.

According to the fund's 2016/17 annual accounts, the trust supports:

> Projects related to education and music associated with the Church of England and those pertaining to the restoration, repair and renovation of Church of England places of worship (particularly smaller churches) and the making of general charitable grants with particular preference being given to those charities associated with the Church of England.

M. E. Priestly Fund

The fund's website states that this fund was:

> Established in 2004 with a legacy of £200,000 from the Estate of Molly Priestly. The fund is directed towards helping members of the armed services who need assistance, such as for health, education or income, particularly as a result of war

service. In addition the Fund provides regular grants to the Army, Sea and Air Cadets.

Kaye's and Labourne's Charity

According to the fund's website:

The objectives of the Kaye's & Labourne's Charity are to relieve persons who are in need, hardship or distress, either generally or individually. In priority these would be Freemen of the Saddlers' Company, their widows and other dependants; those who are or have been employed in the trade of saddler or harness maker, their widows and other dependants who are in need, hardship or distress; and such other persons as the Trustees decide.

Kitchin's charity

The charity was set up by Robert Kitchin who left a property to the company on condition that the income would be used for the maintenance of the Church of St Ethelburga-the-Virgin in Bishopsgate and the poor of its parish. Today 35% of its income is available for discretionary awards for the training and education of people under 25 in need of financial assistance who are or have been resident in or attended educational establishments in the City of London and after that, in Greater London.

Financial information

In 2016/17 the fund had assets of £12.8 million and an income of £333,000. During the year, the fund awarded a total of £377,500 in grants. The fund's 2016/17 accounts state: 'Grants awarded to institutions such as charities, foundations and religious institutions, and in the fields of education and arts amounted to £313,578 and grants awarded to over 100 individuals amounted to £63,954.'

A list of beneficiaries was not included in the accounts.

Applications

Applications to the R. M. Sturdy Trust should be made in writing to the clerk and should state the purpose of the grant, how the proposal meets the eligibility criteria and include such additional and financial information as the trustees may require.

All other applications must be made through the fund's website.

The trustees have stated that they are currently undertaking a review of their grant-making policies. Any new information will be available on the fund's website.

Sources of information

Accounts; annual report; Charity Commission record.

The Jean Sainsbury Animal Welfare Trust

Animal welfare

UK

£427,000 (2016)

CC number: 326358

Trustees: Jacqui Sharp; Gillian Tarlington; James Keliher; Mark Spurdens; Valerie Pike; Michelle Allen; Adele Sparrow; Jill Inglis.

Correspondent: Madeleine Orchard, Administrator, PO Box 469, London W14 8PJ (email: orchardjswelfare@gmail.com)

 jeansainsburyanimalwelfare.org.uk

The trust was established in 1982 with the objective of benefitting animals and protecting them from suffering. The trustees support smaller UK-registered charities that embrace one or more of the following:

- Benefitting or protecting animals
- Relieving animals from suffering
- Conserving wildlife
- Encouraging the understanding of animals

Grant-making information

The trust's website states that it:

Favours applications from smaller animal welfare charities registered in the UK and working in the UK or abroad that:

- Have independently examined up to date annual accounts
- Demonstrate an active re-homing and rehabilitation policy for animals taken into their care
- Are involved with conservation of wildlife, when the rescue, rehabilitation and (where possible) the release of animals is their main aim

The trust expects all applicants to be charities registered with the Charity Commission unless their annual income is under £5,000.

According to the website, grants can be made in the following categories:

- General running costs associated with the rescue, rehabilitation and re-homing of domestic, wild and exotic animals
- Feeding, capture, neutering and release of feral cats
- Assistance with vet's fees and neutering costs of animals owned by those on low incomes
- Donations towards capital purchases involving land, buildings, vehicles, equipment and educational material. The trustees may pledge funds towards large capital building projects, which will only be released when all other funding is in place and the work is ready to commence. The maximum pledge given in the past was £35,000

- Donations towards the purchase or improvement of property or fixed buildings are only considered if:
  1. The property is clearly in the ownership of the charity, or
  2. At least 10 years is left to run on the charity's lease, or
  3. A letter from the landowner states that the charity will be reimbursed for the improvements on sale of the property or at the end of the lease. Otherwise, support for improvements can only be considered when they do not increase the saleable value of the property

There are two subsidiary funds:

- The Joyce Evelyn Shuman Bequest – animal rescue work overseas including rehoming and the neutering of feral cats and dogs, working equines, and endangered species where the rehabilitation and release of the animals is the main aim
- The Colin Russell Award – given to one charity each year

Financial information

In 2016 the trust had assets of £22.8 million and an income of £599,500. There were 73 grants made totalling £427,000, which included £350,000 to 58 charities working in the UK and £77,000 to 15 UK-based charities working overseas.

Previous beneficiaries have included: Society for Abandoned Animals (£30,000); Pennine Pen Animal Rescue (£26,000); Warrington Animal Welfare (£20,000); Essex Horse and Pony Protection Society, Friends of the Strays of Greece and RSPCA Harrogate and District (£5,000 each); Horse Sense Wirral (£4,000); Kathmandu Animal Treatment Centre (£2,000); Pricklepad Hedgehog Hospital (£1,500); Barn Owl Trust (£1,000).

Exclusions

The trust's website states that it will not normally support the following:

- Applications from individuals
- Charities registered outside the UK
- Charities offering sanctuary to animals, with no effort to re-home, foster or rehabilitate (unless endangered species)
- Charities that do not have a realistic destruction policy for animals that cannot be given a reasonable quality of life
- Charities with available reserves equal to more than one year's expenditure will not qualify for consideration unless it can be demonstrated that reserves are being held for a designated project
- Charities that spend more than a reasonable proportion of their annual income on administration or cannot justify their costs per animal helped
- Veterinary Schools, unless the money can be seen to be directly benefiting the type of animals the Trust would want to support e.g. welfare-related or

low-cost first opinion vet treatment projects

Applications

Applications should be completed on a form which is available from the correspondent or can be downloaded from the trust's website. Applicants should complete and return nine copies of the form along with their latest set of audited accounts and any other information which may be relevant to the application.

Note: The trust requests that you do not send originals as these cannot be returned.

There are three trustees' meetings every year, usually in March, August and November and applications should be submitted by 15 January, 1 May and 1 September respectively. Further application information and policy guidelines are available on the website.

The trust encourages charities to maintain contact with it and is also pleased to receive updates on charities' plans and activities. Repeat applications from charities are supported.

Sources of information

Accounts; annual report; Charity Commission record; funder's website.

The Alan and Babette Sainsbury Charitable Fund

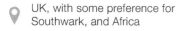 General charitable purposes, arts and education for young people, civil liberties and human rights, overseas aid, medical research into Type 1 Diabetes

UK, with some preference for Southwark, and Africa

£487,500 (2016/17)

CC number: 292930

Trustees: Judith Portrait; The Rt Hon. Sir Timothy Sainsbury; Julian Sainsbury; Lindsey Anderson.

Correspondent: Robert Bell, Director, The Peak, 5 Wilton Road, London SW1V 1AP (tel: 020 7410 0330; email: proposals@sfct.org.uk)

 www.sfct.org.uk

This is one of the Sainsbury Family Charitable Trusts, which share a joint administration and have a common approach to grant-making. The settlor of the fund, Alan Sainsbury, was the grandson of the founders of J Sainsbury plc and former chair of the company. He established the fund in 1953, became Baron Sainsbury in 1962 and died in 1998.

The website states:

> [The fund] concentrates its resources on a small number of programmes, including:
>
> ⬛ arts and education projects which help young people to achieve their potential, particularly within Southwark, from where proposals are particularly encouraged
>
> ⬛ support for UK charities which defend civil liberties and human rights
>
> ⬛ projects in the developing world, especially Africa, which maximise educational and employment opportunities for young people
>
> ⬛ scientific and medical research on Type 1 Diabetes

As with all the Sainsbury Family Charitable Trusts, only registered charities are eligible for support.

Financial information

In 2016/17 the fund held assets of nearly £16.4 million and had an income of almost £494,500. During the year, 30 grants were awarded totalling £487,500 and were categorised as follows:

Civil liberties and community relations	11	£172,500
Youth work	8	£110,000
Scientific and medical research	2	£125,000
Overseas	6	£70,000
General charitable purposes	2	£20,000

Previous beneficiaries have included: University College London Institute of Neurology (£120,000); Holocaust Educational Trust (£45,000); Salmon Youth Centre (£35,000); Chess in Schools and Communities (£30,000); University of York (£20,000); Ashden Sustainable Solutions Better Lives (£15,000); Emms International, Latin American Women's Rights Service and Sharan Project (£10,000 each); Toucan Employment (£7,500); Prisoners of Conscience (£5,000).

Exclusions

None of the Sainsbury Family Charitable Trusts directly supports individuals, education fees or expeditions.

Applications

The fund's website states that it 'will consider proposals, so long as they demonstrably and closely fit their specific areas of interest. However, it should be understood that the majority of unsolicited proposals are unsuccessful.'

Applications should be sent via post with a description of the proposed project covering the organisation, the project requiring funding and a breakdown of costs. Supplementary documentation such as books, brochures, DVDs, annual reports or accounts are not needed. Applicants who do not hear from the fund within eight weeks should assume that their application has been unsuccessful.

Sources of information

Accounts; annual report; Charity Commission record; funder's website.

The Saintbury Trust

 General charitable purposes, social welfare, education, health, community development, arts, culture, heritage and science, sport, human rights and equality, armed forces and emergency services

West Midlands and Warwickshire (which the trust considers to be postcode areas B, CV, DY, WS and WV), Worcestershire and Gloucestershire (post code areas WR and GL)

£410,000 (2016)

CC number: 326790

Trustees: Victoria Houghton; Anita Bhalla; Anne Thomas; Harry Forrester; Amanda Atkinson-Willes; Jane Lewis; Cerian Brogan.

Correspondent: Jane Lewis, Trustee, PO Box 464, Dorking, Surrey RH4 9AF (email: saintburytrust@btinternet.com)

🌐 www.thesaintburytrust.co.uk

The Saintbury Trust was established by Alan and Jean Bryant in 1985. It gives grants for general charitable purposes with grants made to registered charities with four or more trustees in Gloucestershire, West Midlands and Worcestershire. The trust gives to a wide range of causes but the trustees currently have a particular interest in the arts, heritage, the environment and disability.

Financial information

In 2016 the trust held assets of almost £12.5 million and had an income of £1.1 million. Grants were awarded to 82 organisations and totalled £410,000.

Previous beneficiaries have included: Midlands Arts Centre (£40,000); Birmingham Boys and Girls Union (£25,000); The Air Ambulance Service (£20,000); Birmingham YMCA (£15,000); The Amber Foundation (£10,000); Wildfowl and Wetlands Trust (£7,000); Central England Law Centre Ltd (£4,000); Sport4Life UK (£3,000); Castle Vale Tenants and Residents Alliance (£2,000); Sandwell Asian Development Association (£1,000).

Exclusions

Individuals; sponsorship; scouts, guides, sea cadets and similar organisations; village halls; local churches; religious charities; cold-calling national charities or local branches of national charities; animal charities. Note that grants are rarely given for start-up or general running costs.

Note: We have been informed that Herefordshire area (HR postcodes) is not eligible.

Applications

Application forms are available to download on the trust's website. Completed applications should be returned via post to the correspondent accompanied by a short letter and latest set of accounts. The trust will look at the applicant's Charity Commission record to check that there are four or more trustees and that all the accounts and filing obligations are up-to-date.

The trustees meet twice a year to consider applications, once in the spring (usually April or May) and once in the autumn (usually October or November). Details of the application deadlines for these meetings can be found on the trust's website.

Sources of information

Accounts; annual report; Charity Commission record; funder's website.

Samjo Ltd

Jewish causes

Greater Manchester

£1.9 million (2016/17)

CC number: 1094397

Trustees: Rabbi Yisroel Friedman; Joshua Halpern; Samuel Halpern.

Correspondent: The Trustees, Lopian Gross Barnett and Co., 6th Floor, Cardinal House, 20 St Marys Parsonage, Manchester M3 2LG (tel: 0161 832 8721; email: D.Stewart@prestburymanagement. co.uk)

Samjo Ltd is a charity established in 2002 to make grants to charitable causes in the Jewish community. According to the 2015/16 annual report, this includes 'the advancement of religion, the advancement and support of education and the relief of the elderly, vulnerable (such as young children or anyone with special needs) or those suffering poverty or hardship and other charitable purpose for the public benefit'. The charity particularly favours Orthodox Jewish charities.

Financial information

In 2015/16 the charity had assets of £15.5 million and an income of almost £1.7 million. Grants were made to organisations totalling £1.9 million.

Beneficiaries included: Oizer Charitable Trust (£940,000); Shemtov Charitable Trust (£675,000); Teshivoh Tefilloh Tzedokoh (£125,000).

Applications

Apply in writing to the correspondent.

Sources of information

Accounts; annual report; Charity Commission record.

The Basil Samuel Charitable Trust

General charitable purposes, education and training, the promotion of health, people with disabilities, arts and culture, the environment and animals, children and young people, older people

Worldwide, in practice mainly UK

£418,500 (2016/17)

CC number: 206579

Trustees: Coral Samuel CBE; Richard Peskin.

Correspondent: The Trustees, Smith & Williamson, 25 Moorgate, London EC2R 6AY (tel: 020 7131 4376)

This trust was established in 1959 for such charitable purposes as the trustees decide, either in the UK or elsewhere. The trustees describe its activities as making grants to medical, socially supportive, educational and cultural charities as well as making a number of donations to other charities.

Financial information

In 2016/17 the trust had assets of £8.37 million and an income of £34,500. Grants to 60 organisations were made totalling £418,500 and were broken down as follows:

Medical/socially supportive	£293,000
Cultural	£63,500
Educational	£62,000

Beneficiaries included: National Brain Appeal (£50,000); Hazel and Leslie Peskin Charitable Trust and Science Museum Group (£25,000 each); Pancreatic Cancer UK, HomeStart and London Air Ambulance (£10,000 each); Countryside Learning, Epilepsy Research UK, Exmoor Search and Rescue and Future Dreams (£5,000 each); Ospreys Wheelchair Rugby (£1,000).

Exclusions

Registered charities only.

Applications

Apply in writing to the correspondent.

Sources of information

Accounts; annual report; Charity Commission record.

The M J Samuel Charitable Trust

General charitable purposes

UK and overseas

£823,000 (2016/17)

CC number: 327013

Trustees: Hon. Michael Samuel; Hon. Julia Samuel; Lord Bearsted.

Correspondent: Lindsay Sutton, Secretary, Mells Park, Mells, Frome, Somerset BA11 3QB (tel: 020 7402 0602; email: lindsay@mellspark.com)

The trust supports a wide range of charitable causes in the UK.

Financial information

In 2015/16 the trust had assets of £3.7 million, an income of £99,000. Grants were made to 35 charities and totalled £523,000. An exceptional grant of £298,500 was awarded to Civic.

Beneficiaries included: Anna Freud Centre (£250,000); Child Bereavement UK (£120,000); Somerset Community Foundation (£37,000); Game and Wildlife Conservation Trust (£23,000); Chickenshed Theatre Trust and Grange Festival (£2,000 each); Chalke Valley History Trust, Depaul UK, Sudbury Neighbourhood Scheme and WaterAid (£1,000 each).

In addition, 14 other donations of less than £1,000 each were made to organisations, totalling £4,700.

Exclusions

No grants are made to individuals.

Applications

Apply in writing to the correspondent.

Sources of information

Accounts; annual report; Charity Commission record.

The Samworth Foundation

Children and young people, social welfare, education, environment and conservation

UK and overseas

£2.4 million (2016/17)

CC number: 265647

Trustees: Prof. Neil Gorman; Clare Price; Gemma Juma; Susie Culloty; Stephen Hale.

Correspondent: Sarah Wellstead, Chetwode House, 1 Samworth Way, Melton Mowbray, Leicestershire LE13 1GA (tel: 01664 414500; email: samworthfoundation@gmail.com)

www.samworthfoundation.org.uk

Registered with general charitable purposes, the foundation makes grants to support the social and educational needs of children and young people, particularly 'those most neglected and vulnerable'. According to the 2016/17 annual report, there has been a focus on child trafficking, anti-slavery and exploitation in the UK and internationally. The trustees have also expanded their strategy to introduce different targeted areas, notably environmental and conservation issues.

The annual report states:

> The Foundation is currently deciding whether to change its current funds for distribution in each year whilst still maintaining the current funding strategy and priorities. This decision involves members of the Samworth Family and will determine the number, size and nature of grants in the future.

According to the foundation's website, grants currently address 'sexual exploitation and climate change' by supporting organisations which attempt to address the root causes of these issues in the UK and internationally.

Financial information
In 2016/17 the foundation held assets of £67 million and had an income of £599,500. During the year, the foundation awarded 95 grants to organisations amounting to £2.4 million. Grants were distributed as follows:

Family or exceptional grants	59	£1.1 million
UK – core grants	19	£669,000
International – core grants	19	£609,000

Beneficiaries included: Leicester Cathedral Charitable Trust (£1 million); ZOE (£67,500); The Stephen Lewis Foundation – Trauma Centre (£50,000); Anti-Slavery International (£40,000); Well Grounded Ltd (£30,000); Beyond the Streets (£20,000); World Vision UK (£10,000).

Exclusions
No grants are made individuals.

Applications
The foundation's grant-making policy is to support a limited number of causes known to the trustees. Unsolicited applications are not considered.

Sources of information
Accounts; annual report; Charity Commission record.

Santander UK Foundation Ltd

General charitable purposes

UK, including Guernsey, Jersey, and the Isle of Man

£5.4 million (2016)

CC number: 803655

Trustees: Jennifer Scardino; Sue Willis; Keith Moor; Christopher Fallis; Rachel MacFarlane.

Correspondent: Amy Slack, Santander UK plc, Santander House, 201 Grafton Gate East, Milton Keynes MK9 1AN (email: grants@santander.co.uk)

 www.santanderfoundation.org.uk

The Santander Foundation was established by the banking company of the same name. Through Santander UK's flagship community programme, The Discovery Project, the foundation provides grants to support knowledge, skills and innovation in the UK.

Grant-making scheme
The foundation's Discovery Grants scheme, provides grants of up to £5,000 to small, locally registered charities, CICs and credit unions in the UK. Grants are awarded for the following themes:

- **Explorer – improving people's knowledge.** Examples include a series of money management workshops to help people understand how to budget
- **Transformer – developing skills and experience.** Examples include work-based training and mentors to help socially isolated people develop skills to get back into work
- **Changemaker – innovative solutions to social challenges.** Examples include a new social networking programme that uses specially developed braille laptops to help visually impaired young people access the internet

Grants are available for one year only. The foundation prefers to fund a complete project or item, which should be local in scale and may include salaries, equipment or materials.

Financial information
In 2016 the foundation had assets of £15.2 million and an income of £5.8 million. The foundation made 3,263 grants to charities amounting to a total of £5.4 million, under the following categories:

Social inclusion	1,934	£3.7 million
Health	1,200	£1.3 million
Community foundations	60	£300,000
Other	69	£66,500

Beneficiaries of grants of £10,000 or more included: Barnardo's (£203,500); Age UK (£184,000); Macmillan Cancer Support (£54,000); Marie Curie Cancer Care (£24,000); Children's Hospice South West (£20,000); Sense (£14,500); Cumbria Community Foundation (£13,000); British Heart Foundation (£12,000); Alder Hey Children's Charity (£11,000); HCPT – The Pilgrimage Trust (£10,000).

Exclusions
Grants are not awarded to:

- Individuals
- Multi-year funding
- Fundraising activities
- Unregistered charities/not-for-profit groups
- Other funders and grant-makers
- Religious, ethnic or political charities
- Events, conferences and sponsorship
- Shortfall funding
- Beneficiaries outside the UK, Channel Islands or Isle of Man
- Start-up organisations

Applications
Application forms can be found in any local Santander branch. Once completed, applications should be posted in the Discovery Grants post boxes at any branch. Applicants are usually informed of the outcome of their application within six weeks.

Sources of information
Accounts; annual report; Charity Commission record; funder's website.

The Save the Children Fund

Children and families, with a particular focus on: overseas aid, health care and nutrition, disasters and emergencies, education, children's rights, safeguarding and protection

Worldwide

£32.7 million to partner and member organisations (2016)

CC number: 213890

Trustees: Sir Alan Parker; Peter Bennett-Jones; Adele Anderson; Tamara Ingram; Mark Esiri; Naomi Eisenstadt; Sophia McCormick; Sebastian James; Jamie Cooper; Diana Carney; Gareth Davies; Mark Swallow; Fiona McBain; Lisa Rosen; Anne Fahy; Arabella Duffield.

Correspondent: Andrew Willis, Company Secretary, Save the Children, 1 St John's Lane, London EC1M 4AR (tel: 020 7012 6400; email: supporter.care@savethechildren.org.uk)

 facebook.com/savethechildrenuk

 @savechildrenuk

@savechildrenuk

The Save the Children Fund was established in 1919 by two sisters, Eglantyne Jebb and Dorothy Buxton. The fund, also known as Save the Children UK, is a member of the Save the Children Association (SCA), which consists of 30 independent national Save the Children organisations, transforming children's lives in more than 120 countries. SCA also owns 100% of Save the Children International (SCI), a charity incorporated in England and Wales. The charity works with vulnerable children around the world with a focus on the poorest 10%, those who are displaced by crisis and those who are most discriminated against or excluded because they belong to marginalised groups.

The charity's work includes improving access to affordable, good quality healthcare and nutrition; education; and supporting families, communities and governments to provide protection and care for children. The 2016 annual report notes that:

> Much of the charity's programme activity is carried out through grants to local organisations that support long-term sustainable benefits for children, which are monitored by the charity. Grants are also made to fund immediate emergency relief provision in times of crisis, catastrophe or natural disaster.

Eat, Sleep, Learn, Play! programme
This programme provides essential household items to low-income families with young children. The website states:

> We award items during a child's early years to support their well-being and development and contribute to a positive home learning environment. We work with referral partners such as Health Visitors, Family Support Workers, Housing Officers and Early Years Outreach Workers, who are already providing services to families with young children in the community. They know where the need is greatest and can help hard-to-reach families apply for support.

Full guidance, including eligibility and application details, can be found at: www.eatsleeplearnplay.savethechildren. org.uk/Home/ProgrammeInfo.

Grant-making information
The charity awards grants worldwide, mostly to organisations with which they work in partnership but also a small amount is awarded to individuals. Some examples of grants given to individuals include start-up grants for small businesses, food and for times of crisis/ emergency relief. The grant-making policy for awards to organisations is stated in the charity's 2016 annual report as follows:

Save the Children works in partnership with many organisations. This may involve our staff being involved in joint operations, supporting and monitoring work, or funding local partners to deliver services, including immediate emergency relief. The grants we make to partner organisations help local organisations provide sustainable benefits for poor communities...We carefully consider the experience, reach and governance of potential partners, as well as the value they will add to our work with vulnerable children.

Refer to the website (www. savethechildren.org.uk) for the most up-to-date information on the charity's work.

Financial information
In 2016 the fund had assets of £39.35 million and an income of £404.5 million. The fund paid grants to partner and member organisations worldwide totalling £32.7 million. The fund also made a grant of £232.8 million to Save the Children International (SCI). SCI also awards grants worldwide but does not award grants in the UK.

A full breakdown of the countries in which grant recipients were based was not available, so we have been unable to determine the full amount awarded in the UK. However, from a list of beneficiaries that received grants of over £100,000, at least £3.87 million was awarded to UK charities that work internationally.

Beneficiaries included: Action Against Hunger (£3.9 million); Plan International UK (£1.5 million); Mercy Corps Scotland (£1.2 million); CAFOD (£928,000); HelpAge International (£823,000); Doctors of the World UK (£545,000); The Beanstalk Group (£506,000); Durham University (£240,000); Fundacio Bosch Gimpera – University of Barcelona (£110,000).

Applications
The charity selects organisations to work in partnership with and does not accept unsolicited applications.

To apply for Eat, Sleep, Learn, Play!, referral partner organisations must register on the website (eatsleeplearnplay.savethechildren.org. uk).

Sources of information
Accounts; annual report, Charity Commission record; further information provided by the funder; funder's website.

The Savoy Educational Trust

🔍 Hospitality-related projects

📍 UK

£ £1.1 million to organisations (2016/17)

CC number: 1161014

Trustees: Ramon Pajares; Cllr Robert Davis; Sir David Walker; Howard Field; Dr Sally Messenger.

Correspondent: Margaret Georgiou, Room 160, 90 Long Acre, London WC2E 9RZ (tel: 020 7849 3001; email: info@savoyeducationaltrust.org.uk)

 www.savoyeducationaltrust.org.uk

 facebook.com/Savoy-Educational-Trust-712427868829909

The Savoy Educational Trust was registered with the Charity Commission in 2015. The trust's main aim is to advance and develop education, training and qualifications within the hospitality industry.

The trust awards grants for a wide variety of hospitality-related projects to:

▸ Educational establishments to enhance training and education facilities for their hospitality departments
▸ Associations to support those initiatives that will make a real difference to the hospitality industry
▸ Charitable organisations/social enterprises with specific hospitality-related projects
▸ Individuals studying hospitality

Financial information
In 2016/17 the trust had assets of £58.4 million and a total income of £1.5 million. Grants totalled £1.24 million and were broken down as follows:

Educational institutions	£1.1 million
Competitions and prizes	£110,500
Individuals	£3,600

Beneficiaries included: Brooklands College (£50,000); Hospitality Action (£45,000); Hospitality Industry Trust (£25,000); Bradford College (£21,000); East Durham College (£15,000); East Riding College (£9,200); Runshaw College (£4,900); Riverside College (£3,900); Millthorpe School (£200).

Applications
Apply in writing to the correspondent. Details of what should be included in the application are available on the trust's website along with application deadlines.

Sources of information
Accounts; annual report; Charity Commission record; funder's website.

Schroder Charity Trust

 General charitable purposes, health, social welfare, children and young people, education and training, community and economic development, overseas aid, arts and culture, heritage, environment

Worldwide, in practice mainly UK

£ £340,000 (2016/17)

CC number: 214050

Trustees: Bruno Schroder; Timothy Schroder; Charmaine von Mallinckrodt; Claire Fitzalan Howard; Leonie Fane; John Schroder.

Correspondent: Laura Bowman, 81 Rivington Street, London EC2A 3AY

🌐 www.schrodercharitytrust.org

The trust was established in 1944 by the Schroder banking family and it continues to be governed by members of the family and associates. It supports a wide range of general charitable purposes including: the promotion of health; social welfare; children and young people; education and training; community and economic development; overseas aid; arts and culture; heritage; the environment.

Preference is given to UK-registered charities with a proven track record and those in which the trust has a special interest.

Financial information

In 2016/17 the trust had assets of £13.6 million and an income of £434,000. Grants were made to 104 organisations totalling £340,000.

Beneficiaries included: Royal Star and Garter Homes (£6,000); National Youth Orchestra of Great Britain (£5,000); Neuro-Muscular Centre (£4,000); Afasic (£2,500); Amref Health Africa UK, Bowel Cancer UK and Cirencester Housing for Young People (£2,000 each); Durham Wildlife Trust and Stepney City Farm (£1,500 each); Chelsea Old Church (£400).

Exclusions

No grants are awarded to individuals.

Applications

Apply in writing to the correspondent. Applicants should briefly state their case and enclose a copy of their latest accounts or annual review. There is a useful eligibility check at the application stage on the website.

Sources of information

Accounts; annual report; Charity Commission record; funder's website.

The Schroder Foundation

🔍 General charitable purposes

Worldwide, in practice mainly UK

£ £2.03 million (2016/17)

CC number: 1107479

Trustees: Bruno Schroder; Charmaine Mallinckrodt; Leonie Fane; Edward Mallinkrodt; Claire Howard; Michael May; Richard Robinson; Philip Mallinkrodt.

Correspondent: Laura Bowman, 81 Rivington Street, London EC2A 3AY

Established in 2005, The Schroder Foundation shares a common administration with the Schroder Charity Trust (Charity Commission no. 214060). According to the foundation's 2016/17 accounts, the trustees have a policy of 'supporting a broad range of activities within the areas of the environment, education, arts, culture & heritage, social welfare, the community, medical relief and research, and international relief & development'. The foundation does not respond to unsolicited applications.

Financial information

In 2016/17 the foundation had assets of £12.5 million and an income of £1.9 million. Grants were made to 73 organisations totalling £2.03 million.

Beneficiaries included: The Woolf Institute (£100,000); Age UK, Alzheimer's Research UK, The Black Stork Charity and Moorfields Eye Charity (£50,000 each); Family Links and Shannon Trust (£30,000); The Royal National Theatre and The School Home Support (£25,000 each); The Royal Drawing School (£10,000).

Applications

The foundation does not respond to unsolicited applications.

Sources of information

Accounts; annual report; Charity Commission record.

Scott (Eredine) Charitable Trust

🔍 General charitable purposes

UK

£ £426,000 (2016)

CC number: 1002267

Trustees: Keith Bruce-Smith; Amanada Scott; Col. Nick Wills; Lucy Gibson.

Correspondent: Amanda Scott, Trustee, Wise's Farm House, Ampney St Mary, Nr. Cirencester, Gloucestershire

GL7 5SN (email: mandajscott@gmail.com)

The trust was registered with the Charity Commission in 1991 and exists to provide support for general charitable purposes across England and Wales, in particular the armed forces. The trust has also supported organisations in the areas of education, wildlife, animal welfare and disability.

Financial information

In 2016 the trust held assets of £13.6 million and had an income of £521,000. Grants were made to 71 organisations totalling £426,000.

Beneficiaries included: Combined Services Disabled Ski Team and Maggie's Centre (£10,000 each); Youth Options and Tall Ships Trust (£7,000 each); The Gurkha Welfare Trust, Sheldrick Wildlife and Brooke Hospital for Animals (£5,000 each); Langalang Scholarship Fund (£3,000); Life Cycle UK (£2,000); Royal Hospital Chelsea (£1,000).

Applications

Apply in writing to the correspondent.

Sources of information

Accounts; annual report; Charity Commission record.

The Francis C Scott Charitable Trust

🔍 Disadvantaged young people

Cumbria and North Lancashire (comprising the towns of Lancaster, Morecambe, Heysham and Carnforth)

£ £1.2 million (2016)

CC number: 232131

Trustees: Joanna Plumptre; Alexander Scott; Madeleine Scott; Peter Redhead; Melanie Wotherspoon; Christine Knipe; John McGovern; Malcolm Tillyer; Carol Ostermyer; Steven Swallow.

Correspondent: Helen Carter, Director, Stricklandgate House, 92 Stricklandgate, Kendal, Cumbria LA9 4PU (tel: 01539 742608; email: info@fcsct.org.uk)

🌐 www.fcsct.org.uk

The trust was created in 1963 by Peter F. Scott CBE, then Chair of the Provincial Insurance Company. Peter Scott, together with his parents Francis and Frieda Scott and his sister Joan Trevelyan, endowed the trust with a significant holding of Provincial Insurance Company shares.

Grant guidelines

The trust's core purpose is to support charitable organisations who enable young people from the most deprived areas of Cumbria/North Lancashire to achieve their full potential in life.

The trust is particularly interested in effective approaches to addressing the needs of children, young people and young adults (up to 24 years old) in the following areas:

- Victims/survivors of abuse and exploitation
- Homelessness and its underlying causes
- People suffering from mental health problems
- People leaving care
- People leaving the criminal justice system
- Problems of isolation experienced in rural areas
- Enterprising solutions to job creation
- Targeted, issues-based youth work
- People living in poverty

The trust's website states: 'The majority of our grants are multi-year revenue grants for core costs (i.e. salaries and running costs) however Trustees will also fund capital projects that make a tangible difference to a local community.'

Aspiring leaders programme

This programme was created to build leadership talent among young adults in the voluntary sector within the trust's beneficial area. The innovative programme is delivered by The Brathay Trust (Charity Commission no. 1021586) in partnership with the University of Cumbria to provide a three-year programme enabling young people to get a degree in Social Enterprise Leadership. The programme is funded by The Francis C. Scott Charitable Trust, Rathbones, Langdale Leisure and The Sir John Fisher Foundation.

Financial information

In 2016 the trust held assets of almost £32 million and had an income of £777,000. There were 46 grants made totalling £1.2 million. Grants were broken down as follows:

Aspiring leaders programme	1	£444,000
Young people	20	£439,500
Children and family support	9	£120,000
Communities and charity support	7	£112,500
People with disabilities, mental health	6	£94,500
Other	3	£9,800

Beneficiaries included: Project John (£200,000); Safety Net Advice and Support Centre (£40,000); Families Matter, Marsh Community Centre and Strawberry Fields Training (£20,000 each); Achieve Change and Engagement, Depaul UK and Garden Life Services (£15,000 each); Brampton and Beyond Community Trust (£10,000); Furness Multicultural Community Forum

(£5,000); Trumacar Primary School (£700).

Exclusions

The trust will not generally fund the following:

- Individuals
- Statutory organisations
- National charities without a local base/project
- Charities with substantial unrestricted reserves
- Medical/health establishments
- Schools/educational establishments
- Infrastructure organisations/second-tier bodies
- Projects principally benefitting people outside Cumbria/North Lancashire
- Retrospective funding
- Expeditions or overseas travel
- Promotion of religion
- Animal welfare
- Organisations with a turnover of over £1 million

Applications

The trust is always pleased to hear from charities that need help. If an organisation thinks that it may come within the trust's criteria it is encouraged to contact the director for an informal discussion before making an application.

Application forms are available to download from the trust's website or can be requested by phone, email or post. Applications should be completed and returned with the latest set of accounts (via email or post).

Applications for over £4,000 should be submitted at least four weeks before the trustees' meetings in mid-March, early July and mid-November. Check the website for the latest deadlines.

Applications for grants of less than £4,000 will be considered at small grants meetings every three to four weeks.

Applicants should refer to the trust's website which is very comprehensive and covers all aspects of the grant-making process.

Note: Charities should not apply to both The Frieda Scott Charitable Trust and The Francis C Scott Charitable Trust at the same time. Unsuccessful applicants should wait at least a year before applying to the trust again.

Sources of information

Accounts; annual report; Charity Commission record; funder's website.

The Frieda Scott Charitable Trust

Social welfare, community support, general charitable purposes

Old county of Westmorland and the area covered by South Lakeland District Council

£ £255,000 (2016/17)

CC number: 221593

Trustees: Stuart Fairclough; Philip Hoyle; Richard Bronwson; Vanda Lambton; Peter Smith; Samantha Scott; Hugo Pring; Laura Southern; Samuel Rayner.

Correspondent: Celia Forsyth, Trust Secretary, Stricklandgate House, 92 Stricklandgate, Kendal, Cumbria LA9 4PU (tel: 01539 742608; email: info@fcsct.org.uk)

 www.friedascott.org.uk

The trust was established in 1974 and makes grants available to registered charities involved in a wide range of community and welfare activities that meet the needs of local communities and vulnerable and disadvantaged people. Grants are provided to charities and community groups in the South Lakeland district of Cumbria, as well as the area covered by the old county of Westmorland.

Grant-making priorities

The trust's priorities are listed on its website as follows:

- Older people (particularly those who are vulnerable and isolated)
- People with disabilities, mental health problems and/or learning difficulties
- Children and young people
- Family support work
- Victims/survivors of domestic and sexual abuse
- Recovering substance misusers
- Prevention and rehabilitation of offenders
- Carers
- Community facilities
- Improving access to services for rural communities
- Information and support services for charities
- The arts and music in the community (as a medium for personal development rather than an end in itself)
- Local, amateur sporting organisations and uniformed groups (scouts, guides, etc.)

The trustees are also keen to support organisations in their development towards becoming registered charities focused on the trust's priorities.

The trust has two strands of funding – small grants under £3,500 and larger grants over £3,500. The trust awards around 50 grants each year, mostly ranging from £200 to £20,000, although the average grant is usually under £10,000. The trustees will consider funding projects requiring capital or revenue support and, as of 2015, charities can apply for multi-year revenue funding where there is an ongoing or longer-term need.

Financial information

In 2016/17 the trust had assets of over £10 million and an income of £298,000. There were 37 grants made totalling £255,000. Grants were broken down as follows:

People with disabilities	10	£138,500
Children and young people	10	£32,500
Prevention and rehabilitation	3	£26,500
Community support	3	£23,000
Village halls	7	£17,500
Older people	1	£10,200
Family support	1	£4,500
The arts	2	£1,900

Beneficiaries included: Space2Create (£23,000); South Lakes Citizens Advice (£20,000); Mind – Furness (£19,500); Oaklea Trust (£10,000); St Mary's Parish Centre – Ambleside (£8,000); Eden Ventures (£5,000); Rinkfield Area Community Group (£2,000); Friends of the 597 (£1,000); Brigsteer Village Hall (£500).

Exclusions

The trustees will not support the following:

▷ Retrospective appeals
▷ Statutory bodies (including education/health)
▷ Places of worship/promoting religion
▷ Individuals or expeditions
▷ Animal/wildlife/heritage/ environmental causes
▷ Museums and art galleries
▷ National charities (with exceptions made for local branches)

Applications are not considered if they are from outside the beneficial area.

Applications

An application form is available from the correspondent, or from the trust's website, which should be returned by email or post with the latest set of accounts. Potential applicants are encouraged to ring for an informal discussion before submitting an application.

Applications are considered at meetings in March, June, September and December and should be sent to the grants co-ordinator at least a month beforehand. Grants of less than £3,500 are considered by the small grants committee in between main trustee meetings.

Further advice and information about the grant process is available on the trust's website and applicants are invited to contact the trust with any questions asking for Celia Forsyth, the Trust Secretary.

Note: The trust asks that charities do not apply to both The Frieda Scott and The Francis C Scott Charitable Trusts at the same time. If unsure, contact the trust for further guidance.

Previous applicants, whether successful or not, are advised to wait for a year before applying to the trust again.

Sources of information

Accounts; annual report; Charity Commission record; funder's website.

The Finnis Scott Foundation

🔍 Horticulture, fine art, art history

📍 UK

£ £321,000 (2016)

CC number: 1121475

Trustees: Lady Kathryn Robinson; James Miller; David Laing; The Hon. Ursula Wide; Dr William Elliot; Ian Barnett.

Correspondent: The Trustees, c/o Hewitsons, Elgin House, Billing Road, Northampton NN1 5AU (tel: 01604 233233; email: administrator@finnis-scott-foundation.org.uk)

 www.finnis-scott-foundation.org.uk

The Finnis Scott Foundation was established under the Will of Lady Montagu Douglas Scott (Valerie Finnis) in 2006. The trustees can make grants for any charitable purpose but are presently focused on the areas of horticulture and fine art and art history. These were the two main interests of Sir David Montagu Douglas Scott and his wife Valerie Finnis.

Types of grant

The foundation's website states:

> In general the Trustees will only usually consider grants of between £500 and £10,000, although, exceptionally, larger grants may be considered at the Trustees' discretion. Preference is given to making grants to smaller charities where the grant would have a significant impact.

> The Foundation funds both capital and revenue projects.

Financial information

In 2016 the foundation held assets of £9.8 million and had an income of £317,000. Grants to 20 organisations totalled £321,000.

Beneficiaries included: Watts Gallery (£90,000); MK Gallery and The Garden Museum (£60,000 each); Leighton House (£10,000); CHICKS (£7,000); Great Dixter (£6,000); Eureka Children's Charity (£5,000); The British Museum (£3,000); Friends of Amber Primary School (£760).

Exclusions

Grants are not given for expenditure which has already been made.

Applications

Applicants can download an application form and send it with accompanying documents to the grant administrator at: administrator@finnis-scott-foundation.org.uk. In addition to the application form, the trustees require the following:

▷ Governing document
▷ If available, any business plan, project plan or similar document setting out the purpose of the grant
▷ The most recent accounts and annual report
▷ A budget and any separate project budget

Printed application forms can be submitted by post. Applications are typically acknowledged within two weeks. The trustees consider applications at their first meeting following receipt of the application and all necessary accompanying documents. Applications need to reach the foundation three weeks before a meeting.

Sources of information

Accounts; annual report; Charity Commission record; funder's website.

The ScottishPower Foundation

🔍 General charitable purposes, including: education, the environment, community development, arts, heritage, culture and science, social welfare, community development

📍 UK

£ £1.2 million (2016)

OSCR number: SC043862

Trustees: Mike Thornton; Sarah Mistry; Keith Anderson; Ann McKechin; Elaine Bowker.

Correspondent: María Elena Sanz Arcas, 1 Atlantic Quay, Robertson Street, Glasgow G2 8SP (email: scottishpowerfoundation@scottishpower.com)

 www.scottishpower.com/pages/about_the_scottishpower_foundation

ScottishPower is part of the Iberdrola Group, a global energy company with operations focused in the UK, US, Brazil, Mexico and Spain. The foundation was set up in 2013 in order to reinforce the

company's commitment to supporting charitable work throughout Britain.

Areas of work

The following was taken from the foundation's website:

> The Foundation provides funding to registered charities and non-profit organisations for the following purposes:
>
> ◗ the advancement of education
> ◗ the advancement of environmental protection
> ◗ the advancement of the arts, heritage, culture or science
> ◗ the prevention or relief of poverty and the relief of those in need by reason of disability or other disadvantage
> ◗ the advancement of citizenship and community development

Financial information

In 2016 the foundation had both an income and an expenditure of £1.2 million. Grants to 23 charitable organisations totalled £1.2 million.

Beneficiaries included: Music in Hospitals; National Library of Wales; National Museums Scotland; Royal National Institute of Blind People; The 2050 Climate Group; The Aloud Charity; The Manchester College; Theatre Nemo.

Applications

Application forms are available to download from the foundation's website. Check the website for details of application deadlines.

Sources of information

Accounts; annual report; OSCR record; funder's website.

Scottish Property Industry Festival of Christmas (Spifox)

 Children's charities

Scotland

£452,500 (2016/17)

OSCR number: SC020660

Trustees: Andy Clark; Christian Bruce; Lezley Cameron; Alasdair Carlyle; Ross Clephane; Tom Cromar; Bill Colville; Penny Hearn; Alasdair MacConnell; David MacKenzie; Kenneth McDowell; Brian McGhee; Jeremy Milliken; Douglas Moffat; Danny O'Neill; Frances Sim; Ronnie Urquhart; Alan Watt; David Turpie.

Correspondent: Douglas Moffat, Chair of the Beneficiaries Committee, c/o Saffrey Champness LLP, Edinburgh Quay, 133 Fountainbridge, Edinburgh EH3 9BA (email: douglas@spifox.co.uk)

 www.spifox.co.uk

The charity was founded in 1983 by a group of property and construction professionals. The main objective of the charity is to provide funding for Scottish children's charities to enable the purchase of equipment and the provision of facilities.

The following information has been taken from the charity's website:

> Our principal purpose is the donation of cash sums to specific capital projects, these projects being undertaken by Registered (ideally in Scotland) Charities and specifically for the benefit of kids in Scotland. We also seek our contribution to be 'identifiable'; by that we mean if our donation is to be part of a general appeal then our funding should be used for a specific purpose therein. For example, this could be for fitting out works, equipment provision, relevant IT or specific elements within a larger project.

Financial information

In 2016/17 the charity had assets of £121,500 and an income of £585,500. Grants were made to 26 organisations and totalled £452,500.

Beneficiaries included: Sick Kids (£49,500); Kilpatrick School (£36,000); MusicALL (£35,000); Escape Youth Services Hawick (£20,000); Special Needs Adventure Playground (£9,300); Edinburgh Women's Aid (£3,000); Wellington Children's Centre (£1,500).

Exclusions

The charity's website states: 'It is not generally our policy to contribute to revenue or administrative needs, this having become our established practice from when our Charity was set up in 1983.'

Applications

Contact the Chair of the Beneficiaries Committee, Douglas Moffat (douglas@spifox.co.uk) or any of the trustees known to you. Trustees' contact details can be found on the 'Committee Members' section of the website. After an initial discussion the charity will seek further information on the project/cause which will then be considered at the next beneficiaries sub-committee meeting.

Sources of information

Accounts; annual report; OSCR record; funder's website.

Seafarers Hospital Society

 Seafarers and their dependants

UK

£254,500 to organisations (2016)

CC number: 231724

Trustees: Peter McEwen; Jeffrey Jenkinson; Mark Carden; Alexander Nairne; Capt. Colin Stewart; Surgeon Cdr Frank Leonard; Rupert Chichester; Dr Charlotte Mendes da Costa; Graham Lane; Dr John Carter; Mike Jess.

Correspondent: Peter Coulson, 29 King William Walk, Greenwich, London SE10 9HX (tel: 020 8858 3696; fax: 020 8293 9630; email: admin@seahospital. org.uk)

 www.seahospital.org.uk

The Seafarers Hospital Society (formerly known as the Seaman's Hospital Society) was established in 1821 and is dedicated to meeting the health, welfare and advice needs of seafarers and their dependants. Support is provided for merchant seafarers, fishermen, and the Royal Navy and Royal Marines.

The Seafarers Hospital Society provides help in the following ways:

◗ Grants for economic disadvantage – for example, to buy disability aids and equipment, household goods, or to cover unforeseen expenses
◗ Advice service for seafarers – the Seafarers Advice and Information Line (SAIL) is a national telephone advisory service, providing free, confidential and impartial advice on a wide range of issues
◗ Supporting health and fitness for seafarers – including physiotherapy, and diet and exercise advice
◗ Confidential mental health and well-being service – a pilot scheme being run by Big White Wall (currently only available to serving personnel)
◗ The Dreadnought – a hospital based at Guy's and St Thomas's Hospital, offering priority medical treatment for those working at sea
◗ Seafarers link – a fortnightly telephone line that retired seafarers can use to chat to one another, to reminisce and make new friends

Financial information

In 2016 the charity had assets of £9.2 million and an income of £426,500. During the year, the charity gave a total of £460,500 in grants. Of this amount, £310,500 was given to organisations and £150,000 to individuals.

Previous Beneficiaries included: Seafarers Advice and Information Line (£240,500); MCG Development Programme (£5,000); Annual National Service for Seafarers (£150).

Applications

Application forms are available from the correspondent. Applicants are encouraged to contact the correspondent before making application.

Sources of information

Accounts; annual report; Charity Commission record; funder's website.

Seafarers UK (King George's Fund for Sailors)

 Seafarers' welfare

UK and Commonwealth

 £3.5 million (2017)

CC number: 226446

Trustees: Mark Carden; Michael Acland; Christine Gould; Christian Marr; Simon Rivett-Carnac; Mark Dickinson; Vice Adm. Peter Wilkinson; Capt. Roger Barker; Dyan Sterling; Cmdre Peter Buxton; Jeremy Monroe; Evelyn Strouts; Duncan Bain; Natalie Shaw.

Correspondent: Deborah Layde, Grants Director, 8 Hatherley Street, London SW1P 2YY (tel: 020 7932 0000; fax: 020 7932 0095; email: grants@seafarers.uk)

www.seafarers-uk.org

This charity supports people who have served at sea in the Royal Navy, Royal Marines, Merchant Navy and fishing fleets, their equivalents in the Commonwealth, and their dependants. The charity makes grants, often recurrent, for a wide but little-changing range of seafarers' charities. Grants range from a few hundred pounds to several hundred thousand.

The charity gives grants to other charities that help with all aspects of seafarers' welfare including accommodation, medical services, disability services, financial aid, childcare, education and training and youth activities. They describe their four main objectives as:

- to ensure that all former UK and Commonwealth seafarers over normal retirement age and their dependants can live life free of poverty and with access to all reasonable health care and domestic assistance
- to ensure that serving UK and Commonwealth seafarers have access to reasonable shore amenities and communication with their families and financial help where appropriate
- to ensure that the dependent families of UK and Commonwealth seafarers can have access to a reasonable quality of life including adequate accommodation, clothing, education and holidays
- to assist those UK and Commonwealth citizens in maritime youth organisations training for a seagoing career including the Sea Cadets, with the cost of facilities

The fund was set up in 1917 as a central fundraising organisation to support other seafarers' charities. Several years ago the charity underwent a structural overhaul to address its extremely high fundraising costs (35% of income). It succeeded in bringing this figure down to 21% in 2008 and in the process modernised the fund to make it more relevant, including adopting the operational name Seafarers UK. In 2011 fundraising costs were 27.9%; in 2012 they were 29.5%.

In future years the charity will be focusing on raising public awareness of seafarers and the hardship and danger that they face on a daily basis. It intends to do this by holding 'Seafarers Awareness Week'.

The charity operates two grants programmes:

- The Seafarers UK Grants programme
- The Merchant Navy Fund Grants programme

The charity also makes a substantial contribution towards the Sea Cadets annual fund which allocates money to units in need of repairs, maintenance or new equipment. Any sea cadet unit should apply to that fund and will not be considered under the other programmes.

Financial information

At the time of writing (March 2018), the latest accounts available to view on the Charity Commission website are the 2016 accounts, which state that in 2016 the charity had assets of £40 million and an income of £2.8 million. In that financial year, the charity gave a total of £2.6 million in grants; however, we have used the charity's 2017 grants total which is available on its website. The charity's website states: 'In 2017 we awarded 88 grants totalling £3.5 million, including funding eight organisations that were new to us.'

Beneficiaries included: Nautilus Welfare Fund (£554,500); Marine Society and Sea Cadets (£145,000); Royal Navy and Royal Marines Children's Fund (£100,000); Sailors Children's Society (£50,000); SSAFA (£20,000); Mutual Support (£4,000); Merchant Navy Welfare Board (£100).

Exclusions

The charity will not fund:

- Individuals
- Sailing or youth clubs or organisations whose primary purpose is to provide opportunities for people to sail or learn to sail (including young people and people with disabilities)
- Individual Marine Society and Sea Cadet units
- Religious organisations
- Political and campaigning organisations
- Organisations whose primary goal is to undertake beach or sea rescue or lifeboat activities

However, the charity may be able to advise in particular cases about a suitable organisation to approach.

Applications

Applicants to the main grants scheme should download the form available on the charity's website and use the guidance notes available there.

The charity's website states:

> With effect from 01 January 2017 there are no grant application deadlines, as we operate a continuous grant making process and assess applications on a rolling basis. This means you can submit an application to us at any time.
>
> Decisions on grant applications are made a minimum of six times a year. We cannot guarantee that your application will be considered at a particular time and so it is recommended that you plan ahead.

Note that you must pass the grant application eligibility quiz before you can apply for a grant – this is all part of the online grant application process.

Sources of information

Accounts; annual report; Charity Commission record; funder's website; guidelines for applicants.

Sam and Bella Sebba Charitable Trust

 General charitable purposes, particularly Jewish causes

 UK and Israel

£3.6 million (2016)

CC number: 253351

Trustees: Victor Klein; Yoav Tangir; Odelia Sebba; Tamsin Doyle; Leah Hurst; Dr Varda Shiffer.

Correspondent: David Lerner, Chief Executive, Office 19, 5th Floor, 63–66 Hatton Garden, London EC1N 8LE (tel: 020 7723 6028)

This trust was established in 1967 by the late Samuel Sebba for general charitable purposes. The trustees seek to promote a more humane society by supporting vulnerable people and protecting their rights, and does this by funding grants for social innovation and transformative change.

Grant-making policies

The annual report for 2016 explains that the trust:

> Has established its grant-making policy to achieve its objects for the public benefit by making grants to charities whose objectives are clear, that can demonstrate best practice and sustainability, whose operations are transparent and whose commitment to the public benefit is demonstrable.

According to the trust's mission statement, the trustees prioritise making grants 'where others are less active'.

The trustees identify priorities over a three-year grant-making cycle and on a year-by-year basis. In 2016 key areas for funding in the UK were palliative care, refugees and welfare in the Jewish community. The trust also began making grants for assistive technology projects and programmes for the support of mental health, particularly of young people. In Israel the trustees' focus remained on the environment, human rights and social justice, disability and young people at risk. In both the UK and Israel the trust has increased its support for refugee welfare and advocacy.

Financial information

In 2016 the trust had assets of £61 million and an income of £1 million. Grants totalling £3.6 million were made to 122 organisations. Of this number, 108 beneficiaries received grants of £10,000 or more, and 14 received grants of less than £10,000 (accounting for £76,000 of the grant total).

Grants were distributed in the following categories:

Welfare	£728,500
Education	£431,500
Refugees	£407,500
Human rights	£379,500
Disability	£374,000
Environment	£345,000
Social justice	£305,500
Young people at risk	£272,000
Palliative care	£242,000
Assistive technology	£83,000
Other	£35,500
Vulnerable children	£25,000

Beneficiaries included: University District Service League (£149,000); Jewish Care (£122,500); Together for Short Lives (£72,500); Bizchut – The Israel Human Rights Centre for People with Disabilities (£49,500); Alfred Adler Institute (£41,500); Alzheimer's Association of Israel (£39,500); Women Against Violence (£27,000); Richard House Children's Hospice (£25,000); Israel Sports Centre for the Disabled (£24,000); Hospital Kosher Meal Service and Asylum Link Merseyside (£15,000 each); ASSAF Aid Organisation for Refugees and Asylum Seekers (£11,600).

Exclusions

No grants are made to idividuals.

Applications

Apply in writing to the correspondent. Include your organisation's latest annual report and accounts and proof of registered charitable status, as well as a breakdown of the costs required. The trustees meet three times per year.

Sources of information

Accounts; annual report; Charity Commission record.

The Segelman Trust

🔍 Education, arts and culture, social welfare

📍 UK and overseas

💷 £594,000 (2016)

CC number: 1079151

Trustees: Christopher Graves; Wilson Cotton; Rebecca Eastmond; Timothy White.

Correspondent: Grants Administrator, West Wing, Somerset House, The Strand, London WC2R 1LA (tel: 020 7131 4000)

According to its 2016 accounts, the Segelman Trust 'supports and encourages educational, cultural and social values that contribute to enriching our society'. The trust aims to achieve this objective by making grants to organisations 'delivering charitable projects of significant public benefit in a cost effective way'. The trust's grant-making activities are divided across three areas of work:

▶ **Education** – The support of young people, who may be from less advantaged backgrounds, in developing their talents and reaching their full potential

▶ **Social Welfare and Relief of Poverty** – To support people from all parts of society who may be vulnerable or marginalised

▶ **Education and Culture** – To provide access to music and the arts through education for students, school children and the very young

The trust's primary area of focus is the UK; however, grants may also be made to support organisations achieving outstanding work elsewhere in the world.

Financial information

In 2016 the trust has assets of £50.2 million and an income of £1.3 million. During the year, the trustees made or agreed ten grants totalling £594,000. The grants were distributed as follows:

Social Welfare	7	£337,000
Education and Culture	3	£257,000

Beneficiaries included: House of Illustration and Safelives (£125,000 each); The Voices Foundation (£90,000) The Geffrye Museum (£42,000); Chatham House (£12,000); Music as Therapy (£12,000); Acumen (£140).

Exclusions

The trust does not provide grants to individuals.

Applications

The trustees do not consider unsolicited applications, but instead identify projects of interest and provide support to those which complement the charity's aims.

Sources of information

Accounts; annual report; Charity Commission record.

The Jean Shanks Foundation

🔍 Medical research and education, pathology

📍 UK

💷 £297,000 (2016/17)

CC number: 293108

Trustees: Alistair Taylor Jones; Prof. Sir Nicholas Wright; Prof. Andrew Carr; Prof. Sir James Underwood; Eric Rothbarth; Dr Julian Axe; Prof. Adrienne Flanagan.

Correspondent: Paula Price-Davies, Foundation Administrator, Peppard Cottage, Peppard Common, Henley On Thames, Oxfordshire RG9 5LB (tel: 01491 628232; email: administrator@ jeanshanksfoundation.org)

 www.jeanshanksfoundation.org

Registered with the Charity Commission in November 1985, the foundation supports medical research and education, particularly in the area of pathology.

The foundation changed the criteria for grants in November 2017 in order to extend its partnership with The Pathological Society and allow both parties to make bigger and more effective grants to ensure the further development of pathology.

The foundation funds intercalated year awards to allow medical students the benefit of an extra year's research during their training. The 2016/17 annual report states that the foundation now asks medical schools to nominate one candidate for an intercalated grant per medical school. This includes all medical schools in England, Scotland, Wales and Northern Ireland, except those which have a mandatory intercalated year. It also grants research awards in the general medical field.

Financial information

In 2016/17 the foundation held assets of over £24 million and had an income of £409,500. There were grants made to 20 institutions totalling £297,000.

Previous beneficiaries have included: Pathological Society of Great Britain and Ireland (£45,500); University of Cambridge (£21,000); Barts and The

London School of Medicine and Dentistry (£15,000); University of Newcastle (£10,500); Queen's University Belfast (£9,900); University of Liverpool (£7,500); University of Edinburgh (£6,000).

Exclusions

Grants are not made for financial hardship.

Applications

Apply in writing to the correspondent. Full grant guidelines are available on the foundation's website.

Sources of information

Accounts; annual report; Charity Commission record; funder's website.

The Shanly Foundation

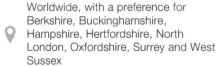

🔍 General charitable purposes

📍 Worldwide, with a preference for Berkshire, Buckinghamshire, Hampshire, Hertfordshire, North London, Oxfordshire, Surrey and West Sussex

£ £1.52 million (2016)

CC number: 1065044

Trustees: Michael Shanly; Tamra Booth; Tim Potter; Donald Tucker.

Correspondent: Maria Mindak, Sorbon, 24–26 Aylesbury End, Beaconsfield HP9 1LW (tel: 01494 671331; email: maria.mindak@shanlyfoundation.com)

 www.shanlyfoundation.com

 @ShanlyFnd

The Shanly Foundation was established in 1997 for general charitable purposes. The foundation aims to support causes that 'help individuals and benefit the local community, including support for young people from disadvantaged backgrounds, the homeless, those with mental health issues and people with physical disabilities, injury or life limiting illness'. In addition to its work in the UK, the foundation also occasionally donates to major international projects such as the 2014 Ebola crisis.

The foundation receives its income from the profits of Shanly Homes Ltd and Sorbon Homes Ltd, and functions as the charitable arm of the Shanly Group of companies established by the foundation's founder Michael Shanly. Since its creation, the foundation has donated over £13 million to thousands of local community groups and charities.

Financial information

In 2016 the foundation had assets of £2.1 million and an income of £1.5 million. Grants were made totalling £1.52 million, and were distributed as follows:

Community	£594,000
Education	£536,500
Health and welfare	£255,000
Disability	£178,000
Wildlife and conservation	£39,500
Religious	£5,800
General	£5,000

Beneficiaries included: Beech Lodge School Ltd (£336,500); Alexander Devine Children's Cancer Trust (£100,000); Adoption UK (£50,000); Thames Valley Adventure Playground (£20,000); Girl Guiding Epsom (£10,000); Shelterbox Trust (£8,000).

Applications

Applicants should state clearly the reasons for making the application and accompany their submissions with relevant documents. Applications can be submitted by post, email or via the online form on the foundation's website.

Sources of information

Accounts; annual report; Charity Commission record.

ShareGift (The Orr Mackintosh Foundation)

🔍 General charitable purposes

📍 UK

£ £2.5 million (2016/17)

CC number: 1052686

Trustees: Alan Scott; Paul Killik; John Roundhill; Susan Swabey.

Correspondent: Lady Mackintosh, Marquis House, 67–68 Jermyn Street, London SW1Y 6NY (tel: 020 7930 3737; email: help@sharegift.org.uk)

 www.sharegift.org

Launched in 1996, this charity was developed by the Viscountess Mackintosh of Halifax and Matthew Orr, a stockbroker whose firm Killik and Co., provides many of the technical support services required to operate ShareGift.

The charity specialises in accepting donations of shares, which it then distributes to a broad range of UK-registered charities. The charity makes donations at its own discretion but is guided by donor suggestions. ShareGift is cause neutral and there are no restrictions on the kind of charitable work it can support, or where in the world it takes place. Grants are typically made to the general funds of the charity concerned, rather than for specific projects. Since 1996, the charity has provided funds of over £29 million to more than 2,600 charities.

Financial information

In 2016/17 the charity had assets of £2.75 million and an income of £3.1 million. 514 grants were made to 416 charities totalling £2.5 million. Grants were made in the following categories:

£1,000–£4,999	382	£591,000
£5,000–£9,999	67	£340,000
£10,000	65	£1.54 million

Beneficiaries included: MQ Transforming Mental Health (£260,000); Alzheimer's Research UK (£37,500); British Red Cross (£27,500); Accounting for Sustainability and Chestnut Tree House Children's Hospice (£25,000 each); Islington Centre for Refugees and Migrants (£15,000); Bradford and Airedale Eyesight Trust (£11,000); National Energy Action, Quaker Social Action and The Royal Shakespeare Company (£10,000 each).

Exclusions

Grants are only made to UK-registered charities.

Applications

Unsolicited applications are not accepted.

Sources of information

Accounts; annual report; Charity Commission record; funder's website.

The Shears Foundation

🔍 Community development, environment, sustainable development, health, social welfare, cultural development, overseas aid

📍 UK, with a preference for the north east of England

£ £779,000 (2016/17)

CC number: 1049907

Trustees: G. Lyall; Lyn Shears; P. J. R. Shears; Patricia Shears; Bruce Warnes; Mark Horner; Richard Shears.

Correspondent: Lyn Shears, Trustee, c/o The Community Foundation, Philanthropy House, Woodbine Road, Gosforth, Newcastle upon Tyne NE3 1DD (email: lyn@shears.onyxnet.co.uk)

The foundation was established in 1994 by Trevor and Lyn Shears following the sale of their transport company.

The foundation's 2015/16 annual report states that it:

Aims to fund selected organisations and projects in the fields of community development, environmental issues, sustainable development, health and welfare and cultural development, all with an emphasis on education and raising awareness. There is also a proportion devoted to overseas projects in the same fields.

Financial information

In 2016/17 the foundation had assets of £17.8 million and an income of £532,500. There were 42 grants made totalling £779,000.

Beneficiaries included: Community Foundation Linden Fund (£100,000); Bradford Grammar School, Community Foundation Local Environmental Action Fund, Royal College of Surgeons in England and Whitley Fund for Nature (£50,000 each); Samling Foundation (£45,000); Alnwick Garden (£35,000); English National Opera (£30,000).

Applications

Apply in writing to the correspondent.

Sources of information

Accounts; annual report; Charity Commission record.

The Sheepdrove Trust

General charitable purposes, arts and culture, medicine and health, farming and wildlife preservation, education

UK, there may be some preference for north Lambeth, London

Around £450,000 (2016)

CC number: 328369

Trustees: Barnabas Kindersley; Juliet Kindersley; Peter Kindersley; Harriet Treuille; Anabel Kindersley.

Correspondent: Juliet Kindersley, Trustee, Sheepdrove Farmhouse, Sheepdrove Organic Farm, Lambourn, Hungerford RG17 7UN (tel: 01488 674726; email: lynn.long@sheepdrove.com)

The trust is endowed with money made by the Dorling Kindersley publishing enterprise, but the trust's holding of shares in the company was sold in 2000, when the endowment was valued at £18 million. The trust has general charitable purposes but there is a particular interest in supporting initiatives involved in sustainability, biodiversity and organic farming.

In previous years the trustees made grants in the following areas of work: education; farming and wildlife preservation; medicine and health; arts and culture.

Financial information

In 2016 the trust had an income of £4,400 and an expenditure of £551,000. Due to the trust's low income accounts were not available to view at the Charity Commission website. We estimate that grants awarded to organisations totalled around £450,000.

Previous beneficiaries have included: Newcastle University – Professorial Fellowship (£500,000); University of the Arts London Scholarships (£75,000); Fundacion Para la Conservacion de Ibiza Formentera (£28,500); Vauxhall City Farm (£15,000); UNHCR – Relief in Syria (£10,000); Alzheimer's Society (£5,000); Greencuisine Trust (£4,300); Newbury Spring Festival (£4,000); Royal Opera House (£350); Oxfordshire Fungus Survey (£250).

Applications

Apply in writing to the correspondent.

Sources of information

Accounts; annual report; Charity Commission record.

The Sheffield Town Trust

General charitable purposes

Sheffield

£359,000 (2016)

CC number: 223760

Trustees: Nicholas Hutton; Adrian Staniforth; Jonathan Brayshaw; Penny Jewitt; Jason Heath; Jane Ferretti; Jim Fulton; Marian Rae; Sarah Thomas; Oliver Stephenson; Zahid Hamid; Julie MacDonald; Mark Swales.

Correspondent: George Connell, Law Clerk, Commercial House, 14 Commercial Street, Sheffield S1 2AT (tel: 0114 276 5555; email: sheffieldtowntrust@hlwkeeblehawson.co.uk)

 www.sheffieldtowntrust.org.uk

The Sheffield Town Trust was established in 1297 by Thomas de Furnival, Lord of Hallamshire and is one of the oldest charities in England. Until late in the nineteenth century it carried out municipal responsibilities such as lighting, policing, highways and water supply. The Sheffield Town Trustees Act 1873 saw the conversion of the trust into a charity with its main object 'other charitable and public purposes for the benefit of Sheffield as a whole and its inhabitants'.

The following is taken from the trust's website:

> The Trust supports a wide range of groups and organisations some on an annual basis but most as one-off grants. The Town Trustees meet four times a year in February, May, August and November to discuss the many applications received and are able to support about 140 charities, groups and organisations each year.
>
> The Town Trust also uses its funds to help protect and safeguard the city's heritage and environment. The Trust has helped with the regeneration of the Botanical Gardens, the development of the Five Weirs Walk, and the restoration of Kelham Island Industrial Museum.

Financial information

In 2016 the trust held assets of £8.6 million and had an income of £498,500. Grants to 178 organisations totalled £359,000.

Beneficiaries included: St Luke's Hospice (£50,000); Cavendish Care (£10,000); Emmaus Sheffield (£5,000); Asperger's Children and Carers Together (£3,000); Friends of Greenhill Park (£2,000); Sick Children's Trust and Victim Support Sheffield (£1,500 each); Sheffield Cathedral (£1,000); Learn for Life Enterprise (£500); Parson Cross Tai Chi Health Group (£300).

Exclusions

Individuals; organisations that do not benefit Sheffield or its inhabitants; animal charities; political organisations; religious groups.

Applications

Apply in writing to the correspondent for consideration at the Town Trustees meeting in February, May, August and November. To be considered at a meeting, applications should be received by post by 12pm (noon) on the 15th of the month prior, i.e. 15 January, 15 April, 15 July and 15 October at the very latest.

Sources of information

Accounts; annual report; Charity Commission record; funder's website.

The Sylvia and Colin Shepherd Charitable Trust

General charitable purposes

North East England, but mostly within a 25-mile radius of York

£204,000 (2016/17)

CC number: 272788

Trustees: Sara Dickson; David Dickson; Sylvia Shepherd; Lucy Dickson; Sophie Dickson.

Correspondent: Sara Dickson, Trustee, c/o 3 Kings Cloisters, Driffield Terrace, York YO24 1EF

The trust was established in 1973 and supports organisations with general charitable purposes within a 25-mile radius of York. It has preferences for: community initiatives; care of older people; childcare; people with learning or physical disabilities; conservation; and medical support and equipment. Grants are given towards projects rather than core costs and range from £40 to £5,000, although most are for £1,000 or less.

Financial information

In 2016/17 the trust held assets of £2.6 million and had an income of £56,500. Grants were made to over 250 organisations and totalled £204,000.

Beneficiaries included: Accessible Arts and Media (£5,100); Ataxia UK (£5,000); University of York (£4,000); Headstart4Babies (£2,500); Yorkshire Air Ambulance (£1,000); Premier Christian Radio, Swaledale Festival and Wellbeing of Women (£500 each); British Hen Welfare Trust (£300); Durham Cathedral (£100).

Exclusions

Applications from individuals will not be considered. Support does not extend to organisations working outside the beneficial area and excludes overseas activities.

Applications

Apply in writing to the correspondent. The trustees meet frequently. Applications should include details of the need to be met, achievements and a copy of the latest accounts.

Sources of information

Accounts; annual report; Charity Commission record.

Sherburn House Charity

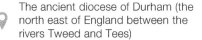

Social welfare, health, disability, community development

The ancient diocese of Durham (the north east of England between the rivers Tweed and Tees)

£186,500 to organisations (2016/17)

CC number: 217652

Trustees: Ray Pye; Margaret Bozic; Michael Laing; Susan Martin; Cllr David Stoker; Kevin Cummings; James Imrie; David Thorne; Margaret Jefferson.

Correspondent: Grants Team, County Durham Community Foundation, c/o County Durham Community Foundation, Victoria House, Whifield Court, St Johns Road, Meadowfield Industrial Estate, Durham DH7 8XL (tel: 0191 378 6340; email: info@cdcf.org.uk)

 www.sherburnhouse.org

The charity was formed from a re-organisation of Christ's Hospital in Sherburn, itself an active charity since 1181. Primarily a housing and residential care charity, the trustees began making grants in the summer of 1998. Funding must be to relieve need, hardship or distress. In January 2017, the trustees outsourced the charity's grants programme to County Durham Community Foundation (CDCF) and will no longer accept applications directly. Applicants must use the CDCF website to apply for grant-funding from the Sherburn House Charity.

Grants programme

The charity only gives grants within the beneficial area of North East England between the rivers Tweed and Tees. The following information is taken from CDCF's website:

> The Sherburn House Community Grants Programme aims to support voluntary and community groups and organisations, including small local groups from 'the ancient Diocese of Durham, that is anywhere in the North East of England between the Rivers Tweed and Tees.
>
> The Programme provides grants [of up] to £5,000 to support charities, voluntary-led organisations and projects that have an incredible impact in their community, enabling them to continue their work and make vital improvements to their service.

Who can apply?

- Voluntary led organisations with charitable aims e.g. Sports clubs
- Registered charities and charitable incorporated organisations (CIO)
- Social enterprises
- Community interest companies

What type of funding can you apply for?

Priority will be given to applications for funding that fall within the following areas:

- Debt Advice
- Crisis Help
- Health and Disabilities
- Social Isolation
- Problems of Long Term Unemployment
- Community Need

Financial information

In 2016/17 the charity had assets of £35.3 million and a turnover of £1.87 million. During the year, 78 grants were made to organisations totalling £186,500. The charity also has a fund for individual hardship, which is also administered by CDCF. There were 342 grants made to individuals in 2016/17 which totalled £56,500.

A list of beneficiaries was not included in the accounts.

Exclusions

The charity will not fund:

- Individuals
- Organisations with substantial reserves or a serious deficit
- Grant-making bodies seeking to distribute grants on the charity's behalf
- Activities which are the responsibility of any statutory body
- Fabric appeals
- Substance abuse
- Family support outside the areas listed for support
- Fundraising events or activities
- General appeals
- Sponsorship
- Expeditions or overseas travel
- Trips and outings
- Mainstream educational activity
- National charities, unless they have a strong representation within the beneficial area
- Hospitals and medical centres (other than hospices)
- Medical research
- Retrospective grants
- Applications from organisations which have received a grant within the previous two years
- Those who do not fully complete the application form and fail to supply the necessary supporting information

Applications

Before applying, read CDCF's general grant-making criteria available on its website, to check that your organisation and activity/project for which you are seeking funding, meets its general criteria.

Contact a member of the grants team on 0191 378 6340 if you have any questions or need help with your application.

The website states (April 2018) that the fund is now closed due to oversubscription. Refer to the website for current information.

Sources of information

Accounts; annual report; Charity Commission record; funder's website.

The Archie Sherman Charitable Trust

Jewish organisations, education and training, arts and culture, health, overseas aid, general charitable purposes

UK and overseas

£1.5 million (2016/17)

CC number: 256893

Trustees: Michael Gee; Allan Morgenthau; Eric Charles; Rhona Freedman.

Correspondent: Michael Gee, Trustee, 274A Kentish Town Road, London NW5 2AA (tel: 020 7493 1904; email: trust@sherman.co.uk)

This trust makes grants to charitable organisations in the UK and overseas to support education and training, overseas aid, arts and culture, health and general charitable purposes. Funding is awarded predominantly, but not exclusively, to Jewish organisations.

The trust's annual report for 2016/17 states that the trustees review all commitments on a forward five-year basis so that a few new projects can be undertaken and for which income is made available.

Financial information

In 2016/17 the trust had assets of £20.8 million and an income of £1.4 million. Grants to 28 organisations totalled almost £1.5 million and were distributed as follows:

Education and training	6	£789,500
Health	8	£354,500
Arts and culture and general charitable purposes	12	£286,000
Overseas aid	2	£41,500

Beneficiaries included: Youth Aliyah Child Rescue (£353,500); Tel Aviv University Trust (£347,000); Shaare Zedek UK (£216,500); British Friends of the Jaffa Institute (£34,500); The Royal National Theatre (£25,000); Jewish Child's Day (£14,400); UK Jewish Film Ltd (£5,000); United Jewish Israel Appeal (£2,500); Magen David Adom UK (£1,200); My Israel – Project Fund (£240).

Applications

Apply in writing to the correspondent. The trustees meet regularly through the year.

Sources of information

Accounts; annual report; Charity Commission record.

Shetland Charitable Trust

 Arts projects for under 18s, activities for older people

 Shetland only

£ £8.4 million (2016/17)

OSCR number: SC027025

Trustees: Bobby Hunter; Andrew Cooper; Geoffrey Hay; Tom Macintyre; Peter Malcolmson; Keith Massey; Ian Napier; Drew Ratter; Margaret Roberts; James Smith.

Correspondent: Ann Black, Chief Executive, 22–24 North Road, Lerwick, Shetland ZE1 0NQ (tel: 01595 744994; email: mail@shetlandcharitabletrust.co.uk)

🌐 www.shetlandcharitabletrust.co.uk

f facebook.com/shetlandcharitabletrust

Shetland Charitable Trust started life as Shetland Islands Council Charitable Trust (SICCT) in 1976 when Sullom Voe Terminal began operating. Money was paid by the oil industry to Shetland as a way of compensating people for the inconvenience of having the terminal based in Shetland. It was decided to establish a charitable trust to receive and disburse this money.

Grant programmes

According to the trust's website, the following grant programmes are open to applications:

Arts Grants

This grant aid scheme is designed to support under 18s and not for profit community groups catering for those under 18 to develop their art form and/or deliver arts related projects and events that meet local needs and make a lasting difference in the community. The scheme can support all forms of arts genres including visual arts, crafts, drama, dialect, film, literature, music, theatre and combined arts.

Senior Citizens Club Grants

This grant aid scheme can support not for profit community groups that organise and deliver social and recreational activities for local Senior Citizens clubs which are exclusively or primarily used by Senior Citizens who are 65 years or older.

Capital Works Bridging Loan Scheme

This bridging loan scheme is available to organisations carrying out work on a public facility or providing a new public facility in Shetland which is eligible for grant funding from EU/Scottish Government/Lottery.

Financial information

In 2016/17 the trust had assets of £271 million and an income of £6.6 million. Grants were made totalling £8.4 million.

Beneficiaries included: Shetland Recreational Trust (£3.3 million); Shetland Amenity Trust (£1.3 million); Shetland Arts Development Agency (£695,000); COPE Ltd (£155,000); Voluntary Action Shetland (£144,500); The Swan Trust (£54,000); Disability Shetland Recreational Club (£12,600).

Applications

Application forms are available to download from the trust's website.

Sources of information

Accounts; annual report; OSCR record; funder's website.

SHINE (Support and Help in Education)

 Education for disadvantaged young people

 England, mainly Greater London and Manchester

£ £1.55 million (2016/17)

CC number: 1082777

Trustees: Gavin Boyle; David Blood; Lord Jim O'Neill; Cameron Ogden; Stephen Shields; Ann Mroz; Mark Heffernan; Sarah Loftus.

Correspondent: Fiona Birkett, Shine Trust, Princes Exchange, 2 Princes

Square, Leeds LS1 4HY (email: info@shinetrust.org.uk)

 www.shinetrust.org.uk

SHINE is a specialist educational grant-maker that works to address educational inequalities and support educational attainment in young people from disadvantaged areas in England. To achieve this goal, the charity helps to co-design and fund educational programmes that raise the attainment and aspirations of children from economically deprived areas in England. To date, the charity has invested over £24.5 million into almost 250 education projects, working with 280,000 children from 5,000 schools.

According to its website, SHINE has the following strategic priorities for all its funding programmes until 2021:

▶ **Ready for School:** improving the school readiness of children during the reception year, with a priority focus on language and communication skills (age four to five)
▶ **Bridging the Gap:** supporting vulnerable children who may not meet age-related expectations at primary school to make better academic progress during Key Stage 3 (age 9 to 14)
▶ **Flying High:** supporting high attaining students to build on their achievements at primary school and stay on a high attaining trajectory during the first few years at secondary school (age 9 to 14)

On its website, the charity states that it is 'interested in supporting projects that involve collaboration between colleagues in the different educational phases, for example professionals in primary and secondary schools working together' and that it is 'also interested in supporting programmes that aim to develop strong relationships with parents'.

Grant programmes

The following is a brief overview of the schemes currently operated by SHINE. See the website for full details.

Teacher-led innovation (Let Teachers Shine)

Supporting innovative teachers across England to develop new ideas to improve the educational attainment of some of the most vulnerable learners.

SHINE Saturday programmes

Helping teachers identify gaps in their students' learning through hands-on and creative learning techniques, including the use of outside trips and external visitors.

School based partnerships
Partnership projects with other schools in science provision and tutoring.

Financial information
In 2016/17 the charity held assets of £5 million and had an income of £1.2 million. A total of £1.55 million was awarded in grants.

Beneficiaries included: London Teacher Innovation Fund (£92,500 11 grants); The Halle Orchestra (£76,000); Active Phonics (£40,000); Bright Futures (£37,000); Barclay Primary School (£30,500); Crowland Primary School (£26,000); The Hyde Primary School (£7,500).

Exclusions
The charity will not fund any of the following:

- Programmes that take place outside England
- Individuals (with the exception of Let Teachers SHINE)
- Short-term or one-off projects
- Bursaries or any kind of student fees
- Direct replacement of statutory funding
- Programmes where the primary aim is the personal development of young people rather than raising academic achievement levels
- Capital building programmes for schools or other education institutions

Applications
Applicants should contact the charity by email, outlining the following points, in no more than three to four paragraphs:

- An overview of the project and its aims, specifically related to academic attainment in maths, literacy or science
- How it would meet SHINE's core priorities
- The number of beneficiaries and schools it would reach
- The overall project budget and the amount of the request to SHINE

If the proposal meets the charity's basic criteria, an initial meeting or phone conversation will be arranged with a member of the grants team. Grants decisions are taken at board meetings, typically in March, June, September and December. On average, it takes three to six months between initial contact with the SHINE office to a grants decision being reached.

Sources of information
Accounts; annual report; Charity Commission record; guidelines for applicants; funder's website.

The Simmons & Simmons Charitable Foundation

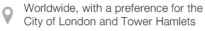

Social welfare, education and training, access to justice and legal aid

Worldwide, with a preference for the City of London and Tower Hamlets

£251,000 (2016/17)

CC number: 1129643

Trustees: Richard Dyton; Fiona Loughrey; Colin Passmore; Ina Vom Feld.

Correspondent: The Trustees, c/o Simmons & Simmons LLP, Citypoint, 1 Ropemaker Street, London EC2Y 9SS (tel: 020 7628 2020; email: corporate.responsibility@simmons-simmons.com)

 www.simmons-simmons.com

The foundation was established in 2009 by the law firm Simmons & Simmons LLP. The following information was taken from the foundation's 2016/17 accounts:

> The foundation seeks to support smaller charitable organisations which are local to the offices of Simmons & Simmons and which seek to address social exclusion. The foundation also seeks to provide access to justice, work and opportunities to those less privileged or fortunate, for example by providing direct grants to talented individuals from low income backgrounds.

Preference is given to charities in which the firm's employees can be involved.

Financial information
In 2016/17 the foundation held assets of £150,000 and had an income of £181,500. Grants totalled £251,000.

Beneficiaries included: Battersea Legal Advice Centre (£36,000); The Big Issue Foundation (£22,000); Bingham Centre for the Rule of Law, The Ethical Property Foundation and Working Families (£10,000 each); Spitalfields Music (£6,000); London's Air Ambulance, Prisoners' Advice Service and School Home Support (£5,000 each).

Grants of less than £5,000 totalled £51,000.

Applications
Application forms are available from the correspondent. Applicants must explain how they meet one of the following objectives:

- Social inclusion (increasing access to education and/or work)
- Governance (supporting the rule of law and access to justice)

They must also explain how they will provide support to communities local to where Simmons & Simmons have offices.

Sources of information
Accounts; annual report; Charity Commission record; funder's website.

The Sino-British Fellowship Trust

Education and training

UK and China

£418,000 to organisations (2016)

CC number: 313669

Trustees: Lady Pamela Youde; Anne Ely; Prof. Hugh Baker; Peter Ely; Ling Thompson; Prof. Wayne Luk; Dr Frances Wood; Prof. George Smith; Prof. Rosemary Foot.

Correspondent: Anne Ely, Trustee, Flat 23, Bede House, Manor Fields, London SW15 3LT (tel: 020 8788 6252)

Established in 1948, the trust makes grants to institutions benefitting individual postgraduate students. Its Charity Commission record notes that financial support is provided for academic exchanges at postgraduate level between the UK and China. According to its objectives, the trust aims to advance education and training by:

- Awarding scholarships or grants to students and academic staff at universities, other higher education institutions and vocational training institutions in [China/Britain] to enable them to undertake study or research, to attend or participate in academic and professional conferences, courses, placements, seminars and similar events in [Britain/China]
- Promoting the study of Chinese languages
- Enabling students and academic staff to participate in joint Chinese/British educational programmes and courses, including academic and other educational exchanges between Hong Kong and China

Financial information
In 2016 the trust had assets of over £17.1 million and an income of £556,000. Grants awarded to organisations totalled £418,000 of which £282,500 was awarded to UK institutions. The amount of grants given to individuals totalled £39,500.

Previous beneficiaries in the UK have included: Royal Society (£70,500); British Academy (£35,000); British Library (£30,500); Universities China Committee London (£29,000); Great Britain China Educational Trust (£20,000); School of Oriental and

African Studies (£17,500); British Museum (£14,100); Needham Research Institute (£12,900 in two grants); Great Britain China Educational Trust (£3,500).

Applications

Apply in writing to the correspondent.

Sources of information

Accounts; annual report; Charity Commission record.

SITA Cornwall Trust Ltd

 Natural environment and community

Cornwall

£736,000 (2016/17)

CC number: 1127288

Trustees: George Hocking; Richard Thomas; Lee Rouse; Paul Brinsley; Betty Hale; Philip Rudin; David Attwell; Anthony Earl.

Correspondent: Wendy Reading, Fund Manager, Spring Cottage, 3 Holmbush Hill, Kelly Bray, Cornwall PL17 8EP (tel: 01579 346816; email: wendyreading@btconnect.com)

 www.sitacornwalltrust.co.uk

SITA Cornwall Trust Ltd is a registered charity that is funded by the Landfill Communities Fund through the company SITA UK. It awards grants to a wide range of facilities that directly benefit communities throughout the county of Cornwall.

To qualify for a grant, your location must fall within a ten-mile radius of one of the 22 landfill sites spread across Cornwall. There is a postcode checker on the website. Projects must meet one of the following objectives:

- Bringing land back into use
- Reducing or preventing pollution
- Public parks and amenities
- Buildings and structures
- Promoting biodiversity

Criteria

The website states that the following have been adopted as the funding criteria for the trust:

- The Trust will normally only consider community project applications up to a maximum grant value of £35,000. Larger projects may be considered by the Trust, but applicants will need to make a very strong case for support
- Projects should be community driven and demonstrate significant fundraising efforts by the community
- Applicants will need to demonstrate that there is a demand for the facility that would result from the project being supported by SCT
- Applicants should be able to demonstrate that the project is financially sustainable and should have

a minimum of ten-year ownership or effective control of the facility

- Projects must be in Cornwall
- A project should be able to demonstrate that it has support of the parish/town council where appropriate
- Works to churches should be fabric related and heating projects will only be considered if they include a sustainable energy element
- SCT support of a project should, where appropriate, increase the potential number of beneficiaries able to use the facility
- The severity of any demonstrated landfill disturbance to a project site will be taken into consideration
- No project or project site can make an application within three years of the date the funding agreement was signed for a previously successful application
- Projects will be expected to start within 3 months of an offer being made and complete within a 12 month period

Financial information

In 2016/17 the trust had assets of £1 million and an income of £553,000. During the year, the trust gave £736,000 in grants to 27 projects.

Beneficiaries included: Flushing Play (£62,500); St Pinnock Band (£47,500); Camborne Community Centre (£35,000); Duloe Skate Park (£25,000); St Gluvias Church (£13,600); Quethiock Church (£10,000); Redruth Tennis Club (£4,000).

Applications

Application forms and guidelines are available to download from the trust's website.

Sources of information

Accounts; annual report; Charity Commission record; funder's website.

The Charles Skey Charitable Trust

 General charitable purposes

UK

£409,000 (2016/17)

CC number: 277697

Trustees: Christopher Berkeley; John Leggett; Revd James Leggett; David Berkeley; Edward Berkeley.

Correspondent: John Leggett, Trustee, Flint House, Park Homer Road, Colehill, Wimborne, Dorset BH21 2SP (tel: 01202 882180)

The trust was registered with the Charity Commission in 1979 and aims to support general charitable purposes. Grants are made on a one-off basis as well as some charities being supported annually or periodically.

Financial information

In 2016/17 the trust had assets of £14 million and had an income of £420,000. During the year, the charity awarded £409,000 in grants to organisations.

Beneficiaries included: Greenwich Foundation for the Old Royal Naval College (£45,500); On Course Foundation (£21,500); Sherborne Girls Foundation (£15,000); Combat Stress Evangelical Movement of Wales, Marine Society and Sea Scouts (£10,000), Food for the Hungry (£5,000) WaterAid (£2,500).

Applications

Apply in writing to the correspondent. The trustees meet several times a year to review grants.

Sources of information

Accounts; annual report; Charity Commission record.

The Slaughter and May Charitable Trust

 Legal advice, education and training, health, social welfare, children and young people and older people

Mainly local to the Slaughter and May offices in Islington and close to Tower Hamlets and Hackney

£385,500 (2016/17)

CC number: 1082765

Trustee: Slaughter and May Trust Ltd.

Correspondent: Kate Hursthouse, Corporate Responsibility Manager, Slaughter and May, 1 Bunhill Row, London EC1Y 8YY (tel: 020 7090 3433; email: corporateresponsibility@slaughterandmay.com)

 www.slaughterandmay.com

Established in 1991 and registered with the Charity Commission in 2000, this trust is the corporate charity of the legal firm Slaughter and May. The trust's annual report for 2016/17 states that it is 'reliant on its key donors, the partners of Slaughter and May with all administrative and other office support being provided by the firm'.

The trust supports a range of legal, educational, health and community projects, with a particular interest in children and young people and older people.

Financial information

In 2016/17 the trust held negative assets of £45,000 and had an income of £405,500. Grants totalled £385,500.

Beneficiaries included: Islington Law Centre (£56,000); National Literacy Trust (£53,500); The Access Project

(£40,000); Action for Kids (£30,500); Moreland Primary School (£17,500); Teach First (£11,300); SBA The Solicitors' Charity (£10,000); Bloodwise (£7,000); Shelter (£5,500); The Costa Foundation (£5,000).

Grants for less than £5,000 totalled £38,000.

Applications

The trust's 2016/17 annual report states that it 'makes annual grants at its discretion to a small number of specific charitable causes and does not generally accept unsolicited funding applications'.

Sources of information

Accounts; annual report; Charity Commission record; funder's website.

Sloane Robinson Foundation

Education and training, higher education students

England and Wales

£317,000 to organisations (2016/17)

CC number: 1068286

Trustees: Hugh Sloane; George Robinson; Deborah Fisher.

Correspondent: Deborah Fisher, Trustee, The Old Coach House, Sunnyside, Bergh Apton, Norwich NR15 1DD (tel: 01508 480100; email: info@fisherlegal.co.uk)

The principal objective of the foundation is the advancement of the education of the public. The foundation maintains long-term relationships with the academic establishments in order to establish scholarships and bursary schemes for overseas students to study in the UK, for British students to study abroad, and generally to provide opportunities for education which would not otherwise be possible.

Financial information

In 2016/17 the foundation had assets of £18.1 million and an income of £86,500. During the year, grants totalling £437,500 were awarded, of which £317,000 was given to organisations and £124,000 to individuals.

Beneficiaries included: Rugby School (£183,500); Keble College, Oxford (£64,500); Lincoln College, Oxford (£59,000); St Laurence PCC (£10,400).

Exclusions

The foundation has previously stated that grants are not awarded for:

- Undergraduate level study
- Funding fellowships and professorships at universities and places of higher education for both teaching and research

- Religion, social sciences and languages

Funding of overseas programmes should be focused on the studies in which the country concerned offers better courses (e.g. Chinese history in China).

Only in exceptional circumstances funding will be provided for the provision of sporting facilities.

Applications

Apply in writing to the correspondent. The foundation is very selective in its grant-making process; therefore, to avoid increased administrative costs, only successful candidates will be notified of the outcome of their application.

Sources of information

Accounts; annual report; Charity Commission record.

The SMB Trust

Religion, social and medical welfare, education and research, famine relief and emergency aid, protection of environment and wildlife

UK and overseas

£279,000 (2016/17)

CC number: 263814

Trustees: Jeremy Anstead; Barbara O'Driscoll; Ian Wilson.

Correspondent: Barbara O'Driscoll, Trustee, 15 Wilman Road, Tunbridge Wells TN4 9AJ (tel: 01892 537301; email: smbcharitabletrust@googlemail.com)

The trust supports charities which meet one of the following criteria:

- Support of the Christian faith
- Provision of social care in the UK and abroad
- Provision of famine or emergency aid
- Protection of the environment and wildlife
- Support of education or medical research

Grants are generally around £1,200, although this does vary. The trustees make regular grants to a large number of 'core' charities, so while new applications are considered, only a small minority is likely to be successful. The founder's preferences are taken into account when deciding which of the applicants will be supported.

Financial information

In 2016/17 the trust held assets of £11.6 million and had an income of £472,000. Grants were made totalling £279,000.

Previous beneficiaries have included: DEC/Concern (£6,000); Pilgrim Friends Society (£4,000); Oasis UK (£2,500); Zimbabwe Educational Trust (£1,200); Designability, Toxteth Women's Centre and Woodland Christian Trust (£1,000

each); Rye Street Pastors (£500); Freedom from Torture (£50).

Exclusions

Individuals.

Applications

Apply in writing to the correspondent, including the aims and principal activities of the applicant, the current financial position and details of any special projects for which funding is sought. There is no application form. Trustees normally meet four times a year to consider applications. Because of the volume of appeals received, unsuccessful applicants will only receive a reply if they enclose an sae. Unsuccessful applicants are welcome to re-apply.

Sources of information

Accounts; annual report; Charity Commission record.

The Mrs Smith and Mount Trust

Mental health, people with disabilities, homeless people, community and economic development

Norfolk, Suffolk, Cambridgeshire, Hertfordshire, Essex, Kent, Surrey and London

£457,500 (2016/17)

CC number: 1009718

Trustees: Richard Fowler; Timothy Warren; Gillian Barnes; Lisa Weaks; Sean Shepley.

Correspondent: Trust Administrator, 6 Trull Farm Buildings, Tetbury, Gloucestershire GL8 8SQ (tel: 020 3325 2590; email: admin@ mrssmithandmounttrust.org)

 mrssmithandmounttrust.org

The Mrs Smith and Mount Trust aims to assist disadvantaged people towards greater independence or a better quality of life.

The trust was originally founded by a wealthy American who chose to make her home in Britain. She stated, and her subsequent actions made clear, that she wished to remain as an anonymous philanthropist even after her death. The original amount donated was increased by a large capital sum following the end of the Second World War, and the sale of works of art, ceramics and other items increased the trust's capital. As the founder grew older she showed that she wished to dispossess herself of all personal wealth and to have the money used for the benefit of those in poverty and need in England.

The Mount Fund

The Mount Fund has the following priority areas, details of which have been taken from the trust's website:

Mental Health – For registered charities with income of up to £1M and unrestricted free reserves of less than six months' annual expenditure. Smaller charities with income of up to £500,000, particularly those working in rural communities, could be considered for larger grants of up to £20,000 paid over 2 or more years under this category.

Homelessness - For registered charities with income of up to £1M and unrestricted free reserves of less than six months' annual expenditure.

Learning Disability – For registered charities with income of up to £1M and unrestricted free reserves of less than six months' annual expenditure.

Health in the Community – Charities working to improve health in the community. This could include groups working in areas such as young people leaving care, people recovering from domestic violence, food poverty, childhood obesity, specific health conditions and hospices. This category is for smaller registered charities (with income of less than £500,000) for services provided primarily to rural communities. Unrestricted free reserves must also be less than six months' annual expenditure. The trustees wish to provide fewer larger grants towards core funding under this category and are inviting applicants to provide details of what they most need funding for and, how this will ultimately benefit the health of people in their community. Grants will be up to £20,000 to be paid in two annual instalments of up to £10,000 each.

What type of grants do we give?
Grants are given for projects; general running costs/core funding; salaries; advice services; furnishings/equipment; organisational development.

The Trustees do not normally consider building costs, only refurbishment or alterations necessary to bring a building up to standards to meet legislative requirements

The Mrs Smith Fund

The Mrs Smith Fund provides block grants to charities that provide small grants to disadvantaged individuals such as:

◗ Young people leaving state care
◗ Those leaving community, residential or long-term hospital care
◗ Individuals who have lost their possessions through theft, fire, flood, vandalism, etc.
◗ Individuals who are being rehoused after living in a refuge and who cannot collect their belongings from previous accommodation
◗ Individuals in rehabilitation
◗ Those who have to be rehoused due to circumstances beyond their

control, e.g. harassment, disability, deterioration of property, etc.

Financial information

In 2016/17 the trust had assets of £8 million and an income of £286,000. The total amount awarded in grants was £457,500 to 63 organisations, categorised as follows:

The Spanoghe Grants Programme	7	£210,000
Mental health	13	£59,000
Learning disabilities	14	£55,500
Health in the community	12	£54,500
Homelessness	12	£53,000
The Mrs Smith Fund	5	£25,000

Beneficiaries included: New Horizon Youth Centre (£50,000); The Kidstime Foundation (£10,000); Assist Trust and Norfolk Carers Support (£5,000 each); Bag Books (£4,300); The Friends of Collett (£3,000); The Hand Partnership (£2,000).

Exclusions

Individuals; general counselling; charities with an income of over £1 million and/or free unrestricted reserves to the value of more than six months of the applicant organisation's annual expenditure.

Applications

All applications must be submitted using the online application form which can be downloaded from the website, where full guidelines and criteria are also available to view.

The trustees meet three times per year in March, July and November and application forms and supporting documentation must be submitted at least six weeks in advance of a meeting or by the date specified on the website. Unsuccessful applicants can re-apply after two years.

The trust's website notes that it 'will only consider appeals from national organisations at branch level where the branch is able to provide separate accounts and is responsible for its own finances'.

Sources of information

Accounts; annual report; Charity Commission record; funder's website.

The DS Smith Charitable Foundation

Education and training, environmental conservation

England and Wales

£310,500 (2016/17)

CC number: 1142817

Trustees: Anne Steele; Rachel Stevens; Emma Ciechan; Mark Reeve; Catriona O'Grady.

Correspondent: Rachel Stevens, Trustee, 7th Floor, 350 Euston Road, London NW1 3AX (tel: 020 7756 1823; email: charitablefoundation@dssmith.com)

 www.dssmith.com/company/ sustainability/our-people/ community-involvement/ charitable-foundation

DS Smith was started by the Smith brothers in 1940. The company provides corrugated packaging in Europe and plastic packaging worldwide. It operates across 25 countries and employs around 21,500 people. Registered in 2011, the foundation supports charities engaged in conservation of the environment and providing training or educational opportunities.

The following information was taken from the foundation's website:

Please note that only charities in the fields of environmental improvement and of education and training, will be considered, so please ensure that any application fulfils this criteria. The charity aims to make a combination of small donations (£1,000 or less) and larger donations each year. We particularly welcome opportunities to develop multi-year partnerships with key selected charities.

Financial information

In 2016/17 the foundation held assets of £2.2 million and had an income of £48,000. Grants totalling £310,500 were made to 41 organisations. Grants were distributed as follows:

Education	24	£161,500
Environment	11	£158,500
Other	6	£12,000

Beneficiaries included: Keep Britain Tidy (£100,000); Unicef (£44,000); Museum of Brands (£40,000); AT Bristol and In Kind Direct (£30,000 each); Arkwright Scholarship Trust (£20,000); Durham University and Edinburgh Science Festival (£5,000 each); Contains Art CIC (£2,500); Action for Kids (£2,000).

Applications

Application forms are available from the foundation's website.

Sources of information

Accounts; annual report; Charity Commission record; funder's website.

The Henry Smith Charity

Social welfare, ethnic groups, carers, community causes, domestic and sexual violence, substance misuse, ex-service people, older people, disability, healthcare, homelessness, LGBT community, mental health, people who have offended, prostitution and trafficking, refugees and asylum seekers, young people

UK. Specific local programmes in the North East and the counties of: East Sussex, West Sussex, Hampshire, Kent, Gloucestershire, Leicestershire, Suffolk, and Surrey

£27.1 million to organisations (2016)

CC number: 230102

Trustees: Anna Scott; Noel Manns; Diana Barran; Mark Newton; Patrick Maxwell; Bridget Biddell; David Allam; Vivian Hunt; James Hordern; Vivienne Hunt; Piers Feilden; Emir Feisal; Revd Canon Paul Hackwood; Lady Bella Colgrain.

Correspondent: The Grants Team, The Henry Smith Charity – Applications, 6th Floor, 65 Leadenhall Street, London EC3A 2AD (tel: 020 7264 4970)

 www.henrysmithcharity.org.uk

The charity was founded in 1628 by Henry Smith, a businessman in the City of London, with the objects of relieving and where possible releasing people from need and suffering. These objects continue in the grant-making policy today, albeit encompassing a broad range of social welfare causes. The Henry Smith Charity is one of the largest independent grant-making charities in the UK, distributing over £30 million each year. The charity is happy to fund revenue funding, such as projects or running costs. The charity's 2017 annual report states that as part of a review, the charity made the difficult decision to stop funding capital, healthcare and

grants to charities helping ex-service people.

Priority is given to work with groups experiencing social and/or economic disadvantage and to work that tackles problems in areas of high deprivation. You do not have to be a registered charity but the organisation must be not-for-profit.

Grant programmes

The charity's 2017 annual accounts state that:

> In November 2015 we commenced a grant-making strategy review. This will be continued through 2016, with the aim of issuing new grant-making guidelines in 2017. The aim of this review is to focus our grant-making more clearly onto those areas where we can make the most difference through the grants we award; as our review develops, the implications for the Charity's development will be worked through by Trustees and staff.

The charity provides a number of grant programmes, each with its own guidelines. Full details of each grant programme can be found on the charity's website, which is where the following summarised information is taken from.

Improving Lives

The Improving Lives grant programme provides grants to charitable organisations that help people when other sources of support have failed, are inappropriate, or are simply not available. We support established organisations delivering services directly to beneficiaries. This grant programme supports organisations which are working to meet at least one of the following priority areas: help at a critical moment; positive choices; accommodation/housing support; employment and training; financial inclusion, rights and entitlements; support networks and family.

Strengthening Communities

The Strengthening Communities grant programme aims to support and strengthen the most disadvantaged and deprived communities across the UK and is only open to organisations with an annual income of between £20k- £500k that are working in areas within the

bottom 10% most deprived areas for England and Scotland, and within the 15% most deprived areas for Northern Ireland and Wales, on the government Indices of Multiple Deprivation.

County Grants Programme

The programme supports the work of small organisations and charities in eight counties with which the Henry Smith Charity has a historical connection. These are: Gloucestershire; Hampshire; Kent; Leicestershire; Suffolk; Surrey; East Sussex; and West Sussex. To be eligible the organisation's annual income must be below £250,000 (unless it is working county-wide in which case the income must be below £1 million). For one year grants applicants can request between £500 and £10,000; for multi-year grants the maximum amount that can be requested is £20,000 spread over two or three years.

Holiday Grants for Children

One-off grants of between £500 and £2,500 are given to organisations, schools, youth groups and so on specifically for holidays or outings for children under the age of 13 who have disabilities or live in areas of high deprivation.

Christian Projects

The Will of Henry Smith included a requirement to fund work which explicitly promotes the Christian faith. We generally support projects that come from a Church of England context and closely fit our four priority areas for the Christian Projects Grants Programme. Please note we are only able to fund work which promotes faith under the Christian Projects Grants Programme. All our other programmes will not fund any work which includes the promotion of religion.

The table below displays some examples of the type of work the trustees prioritise for support through grants, within the programme area classifications.

Financial information

In 2016 the charity held assets of £952.8 million and had an income of £12.8 million. During the year, the charity gave around £28.1 million in grants. Of this amount, £27.1 was given to organisations and £1.4 million to

---

THE HENRY SMITH CHARITY

Category	Example of projects supported
Black, Asian and minority ethnic (BAME)	Projects providing culturally appropriate services to black, Asian and minority ethnic communities, including those that promote integration and access to mainstream services.
Carers	Projects providing advice and support, including respite services for carers and those cared for. Work can include educational opportunities for young carers.
Community service	Projects providing support for communities in areas of high deprivation, including projects providing furniture recycling services, debt advice and community centres.
Disability	Projects providing rehabilitation, training or advocacy support to people with disabilities; this includes learning as well as physical disabilities.
Domestic and sexual violence	Projects providing advice, support and secure housing for families affected by domestic violence or sexual violence. Perpetrator programmes can be considered where organisations have secured, or are working towards, Respect accreditation. The charity is particularly interested in services which can demonstrate their outcomes measurement such as data collected through the CAADA Insights programme.

individuals. Grants were distributed as follows:

Main grants	£24.7 million
County grants	£1.2 million
Clergy	£905,000
Kindred of Henry Smith	£776,000
Parishes	£599,000
Holiday grants	£200,000
Small grants	£150,000

Beneficiaries included: Anah Project (£152,500); Soundabout (£97,000); Age UK Sunderland (£95,000); Albert Kennedy Trust (£75,000); Spark Inside (£30,000); Porch Project (£10,000); Aberdeen Cyrenians (£5,000); 17th Gloucester Girlguiding (£2,500); 186th Sheffield Guides (£900 and £760).

Exclusions

See the charity's website for each grant programme's list of exclusions.

Applications

The application and assessment procedures for each of the grant programmes vary slightly. Candidates are strongly advised to read the full guidelines for the type of grant they seek before making an application. Application forms for all programmes can be downloaded from the charity's website and must be sent by post.

Sources of information

Accounts; annual report; Charity Commission record; funder's website.

The Martin Smith Foundation

General charitable purposes, in particular: education, performing arts, the environment, heritage and culture, science, sport, religious activities, the prevention and relief of poverty

UK

£414,000 (2016)

CC number: 1150753

Trustees: Lady Smith; Sir Martin Smith; Jeremy Smith; Katherine Wake; Elizabeth Buchanan; Bartholomew Peerless.

Correspondent: The Trustees, 5 Park Town, Oxford OX2 6SN (tel: 01865 554554)

The foundation was registered in 2013 and seeks to provide funding for charities and organisations for general charitable purposes, but with a particular interest in the arts and performing arts; education and training; the sciences; environmental sustainability, culture and heritage; sport; religious activities; and the prevention and relief of poverty.

Financial information

In 2016 the foundation held assets of £2.4 million and had an income of

£33,500. Grants awarded to organisations totalled £414,000.

Beneficiaries included: The Smith Family Educational Foundation (£252,500); University of Oxford (£55,000); St Edmund Hall (£10,000); National Orchestra for All (£6,000); The Prince's Countryside Fund (£4,500); The Wigmore Hall Trust (£2,200); MS Society (£2,000).

Applications

Apply in writing to the correspondent.

Sources of information

Accounts; annual report; Charity Commission record.

The Sobell Foundation

Jewish charities, medical care and treatment, disability, care and support for children and older people, homelessness

Unrestricted, in practice England and Wales, Israel and the Commonwealth of Independent States (CIS)

£5.9 million (2016/17)

CC number: 274369

Trustees: Susan Lacroix; Roger Lewis; Andrea Scouller.

Correspondent: Penny Newton, Administrator, PO Box 2137, Shepton Mallet, Somerset BA4 6YA (tel: 01749 813135; email: enquiries@ sobellfoundation.org.uk)

 www.sobellfoundation.org.uk

The Sobell Foundation was established by the late Sir Michael Sobell in 1977 for general charitable purposes and is a grant-making charity with which he was actively involved until shortly before his death in 1993. Grants tend to be made in line with the founder's interests which are principally causes benefitting children, people who are sick, older individuals, those in need and people with disabilities. The foundation's website states: 'The trustees aim to achieve a reasonable spread between Jewish charities (operating principally in the UK and Israel) and non-Jewish charities operating in the UK.' Grants are made towards projects, items of equipment or general running costs.

The following information is taken from the foundation's website:

Guidelines

As a grant-making charity, we provide grants to fund projects and activities carried out by other charities. We receive many different applications for funding, from which our trustees make their funding decisions. For an application to be considered by the trustees, and for it to have the best chance of success,

applicants should note the following guidelines.

Who may apply?
We will only consider applications from charities registered with the Charity Commission, or charities that hold a Certificate of Exemption from the Inland Revenue. Overseas applicants must supply the details of a UK-registered charity through which grants can be channelled on their behalf. We concentrate our funding on small national or local charities; the trustees are unlikely to support large national charities which enjoy wide support. We do not accept applications from individuals.

Which countries do we support?
We restrict our funding on a geographical basis to the following countries: England, Wales, Israel, and Commonwealth of Independent States (CIS). We will only accept applications from charities based in these countries for projects and activities within these countries.

What type of work do we support?
We restrict our funding to charities working in the following areas:

- medical care and treatment, including respite care and hospices
- care for physically and mentally disabled adults and children
- education and training for adults and children with physical and learning disabilities
- care and support of the elderly
- care and support for children
- homelessness
- immigrant absorption (Israel only)
- co-existence projects (Israel only)
- higher education (Israel only)

Financial information

In 2016/17 the foundation held assets of £72.4 million and had an income of £1.9 million. During the year, the foundation awarded 525 grants totalling over £5.9 million. Grants were distributed as follows:

United Kingdom

Medical (care/treatment)	£2.1 million
Hardship alleviation	£677,500
Community	£528,500
Education	£349,000
Medical research	£107,500
Cultural and environmental	£90,000

United Kingdom – Jewish organisations

Education	£434,000
Medical (care/treatment)	£228,000
Community	£100,00
Cultural and environmental	-
Hardship alleviation	£13,000

Israel

Medical (care/treatment)	£768,000
Education	£434,000
Hardship alleviation	£370,000
Community	£310,000
Cultural and environmental	£15,000

Other overseas

Hardship alleviation	£65,000
Medical (care/treatment)	-
Community	£6,400

Approximately one third of grants paid were made to Jewish charities, and two thirds to UK non-Jewish charities. This allocation is within the ranges set by the trustees for grant allocation. Of the grants paid in the year, 76 were of amounts ranging from £20,000 to £50,000 and three grants in excess of £50,000 were paid in the year. A list of beneficiaries was not available.

Exclusions

No grants to individuals will be considered. Only registered charities or organisations registered with the Inland Revenue should apply.

Applications

Application forms are available to download from the website and should be completed and returned to the foundation by post. The foundation notes that it will write with the result of your application as soon as possible, although this may take several months. Applicants, successful or otherwise, may only re-apply to the foundation after 12 months.

Sources of information

Accounts; annual report; Charity Commission record; funder's website.

Social Business Trust

 General charitable purposes

UK

£995,000 (2016/17)

CC number: 1136151

Trustees: Paul Armstrong; Simon Milton; Tim Curry; Guy Davies; Larissa Joy; Michael Crossan.

Correspondent: Adele Blakebrough, Chief Executive, First Floor, 13 St Swithin's Lane, London EC4N 8AL (tel: 020 3011 0770; email: info@ socialbusinesstrust.org)

 www.socialbusinesstrust.org

Previously known as Scale-Up, the trust was registered with the Charity Commission in 2010 and is a partnership of businesses working together to support growing social enterprises with a clear social mission. In this way, it aims to improve the lives of disadvantaged people across the UK.

The trust supports social enterprises with high potential for growth to 'scale-up their impact'. The website states the following information about the trust's approach:

> SBT's mission is to support high growth potential social enterprises to scale-up their impact. We do that by investing cash grants and professional support from our world-class corporate partners in a

carefully selected portfolio of social enterprises.

> We work with established social businesses with revenues of c.£1 million or more that have strong growth potential. Our aim is to help develop a number of social enterprises to national scale or significance.

Eligibility

The trust's website provides the following information:

> The social enterprises we support are special. They have a strong social mission, a proven track record and a robust business model. They are ambitious to grow and extend their social impact. And they have the capacity and willingness to work with volunteers and secondees from our business partners and be open to change. They also need to be:
>
> ▪ Registered as a charity or demonstrate a clear charitable purpose, e.g. as a community interest company (CIC) and/or where there is a clear asset lock in place
> ▪ Making annual revenues greater than £1 million (or be on track to achieve that in 18 months), including a significant proportion of earned income (i.e. not from donations or grants)
> ▪ Based mainly in the UK
>
> We do not make loans or standalone grants but provide organisations with a package of professional business support and targeted grant funding designed to strengthen their capacity to grow.

The trust currently works with 13 social enterprises, covering a wide range of issues such as educational disadvantage, unemployment and care for older people.

Financial information

In the year 2016/17 the trust held assets of £984,000 and had an income of £3.6 million. Cash grants totalled £995,000 with a further £2.6 million given in in-kind services by business partners.

Beneficiaries (of cash and/or in-kind support) included: London Early Years Foundation (£1.14 million); Challenge Partners (£489,500); The Reader Organisation (£233,500); Brightside (£139,000); Twining Enterprise (£69,500); Moneyline (£42,500); Brighter Futures Workshop (£15,600).

Applications

Social enterprises which meet the trust's criteria should contact the trust's staff to discuss working together.

Sources of information

Accounts; annual report; Charity Commission record; funder's website.

Social Investment Business Foundation

 General charitable purposes, community development

UK

£304,000 (2016/17)

CC number: 1117185

Trustees: Hugh Rolo; James Rice; Anand Shukla; Jeremy Newman; Richard Pelly; Rt Hon. Hazel Blears; Jenny North.

Correspondent: Caroline Forster, Interim Chief Executive, 2nd Floor, Can Mezzanine, 7–14 Great Dover Street, London SE1 4YR (tel: 020 3096 7903; email: enquiries@sibgroup.org.uk)

 www.sibgroup.org.uk

The foundation was registered with the Charity Commission in December 2006. It provides loans, grants and strategic support to charities and social enterprises to help them improve people's lives.

The foundation has a number of funds that provide 'investment readiness' grants and social investment for organisations looking to grow their services. Organisations with loans from the foundation can also access legal services and consultancy services.

Financial information

In 2016/17 the foundation had assets of £34.7 million and an income of £4.6 million. Grants paid during the year totalled £304,000. Loans and guarantees of £831,000 were disbursed to beneficiaries during the year.

Previous beneficiaries have included: Beyond Autism (£2 million loan); Hastings Pier Charity (£150,000 loan and £100,000 grant); Bootstrap Company (£198,500 loan and £132,500 grant); The Rare Trust (£168,500 loan); Ashley Community Housing (£75,000); Ecological Land Co-operative (£49,000); Moving on Durham (£23,500); North East Dance (£15,000); The Fox and Hounds Community Co-operative (£8,500).

Applications

Applications can be made via the foundation's website.

Sources of information

Accounts; annual report; Charity Commission record; funder's website.

Social Tech Trust

 Technology projects that transform lives

 UK and overseas

£ £3 million (2016/17)

CC number: 1125735

Trustees: Bill Liao; Sebastien Lahtinen; Elizabeth Murray; Hannah Keartland; Nicolas Temple.

Correspondent: Vicki Hearn, Director, Nominet, Minerva House, Edmund Halley Road, Oxford OX4 4DQ (tel: 01865 334000; email: enquiries@ nominettrust.org.uk)

www.nominettrust.org.uk

@SocialTechTrust

Established in 2008, this is the charitable foundation of Nominet, the company which runs the registry for all.uk domain names.

Innovate Social Tech

Innovate Social Tech is the trust's new grant programme that supports innovative ventures to transform lives with technology. The fund's initial theme will be Tech to Unite Us:

Tech to Unite Us

Grants of up to £45,000 and technical assistance is available to early stage ventures that use technology to unite people in inspirational and informative ways.

The following criteria have been taken from the trust's website:

We'll consider your application if your venture has:

- A social mission embedded in your governance
- Potential to deliver transformative social impact at scale through a deep understanding of the critical social challenge that drives your innovation and an ambition to make a difference through growth
- An innovative approach to tackling a social challenge; this could be through a creative business model, by harnessing emerging tech, or using existing tech in a new and transformative way
- A working product or service that you will continue to test and iterate; you are at the demonstration stage of your venture's evolution
- Evidence of your potential to create user, social and financial value; for example, a theory of change, user co-design and testing, identified social KPIs, or prospective partnerships or routes to market
- The right team with the critical experience and expertise for success – in-house tech capabilities being an essential

- Registration as a UK-based organisation and the potential for social impact in the UK

Financial information

In 2016/17 the trust held assets of £7.8 million and had an income of £5.7 million. Grants were awarded totalling £3 million.

Beneficiaries of grants over £50,000 included: Creative England (£250,000); Inspiring Digital Enterprise (£200,000); My Time to Care (£100,000); Run A Club (£81,500); Wavemaker – Stoke (£85,000); Bounce Works (£50,000).

Grants of less than £50,000 totalled £1.45 million.

Applications

Applications can be made through the trust's website. Refer to the website for application deadlines.

Sources of information

Accounts; annual report; Charity Commission record; funder's website.

Sodexo Stop Hunger Foundation

 Hunger and malnutrition, education, health and well-being

UK and Ireland

£ £388,000 (2016/17)

CC number: 1110266

Trustees: David Mulchay; Gareth John; Patrick Forbes; Niamh Cray; Hayley Michael; Anita Wilson; Gregory Jennings; Samanthan Scott.

Correspondent: Edwina Hughes, Corporate Responsibility Manager, 1 Southampton Row, London WC1B 5HA (email: stophunger@sodexo. com)

 uk.stop-hunger.org/home.html

Registered with the Charity Commission in June 2005, the Sodexo Foundation is the corporate charity of the food services and facilities management company, Sodexo Ltd.

According to its website, the foundation is 'a grant giving organisation that aims to support charities that tackle hunger and malnutrition, provide education and promote health and wellbeing'.

Financial information

In 2016/17 the foundation had assets of £292,000 and an income of £553,000. It made 18 grants totalling £388,000.

Beneficiaries included: FareShare and Trussell Trust (£120,000 each); Outward Bound Trust (£33,500); Coram Life (£18,700); The Prince's Trust (£6,000); Farm Drop, Food Cloud and Future Farm Lab (£2,500 each).

Applications

For further information on the support available, complete the contact form on the foundation's website.

Sources of information

Accounts; annual report; Charity Commission record; funder's website.

Sofronie Foundation

 Education and training for disadvantaged young people

UK, France and the Netherlands

£ £449,500 (2016)

CC number: 1118621

Trustees: Nicholas Kaufmann; Harold Goddijn; Corinne Goddijn-Vigreux; Robert Wilne; Ajay Soni; Boris Walbaum.

Correspondent: Jacqueline Higgin, 16 Great Queen Street, London WC2B 5DH (tel: 020 7421 3330; email: enquiries@sofronie.org)

 www.sofronie.org

The Sofronie Foundation was established in 2008 and aims to help young people by offering them the opportunities with which they can improve their employment chances.

The foundation's website states:

Sofronie is dedicated to supporting projects that provide young people with skills for jobs and programmes that increase access to higher education

The Foundation works with charities and not for profit organisations that focus on improving the lives of disadvantaged young people through educational or vocational programmes.

We particularly encourage a close working relationship with smaller programmes that have the potential to scale up and become more established.

Evaluation processes are important to gauge and review the success of programmes and are an essential component of our grant making terms.

Supporting the STEM specialists of the future

Our focus for the immediate future is improving academic performances with an emphasis on STEM (Science, Technology, Engineering and Mathematics) skills and vocational programmes.

STEM skills are expected to provide many opportunities in the future, and building competencies and awareness around this sector will ensure our young people are better prepared for future employment.

We are currently focusing our work in the UK, France and the Netherlands.

Financial information

In 2016 the foundation had assets of £3.4 million and a total income of

£2.1 million. Grants awarded to organisations totalled £449,500.

Beneficiaries included: Stichting Leerkracht (£89,000); Apps for Good (£50,000); Young Enterprise (£44,000); The Sutton Trust (£30,000); The Smallpiece Trust (£23,000); Impulsion (£17,500).

Exclusions
Individuals are not supported. Only charities or not-for-profit organisations can receive assistance.

Applications
Apply via the foundation's website. Applications can be made at any time but it may take up to three months to receive a decision from the trustees.

Sources of information
Accounts; annual report; Charity Commission record; funder's website.

The Sola Trust

 Advancement of the Christian faith

Worldwide

£ £194,500 to organisations (2016/17)

CC number: 1062739

Trustees: Justin Mote; Simon Pilcher; Rachel Pilcher.

Correspondent: Simon Pilcher, Trustee, Greenend Barn, Wood End Green, Henham, Bishop's Stortford CM22 6AY (tel: 01279 850819; email: admin@ solatrust.org.uk)

 www.solatrust.org.uk

The Sola trust was established in 1997 to support the advancement of the Christian faith and for the relief of poverty.

According to its 2016/17 accounts, the trust seeks to achieve its objectives by:

Making grants available to individuals training for full-time Christian work (especially while at theological college), as well as to those undertaking training within a church (or equivalent) context. Where appropriate these grants may be routed through a church or equivalent body that is providing training to individuals. The charity also seeks to facilitate the strategic placement of trained gospel workers working in new geographical areas (areas of the country where there is little or no biblical ministry at present) and in new types of ministry (for example youth or women's ministry). We are keen to enable ministry among those who can't afford to pay for it (for example among people groups with low or no incomes), and in pioneer situations where there is no established congregation to pay for the ministry. We aim to pump-prime church plants, contributing towards the capital costs associated with setting up a new venture

and to help underwrite the initial years' income requirements.

Grant-making policy
In their 2016/17 annual report, the trustees describe the trust's grant-making policy as follows:

The Trust aims to make grants to supplement other sources of funding for claimants. It is particularly keen to see support (including, but not limited to, financial support) from beneficiaries' 'sending' churches. Trustees require sight of a budget from recipients (detailing anticipated income and expenditure) and also take up references, typically from the 'sending' church and also from the theological college or church offering the training course concerned (or the equivalent relevant organisation). The Trust aims to avoid being the sole source of funding for any applicant and will generally not extend promises of financing beyond one year.

Financial information
In 2016/17 the trust has assets of £389,000 and an income of £917,500. During the year, the trust awarded grants worth a total of £658,500. This total included £464,000 in 136 grants to individuals and £194,500 in 40 grants to organisations. Grants to organisations were distributed as follows:

Other church ministry grants	10	£83,500
Church plants grants	10	£58,000
Theological and ministry training grants	10	£53,000

Beneficiaries included: Friends of JBC (£10,000); Alliance for Transatlantic Theology (£8,000); Brixton Local Church (£7,000); Michael Ots Evangelism Trust and Emmanuel Church (£3,000 each); Dundee Church Plant (£2,000).

Applications
Churches wishing to apply for funding should submit applications in writing, including the following information:

- The rationale for the project
- Information about the key individuals involved
- How the work will develop and at what stage (if any) it is expected to become self-financing
- Budgets for the next three years (where possible)
- Information about any money raised so far
- A copy of the latest church accounts

The trustees also request that applicants arrange for references to be sent direct to the trust. Information for referees is provided on the trust's website. The trustees meet several times a year and accept applications at any time.

Sources of information
Accounts; annual report; Charity Commission record; funder's website.

The Souter Charitable Trust

 Projects engaged in the relief of human suffering in the UK and overseas – particularly, but not exclusively, those promoting spiritual welfare

UK, but with a preference for Scotland, overseas

£ £7.7 million (2016/17)

OSCR number: SC029998

Trustees: Brian Souter; Betty Souter; Ann Allen.

Correspondent: Dion Judd, Administrator, PO Box 7412, Perth PH1 5YX (tel: 01738 450408; email: enquiries@soutercharitabletrust.org.uk)

www.soutercharitabletrust.org.uk

This trust is funded by donations from Scottish businessman Brian Souter, one of the founders of the Stagecoach transport company. The trust supports projects that aid the relief of human suffering in the UK and overseas. The trust's founders, Brian Souter and his wife, Betty, are both committed Christians and are particularly interested in projects that also promote spiritual welfare.

Guidelines
The following guidelines were taken from the trust's website:

The Souter Charitable Trust supports projects engaged in the relief of human suffering in all its aspects in the UK and overseas – especially, but not exclusively, those with a Christian emphasis and ethos.

Grants are restricted to UK-registered charities only. Current legislation does not permit the trustees to give direct grants to overseas organisations as they are unable to carry out the due diligence required of them.

Small grants may be awarded for gap year/short-term projects which extend to at least one calendar year.

All projects for capital building and renovation works are specifically excluded from funding.

The personal health and educational needs of individuals are not normally funded.

Financial information
In 2016/17 the trust had assets of £27 million and an income of £8.2 million. Grants awarded to organisations totalled £7.7 million.

Beneficiaries included: Tearfund (£500,000); The Message Trust (£458,500); Hope for Justice (£263,500); Christians Against Poverty (£250,000); Strathclyde House Trust (£180,000); Lighthouse Group (£125,000); Oasis

Charitable Trust (£100,000); Venture Trust (£80,000); Scripture Union Scotland (£50,000); Preshal Trust (£25,000); Prison Fellowship (£18,000); Urban Saints (£15,000).

Exclusions

The personal health and educational needs of individuals are not normally funded.

Applications

No application forms are required. To make an application, apply in writing to the correspondent via post or email at application@soutercharitabletrust.org.uk. The trust's website states:

> Please keep application brief, 2 sides of A4 is sufficient. The trustees are looking for a brief outline of the project aims and what the funding is required for. A budget maybe included and a copy of your latest audited accounts would be appreciated if available.
>
> Re-application for a grant is permitted, but only after once calendar year has elapsed.
>
> The trustees generally meet once a month and all applications, whether successful or not, are acknowledged in due course.

Sources of information

Accounts; annual report; OSCR record; funder's website.

The W F Southall Trust

 Work of the Society of Friends, peace-making and conflict resolution, alcohol, drug abuse and penal affairs, environmental action, homelessness, community action, overseas development

 UK and overseas

£ £253,000 (2016/17)

CC number: 218371

Trustees: Annette Wallis; Donald Southall; Joanna Engelkamp; Mark Holtom; Claire Greaves; Richard Maw; Hannah Engelkamp; Andrew Southall; Philip Coventry.

Correspondent: The Trustees, School House, Mytholm Bank, Hebden Bridge HX7 6DL (tel: 0300 111 1937; email: Contact form on website)

 wfsouthalltrust.org.uk

The trust was established in 1937 by Wilfred Francis Southall, a pharmacist and manufacturing chemist from Birmingham who was also a Quaker. The trust distributes grants to charities registered in the UK working in one of the following fields:

▶ Supporting the work of the Society of Friends (Quakers)
▶ Peace and reconciliation

▶ Substance abuse, addiction and penal affairs
▶ Environmental action and sustainability
▶ Community action
▶ Overseas development

The trust's website states that:

> Although our approach to grant-making is flexible, generally speaking we favour the following when assessing applications within the six categories above:
>
> ▶ Innovation
> ▶ Imaginative grassroots initiatives
> ▶ Projects that encourage wider support of the categories listed above
> ▶ Projects where grants of between £1,000 and £3,000 will make a quantifiable difference
> ▶ Charities making good use of volunteers
> ▶ Charities that are engaged with their local community and have raised financial support from within it
> ▶ Charities with an annual turnover and assets of less than £5m
> ▶ Charities with a clear and considered reserves policy
> ▶ Charities demonstrating sound governance, leadership and management

Financial information

In 2016/17 the trust held assets of £11 million and had an income of £301,000. Grants were made to 86 organisations totalling £253,000 and were categorised as follows:

Overseas development	38	£81,500
Society of Friends	3	£72,000
Community action	14	£38,000
Peace and reconciliation	10	£23,000
Substance abuse and penal affairs	12	£22,000
Environmental action and sustainability	9	£16,000

Beneficiaries included: Woodbrooke Quaker Study Centre (£14,000); Oxfam (£7,000); Peace Museum and Quaker Congo Partnership (£5,000 each); Campaign Against Arms Trade, Peace Direct and Seeds for Change Network (£3,000 each).

Exclusions

According to its website, the trust will not support the following:

▶ Individuals, groups, families or organisations that are not registered with the Charity Commission of England & Wales (an exception is granted for Quaker Meeting Houses, so long as they hold charitable status.)
▶ Retrospective funding (i.e. funding for a project or work that has already taken place)
▶ Charities with a primary focus not fitting within one of our six categories
▶ Charities that are national household names
▶ Charities with a turnover and/or assets in excess of £5m
▶ Charities that have not complied with Charity Commission regulations (e.g. late annual returns)

▶ Charities with a high level of free reserves and/or no clear reserves policy
▶ Charities spending less than 80% of their annual expenditure on furthering their charitable objects
▶ Emergency appeals
▶ Medical charities
▶ Animal charities
▶ Private schools

Applications

Applicants should first complete the trust's online eligibility checker. Applicants that meet the criteria will then be provided with a link to the downloadable application form.

Sources of information

Accounts; annual report; Charity Commission record; funder's website.

R H Southern Trust

 Education and training, people with disabilities, social welfare, the environment

 England, Wales, Scotland, the Republic of Ireland, Australia, Belgium and India

£ £482,000 to organisations (2016/17)

CC number: 1077509

Trustees: James Bruges; Susan Tuckwell; Rachel Ayres; Rathbone Trust Company Ltd.

Correspondent: James Bruges, Trustee, 23 Sydenham Road, Cotham, Bristol BS6 5SJ (tel: 0117 942 5834; email: cjamesbruges@gmail.com)

 www.rhsoutherntrust.org.uk

The trust was registered with the Charity Commission in 1999. Grants tend to be made to a small number of organisations, mostly for long-term core funding and special projects. The trust's objects are:

▶ The advancement of education (including medical and scientific research)
▶ The relief of poverty
▶ Disability
▶ The preservation, conservation and protection of the environment (especially climate change)

The trust favours projects where the work is innovative, connected to other disciplines/bodies and has diverse application. The grant-making policy used by the trustees is set out in the 2016/17 annual report as follows:

> Grant Making Policy is carefully monitored by the Trustees with potential recipients being assessed against eleven criteria:
>
> 1 Research and development which promotes the Trust's aims and objectives
> 2 The work is innovative

3 Connected – to other disciplines or bodies or there is more than one interested party
4 A product has diverse application
5 An existing staff team which is working creatively together
6 Quality of the proposal – well written, specific, measurable, achievable, realistic in costing and timescale
7 Potential user involvement
8 Could attract matching funding or lever other sources of funding
9 No other source of funding
10 Urgent or limited timescale
11 The Trustees are tremendously enthusiastic

Financial information

In 2016/17 the trust had assets of almost £965,000 and an income of £393,000. During the year, 11 grants were made to organisations which totalled £482,000. A further six grants, totalling £44,000, were made to individuals and businesses, for a soil fertility project.

Beneficiaries included: James Gibb Stuart Trust (£120,000); New Economics Foundation (£40,000); Oxford Research Group and Salt of the Earth (£10,000 each); Global Justice Now (£5,000).

Applications

The trust is currently not accepting any applications for funding, as its funds are fully committed for the foreseeable future.

Sources of information

Accounts; annual report; Charity Commission record; funder's website.

Peter Sowerby Foundation

 Medical research and healthcare provision, education, community and the environment

 UK

£ £612,000 (2015/16)

CC number: 1151978

Trustees: David Aspinall; Dr Peter Sowerby; Dr David Lindsay Stables; Sara Poulios; Professor Longson; Aspinalls Fiduciary Ltd.

Correspondent: David Aspinall, Aspinalls, 10 Buckingham Street, London WC2N 6DF (tel: 020 3909 1600; email: sowerby.foundation@aspinallsgroup.com)

 www.petersowerbyfoundation.com

The foundation was established in 2011 with a large endowment from medical entrepreneur Peter Sowerby.

The foundation makes grants in three areas:

▶ Medical research and healthcare provision

▶ Education
▶ Community and the environment

Financial information

In 2015/16 the foundation had assets of £33.8 million and an income of £1 million. Grants awarded to organisations totalled £612,000.

Beneficiaries included: Multiple Sclerosis Society (£319,500); Target Ovarian Cancer (£50,000); The Economist Education Foundation (£40,500); Field in Trust (£20,000); The Crescent (£10,000).

Applications

Unsolicited applications are not accepted.

Sources of information

Accounts; annual report; Charity Commission record; funder's website.

Sparks Charity (Sport Aiding Medical Research For Kids)

 Medical research into conditions that affect children, babies and pregnant women

 UK

£ £1.2 million (2016/17)

CC number: 1003825

Trustees: Margaret Ewing; Mark Sartori; Prof. Stephen Holgate.

Correspondent: Elvira Morrison, 40 Bernard Street, London WC1N 1LE (tel: 020 7091 7750; email: info@sparks.org.uk)

🌐 www.sparks.org.uk

Sparks raises money to fund pioneering research across the UK that aims to improve understanding of and/or outcomes in child health. Since 1991, the charity has funded more than 285 ground-breaking child health research projects in over 90 hospitals, universities and research institutions across the UK and overseas.

In February 2017, the charity partnered with Great Ormond Street Hospital (GOSH) Charity, merging their national research funds in order to make up to £2 million available. Currently, this is the largest fund in the UK dedicated to child health research, and is intended to benefit children at GOSH, nationally and around the world.

Grant programmes

Through its partnership with GOSH, the charity offers £2 million in research funding annually to support project grant applications for child health research from researchers across the UK. According to its website, the charity is

currently prioritising projects which seek to address complex childhood illness, including rare diseases.

The charity's website provides the following information on what it will support:

> Translational research across the spectrum of medical conditions affecting the fetus, neonates and children directly, as well as pregnancy disorders that affect the child.

> All projects must aim to improve understanding and/or outcomes of the child and have the potential to lead to the development of new diagnostic tools and novel interventions. Proposals will be asked to demonstrate a clear route to clinical application and strong partnership between clinical and laboratory based research.

> We particularly encourage applications from early career researchers and those who are still consolidating their independent research careers.

> The charity would not expect applications to exceed £250,000. Funding will be provided for the direct costs of research (such as research staff and consumables) but will not cover consultant Programmed Activities, team-leader salary time or PhD studentships. Typically, projects will be up to 3 years duration.

Financial information

In 2016/17 the charity had assets of £1.4 million and an income of £4.1 million, mainly from fundraising events. Research grants and other awards were made to institutions totalling around £1.2 million.

Beneficiaries included: University College London (£317,000); Royal Hospital for Children, Glasgow (£150,000); Erasmus MC – Sophia Children's Hospital, Queen Mary University of London and UZ Leuven (£149,000 each); University of Bath, University of Birmingham (£147,000 each); Institute of Child Health (£14,000).

Exclusions

See individual funding calls on the charity's website for details of exclusions applicable to research projects.

Applications

Applications will be received and managed by GOSH and considered by its Research Assessment Panel. Applications can be submitted via the GOSH website. For queries, contact the GOSH grants team at: grants@gosh.org.

Sources of information

Accounts; annual report; Charity Commission report; funder's website.

The Spear Charitable Trust

General charitable purposes, with some preference for animal welfare, the environment and health

Mainly UK

£199,000 (2016)

CC number: 1041568

Trustees: Philip Harris; Francis Spear; Hazel Spear; Nigel Gooch.

Correspondent: Hazel Spear, Trustee, Roughground House, Beggarmans Lane, Old Hall Green, Ware, Hertfordshire SG11 1HB (tel: 01920 823071)

Established in 1994 with general charitable purposes, this trust has particular interest in helping employees and former employees of J. W. Spear and Sons plc and their families and dependants. Grants are given to UK organisations and, occasionally, those working overseas.

Financial information

In 2016 the trust had assets of £4.9 million and an income of £202,000. Grants were made to 59 organisations totalling £199,000. Grants to individuals (former employees of J. W. Spear and Sons plc and their families and dependants) totalled £21,000.

Beneficiaries included: Little Munden Church (£10,500); London Air Ambulance and Tree Aid 2500 (£5,000 each); St Mungo's (£3,000); East and North Hertfordshire Hospital Trust (£2,500); London Wildlife Trust (£2,000); Peta and Salvation Army (£1,000 each).

Exclusions

Appeals from individuals, other than former employees of J. W. Spear and Sons plc and their dependants, are not considered.

Applications

Apply in writing to the correspondent. The trustees state in their annual report that they will make grants without a formal application, but they encourage organisations to provide feedback on how grants are used. Feedback will be used for monitoring the quality of grants and will form the basis of assessment for any further applications.

Sources of information

Accounts; annual report; Charity Commission record.

Spielman Charitable Trust

General charitable purposes, children and young people, older people, people with disabilities, arts and culture, social welfare, the promotion of health (especially oncology and palliative care), economic and community development

Bristol, and the surrounding area

£261,000 (2015/16)

CC number: 278306

Trustees: C. Moorsom; Karen Hann; Paul Cooper.

Correspondent: June Moody, Suite F11B, Kestrel Court Buisness Centre, Harbour Road, Portishead, Bristol BS20 7AN (tel: 0117 929 1929; email: g-s.moody@btconnect.com)

Established in 1979, the trust, according to its Charity Commission record, 'provides grants to a range of charitable institutions and individuals to help them deal with their immediate needs'. It assists 'a number of charities, particularly those engaged in caring for and educating children and young people in Bristol and the South West of England'.

Aims of the trust

The trust's annual report for 2015/16 states that its aims are as follows:

- To broaden possible life experiences
- To improve health, including mental health of parents and children
- To improve opportunities for pre-school children
- To encourage development of new skills for children
- To improve parenting skills

Financial information

In 2015/16 the trust had assets of £5.4 million and an income of £254,000. Grants awarded to organisations totalled £261,000 and were broken down as follows:

Children who are disadvantaged	£153,500
Arts and theatre	£58,000
Children with disabilities or terminal illnesses	£28,500
Older people; older people with disabilities	£19,000
Schools	£2,000

Beneficiaries included: Royal Welsh College of Music and Drama (£25,000); Bristol Children's Help Society, The Wheels Project and Unseen (£15,000 each); NSPCC (£10,000); The Colston Society and Friends of Bristol Oncology (£5,000 each).

Applications

Apply in writing to the correspondent.

Sources of information

Accounts; annual report; Charity Commission record.

The Spoore, Merry and Rixman Foundation

Education and training, arts and culture, children and young people

The (pre-1974) borough of Maidenhead and the ancient parish of Bray, covering the postcode area SL6 1–9 (see the map on the website)

£438,500 to organisations (2016)

CC number: 309040

Trustees: Grahame Fisher; Ann Redgrave; Dorothy Kemp; Tony Hill; Ian Thomas; Cllr David Coppinger; Barbara Wielechowski; Cllr Philip Love; Cllr Gerry Clark; Cllr Judith Diment; The Mayor of the Royal Borough.

Correspondent: Helen MacDiarmid, Clerk to the Trustees, PO Box 4787, Maidenhead SL60 1JA (tel: 020 3286 8300; email: clerk@smrfmaidenhead.org)

 www.smrfmaidenhead.org.uk

The origins of the foundation date back to the 17th century when Abraham Spoore, Elizabeth Merry and Mary Rixman left money derived from rents and investments to be spent for educational purposes on local children. Since then, thousands of schoolchildren have benefitted from their generosity and have been helped to fulfil their educational potential.

The foundation provides grants to children and young people under the age of 25 for items such as school trips, tuition in the arts or music, sporting equipment and musical instruments.

Grants are also made to schools for items not funded by statutory budgets, e.g. for the development of school grounds, or for specialised equipment, lighting, staging, musical instruments and so on. Other organisations for young people, such as youth clubs, are able to apply for grants to provide facilities which are educational in the wider sense.

Financial information

In 2016 the foundation held assets of £12 million and had an income of £394,500. Grants totalled £601,000, of which 438,500 was given to organisations and £162,500 to individuals.

Beneficiaries included: Norden Farm Centre for the Arts (£45,000); Desborough College (£23,500); Holy Trinity School (£20,000); Larchfield Primary School (£17,000).

Applications

The foundation's website has a map of the funding boundary, which was extended in 2016 to cover a wider area. It now covers the current postcode area SL6 1–9.

Application forms are available to download, together with guidelines and criteria, on the foundation's website.

Sources of information

Accounts; annual report; Charity Commission record; funder's website.

The Geoff and Fiona Squire Foundation

 General charitable purposes, medicine, education, disability, children's welfare and health

UK

£762,000 (2016/17)

CC number: 1085553

Trustees: Geoff Squire; Fiona Squire; Bartholomew Peerless.

Correspondent: Fiona Squire, Trustee, The Walton Canonry, 69 The Close, Salisbury, Wiltshire SP1 2EN

Established in 2001, the foundation has general charitable purposes, with a particular interest in medicine, education, disability and the welfare and healthcare of children. The 2016/17 annual report states that the foundation 'will willingly work in partnership with other organisations to fund initiatives beyond the scope of a single organisation'.

Financial information

In 2016/17 the foundation held assets of almost £10.6 million and had an income of £685,000. Grants were made to 40 organisations and totalled £762,000.

Beneficiaries included: Noah's Ark Children's Hospice (£65,000); Grange Park Opera and Queen Elizabeth's Foundation for Disabled People (£50,000 each); Alchemy Foundation (£25,000); Children's Trust (£11,000); Listening Books and Macmillan Cancer Support (£5,000 each); British Disabled Angling Association and London Wheelchair Rugby Club (£3,000 each).

Exclusions

The trustees will only consider organisations or groups which are charitable as defined by UK charity law and whose aims and objectives fall within the scope of the foundation's own charitable objects. The foundation does not normally consider applications from large national charities (with an income of over £10 million or assets of more than £100 million), or from causes

which the trustees deem to be already well funded in the UK.

Applications

Apply in writing to the correspondent.

Sources of information

Accounts; annual report; Charity Commission record.

St James's Place Foundation

 Disadvantaged children, cancer care, hospices, mental health

UK and overseas

£7.3 million (2016)

CC number: 1144606

Trustees: David Bellamy; Ian Gascoigne; Malcolm Cooper-Smith; Andrew Croft; David Lamb; Michael Wilson.

Correspondent: Mark Longbottom, Foundation Manager, St James's Place plc, St James's Place House, 1 Tetbury Road, Cirencester GL7 1FP (tel: 01285 878562; email: Contact form on website)

www.sjpfoundation.co.uk

The foundation is the corporate charity of St James's Place Wealth Management, a UK wealth management company.

Themes

The foundation's grant-making in the UK is guided by four themes:

Cherishing Children

Cherishing Children is the foundation's largest theme and focuses on supporting children and young people under the age of 25 who are disadvantaged, who are young carers, or who have physical or mental health difficulties or life-threatening degenerative conditions. Grants are made for small capital items, support for staff working directly or hands-on with beneficiaries, and support for projects of direct benefit to beneficiaries.

Combating Cancer

Grants are given for capital items of direct benefit to cancer patients; support towards the salaries of staff working directly with cancer patients; and support projects aimed at increasing the quality of life for cancer patients.

Supporting Hospices

Grants are given to hospices working with all age ranges. The foundation is currently working with Help the Hospices which will distribute funds to hospices on the foundation's behalf and, consequently, the foundation does not invite applications from hospices directly.

Mental Health

The foundation supports mental health charities throughout the UK. Unsolicited applications are not accepted.

Grant programmes

- **Small Grants Programme:** grants of up to £10,000 are available to UK charities with an annual income of up to £1 million
- **Major Grants Programme:** the programme is not currently open to unsolicited applications, instead charities are invited to apply. Grants are usually for more than one year and are awarded to charities with an annual income of under £9 million

The foundation's website states: 'Approximately 80% of the money raised goes to supporting UK charities, with the remaining 20% being allocated to charities overseas, particularly those helping children and young people to escape poverty, malnutrition and neglect.'

Financial information

In 2016 the foundation had assets of £2.3 million and an income of £7.3 million. Grants to over 500 charities totalled £7.3 million.

Beneficiaries included: Jamie's Farm (£150,000); Acorns Children's Hospice (£146,500); Brainwave (£101,500); Brain Tumour Charity (£94,000); The Project (£60,000); Children in Crossfire (£28,000); Global Child Dental Fund (£10,000); Hope Support Services (£2,500).

Exclusions

The foundation does not provide support for:

- Charities with reserves of over 50% of income
- Administrative costs
- Activities primarily the responsibility of statutory agencies
- Replacement of lost statutory funding
- Research
- Events
- Advertising
- Holidays
- Sponsorship
- Contributions to large capital appeals
- Single-faith charities
- Charities that are raising funds on behalf of another charity

Applications

Applicants who believe that they fit the criteria are welcome to apply at any time via the foundation's website. The application procedure for all of the programmes can take between four and six months. The following information is given on the foundation's website: 'Applications for a small grant will normally receive a visit from a representative of the foundation, who will subsequently report to the trustees.

Following the trustees' decision, successful applicants will be notified.'

Consult the foundation's website for further details.

Sources of information

Accounts; annual report; Charity Commission record; guidelines for applicants; funder's website.

Stadium Charitable Trust

 General charitable purposes including: medical, health and sickness, sport and recreation

UK

£455,500 (20116/17)

CC number: 328522

Trustees: Edwin Healey; Anne Rozenbroek; Neil Holyoake; Ian Hall.

Correspondent: The Trustees, The Stadium Group, Welton Grange, Cowgate, Welton, East Yorkshire HU15 1NB (tel: 01482 667149; email: info@stadiumcity.co.uk)

The trust was established in 1989 with an initial gift from the Healey family. The trust mainly supports health and recreation and tends to support smaller charities. Its 2016/17 annual accounts state: 'The Charity accepts applicants from a wide range of parties but generally seeks to make small donations to local causes where the Trustees believe they can make the most difference.'

Financial information

In 2016/17 the charity held assets of £1.6 million and had an income of £886,000. Grants to 38 organisations totalled £455,500 and were broken down as follows:

Medical, health and sickness	£373,000
General charitable purposes	£54,000
Sport and recreation	£28,500

Beneficiaries included: Fundacion Alpe (£121,000); Dove House Hospice (£100,000); RNIB Sight Loss Appeal (£30,000); Brough Primary School (£10,000); Sailors Children's Society (£6,500); Special Smiles (£4,000); Pocklington Imagination Library (£1,000); RNLI (£800).

Applications

Apply in writing to the correspondent.

Sources of information

Accounts; annual report; Charity Commission record; funder's website.

The Stafford Trust

 Adult welfare, animal welfare, armed forces, children, community projects, medical research, overseas appeals, sea rescue

UK, with a preference for Scotland

£310,500 (2016/17)

OSCR number: SC018079

Trustees: Gordon Wylie; Ian Ferguson; Robert Hogg; Fiona Gillespie.

Correspondent: Margaret Kane, Trust Administrator, c/o Dickson Middleton CA, PO Box 14, 20 Barnton Street, Stirling FK8 1NE (tel: 01786 474718; email: staffordtrust@dicksonmiddleton.co.uk)

 www.staffordtrust.org.uk

The Stafford Trust was set up in 1991 by the late Mrs Gay Stafford of Sauchie Estate near Stirling. During her lifetime, Mrs Stafford made substantial gifts to the trust and on her death in 2005, the residue of her estate was bequeathed to the trust.

Grants vary, but most are for between £500 and £5,000. Grants are awarded for a variety of purposes including capital projects, running costs and salary support.

Financial information

In 2016/17 the trust had assets of £18.7 million and an income of £517,500. Grants awarded to organisations totalled £310,500 and were broken down as follows:

Community projects	£94,000
Adult welfare	£73,000
Children and young people	£71,500
Medical research and support	£47,000
Services personnel welfare	£15,000
Animal welfare	£10,000

Beneficiaries included: Combat Stress and National Animal Welfare Fund (£10,000 each); Action Medical Research, The Haven and Lomond Mountain Rescue (£5,000 each); St Mungo's Old Folks Centre (£2,600); British Wireless for the Blind Fund (£2,400); Citadel Arts Group (£2,000); Lothian Conservation Volunteers (£700).

Exclusions

The trust does not normally support:

- Religious organisations
- Political organisations
- Retrospective appeals
- Student travel or expeditions
- General appeals or mail shots

Applications

An application form can be downloaded from the trust's website and should include the information specified on the website. The trustees usually meet twice a year, in spring and autumn, to review

applications, and deadlines are posted on the website. Unsuccessful applicants should wait at least one year before re-applying.

Sources of information

Accounts; annual report; OSCR record; funder's website.

Standard Life Foundation

 Financial resilience and well-being

UK

£1.5 million (2016)

OSCR number: SC040877

Trustees: Alistair Darling; James Daunt; Naomi Eisenstadt; David Hall; Lucy Heller; Elaine Kempson; Wendy Loretto; Graeme McEwan; Keith Skeoch; Euan Stirling.

Correspondent: Frances Horsburgh, Secretary, 30 Lothian Road, Edinburgh EH1 2DH (email: enquiries@standardlifefoundation.org.uk)

www.standardlife.com/sustainability

The foundation was established in 2016 and funded with a donation of assets remaining from Standard Life's demutualisation in 2006.

At the time of writing (May 2018) the foundation was conducting a review into financial well-being. Its website states:

Following a careful process of evaluation, the Foundation will be commissioning a systematic review of research into the topic of financial well-being.

This independent review will form the key focus of the Foundation's activity in 2018. It will provide the building blocks for the Foundation to make a real and lasting impact to improving financial well-being and resilience across the UK.

Financial information

In 2016 the foundation had assets of £3 million and an income of £3 million. Grants were made to four organisations totalling £1.5 million.

Beneficiaries included: The Prince's Trust (£600,000); Tomorrow's People (£550,000); Skill Force (£290,000); The Royal British Legion (£107,500).

Applications

At the time of writing (May 2018) the foundation was not accepting applications. Its website states:

At the moment we are not taking unsolicited bids for funding or research projects. However, we do aim to undertake a systematic research review in the future and will be asking for expressions of interests on this project in advance. Please contact the Foundation on enquiries@standardlifefoundation.org.

uk if you would like to be informed about this project when it is launched.

Sources of information

Accounts; annual report; OSCR record; funder's website.

Starlow Charities Ltd

 Judaism, religious education, social welfare

England and Wales

£ £1.4 million (2016/17)

CC number: 1081386

Trustees: Abraham Low; Avraham Shwarts; Eve Low.

Correspondent: Abraham Low, Trustee, 9 Craven Walk, London N16 6BS (tel: 020 8802 9517; email: mail@cohenarnold.com)

Starlow Charities Ltd was established in 2000, to support the activities of Jewish religious organisations. The objects of the charity are:

- The relief of poverty among persons in conditions of need, hardship and distress in the Orthodox Jewish community
- The advancement of the Orthodox Jewish religion
- The advancement of education in accordance with the tenets of the Orthodox Jewish religion
- To promote any charitable purposes for the benefit of the Orthodox Jewish community

Financial information

In 2016/17 the charity had assets of £5.7 million and an income of £2.9 million. During the year, the charity awarded grants of £1.4 million.

Beneficiaries included: Maharim Dushinsky Synagogue (£72,500); Hadras Kodesh Trust (£55,500); Jewish Community of Canvey Island (£51,500); Teshuvoh Tefilloh Tzedokoh (£50,000); The Trust for the Preservation of Jewish Cemeteries (£42,000).

Applications

Apply in writing to the correspondent. According to the 2016/17 annual report, 'grants are made to charitable institutions and organisations which conform to the objects of the charity after the trustees have satisfied themselves as to the bona fides of the recipients'.

Sources of information

Accounts; annual report; Charity Commission record.

The Peter Stebbings Memorial Charity

General charitable purposes, medical research, education, social welfare

UK, worldwide

£ £464,500 (2015/16)

CC number: 274862

Trustees: Andrew Stebbings; Nicholas Cosin; Jennifer Clifford.

Correspondent: Andrew Stebbings, Trustee, 45 Cadogan Gardens, London SW3 2AQ (tel: 020 7591 3333; email: charitymanager@pglaw.co.uk)

 peterstebbingsmemorialcharity.org

The Peter Stebbings Memorial Charity was established 1977, in memory of Hedley Peter Stebbings who was killed during active service during the Second World War. The charity funds projects in the UK, mainly operating in London, and overseas.

In the UK, the charity funds:

- Medical research and care
- Social welfare
- Homelessness
- Hospices
- Mental health/counselling
- Drug and alcohol therapeutic support
- Offender support
- Community regeneration
- Vulnerable families, women and children

In low- and middle-income countries, the charity funds:

- Education
- Basic skills and tools
- Health
- Sanitation, irrigation, hygiene, access to clean water
- Women's education, economics, reproduction
- Help for marginalised communities

According to the website, the charity prefers to assist small to medium-sized charities with annual incomes of up to £5 million. The trustees fund projects but will also consider core funding for organisations they are familiar with. Grants are generally awarded for one year but larger grants may be spread over as long as three years.

Financial information

In 2015/16 the charity had assets of £8.4 million and an income of £196,000. There were 50 grants made totalling £464,500.

Beneficiaries included: The Generation Trust (£40,000); The Women's Trust (£20,000); Harrow Club and New-borns Vietnam (£16,000 each); New Bridge Foundation and Redbridge Concern for Men (£12,000 each); Savannah Education

Trust and Maya Centre (£10,000 each); Trinity Hospice (£5,000); Action Coalition (£3,000); COCO (£2,000).

Exclusions

Individuals; large national/international charities; animal welfare; publications (unless part of a supported project); general appeals; religious organisations; educational institutions; arts organisations.

Applications

An application form is available from the charity's website. Applications made by email rather than post are preferred. The trustees meet twice a year and deadlines for grant applications are November and May.

Sources of information

Accounts; annual report; Charity Commission record; funder's website.

The Steel Charitable Trust

Arts and heritage, education, environment, health, social or economic disadvantage

Mainly UK with a preference for Luton and Bedfordshire

£ £1.2 million to organisations (2016/17)

CC number: 272384

Trustees: Nicholas Wright; Anthony Hawkins; Wendy Bailey; Dr Mary Briggs; Philip Lawford.

Correspondent: Sarah Kilcoyne, Trust Manager, Suite 411, Jansel Business Centre, Hitchin Road, Stopsley, Luton LU2 7XH (tel: 01582 240601; email: administrator@steelcharitabletrust.org.uk)

 www.steelcharitabletrust.org.uk

The trust was established in 1976 for general charitable purposes. Grants are made in five categories: arts and heritage; education; environment; health; social or economic disadvantage.

Grants are made at regular intervals during the year and the total level of grants is approximately £1 million per annum. Grants are generally made as single payments between £2,500 and £25,000.

Financial information

In 2016/17 the trust held assets of £30.9 million and had an income of £1.2 million. During the year, the trust made 121 grants totalling £1.2 million. The trust's 2016/17 accounts state that of this amount:

> 104 grants totalling £1 million were to charities registered in England and Wales, two grants totalling £15,000 were to charities registered in Scotland, two

grants totalling £24,000 were to charities registered in or with charitable status in Northern Ireland, and 13 grants totalling £150,000 were to other charitable organisations in the United Kingdom.

Grants were distributed in the following categories:

Health	33	£316,500
Education	22	£307,500
Arts and heritage	30	£253,500
Social or economic disadvantage	24	£169,500
Other categories	7	£107,000
Environment	5	£43,000

Beneficiaries included: University of Bedfordshire (£51,000); The Rotary Youth Trust for Luton (£50,000); Almeida Theatre Company Ltd (£30,000); The National Youth Orchestra of Great Britain (£25,000); Bowel Cancer UK (£15,000); The Guildhall School Trust (£10,000); Academy Concerts Society (£5,000).

Exclusions

Charities registered outside the UK; expeditions; individuals; political parties; the promotion of religion. Organisations may not re-apply within 12 months.

Applications

All applicants must complete the online application form. Applications submitted by post will not be considered. There is no deadline for applications and all will be acknowledged. The trustees meet regularly during the year, usually in March, June, September and November. All successful applicants will be notified by email and will be required to provide written confirmation of the details of the project or work for which they are seeking a grant.

Sources of information

Accounts; annual report; Charity Commission record; funder's website.

The Steinberg Family Charitable Trust

Q Jewish causes, health, education, social welfare

◉ North West England and Israel

£ £1.4 million (2016/17)

CC number: 1045231

Trustees: Lady Beryl Steinberg; Jonathan Steinberg; Lynne Attias.

Correspondent: The Trustees, 16 Bollinway, Hale, Altrincham, Cheshire WA15 0NZ (tel: 0161 903 8854; email: admin@sfct.co.uk)

This trust is primarily concerned with the support of charities located in the North West region or active within the Jewish community (whether in the North West or Israel), particularly those involved with the provision of

educational or social services. There is a particular emphasis on the needs of children and young people within those areas.

Financial information

In 2016/17 the trust held assets of £35 million and had an income of £2.4 million. Grants were made to 89 organisations totalling £1.4 million. A list of beneficiaries was not provided in the accounts, but the following breakdown was given:

Torah	£426,000
Welfare	£390,500
Community	£297,000
Education	£247,000
Healthcare	£30,000
Miscellaneous	£17,500

Previous beneficiaries have included: Aish (£75,000); Fed, Hathaway Trust, UJIA and World Jewish Relief (£50,000 each); Integrated Education Fund (£25,000); SEED (£22,000); Hale Adult Hebrew Education Trust (£20,000); Centre for Social Justice and Policy Exchange (£15,000); Ascent, Ezer Layeled, Imperial War Museum; MDA Israel, Menachim Begin Heritage Foundation and Yeshiva Bais Yisroel (£10,000 each); Chai Cancer Care and Holocaust Centre (£7,500 each); Hamayon and Hazon Yeshaya (£5,000 each); Henshaw's Society, Jewish Education in Manchester, NATA and Rainbow Trust (£2,500 each); Prostate Cancer Charity (£1,000).

Applications

Apply in writing to the correspondent.

Sources of information

Accounts; annual report; Charity Commission record.

The Sir Sigmund Sternberg Charitable Foundation

Q Interfaith activities

◉ Worldwide

£ £421,500 (2016/17)

CC number: 257950

Trustees: Martin Paisner; Michael Sternberg; Martin Slowe; Revd Dr Marcus Braybrooke; Noam Tamir.

Correspondent: Jan Kariya, Clayton Stark & Co., Charles House, 108–110 Finchley Road, London NW3 5JJ (tel: 020 7431 4200; email: csco@claytonstark.co.uk)

The foundation supports the furtherance of interfaith activities to promote racial and religious harmony, in particular between the Christian, Jewish and Muslim faiths, and the education in, and understanding of, their fundamental

tenets and beliefs. Most grants are made to Jewish and Israeli charities.

Financial information

In 2016/17 the foundation had assets of £4.45 million and an income of £257,000. During the year, the foundation awarded £421,500 in 97 grants, of which 60 were of less than £1,000. Grants were distributed as follows:

The promotion of interfaith understanding	21	£263,500
Religious activities	10	£74,500
Education	16	£60,000
Communal	29	£18,900
Medical care and care of people with disabilities/older people	15	£2,900
Relief of poverty	4	£950
Bereavement care	2	£400

Beneficiaries included: Three Faiths Forum (£258,000 in 15 grants); The Movement for Reform Judaism (£50,000); Alexander Haus (£20,000); Queen's College Cambridge (£13,100 in three grants); Association of Papal Orders in Great Britain (£5,000); Royal College of Speech and Language Therapists (£4,000 in two grants); New Horizons in British Islam (£2,000); International Council of Christians and Jews (£1,600 in two grants).

Exclusions

No grants are made to individuals.

Applications

Apply in writing to the correspondent.

Sources of information

Accounts; annual report; Charity Commission record.

Stevenson Family's Charitable Trust

Q General charitable purposes, arts and culture, conservation and heritage, the promotion of health, education and training, overseas aid

◉ Worldwide, in practice mainly UK

£ £500,000 (2016/17)

CC number: 327148

Trustees: Lady Catherine Stevenson; Sir Hugh Stevenson; Joseph Stevenson.

Correspondent: Sir Hugh Stevenson, Trustee, Old Waterfield, Winkfield Road, Ascot SL5 7LJ (email: hugh.stevenson@ oldwaterfield.com)

This is the family trust of Hugh and Catherine Stevenson. A well known City of London figure, Hugh Stevenson was formerly the chair of one of London's largest investment management companies. The trust is operated personally with no premises or salaried staff of its own and is probably best seen simply as the vehicle for the personal donations of the founders rather than as an institution with an independent existence.

The current policy of the trustees is in the main to support charitable causes in the fields of culture and the arts, conservation and heritage, and education, but they can exercise their discretion to make donations for other charitable purposes.

Financial information

In 2016/17 the trust held assets of over £2.8 million and had an income of £342,500. Grants were made to 50 organisations totalling £500,000.

Previous beneficiaries have included: Royal Horticultural Society (£104,500); Grange Park Opera and St Hilda's College Oxford (£50,000 each); The National Gallery Trust (£35,000); Girl Guiding Wickwood Campsite (£5,000); Grandparents Plus (£2,500); Old Vic Theatre Trust (£1,000); British Heart Foundation, Ethiopiad and The Museum of Army Flying (£500 each); Church of St Mary the Virgin – Aldermaston (£100).

Exclusions

Grants are not awarded to individuals.

Applications

The trust has previously stated that no unsolicited applications can be considered as the trust's funds are required to support purposes chosen by the trustees.

Sources of information

Accounts; annual report; Charity Commission record.

Stewards' Company Ltd

Christian evangelism, general charitable purposes

UK and overseas

£6.1 million to organisations (2015/16)

CC number: 234558

Trustees: Alexander McIlhinney; Philip Symons; Dr John Burness; Paul Young; David Roberts; Denis Cooper; Alan Paterson; Glyn Davies; Andrew Griffiths; Ian Childs; John Gamble; Andrew Mayo; Simon Tomlinson; John Aitken; Keith Bintley; Dr Jonathan Loose; David Crawford Bingham; Joshua Fitzhugh.

Correspondent: Andrew Griffiths, Trustee, 124 Wells Road, Bath BA2 3AH (tel: 01225 427236; email: stewardsco@stewards.co.uk)

The charity supports Christian evangelism, especially (but not exclusively) that of Christian Brethren assemblies. The charity's 2015/16 accounts state that:

> The principal activities of the charity are to act as owner or as custodian trustee of

various charitable properties, mainly used as places of worship and situated either in the United Kingdom or overseas, and to act as administrative trustee of a number of Christian charitable trusts, including The J W Laing Trust and The J W Laing Biblical Scholarship Trust.

The charity supports 'the advancement of the religion in any matter which shall be charitable, and in particular by the furtherance of the gospel of God and education in the Holy Scriptures as contained in the Old and New Testaments, and the relief of the poor'.

Grant-making policy

The charity's 2015/16 accounts state that:

> The trust takes into account the financial resources of the benefiting charities, the efforts made by members of such charities to maximise their own funding, including where appropriate sacrificial giving by themselves and their supporters, and the assessed value of the work of such charities consistent with the objective of the main grant-making charities [i.e. Stewards Company, Laing Trust and Laing Scholarship].

Financial information

In 2015/16 the charity had assets of £145 million and an income of £2.2 million. During the year, 426 grants were awarded to organisations totalling £6.1 million. A further 40 grants were given to individuals which totalled almost £43,000.

Beneficiaries included: Counties (£467,500); Strategic Resource Group (£415,000); Beatrice Laing Trust (£265,500); Christian Workers' Relief Fund (£250,000); Retired Missionary Aid Fund (£225,000); International Fellowship of Evangelical Students (£147,500); Interlink (£140,000); Gospel Literature Outreach (£100,000).

Grants between £25,000 and £99,000 totalled £1.5 million, and 374 grants under £25,000 totalled £2.1 million.

Applications

Apply in writing to the correspondent.

Sources of information

Annual report; accounts; Charity Commission record.

Sir Halley Stewart Trust

Health, social welfare, education, religion

UK, with some work in Africa

£905,000 to organisations (2016/17)

CC number: 208491

Trustees: Prof. Phyllida Parsloe; Joanna Womack; Prof. John Wyatt; Dr Duncan Stewart; Lord Stewartby; Prof. John Lennard-Jones; Prof. Philip Whitfield; Bill Kirkman; Prof. Gordon Wilcock; Theresa Bartlett; Dr James Bunn; Louisa

Elder; Amy Holcroft; Jane Gillard; Celia Atherton; Revd Prof. David Wilkinson; Andrew Graystone; Paul Harrod.

Correspondent: Vicky Chant, Secretary to the Trustees, BM Sir Halley Stewart Trust, London WC1N 3XX (tel: 020 8144 0375; email: email@sirhalleystewart.org.uk)

 www.sirhalleystewart.org.uk

The trust was established in 1924 by Sir Halley Stewart who endowed the charity and established its founding principles.

During the course of his life, Sir Halley Stewart was a non-conformist Christian minister, an MP, a pioneering industrialist and a philanthropist. When he founded the trust, he specified four objects: to advance religion and education, to relieve poverty and to promote other charitable purposes beneficial to the community. He was concerned with the prevention and removal of human misery and in the realisation of national and worldwide brotherhood. He wished the trustees to have the fullest discretion in applying the income of the trust within its objects, but not for dogmatic theological purposes. A tradition of supporting medical research into the prevention of human suffering, not its relief, was established during his lifetime. He died in 1937.

Grants programmes

Although the trust is 'underpinned by Christian values', the trustees welcome applications from other faith and non-faith projects. The trustees state in their 2016/17 annual report:

> All grants are given on the basis defined by our founder, that is, 'to prevent human suffering'. The deliberations that lead to the grant of awards for religious, social or medical purposes explicitly test applications in the context of this aim. In particular trustees need to be convinced that the outcomes proposed by applicants will, if achieved, generate actual benefits to people in the short to medium-term rather than providing theoretical insights that will take many years before they can be translated into such benefits.

Main Grants

The trust's Main Grants scheme awards grants of between £5,001 and £60,000, for between one and three years, usually to cover salary costs, although grants are occasionally made towards the overall costs of a project.

Small Grants

A limited number of smaller grants of up to £5,000 are also available each year. Proposals for small grants are considered all year round and there are no application deadlines.

Both grants programmes have the following criteria, as stated on the website:

The trust funds projects that focus on the prevention (rather than the alleviation) of human suffering. All trust grants must fall under one or both of the following categories:

- Innovative research projects: i.e. those which explore and test new ideas, methods, approaches, interventions and/or devices
- Pioneering/ground-breaking development projects: i.e. those which are original and represent the first of their kind and/or lay the foundations for further developments

The trust has three grant priority areas: Medical, Social and Religious, with education being a central theme that runs across all three. Our trustees are particularly keen to support projects that relate to more than one priority area.

All trust funded projects must have strong dissemination plans, to ensure a positive impact on people beyond the project's immediate beneficiaries.

The trust will consider applications to fund implementation projects that are innovative, for example roll-outs of pioneering pilot work where significant further developments will take place as part of the implementation. However, an application for a straightforward scale-up and expansion of an existing proven model would be less likely to meet the trust's innovation focus.

International projects are supported, but grants are only paid to or through UK charitable organisations – primarily UK-registered charities. Other UK charitable organisational forms may be considered on a case by case basis.

Detailed information on each priority area (medical, social welfare and religious categories) is provided on the trust's website.

Financial information

In 2016/17 the trust had assets of £30.7 million and an income of £1.1 million. Grants to organisations totalled £905,000. There was a further £25,000 paid in grants of less than £10,000 to organisations and individuals.

Beneficiaries included: Spark (£55,500); Durham University (£46,000); Lancaster University (£45,000); Mental Health Foundation (£38,000); Vineyard Compassion (£26,000); Caspari Foundation (£4,000).

Exclusions

According to the trust's website, grants are never made for the following:

- To support individuals directly (grants are only awarded through UK charitable organisations for specific projects)
- General appeals of any kind
- The purchase, erection or conversion of buildings, or other capital costs

- University overhead charges

According to its website, the trust does not usually fund the following:

- Running costs of established organisations or ongoing projects.
- Contributions towards the overall costs of a project (the trust normally provides grants for salary costs, although occasionally it funds other project expenses).
- Conference attendance.
- Projects proposed indirectly through other 'umbrella' organisations.
- Projects from large well-funded charities.
- Personal education fees or fees for taught courses – unless the proposal comes from a senior researcher who is seeking funds for research which could be undertaken by a post-graduate student.
- Completion of a project or PhD initiated by other bodies.
- Educational or 'gap-year' projects for young people.
- Projects where the trust would not be a major supporter, with the trust normally preferring to fund at least 50% of the total project costs.

Applications

Potential applicants are strongly encouraged to first contact the trust's secretary by phone or email to determine the suitability of a project before applying. There is also a short eligibility quiz on the trust's website.

Applications should be made online, using the form on the trust's website. Once an application has been submitted, the applicant will receive a confirmation email and the trust may be in touch to ask for further information. The dates of trustees' meetings are posted on the trust's website. Applicants will be informed around a month before a meeting whether their application will be given further consideration or not.

The website states:

'Please note the Trust does not have hard and fast deadlines for submissions of applications. Meetings are 'closed' to submissions at the discretion of the Trust, and without prior warning, once the meeting capacity is reached.'

The trustees state in their annual report that 'over 100 applications judged unsuitable are rejected during each four month period. Unsuccessful applicants are sent a personalised letter or email explaining the reason for rejection.'

Sources of information

Accounts; annual report; Charity Commission record; funder's website.

The Stewarts Law Foundation

Alleviating poverty, access to justice, supporting disability, providing educational opportunity

Undefined, in practice the UK and financially developing countries

£573,000 (2016/17)

CC number: 1136714

Trustees: John Cahill; Bennett Townsend; Stuart Dench; Paul Paxton; James Healy-Pratt; Stephen Foster; Julian Chamberlayne; Daniel Herman; Andrew Dinsmore; Kevin Grealis; Keith Thomas; Clive Zietman; Sean Upson; Muiris Lyons; Debbie Chism; Helen Ward; Jonathan Sinclair; Ian Gatt; David Hughes.

Correspondent: John Cahill, Trustee, 5 New Street Square, London EC4A 3BF

 www.stewartslaw.com/about/social-impact/the-stewarts-foundation

Established in June 2010 for general charitable purposes and funded by Stewarts Law LLP, this foundation supports organisations in the UK.

Financial information

In 2016/17 the foundation had assets of £89,500 and an income of £658,000. Grants to 12 organisations totalled £573,000.

Beneficiaries included: Access to Justice Foundation (£250,000); Headway (£40,000); Backup Trust, Centrepoint and Coram Children's Legal Centre (£30,000 each); The Children's Trust – Tadworth (£10,000); City Solicitors Horizons (£4,000).

Applications

The foundation does not accept unsolicited applications. The annual report for 2016/17 states: 'It is not the policy of the Trustees to accept direct applications for funds.'

Sources of information

Accounts; annual report; Charity Commission record; funder's website.

The Stobart Newlands Charitable Trust

Christian causes

Worldwide

£1.2 million (2016)

CC number: 328464

Trustees: Ronnie Stobart; Linda Rigg; Peter Stobart; Richard Stobart.

Correspondent: Ronnie Stobart, Trustee, J. Stobart and Sons Ltd, Millcroft,

Newlands, Hesket Newmarket, Wigton
CA7 8HP (tel: 01697 478631)

Registered in 1989 with the Charity
Commission, the Stobart Newlands
Charitable Trust is the corporate charity
of J. Stobart and Sons Ltd, a
manufacturer and retailer of animal
feedstuffs. The trustees are directors and
shareholders of J. Stobart and Sons Ltd,
which is the source of almost all of the
trust's income. This family trust makes
up to 60 grants a year, nearly all on a
recurring basis to Christian religious and
missionary bodies.

Financial information

In 2016 the trust had assets of £62,500
and an income of £1.06 million.
Throughout the year, the trust
awarded almost £1.2 million in grants.
Grants of less than £10,000 totalled
£130,500.

Beneficiaries included: World Vision
(£300,000); Mission Aviation Fellowship
(£250,000); Bible Society (£35,000);
Keswick Ministries (£25,000);
Community Reach (£22,000); Biblica,
Lifewords and Torch Trust (£10,000
each).

Exclusions

Individuals.

Applications

Unsolicited applications are not likely to
be successful.

Sources of information

Accounts; annual report; Charity
Commission record.

Mark Stolkin Foundation

Public education in performing and
visual arts, health and welfare,
education, the furtherance of the
Christian faith, architectural heritage

England, Wales and South Africa

£596,500 (2016/17)

CC number: 1138476

Trustees: Margeaux Stolkin; Mark
Stolkin; Renate Lubert.

Correspondent: Mark Stolkin,
14–16 Egerton Gardens Mews, London
SW3 2EH (tel: 020 7589 0899)

The foundation was registered with the
Charity Commission in 2010 and makes
grants throughout England and Wales
and South Africa.

According to the foundation's 2016/17
accounts, its objects are:

- to educate the public in the art and
  science of music, dancing and the
  performing arts

- to educate the public in the fields of
  painting, drawing, illustration and visual
  arts
- to educate and assist young persons
  through their leisure time activities so
  as to develop their physical, mental
  and spiritual capacities
- to award scholarships, exhibition,
  bursaries or maintenance allowances
  tenable at any school, university or
  other educational or charitable
  establishment approved by the
  Trustees to persons who are in need of
  financial assistance
- to assist in relieving poverty and ill-
  health in all their various forms and the
  causes of poverty and ill-health
  including but not limited to victims of
  terrorism and other forms of trauma
- to further education generally by the
  granting or giving of financial
  assistance to educational institutions of
  all kinds
- to further the religious and charitable
  work for the Christian faith
- to advance the religion(s) of Christianity
- to protect and preserve and/or assist in
  the protection and preservation of
  buildings, monuments and sites of
  special historical and/or architectural
  interest

Financial information

In 2016/17 the foundation held assets of
£2.9 million and had an income of
£711,000. Grants awarded to
organisations totalled £596,500.

Beneficiaries included: Care for
Children (£199,500); Holy Trinity –
Brompton (£198,500); Great Ormond
Street Hospital (£25,000); Oak Hill
College (£8,400); Anne Frank Trust and
Siblings Together (£1,000 each).

Applications

Apply in writing to the correspondent.

Sources of information

Accounts; annual report; Charity
Commission record.

The Stoller Charitable Trust

General charitable purposes including:
children and young people, healthcare
research and cancer relief

North West

£13.1 million (2016/17)

CC number: 285415

Trustees: Roger Gould; Sir Norman
Stoller; Lady Stoller; Andrew Dixon;
KSL Trustees Ltd.

Correspondent: Stephen Lowe, 24 Low
Crompton Road, Royton, Oldham
OL2 6YR (email: enquiries@
stollercharitabletrust.co.uk)

The trust supports a wide variety of
charitable causes, but with particular
emphasis on those that are based in the
North West, medically related or

supportive of children. It also
endeavours to maintain a balance
between regular and occasional
donations and between large and smaller
grants. Trustees include Norman Stoller,
former owner of Seton Healthcare.

Financial information

In 2016/17 the trust had assets of
£20.7 million and an income of
£2.4 million. Grants awarded to
organisations totalled £13.1 million.

Previous beneficiaries have included:
Bauern Helfen Baeurn; Broughton
House; Cancer Research UK; Central
Manchester Children's Hospital; Christie
Hospital, Greater Manchester Appeal;
Church Housing Trust; Commandery of
John of Gaunt; Imperial War Museum
North; Live Music Now; Mines Advisory
Group; National Memorial Arboretum;
Oldham Liaison of Ex-Services
Associations; Onside North West;
Salvation Army; and Windermere Air
Show.

Exclusions

Individuals.

Applications

Apply in writing to the correspondent.

Sources of information

Accounts; annual report; Charity
Commission record.

The Stone Family Foundation

Water and sanitation in the financially
developing world, mental health for
disadvantaged young people in the UK

Sub-Saharan Africa and South East
Asia, particularly Ghana, Kenya,
Uganda, Rwanda and Cambodia, UK

£4.7 million (2016)

CC number: 1164682

Trustees: John Stone; Charles Edwards;
David Steinegger.

Correspondent: Charlotte Lamb,
22 Upper Ground, London SE1 9PD (tel:
020 7663 6825; email: sff@thinkNPC.
org)

 www.thesff.com

The foundation's website states that, in
the early years, it funded a range of
projects in the UK (mental health) and
overseas (education for girls, water and
sanitation and microfinance). Following
a strategic review in 2010, the trustees
decided to focus sharply on:

- Water and sanitation (WASH) in
  financially developing countries.
  Around 80% of funding is committed
  to water and sanitation

- In the UK, mental health and programmes for disadvantaged young people

Financial information

In 2016 the foundation held assets of £56.1 million and had an income of £55.9 million. The foundation's high income is due to an asset transfer following re-registration. Grants to 35 organisations totalled £4.7 million.

Beneficiaries included: IDE Cambodia (£563,000); Grundfos (£300,000); Watershed (£224,000); 17 Triggers (£208,000); Onside Youth Zones (£100,000); Youth Moves (£40,000); Pivot Works (£20,500); Spring Health (£12,000); Bright (£10,000); MSABI (£2,200).

Exclusions

No grants are given to individuals.

Applications

The website states: 'We are a small, family foundation with limited resources and as a result we do not accept unsolicited proposals. If you have any questions, please feel free to email: SFF@thinkNPC.org. Please note, this email inbox is only monitored periodically.'

Sources of information

Charity Commission record; funder's website.

The Stoneygate Trust

General charitable purposes, medical research, health, social welfare, education

England and Wales

£4.8 million (2016/17)

CC number: 1119976

Trustees: Nadine Adderley; Andrew Walden; William Adderley.

Correspondent: Deborah Fisher, The Old Coach House, Sunnyside, Bergh Apton, Norwich NR15 1DD (tel: 01508 480100; email: info@fisherlegal.co.uk)

The trust was established in 2007 and makes grants for general charitable purposes. Its 2016/17 accounts state:

> The Trust is a general purpose charity and the intention of the Trustees is to develop main areas of benefit over the course of time. During the current year the focus has been on medical research, health and welfare and education.

Financial information

In 2016/17 the trust had assets of £6.1 million and an income of £288,500. Grants to 38 institutions totalled £4.8 million.

Beneficiaries included: LOROS (£2 million); The Westminster Abbey Foundation (£1 million); University College London (£341,000); Imperial College London (£170,500); University of Cambridge (£31,000); Institute of Cancer Research (£14,700); University of Sheffield (£12,500); University of Leicester (£3,300).

Applications

Apply in writing to the correspondent.

Sources of information

Accounts; annual report; Charity Commission record.

Stratford-upon-Avon Town Trust

Education, social welfare, general charitable purposes

Stratford-upon-Avon

£1.12 million to organisations (2016)

CC number: 1088521

Trustees: Carole Taylor; Charles Bates; Julia Lucas; Clarissa Roberts; Alan Haigh; Richard Lane; Clive Snowdon; Quentin Wilson; Tessa Bates; Tony Jackson; Julia Lucas.

Correspondent: Rachel Jones, 14 Rother Street, Stratford-upon-Avon, Warwickshire CV32 6LU (tel: 01789 207111; email: engagement@ stratfordtowntrust.co.uk)

 www.stratfordtowntrust.co.uk

The Stratford-upon-Avon Town Trust is a grant-making charity dedicated to supporting local community projects and activities which improve the quality of life for the people living in Stratford-upon-Avon. In accordance with a Charity Commission Scheme of October 2001, the trust derives its income from the properties and funds of two charities, the Guild of Holy Cross and College of Canons estates, whose origins go back to the thirteenth century. Since 2001 the trust has awarded around £1 million each year.

On its website, the trust identifies five key priorities:

- Improve health and well-being
- Create positive activities for young people
- Reduce loneliness and social isolation
- Protect and support vulnerable communities
- Provide support during a time of crisis

To be considered for funding, applications should meet at least one of the above priority themes.

Hardship grants are also provided to individuals in need, through partner organisations.

Grant programmes

There are currently three different types of grant available:

Fast Track Grants

Applicants can apply for up to £2,000 to deliver smaller projects and initiatives, or for one-off equipment and capital costs. A decision is usually given within ten working days.

Main Grant Rounds

There is no restriction on the amount which can be applied for.

Multi-Year Funding

Multi-year funding is available for up to three consecutive years for applications which impact on two or more of the funding priorities outlined and seek to respond to the longer-term needs of communities.

Financial information

In 2016 the trust had assets of £57.4 million and an income of £1.94 million. During the year, the trust awarded a total of £1.82 million in grants.

Non-discretionary grants of £685,000 were made to King Edward VI School, for the maintenance of almshouses and to the vicar of Holy Trinity Church. During the year, the trust also awarded 38 discretionary grants worth a total of £13,000 to individuals. In total 131 discretionary grants were made to organisations, and totalled £1.12 million in 2016. Only beneficiaries of grants above £20,000 were listed in the accounts.

Beneficiaries included: Stratford Artshouse (£199,500); Stratford-upon-Avon Hockey Club (£65,000 over three years); Citizens Advice (£40,000); Domestic Abuse Counselling Service (£27,000); Safeline (£23,500); Lifespace Trust (£15,000); Central England Lip Reading Support Trust (£4,200).

Exclusions

Grants are not awarded for:

- Education costs for individuals (including bursaries, tuition fees, gap year or exchanges, course fees, etc.)
- Organisations that distribute profit to members, or are not classified as 'not for profit'
- Activities promoting business, tourism or local economy
- Activities that are not legally charitable
- Activities which the state is legally obliged to provide
- Fundraising for an organisation on behalf of another
- Retrospective funding
- Projects run by organisations that have not complied with previous monitoring requests
- VAT that can be reclaimed

Applications

Application forms and full guidance for each grant programme is available to download on the trust's website.

All applications are subject to a scoring process which appraises the following key points, as explained in the application guidelines:

- Evidence of need within Stratford-upon-Avon
- Evidence of community/user involvement in the planning and delivery of the proposal
- Ability to make a demonstrable difference to quality of life in Stratford-upon-Avon
- Commitment to collaborative and partnership working
- Financial position, viability and sustainability (where applicable)Application forms can be submitted via email or post

Should applicants have any questions regarding their application, the trust invites them to get in touch via phone prior to submission.

Sources of information

Accounts; annual report; Charity Commission record; funder's website.

Strathnairn Community Benefit Fund Ltd

 General charitable purposes

Strathnairn

£264,000 to organisations (2016/17)

OSCR number: SC036807

Trustees: Sally Moore; Ian Hunt; Isobel McQueer; Scott MacDonald; Pauline Thompson; Mark Burton; Nicolas Boyle; Christine MacPherson.

Correspondent: Secretary, Farr Community Hall, Inverarnie Park, Inverarnie, Inverness IV2 6AX (email: cosec@strathnairncbf.com)

 www.strathnairncbf.com

Strathnairn Community Benefit Fund (SCBF) was established in 2004 to receive and distribute community benefit payments from the developer of the Farr Windfarm.

The key purpose of SCBF is to administer grants to support the objective of 'the promotion, for the benefit of the public, of urban or rural regeneration in areas of social and economic deprivation and in particular in the Strathnairn Community Council area'.

Since its formation, SCBF has begun receiving additional funds from SSE plc in respect of the Dunmaglass Wind Farm.

The fund administers several energy efficiency and renewable energy grant programmes for individuals, but also offers general grants for local community groups, defined by the fund's website as organisations which:

> Consist of a reasonable majority of Strathnairn residents, have open access to all of the target population for that group and have an identifiable relevance to the wider Strathnairn community. Groups must be non-religious and non-political and if a charitable organisation, then need to be established and located within Strathnairn and carry out charitable activity solely for the residents of Strathnairn.

Financial information

In 2016/17 Strathnairn Community Benefit Fund Ltd had assets of £1.34 million and an income of £190,000. During this time, the fund provided grants totalling £375,000. Of this total, £264,000 was provided to local community groups in the form of general grants.

Previous beneficiaries have included: Farr Baby and Toddler Group (£81,500); The Strathnairn Music Initiative (£15,500); Strathnairn Community Access and Transport Association (£12,000); The Strathnairn Community Newsletter (£8,300); Fearnag Growers (£7,800); Daviot Primary School (£7,200); Farr Hall (£7,000); The Community Plan Group (£6,800); The Strathnairn Farmers Association (£3,500); The Strathnairn Seniors Lunch Club (£2,500); Strathnairn Indoor Bowls Club (£1,000); Farr Conversations (£110).

Applications

Applications for general grants can be submitted using an online form available on the fund's website. The fund's board meets each month.

Sources of information

Accounts; annual report; OSCR record; funder's website.

The WO Street Charitable Foundation

General charitable purposes, education, social welfare, family welfare, older people, people with a disability, people who are blind

UK, Lancashire, Jersey

£482,500 (2016)

CC number: 267127

Trustees: Clive Cutbill; Zedra Trust Company UK. Ltd.

Correspondent: The Trustees, Zedra Trust Company UK Ltd, Zedra UK Trusts, Osborne Court, Gadbrook Park, Rudheath, Northwich CW9 7UE (tel:

01606 313327; email: charities@zedra.com)

The WO Street Charitable Foundation is a grant-making charity established by William Openshaw Street. The founder had particular interests in education; the relief of poverty; support for older people, people with disabilities, or people who are blind; family welfare; and social welfare. The current trustees have a particular interest in supporting charities in Lancashire, as well as in Jersey where Mr Street spent a significant part of his life.

Grants are made to UK-registered charities and to organisations with charitable status. The foundation also provides grants to assist with fee-paying schooling where there is unexpected financial difficulty, although the trustees do not normally provide support for individuals, other than through educational bursaries. The trustees support national, regional and local charities, particularly in areas where a grant would make a real difference to the recipients.

According to the foundation's 2016 annual report, the foundation supports a wide range of activities in the following categories:

- Education
- General welfare (particularly older people, the blind and the disabled)
- Family and social welfare

Financial information

In 2016 the foundation had assets of £18.9 million and an income of £509,500. During the year, the foundation gave a total of £482,500 in grants to organisations.

Beneficiaries included: WO Street Charitable Foundation – Jersey (£40,000); Emmott Foundation (£30,000); Bury Grammar School (£15,700); NYAS (£6,000); Royal London Society for the Blind (£5,000); Pimlico Family Workshop Toy Library (£2,500); Sunny Days Children's Fund (£2,000); Warwickshire Vision Support (£1,800).

The foundation gave £42,500 in 'Direct Education Grant Bursaries'.

Exclusions

No grants are made to individuals.

Applications

Apply in writing to the correspondent. Applications are usually considered on a quarterly basis, at the end of January, April, July and October.

Sources of information

Accounts; annual report; Charity Commission record.

The Street Foundation

Education, human rights, disability, poverty, community

Worldwide

Around £405,000 (2016/17)

CC number: 1045229

Trustees: Lucinda Sharp-Smith; Richard Smith; Sarah Sharp-Smith; Millicent Smith; Susan Smith.

Correspondent: Richard Smith, Trustee, Kingsland House, Kingsland, Leominster HR6 9SG (tel: 01568 708744)

The Street Foundation is the charity of Richard Smith a director and shareholder of Techtest Ltd, which is part of the HR Smith Group of Companies. Techtest designs and manufactures advanced aerospace technologies.

The foundation is established for general charitable purposes for the public benefit and awards grants for the relief of poverty, the advancement of education and the advancement of religion.

Financial information

In 2016/17 the foundation had an income of £1,400 and an expenditure of £407,000. No accounts for 2016/17 were available; however, it is estimated that the foundation awarded grants of around £405,000.

Applications

Apply in writing to the correspondent.

Sources of information

Accounts; annual report; Charity Commission record.

Streetsmart – Action For The Homeless

Homelessness

UK – grants are made to charities in the cities in which the Streetsmart campaign runs (a list is available on the charity's website)

£512,500 (2015/16)

CC number: 1071657

Trustees: William Sieghart; Mary Lou Sturridge; Nick Emley; Rosie Boycott; Mark Sainsbury.

Correspondent: Glenn Pougnet, Director, 83 Clerkenwell Road, London EC1R 5AR (tel: 020 7292 5615; email: glenn.pougnet@streetsmart.org.uk)

www.streetsmart.org.uk

facebook.com/StreetSmartUK

@streetsmartuk

 @streetsmartuk

Streetsmart has been running since 1998 and has since raised over £8.2 million for homeless and vulnerable people across the UK. During November and December, participating restaurants add £1 to diners' bills which is then passed on to the charity to distribute to homeless charities. Money raised in a city is spent in that city.

The charity's website states:

> The organisations funded by StreetSmart must work progressively with their client group. Successful applications receive support for projects aimed at helping the homeless to make a better life for themselves, focusing on mental and physical health, employability and sustainable independent living. Grants are given to those who support people through the crucial stages in their progress from vagrant to valued community member.

Financial information

In 2015/16 the charity held assets of £201,500 and had an income of £534,500. Grants awarded to organisations totalled £512,500.

Beneficiaries included: Caravan (£20,000); Sweet Talk Charity UK (£11,000); Ace of Clubs and Alone in London (£10,000 each); Leeds Women's Aid (£3,000); Friends First – Brighton and The Rock Trust (£2,000 each); St Catherine's Convent (£1,000).

Applications

Apply in writing to the correspondent. The charity's website states:

> Homeless charities seeking funding from StreetSmart should submit their application in writing during December.
>
> There is no formal application process, but charities should outline the aims and achievements of the organisation, and explain in detail the specific area of their work in need of financial support, e.g. project worker salary, educational programmes, meaningful occupation. StreetSmart does not provide funding to soup kitchens unless they form part of a drop-in centre linked into other services.
>
> If the project meets our criteria, we will then arrange for a StreetSmart representative to visit the project at some point during January and February and report back to the trustees.
>
> The trustees of StreetSmart meet in April to decide which applications have been successful.
>
> Please contact your regional campaign manager, or email glenn.pougnet@streetsmart.org.uk.

Sources of information

Accounts; annual report; Charity Commission record; funder's website.

The Summerfield Charitable Trust

The arts, museums and built heritage, the environment, community projects, education, sport and recreation, social welfare

Gloucestershire

£516,000 (2016)

CC number: 802493

Trustees: Edward Gillespie; Katrina Beach; Vanessa Arbuthnott; David Owen; James Millar.

Correspondent: Lavinia Sidgwick, Trust Administrator, PO Box 287, Cirencester, Gloucestershire GL7 9FB (tel: 01285 721211; email: admin@summerfield.org.uk)

 www.summerfield.org.uk

 @SummerfieldNews

The trust was established in 1989 by the late Ronald Summerfield, a Cheltenham antique dealer. According to the trust's website, 'charities applying to the trust must either be based in Gloucestershire or they must be engaged in a project that is of specific benefit to residents of the county'. Areas of particular interest to the trustees are:

- The arts, museums and the built heritage
- The environment and natural heritage
- Community work
- Education, sport and recreation
- Vulnerable and disadvantaged sectors of society

The trustees encourage applicants to show they have considered:

- The impact of their projects upon the environment
- Planning for long-term self-sufficiency
- The potential to work in partnership with other statutory and non-statutory funders
- Their active involvement with the people who will benefit
- The outcomes of the project or service

The trustees prefer to award one-off grants to help fund specific projects, rather than to make grants for revenue costs. The trust supports registered charities, CICs, voluntary and community groups, and not-for-profit limited companies. Further eligibility criteria can be found on the trust's helpful website.

Financial information

In 2016 the trust held assets of £10.3 million and had an income of £340,500. Grants were made to organisations totalling £516,000 and were distributed as follows:

Disadvantaged and vulnerable sectors	32	£174,500
Arts, museums and built heritage	10	£142,500
Education, sport and recreation	29	£90,500
Community work	14	£66,000
Environment and natural heritage	8	£43,000

Beneficiaries included: Cotswold Canals Trust (£40,000); Corinium Museum (£20,000); Family Haven (£12,000); Gloucestershire Rape and Sexual Abuse Centre (£9,800); Noah's Ark Children's Venture (£8,000); Watershed Riding for the Disabled (£7,500); The Farm Project CIC (£5,000); Forest of Dean Sculpture Trust (£4,000); Wyldwood Arts CIC (£3,200); Cheltenham Music Society (£1,000); Chalford Village Shop (£930).

Exclusions

Grants are not made for:

- Medical research
- Private education
- Animal welfare appeals
- Trips abroad
- Retrospective projects
- Individuals
- Churches

Charities which have been in receipt of a grant should not re-apply for at least two years, unless they have specifically been asked to do so.

Applications

Applications should be made using the trust's online application form. There is a two-stage application process which is explained step-by-step on the 'how to apply' page of the website. The trustees meet in January, April, July, and October to consider all eligible funding requests received during the previous quarter. Check the website for latest submission deadlines.

Note: If you are not a registered charity your application must include a letter of endorsement from a registered charity, and a copy of audited accounts including a breakdown of salary costs.

Sources of information

Accounts; annual report; Charity Commission record; funder's website.

The Bernard Sunley Charitable Foundation

Community, education, health, social welfare

England and Wales

£2.9 million (2016/17)

CC number: 1109099

Trustees: Dr Brian Martin; Joan Tice; Bella Sunley; Anabel Knight; William Tice; Inigo Paternina; Lucy Evans.

Correspondent: Digby Nelson, Director, 20 Berkeley Square, London W1J 6LH

(tel: 020 7408 2198; email: office@ bernardsunley.org)

 www.bernardsunley.org

The Bernard Sunley Charitable Foundation was established in 1960 by Bernard and Mary Sunley. Today the foundation continues to be a family charitable foundation with the majority of trustees being family members. According to its website, the aim of the foundation is to 'help raise the quality of life, particularly for those who are young, disadvantaged or elderly'. The foundation achieves this goal by providing grants for capital projects worth around £2.5 million each year to a wide range of charities across England and Wales.

Grant programmes

The foundation provides funding for capital projects which fall within the following four categories, as outlined on the website:

Community

The Community programme aims to create cohesive, positive communities throughout England and Wales. This aim is achieved by supporting capital projects that bring local communities together, with a particular focus on enabling young people to become active, responsible citizens.

Applications are considered for:

- New build, refurbishment and improvement of village halls, Scout/ Guide huts, youth clubs, community centres and similar

Education

The Education programme aims to support those with special educational needs and disabilities. The foundation also supports educational nature and farm visitor centres. Mainstream schools and universities should not apply.

Applications are considered for building projects and specialist new transport.

Health

The Health programme supports building projects for residential care and treatment centres, as well as provision of major equipment for medical treatment and care.

Applications are considered for:

- Improvements to hospices and treatment clinics
- Residential care for the elderly and those with special needs
- New major equipment not available through the NHS
- Research medical equipment
- Specialist new transport

Social Welfare

The Social Welfare programme supports capital projects for a range of purposes, such as: residential or day centres for people experiencing homelessness;

charities supporting those who have served in the armed forces; rehabilitation centres; drop-in services; support for those suffering from substance abuse or working with at-risk young people.

Applications are considered for:

- New build and refurbishment of residential and rehabilitation centres; premises for the relief of homelessness, those suffering from substance abuse and young people 'at risk'; emergency centres which do not qualify for statutory funding
- 'Move on' support facilities
- Day care/Drop-in centres

The foundation offers four levels of grants: large grants of above £25,000, medium grants between £5,001 and £25,000, and small grants of £5,000, all considered by the trustees in meetings three times a year. A considerable number of minor grants of less than £5,000 are authorised by trustees on a rolling monthly basis. The foundation rarely funds more than 20% of the total cost of a project. Grants are usually one-off, but may be extended over three years where necessary.

Financial information

In 2016/17 the foundation had assets of £112 million and an income of £4 million. Grants were made to 497 organisations, of which 12 were large grants (above £25,000), 128 medium grants (between £5,000 and £25,000), and 74 small grants (£5,000) and 265 minor grants (less than £5,000). A total of £2.9 million was awarded during the year.

Grants approved were classified as follows:

Community	£1.3 million
Social Welfare	£675,000
Health	£572,000
Education	£500,000

Beneficiaries included: Chailey Heritage Foundation (£50,000); Brooke Hospital for Animals (£45,000); Merlin MS Centre (£25,000); Countryside Learning (£15,000); 1st Goostrey Scout Group, Ketton Sports and Community Centre, St Catherine's Hospice and Stockton-on-Tees Sea Cadets (£10,000 each); Caring for Life and Cumbria Wildlife Trust (£5,000 each); Air Ambulance Service (£2,500).

Exclusions

According to the foundation's website, it does not support:

- Organisations without registered/ exempt/excepted charity status – parish councils, community interest companies and amateur sports clubs
- Charities or projects in Scotland or Northern Ireland
- Revenue or running costs, including salaries, training, software licences, rent and utilities

- Feasibility studies, building surveys or planning applications
- Conservation/heritage projects for churches/church halls
- Mainstream schools and universities
- Projects with a total budget of less than £5,000
- Matched funding
- Non-durable equipment subject to wear and tear – e.g. appliances, camping equipment, furniture, mobility aids, musical instruments, clothing or tablets/laptops

Additional exclusions may apply depending upon the type of funding sought. Check the foundation's website for full details.

Applications

Applications can be made using the form on the foundation's website, where comprehensive guidance, application advice and eligibility criteria are provided. The foundation recommends applying at least six months in advance of the start date of a project. All applications will be acknowledged by email. Applicants who wish to discuss their proposal prior to submission are welcome to contact the foundation by phone.

Sources of information

Accounts; annual report; Charity Commission record; funder's website.

Support Adoption For Pets

Animal welfare

UK

£1.87 million (2016/17)

CC number: 1104152

Trustees: Louise Stonier; George Linwood; Jill Naylor; Brian Hudspith; Dan Laurence; Adrian Bates; Andrew Bickerton.

Correspondent: Laura Messenger, Grant Programme Co-ordinator, Epsom Avenue, Stanley Green Trading Estate, Handforth, Wilmslow, Cheshire SK9 3RN (tel: 0161 486 7538; email: laura@supportadoptionforpets.co.uk)

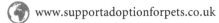

www.supportadoptionforpets.co.uk

facebook.com/ SupportAdoptionForPets

@AdoptionForPets

@supportadoptionforpets

The charity provides support for national animal welfare organisations and locally based re-homing centres through a combination of grants, joint fundraising activities and events. The charity operates small animal adoption

centres in a large number of Pets at Home stores. Since being established in 2006, the charity has supported over 1,000 animal charities across the UK and Northern Ireland.

According to the charity's website, the trustees will consider applications for the following:

- running costs (limited to vet bills and/or boarding costs) to a maximum of 20% of a rescue's annual expenditure
- Trap, Neuter and Release schemes for feral or stray cats
- the purchase of capital items (for example, vehicles, UPVC pens for foster homes, field shelters) and equipment
- low cost vaccination and/or neutering programmes made available to the public
- building renovations and new building work on land which is either owned in the rescue's name, or is on a long-term (min. 25 year) lease to the rescue. We will not fund building work on land which is owned or leased by an individual

Eligible organisations include:

- national pet rescue charities
- branches of national pet rescue organisations which receive minimal or no funding from central funds
- independent pet rescue and rehoming centres
- foster or boarding kennel/cattery based

Organisations must have been operating rescue and re-homing activities for a minimum of 12 months and have accounts for this period, in order to be considered for funding.

A full list of eligibility criteria is available to download from the charity's website.

Financial information

In 2016/17 the charity had assets of £1.8 million and an income of £3.95 million. Grants were made totalling almost £1.87 million.

Beneficiaries included: Hope Rescue (£102,000); Ferne Animal Rescue (£50,000); Eden Animal Rescue (£46,000); Coventry Cat Group, Newcastle Dog and Cat Shelter, Second Chance Animal Rescue Crockenhill and The Cat and Rabbit Rescue Centre CRRC (£20,000 each); Berwick Animal Rescue Kennels BARK, Maria's Animal Shelter, Munchkins Miniature Shetland Rescue, Sally's Cat Rescue and UK German Shepherd Rescue (£10,000 each).

Exclusions

Funding is not given for:

- Salaries, uniforms or expenses
- Education centres and programmes
- The purchase of food
- The cost of leasing a vehicle, road tax, insurance or petrol costs
- Loan or interest payments
- The purchase of land or buildings

- Any costs associated with a charity shop fundraising costs such as marketing materials
- Retrospective appeals for a project that has already been completed
- Wildlife charities

For further details and restrictions, refer to the guidance on the charity's website.

Applications

Prospective applicants are requested to check their eligibility against the charity's detailed online guidance. Eligible organisations can then complete and submit their applications via the charity's website.

The type of information requested varies depending on what applicants propose using the grant type. Broadly speaking, the charity requires that all applications include the following:

- 12 months of financial information
- Some evidence which demonstrates the total cost of the proposed project
- Contact details for two people who can provide a reference, one of whom must be the applicant's main vet

The trustees note that stronger applications may also include:

- Photos and case studies showing examples of pets who would be helped by the grant
- For building projects, photos and possibly videos showing the current state of the facilities
- Ideas on how you will work with Support Adoption For Pets to promote a grant to the charity's supporters and yours

Applications are considered approximately every five to six weeks for projects under £20,000, and quarterly for larger projects.

Sources of information

Accounts; annual report; Charity Commission record; further information provided by the funder; funder's website; guidelines for applicants.

Sutton Coldfield Charitable Trust

Relief in need, education, arts, religion, health, environment, sport, citizenship and community development

The former borough of Sutton Coldfield, comprising four electoral wards: New Hall, Four Oaks, Trinity and almost all of Vesey ward

£1.28 million to organisations (2016/17)

CC number: 218627

Trustees: Cllr Margaret Waddington; Keith Dudley; Carole Hancox; Neil Andrews; Dr Stephen Martin; Malcolm Cornish; Andrew Burley; Andrew

Morris; Inge Kettner; Sanjay Sharma; Cllr Diane Donaldson; Ranjan Hoath; Laurie-Anne Kennedy; Revd John Routh.

Correspondent: John Hemming, Grants Manager, Lingard House, Fox Hollies Road, Sutton Coldfield, West Midlands B76 2RJ (tel: 0121 351 2262; email: info@suttoncharitabletrust.org)

 www.suttoncoldfieldcharitabletrust. com

The trust, which is one of the largest and oldest local charities in the country, dates from 1528 when Bishop Vesey, a native of Sutton Coldfield, persuaded Henry VIII to grant a charter establishing a Warden and Society (corporation) to govern the town. The corporation was obliged to use rental and other income to provide poor relief and improve the locality. Over the next four centuries, other bequests and endowments came within the corporation's oversight. Until 2012, the trust was called the Sutton Coldfield Municipal Charities but now has no direct association with the local authority.

The trust's website states that it makes grants in the following categories:

- The Relief of those in Need by reason of youth, age, ill-health, disability, financial hardship or other disadvantage
- Education
- Arts, Culture, Heritage or Science
- Religion
- Health or the Saving of Lives
- Citizenship or Community Development
- Amateur Sport
- Environmental Protection or Improvement

Grants are awarded to benefit residents in the former borough of Sutton Coldfield, comprised of the wards of New Hall, Four Oaks, Trinity and most of Vesey ward. The website states that applications from organisations based outside this area will only be considered if they 'meet the needs of a significant number of residents and there is no similar local provision. For example, medical, hospice and special needs provision'.

Grants are also made to individuals in need and to families for school uniforms. The trust also maintains almshouses.

Financial information
In 2016/17 the trust had assets of £57 million and an income of £1.9 million. Grants to 63 organisations were made totalling £1.28 million, and a further £92,000 was donated to 399 individuals. Grants to both organisations and individuals were distributed as follows:

Education	£390,000
Amateur sport	£219,000
Relief of those in need	£217,000
Health	£130,000
Religion	£126,000
Citizenship and community development	£87,000
Environment	£67,000
Arts, culture, heritage and science	£58,000

Beneficiaries included: Homestart (£61,500); Sutton Coldfield Town Football Club (£50,000); Boulevard Allotments Association (£23,000); Sutton Coldfield Grammar School for Girls (£21,500); Salus Fatigue Foundation (£8,500); Glovers Trust (£255).

Exclusions
No awards are given to individuals or organisations outside the area of benefit, unless the organisations are providing essential services in the area.

Applications
Contact the grants manager on 0121 351 2262 or info@suttoncharitabletrust.org to make an application or to discuss further details.

Applications may be submitted at any time. The Grants Committee meets at least eight or nine times a year. Where awards requested are for £30,000 or less, the committee makes a decision and applicants are notified as soon as possible. Requests for grants of over £40,000 (previously £30,000), are considered by the committee and may be referred for a final decision to the full board of trustees, which meets quarterly.

Staff at the trust are able give assistance to those making applications at all stages of the process. Projects and applications can be discussed, either at the trust's office or onsite, and advice about deadlines for submitting applications can also be given.

Sources of information
Accounts; annual report; Charity Commission record; funder's website.

The Sutton Trust

 Improving social mobility through education

 UK

£ £3.1 million (2016/17)

CC number: 1146244

Trustees: Sir Peter Lampl; Lady Susan Lampl; Sir Peter Gershon; Oliver Quick.

Correspondent: Dr Lee Major, Chief Executive, Ninth Floor, Millbank Tower, 21–24 Millbank, London SW1P 4QP (tel: 020 7802 1660; email: info@suttontrust. com)

 www.suttontrust.com

The Sutton Trust was established in 1997 by Sir Peter Lampl to improve mobility through education. The trust's mission statement, as given on its website, is:

> We work to raise aspirations of young people from low and middle income backgrounds and to increase their chances of accessing top universities and the professions. We do this by delivering programmes, evidence-based research, and influencing public policy.

The trust runs a range of programmes to support its aims. Recent programmes have included increasing access to independent day schools and improving access to the accountancy profession.

Financial information
In 2016/17 the trust had assets of £7.5 million and an income of £8.9 million. Grants to 104 organisations totalled £3.1 million.

A list of beneficiaries was not included.

Applications
Note the following information taken from the trust's website: 'Currently we are not accepting unsolicited proposals to partner with other organisations. However, if you are looking to develop a programme or project, you may want to engage with our sister charity, the Education Endowment Foundation.'

Sources of information
Accounts; annual report; Charity Commission record; funder's website.

Swansea and Brecon Diocesan Board of Finance Ltd

 General charitable purposes, with a focus on religious activities within the diocese of Swansea and Brecon (Neath Port Talbot, Powys and Swansea)

Diocese of Swansea and Brecon (Neath Port Talbot, Powys and Swansea)

£ £3.35 million (2016)

CC number: 249810

Trustees: Gwyn Lewis; The Most Revd John Davies, the Archbishop of Wales; Revd Alan Jevons; Sonia Jones; The Venerable Jonathan Davies; Very Revd Dr Albert Shackerley; Paul Silk; Andrew Large; Louise Parson.

Correspondent: Louise Parson, Trustee, Diocesan Centre, Cathedral Close, Brecon, Powys LD3 9DP (tel: 01874 623716; email: diocese.swanbrec@ churchinwales.org.uk)

 swanseaandbrecon.churchinwales. org.uk

The charity was established in 1967. It seeks to promote, facilitate and support the work of the church in Wales in the diocese of Swansea and Brecon. The 2016 annual report notes the charity's objectives as follows:

- ▶ Promoting Christian values, and service by members of the Church in and to their communities, to the benefit of individuals and society as a whole
- ▶ Providing facilities for public worship, pastoral care and spiritual, moral and intellectual development, both for its members and for anyone who wishes to benefit from what the Church offers

The report also notes that the trustees manage diocesan funds to support clergy, parishes and communities in the diocese, and to develop and implement the 'Diocesan Vision to encourage mission and church growth strategies', as well as contributing to the work of the Church of Wales nationally and its worldwide mission. Most of the expenditure is in stipends and allowances for clergy and their residences, as well as other activities of the diocese. The 2016 report states, 'At the heart of our mission-shaped vision is the commitment to see lives transformed; this is therefore the fundamental purpose to which funding is directed.'

Financial information
In 2016 the charity had assets of £5.6 million and an income of £3.8 million. A total of £3.35 million was spent on charitable activities. Grant distributions are shown in the table below.

A list of beneficiaries was not included in the annual report and accounts.

Exclusions
Applications from outside the diocese will not be considered.

Applications
The charity does not respond to unsolicited applications.

Sources of information
Accounts; annual report; Charity Commission record; funder's website.

The John Swire 1989 Charitable Trust

🔍 General charitable purposes, arts, welfare, health, sports, education, medicine and research

📍 UK and overseas

💷 £1.4 million (2016)

CC number: 802142

Trustees: Barnaby Swire; Jonathan Swire; Michael Craddock Robinson.

Correspondent: Sarah Irving, John Swire & Sons Ltd, Swire House, 59 Buckingham Gate, London SW1E 6AJ (tel: 020 7834 7717; email: info@scts.org.uk)

Established in 1989 by Sir John Swire, the trust makes donations to a wide range of causes at the trustees' discretion, especially in the area of arts, welfare, health, sports, education, medicine and research. It has a strong affiliation to John Swire & Sons Ltd, a diversified group of global companies.

Financial information
In 2016 the trust held assets of £36.7 million and had an income of £1.4 million. A total of £1.4 million was awarded in donations to 171 organisations.

Beneficiaries included: Breast Cancer Haven and Kent Community Foundation

(£100,000 each); St John of Jerusalem Eye Hospital Group (£51,000); Fynvola Foundation (£25,000); Essex Wildlife Trust and Irish Guards Benevolent Fund (£1,000 each).

Applications
Donations are awarded at the discretion of trustees and unsolicited applications are unlikely to meet with success.

Sources of information
Accounts; annual report; Charity Commission record; funder's website.

The Adrian Swire Charitable Trust

🔍 General charitable purposes

📍 UK and overseas

💷 £844,000 (2016)

CC number: 800493

Trustees: Merlin Swire; Sir Martin Dunne; Lady Judith Swire; Martha Allfrey; Richard Leonard; Samuel Swire.

Correspondent: Sarah Irving, Swire House, 59 Buckingham Gate, London SW1E 6AJ (tel: 020 7834 7717; email: info@scts.org.uk)

The trust, formerly known as the Sammermar Trust, was established in 1988 with general charitable purposes. It has a strong affiliation to John Swire & Sons Ltd, a diversified group of global companies. Grants are made to a wide range of causes at the trustees' discretion.

Financial information
In 2016 the trust had assets of £27.5 million and an income of £1.3 million, including that obtained from investments in John Swire & Sons Ltd. Grants totalled £844,000.

Beneficiaries included: Ashmolean Museum (£125,000); Prior's Court Foundation (£50,000); Wings for Warriors (£30,000); Young Musicians Symphony Orchestra (£20,000); Air Pilots Trust (£10,000); Nilgiris Adivasi Trust (£4,000); Cardinall's Musick (£2,500) Shipwrecked Mariners' Society (£500).

Grants of less than £1,000 totalled £2,100.

Applications
Donations are awarded at the discretion of the trustees and unsolicited applications are unlikely to meet with success.

Sources of information
Accounts; annual report; Charity Commission record.

SWANSEA AND BRECON DIOCESAN BOARD OF FINANCE LTD

Purpose	Sub category	Amount
Support for ministry		
	Stipends and fees	£1.9 million
	Parsonages	£480,000
	Support costs	£115,000
	Training	£61,000
	Clergy expenses	£54,500
Other financial support		
	Diocesan bodies	£136,000
	Anglican, ecumenical and other bodies	£25,500
	Support costs	£9,000
Support for parishes		
	Support costs	£70,000
	Diocesan expenses	£46,000
	Sector ministries	£42,000
Church property		
	Inspections of churches and halls	£25,500
	Support costs	£16,300
	Diocesan Advisory Committee expenses	£11,900
	Churches and Pastoral Committee expenses	£919
Communications		
	Support costs	£8,800
	Newsletters and diocesan publications	£5,800
	Communications and media	£3,200

The Swire Charitable Trust

 General charitable purposes, with a focus on community and social welfare, education and training, heritage

Mainly UK

£2.5 million (2016)

CC number: 270726

Trustees: Barnaby Swire; John Swire; Sir Adrian Swire; Merlin Swire; James Hughes-Hallett; Samuel Swire; Martha Allfrey.

Correspondent: Sarah Irving, Grants Manager, Swire House, 59 Buckingham Gate, London SW1E 6AJ (tel: 020 7834 7717; email: info@scts.org.uk)

www.swirecharitabletrust.org.uk

Established in 1975, the trust's core grant-making programme makes grants to UK-registered charities working in the following areas: community and social welfare; education and training; and heritage. This trust is funded by John Swire & Sons Ltd, a diversified group of global companies. As a result of the merger of the Swire Charitable Trust and the Swire Educational Trust on 31 December 2015, the trust also operates a separate graduate and postgraduate scholarship programme for overseas students.

The following information on the trust's grant programmes and funding types is taken from the application guidelines on its website:

What is funded?

The Swire Charitable Trust awards grants via three funding programmes to UK-registered charities working in England, Scotland, Wales and Northern Ireland. These grant-making programmes are currently open and welcoming eligible online funding requests.

- Community and social welfare
- Education and training
- Heritage

Funding programmes

Community and Social Welfare

We fund charities that help to foster long-term positive change in the lives of disadvantaged people and their communities, we particularly welcome funding requests from charities working with:

- Young people leaving care
- Homeless people
- Ex-Servicemen and women
- Victims of slavery and human trafficking

Education and training

We fund charities that help children and adults from all backgrounds to fulfil their potential and make the most of their talents. We particularly support charities that are:

- Working to narrow the attainment gap for disadvantaged and marginalised children
- Targeting improvements in essential skills such as literacy and numeracy
- Empowering young people not in education, employment or training (NEETs), or marginalised adults, to engage with education or training

Heritage

We fund charities working to restore neglected buildings and monuments which can contribute to community regeneration, particularly in areas of deprivation. We would especially like to hear from smaller heritage charities that focus on providing employment, training or volunteering opportunities for disadvantaged members of their local communities.

Types of funding

Grants from our core programme will aim to meet the needs identified in your application. We will fund individual projects that are aligned with our funding priorities but we also recognise that charities themselves are often best placed to allocate resources within their organisations. Therefore our grants can be awarded on a restricted or an unrestricted basis and we are willing to support core costs, capital expenditure and salaries.

There is no maximum or minimum grant size and, although we base our grants on the amount requested and the size of organisation, we may award more or less than you applied for.

Indeed the amount requested will only be used for guidance and the size of the grant will be entirely at the discretion of the trustees.

While most of our grants are for one year only, we appreciate that charities welcome security of funding. So, where a longer-term commitment can be clearly justified, we are willing to consider multi-year grants of up to three years. But these are likely to come with additional conditions, such as reporting requirements.

Financial information

In 2016 the trust had assets of £10.6 million and an income of £2.8 million. Grants to charitable organisations totalled £2.5 million.

Beneficiaries included: Beanstalk (£50,000); Combat Stress (£30,000); Empire Fighting Chance and The Royal British Legion Industries (£20,000 each); Upper Room, The Passage and Prisoners' Education Trust (£10,000 each).

Exclusions

According to the trust's application guidelines, it is unable to consider:

- Applications received by post or email, i.e. not via the trust's online funding request form
- Organisations that are not UK-registered charities
- Requests from charities that have applied in the last 12 months
- Individual applicants or proposals that will benefit only one person
- Activities taking place outside England, Scotland, Wales or Northern Ireland
- Work that has already taken place
- Statutory bodies or work that is primarily the responsibility of statutory authorities (e.g. residential, respite and day care, housing and provision of mainstream education through individual schools, nurseries and colleges)
- Activities of local organisations which are part of a wider network doing similar work (e.g. uniformed youth groups, YMCA, Mind, Relate, Citizens Advice, Age UK)
- Medicine-related charities, including those that provide care, support and equipment or fund research
- Animal welfare charities
- Academic research, scholarships or bursaries

Applications

The trust welcomes funding applications from UK-registered charities which should be made via the online application form on the trust's website. Applications are considered throughout the year.

Sources of information

Accounts; annual report; Charity Commission record; funder's website.

The Syder Foundation

General charitable purposes

UK and overseas

£287,500 (2015/16)

CC number: 1119373

Trustees: Charlotte Syder; Timothy Syder.

Correspondent: Timothy Syder, Trustee, PO Box 60260, London EC4P 4AN

The foundation was registered with the Charity Commission in 2007 and makes grants throughout the UK and overseas. Its annual report states: 'The object of the charity is to advance monies for any lawful charitable purpose at the discretion of the Trustees, with the exception of the following: The promotion of animal welfare The promotion of research and The advancement of education of individual persons.'

Financial information

In 2015/16 the foundation held assets of £5.26 million and had an income of

£218,000. Grants awarded to organisations totalled £287,500.

A list of beneficiaries was unavailable.

Exclusions

Animal welfare; research; individuals' education.

Applications

Apply in writing to the correspondent.

Sources of information

Accounts; annual report; Charity Commission record.

The Charles and Elsie Sykes Trust

 General charitable purposes, social welfare, medical research

UK, with a preference for Yorkshire

£ £329,000 (2016)

CC number: 206926

Trustees: John Ward; Anne Brownlie; Martin Coultas; Barry Kay; Peter Rous; Dr Rosemary Livingstone; Sara Buchan; Dr Michael McEvoy.

Correspondent: Neil Shaw, Secretary, c/o LCF Barber Titleys, First Floor, The Exchange, Harrogate, North Yorkshire HG1 1TS (tel: 01423 817238; email: katie.davill@lcf.co.uk)

www.charlesandelsiesykestrust.co. uk

Charles Sykes started his career as a twelve-year-old office boy, and became a successful businessman in the West Riding knitting wool trade with his own four-storey mill at Princeville, Bradford. He achieved his life ambition at 82 years old when he launched the Charles Sykes Trust on 16 December 1954.

The trust supports registered charities, education or health/medical organisations based in Yorkshire or benefitting people in Yorkshire directly, for a range of charitable purposes, but with particular interest in: the relief of hardship among children, older people and people with disabilities; and medical research projects. The website states that 'applications from schools, playgroups, cadet forces, scouts, guides, and churches must be for outreach programmes, and not for maintenance projects'.

Grants are given in the following categories:

▶ Medical grants – supporting healthcare and medical research
▶ Annual grants – for ongoing programmes, with funding renewed every year
▶ Special grants – for one-off charitable projects

▶ Exceptional grants/'Super Specials' – grants made for exceptional circumstances, such as the trust's anniversary

Financial information

In 2016 the trust had assets of £16.5 million and an income of £486,500. During the year, 112 grants were made totalling £329,000, distributed as follows:

Medical research	21	£55,000
Social welfare	19	£50,000
Education	5	£45,000
Disability – physical	17	£44,000
Cultural and environmental heritage	13	£34,000
Children and young people	10	£24,500
Older people	4	£18,500
Medical welfare	6	£12,500
Mental health and disability	5	£12,500
Visual impairment	4	£11,500
Hearing and speech impairment	3	£5,500
Overseas aid	1	£3,000
Services and ex-Services	1	£3,000

A wide range of causes are supported, and the trust has sub-committees to consider both medical and non-medical grants.

Beneficiaries included: Opera North (£22,000); Yorkshire Cancer Research (£15,000); York Archaeological Trust (£10,000); Foodcycle and Alzheimer's Research UK (£5,000 each); Samaritans of Leeds (£3,000); Shopmobility Sheffield (£2,400); Deafblind UK, Harrogate Homeless Project and National Eye Research Centre (£2,000 each).

Exclusions

Individuals; building maintenance projects; projects without either a medical link or a link to Yorkshire; recently established charities; applications for overseas work.

Applications

Application forms are available to download from the website, along with a checklist, and should be sent by post along with a copy of the latest accounts and annual report, and any other relevant information. Further guidance on what to include is given on the website. The trustees meet in March, June, September and December, and applications should be submitted by the last Friday of January, April, July and October respectively.

Sources of information

Accounts; annual report; Charity Commission record; funder's website.

The Tajtelbaum Charitable Trust

 Jewish, welfare

Generally UK and Israel

£ £742,500 (2016/17)

CC number: 273184

Trustees: Ilsa Tajtelbaum; Jacob Tajtelbaum; Emanuel Tajtelbaum; Henry Frydenson.

Correspondent: Emanuel Tajtelbaum, Trustee, PO Box 33911, London NW9 7ZX (tel: 020 8202 3464)

The trust makes grants in the UK and Israel to Orthodox synagogues, Jewish educational establishments, homes for older people and hospitals.

Financial information

In 2016/17 the trust held assets of £6.1 million and had an income of £808,000. During the year, the trust gave a total of £742,500 in grants to organisations.

Previous beneficiaries have included: Before Trust; Beth Hassidei; Centre for Torah and Chesed; Comet Charities Ltd; Delharville; Emuno Educational Centre; Friends of Nachlat David; Friends of Sanz Institute; Gur Foundation; Kupat Gemach Trust; Ruzin Sadiger Trust; United Institutions Arad.

Applications

Apply in writing to the correspondent.

Sources of information

Accounts; annual report; Charity Commission record.

The Talbot Village Trust

 General charitable purposes including disability, social welfare and housing

The boroughs of Bournemouth, Christchurch and Poole, the districts of East Dorset and Purbeck

£ £1.36 million (2016)

CC number: 249349

Trustees: Sir Thomas Salt; James Fleming; Christopher Lees; Russell Rowe; Earl of Shaftesbury; George Meyrick.

Correspondent: Darryl Tidd, Director, Trethowans, 5 Parkstone Road, Poole BH15 2NL (tel: 01202 673071; email: darryl.tidd@talbotvillagetrust.org)

www.talbotvillagetrust.co.uk

According to the trust's record on the Charity Commission website, support is given to 'other charitable bodies, churches, schools and the like for projects which support youth, the elderly and the disadvantaged in the boroughs of Bournemouth, Christchurch and Poole and the districts of East Dorset and Purbeck'. The charity owns and manages land and property at Talbot Village, Bournemouth, including almshouses which it maintains through an associated trust. There is a strong property focus in much of the trust's work.

Financial information

In 2016 the trust had of assets of £49.3 million and an income of £2.8 million. Grants were made totalling £1.36 million.

Beneficiaries included: Bournemouth Blind Society (£38,000); Gateway Church (£29,000); Aim Community FYT (£25,000); St George's Church (£15,000); Purbeck Citizens Advice (£10,000); St James the Greater Church (£7,000); St Katharine's CE (VA) Primary School (£2,000).

Exclusions

The trust will not provide grants for individuals, nor contribute to running costs or revenue items of expenditure.

Applications

Applications can be made using the online application form, or by post, including the information specified in the guidelines on the website. The trustees meet twice a year to consider applications and applicants are notified of the outcome within a couple of weeks of a meeting.

Sources of information

Accounts; annual report; Charity Commission record; funder's website.

Tallow Chandlers Benevolent Fund No. 2

 Young people, education, general charitable purposes

London, mostly City of London

£360,000 (2016/17)

CC number: 246255

Trustees: Sir Michael Snyder; John Kurkjian; Nicholas Bull; Ian McIntyre; Michael Bridges Webb; Christopher Tootal; Rupert Travis; Richard Fleck; Robert Nicolle; C. R. Lambourne; N. M. Wells; Brig. N. H. Thompson; Peter Purton; Philip Edwards; R. B. Yates; Timothy Piper; David Simmonds; J. N. Harrington; Michael Sutcliffe; Sir Peter Cazalet; Brig. Keith Prosser; Ian Bowden; Robert Pick; Sir Christopher Pryke; Oliver Kirby-Johnson; Ian Robertson; David Homer; John Baxter; Dr Christopher Gibson Smith; Anthony Green; James Long; Lorraine Green.

Correspondent: David Homer, Clerk, Tallow Chandlers Hall, 4 Dowgate Hill,

London EC4R 2SH (tel: 020 7248 4726; email: clerk@tallowchandlers.org)

 www.tallowchandlers.org

The fund is a charity of the Worshipful Company of Tallow Chandlers.

The fund supports a range of charitable purposes, particularly those supporting disadvantaged young people in Greater London and education and causes relating to the City of London. A proportion of the grant-making budget is reserved for charities proposed by members of the company, which meet the fund's objectives.

The following information is given in the 2016/17 annual report:

> We focus on helping young, disadvantaged people to fulfil their potential and contribute ta society through:
>
> ▸ Supporting education, training and youth activities, primarily in Greater London
> ▸ Supporting health and social welfare programmes
> ▸ Promoting and encouraging excellence

Funding is given to registered charities. One-off grants of between £250 and £1,000 are awarded, as well as longer-term grants for three years, which are usually reserved for those focusing on young people, or education and skills, particularly in STEM subjects.

The fund also works closely with specific schools in London, providing both financial support and other opportunities.

Financial information

In 2016/17 the fund has assets of £8.8 million and an income of £613,000. Grants were made to 73 organisations totalling £360,000.

Beneficiaries of grants over £1,000 included: Greig City Academy (£27,500); Corelli College (£20,000); IntoUniversity (£10,000); The Poppy Factory (£5,500); Clean Break Theatre Company (£4,500 in two grants); Arundel Castle Cricket Foundation (£3,000); Southwark Sea Cadets (£2,500); London Wildlife Trust (£2,000); Shepherd's Bush Families Project and Children's Centre (£1,000 each).

Exclusions

The fund does not generally support large or national charities, or charities operating overseas.

Applications

Apply in writing to the correspondent. Applications are considered by the clerk, the chair and the Education and Charity Committee. All applicants are notified of the outcome of their request.

Sources of information

Accounts, annual report, Charity Commission record; funder's website.

The Talmud Torah Machzikei Hadass Trust

 Jewish causes

UK and international, in practice the London borough of Hackney

£1.7 million (2016/17)

CC number: 270693

Trustees: Jehudah Baumgarten; Yitzchok Sternlicht; Mordechaj Wind.

Correspondent: Yitzchok Sternlicht, Trustee, 28 Leadale Road, London N16 6DA

This trust was founded in 1975 to further the Orthodox Jewish religion in any part of the world. However, in practice, the trust appears to concentrate its activity in Hackney.

Financial information

In 2016/17 the trust had assets of £10.7 million and had an income of £6.3 million. During the year, the trust gave almost £1.7 million in grants to organisations.

A list of beneficiaries was not included in the accounts.

Applications

Apply in writing to the correspondent.

Sources of information

Accounts; annual report; Charity Commission record.

The David Tannen Charitable Trust

Jewish causes, social welfare, education and training

Barnet, Hackney, Haringey and Israel

£436,500 (2016/17)

CC number: 280392

Trustees: David Tannen; Jonathan Miller.

Correspondent: Jonathan Miller, Trustee, c/o Sutherland House, 70–78 West Hendon Broadway, London NW9 7BT (tel: 020 8202 1066)

The trust was established in 1974 and registered with the Charity Commission in 1981. The aims of the trust are to relieve poverty, distress, and suffering in any part of the world, and also to promote and advance Jewish religion and education through charitable means.

Financial information

In 2016/17 the trust had assets of £18.9 million and an income of

£2.7 million. Grants were made totalling £436,500 to eight organisations.

Beneficiaries included: Moreshet Hatorah Ltd (£95,000); ABC Trust and Before Trust (£50,000 each); Cosmon Belz Ltd (£40,000); WST Charity Ltd (£31,000).

Applications

Apply in writing to the correspondent.

Sources of information

Accounts; annual report; Charity Commission record.

Tay Charitable Trust

 General charitable purposes

 UK, with a focus on Scotland, particularly Dundee

£ £249,500 (2016/17)

OSCR number: SC001004

Correspondent: The Trustees, 6 Douglas Terrace, Broughty Ferry, Dundee DD5 1EA

This trust has general charitable purposes and supports a wide range of causes. Grants of up to £5,000 are made to registered charities with first preference given to Dundee-based organisations and then to organisations in Scotland. Some UK national charities have also been supported.

Financial information

In 2016/17 the trust had assets of £7.5 million and an income of £254,500. Grants awarded to organisations totalled £249,500.

Beneficiaries included: Broughty Ferry YMCA and High School of Dundee (£5,000 each); Dundee Botanic Garden (£3,000); Bowel Cancer UK and Dundee Independent Advocacy Support (£2,000 each); Reform Scotland (£1,500); Edinburgh High Blood Pressure Fund, New Caledonian Woodlands and Nordoff Robbins Scotland (£1,000 each).

Exclusions

The trust does not support individuals.

Applications

Apply in writing to the correspondent including a financial statement. The trustees have previously stated that they are unable to notify unsuccessful applicants.

Sources of information

Accounts; annual report; OSCR record.

C B and H H Taylor 1984 Trust

 Healthcare projects, social welfare, education, adult literacy schemes, employment training, youth work, penal affairs, work with offenders and ex-offenders, police projects, the environment and conservation, the arts, cross-community health and social welfare projects in Ireland, overseas development, Quaker causes

Birmingham, the West Midlands, overseas and Ireland

£ £372,000 (2016/17)

CC number: 291363

Trustees: Constance Penny; Elizabeth Birmingham; Clare Norton; John Taylor; Thomas Penny; Robert Birmingham; Simon Taylor.

Correspondent: Carolyn Bettis, Rokesley, Bristol Road, Selly Oak, Birmingham B29 6QF (email: cbandhhtaylortrust.info@gmail.com)

Registered in 1985, the trust supports organisations working in Birmingham, the West Midlands and Ireland, as well as UK-based charities working overseas. The trust also supports organisations based outside these areas with which it has well-established links.

Areas of work

The trust's annual report for 2016/17 describes its general areas of work as:

▸ Quakers and other religious denominations
▸ Healthcare projects
▸ Social welfare for children and young people, older people, people with disabilities, people who are homeless
▸ Community groups including youth groups, housing initiatives and counselling and mediation agencies
▸ Education especially adult literacy schemes and employment training
▸ Projects working with offenders, ex-offenders and the police
▸ The environment and conservation work
▸ The arts, particularly museums and art galleries, music and drama
▸ Ireland: cross-community health and social welfare projects
▸ UK charities working overseas on long-term development projects

The annual report also provides the following information:

> Approximately 60% of grants are for the work and concerns of the Religious Society of Friends. The Trust favours specific applications. It does not usually award grants on an annual basis for revenue costs. Applications are encouraged from minority groups and women-led initiatives.

Financial information

In 2016/17 the trust held assets of £14.8 million and had an income of £537,500. Grants were made to 174 organisations and totalled £372,000.

Previous beneficiaries have included: Britain Yearly Meeting (£58,000); Woodbrooke Quaker Study Centre (£10,000); Shelter (£6,000); Medical Aid for Palestinians and Prison Reform Trust (£5,000 each); Children's Safety Education Foundation and Freedom From Torture (£1,000 each); Bumblebee Conservation Trust, Food Mood, Refugee Women of Bristol and TACT Fostering and Adoption (£500 each).

Exclusions

The trust does not support the following

▸ Individuals
▸ Local projects or groups outside the West Midlands
▸ Annual grants for revenue costs

Applications

Apply in writing to the correspondent.

Sources of information

Accounts; annual report; Charity Commission record.

Humphrey Richardson Taylor Charitable Trust

 Music

Surrey and its adjacent areas

£ £375,000 to organisations (2016)

CC number: 1062836

Trustees: William Malings; Rowena Cox; Colin Edgerton; Ian Catling; Michael Wood; Stephen Oliver.

Correspondent: Mr B. Bennett, Administrator, c/o Palmers, 28 Chipstead Station Parade, Chipstead, Coulsdon, Surrey CR5 3TF (tel: 01737 557546; fax: 01737 554093; email: hrtaylortrust@btconnect.com)

🌐 www.hrtaylortrust.org.uk

This trust was established in 1997 for 'the advancement of public education in, and appreciation of, the art and science of music and allied performing arts'. It is named after its late benefactor, Mr H. R. Taylor, who lived in Surrey and was devoted to music and wished to encourage the advancement of music-making and live performance by people of every age.

Areas of support

The trust supports musical activities in Surrey and its adjacent areas. Through national bodies such as the Royal College of Music and the University of Surrey, it also supports 'musically gifted British residents' outside its primary area of benefit.

Help is given to schools, musical societies and organisations, and individuals, typically for the following:

- Schools: music-related capital projects; purchase of instruments; music computers and software; scores and sheet music; funding of concerts for special occasions; part-funding of instrumental tuition
- Musical societies and organisations: annual grants towards the costs of funding live concerts (choral societies, orchestras, opera and light operatic societies, etc.)
- Individuals: scholarship funding for music-related undergraduate studies; scholarship funding for music-related postgraduate studies; grants towards fees; purchase of instruments

Financial information

In 2016 the trust had assets of £14.6 million and an income of £518,000. Grants totalled £411,000 with £36,000 given to individuals and £375,000 given to organisations.

Beneficiaries included: Royal College of Music (£35,000); Burgess Hill Academy (£30,000); Glenthorne High School (£14,000); Banstead Arts Festival (£4,000); Croydon Symphony Orchestra (£3,5000); Burgess Hill Choral Society (£3,000); Reigate and Redhill Music Festival (£1,500); Thames Philharmonia (£1,000).

Exclusions

Projects or causes that are not associated with music.

Applications

Apply in writing to the correspondent. The trustees meet five times a year to consider applications. Applications should be no longer than four to six pages of A4 when printed. Specific application criteria and guidelines for schools, musical societies and individuals are available to view on the website.

Sources of information

Accounts; annual report; Charity Commission record; funder's website.

The Taylor Family Foundation

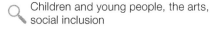

Children and young people, the arts, social inclusion

UK, with a particular focus on the London borough of Merton

£2.9 million (2016/17)

CC number: 1118032

Trustees: Ian Taylor; Cristina Taylor; Neville Shepherd.

Correspondent: Neville Shepherd, Trustee, Hill Place House, 55a High Street, Wimbledon, London SW19 5BA (tel: 020 8605 2629; email: info@ thetaylorfamilyfoundation)

 www.thetaylorfamilyfoundation.co. uk

The foundation was set up by Ian and Cristina Taylor in 2007 and has since given over £16 million to charitable causes in the UK. The main focus of the foundation is supporting charities that give opportunities to children and young people from disadvantaged backgrounds to improve their chances of attaining success and leading fulfilling lives.

Areas of focus

The following information has been taken from the foundation's website:

Children and young people – supporting charitable organisations that provide opportunities for children and young people from disadvantaged backgrounds, to improve their chances of attaining success and to leading fulfilling lives.

The arts – improving access and engagement from young people and those from deprived backgrounds.

Social inclusion - helping the homeless and supporting deprived and struggling families.

Age group - the majority of our future grants will be used to fund projects which focus on young people 11–25 years old.

Geographical focus - we fund charitable organisations based in the UK. For smaller projects we have a particular focus on the London Borough of Merton in which we are based.

Financial information

In 2016/17 the foundation held assets of £957,000 and had an income of £3.1 million. Grants were made to 26 organisations totalling over £2.9 million.

Beneficiaries included: Royal Opera House Covent Garden Foundation (£500,000); Tate Foundation (£260,000); The Lowry Centre Trust (£50,000); Médecins Sans Frontièreses (£40,000); Children's Hospice Association Scotland (£20,000); Prisoners Education Trust (£15,000); Beanstalk (£10,000); Home-Start Merton (£7,000); Mitcham Town Community Trust (£1,500).

Exclusions

No grants are given to individuals.

Applications

Applicants should complete the contact form on the foundation's website. The trustees will then arrange to discuss eligibility and whether the proposed project is something the foundation may fund. The applicant may then be asked to complete a full application form.

Sources of information

Accounts; annual report; Charity Commission website; funder's website.

Khoo Teck Puat UK Foundation

Social welfare, education, health, the promotion of the arts, culture and science

UK

£7 million (2016/17)

CC number: 1142788

Trustees: Elizabeth Khoo; Mavis Khoo Bee Geok; Neil Carmichael; Jennifer Carmichael; Eric Khoo Kim Hai.

Correspondent: Jennifer Carmichael, Trustee, 2–24 Kensington High Street, London W8 4PT (tel: 020 7937 8000)

The foundation is the UK subsidiary of Khoo Teck Puat Foundation, a charitable organisation founded by Khoo Teck Puat which is incorporated in Singapore. Khoo Teck Puat was a banker and hotelier who owned the Goodwood Group of boutique hotels in London and Singapore and was the largest single shareholder of the British bank, Standard Chartered.

Areas of support

According to its 2016/17 annual report, the objects of the foundation are:

- the prevention or relief of poverty or financial hardship of the public
- the advancement of the education of the public
- the relief of sickness and the preservation and advancement of the health of the public
- the promotion and advancement of the arts, culture or science

Financial information

In 2016/17 the foundation held assets of £61.3 million and had an income of £5.7 million. Grants awarded to organisations totalled £7 million.

Beneficiaries included: Guy's and St Thomas's Hospital (£1 million); UCL Cancer Research Trust (£130,000); Lifelites (£125,000); The Stroke Association (£121,000); British Red Cross (£100,000); Sight Savers (£20,000); PAWA (£1,000).

Applications

Apply in writing to the correspondent.

Sources of information

Accounts; annual report; Charity Commission record.

The Tedworth Charitable Trust

 Parenting, children and young people, family welfare, arts and culture, the environment

UK and overseas

£450,500 (2016/17)

CC number: 328524

Trustees: Judith Portrait; Timothy Sainsbury; Jessica Sainsbury; Margaret Sainsbury.

Correspondent: Robert Bell, Director, The Peak, 5 Wilton Road, London SW1V 1AP (tel: 020 7410 0330; email: info@sfct.org.uk)

www.sfct.org.uk

This is one of the Sainsbury Family Charitable Trusts, which share a joint administration and have a common approach to grant-making.

This trust's main areas of interest are parenting, family welfare, child development, arts and the environment; the trust also makes grants for general charitable purposes.

Financial information

In 2016/17 the trust held assets of £12.5 million and had an income of £433,500. Grants were paid to 32 organisations totalling £450,500 and were broken down as follows:

Arts and the environment	14	£212,000
Parenting, family welfare and child development	13	£195,500
General	5	£43,000

Previous beneficiaries have included: Home-Start UK (£50,000); Human Rights Watch, New Economics Foundation and Organic Research Centre (£20,000 each); Family and Childcare Trust (£18,500); Bibliotheraphy Foundation (£15,000); Voices Foundation (£10,000); Women's Environmental Network (£7,500); Migrants Organise (£5,000); Sainsbury Archive (£880).

Exclusions

The trust does not make grants to individuals.

Applications

The trust's annual report for 2016/17 stated that: 'Proposals are generally invited by the Trustees or initiated at their request. Unsolicited applications are unlikely to be successful, even if they fall within an area in which the Trustees are interested.'

Sources of information

Accounts; annual report; Charity Commission record; funder's website.

The Tennis Foundation

 Tennis for young people and people with disabilities

UK

£2.2 million (2017)

CC number: 298175

Trustees: James Jordan; Funke Awoderu; Barry Horne; Karen Keohane; Baroness Margaret Ford; Baroness Tanni Grey-Thompson; Martin Corrie; Nick Fuller; Cynthia Muller.

Correspondent: Joanna Farquharson, Secretary, National Tennis Centre, 100 Priory Lane, London SW15 5JQ (tel: 0845 872 0522; email: info@ tennisfoundation.org.uk)

www.tennisfoundation.org.uk

Registered in 1987, the foundation promotes the participation in tennis for the benefit of young people, older people and people with a disability.

Areas of work

According to the foundation's 2017 annual report, its objectives are:

- the advancement, for the benefit of the public, of the education of children and young persons who are pupils at schools, colleges or universities by organising or providing facilities which will enable and encourage them to play tennis or mini tennis (being a version of tennis adapted for children) and thereby ensuring that due attention is given to the physical education of such pupils as well as the development and occupation of their minds
- the organisation or provision (or assistance in the organisation or provision) of facilities for recreation in the interests of social welfare in any part of the United Kingdom (with the object of improving the conditions of life for the persons for whom the facilities are primarily intended) either for persons who have need of such facilities by reason of their youth, age, infirmity or disablement, poverty or social or economic circumstances or for members of the public at large
- for the benefit of the public to promote community participation in healthy recreation by providing facilities for playing tennis, mini tennis or other sports
- to promote all purposes recognised as charitable under the law of England and Wales from time to time, in particular through an association with tennis

Financial information

In 2017 the foundation had assets of £7 million and an income of £12.4 million. Grants were made totalling £2.2 million and were broken down as follows:

Education	£1.1 million
Community	£380,000
Disability tennis	£374,000
Coaching	£212,000
Tennis development	£183,000

Beneficiaries included: Loughborough University (£153,000).

Applications

Initial enquiries should be made by telephone.

Sources of information

Accounts; annual report; Charity Commission record; funder's website.

Tenovus Cancer Care

 Cancer research

UK, with a preference for Wales

£705,000 (2016/17)

CC number: 1054015

Trustees: Prof. Malcolm Mason; Prof. John Lazarus; Wyn Mears; Melanie Goward; Deborah Fitzsimmons; Geraint Williams; Simons Evans; Paula Kathrens; Annie Proctor; Iestyn Morris; Michael Borrill; Anne-Marie Koukourava; Hugh O'Sullivan.

Correspondent: Rhian Edwards, Director of Research, Gleider House, Ty Glas Road, Cardiff CF14 5BD (tel: 029 2076 8850; email: post@tenovus.org.uk)

www.tenovus.org.uk

facebook.com/tenovuscancercare

@tenovuscancer

According to the charity's Charity Commission record, Tenovus Cancer Care has the general aim of 'identifying opportunities to fund high quality research into major cancers affecting men, women and children'. In addition to its research, Tenovus also aims to provide 'psychological, psychosocial and practical financial help to people affected by cancer, and to educate and raise awareness of cancer issues of both the public and healthcare professionals'.

The majority of the charity's funds are raised through its retail activities as well as donations and legacies from its supporters.

Grant programmes

At the time of writing (April 2018), the charity offered the following types of funding:

- **iGrants:** grants for research projects which 'meet the needs of cancer patients and their families, including cancer prevention research'. Grants are available to individuals, patient groups, academic institutions, health professionals and voluntary organisations, where the lead applicant is based in Wales, although co-applicants or collaborators may be from outside Wales. Applications are accepted for projects from £1,000 up to a maximum of £30,000

- **PhD studentships:** funding for postgraduate cancer research, both in the laboratory and in the social sciences. PhD studentships are open to any academic institution based in Wales. They will be for a period of up to four years at a maximum of £30,000 per annum for laboratory based projects, and £20,000 per annum for non-laboratory projects
- **KESS studentships:** Knowledge Economy Skills Scholarships (KESS) is a major European Convergence programme led by Bangor University on behalf of the Welsh higher education sector. KESS offers collaborative research projects (Research Masters and PhD) linked with a local company partner, with scholarships supported by European Social Funding across Wales. Tenovus is an active KESS partner, and welcomes applications for research projects across Wales which will help it to meet its charitable aims
- **Research strategy grants:** funding to advance the service and activity provision of Tenovus Cancer Care as well as evaluate the effectiveness of current services. Research strategy grants are open to projects where the lead applicant is based in Wales, although co-applicants or collaborators may be from outside Wales. Applications for projects up to a maximum of £60,000 in total, for funding for up to two years are accepted. Each funding call will have its own priority themes which applications should meet. See the charity's website for guidance on the most recent call for funding

Financial information

In 2016/17 the charity had assets of £5.3 million and an income of £9 million. During the year, the charity provided grants totalling £705,000 to ten organisations.

Beneficiaries included: University of Cardiff (£335,500); Royal College of Music (£155,000); University of Aberystwyth (£50,000); Cardiff and Vale UHB (£39,500); Hywel Dda University Health Board (£36,500); University of Swansea (£14,600); University of Wales Bangor (£5,700); University Hospital of Wales (£100).

Applications

Application processes vary depending upon the grant programme. Full guidance for all open grant programmes is available on the charity's website, where prospective applicants can register

to receive updates about new programmes and funding calls.

Sources of information

Accounts; annual report; Charity Commission record, funder's website.

Tenovus Scotland

Medical research

Scotland

£661,000 (2016/17)

OSCR number: SC009675

Trustees: Prof. Andrew Calder; Colin Black; Prof. John Connell; Prof. James Grieve; Mary Marquis; Francis McCrossin; Malcolm McIver; Prof. Kenneth Paterson; Graham Philips; Dr Heather Reid; James Watson.

Correspondent: Iain McFadzean, General Secretary, The Royal College of Physicians and Surgeons of Glasgow, 232–242 St Vincent Street, Glasgow G2 5RJ (tel: 0141 221 6268; email: gen. sec@talk21.com)

 www.tenovus-scotland.org.uk

The charity was established in 1967 and provides early pilot funds for initial research in medicine and healthcare. It has regional committees in Edinburgh, Grampian, Strathclyde and Tayside.

The following information on the charity's grant programmes has been taken from its website:

Small Pilot grants of up to £20,000

Our main focus is on awarding small grants to allow researchers, usually at the start of their research career, to produce preliminary data in a new area of scientific research. This then allows them to apply for funding from larger research funding organisations, further developing exciting medical possibilities.

Each of the four regions (Edinburgh, Grampian, Strathclyde and Tayside) raises its own funds to support research within its region.

Recent projects funded have included: research into the development of novel approaches to reduce vascular diseases, a potential new drug target for resolving sepsis and investigating new therapies for osteoarthritis.

Large grants of up to £100,000

A small number of larger awards (between £50,000 and £100,000) are available only in the Tayside region. This level of support is aimed at more ambitious research projects than the small research grants as they require a higher level of funding and a project duration of two to three years. These awards, however, are still primarily aimed at early career researchers or pilot projects that have potential to lead to more ambitious programmes of research

than can be supported by major Research Councils or Charities.

Recent projects funded have included: research into enzyme inhibitors in asthma, investigation into the causes of kidney cancer and research into the inflammation effect on heart and blood vessel disease.

Medical research PhD scholarships

The Princess Royal Tenovus Scotland Medical Research Scholarship Scheme gives scholarships to support young researchers through a three-year programme of training and research activity towards a PhD degree. We aim to offer at least one scholarship a year.

The Moulton-Barrett Research Scholarship is a Grampian region initiative to fund talented PhD medical students for four years of full-time study

Recent scholarship holders include: Anna Muriano, studying the debilitating condition of Huntingdon's Disease at the University of Dundee; Angela Ianniciello at the University of Glasgow studying Chronic Myeloid Leukaemia; and Vasiliki Mallikourti, researching non-invasive mapping of lipid and metabolite profiles in breast cancer, involving MRI methods, at the University of Aberdeen.

Researcher awards

We make one-off awards to researchers in recognition of the quality and importance of their work and to support further research, including awards for:

- Most outstanding final research report
- Best research in Scotland in a nominated field
- Pathology intercalated degree students at the University of Glasgow
- Contribution to the understanding of the disabilities affecting elderly people

Financial information

In 2016/17 the charity had assets of £2.5 million and an income of £1.2 million. Expenditure on projects and grants totalled £661,000.

A list of beneficiaries was not available.

Exclusions

Grants are not made to individuals other than as members of institutions engaged in research approved by such institutions and by the National Scientific Advisory Committee of Tenovus Scotland.

Applications

An application form can be requested from the relevant regional correspondent – refer to the website for contact details. Application deadlines are also posted on the website.

Sources of information

Accounts; annual report; OSCR record; funder's website.

Theatres Trust

 Capital improvements for theatres

 UK

 £200,000 (2016/17)

CC number: 274697

Trustees: Ann Skippers; Gary Kemp; Ruth Eastwood; David Blyth; Dara O'Briain; Peter Roberts; Anna Stapleton; Tim Eyles; Patrick Dillon; Richard Baldwin; Paul Cartwright; David Ian; Richard Johnston; Simon Ricketts; Pamela Bone.

Correspondent: Jon Morgan, 22 Charing Cross Road, London WC2H 0QL (tel: 020 7836 8591; email: advice@ theatrestrust.org.uk)

🌐 www.theatrestrust.org.uk

f facebook.com/theatres.trust

🐦 @TheatresTrust

The Theatres Trust was established in 1976 and is the national public body for theatres. It works to promote the better protection of theatres for the benefit of the nation.

Grant schemes

The trust has three grant schemes, details of which have been taken from its website:

The London Small Theatres Grants Scheme is a capital fund that awards up to £5,000 to small theatres in London which are undertaking building projects.

The UK Theatres Small Grants Scheme is a capital fund that awards up to £5,000 to theatres across the UK run by charities and not-for-profit groups that can clearly demonstrate the value capital improvements to their theatres would make to their work in local communities.

The Theatres Trust's Theatre Improvement Scheme, in association with the Wolfson Foundation, is a capital fund that awards grants of up to £20,000. The scheme will run for three years, and each year will fund projects with a specific theme. The theme for 2018 will be **Improving Accessibility**.

Who can apply

To be eligible to apply to the scheme, applicants must demonstrate that they:

▶ own or manage theatres with titles or signed leases of more than 15 years on buildings in England, Scotland, Wales and Northern Ireland

▶ run a year-round programme of live performance, of no less than 30 performances a year

▶ have a bona fide UK charitable or not-for-profit legal structure and be able to provide certified or audited accounts for at least two years

▶ operate theatres that achieve excellence through their producing and programming or architectural significance

Financial information

In 2016/17 the fund had assets of £1 million and an income of £861,000. Grants to 25 organisations totalled £200,000.

Beneficiaries included: Marine Theatre – Lyme Regis and Shelley Theatre Trust (£15,000 each); Marine Theatre, Theatre Peckham and Tron Theatre (£5,000 each); Bedford Players Trust (£3,300); Bridgewater Arts Centre (£3,000).

Applications

Application forms are available to download from the trust's website.

Sources of information

Accounts; annual report; Charity Commission; funder's website.

DM Thomas Foundation for Young People

 General charitable purposes, children and young people, disaster relief and international development

 UK and Europe

£956,500 (2016)

CC number: 1084220

Trustees: Ramesh Dewan; Dame Maureen Thomas; Christopher Ring; Simon Vincent; William Differ; Paul Farrow.

Correspondent: Louise James, Grants Manager, 179–199 Holland Park Avenue, London W11 4UL (tel: 020 7605 7733; fax: 020 7605 7736; email: grant@ dmtfyp.org)

 dmthomasfoundation.org

🐦 @DMTFYP

DM Thomas Foundation for Young People (formerly known as Hilton in the Community Foundation) was established in 2000. It changed its name in 2015 'in honour of the dedication of the foundation's founding Trustee Dame Maureen Thomas'.

The website states: 'Our mission is to transform young lives. We do this by raising money to support a wide range of fantastic projects that help disadvantaged young people to Achieve It, Beat It, Live It and Experience It.'

We have a special focus on supporting young people with disabilities, supporting employability and training programmes, enhancing the experiences of life-limited children in hospice care and supporting sick children in hospital. Our projects provide training, equipment, experiences and support so that young people can reach their full potential. We focus on partnering with local organisations which often struggle to attract support.

Grants programmes

Central grants fund

Within the remit of education and health, the foundation's central grants fund has a particular focus on the following target groups, as stated in the application guidelines:

▶ Children and young people with disabilities

▶ Children and young people who are sick in hospital

▶ Children and young people who are life limited (requiring palliative care)

If favoured, grant applications for up to £5,000 can be approved by the Director, up to £10,000 can be approved by the Grants Committee, and applications for more than £10,000 are recommended to the Trustees for final approval. The Foundation is a small charity and generally will not make awards of over £30,000 (per year). Funding can be requested for up to 2 years for any particular project Local funds

In addition to the central grants fund, the foundation also operates donor-advised funds; however, the website states:

There is no application process for these local funds. Business partners work with the Foundation to make these grants to local charities and schools that they have identified and nominated, using funds raised for the Foundation and held by the charity. Nominated causes must fall within our giving remits and relationships are maintained locally.

Foundation giveaways

In the course of the year the foundation organises regional giveaways which 'gives smaller charities a chance to apply for a grant and for the foundation to reach a new audience'. This scheme is held in partnership with local volunteers and a local media partner. A list of organisations and projects supported through giveaways is given on the website.

Disaster relief

The annual report and accounts note:

Although there is no designated fund, at times the Trustees may at their own discretion decide to award international or disaster response grants from general funds that support relief, reconstruction and development work affecting young people. To ensure a rapid response, Trustees may approve these disaster relief grants between the regular scheduled meetings.

The Les Mills Children's Fund

The charity also operates the Less Mills Children's Fund which provides funding for the education and physical and emotional well-being of children. Further information can be found on the fund's website: www.lesmillsfundforchildren.org.uk.

Financial information

In 2016 the foundation had assets of £1.5 million and an income of £1.55 million. Grants to 300 organisations totalled £956,500.

Beneficiaries included: Aga Khan Foundation UK (£80,000); Disability Challengers, The Orpheus Centre and Wessex Children's Hospice Trust (£30,000 each); Rockinghorse (£20,000); Teens Unite Fighting Cancer (£12,800); Tall Ships Youth Trust (£12,000).

Exclusions

According to the application guidelines, the foundation's central grants programme will not fund:

- Applicants whose projects do not fit one of DMTFYP's four target groups: disabled children, children in hospital, employability/training programmes, life-limited children
- Organisations which are not registered charities
- Charities which have: an income above £2 million (except hospices); been registered for under 12 months; present financial information which is incomplete or out of date; management and administration costs (including fundraising costs) above 30% of their annual expenditure
- Projects and organisations outside the UK or Ireland
- Funding requests over £30,000 pa for up to 2 years (£60,000 total)
- Requests solely for day-to-day administrative running costs (rent, lighting, heat, etc.)
- Requests solely for staff salaries or other staff costs
- Where outcomes are unclear or where the grant will not make an impact
- Requests by individuals, general donations
- Fundraising events or other fundraising costs
- Work with adults over the age of 25
- Medical research, individual medical treatment
- Capital appeals or construction of new buildings
- Overseas expeditions or exchange programmes
- Training or conferences for professionals or staff, e.g. teacher training, parenting training
- Loans
- Work which excludes some faith groups
- Work with only boys or only girls

Applications

Applications should be made using a form available to download from the foundation's website, where guidelines are also provided.

Sources of information

Accounts; annual report; Charity Commission record; funder's website.

The Thompson Family Charitable Trust

 General charitable purposes, health/medical research, horse welfare

UK

£6 million (2016/17)

CC number: 326801

Trustees: David Thompson; Patricia Thompson; Katie Woodward.

Correspondent: The Trustees, Hillsdown Court, 15 Totteridge Common, London N20 8LR (tel: 01608 676789; email: roy.copus@btinternet.com)

The trust makes grants for general charitable purposes throughout the UK.

Financial information

In 2016/17 the trust had assets of £121.4 million and an income of £8 million. Grants were made to 55 organisations totalling £6 million.

Beneficiaries included: Haileybury (£750,000); Macmillan Cancer Support (£305,000); East Anglia's Children's Hospices (£300,000); National Gallery (£200,000); Centrepoint (£100,000); Cambridge Women's Aid (£50,000); London Youth Rowing (£10,000); North London Hospice (£1,000).

Exclusions

No grants are made to individuals.

Applications

Apply in writing to the correspondent. The trust's 2016/17 accounts state: 'The Trustees meet as regularly as is necessary to assess grant applications. Applications for donations are invited from all categories of registered charity. Applications should be in writing in the first instance, and sent to the Trustees at the Charity's address'.

Sources of information

Accounts; annual report; Charity Commission record.

The Sir Jules Thorn Charitable Trust

 Medical research, medicine, social welfare

UK

£2.9 million (2016)

CC number: 233838

Trustees: John Rhodes; Prof. Sir Ravinder Maini; Prof. David Russell-Jones; Sir Bruce McPhail; Elizabeth Charal; William Sporborg; Mark Lever; Julian Ide.

Correspondent: David Richings, Director, 24 Manchester Square, London W1U 3TH (tel: 020 7487 5851; fax: 020

7224 3976; email: info@julesthorntrust.org.uk)

 www.julesthorntrust.org.uk

The trust was established in 1964 for general charitable purposes and its primary interest is in the field of medicine. The founder of the trust, Sir Jules Thorn, made his fortune through his company Thorn Electrical Industries. Grants are awarded to universities and hospitals in the United Kingdom to support medical research, with modest donations provided also for medicine-related purposes. The trust is a member of the Association of Medical Research Charities. Outside of medicine, small grants are also made for more general causes.

Areas of interest

The charity's website states that the trustees' areas of interest can be categorised into the following five broad categories:

- Medical science
- Serious illness
- Disability
- Disadvantage
- Overcoming adversity

The 2016 annual report states that 'the trust's primary interest is in supporting medical research and medical science generally, while other grants assist charities whose work is relevant to the Trust's humanitarian objectives'.

Grant programmes

Resources for grant-making are allocated each year and distributed competitively. The trust has three core areas of grant-making:

- **Medical research grants** – funding is considered for all areas of clinical research other than for cancer or AIDS, for the sole reason that such research is already well supported
- **Medicine-related grants** – appeals from universities, hospitals and other charitable organisations to assist with capital projects related to medical science or to the care and treatment of people suffering from severe clinical conditions
- **The Ann Rylands Small Donations** – allocated to charities in response to appeals of a humanitarian nature (donations may be for core funding)

Applications are by invitation only for the medical research grants programme. Applications for medicine-related grants and for the Ann Rylands Small Donation programme are accepted from any charity which considers it meets the criteria.

Financial information

In 2016 the charity had assets of £120.4 million and had an income of

£1.5 million. During the year, the charity gave a total of £2.9 million in grants which was distributed as follows:

Medical research grants	£1.6 million
Medicine-related grants	£979,000
The Ann Rylands small donations	£308,500

Beneficiaries include: University College London (£1.4 million); The Brendoncare Foundation (£150,000); Chelsea and Westminster Health Charity (£100,000); DEBRA, Heads On and North East Autism Society (£50,000 each); Beatson Cancer Charity and Haven House Foundation (£10,000 each); Swings and Smiles (£1,500); REACT (£1,250); The Back-Up Trust (£1,000); Music Alive (£750); The Pod (£500).

Exclusions

Refer to the website for exclusions from each specific grant scheme.

Applications

Refer to the website for detailed guidance notes for each of the grants programmes, along with details of how to apply.

Sources of information

Accounts; annual report; Charity Commission record; funder's website.

The Three Guineas Trust

 Autism

UK

£ £1.8 million (2016/17)

CC number: 1059652

Trustees: Clare Sainsbury; David Wood; Dominic Flynn.

Correspondent: Robert Bell, Director, The Peak, 5 Wilton Road, London SW1V 1AP (tel: 020 7410 0330; email: proposals@sfct.org.uk)

🌐 www.sfct.org.uk

The Three Guineas Trust was established by Clare Sainsbury in 1996 and forms part of the Sainsbury Family Charitable Trusts – an operating office for 17 independent grant-making trusts established by members of three generations of the Sainsbury family.

Applications are accepted for any practical projects in the field of autism. In 2014 the trustees began to explore the field of disability, violence and access to justice and in 2016/17 made five new grants in this area. In the most recent accounts (2016/17), the trustees note that they expect to fund other carefully chosen projects in this field in due course. The trust also runs an annual small grants programme for play schemes run in the summer school holidays which support children with ASD.

On the trust's website, the trustees advise that they are particularly keen to support projects which include service users in decision-making.

Financial information

In 2016/17 the trust had assets of £24.6 million and an income of £1.6 million. During the year, the trustees awarded 37 grants worth a total of £1.8 million. Grants were distributed as follows:

Disability, violence and access to justice	5	£919,000
Autism	31	£839,500
General	1	£10,000

Beneficiaries included: Respond (£300,000); Disability Law Service (£240,000); Sunbeams Play (£176,000); Harrow Law Centre (£144,000); Autism Concern (£99,000); Assert (88,000); National Autistic Society (£50,000); Carmarthenshire Autism Community Group (£6,300); Spectrum (£6,000); Helping Hands Autism Support Group (£5,000).

Exclusions

The trust does not provide grants for:

▶ Individuals
▶ Research
▶ Capital projects

Applications

Applications should be submitted in writing to the correspondent. Applications should comprise a single document of no more than two pages, and should include the following:

▶ A brief description of the applicant's charity – explaining its charitable aims and objectives, and stating its most recent annual income and expenditure
▶ An outline of the project requiring funding – why it is needed, who will benefit and in what way
▶ The budget for the project – including a breakdown of costs, the amount requested, and any money raised so far
▶ The timescale for the project
▶ Any plans for monitoring and evaluation
▶ The name and contact details of the person responsible for the application (this must include the full name, postal address and telephone number)

The trust requests that applicants do not send more than one application; or books, brochures, DVDs, annual reports or accounts.

Applications are usually processed within eight weeks. Applicants who do not receive a response within this time must assume they have been unsuccessful.

Sources of information

Accounts; annual report; Charity Commission record; funder's website.

The Tinsley Foundation

 Human rights, relief of poverty, homelessness, health education

UK and overseas

£ £250,000 (2016/17)

CC number: 1076537

Trustees: Henry Tinsley; Rebecca Tinsley; Tim Jones; Jane Hogarth.

Correspondent: Henry Tinsley, Trustee, Office 313, 31 Southampton Row, London WC1B 5HJ (tel: 01780 762056; email: lesleyedmunds@btconnect.com)

The foundation was founded by Henry Tinsley, former chair of chocolate company Green and Blacks, in 1999.

Areas of support

The foundation's annual report for 2016/17 states that it will support:

▶ charities which promote human rights and democratisation and/or which educate against racism, discrimination and oppression
▶ charities which promote self-help in fighting poverty and homelessness
▶ charities which provide reproductive health education in underdeveloped countries, but specifically excluding charities whose policy is against abortion or birth control

The foundation makes grants and social investments to small grassroots organisations as well as larger organisations that aim to deliver a real and lasting positive impact.

Financial information

In 2016/17 the foundation had assets of £5.9 million and an income of £631,000. During the year, the charity awarded £250,000 to 20 organisations. The foundation aims to spend at least 5% of its net assets on grants each year.

Beneficiaries included: Tinsley Charitable Trust (£56,000); Network for Africa (£50,000); Client Earth (£25,000); Soil Association (£10,000); Citizens UK and Big Issue Foundation (£1,000 each); Inspiration (£500); The Ecology Trust (£250).

Applications

Apply in writing to the correspondent. The 2016/17 annual accounts state: 'While the charity welcomes applications from eligible potential grantees, the trustees seek out organisations that will effectively fulfil our objectives. Individual trustees have a close working relationship with charities in receipt of our larger grants.'

Sources of information

Accounts; annual report; Charity Commission record.

The Tolkien Trust

 Emergency and disaster relief, overseas aid and development, the homeless and refugees, healthcare charities, especially those focusing on illnesses of childhood and old age, the needs of disadvantaged communities and medical research, religious causes promoting peace and reconciliation and work with impoverished communities, environmental causes, education and the arts

UK, with some preference for Oxfordshire, overseas including Malawi, Rwanda, Democratic Republic of Congo, Haiti and Europe

£1.7 million (2016)

CC number: 1150801

Trustees: Priscilla Tolkien; Michael Tolkien; Baillie Tolkien.

Correspondent: Cathleen Blackburn, Prama House, 267 Banbury Road, Oxford OX2 7HT (tel: 01865 339330; email: info@tolkientrust.org)

www.tolkientrust.org

The trust was established in 1977 by the four children of the author J. R. Tolkien, to enable the family to give to its chosen causes on a regular basis.

The following information is taken from the trust's website:

The trust is wholly discretionary, which means that its constitution does not impose any limitations on the charities it may benefit; it is therefore free to select those causes of interest to it.

The trust does not publish any guidelines concerning the charities of interest to it but its filed accounts give an indication of the nature and number of causes benefited in recent years. Many of the chosen charities are benefited on an annual basis, and a large number have received support from the trust for many years.

The trust has traditionally supported a wide spectrum of charitable causes throughout the world including:

- emergency and disaster relief
- overseas aid and development
- the homeless and refugees
- healthcare charities, especially those focusing on illnesses of childhood and old age, the needs of disadvantaged communities and medical research
- religious causes promoting peace and reconciliation and work with impoverished communities
- environmental causes
- education and the arts

Financial information

In 2016 the trust had assets of £28.1 million and an income of £1.8 million. Grants to 56 organisations totalled £1.7 million.

Beneficiaries included: Motor Neurone Disease Association (£370,000); Find Your Feet (£75,000); Oxford Botanic Garden (£60,000); Action Aid UK (£50,000); Asylum Welcome (£30,000); British Deaf Association, Human Rights Watch and Oxford Food Bank (£10,000 each); St Lukes Oxford (£2,500).

Exclusions

No grants are given to individuals.

Applications

The trust's website states:

Please note that The Tolkien Trust is no longer accepting unsolicited applications. Please do not send an application unless you have been specifically requested to do so by the Trust. The Trust does not have the capacity to process the volume of unsolicited applications it has been receiving, and does not wish applicants to waste time writing applications that will not be appraised.

Sources of information

Accounts; annual report; Charity Commission record; funder's website.

Jane Tomlinson Appeal

 Projects supporting people with cancer

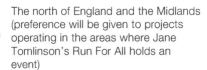 The north of England and the Midlands (preference will be given to projects operating in the areas where Jane Tomlinson's Run For All holds an event)

£273,000 (2016/17)

CC number: 1113894

Trustees: Suzanne Tomlinson; Craig Maher; Mark Mills; Robert Shaw; Stephen Whiteside; Adrian Fitzpatrick.

Correspondent: Vicki Robinson, The Jane Tomlinson Appeal, PO Box 314, Rothwell, Leeds LS25 1BY (tel: 0113 826 7766; email: info@janetomlinsonappeal.com)

 www.janetomlinsonappeal.com

 facebook.com/janetomlinsonappeal

 @janesappeal

 @janetomlinsonappeal

The appeal was established as a legacy to Jane Tomlinson who raised £1.8 million for children's and cancer charities before her death in 2007. Jane was awarded the MBE and later the CBE for her charitable work.

The following information has been taken from the appeal's website:

Jane Tomlinson Appeal Grants Criteria

The Jane Tomlinson Appeal is committed to supporting good causes in the areas in which we operate. Grants are available for projects supporting children or anyone affected by cancer. Read on to find out if your project is eligible for funding.

What type of grants do we offer?

We fund anything from £250 to £10,000. Grants are usually one-off, however on occasion the trustees have been known to fund over multiple years at their discretion.

Who do we fund?

We fund UK-registered charities and community interest companies (CICs)

Organisations applying must have had at least two years of activity and be able to submit their latest annual accounts.

What do we fund?

Projects supporting children or anyone affected by cancer

We fund projects operating in the North or the Midlands. Preference will be given to projects operating in the areas where 'Jane Tomlinson's Run for All hold an event'.

We cover capital and revenue costs.

We will support specific project costs or core costs.

Financial information

In 2016 the charity had assets of £1.2 million and an income of £2.7 million. Grants awarded to organisations totalled £273,000.

Beneficiaries included: Martin House (£19,500); St Leonards (£12,500); Prince of Wales Hospice (£10,000); Pendleside (£9,900); East Lancashire People (£7,800); Snappy (£5,000); Mini Mermaid (£2,200); Manorlands (£1,200).

Exclusions

According to its website, the charity cannot fund:

- Individuals
- Public bodies
- Organisations that mainly distribute grants to other organisations
- Organisations with an income over £5 million annually
- Organisations with excessive reserves, unless this can be justified
- Organisations with political associations or interests

Applications

The charity's website states:

If you meet all the criteria ... and would like to request a grant application form, please contact 'info@janetomlinsonappeal.com' with the name of the applicant organisation and a sentence or two about the project. This will help to confirm your project is eligible and then an application will be sent out to you.

Sources of information
Accounts; annual report; Charity Commission record; funder's website.

The Tompkins Foundation

 General charitable purposes, education and training, recreation, religious causes, the promotion of health, children and young people

UK, with a preference for the parish of Hampstead Norreys in Berkshire and the parish of West Grinstead in West Sussex

£288,000 (2016/17)

CC number: 281405

Trustees: Peter Vaines; Elizabeth Tompkins; Victoria Brenninkmeijer.

Correspondent: The Accountant, 7 Belgrave Square, London SW1X 8PH (tel: 020 7235 9322)

The foundation was established in 1980 by Granville Tompkins, founder of Green Shield Stamps and the Argos retail chain, primarily for the advancement of education, learning and religion and the provision of facilities for recreation and other purposes beneficial to the community.

Financial information
In 2016/17 the foundation held assets of £12.8 million and had an income of £355,500. Grants were made to 14 organisations and totalled £288,000.

Previous beneficiaries have included: The Foundation of Nursing Studies (£30,000); Arthroplasty for Arthritis, Chickenshed Theatre, St Johns Hospice, St Mary's Coronary Flow Trust and The Police Foundation (£25,000 each); City of London School (£20,000); Restart (£10,000); London Early Opera Co. (£7,000).

Exclusions
Individuals are not supported.

Applications
Apply in writing to the correspondent. Unsolicited applications are unlikely to be successful as the trust has a regular list of charities which receive support.

Sources of information
Accounts; annual report; Charity Commission record.

Toras Chesed (London) Trust

 Jewish causes, education and training, social welfare, children and young people, older people

UK

£541,500 to organisations (2016/17)

CC number: 1110653

Trustees: Aaron Langberg; Akiva Stern; Simon Stern.

Correspondent: Aaron Langberg, Trustee, 14 Lampard Grove, London N16 6UZ (tel: 020 8806 9589; email: ari@toraschesed.co.uk)

Registered with the Charity Commission in 2005, its record states that the trust's charitable objects are as follows:

- The advancement of the Orthodox Jewish faith
- The advancement of Orthodox Jewish religious education
- The relief of poverty and infirmity among persons of the Jewish faith
- To provide a safe and user friendly environment to share mutual problems and experiences
- To encourage active parental participation in their children's education

The trust achieves its objectives by making grants to qualifying organisations and individuals.

Financial information
In 2016/17 the trust had an income of £597,500. According to its annual report, the trust awarded grants worth a total of £599,000, including £541,500 to organisations and £57,500 to individuals.

Beneficiaries included: Central UTA of Moncey (£18,000); Cong. Yeshiva Kinyan Torah (£13,300); American Friends of Toras Chesed and Kolel L'Metzyonim (£6,000 each); Be'er Shmual (£2,500).

Applications
Apply in writing to the correspondent.

Sources of information
Accounts; annual report; Charity Commission record.

The Tottenham Grammar School Foundation

Education, children and young people

Haringey

£677,500 to organisations (2016/17)

CC number: 312634

Trustees: Keith Brown; Terry Clarke; Paul Compton; Roger Knight; Frederick Gruncell; Peter Jones; Graham Kantorowicz; Keith McGuinness; Victoria Phillips; Andrew Krokou; John Fowl.

Correspondent: Graham Chappell, Clerk, PO Box 34098, London N13 5XU (tel: 020 8882 2999; email: trustees@tgsf.org.uk)

www.tgsf.info

In 1686 Sarah, Duchess of Somerset left money in her will to permanently endow a school in Tottenham by purchasing land and covering the headmaster's salary. Unfortunately, the school closed in 1988 after more than 300 years but many of the school governors became the trustees of this charity and continue to act within the spirit of her will by making grants for the education of young people from Tottenham.

Grants are made to schools and voluntary organisations in the borough of Haringey for equipment and activities not provided by local authorities. Activities supported include youth clubs, Saturday schools and sports promotion. Grants are also made to individuals under 25 who, or whose parents, live in the borough or who have attended school in the borough.

Financial information
In 2016/17 the foundation had assets of £26.8 million and an income of £503,500. Grants to schools and organisations totalled £677,500 and a further £374,500 was awarded to individuals.

Beneficiaries included: Haringey Sports Development Trust (£107,000 in 101 grants); Chaverim Youth Organisation (£51,000 in six grants); Haringey Council Music Service (£30,000 in two grants); Rowland Hill Children's Centre (£19,200 in 11 grants); HR Sports Academy CIC (£12,800 in seven grants); Alexandra Park and Palace Charitable Trust (£10,000); Haringey Police and Community Amateur Boxing Club (£7,000); Face Front Inclusive Theatre, Stamford Hill Primary School and St Mary's Church (£5,000 each); Jackson Lane Community Arts Centre Association (£4,500).

Exclusions
The foundation cannot fund:

- The direct delivery of the national curriculum
- The employment of staff
- The construction, adaptation, repair and maintenance of school buildings
- The repair and maintenance of school equipment
- Vehicle purchase
- Staff training
- Resources exclusively for parents
- The costs of adults attending school trips

People aged 25 or over, or those who do not live in the borough of Haringey, unless they attend or have attended a school there

Applications
Apply on a form available from the foundation's website, where further guidance is also given. The trustees' meetings take place around every eight to ten weeks and applications should be submitted at least ten days in advance; dates of upcoming meetings are posted on the website. Grants of less than £1,000 may be approved by the clerk between meetings.

Sources of information
Accounts; annual report; Charity Commission record; funder's website.

The Toy Trust

 General charitable purposes, the promotion of health, social welfare, overseas aid, children and young people, people with disabilities

UK

£441,000 (2016)

CC number: 1001634

Trustees: Phil Ratcliffe; Jon Diver; Christine Nicholls; Foye Pascoe; British Toy and Hobby Association Ltd.

Correspondent: Tracey Butcher, British Toy & Hobby Association, BTHA House, 142–146 Long Lane, London SE1 4BS (tel: 020 7701 7271; email: admin@btha.co.uk)

 www.btha.co.uk/toy-trust

This trust was registered in 1991 to centralise the giving of the British Toy and Hobby Association (BTHA). Its website states: 'Founded by the BTHA, the Toy Trust – the industry's charity – exists to raise money predominantly from the toy industry, its suppliers and friends; and distribute the money raised to charities helping disadvantaged and disabled children within the UK and abroad.'

Financial information
In 2016 the trust had assets of almost £91,000 and an income of £408,000. Grants were awarded to 95 organisations totalling £441,000.

Beneficiaries included: East African Playgrounds (£60,000); Acorn's Children's Hospice (£15,000); St Neots Rotary Club (£8,000); Children's Hospices Southwest, Friends of Sherwood Park School and Medic Malawi (£5,000 each).

Applications
Application should be made by downloading an application form from the charity's website, completing it and sending with relevant documents to the correspondent's address. There is a useful checklist on the charity's website.

Sources of information
Accounts; annual report; Charity Commission record; funder's website.

The Constance Travis Charitable Trust

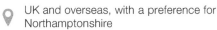 Relief of poverty, medical and health, environment, conservation and heritage, economic and community development, arts and culture, disability, animals, education and training, overseas aid, religious activities, accommodation/housing, sport and recreation

UK and overseas, with a preference for Northamptonshire

£1.46 million (2016)

CC number: 294540

Trustees: Ernest Travis; Peta Travis; Matthew Travis.

Correspondent: Ernest Travis, Trustee, 86 Drayton Gardens, London SW10 9SB (email: travistrust86@yahoo.co.uk)

Established in 1986, the trust has general charitable purposes, supporting local organisations in Northamptonshire as well as organisations working UK-wide and internationally.

Financial information
In 2016 the trust had assets of £124.1 million and an income of £18.7 million. Grants awarded to organisations totalled £1.46 million and were broken down as follows:

Relief of poverty	£401,000
Medical/health/sickness	£388,000
Environment/conservation/heritage	£169,500
Economic/community development/employment	£137,500
Arts/culture	£81,500
Disability	£81,000
Animals	£44,000
Education/training	£41,500
Overseas aid/famine relief	£35,000
Other/general	£29,000
Religious activities	£27,500
Accommodation/housing	£15,000
Sport and recreation	£7,000

Previous beneficiaries have included: Institute of Cancer Research (£130,000); British Red Cross (£120,000); Beanstalk (£20,000); Motor Neurone Disease Association (£18,000); Dyslexia Teaching Centre and National Trust (£15,000 each); Northamptonshire Historic Churches and Royal Shakespeare Company (£12,000 each); Royal Air Force Benevolent Fund and Unicef (£10,000 each).

Applications
Apply in writing to the correspondent. The trustees meet at least quarterly. The trust does not welcome contact prior to applications.

Sources of information
Accounts; annual report; Charity Commission record.

The Triangle Trust (1949) Fund

Carers, rehabilitation of offenders and ex-offenders

Worldwide, in practice UK

£762,000 to organisations (2016/17)

CC number: 222860

Trustees: Andrew Pitt; Julian Weinberg; Bruce Newbigging; Karen Drury; Helen Moss; Dr James Anderson; Alison Hope.

Correspondent: Dr Joanne Knight, Director, Foundation House, 2–4 Forum Place, Fiddlebridge Lane, Hatfield AL10 0RN (tel: 01707 707078; email: info@triangletrust.org.uk)

This charity was set up in 1949 by Sir Harry Jephcott, a pharmaceutical industrialist and former managing director of Glaxo Laboratories Ltd. In 2012 the trustees made the decision to become more focused and only support specialist organisations working with carers or the rehabilitation of ex-offenders.

Areas of support
The trust supports two areas of work:

- Carers – organisations supporting unpaid carers
- Rehabilitation of offenders and ex-offenders – organisations working with offenders in prison and after they are released

The trust will only support specialist organisations in these two areas – not organisations with a broader remit running relevant projects. Grants are made to registered charities, not-for-profit social enterprises or community interest companies. Organisations providing direct support or services are eligible, as well as those undertaking research, policy or campaigning work. There must be some volunteer input in the organisation.

Type of grant
The trust's development grant scheme, according to the website, aims to provide 'core funding to support organisations to implement a step change in their development and therefore build increased sustainability for the future'. The trustees are open minded about the ways in which organisations may wish to use their grant to achieve this; a few

examples of previous grants are given on the website. Grants of up to £80,000 can be awarded over three years, with a maximum of £35,000 in the first year, decreasing in subsequent years as the trustees expect other income streams will be developed to replace this.

Grants are also awarded to individuals.

Financial information

In 2016/17 the trust had assets of £20.3 million and an income of £664,500. Grants were made to 33 organisations totalling £762,000, broken down as follows:

Rehabilitation	18	£407,500
Carers	15	£354,500

Beneficiaries included: Caring Breaks (£39,500); Koestler Trust and Spark Inside (£35,000 each); Prison Arts Foundation (£30,000); Creative Carers (£20,000); Family Tree Wirral (£17,000); Powys Carer Service (£15,000); Storybook Dads (£15,000); Renfrewshire Carers Centre (£14,700); Open Gates (£8,000).

Exclusions

The trust will not give funding for:

- Appointment of a trust, corporate or community fundraiser
- Expanding the coverage of a particular service, unless there is a tangible increase in sustainability as a result
- Matched funding, unless associated with a sustainability development
- Covering the loss of a statutory contract or grant income
- General running costs
- Organisations which are not solely focused on either carers or rehabilitation
- Crime prevention or restorative justice initiatives
- Organisations providing support for people who are cared for, as well as carers

Applications

The trust holds one funding round for carers organisations and one for rehabilitation each year – deadlines and a timetable are posted on its website. An initial application can be made online; shortlisted applicants will then be visited by a representative from the trust, where they should present a strategic plan for the next few years. The trust welcomes potential applicants to get in touch to discuss their ideas before applying.

Sources of information

Accounts; annual report; Charity Commission record; funder's website.

The True Colours Trust

Children and young people with disabilities and life-limiting conditions, palliative care

UK and Africa

£1.3 million (2016/17)

CC number: 1089893

Trustees: Lucy Sainsbury; Dominic Flynn; Bernard Willis; Tim Price.

Correspondent: Robert Bell, The Peak, 5 Wilton Road, London SW1V 1AP (tel: 020 7410 0330; fax: 020 7410 0332; email: truecolours@sfct.org.uk)

 www.truecolourstrust.org.uk

Established in 2001, this is one of the newest of the Sainsbury family charitable trusts. According to its website, the trust focuses on the following three areas:

- Improving the service delivery and support offered to children with complex disabilities, their families and siblings in the UK
- Strengthening palliative care services for children in the UK
- Promoting and developing palliative care for adults and children in Africa

Grants programmes

Children and young people in the UK

The trust looks to make a difference in the lives of children and young people with disabilities and/or life-limiting or life-threatening illnesses in the UK, as well as their families. Grants focus on the following areas, according to the website:

- Support for organisations leading the way in developing services and opportunities for children and their families.
- Raising the profile of these children and their families with central and local government.
- Raising the profile of the siblings of these children and supporting services to meet their needs.

Palliative care in Africa

The trust works with other organisations in Africa as part of the Waterloo Coalition. The website states that grant-making focuses on:

- Improving access to affordable palliative care for adults and children in Africa, prioritising the need for appropriate pain relief and integration of palliative care services into established health systems.
- Increasing awareness of palliative care and influencing policy at a regional and international level through strategic grants to the African Palliative Care Association and the International Children's Palliative Care Network.
- Supporting palliative care services across Africa through a small grants programme, administered by the African Palliative Care Association.

Small grants – UK and Africa

The trust accepts applications for its small grants in the UK and Africa.

For projects in the UK grants of up to £10,000 are provided to smaller organisations working with children with disabilities and their families. Grants are mainly given for one-off projects or core costs rather than multi-year grants for ongoing revenue costs. The trustees particularly support:

- Hydrotherapy pools
- Multi-sensory rooms
- Mini buses
- Sibling projects
- Bereavement support
- Specialised play equipment/access to play and leisure
- Family support/parent-led peer support

In addition to its work in the UK, the trust has also set aside funds towards a small grants programme to support the development of palliative care across Africa. Funding is primarily for one-off projects, although the trustees are willing to consider funding for core costs. The size of grants ranges from £500 to £5,000. The trustees particularly favour applications from organisations which directly improve the patient experience and the standard of palliative care services. Priority is given to the following:

- Equipment for patients
- Palliative care for children and young people
- Palliative care medicines
- Capital improvement costs
- Increasing access to palliative care in rural areas
- Training courses for palliative care service providers held in Africa

Financial information

In 2016/17 the trust had assets of almost £9.4 million and an income of £2.2 million. The trustees approved 64 grants totalling £1.3 million. Grants were distributed as follows:

Palliative care in Africa	16	£798,500
Children and young people – UK	6	£317,000
Small grants – UK	42	£198,500

Beneficiaries included: African Palliative Care Association (£152,000); World Health Organization (£140,000); International Children's Palliative Care Network (£81,500); Island Hospice, Zimbabwe (£70,000); Epilepsy (£53,000); Contact a Family (£50,000); Shepherd's Hospice, Sierra Leone (£47,500); Bradford Toy Library, Crossroads Care Oxfordshire and Fair Play Barnet (£5,000 each).

Exclusions

The trust no longer makes grants to individuals. Exclusions for grants for organisations may vary depending on the specific grant programme. Refer to the website for more details.

Applications

The trustees only consider unsolicited applications for their Small Grants Programmes (UK and Africa).

Small grants – UK

Applications can be made using the online form on the trust's website, or by downloading the application form and submitting by post or email. Applications can be submitted at any time. The trustees meet quarterly to review applications. If you do not hear from the trust within 12 weeks of receiving an acknowledgement, you should assume that you have been unsuccessful. Further guidance is given on the trust's website.

Small grants – Africa

This programme is administered by the African Palliative Care Association (APCA) – application forms can be downloaded from the website and should be submitted directly to APCA at truecolourssmallgrants@ africanpalliativecare.org. If you have any questions about the form, contact Pamela Kalema at APCA at pamela. kalema@africanpalliativecare.org.

Sources of information

Accounts; annual report; Charity Commission record; funder's website.

Truedene Co. Ltd

 Jewish causes, general charitable purposes, education, alleviation of poverty

UK and overseas

£743,000 (2016/17)

CC number: 248268

Trustees: Sarah Klein; Samuel Berger; Solomon Laufer; Sije Berger; Zelda Sternlicht.

Correspondent: The Trustees, Truedene Co. Ltd, Cohen Arnold, New Burlington House, 1075 Finchley Road, London NW11 0PU (tel: 020 8731 0777)

This charity supports organisations providing religious education in accordance with traditional Jewish doctrines and principles. The trust also gives grants to organisations that provide aid to Jewish people facing disadvantage or hardship.

Financial information

In 2016/17 the charity had assets of over £7 million and an income of £661,500. During the year, the trustees awarded almost £743,000 in grants to organisations. The charity's 2016/17 accounts state that 'all grants were made for general charitable purposes and for

the advancement of education or the alleviation of poverty'.

A list of beneficiaries was not included in the annual accounts.

Beneficiaries included: Yetev Lev London Jerusalem Trust (£110,000); Asser Bishvil Foundation (£83,000); Chevras Mo'oz Ladol (£50,000); Kolel Shomrei Hachomoth (£45,000); Yeshiva Gedolah Torah Veyirah (£30,000).

Grants below £30,000 totalled £309,000.

Applications

Apply in writing to the correspondent.

Sources of information

Accounts; annual return; Charity Commission record.

The Trusthouse Charitable Foundation

General charitable purposes

UK and overseas

£2.55 million (2016/17)

CC number: 1063945

Trustees: Crispian Collins; The Hon. Olga Polizzi; Lady Janet Balfour of Burleigh; Sir John Nutting; Revd Rose Hudson-Wilkin; Lady Anthony Hamilton; Philippa Hamilton; Nicholas Melhuish; Carole Milner; Charlie Polizzi Peyton; Patrick Reed.

Correspondent: Judith Leigh, Grants Director, 6th Floor, 65 Leadenhall Street, London EC3A 2AD (tel: 020 7264 4990)

 www. trusthousecharitablefoundation. org.uk

The Trusthouse Charitable Foundation was formed out of a trust operated by the Council of Forte plc in 1997 which inherited investments in the Granada Group. The foundation is administered on a day-to-day basis on behalf of the trustees by the Henry Smith Charity, although each charity is entirely independent.

Areas of support

The foundation makes grants to charitable organisations in the UK, with a focus on small and medium-sized organisations with a 'demonstrable track record of success working to address local problems in communities in areas of extreme urban deprivation or remote and deprived rural districts'. The foundation's grant-making is directed by two overarching themes:

- Rural issues: (organisations working in areas with 10,000 or fewer inhabitants, and which are in the most deprived 50% according to the latest indices of multiple deprivation)
- Urban deprivation (organisations working in urban areas which are in

the most deprived 20% according to the latest indices of multiple deprivation

Applicants must clearly show in their application how their project fits into one or both of these categories.

Within these overarching themes, the trustees are interested in two areas:

Community support

For example: work with young people; community centres; support for carers; older people's projects; help for refugees; family support; community transport; sports projects; rehabilitation of ex-offenders; alcohol and drug misuse projects; domestic violence prevention and aftermath; support groups for people with disabilities.

Arts, education and heritage

For example: arts projects for people with disabilities; performance or visual arts with a clear and strong community impact; alternative education projects; supplementary teaching; heritage projects in marine or industrial areas which involve local people and have a demonstrable community benefit.

Grant programmes

Major Grants programme

Open to any eligible organisation with a total annual income under £500,000. Grants can be awarded in any of the following three ways, as outlined in the funding guidelines:

- Single year grants between £7,500 and £20,000 for core costs, salaries, running and project costs. Successful applicants can apply in two further successive calendar years. No further applications can be made for two years after the completion of any third grant
- Multi-year (maximum 3 years) grants between £7,500 and £20,000 a year for core costs, salaries, running and project costs. Successful applicants will not be able to make any further applications until two years after the completion of the final year of the grant
- Grants between £7,500 and £60,000 for one-off capital costs, where the total project cost does not exceed £2M. Applicants must have secured a minimum of 50% of the total project cost before applying. Successful applicants will need to contact the office to discuss further applications

Small Grants programme

The funding guidelines state that the programme is open to any eligble organisationas long as it has a total annual income of no more than £250,000, and give the following details about the programme:

- Single year grants between £2,000 and £7,500 for core costs, salaries, running and project costs or one-off capital costs.
- Applicants cannot apply for more than 50% of the total cost of the project,

and grants will not be paid until the remaining 50% has been secured.

- Successful applicants can apply in two further successive calendar years. No further applications can be made for two years after the completion of the third grant.

Community centres and village halls

In addition to its main grant programmes, the foundation is also interested in applications for capital projects at community centres in the most deprived urban areas and village halls in remote and economically deprived rural areas. Applications will be considered for 'new buildings; upgrading, renovating or extending buildings; improving or creating outside space (but not car parks)'. See the foundation's website for full details.

Themed Grants programme

The foundation also runs three-year themed grants programmes, focusing on an issue of interest to the trustees. The most recent programme focused on young families; however, according to the foundation's website, the budget for this themed grant programme has now been fully allocated and the programme is closed to new applications. See the website for the latest information.

Refer to the foundation's detailed funding guidelines available on the website for more comprehensive information regarding eligibility and examples of previously supported projects.

Financial information

In 2016/17 the foundation had assets of £83.2 million and an income of £2.06 million. During the year, 257 grants were awarded totalling £2.55 million.

Beneficiaries included: South London Gallery, Iona Community (£125,000 each); South Bristol Advice Services (£11,800); Creggan Preschool and Training Trust (£8,400); Kesh Evergreens Senior Citizens Club (£4,100); Waterside Women's Centre (£3,800).

Exclusions

According to the funding guidelines, the foundation will not fund the following:

- Individuals, whether direct or through a third party
- Charities or NGOs registered outside the UK
- Statutory services including state schools (unless these are specifically and only for pupils with disabilities), local or national authorities, prisons, NHS hospitals or services
- Universities, further education colleges and independent schools
- Organisations with a total annual income in excess of £500,000
- Hospices
- Organisations with primarily an ecological aim

- Grant-making organisations
- Umbrella organisations

Furthermore, according to its guidelines, the foundation is not currently funding:

- Set up costs for new organisations
- Projects outside the UK
- Animal welfare/conservation
- Medical research
- Feasibility studies
- Capital appeals for places of worship unless these are primarily for wider community use, such as an adjoining church hall or a clearly defined community area within a place of worship
- One-off events (except under the Small Grants programme)
- PR and awareness raising; fundraising salaries, events or initiatives
- Projects primarily concerned with the productions of DVDs or other media

Applications

Applications can be submitted via the foundation's website. Grants Committee meetings are held in February, late April/early May, July and late October/early November. Applications need to be received at least six weeks before a meeting to be included on the agenda.

Sources of information

Accounts; annual report; Charity Commission record; guidelines for applicants; funder's website.

The James Tudor Foundation

Relief of sickness, medical research, health education, palliative care, overseas health projects

UK and overseas

£918,500 (2016/17)

CC number: 1105916

Trustees: Cedric Nash; Richard Esler; Susan Evans; Anne McPherson; Stephanie Wren.

Correspondent: Sarah Stewart, Foundation Director, WestPoint, 78 Queens Road, Clifton, Bristol BS8 1QU (tel: 0117 985 8715; fax: 0117 985 8716; email: admin@jamestudor.org.uk)

 www.jamestudor.org.uk

The foundation was established in 2004. It makes grants for charitable purposes, usually in the UK, with the principal objective being the relief of human sickness. In line with this objective, the foundation seeks to help small charities stay on their feet; to significantly improve the financial position of medium-sized to large charities; and to contribute to medical research where there is a probability of positive clinical outcomes.

Grant-making information

Examples of the types of organisations and projects funded can be found on the foundation's website. The foundation usually supports project costs; core costs are generally only considered for organisations with which the foundation has had a long relationship. The majority of grants are for one year. Occasionally, multi-year grants are awarded, but these are never for longer than three years.

The foundation awards grants over the following six main funding areas:

Palliative care

Grants under this category usually range from £5,000 to £20,000, normally have a term of 12 months and are distributed all over the UK. The foundation considers this to be a public health priority and supports both adult and children's hospices.

Medical research

The foundation supports medical research that has a high probability of positive clinical outcomes. The following key themes have been previously supported by the foundation:

- Clinical trials for a new drug delivery service for cancer treatments
- Blood tests research to indicate the risk of pregnant women developing post-natal depression
- Equipment, such as a custom-built perfusion system to develop a safe transplantation environment of islet cells
- Stem cell research into possible therapies for Parkinson's disease
- Research into childhood brain tumours

Health education

The annual report states that:

The key benefits in this area of funding are the publication and dissemination of health related information, the benefits accrued through scholarship and the introduction of newly acquired practices to medical practitioners, sufferers, carers and the general public.

Relief of sickness

This tends to be the foundation's most popular category. Awards made contribute to the preservation of health and assist in the treatment and care of people living with mental or physical health issues. Preference is generally given to applications that are condition related.

Overseas projects

The foundation supports overseas projects for the relief of sickness that are run by UK-registered charities.

Other means

The foundation will consider supporting applications that do not fit into any of the above categories as long as it meets the requirement of the relief of sickness.

Some examples of what the charity has previously supported include:

- Disability advisers
- Assisted housing
- Assisted technology
- Equipment, such as a multi-sensory room for children and young adults

Financial information

In 2016/17 the foundation had assets of £30 million and an income of £1.16 million. There were 107 grants made to organisations totalling £918,500. Grants were distributed as follows:

Relief of sickness	37	£309,500
Medical research	11	£185,500
Palliative care	9	£168,000
Health education	16	£130,000
Other means	14	£71,000
Overseas	20	£53,500

Previous beneficiaries have included:

University of Bristol (£40,500); St Peter's Hospice (£18,000); National Rheumatoid Arthritis Society (£17,500); Teenage Cancer Trust (£15,000); Cerebra (£10,000); World Medical Fund (£8,800); York Mind (£5,000); Asthma Relief (£4,000); Action on Pre-Eclampsia (£2,000); Bristol Area Stroke Association (£500).

Exclusions

The foundation will not accept applications for grants:

- That directly replace, or negatively affect, statutory funding
- For work that has already taken place
- For endowment funds
- For economic, community development or employment use
- For adventure or residential courses, expeditions or overseas travel, or for respite holidays
- For sport or recreation uses, including festivals
- For art and music therapies
- For environmental, conservation or heritage causes
- For animal welfare
- For capital and refurbishment projects
- From applicants who have applied within the last 12 months
- From individuals
- From overseas organisations

Note that the foundation prefers to fund small and medium-sized organisations that have been established for at least two years and are UK-registered charities. Local organisations that are part of a wider network are unlikely to be funded.

Applications

Potential applicants must read the foundation's guidelines and can complete an initial eligibility check, both of which can be found on the website. Organisations that are eligible at this stage can send an outline application along with a coversheet to the foundation and, following this, may be invited to submit a full application.

Sources of information

Accounts; annual report; Charity Commission record; guidelines for applicants; funder's website.

The Tudor Trust

 General charitable purposes, social welfare

 UK and overseas

£ £16.1 million (2016/17)

CC number: 1105580

Trustees: Amy Collins; James Long; Catherine Antcliff; Monica Barlow; Nell Buckler; Louise Collins; Elizabeth Crawshaw; Ben Dunwell; Helen Dunwell; Matt Dunwell; Christopher Graves; Francis Runacres; Rosalind Dunwell; Vanessa James.

Correspondent: The Information Team, 7 Ladbroke Grove, London W11 3BD (tel: 020 7727 8522; fax: 020 7221 8522; email: general@tudortrust.org.uk)

🌐 www.tudortrust.org.uk

🐦 @thetudortrust

This trust, established for general charitable purposes, was founded in 1955 by Sir Godfrey Mitchell who endowed it with shares in the Wimpey construction company. Today, the trustees make grants, and provide other types of support, to voluntary and community groups working in any part of the UK. They are particularly keen to help smaller, community-led organisations that work directly with people who are at the margins of society.

Grant-making policy

The trustees tend to support smaller and under-resourced organisations with an annual income of less than £1 million. On its website, the trustees state that:

In our experience, smaller organisations are particularly well-placed to deliver positive change because they know their communities and can be highly responsive to need, providing an individualised and holistic response to the people they support. The best smaller-scale organisations also encourage participation and inclusion and contribute to the resilience of communities by offering opportunities for connection and engagement.

The trustees believe that the organisations they support are best placed to identify challenges and develop solutions. As such, there are no specific funding programmes and many of the trust's grants take the form of core funding.

Grants are made in four categories:

- Core funding
- Project grants
- Capital grants
- Grants to help strengthen an organisation

There is no maximum or minimum grant, although in practice it is unusual for the trust to make a grant of less than £10,000. Usually grants are made over one, two or three years.

According to the trust's website, the trustees want to support organisations which meet the following criteria

Display positive organisational characteristics

- Encourage and develop positive social connections and relationships
- Are embedded in their community and can identify and channel the potential within that community
- Have vision, energy and commitment and are reflective and open to change
- Want to make a step change in the way they work, but need support to do this
- Listen to and are responsive to their users and give users a voice
- Offer longer-term engagement and support
- Make good use of the resources they have

Address marginalisation

- Engage with a marginalised community or engage with a particularly marginalised group of people or 'community of interest
- Provide direct support to individuals who are in real need
- Are rooted in overlooked and neglected areas where funding is hard to come by
- Affect the lives of marginalised people and communities in a positive way

Make a difference

- Generate a ripple effect – a wider impact beyond the immediate beneficiaries of the work
- Display new thinking or demonstrate best practice: offer an exemplar others can learn from
- Are interested in reflecting on their work and are generous in sharing their findings with others

The trustees publish a grant review each year to report on the trust's grant-making strategy and to detail what grants were made and how much was given. A key feature of grant-making is awarding grants which respond directly to the priorities identified by applicants.

Although the trust's primary focus is grant-making, it also engages with the organisations it supports in other ways, offering advice and development support where this is needed.

For more information, consult the trust's detailed and helpful website.

Financial information

In 2016/17 the trust had an income of £6.6 million and assets of £249.2 million. Grants were made to 327 organisations totalling £16.1 million. The annual report details how grants were distributed in the following areas:

Community	£6.5 million
Young people	£1.9 million
Relationships	£1.6 million
Housing	£1.4 million
Mental health	£1 million
Substance misuse	£741,000
Criminal justice	£697,000
Older people	£320,000
Learning	£295,000
Financial security	£285,000

Beneficiaries included: Barnardo's (£266,000); Care Leavers' Association (£209,000); Finance Innovation Lab (£150,000); Caldmore Village Festival (£100,000); Art Against Knives (£95,000); Alive Activities Ltd, DASH – Destitute Asylum Seekers Huddersfield and East Cleveland Youth Housing Trust (£90,000 each); Citizens Advice Bassetlaw (£80,000); Felix Road Adventure Playground (£45,000); Ghost Academy CIC (£30,000); Global Justice Now Trust (£10,000); Greater Easterhouse Alcohol Awareness Project (£7,500); Highfield Hall Community Club (£3,000).

Exclusions

According to the website, grants are not made to/for:

- Individuals, or organisations applying on behalf of individuals
- Larger charities (both national and local) enjoying widespread support
- Statutory bodies
- Hospitals, health authorities or hospices
- Medical care, medical equipment or medical research
- Universities, colleges or schools
- Academic research, scholarships or bursaries
- Nurseries, playgroups or crèches
- Uniformed youth groups
- One-off holidays, residential, trips, exhibitions, conferences, events, etc.
- Animal charities
- The promotion of religion
- Routine repairs and minor improvements to community buildings (community centres, church halls, village halls etc.)
- Landscaping or equipment for playgrounds, parks or recreation areas
- Sports and leisure (where there isn't a strong social welfare focus)
- The restoration or conservation of buildings or habitats (where there isn't a strong social welfare focus)
- Work outside the UK. The trust runs a targeted grants programme promoting ecological agriculture in Zimbabwe, Kenya and Uganda. However, it does not consider unsolicited proposals from groups working overseas
- The promotion of philanthropy and endowment appeals

- Retrospective funding: costs that have already been incurred

Applicants are encouraged to call the information team for advice concerning applications.

Applications

According to the trust's website, the application process is made up of two stages.

A first stage application must include the following:

- A brief introductory letter on your organisation's letterhead
- A completed organisation details sheet (available from the funding section of the trust's website)
- A copy of your most recent annual accounts, and annual report if you produce one
- Answers to the following five questions, on no more than two sides of A4:

  1 Tell us about the work you do
  2 What practical difference do you want to make?
  3 Tell us something about the community you work with and the challenges it is currently facing
  4 What strengths and opportunities do you see in your community?
  5 How can Tudor best help you?The proposal should be addressed to the trustees and sent via post or email. Proposals will be acknowledged within a few days of being received. If the first-stage proposal is successful, applicants will receive an acknowledgement letter plus details about the second-stage of the process. The second stage will be conducted by telephone or a visit. The trust aims to let applicants know within a month whether or not they have progressed to the second stage application. The trust aims to make a decision on most applications three months after progressing to the second stage. Trustees and staff meet every three weeks to consider applications.

The trust's website provides helpful and very detailed information on the application process and how to apply. Check that you have followed all the requirements before you make an application or it will be ineligible. It is worth noting that while 98% of applications meet the trust's criteria, due to the number of applications received, only approximately one in ten receive funding. The trustees encourage potential applicants to look at the grants list published every three months on the website to get a sense of the level and range of funding they provide.

Sources of information

Accounts; annual report; Charity Commission record; guidance for applicants; funder's website.

The Tuixen Foundation

 General charitable purposes, particularly education, health, disability, social welfare, children and young people

 UK

£ £948,500 (2016/17)

CC number: 1081124

Trustees: Peter Englander; Dr Leanda Kroll; Stephen Rosefield; Paul Clements; Simon Englander.

Correspondent: Paul Clements, Trustee, 440 Strand, London WC2R 0QS (tel: 020 7649 2903; email: jandoole@tuixen.org.uk)

tuixen.org.uk

Set up in 2000, this foundation spent its first few years of operation building up its assets. The trust states in its 2016/17 annual report that grants are made to registered charities, hospitals, schools and other charitable organisations. The foundation's areas of interest include: children and young people; education; people with disabilities or learning disabilities; mental health; hospices; homelessness; and the relief of poverty. Grants are given towards core costs and some organisations are supported on an ongoing basis.

Financial information

In 2016/17 the foundation had assets of £41.95 million and an income of £2.67 million. Grants were made to 32 organisations totalling £948,500.

Beneficiaries included: Impetus Trust (£100,000); Leap Confronting Conflict and Teens and Toddlers (£50,000 each); Street League and Whizz-Kidz (£30,000 each); New Philanthropy Capital (£25,000); Jewish Care and Storybook Dads (£20,000); Camp and Trek and Oily Cart (£10,000 each).

Exclusions

The foundation does not give grants to individuals.

Applications

The foundation's website states that 'unsolicited applications are not sought and correspondence will not be replied to'.

Sources of information

Accounts; annual report; Charity Commission record; funder's website.

The Roger and Douglas Turner Charitable Trust

Older people, medical research, children and young people, environment and heritage, the arts, work in the community, social support, disability and health, international aid, hospices

Birmingham, Dudley, Sandwell, Walsall, Wolverhampton and Worcestershire

£629,000 (2016)

CC number: 1154467

Trustees: Stephen Preedy; Ronald Middleton; Geoffrey Thomas; Peter Millward; Dawn Long; Amanda McGeever.

Correspondent: Tim Patrickson, Arley House, Lion Lane, Upper Arley DY12 1SQ (tel: 01299 861368; email: tim@turnercharitabletrust.co.uk)

The trust was established in 2013 and then later merged with The Douglas Turner Trust and The R. D. Turner Charitable Trust. The aims of the trust are to support local charities, maintain the amenities of Upper Arley Village and provide public access to Arley Arboretum as an educational resource.

The trust makes grants to charities in the following areas:

▪ Older people
▪ Medical research
▪ Children and young people
▪ Environment and heritage
▪ The arts
▪ Work in the community
▪ Social support
▪ Disability and health
▪ International aid
▪ Hospices

Financial information

In 2016 the trust held assets of £55.8 million and had an income of £1.7 million. Grants were made to 192 organisations totalling £629,000 and broken down as follows:

Health and disability	62	£180,000
Work in the community	44	£118,000
Children and young people	29	£87,000
Hospices	8	£84,000
The arts	20	£70,000
Social support	17	£51,000
Environment and heritage	8	£24,000
International aid	4	£15,000

Beneficiaries included: Birmingham St Mary's Hospice (£20,000); Stonehouse Gang (£15,000); Cerebral Palsy Midlands (£12,000); National Churches Trust (£10,000); Primrose Hospice – Bromsgrove (£8,000); Cotteridge Church Day Centre (£7,000); Dorothy Parkes Centre (£6,000); Birmingham Settlement and YMCA Birmingham (£5,000 each).

Applications

Contact the administrator for grant appeal guidelines and an application form.

Sources of information

Accounts; annual report; Charity Commission record.

G J W Turner Trust

General charitable purposes

Birmingham and the Midlands area

£362,500 (2016/17)

CC number: 258615

Trustees: Lesley Davis; Hugh Carslake; Kate Honeyborne.

Correspondent: Chrissy Norgrove, SGH Martineau LLP, 1 Colmore Square, Birmingham B4 6AA (tel: 0870 763 1000)

The trust awards grants to a wide variety of registered charities in the Birmingham and Midlands area, some of which are supported on an annual basis.

Financial information

In 2016/17 the trust had assets of £11.9 million and an income of £345,500. Grants totalled £362,500.

A list of beneficiaries for the year was not included in the accounts.

Previous beneficiaries have included: Birmingham St Mary's Hospice and Sunfield Children's Homes (£40,000 each); Birmingham Rathbone Society (£30,000); Victoria School and Shakespeare's Hospice (£15,000 each); Elmhurst Ballet School – Bursary Fund and The Diabetic Foot Trust Fund (£10,000 each); Barnardo's, Birmingham Hippodrome, Children's Hand and Arm Surgery, County Air Ambulance and Queen Alexandra College (£5,000 each); Saltley Neighbourhood Pensioners Centre (£3,000); St Margaret's Church Short Heath (£2,000); The National Children's Orchestra of Great Britain (£1,000).

Applications

Apply in writing to the correspondent. The trustees meet annually, usually in July.

Sources of information

Accounts; annual report; Charity Commission record.

The Turtleton Charitable Trust

Arts, culture and heritage

UK, with a strong preference for Scotland

£202,500 (2016/17)

OSCR number: SC038018

Correspondent: Kenneth Pinkerton, c/o Turcan Connell, Princes Exchange, 1 Earl Grey Street, Edinburgh EH3 9EE

 www.turcanconnell.com/turtleton

Established in 2007, the trust makes grants in the fields of heritage and the arts, principally in Scotland. According to its website, grants are made to charities in support of the following causes:

▪ The advancement of the arts, culture and heritage – the Trustees particularly favour heritage and the visual arts, but other aspects of the arts and culture will be considered. The vast majority of grants are made in this field.
▪ Support of the disadvantaged and the advancement of education – the Trustees consider only a small number of grants in this field in any one year.

There is a preference for causes in Scotland.

Grants typically range between £5,000 and £25,000; larger or multi-year grants are made occasionally.

Financial information

In 2016/17 the trust held assets of £5.9 million and an income of £180,000. Grants were made to 23 organisations totalling £202,500.

Beneficiaries included: The National Galleries of Scotland (£50,000); National Youth Choir of Scotland (£20,000); Scottish Traditional Skills Training Centre (£11,100); The Place – London Contemporary Dance School and Scotland Yard Adventure Centre (£10,000 each); National Theatre of Scotland (£6,000); Art in Healthcare and Edinburgh International Book Festival (£5,000 each); Sound Festival and The Leith Trust (£3,000 each); Centre for Moving Image (£1,000).

Exclusions

Grants are not made to individuals.

Applications

Applications should be made using the online application form, and should not exceed three sides of A4. If an online application is not possible for your organisation, an application can be sent by post to the address given, marked for the attention of Kenneth Pinkerton. Additional literature or other materials should not be sent. Note that the maximum combined size of the application documents is 10MB.

The trustees meet in spring every year to consider applications; the deadline is 31 December. In order to save administration costs, applications are not acknowledged and only successful applicants will be contacted.

Sources of information
Accounts; annual report; OSCR record; funder's website.

Tzedakah

 Jewish causes, education and training, social welfare, children and young people

Worldwide, in practice mainly UK and Israel

£261,500 (2016/17)

CC number: 251897

Trustees: Leonard Finn; Michael Lebrett.

Correspondent: Michael Lebrett, Trustee, Brentmead House, Britannia Road, London N12 9RU (tel: 020 8446 6767; email: lfinnco@aol.com)

The objectives of this charity are the relief of poverty, advancement of education, advancement of religion, and general charitable purposes. It makes over 300 grants to organisations in a year. The 2016/17 annual report states that 'the charities are chosen by the individual members'. It is not clear who the members are or if this precludes general applications to the charity.

Financial information
In 2016/17 the charity had assets of £247,000 and an income of £223,500. Grants totalled £261,500 and were distributed mainly in Great Britain and Israel but the trustees may also consider worldwide appeals. The annual report states that grants were made to over 300 charities during the year. There was no list of beneficiaries in this year's accounts.

Previous beneficiaries have included: Gertner Charitable Trust; Hasmonean High School Charitable Trust; Hendon Adath Yisroel Synagogue; Medrash Shmuel Theological College; Sage Home for the Aged; Society of Friends of the Torah; Tifferes Girls School; Torah Movement of Great Britain; Torah Temimoh; Willow Foundation; Wizo.

Exclusions
Individuals are not awarded grants.

Applications
Apply in writing to the correspondent.

Sources of information
Accounts; annual report; Charity Commission record.

Ufi Charitable Trust

 Vocational education

UK

£ 1.65 million (2016)

CC number: 1081028

Trustees: Tom Wilson; Brynley Davies; Valerie Dias; Bob Harrison; Dominic Gill; Prof. Rosemary Luckin.

Correspondent: The Trustees, 26 Red Lion Square, London WC1R 4AG (tel: 020 7969 5500; email: info@ufi.co.uk)

 www.ufi.co.uk

 facebook.com/UfiCharitableTrust

 @ufitrust

The Ufi charitable trust is a UK-based charity which, as stated on its website:

> Aims to improve UK productivity by making innovative use of digital technology to increase the skills of the UK workforce. Its projects are all intended to demonstrate how digital approaches can bring more learning to more people, more of the time in order to improve the workforce skills available to UK businesses and organisations, and improve outcomes for individuals by enhancing their workplace skills.

According to its website, the trust is especially keen to support projects focused on areas, sectors or communities where the existing vocational learning system fails to adequately address vocational learning needs and where digital technology could make a difference. This might include:

> - areas where geography makes it harder to access learning;
> - sectors where industry structure, low productivity/low margins etc. makes it difficult for employers to provide training;
> - communities of learners who (for social, economic or other reasons) have not engaged with traditional learning approaches earlier in their lives and might be better engaged by new approaches.

In its five-year funding strategy, the trust identifies the following funding priorities:

> - Seeding the market by supporting emerging digital vocational learning innovation at an early stage of either the technology or the learning approach
> - Market test projects that engage learners and employers to showcase how the idea works in practice
> - Large-scale partnerships near to market to demonstrate that the use of digital tech can deliver significant scale

On its website the trust notes that it will only fund activity that is 'scalable' through technology, i.e. projects that use digital methods to widen access to vocational learning.

The trust opens and closes funding programmes periodically. Some competitions will have a time limit but others may be open for proposals over an extended period. Full information about current programmes including eligibility criteria and deadlines is available on the trust's website.

Financial information
In 2016 the trust had assets of £59.7 million and an income of £1.16 million. During the year, the trust awarded grants totalling £1.65 million.

Beneficiaries included: Calderdale College (£296,500); National Numeracy (£155,000); Myerscough College (£40,000); Rapid English Ltd (£22,500); Sussex Downs College (£16,500).

Exclusions
Each funding programme will have its own specific eligibility criteria.

According to its website, the trust has the following general exclusions:

> - projects which address generic 'access to work' skills, such as time management, CV building or interview skills training
> - basic digital skills training aimed at enabling generic digital capability and overcoming digital exclusion, but can fund specific digital skills required in the workplace
> - projects which do not represent a step change in how vocational learning happens – it is not sufficient for a project to describe an incremental improvement in vocational learning
> - standard content development work, that aims, for example, to simply digitise existing content or add further content to an existing platform
> - projects in HE
> - research projects
> - projects in schools, unless these can demonstrate that they are addressing specific workplace skills provision to those aged over 16, where there is an identifiable employer need

Check the trust's website for full details.

Applications
Applications can be made via the trust's website.

Sources of information
Accounts; annual report; Charity Commission record; funder's website.

Ulster Garden Villages Ltd

 Housing and social welfare

Northern Ireland

£1.2 million (2016)

CC number: 101248

Trustees: Martie Boyd; Sir Desmond Lorimer; W. A. Crawford; Erskine Holmes; Kevin Baird; Dr Anthony Hopkins; Susan Crowe; Brian Garrett; William Webb.

Correspondent: The Administration Officer, Forestview, Purdys Lane, Newtownbreda, Belfast BT8 7AR (tel: 028 9049 1111; fax: 028 9049 1007; email: admin@ulstergardenvillages.co.uk)

www.ulstergardenvillages.co.uk

Ulster Garden Villages Ltd was established under the Industrial and Provident Societies Acts (Northern Ireland) in 1946 with the principal objective of providing good quality housing and associated amenities for the disadvantaged and elderly people. The following information is taken from the charity's website:

> Since that time government's approach to housing has changed dramatically and in Northern Ireland the establishment of the Northern Ireland Housing Executive and the Housing Association movement has largely catered for housing needs. In 1983 the Committee of Management of Ulster Garden Villages took the necessary steps to convert the Society into a charity and under its amended regulations empowered it to transfer from reserves to a common fund such amounts to be available for distribution for general charitable purposes, as the Committee shall from time to time determine.

> The Society primarily allocates funds to projects within Northern Ireland that will have a positive impact in Northern Ireland. National Charities making an approach to the Society should relate their appeal to specific needs or projects within Northern Ireland.

> Funds are not given retrospectively and it is not usual to give grants for office expenses or administrative staff salaries. In addition to outright grants, assistance may be given by way of loans which may carry certain conditions at the discretion of the Committee.

> The purpose of any application must be charitable and normally the committee will only consider requests from registered charities.

> Preferred projects will be those demonstrating active participation and self-help. They should be innovative and developmental with an achievable, practical and sustainable objective.

> We will not fund activities which are the responsibility of any statutory agency, neither will we fund the direct replacement of statutory funding.

> The Committee will only make donations toward specific projects under the control of a responsible organisation and when large capital projects are involved, only when satisfied that the sponsoring organisation has raised or is capable of raising the remainder of the finance required.

Grants have been made in the following areas:

- Health
- Culture and heritage
- Disadvantaged sections of society
- Environment
- Young people

Considerable support is provided to umbrella organisations representing the community and voluntary sector and, therefore, applications from individual groups are a low priority.

Financial information

In 2016 the charity had assets of almost £52.5 million and an income of £2.4 million. Grants were made to organisations totalling £1.2 million.

Previous beneficiaries have included: Belfast City Hospital – the Garden Village Suite; Belmont Tower; Clifton Nursing Home; Croft Community; Disability Sport NI; Habitat for Humanity Northern Ireland; Northern Ireland Children's Hospice; QUB Foundation Great Hall; Rams Island; Royal Victoria Hospital – Institute of Vision Science; Royal Victoria Hospital – Percutaneous Aortic Valve Replacement; The Scout Association; Ulster Waterways Group.

Exclusions

Grants are not made to/for:

- Individuals
- Organisations whose application is not charitable and with public benefit
- Activities which are primarily the responsibility of central and local government
- Sponsorship or marketing appeals
- Promotion of religion
- Expeditions or overseas travel
- Charities who collect funds for distribution to other charities

Applications

Apply on an application form available from the charity's website. Guidelines on how to apply can also be found on the website.

Sources of information

Charity Commission NI record; funder's website.

The Underwood Trust

 Medicine and health, social welfare, education, arts, environment and wildlife

UK

£3.5 million (2016/17)

CC number: 266164

Trustees: Robin Clark; Briony Wilson; Reg Harvey; Richard Bennison.

Correspondent: Michele Judge, Manager, Ground Floor, 20 York Street, London W1U 6PU (email: michelej@ taylorclark.co.uk)

www.theunderwoodtrust.org.uk

The Underwood Trust was established in 1973. The name derives from Underwood Lane, Paisley, Scotland, which was the childhood home of one of the founders. It currently supports registered charities and other charitable organisations which benefit society nationally and locally in Scotland and Wiltshire.

The general aims of the trust are to cover a wide spectrum of activities so as to benefit as many charitable causes as possible and to make donations to organisations where its contribution really can be seen to make a difference. The trust does not wish to be the principal funder of a charity and medium-sized bodies are more likely to receive grants than either very small charities or well-known large national ones.

Grants are categorised under the following headings:

- Medicine and health
- Social welfare
- Education and the arts
- Environment and wildlife

The allocation between these headings varies from year to year.

Financial information

In 2016/17 the trust had assets of £21.2 million and an income of £536,000. There were 26 grants made to organisations totalling £3.5 million.

Beneficiaries included: Wiltshire Air Ambulance (£2.5 million); Greenpeace – LIFE project phase IV (£419,000); The Living Paintings Trust (£75,000); Bristol Speech Language Therapy Research Unit (£50,000); British Red Cross (£45,000); Friends of the Earth, Music for Youth and NSPCC (£20,000 each); Pimlico Opera (£10,000).

Exclusions

No grants are given to/for:

- Individuals directly
- Political activities
- Commercial ventures or publications

- ⟩ The purchase of vehicles including minibuses
- ⟩ Overseas travel, holidays or expeditions

Applications

The trust's website states: 'The Trust is unable to accept unsolicited applications. We are keen that applicants do not waste their own time, and our limited resources in applications which have little chance of success, therefore please do not apply to The Trust unless specifically asked to do so.'

Information on how to apply, if you have been invited to do so, is given on the website.

Sources of information

Accounts; annual report; Charity Commission record; funder's website.

The Union of Orthodox Hebrew Congregations

 Orthodox Judaism

 UK

£ £794,500 to organisations (2016)

CC number: 1158987

Trustees: Myer Rothfeld; Benzion Freshwater; David Frand; Moses Bibelman; Henri Konig; Jehuda Baumgarten; Jacob Goldman; Alexander Heilpern; Sydney Sinitsky; Benjamin Roth; Judah Feldman; Michael Lobenstein; Dr Percy Mett; Rabbi Abraham Pinter.

Correspondent: David Passey, Landau Morley LLP, York House, Empire Way, Wembley HA9 0FQ

The main objects of this charity are to advance the Orthodox Jewish faith and to establish and support institutions which will help to achieve this. Support is also given to individuals who are in need to help with expenditure at Jewish festivals.

Financial information

In 2016 the charity held assets of £1.2 million and had an income of £2.7 million. Grants awarded to organisations totalled £794,500 and those to individuals a further £25,000.

Beneficiaries included: United Torah Association (£250,000); CMZ Trust (£175,000); Kehal Chasidei Wiznitz Ltd (£32,500); Milah UK (£8,000); Initiation Society (£1,000).

Applications

Apply in writing to the correspondent.

Sources of information

Accounts; annual report; Charity Commission record.

The Union of The Sisters of Mercy of Great Britain

 Christian missionary work, education, health, social welfare

 UK and overseas

£ £425,500 to organisations (2016/17)

CC number: 288158

Trustees: Sister Philomena Bowers; Sister Evelyn Gallagher; Sister Geraldine Lawlor; Sister Mary Horgan; Sister Monica Killeen.

Correspondent: Alan Wraight, Finance Director, Mercy Union Generalate, 11 Harewood Avenue, London NW1 6LD (tel: 020 7723 3221; email: admin@mercyunion.org.uk)

 sistersofmercyunion.org.uk

The Congregation of the Sisters of Mercy was founded by Catherine McAuley in 1831 in Dublin, Ireland. The Union of the Sisters of Mercy have convents throughout England, Scotland and Wales and residential care homes in England and Wales. The main activities of the charity are caring for the members of the congregation, supporting members of the congregation in their social and pastoral work and running the residential care homes it owns.

The charity also makes grants to organisations and individuals for the following purposes:

- ⟩ Education
- ⟩ Care for older people
- ⟩ Women
- ⟩ Evangelical work
- ⟩ Refugees and migrants
- ⟩ Children
- ⟩ Homelessness
- ⟩ Social welfare

The charity also supports overseas mission work in South Africa, Lebanon and Romania.

Financial information

In 2016/17 the charity held assets of £65 million and had an income of £5.3 million. Grants were made to 59 organisations and totalled £425,500 with a further £31,000 awarded to individuals. The following information is taken from the 2016/17 accounts:

Relief of hardship	£145,500
Evangelisation	£102,000
Care for older people	£67,000
Homeless	£37,500
Missions	£29,500
Women's charities	£27,000
Education	£24,000
Children's charities	£23,700

Previous beneficiaries have included: The St Mary's Convent Handsworth (£144,000); Mercy International

Association (£36,500); CAFOD, International Refugee Trust, Scottish Catholic International Aid Fund and St Joseph's Hospice (£10,000 each); Irish Community Services, Irish in Britain, Our Lady of the Rosary RC Church and St Mary's University Twickenham (£5,000 each).

Applications

Apply in writing to the correspondent.

Sources of information

Accounts; annual report; Charity Commission record; funder's website.

United Jewish Israel Appeal

 Jewish causes, particularly: education, welfare, youth engagement

 Israel and UK

£ £6.5 million (2016/17)

CC number: 1060078

Trustees: Louise Jacobs; Melvin Berwald; Marc Cave; Karen Goodkind; Ruth Green; Steven Kaye; Samantha Leek; Marc Lester; Brian May; Jonathan Morris; Hilton Nathanson; Robert Randall; Nicola Wertheim; Miles Webber.

Correspondent: Maurice Stone, Company Secretary, 1 Torriano Mews, London NW5 2RZ (tel: 020 7424 6400; email: central@ujia.org)

 www.ujia.org

f facebook.com/UJIAcharity

🐦 @ujiacharity

📷 @ujiacharity

United Jewish Israel Appeal, or UJIA, was registered with the Charity Commission in 1997. The charity supports young people in Israel and in the Jewish community in the UK. The charity runs and funds a wide range of programmes. In Israel (mainly the northern region of Galil), activities focus on education, welfare and other humanitarian projects. In the UK, the focus is on youth engagement in the Jewish community, through projects such as youth activities, school programmes, gap year projects and opportunities for university students. Further information on projects currently supported by the charity can be found on the website.

Financial information

In 2016/17 the charity had assets of £6.6 million and an income of £9.9 million. Grants to organisations during the year totalled £6.5 million, of which £4.6 million was given to organisations in Israel, and £1.9 million to organisations in the UK.

Beneficiaries included: Jewish Agency for Israel (£1.16 million); Danciger High School (£1.1 million); UJIA Israel (£613,000); Ort Yussefiya (£240,000); Birthright Israel (£221,000); Tsfat Medical School Scholarships (£207,000); Karmiel Youth Village (£154,000); Bell Scholarships for Tel Hai University (£154,000); B'nei Akiva (£147,000); Union of Jewish Students (£143,000); Tel Hai Learning Disabled Centre (£130,000); Maccabi GB (£110,00).

Applications

The application process is explained in the 2014/15 annual report as follows:

Following informal discussions and shared development of ideas with UJIA staff, partner organisations are invited to apply in writing (including project narrative and financial information) for grants for specific charitable activities that are aligned with UJIA's goals. This enables us to support partners and to make strategic connections between grantees.

The professional staff work with Trustees and Lay Leaders to develop and monitor the programme.

Partner Grants are monitored carefully for delivery in both financial and programme terms and checked for charitable activities and compliance. Payment is generally made in three instalments in January, May and October.

Sources of information

Accounts; annual report; Charity Commission record; funder's website.

United Purpose

Partnership and local capacity strengthening, emergency prevention, preparedness and response, health, including HIV/AIDS, rights and equity, water and sanitation, and sustainable livelihoods, including food security and micro-enterprise. In the UK, the charity also works to generate public interest in and support for international development

Mainly Africa, Asia and Latin America, also UK

£2.9 million (2016/17)

CC number: 272465

Trustees: Peter Ayres; Hadi Husani; Adam Wynne; Nicola Mushet; Robin Todd; Alan Davies; Steven Marshall; David Bull; Ceri Briggs; Martin Davidson.

Correspondent: Kathryn Llewellyn, Chief Executive Officer, 14 Cathedral Road, Cardiff CF11 9LJ (tel: 029 2022 0066; email: up.uk@united-purpose.org)

 www.united-purpose.org

 facebook.com/UnitedPurposeUP

 @United_Purpose

 @united.purpose

United Purpose was previously known as Concern Universal. The charity is a global development organisation with an innovative, community-led approach to tackling poverty and inequality. Working in 14 countries across Asia, Africa and South America, the charity aims to lift people up out of poverty by providing solutions to poverty that last. The charity's head office is in Cardiff and it currently has country offices in Bangladesh, Brazil, Ghana, Guinea, Malawi, Mozambique, Nigeria, Senegal and The Gambia, and manage projects through local partners in: Ethiopia, Kenya, India and Zambia.

Grant-making

The charity currently works with 93 local partners. The grants made to partners help local organisations provide sustainable benefits for poor and marginalised communities, furthering the charity's own objectives. The charity's 2016/17 annual accounts state: 'We carefully consider the experience, reach and governance of potential partners, as well as the value they will add to our work. We monitor how all grants are spent.'

Areas of work

During 2016/2017, United Purpose worked across three strategic change objectives set out in their previous strategy (2014–2019):

▶ **Resilient Lives:** To ensure that vulnerable people have more resilient and sustainable livelihoods and that economic growth is equitable

▶ **Better Health:** To improve health by increasing access to basic services, such as water, sanitation, primary healthcare and emergency food/shelter

▶ **Upholding Rights:** To improve government accountability to vulnerable people and to increase citizen engagement in decision-making processes, as well as

increasing the respect for the rights of all people

Financial information

In 2016/17 the charity held assets of £5.8 million and had an income of £30.2 million. Charitable expenditure amounted to £30.2 million and included grants paid to partners totalling £2.9 million, of which £1.9 million was given in the UK. Grants distributed are shown in the table below.

Awards of more than £50,000 each accounted for £2.9 million of the grants total.

Beneficiaries included: World Agroforestry Centre (ICRAF) (£645,500); Cooperazione Internazionale (£507,000); GOAL (£358,000); Self Help Africa (£214,000); Concern Universal Microfinance Operrations (CUMO) (£7,400).

A further £11.3 million was given as gifts in kind in the following forms: mosquito nets (to Against Malaria Foundation); foodstuffs for distribution (World Food Programme); rent discount (in the UK).

Applications

Apply in writing to the correspondent.

Sources of information

Accounts; annual report; Charity Commission record; funder's website.

United St Saviour's Charity

Social welfare, community development and social justice

North Southwark and Bermondsey

£724,000 (2016/17)

CC number: 1103731

Trustees: Julia Tybura; Camilla McGibbon; Richard Heaton; Lord Kennedy of Southwark; Claire Treanor; Nicola Steuer; Stephen Burns.

Correspondent: Matthew Allgood, Grants Manager, United St Saviour's Charity, St Saviour's House, 39–41 Union Street, London SE1 1SD (tel: 020 7089 9014; email: matthew. allgood@ustsc.org.uk)

UNITED PURPOSE

Country	Resilient Lives	Strategic area Better Health	Upholding Rights	Amount
UK	£1.86 million	£29,500		£1.9 million
Nigeria		£506,000		£506,000
Gambia	£239,000			£239,000
Bangladesh	£184,500			£184,500
Ghana	£37,000	£25,000		£62,000
Guinea	£52,500			£52,500
Mozambique	£980		£17,500	£18,500
Brazil			£3,000	£3,000
Malawi	-	-	-	-

www.ustsc.org.uk

 facebook.com/
unitedstsaviourscharity

 @UnitedStSaviour

United St Saviour's is a charity that supports the people and communities of North Southwark. Through its grant-making programmes, the charity aims to help communities tackle social need by investing in projects that offer 'both proven and innovative ways of solving problems'. In addition to its grant-making activities, the charity also administers several almshouses in Southwark.

According to its website, the charity's work is guided by the following themes:

> **Strong, resilient communities:** connecting, enabling and strengthening communities
> **Positive ageing:** reducing isolation and increasing well-being among older residents
> **Levelling the playing field:** targeted and life-changing support for population groups disproportionately experiencing social and economic disadvantage

Grants programmes

Currently the charity operates two open grants programmes:

> **Community Investment Programme (large grants)** – grants of more than £5,000
> **Community Engagement Programme (small grants)** – grants up to the value of £5,000. Most applications are in the region of £1,000 to £4,000 and the average size of a grant in 2016/17 was around £2,000

Applications for both programmes should demonstrate engagement with one or more of the themes listed above.

Financial information

In 2016/17 the charity had assets of £44.25 million and an income of £1.97 million. During the year, the charity awarded £724,000 in grants.

Beneficiaries included: Pembroke House (£90,500); Advising London (£63,500); Bede House Association (£53,000); Ripe Enterprises (£35,000); Surrey Docks Farm (£33,500); Cargobike Life CIC (£30,500).

Exclusions

The charity does not fund any of the following:

> Projects where the main beneficiaries are living or working outside our area of benefit
> Individuals (including sole traders)
> For-profit private companies
> Local authorities and public bodies

> Purely religious activity
> Political or animal welfare activity

Applications

Applications for both programmes can be submitted through the charity's online portal, which can be accessed via its website. For Community Engagement (small) grants, applicants will typically be notified about the outcome of their application within four weeks of applying. For the Community Investment (large) grants, the charity operates a two-stage application process. See the website for full details.

Sources of information

Accounts; annual report; Charity Commission record; funder's website.

United Utilities Trust Fund

 Money advice, debt counselling, financial literacy

The area supplied by United Utilities Water plc (predominantly the north west of England)

£377,000 to organisations (2016/17)

CC number: 1108296

Trustees: Deborah Moreton; Alastair Richards; Simon Dewsnip; Robert Harrison; Lynne Heath; Sandra McCaughley.

Correspondent: Gay Hammett, Emmanuel Court, 12–14 Mill Street, Sutton Coldfield B72 1TJ (tel: 0121 362 3625; email: communitygrants@aurigaservices.co.uk)

 www.uutf.org.uk

United Utilities Trust Fund is an independent grant-making charity established in early 2005. Grants are mainly awarded to individuals in financial hardship who have a liability to pay water charges to United Utilities Water (directly or indirectly) and who are unable to pay.

Grants are also given to organisations that can deliver money advice and financial literacy services. The trustees' annual report for 2016/17 provides the following information: 'Trustees recognise the value of offering long-term help and support to individuals experiencing hardship and have adopted a policy of making grants available to organisations that provide free money advice and debt counselling services.'

Financial information

In 2016/17 the charity had assets of £337,000 and an income of £5 million. Grants to 4,971 individuals or families totalled £4.4 million and grants to 18 organisations totalled £377,000.

Beneficiaries included: Age UK – South Lakeland (£39,500); Blackpool Citizens Advice (£29,500); St Helens Citizens Advice (£20,000); Involve Northwest (£15,100); St Andrew's Community Network (£6,300).

Applications

Details of open funding rounds can be found on the fund's website.

Sources of information

Accounts; annual report; Charity Commission record; funder's website.

UnLtd (Foundation for Social Entrepreneurs)

Social entrepreneurship

UK

£2.3 million (2016/17)

CC number: 1090393

Trustees: Rajeeb Dey; Norman Cumming; Martin Wyn Griffith; Lynne Berry; Susan Charteris; Stephen Bediako; Nicolas Farhi; Elizabeth Sideris; Nicholas Petford; Rachel Barton; Krishna Vishnubhotla; James Lawson; Tim Davies-Pugh.

Correspondent: Mark Norbury, Chief Executive, 123 Whitecross Street, Islington, London EC1Y 8JJ (tel: 020 7566 1100; email: info@unltd.org.uk)

www.unltd.org.uk

UnLtd is unique in that it exists to make grants to individuals to undertake social initiatives. In effect, it makes grants for the start-up costs of new organisations and community groups to enterprising individuals who need support to implement their ideas and projects for improving their communities.

The charity was established in 2000 by seven partner organisations: Ashoka (since resigned), Changemakers, Comic Relief, Community Action Network, Scarman Trust, School for Social Entrepreneurs and Senscot. In 2003, the Millennium Commission invested £100 million in the organisation after a competitive process in which UnLtd was successful. UnLtd now works with a wide network of partner organisations.

UnLtd's core start-up awards are funded by the income generated from an endowment from the Millennium Commission. Award winners receive a complete, tailored package of money, training and advice at every stage of their project. Networking opportunities are also provided by UnLtd, along with intensive business support and mentoring to the most promising social entrepreneurs.

Awards are for people living in the UK, who are applying as an individual or informal group for support to run projects 'that benefit the public or community in the UK; that need an UnLtd Award to ensure success; that offer a new learning opportunity for the applicant(s); that are a new initiative'.

In addition to its core awards, UnLtd also manages several other funding schemes, the details of which can be found on the foundation's website.

Financial information

In 2016/17 the charity had assets of £149.2 million and an income of over £5.6 million. During the year, the charity awarded around £2.3 million in grants.

Exclusions

Ideas and ventures are not eligible for start-up awards if they:

- Are part of paid employment where the social entrepreneur is an employee
- Involve political or religious campaigning
- Involve activities outside the law or against public policy, or anything that encourages ethnic, religious or commercial disharmony
- Are mainly for the benefit of the social entrepreneur and/or others to achieve academic qualifications

Other programmes may have their own specific eligibility criteria. Check the website for full details.

Applications

Applications for all UnLtd's programmes can be made via the application portal on the charity's website.

Sources of information

Accounts; annual report; Charity Commission record; funder's website.

UPP Foundation

🔍 Higher education

📍 UK

💷 £220,000 (2015/16)

CC number: 1166323

Trustees: Rt Hon. David Laws; Dr Paul Marshall; Robin Bailey-Watts; Joanne Midren; Mary Stuart.

Correspondent: Richard Brabner, Head of Foundation, UPP, 40 Gracechurch Street, London EC3V 0BT (tel: 020 7398 7200; email: upp-foundation@upp-ltd.com)

 upp-foundation.org

 @upp_foundation

This foundation was established in 2015 and aims to tackle issues facing the UK higher education sector. It was established and is fully funded by University Partnerships Programme (UPP), a UK company which provides student accommodation infrastructure and support services.

According to its website, the foundation:

> Offers grants to universities, charities and other higher education bodies. In recent years, as higher education has expanded, the burden of paying for a degree has shifted towards the individual. This presents difficulties in maintaining the 'University for the Public Good', as well as ensuring there is greater equity in going to, succeeding at and benefiting from the university experience. The UPP Foundation helps universities and the wider higher education sector overcome these challenges.

Grants

The trustees are focusing on four main themes:

- Increasing access and retention to higher education
- Improving employability
- Enhancing civic universities
- Developing global citizens

Further detail on each of these priorities is provided in the eligibility guide on the foundation's website.

Grants can be awarded to registered charities and universities, but applications from other organisations with a clear social purpose, such as social enterprises and community groups, will also be considered. Grants are generally between £5,000 and £20,000, although larger grants will occasionally be considered if greater impact and value can be demonstrated.

The website states that in particular, the foundation supports applications which can demonstrate:

> - A new or innovative approach to tackling relevant issues
> - A commitment to collaboration and/or working in partnership
> - How the UPP Foundation can measurably add value to the project
> - A clear plan for long-term sustainability independent of support from the UPP Foundation

In 2015/16 the foundation had assets of £82,000 and an income £335,000. Grants awarded totalled £220,000. There was no list of beneficiaries included in the accounts.

Previous beneficiaries have included: Birkbeck, University of London; The Bridge Group (£16,000); MyBigCareer (£14,000); The Prince's Trust (£100,000 over four years); Queen Mary University of London (£18,500).

Exclusions

According to the website, the foundation will not support:

- Applications from individual students or persons (to clarify we will not accept applications directly from an individual but can accept applications from institutional bodies that meet the 'organisation criteria' wishing to support individuals within the Foundation's themes)
- Organisations directly affiliated to any political party
- Single faith religious organisations – it is understood that many charities have religious affiliations, foundations and history. The restrictions on single faith religious organisations only applies to charities or organisations where the observance to a specific faith is a prerequisite of support from the charity or organisation
- Recipients of funding from The UPP Foundation in the last 6 months, except at the discretion of the trustees

It will not support applications which:

- Risk bringing the name of The UPP Foundation and associated corporate parent UPP Group Ltd into disrepute
- Relate to the purchase of land or existing buildings (including a building's freehold) or the repayment of loans
- Represent a disproportionate percentage of the overall turnover of the organisation
- Relate to non-specific appeals, endowment funds, conduit organisation

Applications

Application forms can be requested by emailing upp-foundation@upp-ltd.com and can be submitted at any time during the year for consideration at quarterly trustees' meetings.

Further guidance is provided on the website, refer to the eligibility guidelines.

Sources of information

Charity Commission record; funder's website; guidelines for applicants.

The Michael Uren Foundation

🔍 Armed forces, medical research and facilities, animal welfare, education, with a focus on the sciences, engineering and technology, historic buildings

📍 UK and overseas

💷 £17.3 million (2016/17)

CC number: 1094102

Trustees: John Uren; Anne Gregory-Jones; Janis Bennett; Roger Gould; David Uren; Robert Uren.

Correspondent: Mark Pattenden, Haysmacintyre, 26 Red Lion Square, London WC1R 4AG (email: mpattenden@haysmacintyre.com)

The foundation was established in 2002 with general charitable purposes following an initial gift from Michael Uren.

The trustees state in their annual report that they intend to expand the foundation's charitable activities in the future, with the hope of making a high level of distributions to chosen charities. The foundation has previously stated that: 'The trustees are particularly keen on making grants for specific large projects. This could mean that, to satisfy this objective, no significant grants are paid in one year. With the resultant reserves retained a large grant could be made in the following year.'

The trustees set out the following primary objectives in their 2016/17 annual report:

▶ **Armed forces** – support of charities relating to the armed forces, and the support of ex-service personnel
▶ **Medical** – support of advanced medical research, and expansion and modernisation of medical facilities
▶ **Animal welfare** – support of endangered species, regardless of location
▶ **Education** – supporting the furtherance of education, with a specific focus on the sciences, engineering and technology
▶ **Historic buildings** – the restoration and continued maintenance of historic buildings

Financial information
In 2016/17 the foundation had assets of £48.3 million and an income of £2.5 million. There were grants made to 19 organisations totalling £17.3 million.

Beneficiaries included: King Edward VII Hospital (£10 million); Imperial College Trust (£4.5 million); Moorfields Eye Hospital (£600,000); Chatham Historic Dockyard Trust (£200,000); The Royal British Legion, Marine Society and Sea Cadets (£50,000 each); Friends of St Mary's Kenardington, Kent Wildlife Trust (£30,000 each); Royal Society of Wildlife Trusts (£20,000); Selby Abbey Organ Appeal (£10,000).

Applications
The foundation does not consider unsolicited applications.

Sources of information
Accounts; annual report; Charity Commission record.

The Utley Family Charitable Trust

 General charitable purposes, health, children, education, dementia

Worldwide

£ £317,500 (2016/17)

CC number: 1157399

Trustees: Raja Balasuriya; Melvyn Sims; Neil Utley; Nicky Utley.

Correspondent: The Trustees, 199 Nine Ashes Road, Nine Ashes, Ingatestone CM4 0JY (tel: 020 7842 2000)

This trust, registered in June 2014, was established by Neil and Nicky Utley. Neil Utley is an entrepreneur who made his career in the insurance industry and currently sits as a non-executive director on the board of Hastings Insurance Services Ltd. Together with Nicky Utley, his wife, he founded the record label NUA Entertainment.

The trust's Charity Commission record states that it operates as a grant-making charity with general charitable purposes. The trust can support organisations based anywhere in the world. The record also states that, initially, the trustees have focused on causes related to children, education, health and dementia.

Financial information
In 2016/17 the trust had assets of £20.8 million and an income of £1.8 million. Grants to 45 organisations totalled £317,500.

Beneficiaries included: Dementia and Power of Music (£72,000); BRIT Trust (£47,500); Great Ormond Street Hospital (£20,500); Pebble Beach Charitable Trust (£15,000); Cerebral Palsy Plus (£10,000); Fight for Sight and Street Child (£5,000 each); The Brainwave Centre Ltd (£2,500); Wildlife Management Ltd (£1,500); Quest School (£1,000); Spring Hill (£145).

Applications
Apply in writing to the correspondent.

Sources of information
Accounts; annual report; Charity Commission record.

The Vail Foundation

 General charitable purposes, Jewish causes

 UK and overseas

£ £1.12 million (2015/16)

CC number: 1089579

Trustees: Michael Bradfield; Paul Brett; Michael Goldstein.

Correspondent: Michael Bradfield, Trustee, 5 Fitzhardinge Street, London W1H 6ED (tel: 020 7317 3000)

This foundation was set up in 2001 with general charitable purposes. Grants are made to a wide variety of charitable organisations including those engaged in medical ancillary services (including medical research), education, helping people with disabilities and older people, relieving poverty, providing sheltered accommodation and developing the arts. In practice, predominantly Jewish causes and organisations are supported.

Financial information
In 2015/16 the foundation had assets of just over £5.4 million and an income of £631,000. Grants were made to 20 organisations and totalled £1.12 million. As in previous years, the organisations receiving the largest grants were: KKL Charity Ltd (£727,500 in total); the London School of Jewish Studies (£100,000 in total); and the United Jewish Israel Appeal (£80,000 in total).

Previous beneficiaries have included: JW3 Trust Ltd (£25,000); Anne Frank Trust UK (£4,000); The Mental Health Foundation (£2,500); Institute of Higher Rabbinical Studies (£1,500); Langdon Foundation (£1,000).

Applications
Apply in writing to the correspondent. The foundation's Charity Commission record states that 'the trustees consider all requests which they receive and make such donations as they feel appropriate'.

Sources of information
Accounts; annual report; Charity Commission record.

The Valentine Charitable Trust

 General charitable purposes

UK and overseas with a preference for Dorset

£ £915,000 (2015/16)

CC number: 1001782

Trustees: Douglas Neville-Jones; Peter Leatherdale; Susan Patterson; Roger Gregory; Diana Tory; Wing Cdr Donald Jack; Susan Ridley.

Correspondent: The Trustees, Hinton House, Hinton Road, Bournemouth BH1 2EN (tel: 01202 292424)

The Valentine Charitable Trust was founded by the late Miss Ann Cotton in 1990. It supports general charitable purposes with a particular focus on the provision of amenities and facilities for the benefit of the public, the protection and safeguarding of the countryside and wildlife and the control and reduction of pollution. Miss Cotton lived most of her life in Dorset, as such the trust particularly welcomes involvement in local projects in Dorset.

Grant-making policy

There are no boundaries on what the trustees consider local; however, when charities have a limited area of interest, preference will be given to those which operate in Dorset. The trustees will also consider making grants to charities which, while not based in the local area, operate there.

In addition to local grants, the charity also supports a small number of initiatives in financially developing countries. The trustees are particularly interested in projects which offer sustainability to local communities.

The trustees are prepared to make donations towards core funding on a repeat basis. Recurring donations require a report from the applicant charity and a new application so that the position can be reviewed. If a particular charity has been supported once, then the trust takes the stance that it will be supported again, unless there have been substantial changes that do not fit in with the trust's objectives since the last grant.

Offers of funding are regularly conditional upon the applicant raising other funds before the donation will be forthcoming. Similarly, offers of donations are sometimes made on the basis that they will only be made once the project actually proceeds.

Financial information

At the time of writing (June 2018), the trust's most recent set of accounts were unavailable. In 2015/16 the trust held assets of almost £33.5 million and had an income of £986,500. Grants were made to 142 organisations totalling £915,000.

Beneficiaries included: Dorset County Hospital Charity (£25,000); Game and Wildlife Conservation Trust, Macmillan Cancer Support and Shine Project (£10,000 each); Refresh Weymouth and Portland (£7,500); Royal Agricultural Benevolent Institution and Salisbury Cathedral Trust (£5,000 each).

Exclusions

No grants are given to individuals. The trust would not normally fund appeals for village halls or for the fabric of church buildings.

Applications

Apply in writing to the correspondent. All applications will be acknowledged and decisions are made at quarterly trustees' meetings.

Sources of information

Accounts; annual report; Charity Commission record.

The Van Neste Foundation

Social welfare, community projects, Christian causes, financially developing countries, people who are older or who have a disability, environment, respect for the sanctity of life

UK (especially the Bristol area) and overseas

£276,000 (2016/17)

CC number: 201951

Trustees: Martin Appleby; Fergus Lyons; Gerald Walker; Jeremy Lyons; Benedict Appleby; Tom Appleby; Joanna Dickens.

Correspondent: Fergus Lyons, Trustee, 15 Alexandra Road, Clifton, Bristol BS8 2DD (tel: 0117 973 5167; email: fergus.lyons@virgin.net)

The trustees of this charity currently give priority to the following:

- Financially developing countries
- People who are older or who have a disability
- Advancement of religion
- Community and Christian family life
- Environment
- Respect for dignity and sanctity of life

These priorities are reviewed by the trustees from time to time but applications falling outside them are currently (April 2018) unlikely to be considered. Applications are only accepted from registered charities or CICs and are typically for one-off projects rather than ongoing support.

Financial information

In 2016/17 the foundation held assets of £9.3 million and had an income of £320,500. Grants were made to 34 organisations totalling £276,000. Grants were broken down as follows:

Community and Christian family life	19	£128,000
Developing world	5	£57,500
Advancement of religion	3	£35,500
Environment	4	£30,000
Respect for dignity and sanctity of life	2	£20,000
People who are older or who have a disability	1	£5,000

Beneficiaries included: Housing Advice Bristol (£30,000); CAFOD (£25,000); Above and Beyond (£15,000); Independent People, Fauna and Flora and COAST (£10,000 each); Hop, Skip and Jump, Womankind and Young and Free (£5,000 each); The Daisy Garland Trust (£3,000); St Luke's Hospice (£2,000); Mercy Ships (£1,500).

Exclusions

Usually, grants are not given to individuals or to large, well-known charities. Applications are only considered from registered charities.

Applications

Applications should be made in writing in the form of a concise letter setting out: the objectives of the appeal; funding agreed from other sources; and a timetable for achieving the planned objectives. Applications should be made by post and should include a copy of the latest accounts. The foundation will not deal with enquiries by email, telephone or fax. Applications are considered by the trustees in January, June and October. Unsuccessful applicants will not be notified, to keep administration costs down; successful applicants will be notified within two weeks of a meeting.

Sources of information

Accounts; annual report; Charity Commission record.

The Vandervell Foundation

General charitable purposes, particularly: education, medical care and research, performing arts, social welfare, environmental regeneration

UK

£340,000 (2016)

CC number: 255651

Trustee: Directors of the Vandervell Foundation Ltd.

Correspondent: Valerie Kaye, Administrator, Hampstead Town Hall Centre, 213 Haverstock Hill, London NW3 4QP (tel: 020 7435 7546; email: vandervell@btconnect.com)

This foundation gives grants for a wide range of charitable purposes, but particularly in the areas of education, medical care and research, the performing arts, social welfare and environmental regeneration.

A wide range of organisations have been supported, including schools, educational establishments, hospices and other health organisations. Grants generally range up to £30,000.

Financial information

In 2016 the foundation had assets of £7.8 million and an income of £259,000. A total of 90 grants to organisations amounted to £340,000.

Social welfare	47	£166,500
Medical care and research	31	£80,500
Education	3	£45,000
Performing arts	7	£42,000
Environmental regeneration	2	£6,000

Beneficiaries included: Big Issue (£30,000); British Exploring Society and King's College London School of Medicine (£15,000 each); The Outward Bound Trust (£10,000).

Applications

Apply in writing to the correspondent. Grants are reviewed by the board of trustees every other month.

Sources of information

Accounts; annual report; Charity Commission record.

The Vardy Foundation

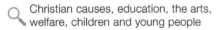 Christian causes, education, the arts, welfare, children and young people

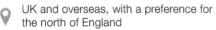 UK and overseas, with a preference for the north of England

£2.46 million to organisations (2016/17)

CC number: 328415

Trustees: Lady Margaret Vardy; Peter Vardy; Richard Vardy; Sir Peter Vardy; Victoria Vardy.

Correspondent: Sir Peter Vardy, Trustee, 4 Admiral Way, Doxford International Business Park, Sunderland SR3 3XW (tel: 0191 501 8555)

The foundation was set up in 1989 with general charitable objectives by Sir Peter Vardy. Sir Peter Vardy made his fortune in the motor retail business through his company, Reg Vardy plc, founded by his father. According to the trustees' report for 2016/17, the foundation supports 'initiatives and programmes committed to strengthening families, the relief of poverty, supporting ex-offenders and those in prisons, addiction rehabilitation, the homeless and the unemployed'. The foundation also supports 'a range of programmes in education, the arts, skills enhancement, mentoring and leadership development'.

Grant-making information

The trustees' report for 2016/17 states that the foundation 'considers and measures applications against two main criteria:'

▶ Projects should involve, help and encourage young people
▶ Projects, if in the UK, should ideally be based in the North of England

Projects are supported primarily in northern England, but also throughout the UK and internationally. The foundation also established the Safe Families for Children charity, which seeks to keep families together and avoid children being taken into the care system.

The Peter Vardy Foundation

The Peter Vardy Foundation is a fund within the Vardy foundation. It funds projects that support, educate and care for children and young people both internationally or near Reg Vardy motor dealerships in Scotland.

Financial information

In 2016/17 the foundation held assets of £36.3 million and had an income of almost £1.8 million. There were 434 grants made with £2.46 million awarded to organisations and £69,000 awarded to individuals. Grants were distributed as follows:

Religion	81	£986,500
Welfare	334	£923,500
Education	10	£544,500
Arts	9	£77,500

Beneficiaries included: Beacon of Light (£500,000); Dumfries Baptist Church (£200,000); North Music Trust (£150,000); Hope For Justice (£50,000); The Vine Church and Urban Saints (£25,000 each).

Grants of less than £25,000 totalled £463,000.

Applications

The Vardy Foundation: Apply in writing to the correspondent. The trustees meet every two months to review grants. Each application is considered against the criteria outlined above.

The Peter Vardy Foundation: Apply via the foundation's website: www. petervardy.com/peter-vardy-foundation.

Sources of information

Accounts; annual report; Charity Commission record.

Variety, the Children's Charity

 Children and young people (up to the age of 18)

UK

£2.2 million to organisations (2016)

CC number: 209259/SC038505

Trustees: Jason Lewis; Ronald Sinclair; Nicholas Shattlock; William Sangster; Rodney Natkiel; Tushar Pradhu; James Martin; Duncan Syers; Jonathan Gold; Dilaram Williamson.

Correspondent: Julie Thomas, Grants Programme Manager, Variety House, 93 Bayham Street, London NW1 0AG (tel: 020 7428 8100; email: julie.thomas@variety.org.uk)

 www.variety.org.uk

 facebook.com/VarietyGB

 @VarietyGB

 @VarietyGB

Variety aims to improve the lives of children and young people across the UK who are disadvantaged, sick or have disabilities. The charity belongs to Variety International – 'a global charity with three core initiatives: Freedom, Future and Caring', which are also reflected in the UK programmes.

The charity's annual report and accounts state: 'Variety is not about stopping a crisis or preventing a drama; it is about providing both practical help (including coaches, wheelchairs and specialist equipment) and memorable childhood experiences.'

Support is given to both organisations (including schools, hospitals, hospices and youth clubs) and individuals (principally for the purchase of specialist care or play equipment). Each year, Variety also takes children on day trips to seaside, zoo, theme parks and so on.

According to the annual report, the charity's objectives are as follows:

▶ to promote and provide for the care and upbringing of sick, disabled and disadvantaged children within the United Kingdom
▶ the advancement of education and the relief of financial need of children within the United Kingdom
▶ to undertake, and to assist others to undertake, research into any illness or affliction affecting children which will advance knowledge and to publish the useful results of research
▶ the provision of facilities for recreation and other leisure time occupation for children in the interests of their social welfare with the object of improving the conditions of life for such children.

The four main areas of work covered are:

1 **Sunshine coaches** – funding is provided towards coaching for organisations. Funding is a joint effort between the organisation, Variety and sponsors.
2 **Wheelchairs** – manual, powered and sports wheelchairs are provided to children and young people with disabilities.
3 **Equipment grants** – grants are provided to organisations and individuals. The charity tries to provide whatever is needed whether it is medical equipment, basic care or mobility/play equipment. Grants are typically between £100 to £6,000.
4 **Great Days Out** – the charity runs days out for children who have a disability, are sick or disadvantaged.

Financial information

In 2016 the charity had assets of £2.8 million and an income of £3.6 million. Grants totalled £2.7 million with £521,000 awarded to individuals and £2.2 million awarded to organisations. Grants were broken down as follows:

Sunshine Coaches	£2.04 million
Equipment grants	£435,000
Wheelchairs	£376,000

Beneficiaries included: Marian Vann Primary School (£60,500); Seashell Trust (£38,000); Three Ways Close (£38,000); Royal School for the Deaf (£34,000); Harbour School (£28,000); Ravensbourne Project (£7,700).

Applications

Details of how to apply for each type of grant can be found on the charity's website.

Sources of information

Accounts; annual report; Charity Commission record; guidelines for applicants; funder's website.

The Veolia Environmental Trust

 Community and environmental projects

 UK

(£) £3.78 million (2016/17)

CC number: 1064144

Trustees: Oswald Dodds; Tom Spaul; Caroline Schwaller; Derek Goodenough; Malcolm Marshall; Mike Smith; John Brown; Robert Hunt; Maggie Durran; Ben Slater; Donald Macphail; Malcolm Marshall.

Correspondent: Robert Hunt, Secretary, Ruthdene, Station Road, Four Ashes, Wolverhampton WV10 7DG (tel: 020 3567 6820; email: info@veoliatrust.org)

 www.veoliatrust.org

The Veolia Environmental Trust was established in 1997. The trust supports community and environmental projects that fulfil the following objective: the reclamation and reduction of polluted land; the protection, preservation and improvement of the environment for the benefit of the public; and the delivery of biodiversity conservation for UK species.

According to its website, the trust will consider applications for capital improvement projects at a single site with discrete start and end dates, and which fall into the one of the following categories:

- **Community buildings and rooms:** e.g. community centres; village halls; community spaces within religious buildings, Scout or Girlguiding buildings
- **Outdoor spaces:** e.g. public parks, nature reserves, community gardens, footpaths, bridleways or cycle paths
- **Play and recreation:** e.g. play areas, skateparks, Multi Use Games Areas (MUGAs), sports grounds, pavilions or changing rooms
- **Biodiversity**

The website states that competition for funding is considerable and therefore applicants need to submit an application that does justice to their project and highlights how it is going to make a real difference to people's lives or the environment. Grants provided by the trust are usually between £10,000 and £75,000.

Financial information

In 2016/17 the trust had assets of £2.48 million and an income of £4 million. Grants were made totalling £3.78 million to 255 projects, of which 247 grants were for less than £50,000.

Beneficiaries included: The JPK Sussex Project (£95,000); Copleston Centre, River Thames Boat Project (£76,000); Brewood Bowling Club (£71,000); Surrey Docks Farm Provident Society (£62,000); Salford City Council (£57,000); Birmingham City Council and Rugby Borough Council (£52,000 each).

Exclusions

Funding is limited to projects which are in the proximity of a qualifying Veolia site. Eligibility can be checked using the 'postcode checker' on the trust's website. In addition, the trust's website notes that grants will not be provided for the following:

- Regulatory bodies (e.g. Forestry Commission, Environment Agency)
- Zoos, museums, libraries, theatres or arts organisations
- Educational or arts establishments
- Projects where the public amenity is subject to a lease of less than six years remaining duration
- Shops or projects established to generate an income for use other than for the upkeep of the project
- Projects that involve the purchase of land or buildings
- Exhibitions, sculptures, statues or memorials
- Allotments, graveyards or crematoria areas
- Portable equipment, including sports and fitness kits, furniture or white goods
- Access roads or car parks
- Restoration of buildings
- Street scene improvements street trees, hanging baskets, aesthetic improvements, village or highway signs
- CCTV and portable equipment, including sports and fitness kit, lawnmowers, furniture and white goods
- Renewable energy projects to access feed-in tariffs, e.g. solar panels
- Staff costs that do not relate to the physical project
- Projects that have already started
- Projects with a total cost of over £250,000 (including VAT and professional costs)

Applications for biodiversity projects must be submitted by registered Environmental Bodies and comply with ENTRUST requirements.

Applications

Full details of the eligibility criteria, application process and deadlines are provided on the trust's helpful website. Information on the website is divided into three sections:

- **Know:** gives details about the trust's criteria, closing dates, and application process
- **Prepare:** provides information to help applicants have a complete picture of what the trustees are looking for in a project in order to develop the best possible project proposal
- **Apply:** allows applicants to check their projects eligibility using the 'Eligibility Checker', and access the trust's stage one application form

The trust has a two-stage application process.

Stage 1 Application requires:
- A project overview
- Identify the elements/activities you are requesting funding for
- Have 20% of your total project cost already secured
- Have an idea of timescales

Stage 2 Applications requires you to provide:
- Detailed information about the project
- Copies of required permission(s) to complete the project (e.g. planning approval)
- Evidence of need for the project
- Evidence of the benefit of the project
- A copy of the design
- A cost breakdown

Applicants are encouraged to make contact if they want to discuss their project. Applications are considered quarterly by the trustees.

Sources of information

Accounts; annual report; Charity Commission record; funder's website.

VHLT Ltd

 Orthodox Jewish causes, social welfare

 London and Israel

(£) £618,000 to organisations (2015/16)

CC number: 1101241

Trustees: Avrohom Streicher; Yoel Marmorstein; Yehiel Frand; Raymond Frand.

Correspondent: Yehiel Frand, Trustee, 61 Fairholt Road, London N16 5EW (tel: 020 8809 5700)

According to the charity's 2015/16 accounts, the objectives of the charity are: to advance religion in accordance with the Orthodox Jewish faith and the relief of poverty, in particular by assisting individuals in need of food, clothing, shelter or medical services who are unable to afford these from their own means. The charity also supports educational and religious institutions and gives grants and scholarships to suitable qualified students.

Financial information

At the time of writing (June 2018), the charity's latest accounts were unavailable. In 2015/16 the charity had assets of £63,500 and an income of £720,500. During the year, the charity awarded grants totalling £653,000, including £618,000 to organisations and £35,500 to individuals. The grant total for organisations included a very large grant of £540,000 to Vaad Harabonim Israel for the relief of poverty.

A full list of beneficiaries was unavailable.

Applications

Apply in writing to the correspondent.

Sources of information

Accounts; annual report; Charity Commission record.

The Vintners' Foundation

 Alcohol and drug abuse, education

Generally in Greater London only

£ £215,000 (2016/17)

CC number: 1015212

Trustees: Andrew Parmley; Nicholas Arkell; Marcia Waters; Christopher Davey.

Correspondent: Stephen Freeth, Archivist and Charities Secretary, Vintners' Company, Vintners' Hall, 68 Upper Thames Street, London EC4V 3BG (tel: 020 7651 0753; email: charity@vintnershall.co.uk)

 www.vintnershall.co.uk

The Vintners' Foundation, set up by the Vintners' Company, receives donations primarily from members of the company and supporters of the foundation's objectives. The foundation makes grants to charities concerned with the prevention of alcohol and drug abuse in Greater London. Grants are also made to other causes including education, the services, welfare of people in need, churches and other charities requested by the company's members.

The trustees tend to focus support more specifically on charities dealing with the social consequences of alcohol abuse, including support for the families and dependants of abusers and preventative education around substance misuse for young people. It also supports fewer

charities, but to a greater extent and for longer periods of time.

The trustees favour small, localised charities who may be more in need of funds than larger, well-known charities and grants are generally made in the range of £3,000 to £5,000. Grants are made for specific projects rather than running costs. The foundation supports a number of charities on a continuous basis. In addition to grants, organisations that are supported by the foundation may also benefit from the skills of members of the Vintners' Company as volunteers.

Financial information

In 2016/17 the trust held assets of £2.3 million and had an income of £334,500. Grants were made to 53 organisations and totalled £215,000.

Beneficiaries included: Spitalfields Crypt Trust (£50,000); Anthony Nolan Charity (£12,500); Chain Reaction Theatre Company and Counselling Pastoral Trust (£10,000 each); Emmaus South Lambeth Community and Toy House Libraries Association (£5,000 each); Alzheimer's Research (£4,000); Maytree Respite (£3,000); ABF Soldier's Charity, Guildhall School of Music and Drama and St Paul's Cathedral (£1,000 each).

During the year, 20 grants were made of less than £1,000 and totalled £4,800.

Exclusions

Grants are not given to/for:

- Medical research
- The restoration of buildings
- National charities
- Overseas organisations
- General running costs

Applications

Although much of the foundation's grant-making is directed to its current selected charities, some limited funds are still available for new applications. New petitions also provide an essential mechanism for bringing potential new selected charities to the notice of the trustees. The foundation's website provides the following information on how to make a petition:

- There is no application form. Applicants have a free hand to state their case, preferably in not more than three sides of A4 (by email in electronic format – see below)
- Applications for specific projects are much preferred. The Committee is unwilling to support general running costs
- All applications should include a breakdown of the budget for the proposed project together with the charity's most recent audited accounts
- All agenda papers for the Vintners' Foundation Committee are now circulated electronically and hard copy petitions are not accepted

- Documents sent as attachments should be on the headed notepaper of the charity

The committee meets four times a year, usually in March, June, September and December. Petitions which are too late for the next meeting will be postponed to the following scheduled meeting. See the website for further details.

Sources of information

Accounts; annual report; Charity Commission record; funder's website.

The Virgin Money Foundation

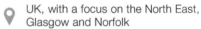 Community development and regeneration, social enterprise, children and young people

UK, with a focus on the North East, Glasgow and Norfolk

£ £1.04 million (2016)

CC number: 1161290

Trustees: Sir Thomas Shebbeare; Ruth Ibegbuna; Edward Wakefield; Joanne Curry; Timothy Davies-Pugh; Stephen Pearson; Tim Arthuer; Emma Morris.

Correspondent: The Trustees, Jubilee House, Gosforth, Newcastle upon Tyne NE3 4PL (tel: 0330 123 3624; email: info@virginmoneyfoundation.org.uk)

 virginmoneyfoundation.org.uk

 @VMFStartLocally

The foundation was registered with the Charity Commission in April 2015. It was set up following the demise of the Northern Rock Foundation (established by the Northern Rock Bank which was purchased by the Virgin Money bank) 'to promote the sustainable regeneration of economically and socially deprived communities in the United Kingdom'.

Grant programmes

At the time of writing (May 2018) the foundation has five funding programmes, details of which have been taken from its website:

The North East Fund – The North East Fund works with organisations that promote long-term change in the communities that need it most in the North East.

The Ripple Fund – The Ripple Fund supports sustainable regeneration in local communities, particularly enabling activity that is likely to have a 'ripple effect', that is activity which will create skills and confidence to tackle other important issues and therefore build stronger communities.

#iwill Take Action Fund – The #iwill Take Action Fund supports organisations working with young people aged 10 to 20 to engage in meaningful social action across the North East.

Heart of the Community Fund – Helping causes at the heart of Glasgow. Every two months, the Virgin Money Foundation is giving a local charity in Glasgow the chance to receive £1,000.

Making a Splash in Norfolk – A grants programme to enable organisations working in community regeneration across Norfolk to think outside the box helping them to develop new initiatives and sustainable enterprises.

Financial information

In 2016 the foundation held assets of £2.1 million and had an income of £2.4 million. Grants awarded to organisations totalled £1.04 million and were broken down as follows:

Helping homeless people find and keep a home	£477,000
Helping disadvantaged young people into employment	£451,000
Supporting new or existing social enterprises	£117,00

Beneficiaries included: Newcastle upon Tyne YMCA (£50,000); Young Asian Voices (£41,000); Depaul UK (£40,000); East Cleveland Youth Housing Trust (£35,000); Youth Almighty Project (£31,000); Bluewatch Youth Project (£28,000); Cleveland Ironstone Mining Museum (£25,000); Actes Trust (£24,000).

Applications

Consult the website for application details.

Sources of information

Accounts; annual report; Charity Commission record; funder's website.

Viridor Credits Environmental Company

 Environment, community development, heritage

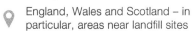 England, Wales and Scotland – in particular, areas near landfill sites

 £8.4 million (2016/17)

CC number: 1096538

Trustees: David Robertson; Peter Renshaw; Simon Catford; Mary Prior.

Correspondent: Alison Salvador, General Manager, Aintree House, Blackbrook Park Avenue, Taunton TA1 2PX (tel: 01823 476476; email: enquiries@viridor-credits.co.uk)

 www.viridor-credits.co.uk

@viridorcredits

Viridor Credits Environmental Company is a registered charity that provides funding for community development, heritage and biodiversity projects

through the Landfill Communities Fund and the Scottish Landfill Communities Fund.

Grants schemes – England and Wales

According to the charity's website, the charity has the following grants schemes for England and Wales:

Small Grants Scheme
The Small Grants scheme is for Community, Heritage and Biodiversity projects that request up to £20,000. Small grant projects are considered by our local Steering Groups and must start drawing down funding within three months of the offer of funding and finish within six months. We can support projects in the Funding Areas located within 10 miles of an active Viridor Landfill site or within 10 miles of the Viridor Energy Recovery Facilities located in Peterborough, Bolton, Cardiff, Exeter, Oxford and Runcorn.

Main Grants Scheme
The Main Grants scheme is for Community, Heritage or Biodiversity projects that request £20,001 to 50,000.Main grant projects are considered by our local Steering Groups and must start drawing down funding within six months of receipt of a funding decision and finish within 12 months. We can support Community & Heritage projects in Funding Areas located within 10 miles of an active Viridor Landfill site. We can support Biodiversity project located within 10 miles of any active Landfill site.

Large Grants Scheme
The Large Grants band is for Community, Heritage or Biodiversity projects that request £50,001–100,000 from Viridor Credits. Large grant projects are considered by the main Viridor Credits Board and must start drawing down funding within six months of receipt of a funding decision and finish within 18 months. We can support Community & Heritage projects in Funding Areas located within 10 miles of a Viridor Landfill site. We can support Biodiversity project located within 10 miles of any active Landfill site.

All three of these grants schemes are open to constituted charitable organisations, including charities, community groups and parish or town councils. To be eligible for funding, projects must fulfil one of the following Landfill Communities Fund's objects:

▶ **Object D** – The protection of the environment; the provision, maintenance or improvement of public amenities and parks, which are open and accessible to the public
▶ **Object Da** – The protection of the environment; the enhancement, protection and/or promotion of biological diversity of a species or habitat
▶ **Object E** – The protection of the environment; the maintenance, repair or restoration of a building or structure that is of historic or architectural

interest, and is open and accessible to the public

Projects must have 'no restrictions on access or use and, in the case of community facilities, are available to the public at all times for at least 104 days per year'.

Pennon Environmental Fund
The Pennon Environmental Fund (PEF) was set up in 1999 to distribute awards from the Landfill Communities Fund in South West Water's (SWW) operating area. The fund allows non-profit groups to apply for funding up to £20,000 in areas served by SWW, mainly Cornwall and parts of Devon.

For more information on each of the grants schemes, including upcoming deadlines, refer to the charity's website.

Grants schemes – Scotland

Grants of up to £50,000 are available for projects in Scotland, through the Scottish Landfill Communities Fund. The website states the following information:

Projects under objects C, D & E must be located within 10 miles of an active landfill site, or a transfer station that processes more than 2,500 tonnes of waste per year.

▶ **Object C** - To provide, maintain or improve a public park or other public amenity
▶ **Object D** – The conservation or promotion of biological diversity through the provision, conservation, restoration or enhancement of a natural habitat or the maintenance or recovery of a species in its natural habitat
▶ **Object E** – The maintenance, repair or restoration of a building, other structure or a site of archaeological interest which is a place of religious worship, or a site of historic or architectural or archaeological interest and is open to the public
▶ **Objects A, B & F** – To apply for funding under objects A, B & F, please call 01823 476476 to discuss your application. Projects under objects A, B and F can be located anywhere in Scotland

For further information on each of the above priorities, as well as deadlines and application guidance, refer to the charity's website.

Contributing Third Party payments

For any grants made by the charity, a Contributing Third Party payment must be made. The website explains this as follows:

The Contributing Third Party payment is a transaction between a third party (that is neither the applicant organisation nor Viridor Credits) and Viridor Waste Management.

When Viridor Credits awards funding, it awards a gross amount to the applicant, which is inclusive of the ENTRUST fee.

10% of this gross amount is the total sum payable by the Contributing Third Party to Viridor Waste Management.

More information is provided on the charity's website.

Financial information

In 2016/17 the charity had assets of £2.4 million and an income of almost £7 million. During the year, the charity awarded grants worth a total of £8.4 million.

Beneficiaries included: Milton Abbey, Stonham Aspal Village Hall (£100,000 each); Fleet Air Arm Museum (£74,500); Tottington St John's Cricket Club (£65,500); Arundel Wetland (£60,000); West Barns Village Hall and Paisley Methodist Central Hall (£50,000 each).

Exclusions

According to the application guidance notes, the charity is unable to consider funding for the following:

- Aspects of a project that have already started
- Contingencies, fees and preliminaries
- Works to public highways; anything that may be the statutory or discretionary responsibility of the local authority
- Projects located on/in:
  - Allotments
  - School grounds
  - Facilities owned and managed by a local authority (except parks and play areas)
  - Facilities primarily used for service provision or not considered a general public amenity, such as hospitals, day centres, hospices or accommodation
- Proportional projects
- Salaried posts or revenue funding
- Core costs of an organisation e.g. rent, energy bills, supplies
- Community Cafes
- Purchase or lease of vehicles
- Purchase of land or buildings that are not at risk of closure or loss to the community
- Multimedia or CCTV equipment, events, CDs, website or marketing materials
- Energy saving or green technology projects that generate an income, such as Feed in Tariff or Renewable Heat Incentive

Applications

For information on how to apply to each scheme, along with guidance notes and deadlines, refer to the charity's website.

Sources of information

Accounts; annual report; Charity Commission record; funder's website.

The Vodafone Foundation

General charitable purposes, with a preference for, technology, disadvantaged communities, humanitarian and disaster relief

UK and overseas (where Vodafone operates)

£20.6 million worldwide, of which £515,000 was given in the UK (2016/17)

CC number: 1089625

Correspondent: Andrew Dunnett, Foundation Director, Vodafone House, The Connection, Newbury, Berkshire RG14 2FN (email: groupfoundation@vodafone.com)

 www.vodafonefoundation.org

 facebook.com/VodafoneFdn

 @vodafonefdn

 @vodafonefoundation

The Vodafone Foundation was established in 2001. Its 2016/17 trustees' annual report states that during that year it distributed funds to:

- Charities and individual programmes selected by its 28 local Vodafone foundations
- Global programmes that fit with the foundation's grant-making strategies

The report also states that:

The Vodafone Foundation has a funding partnership with Vodafone's local foundations to provide public benefit by investing in programmes that support communities in which Vodafone has commercial roots. The trustees also allocate funds to global programmes, run in partnership with NGOs.

The strategic report for this financial year notes that the foundation supports projects within the following major themes:

- **Connecting for Good** – connecting our giving to our technology, maximising the impact of our charitable giving by funding projects that can benefit from leveraging Vodafone's technologies and expertise to address some of the world's most pressing humanitarian challenges. During 2017, around 70% of our giving was allocated to Connected for Good
- **Disaster relief** – through our Instant Network programme we aim to deploy Vodafone Volunteers and technology in emergencies to provide free communications and technical support to aid agencies and victims and develop new technologies to support the humanitarian community. Vodafone continues to enable customers to donate to charity via our network and through The Vodafone Foundation's mobile giving programme
- **In-country Grants** – through the 28 local Vodafone Foundations, we give financial support to projects that benefit local communities in significant and timely ways

UK programme

The trustees' annual report for 2016/17 states that the Vodafone Foundation is responsible for Vodafone UK's social investment activities. The programmes include:

- **JustTextGiving:** JustTextGiving enables charities in the UK, to raise money via text donations. Since its inception in May 2011, JustTextGiving has been used by more than 300,000 individual fundraisers and by 25,000 charities and has helped raise more than £41 million for charity
- **TecSOS:** This is a specialised handset designed for use by victims of domestic violence which connects them directly to the police wherever they are. Six European countries are using the handset with almost 13,300 UK victims benefitting. The report states that over 88% of UK police forces are using the service to support victims of domestic violence in their area
- **Matched Funding:** The Vodafone Foundation gives financial support to UK-based Vodafone employees or teams that fundraise in their own time. This is processed through matched funding of up to £350 per employee, per event, and up to four times per year. In 2016/17, Vodafone employees raised nearly £2.2 million for their chosen causes and the Vodafone Foundation contributed £661k towards employee fundraising

Financial information

In 2016/17 the foundation had assets of over £4.2 million and an income of almost £22 million. During the year, the foundation made grants worldwide totalling £20.6 million. This included £12.4 million given to the 28 local Vodafone foundations. A total of £515,000 was given in the UK.

Beneficiaries included: The Prince's Trust (£151,500); PK Trust (£120,000); Diana Award (£106,000 in two grants); Digital Scouts (£84,000); Story Time project (£12,600); British Heart Foundation (£1,500).

Applications

Contact the foundation or see the website for details of all application processes for different grant programmes.

Note: The foundation's website states that the foundation receives an average of 12,000 requests per year for funding and support and that, while seeking to respond to all requests for information, it normally approaches only those charitable organisations which it believes can help in the delivery of its charitable aims.

Sources of information

Accounts; annual report; Charity Commission record; funder's website.

Volant Charitable Trust

 Social welfare, women, children

 Scotland

£3.1 million (2016/17)

OSCR number: SC030790

Correspondent: Jennifer McPhail, Grants Programme Executive, Princes Exchange, 1 Earl Grey Street, Edinburgh EH3 9EE (tel: 0141 341 4964; email: jennifer@foundationscotland.org.uk)

 www.volanttrust.com

This trust was established in 2000 by the author J. K. Rowling for general charitable purposes. The trust has three broad areas of funding:

» Charitable organisations involved in the support and protection of women, children, relief of poverty and alleviating social deprivation and the provision of social benefit to the community and the public at large
» Research and teaching related to the treatment, cure and nursing of multiple sclerosis and related conditions
» Major disaster appeals

Open Grants programme

Applications are only accepted for the Open Grants programme which support Scottish charities and projects, whether national or community-based, that alleviate social deprivation, particularly supporting women, children and young people at risk. The following information on the programme has been taken from the trust's website:

Projects must demonstrate a strong focus on supporting women and children affected by hardship or disadvantage and on tackling the issues they face in order to make a lasting difference to their lives and life chances.

Specific programme areas that we cover include support for:

Women – Victims of sexual abuse, rape, domestic violence and those working in the sex industry; care for young mothers and those affected by postnatal depression, isolated and lone parents; community support for black and minority ethnic women and asylum seekers; support services for women prisoners and their families.

Children and young people – Counselling, support services and outreach projects for those who are disadvantaged or deemed to be at risk through neglect, emotional and physical abuse, alcohol or drug misuse.

Poverty and deprivation – Mental health projects for women and children; support for vulnerable families; promotion of healthy eating for families in areas of extreme deprivation.

Eligibility

Both one-off projects and multi-year applications are accepted.

Grants are made at any level up to £10,000 per year.

The trust will only fund core costs and projects costs. No grants are made for capital expenditure.

Financial information

In 2016/17 the trust held assets of £66.6 million and had an income of £2.8 million. Grants awarded to organisations totalled £3.1 million and were broken down as follows:

International aid relief	£1.3 million
Women	£805,500
Relief of poverty and social deprivation	£798,000
Children and young people	£157,500

Beneficiaries of major grants included: Disasters Emergency Committee (£1 million); Gingerbread (£300,000); British Red Cross (£100,000); Christian Aid and Oxfam (£50,000 each).

Exclusions

The Volant Trust will not support:

» Individuals
» Projects which do not benefit people in Scotland
» General fundraising appeals or activities
» Contributions to major capital projects
» Groups who will then distribute the funds as grants or bursaries
» The repayment of loans or payment of debts
» Retrospective funding (i.e. costs already incurred/activities already taken place)
» Trips abroad
» Purchase of second-hand vehicles

Applications

Applications can be made online via the Foundation Scotland website. Applicants should first complete an initial enquiry form. Once Foundation Scotland has reviewed the form, you may then be invited to submit a full application.

Sources of information

Accounts; annual report; OSCR record; funder's website.

Voluntary Action Fund (VAF)

 Social welfare, capacity building, equality, violence against women, isolation, employment, nutrition

 Scotland

£14.4 million (2016/17)

OSCR number: SC035037

Trustees: Joanna McLaughlin; Anela Anwar; John McDonald; Sarah Kersey; Pervin Ahmed; Graham Leydon; David McNeill; Ahmed Yousaf; Rosalind McKenna; James Nicol; Claire Stevens; Pauline Hinchion; Dalvir Johal.

Correspondent: Programmes Team, Suite 3, Forth House, Burnside Business Court, North Road, Inverkeithing, Fife KY11 1NZ (tel: 01383 620780; email: info@vaf.org.uk)

 www.voluntaryactionfund.org.uk

 facebook.com/Voluntary-Action-Fund-255493851220324

@volactionfund

Set up in 1982, this was originally a fund called the Unemployed Voluntary Action Fund (UVAF) managed under the auspices of the Carnegie UK Trust. In response to the economic and social challenges of the day, the initial Scotland-wide fund of £400,000 aimed to support volunteering opportunities for unemployed people, in health projects, social services and community development.

In 1990 UVAF became an independent charitable organisation. Later, as the scope of the funding expanded, the name changed and in 2003 the Voluntary Action Fund (VAF) was re-established as a charitable company limited by guarantee.

Grant-making

VAF manages a number of programmes on behalf of the Scottish Government and other funders. These are:

» Democracy Matters Community Engagement Fund
» Glasgow Children's Food Programme
» Workplace Equality Fund
» Wellbeing for Longer in Glasgow Fund
» Promoting Equality & Cohesion Fund
» Equally Safe (Violence against Women and Girls Fund)
» Rape Crisis Specific Fund
» Volunteering Support Fund

Financial information

In 2016/17 the fund had assets of £583,500 and an income of £15.4 million. Grants awarded to organisations totalled £14.4 million and were distributed through the following funds:

Violence Against Women	£8.9 million
Equality Programme	£2.9 million
Volunteering Scotland Grant Scheme	£1.1 million
Drugs and Community Safety Division	£986,000
Social Isolation and Loneliness Fund	£482,000
American Mothers	£11,000
Healthier Scotland Engagement Fund	£1,500

Previous beneficiaries have included:
Lothian and Borders Community Justice Authority (£375,000); South West Scotland Criminal Justice Social Work Services (£372,000); Barnardo's Scotland (£228,500); Zero Tolerance (£177,000); Sense over Sectarianism (£169,500); South Lanarkshire Women's Aid (£158,500); Citizens Theatre (£151,000); Youthlink Scotland (£131,000); Motherwell and Districts Women's Aid (£103,500); Scottish Book Trust (£79,500).

Exclusions

See the fund's website for details of any individual exclusions for each fund.

Applications

Application forms and guidance notes for open programmes are available on the fund's website. The trustees recommend that interested parties contact them to discuss the project before making any application. Grant programmes may open and close so applicants should check the website for the most recent updates. Different funds have different application guidance.

Sources of information

Accounts; annual review; OSCR record; funder's website.

Sylvia Waddilove Foundation UK

 General charitable purposes, education, arts, medical research, disability, heritage, housing

 UK

£ £268,500 (2016)

CC number: 1118097

Trustees: Gerald Kidd; Percy Robson; Peter Spencer.

Correspondent: The Trustees, c/o Pothecary Witham Weld Solicitors, 70 St George's Square, London SW1V 3RD (tel: 020 7821 8211; email: waddilove@pwwsolicitors.co.uk)

 www.pwwsolicitors.co.uk/charity-grants/13-the-sylvia-waddilove-foundation-uk

The foundation was established in 2006 from part of the estate of Sylvia Waddilove, who died five years earlier. Ms Waddilove was born in Bradford in

1911 and her family was successful in the textile industry. There is a strong connection with agriculture as Ms Waddilove lived at Chevin Grange Farm, Menston near Ilkley, Yorkshire. Her father, Joshua Kelley Waddilove, founded Provident Financial in Bradford in 1880.

The following information is taken from the administrator's website:

> The Trustees welcome applications from charities, CICs and Registered Societies. Grants are provided for projects relating to the following charitable purposes:
>
> - Education (organic farming, animal husbandry, veterinary science, animal welfare and animal surgery)
> - The visual and performing arts
> - Medical research
> - The relief of disability and severe illness
> - The preservation of buildings of architectural or historical significance
> - The accommodation of those in need

There are detailed individual eligibility criteria for each of the above charitable purposes – these are available on the administrator's website and should be checked before making an application.

The following criteria apply to all applicants:

> - The applicant has used the application form
> - The applicant has not applied within the last two years
> - The applicant is a registered charity (including a CIO), CIC, Registered Society, or an exempt charity. Small charities which are not required to register with the Charity Commission because their income is less than £5,000 may also apply. The applicant may be an individual if the project relates to medical research
> - The applicant and the beneficiaries benefitting from the project are based in the United Kingdom
> - The applicant has been in existence for at least two years and has a track record of delivering projects
> - The project relates to one of the six charitable purposes listed above
> - The application relates to a project that is either new or has been running for less than five years

The trustees may occasionally allocate a separate budget for grants in order to advance one of the charitable objects of the foundation. This is known as the Allocated Grants Programme. The trustees decide which purpose to concentrate on and then research potential applicants themselves.

Financial information

In 2016 the foundation had assets of £3.6 million and an income of £108,000. Grants were made to 93 organisations totalling £268,500 and were distributed in the following categories:

Allocated Grant Programme	£87,500
Relief of disability and severe illness	£40,000
Visual and performing arts	£33,500
Medical research	£33,000
Accommodation of those in need	£25,000
Preservation of buildings	£23,500
Skills-based training for young people	£17,700
Education	£8,500

Beneficiaries included: Hay Castle (£35,000); Southbank Sinfonia (£4,000); Crossroads Derbyshire and Uplands Educational Trust (£3,500 each); Wellbeing of Women (£3,000); Future Talent (£2,000); Bournemouth University (£1,500); Vauxhall City Farm (£1,000); Futures Theatre Company and Oxford Hub (£500 each).

Applications

Application forms are available from the administrator's website and should preferably be returned by email. Alternatively, the application can be printed and sent in hard copy to Pothecary Witham Weld Solicitors.

The trustees usually meet in January, April, July and October. Note that 'the trustees receive a large number of applications and can only open the application dates for a short period of time'. Deadlines are posted on the website.

Sources of information

Accounts; annual report; Charity Commission record; funder's website.

The Bruce Wake Charitable Trust

 Disability and recreation

UK

£ £552,500 to organisations (2016/17)

CC number: 1018190

Trustees: Peter Hems; Robert Rowley; Penny Wake; Thomas Wake.

Correspondent: Peter Hems, Trustee, PO Box 9335, Oakham, Rutland LE15 OET (tel: 0344 879 3349; email: wake@webleicester.co.uk)

www.brucewaketrust.co.uk

The Bruce Wake Charitable Trust was established in 1993 to encourage and assist the provision of leisure activities for people with disabilities, in particular boating holidays.

According to the trust's website, the trustees will consider a broad range of grant applications related to the provision of leisure activities for people with disabilities, but particularly favour applications which support the following:

> - Wheelchair users with physical disabilities

- Improved access for wheelchair users
- A sporting or leisure activity involving wheelchair users with disabilities

Applications are considered from both individuals and organisations.

Financial information

In 2016/17 the charity had assets of £9.2 million and an income of £213,500. During the year, a total of £604,000 was awarded in grants, with £552,500 given to 196 organisations and £52,000 granted to individuals.

Beneficiaries included: Motor Neurone Disease Association (£25,000); Wheelpower (£20,000); The Back-Up Trust (£10,000); Disability Snowsport UK (£10,000); Leicester Charity Link (£7,000); Southern Spinal Injuries Trust (£7,000); Leonard Cheshire Disability (£5,900); Revitalise Respite Holidays, Stockport Wheelchair Racing and The Jubilee Sailing Trust (£5,500 each); Sheffield Steelers Wheelchair Basketball Club, The Nancy Oldfield Trust Ltd, Whizz-Kidz, West of Scotland Wheelchair Sports Club, Evening Chronicle Sunshine Fund and Jumbulance Trust (£5,000 each).

Exclusions

The trust will not fund for-profit organisations.

Applications

Apply in writing to the correspondent. The trustees meet quarterly to consider grant applications. Charitable organisations should include a copy of their latest financial statements as part of their application.

Sources of information

Accounts; annual report; Charity Commission website; funder's website.

The Wakefield and Tetley Trust

 Social welfare and general charitable purposes

 London boroughs of Tower Hamlets, Southwark and the City of London

£340,500 (2017)

CC number: 1121779

Trustees: Helal Rahman; Lady Judith Moody-Stuart; Stuart Morgenstein; Peter Delaney; Patrick Kelly; Clare Murphy; Lawrence Kilshaw; Dawn Plimmer; Fozia Irfan; Tim McNally; Susan Reardon Smith.

Correspondent: Clerk to the Trustees, Oxford House, Derbyshire Street, London E2 6HG (tel: 020 7749 1118; email: enquiries@wakefieldtrust.org.uk)

 www.wakefieldtrust.org.uk

Established in 2008, this trust was formed as a result of a merger between the Wakefield Trust and the Charity of Charlotte Tetley. The trustees aim to support charitable activity that will make a positive difference to the lives of people who face significant disadvantage and have limited choices and opportunities, in the London boroughs of Tower Hamlets, Southwark and the City of London. The trustees' annual report is interesting, informative and helpful in understanding the activities of the charity.

Who can apply
You will need to demonstrate that your organisation:

- Benefits people resident or working in Tower Hamlets and/or Southwark and/ or the City of London
- Undertakes charitable work (however you do not have to be a registered charity)
- Has a constitution or a set of rules which governs its activities
- Has its own bank or building society account where two or more named people (including one trustee or management committee member) have to sign all the cheques
- Can provide annual accounts for the previous year (If your organisation is new, copies of your most recent bank or building society statements will suffice)

Grant programmes
The trust has two grant programmes:

Main Programme
Average grants are in the region of £8,500 and are usually awarded to organisations with a turnover of less than £500,000.

Fast Track
Grants are awarded for smaller projects, under £2,500, and are aimed at groups with an income of less than £300,000. Organisations that can demonstrate their track record and experience are more likely to receive funding.

Financial information
In 2017 the trust held assets of £9 million and had an income of £391,000. Grants paid in the year totalled £340,500. The trust made a grant of £58,500 to All Hallows by the Tower, which is supported on an annual basis.

Previous beneficiaries have included: All Hallows by the Tower Church (£58,500); ATD First World (£7,000); Age Concern City of London, Bike Project, Pembroke House and Wheels for Wellbeing (£5,000 each); Marshalsea Tenants (£2,500); Southwark Daycentre for Asylum Seekers (£2,000).

Exclusions
The trustees will not support:

- Grants to individuals
- Work that has already taken place
- Applicants who have been rejected by the trust within the last twelve months
- Organisations with significant unrestricted reserves
- Organisations in serious financial deficit
- The promotion of religion
- Animal charities
- Statutory bodies and work that is primarily the responsibility of central or local government
- Health trusts, health authorities and hospices (or any sort of medical equipment or medical research)
- Environmental improvements
- Building restoration or conservation
- Uniformed youth groups
- Schools or projects working with schools, supplementary schools or vocational training

Applications
The trust's website states that it:

Has launched a new online application process for both Programmes. The application portal can now be accessed at wtt.flexigrant.com

Applications will no longer be accepted through the post or by email. The application portal provides more details of our funding criteria and guidelines. Do get in touch with us if you need help filling out the form, and we can provide support as necessary.

Sources of information
Accounts; annual report; funder's website.

The Walcot Foundation

 Education, social welfare

The borough of Lambeth

£1.8 million to organisations (2016/17)

CC number: 312800

Trustee: The Walcot and Hayle's Trustee.

Correspondent: Grants Team, 127 Kennington Road, London SE11 6SF (tel: 020 7735 1925; email: grants@ walcotfoundation.org.uk)

www.walcotfoundation.org.uk

The Walcot Foundation (formerly the Lambeth Endowed Charities), with roots dating back to the 17th century, is an umbrella title for what are now four charities: the Walcot Educational Foundation, Hayle's Charity, The Cynthia Moseley Memorial Fund and the Walcot Non-Educational Charity. The Walcott charities spring from the generosity of Edmund Walcot, a citizen of London and a haberdasher by trade, who, by his will of 1667, left provision for the needs of the poor of Lambeth.

The following information has been taken from the foundation's website:

Who can apply? Applicants must be not-for-profit organisations. This includes properly constituted voluntary or community groups, registered charities or social enterprises.

Grant size
We offer revenue grants up to £25,000 per year for up to three years. The Foundation will consider providing up to 100% of reasonable project costs. A project is considered more favourably if the applicant organisation can make a contribution, either from its own resources or from funds raised elsewhere. *If a project is working in a school we expect match-funding from the school's budget.*

Types of projects
We exist exclusively for the benefit of Lambeth individuals from low-income households. Our grants to organisations and schools are solely a means of reaching those individuals. Our grants are targeted at specific individuals or groups of individuals that meet our criteria as opposed to, for example, whole-school or whole-community projects.

The strategy underpinning all our grant making is to help individuals move along these key paths:

▶ from academic underachievement to achievement
▶ from unemployable to employable
▶ from unemployed to employed
▶ from financially disadvantaged to financially self-sufficient

Financial information
In 2016/17 the foundation had assets of £99.4 million and an income of £2.25 million. Grants totalled £2 million with £1.8 million awarded to organisations and £253,000 awarded to individuals.

Beneficiaries included: Tomorrow's People Trust Ltd (£50,000); The Creative Society (£40,000); Garden Museum (£35,000); Tree Sheperd (£25,000); Advising London (£20,000); Ace of Clubs (£15,000); Creative Sparkworks (£11,000); Upper Norwood Library Trust (£10,000).

Exclusions
The foundation does not fund anything that is the responsibility of central or local government, organisations that cannot show they are working with Lambeth residents who are in financial need, debt repayments, crisis payments or research.

Applications
Applicants for a grant for an individual should apply using the online form on the charity's website.

There are several rounds of applications for grants to organisations and details are available on the foundation's website which states:

> If the Grants to Organisations scheme is open, please contact a member of our Grants Team to discuss your proposal on 020 7735 1925. If your proposal fits with our criteria, we will send you an application form.

> We negotiate application deadlines with each applicant. When you ring a member of the grants team to discuss a potential application, we will suggest a deadline that suits both you and us. We will also let you know when you can expect your application to be considered by the Board of Governors. No guarantee is ever given about which meeting will consider an application even if an application deadline has been met. Ensuring that an application is clear and complete and that a site visit can be easily arranged does greatly increase the likelihood that your application will be submitted to the next Board meeting.

Sources of information
Accounts; annual report; Charity Commission record; funder's website.

The Walker Trust

 Health, education

📍 Shropshire

£ £110,000 to organisations (2016/17)

CC number: 215479

Trustees: Sir Algernon Heber-Percy; Carolin Paton-Smith; Shirley Reynolds; Lady Lydia Forester; Ann Hartley.

Correspondent: Edward Hewitt, Clerk, 2 Breidden Way, Bayston Hill, Shrewsbury SY3 0LN (tel: 01743 873866; email: edward.hewitt@btinternet.com)

The 2016/17 annual report states that:

> The objective of the Trust is to make grants in accordance with the criteria set out by the Benefactor. These cover in broad terms the assistance of health and disability, orphans and education and training. The Trustees consider applications under any of these heads and interpret them in a wide and general sense.

The aim of the trustees is to make grants in order to improve the quality of life and opportunities for the people of Shropshire. The trust gives grants to local health and disability organisations and institutions; schools and other local charitable organisations; as well as grants for individuals. When awarding grants for individuals, the trustees focus on those with low incomes, young people leaving care or estranged from families, orphans, single parents and children from low-income families and those relying on state benefits.

Financial information
In 2016/17 the trust had assets of £6.59 million and an income of £455,000. During the year, the trust awarded £110,000 in grants to organisations and £93,500 to individuals.

Beneficiaries included: Shropshire Youth Support Trust and University Centre Shrewsbury (£25,000 each); Bookfest Shrewsbury (£10,000); Soil Association (£5,000); The Firefighters Charity (£2,000).

Exclusions
Appeals from outside Shropshire will not be considered or replied to. The trustees generally do not assist students in higher education (due to the assistance available from student finance) apart from in exceptional circumstances, such as disability, or for medical or veterinary courses.

Applications
Apply in writing to the correspondent. Details of other assistance applied for must be given and, in the case of organisations, the latest annual report and accounts have to be provided. The trustees meet four times a year, but arrangements can be made for urgent applications to receive consideration between meetings. Individuals receiving larger grants are paid termly subject to reports from university/college at end of previous term.

Sources of information
Accounts; annual report; Charity Commission record.

Walton On Thames Charity

🔍 Community, social welfare

📍 Ancient parish of Walton-on-Thames, Surrey

£ £277,000 to organisations (2016/17)

CC number: 230652

Trustees: Steve Wood; Chris Sadler; Graham Victor Mann; Juliet Hobbs; Ben White; James Vizzini; Nicolas Stuart; Timothy Mark Armstrong Hewens; Robert Douglas; Elizabeth Kennedy; David Nash; Marta Ing; Paul Tajasque.

Correspondent: Jackie Lodge, Walton On Thames Charity, Charities House, 2 The Quintet, Churchfield Road, Walton On Thames KT12 2TZ (tel: 01932 220242; email: admin@waltoncharity.org.uk)

 www.waltoncharity.org.uk

The Walton On Thames Charity supports charities which aim to improve quality of life for disadvantaged people in the local community. The grant-making policy on the charity's website states that it will:

- Provide core and revenue funding, for new and existing projects
- Enable organisations to test new ideas and approaches
- Help organisations access funding from other sources
- Support the development of organisational capability, capacity and sustainability
- Actively encourage organisations and individuals to work in partnership with the Charity and other local organisations

Grants for equipment or other items may be considered to a limited extent and, in exceptional cases, short-notice substitute or replacement funding for activities where funding has been unexpectedly withdrawn may be provided. The charity provides one-off grants; multi-year grants, for up to three years (or more in exceptional cases); and grants to support specific needs of smaller organisations.

Financial information

In 2016/17 the charity had assets of £31.1 million and an income of £3.2 million. The annual report states that, during the year, grants were committed to 39 organisations (of which 16 organisations were new beneficiaries). The accounts state that grants paid during the year totalled £331,000 altogether, broken down as follows:

Community grants	£239,500
Individual crisis grants	£54,000
Schools	£14,500
Community projects	£13,500
Learning and development	£9,200

Beneficiaries have previously included: Elmbridge Mencap; Frost Festival; Hersham Youth Trust; Mount Felix Tapestry Project; Music in Hospitals; River House Barn; Surrey Fire and Rescue Service Youth Engagement Scheme.

Exclusions

The charity will not fund:

- Activities which take place exclusively outside its area of benefit
- Activities which should be provided/ funded by statutory bodies
- Medical research
- Funding for major capital projects or items
- Fundraising appeals
- Advancement of any religion or religious group, unless the application is to provide non-religious services to the local community
- Animal welfare
- Retrospective requests
- Commercial or business activities, apart from social enterprise

Applications

The charity recommends that any organisations wishing to apply should first contact the community services manager by telephone or email. An initial outline application (two sides of A4) may then be submitted, along with organisation details, a budget and the latest accounts. The next steps are dependent on the size of the grant requested – refer to the guidance on the website for more information. The charity aims to keep in close contact with applicants and encourages applicants to view it as an iterative process.

Sources of information

Accounts; annual report; Charity Commission record; funder's website.

The Barbara Ward Children's Foundation

🔍 Children and young people

📍 Mainly UK, some overseas

💷 £565,000 (2017)

CC number: 1089783

Trustees: Barbara Ward, Chair; David Bailey; John Banks; Alan Gardner; Kenneth Parker; Brian Walters; Christopher Brown.

Correspondent: Chris Banks, Trustee, 85 Fleet Street, London EC4 1AE (tel: 020 7222 7040; fax: 020 7222 6208; email: info@bwcf.org.uk)

 www.bwcf.org.uk

This foundation makes grants to organisations working with children who are disadvantaged in some respect, whether through serious or terminal illness, poverty, disability or otherwise. Grants may also be given for organisations supporting adults who have learning disabilities. Grants made can range from one-off grants to project-related grants that run for two to five years.

In particular, the foundation prefers to support 'financially healthy children's charities where funding is not forthcoming from statutory bodies, where incomes and fund balances are constantly put to good use and where administration overheads are kept to a minimum'. In previous years, grants have been given for purposes including:

- Educational projects
- Support, care and respite
- Holidays
- Sport, play and leisure
- Health and well-being

Financial information

In 2017 the foundation had assets of £11.1 million, an income of £507,500. Grants were made to 51 organisations totalling £565,000.

Beneficiaries included: Well Child (£27,500); Whoopsadaisy (£15,000); Sussex Association for Spina Bifida and Hydrocephalus, Skipton Extended Learning for All, Space4Autism and Street-Teams Multi-Sports Club (£5,000 each); Friends of Chums, Mondo Challenge Foundation and Perth Autism Youth Theatre (£3,000) each); Leeds Community Trust (£500).

Exclusions

Religious charities.

Applications

Apply in writing to the correspondent detailing the purpose for which the grant is requested and including latest annual report and set of audited financial statements. Beneficiaries or applicants may be visited by trustees, who usually meet on a quarterly basis to review and award grants (although subgroups may meet more frequently to assess applications).

Sources of information

Accounts; annual report; Charity Commission record; funder's website.

Mrs Waterhouse Charitable Trust (formerly known as the Houghton Dunn Charitable Trust)

🔍 Medical/health, welfare, environment, wildlife, churches, heritage

📍 UK, with an interest in the north west of England and particularly the Lancashire area

💷 £326,000 (2016/17)

CC number: 261685

Trustees: Alistair Houghton Dunn; Helen Dunn.

Correspondent: Mark Dunn, Carlton Place, 28–32 Greenwood Street, Altrincham WA14 1RZ (email: markdunnamalg@btconnect.com)

The trust's annual report for 2016/17 states that 'the trust makes donations to bodies embracing a wide range of charities; the main fields supported being medical and health, welfare in the community, environment and wildlife, and church and heritage with special reference to charities in, or with branches in the North West of England'.

Financial information

In 2016/17 the trust had assets of £8.7 million and an income of £347,500. During the year, the trust gave around £326,000 in grants to 34 organisations. Grants totalling £154,000 were made to charities based in the north west of England, plus a further £65,000 was awarded where national charities have pledged funds to North West-based projects. Grants were distributed as follows:

Medical and health – general	9	£93,000
Welfare in the community – general	9	£72,000
Medical and health – children	4	£52,000
Welfare in the community – children and young people	9	£19,000
Environment and wildlife	1	£15,000
Medical and health – research	2	£15,000

A list of beneficiaries was not included.

Exclusions
No grants are given to individuals.

Applications
Apply in writing to the correspondent.

Sources of information
Accounts; annual report; Charity Commission record.

The Waterloo Foundation

 Child development, environment, developing countries, projects in Wales

 UK, with a preference for Wales, and overseas

£ £6.6 million (2016)

CC number: 1117535

Trustees: Heather Stevens; David Stevens; Janet Alexander; Caroline Oakes.

Correspondent: The Trustees, c/o 46–48 Cardiff Road, Llandaff, Cardiff CF5 2DT (tel: 029 2083 8980; email: info@ waterloofoundation.org.uk)

 www.waterloofoundation.org.uk

The foundation was established in early 2007 with a substantial endowment of £100 million in shares from David and Heather Stevens, co-founders of Admiral Insurance. The foundation's website states:

> The Waterloo Foundation (TWF) is an independent grant-making Foundation. We are most interested in projects that help globally, with particular focus on the disparity of opportunities, wealth and the unsustainable use of the world's natural resources. To that end, our main programmes support:

World Development – supporting people and communities to build the basis of sustainable prosperity within developing countries, through their access to sexual and reproductive health services, excellent nutrition, high-quality education and clean water, sanitation and hygiene systems. Further information about each of these areas can be found on the foundation's website.

Environment – support for projects which counter damage to the environment, especially human-caused effects, through increasing marine fish stocks and protecting tropical rain forests.

Child Development – support for research, knowledge dissemination, and small Wales-based intervention projects about certain child development conditions.

Wales – support for organisations working in Wales which provide support for unpaid carers, increase employment opportunities or address educational inequality.

The themes within each area of support change regularly. Check the foundation's website for the latest information.

Financial information
In 2016 the foundation had assets of £128.4 million and an income of £8.2 million. During the year, the charity awarded 325 grants which totalled over £6.6 million. Grants were broken down as follows:

World development	116	£2.5 million
Environment	47	£2.1 million
Wales	58	£779,000
Other	78	£639,000
Child development	26	£633,000

Beneficiaries included: Carers Trust Wales; Ethiopaid; Hope International; Institute of Physics; Rainforest Foundation UK; Stromme Foundation; SV Effect; Teach First; The Open Seas Trust; Young Enterprise Wales.

Exclusions
Each grant programme has specific criteria and exclusions, which are detailed on the foundation's website.

In general, the foundation will not support:

▶ The promotion of religious or political causes
▶ General appeals or circulars

Applications
Application guidelines, criteria and deadlines for each of the grants programmes are available on the foundation's website, which potential applicants are encouraged check before making an application.

There is no application form and all applications should be submitted by email to applications@ waterloofoundation.org.uk. Details of what should be included in the application are specific to each grant programme and can be found on the foundation's website. Applications are welcomed from organisations with a clear charitable purpose.

The foundation's website states:

> All funding applications we receive are reviewed at a first assessment stage. Applications which are deemed to be ineligible or do not clearly meet our main priorities are rejected at this assessment stage. We aim to contact all organisations after this first assessment to let them know if they have been unsuccessful.
>
> The applications which are deemed to have best met our criteria are then taken

forward to our second assessment stage. These are researched by the relevant Fund Manager, who will contact grant applicants to ask for further details about the funding proposal. The strongest applications are then taken forward for discussion with our Trustees who will make a final decision whether a grant can be awarded.

A helpful list of FAQs can be found on the website.

Sources of information
Accounts; annual report; Charity Commission record; funder's website.

Wates Family Enterprise Trust

 Education, employment and training, community projects, social enterprise, sustainability, thought leadership

 UK

£ £870,000 (2016)

CC number: 1126007

Trustees: Andrew Wates; Paul Wates; Tim Wates; James Wates; Andy Wates; Michael Wates; Charles Wates; Jonathan Wates.

Correspondent: Jerry Wright, Director, Wates House, Station Approach, Leatherhead, Surrey KT22 7SW (tel: 01372 861251; email: director@ watesfoundation.org.uk)

 watesgiving.org

Registered in 2008, the trust is the vehicle for the philanthropic and charitable activities of the Wates family, owners of the Wates Group.

The trust's charitable grants programme is called Wates Giving. It supports the following causes:

▶ Education
▶ Employment and training
▶ Community building
▶ Social enterprise
▶ Sustainability
▶ Thought leadership

Further information and examples of causes supported in each of these categories are provided on the website.

There are three types of grant which may be made by the trust, according to the 2015 annual report:

▶ **Major awards** – in support of bids originating from initiatives of the Wates Group and its business units
▶ **Family awards** – in support of bids which are the initiative of the Wates family
▶ **Employee awards** – in support of initiatives of employees of the Wates businesses acting in a private capacity.

Financial information

In 2016 the trust had an income of just over £1 million, almost all of which came from the Wates Group. Grants awarded to organisations totalled £870,00. Grants to organisations were broken down as follows:

Major projects	£578,000
Family projects	£227,000
Community projects	£71,200
Matched funding	£62,500
Give As You Earn	£20,500
Supply chain fund	£3,400

Beneficiaries included: Wolverhampton Youth Zone (£30,000); Housing Finance Institute (£20,000); Julia's House Hospice (£18,900); Housing Finance Institute (£10,000); Downside Fisher Youth Club (£500); The Children's Society (£250); Shooting Star Chase Children's Charity (£200).

Applications

All proposals come from Wates employees or the Wates family – unsolicited applications are not considered.

Sources of information

Accounts; annual report; Charity Commission record; funder's website.

The Wates Foundation

 Social welfare, employment and education, health, community safety, voluntary sector capacity building

UK

£389,000 (2016/17)

CC number: 247941

Trustees: Andy Wates; Jonathan Heynes; Claire Spotwood-Brown; Christopher Wates; Neil Wates; Nick Edwards.

Correspondent: Jerry Wright, Director, 7 Langside Avenue, London SW15 5QT (tel: 01372 861250; email: director@watesfoundation.org.uk)

 www.watesfoundation.org.uk

In 1966, three brothers Norman, Sir Ronald and Allan Wates of the Wates building firm (now the Wates Construction Group), amalgamated their personal charitable trusts into the single entity of The Wates Foundation. The foundation has three grant-making committees, each named after its respective founder: the Allan Wates Family Committee, the Norman Wates Family Committee and the Ronald Wates Family Committee. Each of the committees usually meets once a year.

Grants

Following a review of its grant-making policy in 2011, the Wates Foundation decided to take a new proactive grant-making strategy. The trustees seek out charities to support, often in their local communities. Unsolicited applications are not accepted.

Grants may be paid over between one and four years. The foundation awards grants under the following six themes:

- Building social values
- Employment and education
- Community health
- Safer communities
- Life transitions
- Strengthening the charitable and voluntary sector

Financial information

In 2016/17 the foundation had assets of £19 million and an income of £568,000. Grants were made to 43 organisations totalling £389,000 and were distributed in the following categories:

Education and employment	£154,000
Community health	£102,500
Social values	£83,500
Strengthening the sector	£18,200
Safer communities	£17,000
Other	£4,000

Beneficiaries included: University of Sussex (£30,000); St Andrew's Club (£20,000); Jamie's Farm (£10,000); Cotswold Friends (£9,200); Magic Breakfast (£9,100); Family Line – Surrey (£6,500); Thomley Trust (£5,000); Goatacre Village Hall (£4,000); Dementia UK (£2,000).

Applications

Applications are by invitation only. Unsolicited applications are not accepted.

Sources of information

Accounts; annual report; Charity Commission record; funder's website.

The William Wates Memorial Trust

 Young people, the arts, sports, education

London and the South East (the trust will also support projects throughout the UK proposed by their Le Loop riders)

£373,000 (2016/17)

CC number: 1011213

Trustees: Andrew Wates; Sarah Wates; Jonathon Wates; Richard Wates; Monty Wates; Timothy Wates; Susan Laing.

Correspondent: Jane Lowe, Wates House, Station Approach, Leatherhead, Surrey KT22 7SW (email: wwmt@wates.co.uk)

 wwmt.org

facebook.com/williamwatesmemorialtrust

The trust was established in 1998 and exists to celebrate the life of William Wates who was killed while travelling through South America.

The aim of the trust is to help disadvantaged young people stay away from crime and fulfil their potential. The trust achieves this by supporting charities that engage young people through the mediums of sports, arts and education.

Projects should help the most disadvantaged young people between the ages of 5 and 19.

Financial information

In 2016/17 the trust held assets of £962,000 and had an income of £590,000. Grants to organisation totalled £373,500 and were broken down as follows:

Sports	£176,500
Mentoring	£134,500
Arts	£27,000
Other	£25,000
Crime prevention	£9,700

Beneficiaries included: Access Sport (£169,000); Winchester Project (£50,000); St George's Hanworth (£25,000); BIGKID Foundation (£10,000); Ride High (£7,500).

Applications

Applications can be made through the trust's website.

Sources of information

Accounts; annual report; Charity Commission record; funder's website.

The Geoffrey Watling Charity

 General charitable purposes, particularly: social welfare, education and the arts, conservation, sports, health

Norfolk and Suffolk

£458,000 (2016/2017)

CC number: 1025258

Trustees: Susan Watling; David Walker; Alan Watling; Anthony Gilbert; Richard Marks.

Correspondent: David Lundean, Clerk, The Geoffrey Watling Charity, 8A Ber Street, Norwich NR1 3EJ (email: enquiries@geoffreywatling.org.uk)

 www.geoffreywatling.org.uk

The Geoffrey Watling Charity was established in 1993 to support general charitable purposes in Norfolk and Suffolk. Its founder, Geoffrey Watling, was a local entrepreneur and former chair and president of Norwich City F.C. who bequeathed much of his estate to the charity so that it could continue to work with and support local charitable organisations.

Financial information

In 2016/17 the charity had an income of £856,500 and assets of £14.3 million. Grants to 99 charitable organisations were made totalling £458,500. Grants were distributed as follows:

Social welfare	54	£201,000
Churches and historic buildings	25	£92,000
Education and arts	13	£78,500
Environment	6	£61,000
Medical	1	£30,000
Sporting	4	£15,000

Beneficiaries included: Norfolk Museums Development Foundation (£40,000); University of East Anglia (£30,000); Norfolk Wildlife Trust, Suffolk Wildlife Trust (£25,000); Harleston Magpies Hockey Club, Home-Start Norfolk, Norfolk Deaf Association and St Stephen's Church Norwich (£10,000 each).

Exclusions

The charity will not consider grant applications from organisations which have not submitted their annual accounts/annual return to the Charity Commission or to Companies House.

Applications

Applications can be made in writing or submitted on the charity's website, where there are detailed guidelines for prospective applicants. The trustees meet once every three months to consider applications and make decisions on the grants to be awarded in accordance with the charity's objectives.

The guidelines for applicants state that applications for funding 'towards a specific project are more likely to be looked on favourably by the trustees than those to help core costs or salaries'.

Sources of information

Accounts; annual report; Charity Commission record; funder's website.

The Weavers' Company Benevolent Fund

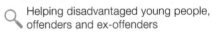

🔍 Helping disadvantaged young people, offenders and ex-offenders

📍 UK

💷 £451,500 (2016)

CC number: 266189

Trustee: Bailiffs Wardens and Assistants of the Worshipful Company of Weavers.

Correspondent: Anne Howe, Charities Officer, The Weavers Company, Saddlers' House, Gutter Lane, London EC2V 6BR (tel: 020 7606 1155; fax: 020 7606 1119; email: charity@weavers.org. uk)

 www.weavers.org.uk

This benevolent fund was set up in 1973 with funds provided by the Worshipful Company of Weavers, the oldest of the City of London livery companies. Its priorities are listed on the website as:

1. Helping disadvantaged young people

The trustees are keen to support projects working with disadvantaged young people to ensure that they are given every possible chance to meet their full potential and to participate fully in society. We normally define young people as being aged from 5 to 30 years.

2. Offenders and ex-offenders, particularly those under 30 years of age

Many offenders and ex-offenders suffer from a variety of difficult and complex problems and they are amongst the most vulnerable members of society. We will fund work that addresses the social and economic problems faced by this group and their families, and provide them with support, life skills training and a way back into education, training and/or employment, so that they may reintegrate and make a positive contribution to society.

We are especially interested in helping smaller organisations which offer direct services. They must be registered charities or in the process of applying for registration. Our grants are relatively modest, usually with an upper limit of £15,000 per annum, and to make sure grants of this size have an impact, we will not fund large organisations.

Applicants must show that they have investigated other sources of funding and made plans for the future, which should include replacement funding if appropriate.

The trust also has a textile education fund to encourage excellence in all spheres of the UK woven textile industry by supporting and nurturing students during their training and sponsoring young talent working within the industry. Full details of funding for individuals can be found on the website.

What is funded?

The appication guidelines on the charity's website give the following information:

Size of organisation: 'To be eligible for funding, local organisations such as those working in a village, estate or small town should normally have an income of less than about £100,000. Those working across the UK should normally have an income of not more than about £250,000.'

Funding limit: Grants are usually of up to £15,000 per annum but smaller applications are also welcomed.

Duration: Grants may be awarded for up to three years.

Project funding: The trustees prefer to support projects where the grant will be used for an identified purpose.

Pump-priming: The trust particularly welcomes applications for pump-priming grants from small community-based organisations where a grant would form a major element of the funding. It prefers to support projects where grants will be used for an identified purpose.

Core costs: Applications for core funding will be considered, such as general administration and training that enable an organisation to develop and maintain expertise.

Innovative or pioneering work: 'We like to encourage new ideas and to fund projects that could inspire similar work in other areas of the country.'

Continuation funding: The trust appreciates the importance of providing ongoing funding for successful projects, which have 'proved their worth'.

Emergency or deficit funding: In exceptional circumstances, the trust may provide emergency or deficit funding for an established organisation. Applicants most likely to be granted emergency funding are charities which the charity knows or has previously supported.

Associated costs: 'If you are applying for project funding, you should make sure you have included the cost of any overheads associated with the work, such as office/secretarial support, so that the project is not under-funded. It is in your best interest to ensure that you have realistically assessed the cost of the project.'

Financial information

In 2016 the fund held assets of £13.1 million and had an income of £610,500. During the year, the fund gave a total of £451,500 in grants to organisations.

The grant total includes the following categories: charitable grants (major grants under the fund's main focus and casual grants which fall outside these criteria); grants from the Millennial Fund (formed from donations of members of the company); grants for primary schools (working with selected London schools); and textile-related grants (mainly educational scholarships and awards).

Beneficiaries included: People Arise Now (£15,000); Inside Out and The Clink Charity (£10,000 each); Chaos Theory (£6,500); Lets Get Talking (£5,000); Words of Wisdom 4 Young People (£4,000); Christ Church (£500); Crazy Hats and the National Army Museum (£300 each).

Exclusions

The following details are given on the charity's website:

What will we not fund?

- General appeals – We will not support sponsorship, marketing or other fundraising activities
- Endowment funds – We will not support endowment funds, nor bursaries or long-term capital projects
- Grant-giving charities
- Retrospective funding – We will not make grants for work that has been completed or will be completed while the application is being considered
- Replacement funding – We will not provide grants for work that should be covered by statutory funding
- Building projects – We will not fund building work but may help with the cost of equipment or furnishings
- Disability Discrimination Act – We will not fund capital projects to provide access in compliance with the DDA
- Personal appeals – We will not make grants to individuals. Applicants must be registered charities, in the process of registering, or qualified as charitable
- Umbrella bodies or large, established organisations – We will not normally support projects in which the charity is collaborating or working in partnership with umbrella bodies or large, established organisations
- Overseas – We will not support organisations outside the UK, nor overseas expeditions or travel
- Long-term support – We will not normally provide long-term support

Work that we cannot normally support includes:

- Work with children under 5 years of age
- Universities or colleges
- Medical charities or those involved in medical care
- Organisations of and for disabled people
- Environmental projects
- Work in promotion of religious or political causes

Applications

Detailed guidelines for applicants are available from the Weaver's Company website.

Applicants must complete an on-line form on the funders' website and then print it off, sign it and send it by post with all required accompanying documents to the trust. The completed form cannot be submitted online or by email.

The grants committee meets in February, June and October of each year. Deadlines are available on the website; they are typically about three months prior to the meetings.

Sources of information

Accounts; annual report; Charity Commission record; funder's website.

The David Webster Charitable Trust

 Conservation (wildlife habitats, woodland, birds, etc.), the preservation of historical/cultural buildings and churches

UK

£327,000 (2015/16)

CC number: 1055111

Trustees: Thomas Webster; Nikola Thompson.

Correspondent: Nikola Thompson, Trustee, Marshalls, Marshalls Lane, High Cross, Ware SG11 1AJ (tel: 01920 462001)

This trust was registered with the Charity Commission in 1996 and provides grants to organisations working in conservation (wildlife habitats, woodland, birds, etc.). Funding is also given to assist with the preservation of buildings and churches of historical or cultural interest.

Financial information

At the time of writing (June 2018) the 2015/16 annual report and accounts were the latest available at the Charity Commission.

In 2015/16 the trust had assets of £3.7 million and an income of £194,500. A total of £327,000 was awarded in grants to nine organisations.

Beneficiaries included: Bird Life International and The National Trust (£125,000 each); Wells Cathedral School (£25,000); Isabel Hospice (£20,000); Future Trees Trust and Tank Museum (£10,000 each); National Churches Trust and Wherry Trust (£5,000 each); Bat Conservation Trust (£2,000).

Applications

Apply in writing to the correspondent.

Sources of information

Accounts; annual report; Charity Commission record.

The Weinstock Fund

 Medical care, care and education for people with disabilities, care and support of children and older people, welfare, the arts

UK

£449,000 (2016/17)

CC number: 1150031

Trustees: Dr Susan Lacroix; Patrica Milner; The Hon. Laura Weinstock.

Correspondent: The Administrator, PO Box 2318, Salisbury SP2 2JX (email: enquiries@weinstockfund.org.uk)

 www.weinstockfund.org.uk

The Weinstock Fund was originally established by the late Lord Weinstock in 1962 for general charitable purposes and is a grant-making charity with which he was actively involved until his death in 2002. It was wound up in December 2012 and this successor charity with similar aims was created in its place.

The following information has been taken from the fund's website:

Who may apply?

We will only consider applications from UK charities registered with the Charity Commission, or charities holding a Certificate of Exemption from the Inland Revenue. We do not accept applications from individuals.

Which countries does the Weinstock Fund support?

We tend to restrict our funding on a geographical basis to the UK.

What type of work does the Weinstock Fund support?

We support charities working in the following areas:

- Medical care and treatment, including respite care and hospices
- Care for physically and mentally disabled adults and children
- Education and training for adults and children with physical and learning disabilities
- Care and support of the elderly
- Care and support for children
- Welfare
- Music and the Arts

Financial information

In 2016/17 the fund held assets of £18.3 million and had an income of £607,500. Of the 100 grants made during the year, 83 were between £1,000 and £5,000. Grants totalled £449,000 and were broken down as follows:

Arts	£131,000
Disability	£91,000
Education	£67,000
Medical (care/treatment)	£55,500
Community	£48,500
Hardship alleviation	£25,500
Other	£18,000
Cultural and environment	£12,500

A list of beneficiaries was not available.

Exclusions

The trust tends not to support research projects or charities abroad.

Applications

Applications should be made using the form available to download from the website, where further guidance is given on what to include. Two copies should be sent, along with the current year's summary income and expenditure budget and the most recent annual report and accounts. There are no deadlines and applications are considered on a rolling basis, with the trustees meeting three or four times each year. Applicants must wait 12 months before reapplying.

Sources of information

Accounts; annual report; Charity Commission record; funder's website.

The Weir Charitable Trust

 Sport and recreational activities, animal welfare, health, culture

 Scotland

£198,000 (2016)

OSCR number: SC043187

Trustees: Jacqui Low; Martin McLellan; Colin Weir; Christine Weir; Carole Weir; James Weir.

Correspondent: The Trustees, 27 Maritime Street, Leith, Edinburgh EH6 6SE (tel: 0131 554 7806; email: enquiries@weircharitabletrust.com)

 www.weircharitabletrust.com

The trust supports smaller charities and community groups that provide services to help communities across Scotland.

Areas of work

The following information was taken from the trust's website:

We support services/projects, run by Scottish-based community groups and small charities, in the following qualifying categories that address any aspect of the following purposes

▶ **Sport:** encouraging and increasing public participation in sport (activities which involve physical skill and exertion)

▶ **Recreational facilities:** the provision or organisation of recreational facilities (buildings, pitches or similar) with the aim of improving the conditions of life for the people for whom the facilities are primarily intended. This is only in relation to facilities which are primarily intended for people who need them due to age, ill-health, disability, financial hardship or other disadvantage

▶ **Animal welfare:** for the advancement of animal welfare

▶ **Health:** the advancement of health, including prevention or relief of sickness, disease or human suffering

▶ **Culture:** supporting the heritage – tangible or otherwise – of Scotland, through projects that encourage participation in and preservation of Scotland's distinctive culture

Types of funding

Funding can be used for capital projects (such as equipment, fixtures, fittings and refurbishments), running costs, one-off projects, core costs and salaries. In summary, anything you need it for as long as it contributes to providing a benefit to your community. If you receive an award,

the money must be used for the purposes laid out in your application.

Financial information

In 2016 the trust held assets of £4.6 million and had an income of £213,000. Grants were made to 39 organisations totalling £198,000 and were broken down as follows:

Health	10	£69,000
Animal welfare	10	£68,000
Sport	9	£26,000
Culture	6	£19,700
Recreational facilities	4	£15,800

Beneficiaries included: Kids in the Street (£16,400); Boxer Welfare Scotland and South of Scotland Wildlife Hospital (£10,000 each); Combat Cancer and Greenock United (£5,000 each).

Exclusions

According to the trust's website it does not fund:

▶ Small group or charity with income of £100,000 or more a year

▶ Individuals

▶ Commercial ventures, including start ups

▶ Social enterprises

▶ Requests for amounts over £25,000

▶ Requests for sponsorship if fundraising for a charity or good cause

▶ Debt reduction, redundancy payments, fees or payouts for legal actions raised against an individual, group or charity

▶ Applications for retrospective funding

▶ Applications from people based outwith Scotland or for activities carried out outwith Scotland

▶ one-off events such as Gala Days, exhibitions

▶ Large capital projects

▶ Community Councils, Parent Teacher Associations, Active Schools activities

Applications

Applications can be made through the trust's website or on an application form available from the website. Details of application deadlines are also available on the website.

Sources of information

Accounts; annual report; Charity Commission record; funder's website.

The James Weir Foundation

 General charitable purposes

Scotland with a preference for Ayrshire and Glasgow

£212,000 (2016/17)

CC number: 251764

Correspondent: Louisa Lawson, Secretary to the Trustees, PO Box 72361, London SW18 9NB (email: info@jamesweirfoundation.org)

jamesweirfoundation.org

The James Weir Foundation was established in 1967. The foundation has general charitable purposes, giving priority to Scottish organisations, especially local charities in Ayrshire and Glasgow. The foundation also makes grants to six bodies named in the trust deed which are:

▶ The Royal Society of Edinburgh

▶ The British Science Association

▶ The RAF Benevolent Fund

▶ The Royal College of Surgeons of Scotland

▶ The Royal College of Physicians of Scotland

▶ The University of Strathclyde

Financial information

In 2016 the foundation had assets of £8.2 million and an income of £304,500. Grants awarded to organisations totalled £212,000 with £45,000 awarded to named beneficiaries and £167,000 awarded to other charities.

Beneficiaries included: Action for Blind People, Back Up, Brainwave, Larkfield Centre, Peebleshire Youth Trust and St Andrew's Children's Society (£3,000 each); Military Debt Help UK (£1,000).

Exclusions

No grants are given to individuals, or to organisations that are not UK-registered charities, or whose beneficiaries are not located in the UK.

Applications

The trustees' report for 2016 states that:

Applications should be received by letter with supporting evidence and a copy of the latest annual report. No applications can be received by email. The trustees meet twice a year in furtherance of the trust's objective of making grants to charitable bodies. Successful applicants are not able to submit a further application for two years.

Applicants that are not successful will be notified by postcard after the meeting has taken place.

Sources of information

Accounts; annual report; Charity Commission record; funder's website.

Welcome To Our Future (Local Agenda 21)

 Environment, conservation, community development, sports and recreation

Herefordshire, Shropshire, Worcestershire

£422,500 (2016/17)

CC number: 1075371

Trustees: Adrian Bourne; Cllr Banks; James Haywood; Keith Chandler; Cllr Sebastian Bowen; Sarah Wilkins; Val Wood; Michael Parker.

Correspondent: George Mackison, The Garden House, Queen Elizabeth Drive, Pershore WR10 1PZ (tel: 01386 556222; fax: 01386 556000; email: george@wtof.org.uk)

 wtof.org.uk

The Welcome To Our Future (Local Agenda 21) charity was established in 1999 to educate and raise awareness on issues relating to sustainable development in Herefordshire and Worcestershire – specifically to promote the well-being of people, their communities and their environment.

The charity's income is generated from a range of sources, including funds derived from grant administration, project management, and consultancy such as acting as a facilitator on community planning projects.

According to its website, the charity's projects aim to realise the following objectives:

- Biodiversity and natural environment
- Sustainable agriculture
- Green build technology
- Alternative economic systems
- Sustainable business practice
- Sustainable transport
- Waste minimisation
- Energy efficiency and generation

Grant programmes

In addition to running its own environmental projects and campaigns, the charity is responsible for the administration of the Severn Waste Environmental Fund (SWEF) in Herefordshire and Worcestershire. The fund, designed to help mitigate the effects of landfill, uses the Landfill Tax Credit Scheme to help local communities.

Since it began in 2000, the fund has helped numerous community projects related to sustainability and which encourage good environmental practice. This has ranged from improving disability access to installing renewable energy heating and other green technologies in community buildings in the two counties.

Under the scheme regulations, projects can be funded which:

- Reclaim land, the use of which has been prevented by some past activity
- Reduce or prevent pollution on land
- Provide or maintain public amenities and parks
- Conserve biodiversity for UK species habitats
- Restore or repair buildings for religious worship, or of architectural or historical interest

Financial information

In 2016/17 the charity had assets of £294,000 and an income of £556,000. During the years grants were made totalling £422,500.

Beneficiaries included: Hartlebury Village Hall (£89,000); Herefordshire Wildlife Trust (£30,000); Evesham Sports Club Ltd (£9,400); Friends of St Peters (£8,500); Wellington Tennis Club (£5,000); Friends of Avon Meadows (£3,500); Hereford Squash Centre (£2,900).

Applications

For further information about the Severn Waste Environmental Fund, or for an application form, applicants should contact Bill Richardson on 01386 556222 or email severnwastefund@aol.com.

Sources of information

Accounts; annual report; Charity Commission record; funder's website.

The Wellcome Trust

 Biomedical research, history of medicine, biomedical ethics, public engagement with science

 UK and overseas

£931.7 million (2016/17)

CC number: 210183

Trustees: The Wellcome Trust Ltd (Corporate Trustee). The board of governors are: Baroness Eliza Manningham-Buller; Prof. Dame Anne Johnson; Sir Damon Buffini; Prof. Michael Ferguson; Prof. Bryan Grenfell; Alan Brown; William Burns; Prof. Tobias Bonhoeffer; Fiona Powrie.

Correspondent: See website, Gibbs Building, 215 Euston Road, London NW1 2BE (tel: 020 7611 8888; email: gtsupport@wellcome.ac.uk)

 www.wellcome.ac.uk

 facebook.com/wellcometrust

 @wellcometrust

The pharmacist, entrepreneur, philanthropist and collector Sir Henry Wellcome died in 1936. On his death, his will established a charity for 'the advancement of medical and scientific research to improve mankind's wellbeing'. The Wellcome Trust is now one of the world's leading biomedical research charities, supporting scientists and researchers, and is the UK's largest non-governmental source of funds for biomedical research. It is also the UK's largest charity dedicated to improving health.

The trust is committed to realising the full potential of biomedical research to improve health and its mission is 'to support the brightest minds in biomedical research and medical humanities'.

The trust supports researchers in the UK and in low- and middle-income countries.

Funding from the trust has supported a number of major successes including:

- Sequencing of the human genome
- Development of the antimalarial drug artemisinin
- Pioneering cognitive behavioural therapies for psychological disorders
- Establishing UK Biobank
- Building the Wellcome Wing at the Science Museum

Strategic plan

The 2016/17 trustees' report states:

Wellcome benefits people around the world by improving health through three complementary approaches across science, research and engagement with society. This framework allows us to adapt as new ideas and challenges arise, drawing on insights from more than 80 years of achievement and our broad network of experts.

Advancing ideas

We support excellent research addressing fundamental health challenges of our time, across discovery science, medical innovation and the humanities and social sciences. Supporting ideas from people dedicated to discovery, creativity and innovation will always be at the heart of Wellcome's activities. We are open to proposals and give grants through schemes run by our three funding divisions: Science, Innovations, and Culture and Society. We also initiate and maintain direct activities, such as Wellcome Collection.

Seizing opportunities

When we judge that concerted intervention will accelerate progress towards better health, we provide focused, intensive support to create a step change in a priority area within five to ten years. Current priority areas: Vaccines, Drug resistant infections, Research in Africa and Asia, and Our Planet, Our Health.

Driving reform

We promote change in practices and the removal of barriers so that ideas can reach their full potential – leading by example, convening alliances, and campaigning for wider reform in priority areas. Current priority areas: Diversity and inclusion, and Science education.

The trust's strategic plan for 2010–20 can be found on its website at www.wellcome.ac.uk/strategicplan and sets out the strategy for this decade. The 'plan provides the basis on which we will develop our funding strategies. It sets out how we will assess progress towards our goals, so that we can help to realise extraordinary improvements in health'.

Grant-making policy

In the 2016/17 annual report, the trustees state:

> For 2016/17, we used an established formula to identify the amount of funding that we would plan to commit over a five year period, including the value for the first year. Based on this plan our charitable expenditure was £1,134 million this year. As announced in September 2017, from 2017/18 onward, we have adopted a new approach to how we fund our charitable activities.
>
> The new approach will protect our core activities in Advancing Ideas and provide stability and predictability for our spending plans. We plan a funding level of around £900 million a year, on average, over a five year period, which we intend to increase annually with inflation. In addition, to support the Priority areas, and potentially other large-scale and high-impact activities, we plan additional discretionary funding. We have currently identified funding of £865 million, of which £365 million has been budgeted to existing priority areas. We will add to this funding only when the investment portfolio performance is sufficiently strong. New priority areas or other activities supported through this funding will be highly ambitious projects aiming to bring about significant change within a specific time period.
>
> The approach outlined above will help us manage our internal resources for achieving our long-term vision of improving health, as set out in our strategic framework.

Financial information

In 2016/17 the Wellcome Trust had net assets of over £21.87 billion and an income of £425.3 million. During the year, the charity awarded £931.7 million in grants (this excludes support costs and expenditure on direct charitable activities), which can be broken down as follows:

Science	£636.4 million
Priority areas	£151.1 million
Innovations	£87.7 million
Culture and society	£56.5 million

Below are examples of the many grants awarded during the year to universities and other institutions, mainly in the UK (these figures represent the total amount awarded to the organisation during the year and may comprise many grants):

University of Cambridge	£120.7 million
University of Oxford	£98.6 million
Imperial College London	£42.9 million
University of Dundee	£32.2 million
Boston University USA	£30 million
University of Bristol	£17.4 million
UK Biobank Ltd	£12.4 million
University of Leeds	£8.9 million
University of Cape Town, South Africa	£8.3 million
Wellcome Trust/DBT India Alliance, India	£7 million

Extensive information on the work of the trust is available on its excellent website www.wellcome.ac.uk.

Exclusions

Generally, the trust will not fund:

- Scientific research outside its remit
- Project or research costs you've already incurred
- Costs to top up individual grants already awarded by another funder
- Standalone travel or conference costs (although you can ask for them as part of a wider grant application)
- Healthcare for patients
- The building of hospitals
- Other charities if their sole intention is to redistribute the funds
- Humanitarian aid or charities that give out humanitarian aid
- People who are applying for, hold, or are employed on a research grant from the tobacco industry

The costs of master's courses or PhD studentships will not be considered, except in certain circumstances. Refer to the trust's website for full information.

The trust does not fund undergraduate courses. Its only scheme for undergraduates is the Biomedical Vacation Scholarship. Full details can be found on the trust's website.

Applications

The trust has recently launched a new application and grants management system.

This new system is the WT Grant Tracker and has replaced the previous eGrants as the way to submit online applications. It handles all aspects of the application review process up to the point when a grant is awarded and accepted. It is also the mechanism by which peer reviewers and committee members access and review applications.

As criteria, processes and deadlines vary according to which award fund you are applying to, you need to check these details on the trust's website.

For more information about WT Grant Tracker or the implementation arrangements, contact the grants information desk on +44 (0)20 7611 8383 or email gtsupport@wellcome.ac.uk.

Sources of information

Accounts; annual report; Charity Commission record; funder's website.

The Welton Foundation

 Mainly health and medical projects, also, education, welfare and arts organisations

 UK and overseas

(£) £1.6 million (2016/17)

CC number: 245319

Trustees: Sir Hugh Stevenson; D. B. Vaughan; Dr Michael Harding.

Correspondent: The Trustees, Old Waterfield, Winkfield Road, Ascot, Berkshire SL5 7LJ (email: hugh. stevenson@oldwaterfield.com)

The foundation was registered in 1965. The trustees' report for 2016/17 states that 'the current policy of the trustees is in the main to support charitable causes in the fields of health and medicine, but they can exercise their discretion to make donations to any other charities'.

Financial information

In 2016/17 the foundation had assets of £427,000 and an income of £38,000. During the year, the charity awarded a total of £1.6 million to 42 organisations in the following categories:

Health and medicine	£799,500
Education and training	£526,000
Community development	£172,500
Culture and the arts	£69,000
Disability	£42,000

Beneficiaries included: Arnold Foundation for Rugby School (£509,500); Berkshire Community Foundation (£100,000); Royal College of Psychiatrists and Dementia UK (£50,000 each); Paddington Development Trust (£20,000); Child Bereavement UK, Westminster Synagogue and Tricycle Theatre (£5,000 each); Jewish Museum (£2,000); Prism the Gift Fund (£240).

Exclusions

Grants are only awarded to registered charities and organisations with a charitable purpose.

Applications

No grants are given to unsolicited applications.

Sources of information

Accounts; annual report; Charity Commission record.

The Wembley National Stadium Trust

 Sports and recreation

England with a preference for the London Borough of Brent

(£) £2.2 million (2016/17)

CC number: 1072392

Trustees: Alderman Gordon Haines; Cllr Ann Marie John; Sir Rodney Walker; Dinah Cox; Baroness Tanni Grey-Thompson; Peter Ackerley.

Correspondent: Martin Hall, Grants Administrator, Guildhall, Po Box 270, London EC2P 2EJ (tel: 020 7332 1055; email: info@wnst.org.uk)

 www.wnst.org.uk

The Wembley National Stadium Trust (WNST) makes grants to organisations which help to address inequalities in access to sport and enable the widest possible participation in various community sports activities. WNST is funded by donations made by the Wembley National Stadium, amounting to one per cent of its gross annual takings. This contribution is estimated to be worth approximately £1 million per year.

The charitable activities of the trust are divided into a number of geographical and thematic programmes.

Community sports activities in the London borough of Brent

The trust supports local sports clubs as well as larger or more general community organisations providing sports activities or facilities in the London borough of Brent. Grants are available for both revenue and capital costs. There are usually two funding rounds a year, each distributing around £150,000. Each round is comprised of two programmes:

- Community awards – grants of up to £2,500 to local sports clubs or other organisations towards general running costs, coaching, training courses, equipment, etc.
- Strategic awards – a smaller number of larger grants (generally of up to £25,000) to fund broader revenue projects or larger capital works

London-wide

Following the completion of the trust's disability sports programme which ran during 2013–17, the trust is currently working to increase the number of girls playing team sports in London by funding the London-based work of TeamUp – a campaign to raise the profile of women's sport and boost the membership of women's sports clubs.

This programme is being delivered in partnership with three National governing bodies – the ECB, England Netball and England Hockey – and will run in 2017–20.

England-wide

Working in partnership with the EFL Trust, WNST supports the community trusts of professional football clubs playing in the EFL to deliver disability football projects across the country. These projects encompass a wide range of needs for people with physical disabilities, wheelchair users, children with autism, people with sensory impairments, adults with enduring mental ill health or those with learning difficulties.

One-off Haringey Small Grants programme

In 2018 the trust announced a one-off grants programme for community organisations and sports clubs working in the London Borough of Haringey. Grants of up to £2,500 will be provided for new kits or equipment, minor capital works to sports premises, or the delivery of new sporting activities.

Financial information

In 2016/17 the trust had assets of £17,700 and an income of £1.05 million. Grants provided to organisations totalled £2.2 million.

Beneficiaries included: Capital City Sports Partnership (£22,000); Brent Mencap (£20,000); London Youth (£15,000); Tottenham Hotspur Foundation (£10,000); London Playing Fields Foundation (£6,500); Tamil Association of Brent and The Crest Academy (£2,500 each); Anson Primary School, Braintcroft Primary School, Edgware Town FC and London Basketball Association (£1,500 each); RollaDome All Skate (£1,000).

Exclusions

The trust will fund any of the following:

- Individuals
- Items already purchased or ordered, or works already undertaken
- Core PE school curricula
- Activities which promote religion

Applications

Applications can be submitted using the trust's online application form. The trust requests that applicants also provide:

- Rules or constitution
- Latest end-of-year accounts
- A forecast of income and expenditure for this financial year
- Evidence of the cost of any purchase or expenditure

These can be attached electronically to the application, emailed separately or sent by post.

Sources of information

Accounts; annual report; Charity Commission record; funder's website.

The Westfield Health Charitable Trust

 Health, welfare

South Yorkshire

(£) £684,500 (2016/17)

CC number: 246057

Trustees: Graham Moore; David Whitney; Dr Catherine Ryan.

Correspondent: Graham Moore, Trustee, Westfield House, 60 Charter Row, Sheffield S1 3FZ (tel: 0114 250 2000; email: charity@westfieldhealth.com)

 www.westfieldhealth.com

This trust was previously known as The Sheffield and District Hospital Services Charitable Fund.

The objectives of the charity are to provide grants for the provision of assistance in the treatment and care of sick, infirm or convalescent people and women in pregnancy and childbirth and to provide grants to various medicine-related charities. The fund receives its income from the pre-tax profits of a medical insurance company based in Sheffield. The following was taken from the charity's website:

> Our Charitable Trust has a long history of supporting people, communities and charities. It's something we put our heart and soul into. As a not for profit company, we've always believed in giving something back to the communities we work in. And with the NHS facing increasing pressures and charitable donations more essential than ever, our support can be invaluable.
>
> Since 1996, we've donated more than £11 million to the NHS and medically related charities, helping to keep thousands of people at their healthy best.
>
> We donate to both large national and smaller, local charities, helping out wherever we can and working harder to nurture the health and wellbeing of communities across the UK.

Financial information

In 2015/16 the trust had assets of £82,500 and an income of £562,500. Grants to 168 organisations totalled £684,500.

Beneficiaries included: Transplant Sport UK (£184,000); Age UK Sheffield (£90,000); Ashgate Hospice (£51,000); Support Dogs (£12,000); Sheffield Young Carers (£9,500); Nottinghamshire Hospice (£5,000); Kidney Research UK (£2,000); Radio Nightingale (£250); Action Medical Research (£200); Brain

Tumour Support and Mind (£100 each); Bliss (£50).

Applications

Apply in writing to the correspondent.

Sources of information

Accounts; annual report; Charity Commission record.

Westhill Endowment

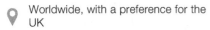 Formal and informal religious education projects and faith-motivated activities that enable people to transform their lives and the lives of people in their communities

Worldwide, with a preference for the UK

£286,500 (2016/17)

CC number: 1104736

Trustees: Simon Rowntree; Sarah Evans; Revd Edward Coleman; Martin Woodward; Peter Ullathorne; Lorna Hewitt; Andrew Morris; Julie Grove; Margaret Rendle; Philip White; David Slade; Rachael Royal.

Correspondent: Diane Webb, Trust Office Manager, The Lodge Westhill, South Drive, Selly Oak, Birmingham B29 6WE (tel: 0121 472 8000; email: admin@westhilltrust.com)

 www.westhillendowment.org

 @westhillcharity

The charity was established in 2004 and provides grants and other resources to support religious education projects and faith-motivated activities that enable people to transform their own lives and their communities.

The charity usually provides grants of between £1,000 and £20,000. Larger sums for projects running over two years are available but the charity advises that applicants should also have to seek matched funding in such cases.

Most grants are for work in the UK but the charity is able to consider some applications for international work with accountable UK-based partner organisations.

Financial information

In 2016/17 the charity held assets of £11.3 million and had an income of £351,500. Grants awarded to organisations totalled £286,500.

Beneficiaries included: Free Churches Education Group (£33,000); National Association of Teachers of Religious Education (£21,000); Citizens UK (£21,000); Faith Encounter Project (£13,000); Birmingham Methodist Circuit Chaplaincy (£11,600); Manchester Community Spirit (£10,500).

Exclusions

The charity's website states:

> Applications for the following activities are very unlikely to be successful:
>
> ▷ If the expected impact of the project is unclear or considered to be very unlikely to be achievable
> ▷ Capital appeals for building projects
> ▷ Requests for funding that seek to persuade people of one faith/political belief or none to adopt another faith/political belief
> ▷ Requests for contributions towards ongoing salary costs, although Westhill does consider applications to fund the costs of sessional, part-time or project staff
> ▷ If Westhill has provided a grant to the same applicant within the past 12 months
> ▷ Where the beneficiaries of the project do not involve humans, i.e. projects that work exclusively for the benefit of animals or for the environment
> ▷ If the activity to be funded is a statutory responsibility of the State
> ▷ If it is clear that the applicant has sufficient unrestricted reserves to self-fund the project

Applications

Application forms can be requested using the contact form on the charity's website.

Sources of information

Accounts; annual report; Charity Commission record; funder's website.

The Westminster Amalgamated Charity

 Social welfare

 City of Westminster

£213,500 to organisations (2016)

CC number: 207964

Trustees: Mark Studer; Jenny Bianco; Dr Cyril Nemeth; Paul Gardner; Eileen Terry; Jean Rymer; Linda McHugh; Graham Mordue; Simon Carruth; David Cavaye; Kate Bowyer; Mark McPherson.

Correspondent: Julia Moorcroft, Grants Administrator, School House, Drury Lane, London WC2B 5SU (tel: 020 7395 9460; email: wac@3chars.org.uk)

 www.w-a-c.org.uk

The charity was formed in 1961 through the amalgamation of seven Westminster-based charities: Earl Craven's Pest House Charity; Westminster General Aid in Sickness Charity; Charity of Albert Reitlinger in the City of Westminster; Drury Lane Public Dispensary Fund; St Henry Convalescent Fund; Charity of John Barlow; and Louie and Cecilia Holiday Fund. In 1994 it grew further, amalgamating with the St James' Relief-in-Need Fund.

The charity aims to alleviate poverty and need, either by providing grants to organisations who share the same aim, or by supporting individuals in need directly.

Eligibility

Applications are welcome from local organisations as well as large national organisations provided that the service or project will benefit a significant number of Westminster residents who are in need. Priority is given to local organisations and, therefore, national applications are deferred to the final trustee meeting of the year.

The charity will fund specific capital costs, revenue funding and project or service costs. The current funding priorities are: addiction, children and young people, community, older individuals, health and disability and homelessness. The charity must be able to visit your project as part of the grant verification process.

Financial information

In 2016 the charity had assets of £7.5 million and an income of £318,500. Grants, excluding governance and support costs, totalled £252,000 with £213,500 given to 42 organisations and £38,000 given to individuals.

Beneficiaries included: Working with Men (£10,000); Real Action (£8,000); Royal Trinity Hospice (£6,000); Carers Network and Royal Trinity Hospice (£5,000 each); Live Music Now (£4,000); African Women Group (£2,000); Hands on London (£500).

Exclusions

Applications from outside the City of Westminster are not supported.

Applications

Applications can be made using the online form on the charity's website, where deadlines for the five meetings of the trustees through the year are also posted. Applications from national charities are automatically deferred to the last meeting of the year. Applicants will be notified of the outcome within two weeks of a meeting. Any queries should be directed to the grants administrator.

Sources of information

Accounts; annual report; Charity Commission record; funder's website.

The Westminster Foundation

 Social welfare, with an emphasis on poverty and supporting communities

In the UK, there is a preference for: Westminster (parts of the Old Metropolitan Borough of Westminster), Cheshire West and Cheshire, North West rural Lancashire (near Forest of Bowland), and North West Sutherland. Overseas grants are awarded in areas where the Grosvenor Group operates

(£) £1.4 million (2016)

CC number: 267618

Trustees: Jane Sanders; Mark Preston; The Duke of Westminster.

Correspondent: Jane Sandars, Director, The Grosvenor Office, 70 Grosvenor Street, London W1K 3JP (tel: 020 7312 6157; email: westminster.foundation@ grosvenor.com)

www.westminsterfoundation.org.uk

The foundation was established in 1974 for general charitable purposes by the fifth Duke of Westminster and continues to make grants to a wide range of charitable causes. In 1987 the Grosvenor Foundation, a separately registered charity, transferred all its assets to the Westminster Foundation. The foundation continues to receive regular donations from Grosvenor Group Ltd and supports a wide range of charities through its grant-making, with a focus on the areas in which the group operates.

Grant-making
The foundation's grant-making currently focuses on poverty, through the Supporting Communities programme. The website states that the foundation is interested in the following two issues:

- **Supporting vulnerable groups:** projects to tackle the challenges faced by people who are isolated or alone whether they are in rural or urban areas. This might include those who are suffering because of the absence of family and social networks to turn to for help and support, such as vulnerable older people. For example, outreach and community groups, befriending schemes, help on the doorstep, nutrition, welfare advice, emergency alarms, learning new skills, access to specialist transport services and communication.
- **Building resilience through strengthening local voluntary organisations:** initiatives such as volunteer training to help organisations develop the skills they need to become better equipped to provide more effective and sustainable support to vulnerable people within our communities.

Grants of up to £5,000 are available, and are made only to registered charities or organisations with exempt or excepted status, such as schools or churches.

According to the foundation's 2016 annual report, there were two themes to the foundation's grant-making in 2016:

- **Supporting Communities** targeted issues of isolation and loneliness, in both rural and urban contexts, and contributes to improved community cohesion within defined geographic focus areas.
- **Youth Homelessness** focused on charitable organisations supporting young people who have become homeless or are at risk of doing so, and helping prevent homelessness amongst young adults.

Financial information
In 2016 the foundation held assets of £5.3 million and had an income of almost £2.7 million. During the year, the foundation awarded 119 grants to organisations totalling £1.4 million. Overseas grants (only where nominated by Grosvenor overseas operating company) totalled £364,000.

Beneficiaries of grants of £20,000 or more included: Community Foundation for Merseyside (£200,000); The Game and Wildlife Conservancy Trust (£62,000); Medical Detection Dogs (£50,000); Atlantic Salmon Trust (£40,000); Better Living Blue House (£34,500); Habitat et Humanisme (£34,000); St Vincent's Family Project (£20,000).

Exclusions
According to its application guidelines, the foundation does not consider:

- General appeals or letters requesting non-specific donations
- Organisations that do not have charitable aims (e.g. commercial companies and companies limited by shares)
- Overtly political projects (including party-political and campaigning projects)
- Individuals (or organisations applying on behalf of an individual)
- Student fees/bursaries
- Projects taking place or benefiting people outside the UK
- Projects/work benefiting people outside our specific geographical criteria
- Overseas trips
- Holidays/trips
- Organisations that have applied to us unsuccessfully within the previous 12 months
- Projects where the main focus is website development or maintenance
- Start up costs, organisations that do not yet have a demonstrable track record

Applications
Applicants should first refer to the website to ascertain whether they are eligible for funding from the foundation.

Applications should be made through the foundation's application form provided on the website, alongside application guidelines. The Grants Review Panel meets around every eight weeks and successful applicants will be notified within two weeks. If you do not hear back in this period, you should assume that you have not been successful.

Sources of information
Accounts; annual report; Charity Commission record; funder's website.

The Garfield Weston Foundation

 Arts, education, young people, health, museums and heritage, community, environment, faith, welfare

UK

(£) £62.75 million (2016/17)

CC number: 230260

Trustees: Guy Weston; Jana Khayat; Camilla Dalglish; Eliza Mitchell; Galen Weston; George Weston; Sophia Mason; Melissa Murdoch; Kate Hobhouse.

Correspondent: Philippa Charles, Director, Weston Centre, 10 Grosvenor Street, London W1K 4QY (tel: 020 7399 6565; email: see contact form on website)

 www.garfieldweston.org

 @GarfieldWFdn

The Garfield Weston Foundation was established in 1958 by Willard Garfield Weston, a Canadian businessman who moved to the UK with his family in 1932. He was the creator of Associated British Foods and the foundation was endowed with the donation of family-owned company shares. According to the foundation's 2016/17 annual report, at 5 April 2017 it owned 79.2% of Wittington Investments Ltd, the ultimate holding company of Associated British Foods plc.

Areas of work
The following information has been taken from the foundation's website:

The Foundation aims to be responsive to where need is greatest and therefore supports a wide range of charitable activity in the following categories:

- Arts
- Education
- Youth
- Health
- Museums & Heritage
- Community
- Environment
- Faith
- Welfare

The Trustees have a preference for charities directly delivering services and activities to those in need, and are especially keen to see applications from charities in the Welfare, Youth and Community sectors and also in regions of economic disadvantage.

Almost 2000 charities across the UK benefit each year from grants made by the Foundation, ranging from small community and volunteer projects to large national organisations. Despite this range, the common theme is that charities demonstrate they are meeting a need effectively with clear outcomes and benefits, good leadership, sensible business plans and a commitment to excellence.

Types of grant

The types of grant we make, whatever their size, tend to fall into one of three categories – Capital, Revenue (often called 'core costs') and Project work. The most important thing is that you apply for *what you need* as this will be your priority and therefore the most compelling for our Trustees.

Grant programmes

Regular grants

For applications below £100,000. These applications are reviewed by our Trustees on an ongoing basis so there are no specific deadlines to worry about. You can apply when you are ready and when your plans and priorities are sufficiently clear to be able to make a compelling case – see our guidelines for details of what to include.

Major grants

For application of £100,000 or more. These are reviewed at one of the Foundation's eight Board meetings a year and are carefully planned in advance to be fair to all applicants. If you are considering applying for a major grant, please start by sending a one page summary to Grace da Rocha via gdarocha@garfieldweston.org outlining what you are raising funds for, the total cost and fundraising target. We can give you bespoke guidance on whether you are eligible. Please note that if you are applying for £100,000 or more we typically expect your project and/or annual income to be in excess of £1 million. Please *do not* apply for a major grant through our website.

Financial information

In 2016/17 the foundation had assets of £9.9 billion and an income of £65.9 million. Grants awarded to organisations totalled £62.75 million and were broken down as follows:

Welfare	111	£11.8 million
Education	159	£8.7 million
Environment	55	£8 million
Young people	273	£7.2 million
Arts	160	£6.2 million
Museums and heritage	45	£6 million
Community	252	£5.6 million
Health	139	£5.5 million
Other	5	£455,000

Beneficiaries included: The Prince's Trust (£1 million); Dorset County Museum (£300,000); Roman Baths Foundation (£75,000); Pecan (£40,000); St Augustine of Hippo (£25,000); Ballet Black (£10,000); Redbrook Village Hall (£1,000); West Action for Children (£250).

Exclusions

According to its website, the foundation's regular and major grant programmes are unable to support:

- Individuals
- Charitable Incorporated Companies (CICs)
- Social enterprises without UK Charity Commission registration
- Sporting associations that are not registered charities
- Work that does not deliver a direct benefit in the UK, even if the organisation is a registered charity within Britain
- Animal welfare charities
- Charities that spend the majority of their income outside the UK
- Local authorities and councils

Applications

Regular grants: Applications for regular grants can be made using the foundation's online system or by downloading an application form from the website and submitting it by post. The foundation's website states that applications are accepted at any time during the year and that there are no formal deadlines for the submission of applications. Full information on criteria and how to complete an application are given in the foundation's guidelines, available from the website or by request. The trust asks that you do not apply both online and by post.

Major grants: Applicants should send a one-page summary to Grace da Rocha at gdarocha@garfieldweston.org outlining what you are raising funds for, the total cost and fundraising target. The trustees meet eight times a year to review applications.

Sources of information

Accounts; annual report; Charity Commission record; funder's website.

Westway Trust

Arts, culture and heritage, community causes, health and well-being, education and training, sports

Kensington and Chelsea, with particular focus on North Kensington and the area in and around the Westway

£379,000 to organisations (2016/17)

CC number: 1123127

Trustees: Cllr Malcolm Spalding; Cllr Anne Cyron; Christopher Ward; Karen Bendell; Sheraine Williams; Alan Brown; Angela Spence; Cllr Monica Spence; Howard Richards; Jeannette Davidson; Thomasin Renshaw.

Correspondent: Phil Nicholas, Head of Charity Income & Impact, Westway Trust Office, 1 Thorpe Close, London W10 5XL (tel: 020 8962 5720; email: info@westway.org or grants@westway.org)

 www.westway.org

The trust (previously known as Westway Development Trust) was originally established in 1971 when the A40 Westway Flyover was built leaving 23 acres of derelict land. It manages and regenerates the land on behalf of the local community. The trust's activities focus on: economic well-being and learning; health and well-being; arts, heritage and culture; and the environment.

Community Grants programme

The trust's Community Grants scheme offers grants of between £500 and £2,500 to charitable, voluntary and community organisations and social enterprises working in the Royal Borough of Kensington and Chelsea, with particular focus on North Kensington, in and around the Westway. Collaborative projects are also welcomed and priority is given to new applicants. Projects should be making an impact on the following priority areas:

- Enterprise and economic well-being
- Sport, health and fitness
- Environment
- Arts, culture and heritage

There are three types of grant available:

1. **Community celebration grants** – up to £500 for community events and celebrations
2. **Small grants** – up to £2,500 for projects which improve the health or economic well-being of local people and celebrate the area's rich cultural heritage
3. **Pledges to a crowdfunding campaign** – up to £4,000 (or 50% of the total amount) for larger projects which commit to a Spacehive crowdfunding campaign

The trust's website also states: 'The fire at Grenfell Tower has had a devastating impact on the North Kensington community and we welcome applications for projects that will help contribute to the process of healing and rebuilding.' Full guidance notes are available on the trust's website.

Festivals Fund

Grants of up to £5,000 are available to support arts and cultural festivals 'in the area of benefit which support and recognise local talent, diversity and heritage' and 'bring communities together and have a lasting impact on the local area and local people'.

Creative Futures

The trust offers up to £3,800 to employers in the creative industries in support of 'high quality, entry level employment opportunities for local young people', which pay the London Living Wage, either full- or part-time roles. Applications are accepted from employers in the Royal Borough of Kensington and Chelsea; Westminster; Hammersmith; Fulham; and Brent.

Sports bursaries

Awards of up to £500 are available for 'adults or children who want to take part in sports and fitness activities but find it hard to pay the fees'. Bursaries can be given for training, coaching or education. The Tim Davis Sports Scholarship is also awarded to a young person with outstanding sporting potential who is in need of financial support.

Financial information

In 2016/17 the trust had assets of £58.1 million and an income of £7.1 million. Grants were made to 54 projects totalling £379,000. The amount of grants given to individuals totalled £11,700.

Beneficiaries included: Eritrean Parents' and Children's Association (£10,500); Somali Women's Association (£5,600); Clement James Centre (£2,500); Corner Nine Arts Project (£2,400); The Cardinal Vaughan Memorial School (£500).

Exclusions

Community grants will not be given for:

- Projects or activities taking place outside the Royal Borough of Kensington and Chelsea and/or that do not benefit local residents
- Individuals (either directly or via a third party) – apart from through the sports bursary scheme
- Organisations with an annual income of more than £10 million
- Grant-making organisations
- Set-up costs of an organisation
- Ongoing running costs of an organisation
- Cost of anything which has already taken place
- Contributions to reserve funds or the payment of any debts
- Animal welfare organisations
- Political organisations
- Religious activities
- Organisations that have debt outstanding for the trust's services
- Organisations that wish to use the grant funding to pay for services provided by the trust

Refer to the website for exclusions from specific programmes.

Applications

Applications for Community Grants or the Festivals Fund can be made via the trust's website, where guidance notes and deadlines are also posted. Refer to the website for up-to-date information about what is currently available. Any queries should be directed towards Phil Nichols: 020 8962 5720 or grants@ westway.org.

Sources of information

Accounts; annual report; Charity Commission record; funder's website.

The Wheeler Family Charitable Trust

🔍 Education

📍 England and Wales

💷 £600,000 (2016/17)

CC number: 1156928

Trustees: Belinda Wheeler; Nicholas Wheeler.

Correspondent: The Trustees, RSM, Central Square, 29 Wellington Street, Leeds LS1 4DL (tel: 0113 285 5000)

The trust's previous annual accounts have stated that its objectives are: 'the advancement of education for the public benefit by the provision of grants, donations, scholarships and by such other means as the trustees may determine to assist in the provision of and access to practical, vocational and academic education'.

Financial information

In 2016/17 the trust had an income of £21,000 and a total expenditure of £612,500. We estimate that grants awarded to organisations totalled around £600,000. The trust's accounts were not available to view on the Charity Commission website due to its low income.

Previous beneficiaries have included: Place2Be (£154,500); Buckinghamshire Community Foundation and Eton College Charitable Trust (£100,000 each); Best Beginnings (£30,000); Child Bereavement UK (£20,000); Peter Jones Foundation (£10,000); Wellington College (£1,400).

Applications

Apply in writing to the correspondent.

Sources of information

Accounts; annual report; Charity Commission record; funder's website.

The Melanie White Foundation Ltd

🔍 Areas of interest to the trustees (including health, medicine and social welfare)

📍 Mainly UK

💷 £215,500 (2016/17)

CC number: 1077150

Trustees: Melanie White; Andrew White.

Correspondent: Paula Doraisamy, Secretary, 61 Grosvenor Street, London W1K 3JE (tel: 020 3011 1041; email: melaniewhitefoundation@gmail.com)

The principal activity of the foundation is its grant-making programme, through which the trustees support charitable causes in areas of particular interest to them. These areas include health, medicine and social welfare.

Financial information

In 2016/17 the foundation had assets of £13.5 million and an income of £272,500. Grants totalling £215,500 were made to 14 organisations.

According to the annual report, 'it is expressly contemplated that CLIC Sargent may be a beneficiary of the charity'; during the year, CLIC Sargent received two grants totalling £51,000.

Other beneficiaries included: Tiger Woods Charity (£68,500); Royal Parks Foundation (£20,000); Wetherby School Charity (£11,500); WWF UK (£200).

Applications

At the time of writing (June 2018), the foundation's Charity Commission record provided the following helpful advice: 'The directors take a strategic approach to grant-making and do not therefore suggest sending unsolicited applications. Instead, if an organisation identifies that it has strong links to the foundation's funding objectives, the directors request that they contact them via the foundation's email address.'

Sources of information

Accounts; annual report; Charity Commission record.

White Stuff Foundation

🔍 General charitable purposes

📍 UK

💷 £440,500 (2016/17)

CC number: 1134754

Trustees: Rebecca Kong; Victoria hodges; Sean Thomas; Julian Baker; Helen Marshall.

Correspondent: Foundation Manager, Canterbury Court, 1–3 Brixton Road,

London SW9 6DE (tel: 020 7735 8133; email: giving@whitestufffoundation.org)

 www.whitestuff.com

The foundation was established in 2010 by the directors of White Stuff Ltd. The company has committed to donating at least one per cent of its annual profits to the foundation and, as such, provides its principal source of income.

The 2016/17 annual report states:

Each White Stuff shop, together with its head office, and distribution centre is partnered with a charity operating within their local area and White Stuff employees are encouraged to develop a positive relationship with their partner charity through regular contact, fundraising activities and the provision of financial and non-financial support.

Distributions to partner charities are made on a quarterly basis from core income received from White Stuff Ltd and from the specific fundraising activities of White Stuff shops, its customers and employees. A discretionary fund allows the Foundation's Trustees to make ad hoc grants to other charities where they feel it appropriate to do so.

Before selection, each potential charity is assessed according to specific criteria which, during the year under review, included the need to:

- Be registered with the Charity Commission (or equivalent in another country)
- Demonstrate operational and financial compliance, including the filing of unqualified audited accounts
- Work to make a positive difference within the local community in which it operates
- Operate in an area local to a White Stuff shop, office, distribution centre or supplier
- Be a smaller charity, with an annual income of generally no more than £3 million per annum
- Engage with the local White Stuff representatives

Financial information

In 2016/17 the foundation had assets of £377,500 and an income of £611,000. Grants were made to 180 charities totalling £440,500.

Beneficiaries included: The Spires Centre (£79,500); The Laura Centre (£32,500); The Rathbone Society (£26,500); Wood Street Mission (£5,400); Lothian Autistic Society (£5,000); Go Commando (£4,000); The Joshua Tree (£3,800); Winston's Wish (£3,200); Bendrigg Trust (£3,000).

Grants below £3,000 totalled £204,000.

Applications

Refer to the website or contact your local White Stuff shop, distribution centre or supplier.

Sources of information

Accounts; annual report; Charity Commission record; funder's website.

Whitley Animal Protection Trust

 Animal welfare

UK and overseas

£ £370,500 (2016)

CC number: 236746

Trustees: Edward Whitley; Edward Whitley; Jeremy Whitley; Penelope Whitley; Vivien Thompson.

Correspondent: Michael Gwynne, Secretary, Padmore House, Hall Court, Hall Park Way, Telford TF3 4LX (tel: 01952 641651)

This trust makes grants to registered charities working to prevent cruelty to animals or to promote the welfare of animals.

The annual report for 2016 states that 'a majority of the grants undertaken are repeat donations, however the trustees do provide essential core funding to these smaller charities without which they would find it hard to maintain their activities'. One-off grants are also awarded, but the majority of support is given on a longer-term basis.

Financial information

In 2016 the trust had assets of £10.4 million and an income of £408,500. Grants to 20 organisations totalled £370,500.

Beneficiaries included: Whitley Fund for Nature (£150,000); Shropshire Wildlife Trust – The Wildlife Sites Project (£60,000); Fauna and Flora International (£25,000); Cardiff University Otter Appeal (£10,000); Rivers and Fisheries Trusts of Scotland (£3,000); Brooke Hospital for Animals (£2,500); Welsh Dee Trust (£250).

Exclusions

No grants are given to non-registered charities.

Applications

Apply in writing to the correspondent. The trustees meet twice a year to decide on grants to be made.

Note: The majority of beneficiaries have been supported by the trust on a longer-term basis and so the potential for new applicants to receive support may be limited.

Sources of information

Accounts; annual report; Charity Commission record.

Charity of Sir Richard Whittington

 Social welfare, young people, older people, families

Within the boundaries of the M25

£ £1 million to organisations (2016/17)

CC number: 1087167

Trustee: The Mercers' Company.

Correspondent: R. M. Abernethy, Clerk To The Mercers' Company, Worshipful Company of Mercers, Mercers' Hall, Ironmonger Lane, London EC2V 8HE (tel: 020 7726 4991; email: info@mercers.co.uk)

 www.mercers.co.uk

The Charity of Sir Richard Whittington was founded in 1424 under the will of Richard Whittington who was mayor of London four times and master of the Mercers' Company three times. The charity is the amalgamation of both The Charity of Sir Richard Whittington and Lady Mico's Almshouse Charity and is regulated by a scheme of the Charity Commission, dated April 2001.

Areas of work

Today, the charity offers grants to organisations based within the M25 under the following four strategic priorities:

1. **Care for older people:** work which seeks to provide care and support, and develop improved services to improve the health of older people, particularly those who are frail and isolated
2. **Family welfare:** work which supports vulnerable families by helping to improve parenting skills and develop more resilient children
3. **Support to young people:** work which prepares disadvantaged young people for adult life by offering positive activities that enable them to reach their full potential. There is also a focus on supporting young people through important transitions: leaving school, leaving care, entering and sustaining employment
4. **Social welfare:** work which seeks to improve the quality of life for those with learning and/or physical disabilities by increasing social and community participation and access to opportunities, and to alleviate the challenges of a carer's role

As part of a philanthropic review, the trustees have stated that in coming years they will begin to look more at the changing needs of older people, particularly as the population ages significantly and more people are living longer with chronic long-term conditions, often in very much reduced financial circumstances.

In addition to its open grants programme, each year the charity also offers small donations to around 200 older individuals in London in financial need. Further to its grant-making activities, the charity is also responsible for the administration of almshouses at Whittington College, Felbridge, Surrey and at Stepney, London.

Financial information

In 2016/17 the charity had assets of £106 million and an income of £3.2 million. During the year, the trustees awarded grants worth around £1.24 million, of which £1 million was given to institutions and £237,500 to individuals.

Beneficiaries included: The Royal Foundation (£75,000); Carefree Kid (£27,000); Age Concern – Waltham Forest (£21,000); Urban Hope (£16,000); Superkidz Community Trust (£15,000); Blue Elephant Theatre (£13,000); Home-Start London, Reaching Higher (£10,000 each); Royal London Hospital (£750).

Applications

Apply in writing to the correspondent.

Sources of information

Accounts; annual review; Charity Commission record.

The Wigoder Family Foundation

General charitable purposes

England and Wales

£1.6 million (2015/16)

CC number: 1086806

Trustees: Elizabeth Wigoder; Charles Wigoder; Martin Rose.

Correspondent: Charles Wigoder, Trustee, 9 Hyde Park Gardens, London W2 2LT

The Wigoder Family Foundation was established in 2000 by Charles Wigoder, a telecommunications entrepreneur, and his wife Elizabeth to support general charitable purposes throughout England and Wales.

The foundation does not specify any particular aims or objectives in its Charity Commission record or annual report but its beneficiaries have included charities that support Jewish causes.

Financial information

At the time of writing (March 2018), the 2015/16 accounts were the latest available. In 2015/16 the foundation had an income of almost £1.5 million and net assets of £40 million. During the

year, the foundation made grants totalling £1.6 million.

Beneficiaries included: The Prince's Trust Institute (£1 million); One Family UK (£25,000); Young Dancers Charitable Academy (£12,300); Henry Jackson Society, Holocaust Education Trust and One To One Children's Fund (£10,000 each); Du Boisson Dance Foundation (£7,100).

Applications

Apply in writing to the correspondent. According to the 2015/16 annual report, 'The Trustees meet as many times as deemed appropriate but not less than twice a year to discuss grants, based on applications received throughout the year'.

Sources of information

Accounts; annual report; Charity Commission record.

The Will Charitable Trust

Blindness, cancer, learning disabilities

UK

£1.1 million (2016/17)

CC number: 801682

Trustees: Alastair McDonald; Rodney Luff; Vanessa Reburn.

Correspondent: Grants Administrator, Bridge House, 11 Creek Road, East Molesey KT8 9BE (tel: 020 8941 0450; email: admin@willcharitabletrust.org.uk)

willcharitabletrust.org.uk

Established in 1990, the trust supports UK-registered or exempt charities whose activities fall within the following three categories:

▶ **Blind people** – the care of and services for blind people, and the prevention and/or cure of blindness
▶ **People with learning disabilities** – the long-term care of people with learning disabilities either in a residential care or supported living environment, especially those that provide a family environment and a wide choice of activities and lifestyle or by providing long-term day/employment activities
▶ **People with cancer** – care of and services for people suffering from cancer, and their families

Other categories may be supported but this is rare and reserved for causes that have come to the attention of individual trustees. Unsolicited applications for causes outside the three areas listed above are not welcomed by the trust and will not be considered.

Larger exceptional grants are occasionally considered but this is unusual and generally confined to charities that are well known by the trustees. There is no separate application process for this and applicants will be identified from the normal grant round.

Grants are exclusive to UK-registered or exempt charities. They must have proven track records of successful work in their field of operation or, in the case of newer charities, convincing evidence of ability. Charities of all sizes are considered and grants vary in amount accordingly. Grants generally fall within the range of £3,000 to £30,000 and are typically made on a one-off annual basis, although successful grantees are encouraged to apply in the next and subsequent years.

Financial information

In 2016/17 the trust held assets of £20.5 million and had an income of £728,500. Grants totalled £1.1 million and were made for the following purposes:

Exceptional grants	4	£375,000
Blind people	24	£267,000
People with cancer	19	£253,000
People with learning disabilities	21	£229,000

Beneficiaries included: Deafblind Scotland and Stable Family Home Trust (£25,000 each); Hospiscare (£20,000); Living Paintings (£15,000); Relate Greater Manchester South (£13,000); Teamwork Trust (£12,000); National Autistic Society (£10,000); Mousetrap Theatre Projects (£5,000); Speakup Self Advocacy (£4,000); Pathfinder Dogs (£3,000).

There were four exceptional grants committed during the year to Jigsaw Trust and St David's Hospice (£150,000 each), St Wilfred's Hospices (£100,000), and Sightsavers (£50,000).

Exclusions

It is unlikely that applications relating to academic research projects will be successful.

Applications

Applications should be made in writing to the correspondent and sent by post – emailed applications will not be accepted. Guidance on what to include in your application is given on the website, along with more detailed eligibility criteria. There are separate deadlines for each area of focus:

▶ Blind people and learning disabilities – applications should be submitted between November and 31 January, for consideration in April
▶ Cancer care – applications should be submitted between June and 31 August, for consideration in November

The trust advises applicants not to submit their applications too early, but in plenty of time ahead of the deadlines to allow enough time for consideration. Potential applicants can discuss an application or any queries with the grants administrator. Applications are usually acknowledged within three weeks.

Sources of information
Accounts; annual report; Charity Commission record; funder's website.

The Williams Family Foundation

 Welfare, young people, older people, people with learning or physical disabilities, people who are ill

Cheshire West, Chester, Denbigh, Flint and Wrexham (a map is available on the foundation's website)

£494,500 (2016)

CC number: 1157478

Trustees: John Gregory; Amy Sheppard; Barbara Williams; Mark Williams; Thomas Williams.

Correspondent: The Trustees, PO Box 3809, Chester CH1 9ZW (tel: 01244 570292; email: enquiries@williamsfamilyfoundation.org.uk)

www.williamsfamilyfoundation.org.uk

The foundation was established and registered in 2014 by the Williams family, who have roots in North Wales and have lived in Cheshire West. The family wished to give back into their local community, and the foundation exists to provide grants and funding support to local charities who make lives better in these areas.

Areas of support
The foundation's website states:

We support charities that help people within our community. In particular we focus on charities that aid those in need, including:

- young people
- the elderly
- people with learning or physical disabilities
- people of ill health

Our efforts will go into funding projects that we believe will benefit our target groups and have a positive impact on the lives of these individuals.

Principles of grant-making
- The trustees will normally only fund the work of charities operating in North Wales and Cheshire. Exceptionally the trustees will fund charities operating nationally and internationally e.g. in the case of disaster appeals
- The trustees prefer to contribute to specific appeals and projects rather than to contribute to general running costs or expenditure of a charity
- The trustees are willing to contribute both to large charities and small charities
- The trustees will not normally approve any grant without seeing the most recently published annual report and accounts of the charity that they intend to benefit
- The trustees do not normally make grants of less than £1,000
- The trustees will consider funding an ongoing project of another charity on a regular basis in appropriate circumstances

Eligibility
Your organisation must be:

- based in our remit area
- a registered charity or charitable incorporated organisation (CIO)
- asking us to fund/part-fund a specific project (this does not include the funding of salaries)

Financial information
In 2016 the foundation held assets of £229,000 and had an income of £500,000. Grants awarded to organisations totalled £494,500 and were broken down as follows:

Refurbishment costs	£154,500
Charitable project funding	£142,000
Capital projects	£117,500
Equipment purchases	£74,000
Christmas project funding	£5,100
Sponsorship	£1,400

Beneficiaries included: Hospice of Good Shepherd (£75,000); COCH Charity Trust (£32,500); Ashton Village Hall (£28,000); Awyr Las Blue Sky (£15,000); Claire House (£13,000); Cheshire Without Abuse and DEBRA (£10,000 each).

Exclusions
According to the foundation's website, the trustees will not normally fund any of the following:

- General appeals from national charities
- Small contributions to large appeals for vehicles or buildings
- Animal charities
- Religious organisations
- Individuals
- Community interest companies

Applications
Applications can be made through the foundation's website. Application forms are also available on the website and can be completed and returned to applications@williamsfamilyfoundation.org.uk.

Sources of information
Accounts; annual report; Charity Commission record; funder's website.

The Willmott Dixon Foundation

 Young people, people with disabilities

UK

£343,500 (2016/17)

CC number: 326530

Trustees: Richard Willmott; Colin Enticknap; Andrew Telfer.

Correspondent: Wendy McWilliams, Spirella 2, Icknield Way, Letchworth Garden City, Hertfordshire SG6 4GY (tel: 01462 671852; email: company.secretarial@willmottdixon.co.uk)

www.willmottdixon.co.uk/how-we-do-it/the-willmott-dixon-foundation

Willmott Dixon Group is a privately owned construction, housing and property development business. The Willmott Dixon Foundation was set up in 1984 and is chaired by the Group Chief Executive, Rick Willmott.

According to its 2016/17 annual accounts, the object of the foundation is: 'to support projects and causes which promote the training of young people and the welfare of people with special needs'.

Financial information
In 2016/17 the foundation had assets of £26,500 and an income of £350,500. A total of £343,500 was awarded in grants to 41 projects. Donations of less than £2,500 totalled £21,000.

Beneficiaries included: Shelter (£109,500); Chesnut Tree House (£104,000); Action Medical Research (£63,500); Wide Horizons (£9,500); Cancer Research UK (£6,300).

Applications
Applications can be made in writing to the correspondent. Note that the foundation tends to work with a small number partner charities.

Sources of information
Accounts; annual report; annual review; Charity Commission record; funder's website.

The HDH Wills 1965 Charitable Trust

 General charitable purposes with particular preference towards wildlife and conservation

UK

£887,500 (2016/17)

CC number: 1117747

Trustees: John Carson; Dr Catherine Wills; Liell Francklin; Martin Fiennes; Tom Nelson; Richard Tulloch.

Correspondent: Sue Trafford, Trust Administrator, Henley Knapp Barn, Fulwell, Chipping Norton, Oxfordshire OX7 4EN (tel: 01608 678051; email: hdhwills@btconnect.com)

 www.hdhwills.org

The trust has been endowed by the family of Sir David Wills, from a fortune derived largely from the tobacco company of that name. The trust's website states that it makes grants to 'general, environmental and wildlife charities, so long as they are registered with the Charity Commission of England and Wales or they are exempt or excepted charities'.

The trust has two main grant schemes – monthly grants and large grants. The following information on these grants has been taken from its website:

Monthly grant criteria
- We seek to make donations to general charities which are small enough in size or are applying for support for a modest project such that the charity will benefit substantially from a donation of between £250 and £1,000, though we will consider grants of up to £5,000
- We also make grants to charities which focus on the conservation of wildlife and the environment which are typically in the £1,000 to £2,000 range
- We will generally only support charities which are registered with the Charity Commission of England and Wales, or which are exempt or excepted charities (within the meaning of the Charities Act 2011)
- We will not generally make a grant to an organisation that the Trust has supported within the previous 18 months
- We will not support applications from individuals seeking personal support
- Grants may be made towards revenue, capital or project expenditure
- Grants are made on a periodic basis and there is no deadline for applications

Large grant criteria
- We will next be making large grants to registered charities dedicated, or primarily dedicated, to the conservation of wildlife and the environment in 2016 and 2017
- We will accept applications for these two grant years from June 2015
- Grants will be for £2,000 to £25,000, and in some cases could be up to £50,000
- We will generally only support charities which are registered with the Charity Commission of England and Wales, or which are exempt or excepted charities (within the meaning of the Charities Act 2011)
- Grants may be made towards revenue, capital or project expenditure

Financial information
In 2016/17 the trust held assets of £87.3 million and had an income of £2.8 million. Grants awarded to organisations totalled £887,500.

Beneficiaries included: Sanford St Martin Parish Trust (£25,000); 21st Century Trust (£12,500); Sandford St Martin PCC (£10,000); Alzheimer's Research (£5,000); Spelsbury Memorial Hall and Fountain (£2,000); Enstone and Uplands Conservation Trust, Gamekeepers Welfare Trust and Racing Welfare (£1,000 each).

Applications
Monthly grants can be applied for using the online form on the trust's website, or by downloading a form to send by post or email, along with supporting documents. Details on what should be included are given on the website.

The large grants scheme was closed at the time of writing (March 2018). Check the trust's website for the latest information on these grants.

Sources of information
Accounts; annual report; Charity Commission record; funder's website.

Brian Wilson Charitable Trust

 General charitable purposes

UK, with a preference for Cheshire

£340,500 (2016)

CC number: 1059736

Trustees: John Pickup; Vivien Roberts; Ruth Downes.

Correspondent: John Pickup, Trustee, 36 Landswood Park, Hartford, Northwich CW8 1NF (tel: 01606 74970; fax: 01606 852733)

This trust has general charitable purposes, with a preference for Cheshire and the surrounding counties.

Financial information
In 2016 the trust had assets of £4.25 million and an income of £128,500. During the year, grants were made totalling £340,500.

Previous beneficiaries have included: Leonard Cheshire Disability Support (£115,000); Help for Heroes (£25,000); The Friends of Russett School (£10,000); Cross Roads Care – North Wales (£7,000); St Luke's Cheshire Hospice (£5,000).

Applications
Apply in writing to the correspondent. The trustees meet on a quarterly basis to consider requests and approve grants.

Sources of information
Accounts; annual report; Charity Commission record.

Sumner Wilson Charitable Trust

General charitable purposes

UK

£263,500 (2016/17)

CC number: 1018852

Trustees: Michael Sumner Wilson; Amanda Wordsworth Sumner Christie; Anne-Marie Challen.

Correspondent: Nathan Steinberg, Kreston Reeves LLP, 24 Chiswell Street, London EC1Y 4YX (tel: 020 7269 7680; email: nathan.steinberg@krestonreeves.com)

This trust has general charitable purposes and supports charities working in a wide range of areas. The trustees favour causes supported by the settlor.

Financial information
In 2016/17 the trust had assets of more than £6.7 million and an income of £149,500. Grants were made totalling £263,500.

Beneficiaries included: Listen Media Campaign (£100,000); MQ: Transforming Mental Health (£51,000); St James's Place Foundation (£32,000); Young Gloucestershire (£10,000); Duke of Edinburgh Awards (£5,000); Science Museum Group and Spinal Research (£2,500 each).

Grants of less than £2,500 each totalled £24,500.

Applications
Apply in writing to the trustees.

Sources of information
Accounts; annual report; Charity Commission record.

The Wimbledon Foundation

General charitable purposes, children and young people, sport, education

The London boroughs of Merton and Wandsworth

£398,000 (2016/17)

CC number: 1156996

Trustees: Sir Nicholas Young; Nicholas Bitel; I.L. Hewitt; P.G.H. Brook; Ashley Tatum; Sir Keith Ajebo; Hon. Henry Weatherill.

Correspondent: Helen Parker, Church Road, Wimbledon SW19 5AE (tel: 020 8971 2702; email: foundation@aeltc.com)

www.wimbledon.com/en_GB/
foundation/index.html

The Wimbledon Foundation was established in 2013 and is the charity of The All England Lawn Tennis Club and The Championships. The aim of the Wimbledon Foundation is to help change people's lives using the resources and heritage of Wimbledon.

The foundation's website states that its three main areas of focus are:

1 The London Boroughs of Merton and Wandsworth
2 Charities associated with or promoted by key groups involved in The Championships
3 Projects and charities that use the power of sport (and particularly tennis) to provide opportunities to assist people, especially the young, with education and personal development

At the time of writing (June 2018), the foundation had two grant programmes to provide support in the boroughs of Merton and Wandsworth, both of which were closed: Wimbledon Foundation Community Fund, for grants of up to £5,000 to community organisations; and Get Set, Get Active Fund, for grants of up to £2,500 to community groups and sports clubs.

Financial information
During 2016/17 the foundation had total assets of £1.78 million and a total income of £1.28 million. Grants awarded to organisations totalled £398,000.

Previous beneficiaries have included: Age UK – Wandsworth; Attic Roots and Shoots; Catch 22; Endevour Club; London Athletics; Jigsaw4u.

Applications
Full details on how to apply for various grant funds are available on the foundation's website.

Sources of information
Accounts; annual report; Charity Commission record; funder's website.

The Harold Hyam Wingate Foundation

🔍 Jewish life and learning, performing arts, music, education and social exclusion, overseas development, medical research

📍 UK and financially developing world

💷 £408,000 (2016/17)

CC number: 264114

Trustees: Roger Wingate; Tony Wingate; Prof. Robert Cassen; Prof. David Wingate; Jon Drori; Daphne Hyman; Emily Kasriel; Dr Richard Wingate; Barbara Arnold.

Correspondent: Sarah Mitchell, Somerset House, New Wing (S93), Strand, London WC2R 1LA

 www.wingatefoundation.org.uk

The foundation was established in 1960 and aims to support Jewish life and learning, performing arts, music, education and social exclusion, financially developing countries and medical organisations. The trust also administers the Wingate Scholarships which makes grants to young people with outstanding potential for educational research.

Grant-making policy
Further information is provided on the foundation's website about the different criteria and exclusions for each programme. The foundation has the following areas of interest:

- **Jewish life and learning** – projects that encourage Jewish cultural, academic and educational life, particularly academic institutions specialising in Jewish subjects and from bodies promoting Jewish culture, including museums, libraries and literary publications. Applications are also welcomed from organisations able to demonstrate a record in interfaith dialogue, in the promotion of reconciliation between Jews in Israel and their Arab neighbours and the encouragement of liberal values in both communities

- **Performing arts (excluding music)** – the foundation has a preference for supporting not-for-profit companies with a record of artistic excellence that require additional funding, not available from public sources or commercial sponsorship, to broaden their repertoire or develop work of potentially outstanding interest which cannot be funded from usual sources. Assistance will also be considered for training and professional development for creative talent or the technical professions

- **Music** – the trustees recognise that music is seriously under-funded in the UK and will consider applications for support in those areas of music performance and education which do not readily attract backing from commercial sponsors or other funding bodies, or which are not eligible for public funding. Priority will be directed towards supporting the work or education of musicians based in, or wishing to study in, the UK, but by no means exclusively so. The foundation will be prepared to consider applications for support for ongoing expenses and will be willing to consider such support for a period up to three years. Priority will be given to those organisations which give opportunities to young professionals and to education projects for young people as well as for new adult audiences. This would include direct assistance as well as funding for organisations which promote their work or performance, and support for master classes

- **Medical research travel grants** – grants can be made for travel costs to laboratories for the acquisition of new skills, and for setting up inter-institutional collaborative research. The trustees are prepared to consider applications for funds to cover the expenses of travel and subsistence for such visits up to a maximum of £1,000

The foundation also offers an annual literary prize awarded in spring, visit the website for further information.

Financial information
In 2016/17 the foundation had assets of £6.9 million and an income of £86,000. During the year, the foundation gave a total of £408,000 in grants to organisations.

The ratio of the value of grants made to organisations during the year were categorised as follows:

Performing arts	41%
Music	23%
Jewish life and learning	16%
Education and social exclusion	10%
Development projects	6%
Literary prizes	3%
Medical research including travel grants	1%

Beneficiaries included: Donmar Warehouse Theatre and Grapevine (£15,000); Arava Institute for Environmental Studies – AIES (£12,000); Little Angel Theatre (£8,300); London Master Classes (£5,000); HOME – Greater Manchester Arts Centre (£3,000); Dorset Wildlife Trust (£2,000); Royal Philharmonic Society (£1,500); Coventry and Warwick University Hospitals for Dr Joseph Hardwick (£1,000 each).

Exclusions
No grants are given to/for:

- Individuals, including students or individuals undertaking research projects (except for those covered in the Medical Research Travel Grants category)
- Large, well-known charities, including local branches
- Gap year projects, Duke of Edinburgh Awards or Raleigh International projects

Applications
Applications should be made using the application form available from the foundation's website, sent with supporting documentation and most recent accounts. Applications are only

acknowledged if a stamped addressed envelope is enclosed or if the application is successful.

The administrator of the foundation only deals with enquiries by post and it is hoped that the guidelines and examples of previous support for successful applicants, given on the foundation's website, provides sufficient information. There is no email address for the foundation. Trustee meetings are held quarterly and further information on upcoming deadlines can be found on the foundation's website.

Sources of information
Accounts; annual report; Charity Commission record; funder's website.

The Francis Winham Foundation

 Welfare of older people

England

£355,500 (2016/17)

CC number: 278092

Trustees: Josephine Winham; Elsa Peters; Desmond Corcoran; Fuschia Peters.

Correspondent: Josephine Winham, Trustee, 18 Gilston Road, London SW10 9SR (tel: 020 7795 1261; email: francinetrust@outlook.com)

This charity was registered with the Charity Commission in 1979, for the benefit of older people in England. Grants are given to both national organisations (including their local branches) and local charities. Many organisations are regular recipients, although not necessarily on an annual basis.

The foundation's 2016/17 annual accounts state: 'The majority of grants are made to institutions, which may in turn make grants to individuals.'

Financial information
In 2016/17 the charity had assets of £8.8 million and had an income of £72,000. During the year, the charity awarded a total of £355,500 in grants to organisations.

Beneficiaries included: SSAFA (£17,300); Care and Repair (£16,200); Age UK, Buckingham Almshouses and Welfare (£10,000); Age Concern (£7,000); Aspire, Cavell Nurses Trusts, Pengarth Day Centre (£5,000); U Can Do It (£3,000).

During the year, 103 grants of less than £5,000 were awarded to organisations.

Applications
Apply in writing to the correspondent. The trust regrets it cannot send replies

to applications outside its specific field of help for older people.

Sources of information
Accounts; annual report; Charity Commission record.

Winton Philanthropies

 Scientific education and research, general charitable purposes

 UK and overseas, particularly London and areas local to Winton offices

£6.3 million (2016)

CC number: 1110131

Trustees: David Winton Harding; Claudia Harding; Martin Hunt.

Correspondent: Alexandra Openshaw, Grove House, 27 Hammersmith Grove, London W6 0NE (email: philanthropies@winton.com)

 www.winton.com/philanthropies

Winton Philanthropies is the corporate charity of Winton, a global investment management company. Formerly known as The Winton Charitable Foundation, the charity changed its name in 2016.

According to its website, the charity focuses on the following four areas of support:

▶ Funding scientific research – particularly 'experimental, bold and risk-taking research'

▶ Communication of scientific ideas – particularly around the public understanding of risk and statistics

▶ London – in the city where Winton's head office is located, it supports 'projects and institutions that add to the character, culture and beauty of the city'

▶ Local initiatives – charities in areas local to Winton offices around the world

Financial information
In 2016 the charity had assets of £2.6 million and an income of £8.6 million. Grants awarded totalled £6.3 million.

Beneficiaries included: The Cambridge Foundation (£3 million); The Science Museum Foundation (£1.25 million); Foundation and Friends of the Royal Botanical Gardens Kew (£1 million); The Max Planck Institute (£569,000).

The foundation also provides match funding for charitable donations of up to £10,000 made by Winton Capital Management employees.

Applications
The following information is provided on the charity's website:

Please note that grant proposals are by invitation only – we do not accept

unsolicited proposals. Because of our tightly defined grant-making themes, many worthwhile projects fall outside the scope of our funding priorities. However, if you have thoughts or enquiries related to our work that you would like to share, you can contact us at philanthropies@ winton.com. Please understand that due to the volume of enquiries we receive, we are only able to commit to reviewing those which are aligned to our strategic themes.

Sources of information
Accounts; annual report; Charity Commission record; funder's website.

The Wixamtree Trust

 General charitable purposes

 UK, Bedfordshire

£1.1 million (2016/17)

CC number: 210089

Trustees: Sir Samuel Whitbread; Lady Whitbread; Charles Whitbread; Ian Pilkington; Geoff McMullen; Elizabeth Bennett; Paul Patten; Harry Whitbread.

Correspondent: Mia Duddridge, Clerk to the Trustees, 6 Trull Farm Buildings, Tetbury, Gloucestershire GL8 8SQ (tel: 020 8777 4140; email: wixamtree@ thetrustpartnership.com)

 www.wixamtree.org

This trust was established by Humphrey Whitbread in 1949 for general charitable purposes. According to the trust's website, the trustees focus most support on organisations and projects based or operating in Bedfordshire. In addition, they support a small number of national charities with whom the trust's main benefactor, Humphrey Whitbread, had been associated with during his life.

Financial information
In 2016/17 the trust had assets of £33.8 million and an income of £1 million. The trust received 228 applications and grants were made to 175 organisations totalling £1.1 million. They were categorised as follows:

Social welfare	£470,500
Environment and conservation	£222,000
Medicine and health	£102,500
Education	£86,000
The arts	£60,000
Sports and leisure	£31,500

Beneficiaries were not listed in the accounts but could be viewed on the trust's website which includes details of the purpose of each grant.

Beneficiaries included: Age Concern Luton; Age UK Bedfordshire; Bedford Guild House; Bibles for Children; Happy Days Children's Charity; Meningitis Now; Migraine Action Association; Motor Neurone Disease Association; Signposts – Luton; Tall Ships Youth

Trust; Unseen; Zoological Society of London.

Exclusions

The trust will not give grants to individuals.

Applications

Applications are welcomed from organisations either based or operating within the county of Bedfordshire which are either a registered charity or considered to be charitable in nature by the Inland Revenue. Applications can be made using an online application form on the trust's website. Guidance, future meeting dates and application deadlines are also on the website.

Along with the application form, applicants must provide a copy of their latest audited report and accounts. If the organisation is not a charity, then a copy of its constitution/rules must also be provided. Applicants are permitted to provide additional information to support their application if they wish to do so.

Successful applicants will be notified within 14 days of the trustees' meeting of the amount that has been approved. Unsuccessful applicants will receive a letter detailing the trustees' decision within seven days of the meeting.

The trustees are happy for further applications to be made on the anniversary of an award. Before another application can be submitted, the trust asks previously successful organisations that already hold grants to submit an annual report on how the earlier grant has been used.

Support for churches

The trustees of The Wixamtree Trust have entered into an arrangement with the trustees of the Beds and Herts Historic Churches Trust (BHHCT) who consider applications from Bedfordshire churches that are seeking support for repairs to the fabric of their buildings. Bedfordshire churches seeking such support should therefore contact BHHCT via its website www. bedshertshct.org.uk.

An annual donation is given to BHHCT to support such appeals on behalf of The Wixamtree Trust.

Sources of information

Accounts; annual report; Charity Commission record; funder's website.

The Maurice Wohl Charitable Foundation

 Jewish causes, health, medical science, social welfare

UK and Israel

£1.5 million (2016)

CC number: 244519

Trustees: Ella Latchman; Martin Paisner; Prof. David Latchman; Sir Ian Gainsford; Daniel Dover.

Correspondent: Joseph Houri, Secretary, Fitzrovia House, 2nd Floor, 153 – 157 Cleveland Street, London W1T 6QW (tel: 020 7383 5111; email: jh@wohl.org. uk)

 www.wohl.org.uk

The Wohl Legacy is a group of three charitable foundations established by the late Maurice and Vivienne Wohl, which now continues their legacy of support for medical science, welfare and education in the UK, Israel, Central and Eastern Europe, the former Soviet Union and other Jewish populations in need around the world.

The foundation mainly funds capital projects, with particular focus given to the following areas:

Health and medical sciences

In the field of health, welfare and medical sciences, the trustees make a range of grants that reflects the wider field, encompassing medical care, advancement of knowledge and education, and new models of engagement.

Welfare within the Jewish community

Through both capital projects and programme funding, the foundation aims to achieve its objective of promoting welfare and the relief of poverty for the benefit of the public

Jewish education

The foundation continues to support Jewish education with grants to both formal education through the Jewish School Network, and to informal education through the Union of Jewish Students, United Jewish Israel Appeal (UJIA) and Jewish Lads' and Girls' Brigade (JLGB). Through these and other grants the foundation intends to strengthen Jewish children and young adults' commitment to thriving communal life.

The foundation continues to follow the example set by Maurice and Vivienne Wohl in their help and support of those, primarily in the Jewish community, in direct medical, financial, emotional or material need. The foundation continues to fund a wide variety of local communal organisations within the Jewish community that research, identify and support those in urgent need.

Financial information

In 2016 the foundation had assets of £84.5 million and an income of £1.6 million. During the year, the foundation gave a total of £1.5 million in grants to organisations. Grants were distributed as follows:

Jewish education	£620,500
Health and medical sciences	£607,000
Welfare within the Jewish community	£245,000
Miscellaneous	£16,000
The arts	£2,800

Beneficiaries included: Central Synagogue London (£342,000); Children Ahead Ltd (£50,000); Shaarei Parnosoh Toiva (£34,000); Jewish Lad's and Girl's Brigade (£50,000) Mitzvah Day UK Trust, Kesher (£10,000); King David Religious Education (£5,000); Shema Koli (£2,000); Keren Hatzolas Doros Alei Siach (£1,000); Seed (£400).

Exclusions

No grants are made to individuals.

Applications

The foundation does not accept unsolicited applications, as trustees identify suitable projects.

Sources of information

Accounts; annual report; Charity Commission record; funder's website.

The Charles Wolfson Charitable Trust

 Medical research, education, social welfare

Unrestricted, mainly UK

£6.4 million (2016/17)

CC number: 238043

Trustees: Lord Simon Wolfson; Dr Sara Levene; The Hon. Andrew Wolfson; Lord David Wolfson.

Correspondent: Joanne Cowan, Correspondent, 8/10 Hallam Street, London W1W 6NS (tel: 020 7079 2506)

The trust was established in 1960 for general charitable purposes. The intention of the trust is to make grants to organisations which fall within the areas of medicine, education and welfare, especially for capital or fixed-term projects and the provision of rent-free premises. Particular regard is given to the needs of the Jewish community.

The bulk of the trust's income derives from grants received from Benesco (Charity Commission no. 269181) which has its investments held in property.

Financial information

In 2016/17 the trust had assets of £236 million and an income of £5.4 million. During the year, the trust gave a total of £6.4 million in grants to organisations. Grants were distributed as follows:

Medicine	£2.7 million
Welfare	£2.5 million
Education	£1.2 million

Beneficiaries were not listed in the accounts.

Previous beneficiaries have included: Addenbrooke's Charitable Trust and Yavneh College Trust (£500,000 each); Jewish Care (£350,000); Cure Parkinson's Trust (£200,000); Huntingdon Foundation (£125,000); Royal Marsden Cancer Campaign (£50,000); Sir George Pinker Appeal (£30,000); Zoological Society of London (£25,000); Priors Court Foundation (£10,000); Tavistock Trust for Aphasia (£5,000); the Roundhouse Trust (£1,000).

Exclusions

No grants are given to individuals.

Applications

Apply in writing to the correspondent.

Sources of information

Accounts; annual report; Charity Commission record.

The Wolfson Family Charitable Trust

 General charitable purposes

UK, Israel

£ £1.5 million (2016/17)

CC number: 228382

Trustees: Martin Paisner; Sir Ian Gainsford; Sir Bernard Rix; Sir Eric Ash; The Hon. Laura Wolfson Townsley; The Hon Janet De Botton; Lord Turnberg; The Hon. Elizabeth Wolfson Peltz; Alexandra Wolfson Halamish.

Correspondent: Paul Ramsbottom, Chief Executive, 8 Queen Anne Street, London W1G 9LD (tel: 020 7323 5730; email: grants@wolfson.org.uk)

www.wolfson.org.uk

The trust was founded in 1958 by Sir Isaac Wolfson, his wife, and their son Leonard, and it was registered with the Charity Commission in 1966. The Wolfson Family Charitable Trust is a sister organisation to the Wolfson Family Foundation, and provides grants to fund general charitable purposes, mainly in Israel. The trust considers its funding a catalyst to lever additional support and hopes its funding will support areas that are under-researched or unpopular.

Financial information

In 2016/17 the trust held assets of £36.2 million and had an income of £924,000. During the year, the trust gave a total of £1.5 million in grants to organisations, broken down as follows:

Science and medicine	8	£940,000
Health and disability	11	£292,000
Arts and humanities	4	£135,000
Education	3	£46,000

Beneficiaries included: Tel Aviv Sourasky Medical Centre (£156,000); Rambam Healthcare Campus – Haifa (£120,000); Shaare Zedek Medical Center – Jerusalem (£100,000); Central Synagogue W1 (£50,000); Alin Beit Noam, Kiryat Ono, Israel (£20,000); CLS Care Services Group – Manchester (£10,000).

Exclusions

Funding is not provided for:

- Individuals
- Overheads, maintenance costs, VAT or professional fees
- Non-specific appeals
- Endowment funds
- Purchase of land or existing buildings
- Film or promotional materials
- Loan repayment
- Projects which already are or will be completed by the time the award is made

Applications

Applications are made in two stages and should include proof of an income over £50,000 per year and show evidence of financial viability.

Stage one of the application should be returned by 1 June. Stage two should be returned by 15 July. See the website for more details.

Sources of information

Accounts; annual report; Charity Commission record; funder's website.

The Lord Leonard and Lady Estelle Wolfson Foundation

 Preventative healthcare research and initiatives

UK

£ £1.36 million (2016/17)

CC number: 1148663

Trustees: Ian Burman; Lord Ara Darzi; Lady Estelle Wolfson of Marylebone; Sir Ian Gilmore.

Correspondent: Michael Feldman, 74 Portland Place, London W1B 1NR (tel: 020 7636 6446; email: admin@lordandladywolfson.org.uk)

 lordandladywolfson.org.uk

The foundation supports and promotes projects calculated to promote the advancement of research and education for the public benefit in preventative medicine or surgery and research.

The foundation's website states:

> The Foundation will fund cutting-edge research and related initiatives into a wide range of areas of preventative healthcare.

> One specific area of focus for the Foundation will be the important role that art, music and architecture can play in preventing and mitigating certain illnesses and in creating innovative healthcare delivery mechanisms.

> The Foundation will support pioneering research that is, increasingly, demonstrating this important cultural/ healthcare link.

Financial information

In 2016/17 the foundation held assets of £26.7 million and had an income of £784,500. Grants awarded to organisations totalled £1.36 million.

Beneficiaries included: Cancer Research (£380,000); Alcohol Health Alliance (£180,000); University College London (£70,000); Tommy's (£50,000); National Gallery (£15,800); Academy of Medical Sciences (£15,000); Great Ormond Street Hospital (£10,000); Chickenshed and Chabad (£5,000 each).

Applications

The foundation has a three-stage application process. Application guidelines are available to download from the foundation's website.

Sources of information

Accounts; annual report; Charity Commission record; funder's website.

The Wolfson Foundation

 Medical and scientific research, education, health and welfare, heritage, arts

UK

£ £30.4 million (2016/17)

CC number: 1156077

Trustees: Lord McColl; Sir Eric Ash; Hon. Laura Wolfson Townley; Sir David Cannadine; Dame Janet Wolfson de Botton; Rebecca Marks; Lord Turnberg; Dame Jean Thomas; Dame Hermione Lee; Sir Michael Pepper; Hon. Deborah Wolfson Davis; Sir Peter Ratcliffe.

Correspondent: Paul Ramsbottom, 8 Queen Anne Street, London W1G 9LD (tel: 020 7323 5730; email: grants@wolfson.org.uk)

 www.wolfson.org.uk

facebook.com/WolfsonFoundation

 @wolfsonfdn

The trust was founded in 1955 by Sir Isaac Wolfson, his wife, and their son Leonard, and it was registered with the Charity Commission in 1966. The Wolfson Family Charitable Trust provides grants to promote and support excellence in science, health, education, and the arts and humanities. The trust considers its funding a catalyst to lever additional support, and hopes its funding will support areas that are under-researched.

Grant-making

The foundation's grant-making has four main areas of focus, details of which have been taken from the foundation's website:

Science and medicine – The Wolfson Foundation supports excellence in science and biomedicine, funding research of the highest quality and supporting medical and science education

Arts and humanities – The Wolfson Foundation supports excellence in the arts and humanities, funding across museums and galleries, historic buildings and landscapes, the performing arts and education

Education – The Wolfson Foundation supports excellence in secondary and higher education through infrastructure funding and the provision of bursaries and scholarships.

Health and disability – The Wolfson Foundation supports excellence for health and disability by funding improved facilities for organisations delivering outstanding care and support for people with a range of needs

Financial information

In 2016/17 the trust had assets of £774.5 million and an income of £19.6 million. The total amount awarded in grants was £30.4 million, broken down into the following categories:

Science	£14.5 million
Arts and humanities	£7 million
Education	£5.3 million
Health	£3.6 million

Beneficiaries included: University of Edinburgh (£2 million); National Youth Orchestra of Great Britain (£300,000); York Archaeological Trust (£250,000); Story Museum – Oxford (£150,000); Havering Sixth Form College (£100,000); Birmingham Conservatoire (£60,000); Cardiff High School (£35,000); Stroud High School (£16,000); Castle Leod (£10,000).

Exclusions

The following are ineligible for funding:

- Individuals
- Conduit organisations
- Overheads, maintenance costs (including for software), VAT and professional fees
- Non-specific appeals (including circulars) and endowment funds
- Costs of meetings, exhibitions, concerts, expeditions, etc.
- Purchasing of land or existing buildings (including a building's freehold)
- Film or promotional materials
- Repayment of loans
- Completed projects
- Projects where the total cost is below £15,000

Applications

Applications are made in a two-stage process and can be submitted at two points during the year:

- **Spring:** first-stage application due on or before 5 January, second-stage application due in March. Funding decision made in June.
- **Autumn:** first-stage applications due on or before 1 July, second-stage applications due in September. Funding decision made in December.

See the website for full details of how to apply and what to include in your application.

Sources of information

Accounts; annual report; Charity Commission record; funder's website.

The Foster Wood Foundation

 The advancement of the Christian religion, education and training, social welfare

England and Wales

£497,000 (2016/17)

CC number: 1101364

Trustees: Geoffrey Hill; Margaret Lodge; Paul Lodge.

Correspondent: Geoffrey Hill, Trustee, 21–27 Lamb's Conduit Street, London WC1N 3GS (tel: 020 7935 3793; email: ghill@gsmaccountants.co.uk)

The Foster Wood Foundation was established in 2003. According to its annual report for 2016/17, the foundation primarily provides funding to organisations which fall into one of the following categories:

- Christian organisations
- Medical charities
- Charities relieving poverty
- Social welfare institutions

Financial information

In 2016/17 the foundation had assets of £85,000 and an income of £520,000. During the year, grants worth a total of £497,000 were awarded to 26 organisations. Grants were distributed as follows:

Christian organisations	£270,000
Medical	£141,000
Relief of poverty	£66,000
Social welfare	£20,000

A list of beneficiaries was not available.

Applications

The foundation's annual report states the following:

In the past applications have been invited from suitable charities able to demonstrate that they can use the funds they apply for in an effective manner to achieve their stated aims which must be consistent with the objects of the foundation. However, as it is the intention of the trustees to reduce the activities of the foundation, no applications are being sought from any other charity other than those already being supported.

Sources of information

Accounts; annual report; Charity Commission record.

Wooden Spoon Society

 Children and young people who are disadvantaged or have disabilities

UK

£1.04 million (2016/17)

CC number: 326691

Trustees: Nigel Timson; David Allen; Martin Sanders; Alison Lowe; Richard Smith; John Gibson; Mark McCafferty; Quentin Smith; Joanna Coombs.

Correspondent: The Trustees, Sentinel House, Ancells Business Park, Harvest Crescent, Fleet, Hampshire GU51 2UZ (tel: 01252 773720; email: charity@ woodenspoon.org.uk)

www.woodenspoon.com

Wooden Spoon Society was established in 1983 and supports children and young people who are disadvantaged or have disabilities.

Grant guidelines

The charity awards grants for the following purposes:

- Health and well-being
- Sensory rooms and gardens
- Specialist equipment and facilities
- Playgrounds and outdoor activity areas
- Education projects

The following information is taken from the charity's website.

For capital projects, the following criteria apply:

- It must have a minimum predicted life-span of five years (preferably ten years), be non-transferable and of a permanent nature. Special consideration may be given to funding

- life-enhancing/medical treatment equipment if it can be shown that the useable life of such equipment is likely to be at least five years
- Grants will not be considered for salaries, administration costs, professional fees and on-going overheads related to a capital project

For projects focused on education or disability sports, the following criteria apply:

- There must be a key rugby element to engage children and young people
- It must have a clearly-defined brief to detailing the project's need and objectives; stakeholders; description of participants (age, gender, geography); recruitment of participants; project activity and budget; legacy planning; monitoring and evaluation and mechanism for reporting to Wooden Spoon
- Grants will be considered for kit and equipment, salaries and administration costs

Projects must:

- Enhance and support the lives of children and young people (under the age of 25) who are disadvantaged physically, mentally or socially
- Work directly with children and young people and have a positive influence on their lives as a result of the activities or service provided
- Benefit those located in the UK or Ireland
- Support a group – we cannot make grants to individuals

Although there is no minimum or maximum grant available, it is unlikely that capital projects under £5,000 will meet the charity's criteria.

Financial information

In 2016/17 the charity had assets of £974,000 and an income of £2.8 million. Grants were made in support of 70 projects, totalling £1.04 million and broken down as follows:

Special equipment and facilities	20	£289,000
Transport	2	£289,000
Sensory rooms and gardens	14	£177,000
Health and well-being	11	£103,000
Playgrounds	15	£99,000
Buildings and extensions	5	£79,000
NEET	2	£68,000
Disability rugby	1	£6,000

A list of beneficiaries was not included in the annual report and accounts. Information about previous beneficiaries is provided on the charity's website.

Previous beneficiaries have included: Rugby Football League (£80,000); 999 Club (£58,500); Quarriers Epilepsy Centre (£50,000); Camphill School (£29,000); Claytons Primary School (£23,000); Greenbank Sports Academy (£15,000); Horseworld (£11,000); PACT (£10,000); Printfield Community Project (£6,500); Scottish Spina Bifida Association (£5,000); Our Lady of Walsingham School (£1,000).

Applications

If you have read the guidelines and criteria on the website and think you are eligible for a grant, you should contact the charity for an application form: projects@woodenspoon.org.uk or 01252 773720.

Sources of information

Accounts; annual report; Charity Commission record; funder's website.

The F Glenister Woodger Trust

 General charitable purposes

West Wittering and surrounding areas

£255,500 (2016/17)

CC number: 802642

Trustees: Richard Shrubb, Chair; Rosamund Champ; William Craven; Stuart Dobbin; Maxine Pickup; Rosamund Gentle.

Correspondent: Richard Shrubb, Trustee, Wicks Farm Caravan Park, Redlands Lane, West Wittering, Chichester PO20 8QE (tel: 01243 513116; email: office@wicksfarm.co.uk)

The trust was established in 1989 and its object is to improve the quality of life for people who live in West Wittering and the surrounding area.

Financial information

In 2016/17 the trust held assets of £43 million and had an income of £1.5 million. Grants were awarded to 12 organisations and totalled £255,500.

Beneficiaries included: St James Centre, Birdham (£150,000); Chichester Harbour Conservancy (£15,000); Birdham and Wittering Scout Group, Birdham CE Primary School (£10,000); British Wireless for the Blind (£2,200); Home-Start (£2,000); Redlands Camp (£1,000); Birdham Village Choir (£500).

Exclusions

No grants are given to individuals.

Applications

Apply in writing to the correspondent. The trustees meet quarterly to review grant applications.

Sources of information

Accounts; annual report; Charity Commission record.

Woodroffe Benton Foundation

 Social welfare, older people, education and development of young people, environment and conservation

UK

£425,500 (2016/17)

CC number: 1075272

Trustees: James Hope; Philip Miles; Colin Russell; Anthony Behrens; Richard Page; Jill Wesley.

Correspondent: Joanna Noles, Secretary, PO Box 309, Cirencester GL7 9HA (email: secretary@woodroffebenton.org. uk)

www.woodroffebenton.org.uk

This foundation was set up by trust deed in November 1988 by the late Alfred Woodroffe Benton. It later amalgamated with the S. Wolfe Memorial Fund.

The foundation makes grants to registered and exempt charities in the following categories:

- Relief of hardship
- Care for older people
- Education and development of young people
- Environment and conservation

The trustees currently focus on making grants of between £500 and £2,500 to smaller organisations (generally with an income of less than £1 million) for core operating costs (although applications for specific projects are considered).

The foundation will also support 'human physical well-being' but the website states that the trustees do not accept unsolicited applications for this purpose.

Financial information

In 2016/17 the foundation held assets of £8 million and had an income of £339,500. The annual report states that 213 grants were paid during the year in the following categories:

- Ongoing support – 24 grants to 20 charities totalling £271,000
- Small grants – 166 grants totalling £141,000
- Trustee-directed grants – 22 grants totalling £13,700
- The funding pot – £50,000 spread over two years to finance research into causes of and support for stammering children

During the year, the trustees received 408 applications through the small grants programme. The accounts state that £425,500 of these grants were actually paid during the year, with a further £117,500 committed for future grants. Beneficiaries for the year were not listed in the accounts.

Previous beneficiaries have included:
Community Links (£250,000); Ilfield Park Care Home (£22,500); Queen Elizabeth's Grammar School (£19,000); Action for Stammering Children, Furniture Re-Use Network and Prisoners' Families and Friends Service (£5,000 each); Beauchamp Lodge Settlement (£4,000); Theatre Peckham (£1,500).

Exclusions

The foundation does not usually make grants for:

▶ Organisations that operate primarily outside the UK or for the benefit of non-UK residents
▶ Places of worship seeking funds for restoration or upgrade of facilities
▶ Students requesting a grant for tertiary education or a gap year
▶ Educational organisations based outside the Derbyshire region
▶ Museums, historical or heritage organisations
▶ Palliative care
▶ Organisations that are not registered charities
▶ Organisations that have been operating for less than 12 months
▶ Animal welfare organisations whose primary purpose is not conservation of the environment except those that help the survival of wild species in the UK
▶ Bodies affiliated to or a local branch of a national organisation, even when registered as a separate charity – if you are unsure whether you would fall within this category, submit a query via the foundation's website
▶ Individuals

The trust is also unlikely to provide multiple grants to the same charity within a 12-month period.

Applications

Applications are made using an online form on the foundation's website, where guidance is also available. No supporting documentation is required. If it is not possible to submit an application online, alternative methods of submission may be arranged by contacting the foundation.

The website also states:

Meetings of the trustees are held quarterly, in the second or third week of January, April, July and October. The deadline for the receipt of applications is approximately six weeks prior to each meeting. Any applications not received by the deadline will be held over for consideration at the following meeting.

We will contact successful applicants as soon as possible following the meeting at which their proposal has been considered. We generally do not contact unsuccessful applicants as we are a small organisation with limited administrative resources. Although we are always happy to respond to enquiries or queries, the Foundation does not generally provide feedback on why an application was unsuccessful. If you do not hear from us by the end of the month in which the meeting took place, it will normally mean that your application has not been successful.

Sources of information

Accounts; annual report; Charity Commission record; funder's website.

The Woodstock Family Charitable Foundation

🔍 Rehabilitation of offenders

📍 England and Wales

£ £226,000 (2016/17)

CC number: 1156449

Trustees: Paul Woodstock Harris; Peter Woodstock Harris; Thomas Woodstock Harris; Alison Swinburn; Margaret West.

Correspondent: Peter Woodstock Harris, Trustee, Sallow Copse, Ringshall, Berkhamsted, Hertfordshire HP4 1LZ (tel: 01442 842480)

This foundation was established in 2014 by the Woodstock family, members of which sit as trustees.

The trustees of the foundation include Peter Harris, the founder and Chair of Bourne Leisure, a Hemel Hempstead-based leisure and holiday company.

The Charity Commission record of The Woodstock Family Foundation states that it operates as a grant-making charity in England and Wales. The primary objective of the foundation is 'to promote and support the rehabilitation of offenders for the public benefit by the provision of grants and donations as the trustees in their absolute discretion think fit', although general charitable purposes may also be supported.

The annual report for 2016/17 states that: 'In addition to, and consistent with the principal object, the Trustees support projects to assist minors considered at-risk from offending to provide them guidance, coaching and life skills to prevent them going to prison. The Trustees also continue to support causes with which a number of the Trustees have a longstanding relationship.'

Financial information

In 2016/17 the foundation had assets of £204,000 and an income of £125,000. Grants were made to three organisations totalling £226,000.

Beneficiaries were: St Francis Hospice (£125,000); TurnAround (£86,000); St Andrew's Mission Orphanage (£15,000).

Applications

Apply in writing to the correspondent.

Sources of information

Accounts; annual report; Charity Commission record.

The Woodward Charitable Trust

🔍 General charitable purposes

📍 UK and overseas

£ £261,500 (2016/17)

CC number: 299963

Trustees: Camilla Woodward; Shaun Woodward; Eleanor Woodward; Thomas Woodward.

Correspondent: Karin Hooper, Administrator, The Peak, 5 Wilton Road, London SW1V 1AP (tel: 020 7410 0330; email: contact@woodwardcharitabletrust. org.uk)

 www.woodwardcharitabletrust.org. uk

This is one of the Sainsbury Family Charitable Trusts, which share a joint administration, but this charity operates somewhat differently to others in this group in that it gives a large number of small grants in response to open application. It is the trust of Camila Woodward (nee Sainsbury) and her ex-husband Shaun Woodward, previously MP for St Helens South and Whiston. The trust primarily supports charitable organisations in the UK, although occasionally overseas projects are supported through UK charities.

Grant information

The trust offers the following guidance on its website:

Woodward favours charities which make good use of volunteers and encourage past and current users to participate. Our grant-making continues to be primarily reactive but with selected projects initiated by the trustees. The trust's grant-making focuses on the following areas:

▶ **Children and young people** who are isolated, at risk of exclusion or involved in antisocial behaviour
▶ **Prisoners and ex-offenders.** Projects that help the rehabilitation and resettlement of prisoners and/or ex-offenders are supported as well as requests to help prisoners' families
▶ **Disadvantaged women**, covering refuges, domestic violence and parenting
▶ **Disability** projects which can include rehabilitation and training for people who are either physically disabled or learning disabled
▶ **Arts** outreach work by local groups for the benefit of disadvantaged people

- Projects that promote integration and community cohesion amongst **minority groups**, including refugees and travellers

The trustees favour small-scale, locally based initiatives. Funding is primarily for one-off projects, but the trustees are willing to consider funding core costs and salaries. The 2016/17 annual report notes that prospective applicants should be aware that less than 15% of the applications received are successful. The 2016/17 annual report also notes that the trust 'will fund social enterprises and community interest companies providing their aims are purely charitable'.

Types of grant

The following types of grant are available:

- Small grants ranging between £100 and £5,000
- Large grants of over £5,000. These are normally only given to charities known by the trustees; applications will automatically be rejected unless they are discussed with the administrator prior to submission. Normally around five large grants are awarded each year
- Children's summer play scheme grants for disadvantaged children between the ages of 5 and 16. Grants range between £200 and £1,000. Applicant organisations must have an income of under £100,000 to be eligible. Programmes must run for a minimum of two weeks

Financial information

In 2016/17 the trust held assets of £10.5 million and had an income of £182,500. There were 206 grants paid in the year totalling £261,500, broken down as follows:

Community and social welfare	93	£145,000
Summer schemes	71	£35,000
Arts	15	£31,500
Education	3	£29,500
Disability and health	24	£20,500

Previous beneficiaries have included:
Weidenfeld-Hoffman Trust (£30,000); London Academy of Music and Dramatic Art (£10,000); Unlock (£2,000); Action for Refugees in Lewisham, Haringey Migrant Support Centre, Nurture by Nature Forest School and Tomorrow's Women Wirral (£1,000 each); Families First Southampton, Osprey's Wheelchair Rugby Club and Tools for Solidarity Downpatrick (£500 each); Woodthorne Primary School PTA (£200).

Exclusions

The trustees will not fund:

- Charities whose annual turnover exceeds £300,000
- Construction projects such as playgrounds, village halls, and disability access

- General school appeals including out-of-hours provision
- Hospices
- Medical research
- Parish facilities
- Playgroups and pre-school groups
- Requests for vehicles
- Individuals in any capacity
- Educational fees

For the summer playschemes grant, trustees will not fund:

- Trips that are only social; preference is given to trips that are educational and motivational
- Charities with a turnover of over £100,000
- Overseas projects
- Playgroups
- Individuals
- Educational fees

Applications

Application forms are available from the trust and can be downloaded from its website. Potential applicants whose project falls within the criteria are invited to telephone the administrator in advance to discuss the advisability of making an application. Do not skip sections on the application form and refer instead to supplementary material. Only send your accounts if they are not already available on the Charity Commission website.

Main grant applications are usually reviewed in February/March and October/November and summer playscheme grants are normally considered in April. Applicants are advised to check the trust's website for the latest deadline dates. All application forms are assessed on arrival and acknowledged within six to eight weeks. Applicants will be contacted if additional information is required.

The website has a useful diary of trustees' meetings and of the cut-off dates for applications. The trust advises that only around 15% of applicants are successful and the majority of grants are for less than £5,000.

Sources of information

Accounts; annual report; Charity Commission record; funder's website.

Worth Waynflete Foundation

 General charitable purposes

UK, with a preference for Lincolnshire

£330,000 (2016)

CC number: 1068892

Trustees: Michael Worth; Graham Scrimshaw.

Correspondent: Margaret Dawson, Foundation Manager, PO Box 9986,

Grantham, Lincolnshire NG31 0FJ (tel: 01400 250210; email: info@ waynfletecharity.com or margaretdawson@waynfletecharity.com)

 www.waynfletecharity.com

This trust was established in 1986 and aims to support voluntary organisations in South Lincolnshire.

The trust states on its website that it prefers to give grants in support of the following:

- Lincolnshire based charities and organisations
- National charities and organisations where Lincolnshire residents are involved
- Individual initiatives
- Rural projects promoting the enhancement of the Lincolnshire landscape and ecology
- Preservation of heritage assets

Activities that the trust supports include:

- Enhancement of skills and qualifications of existing staff
- Training and proficiency of new volunteers
- Core day to day running costs and special needs
- Start-up initiatives with additional staged funding programmes

Alongside its main community grants, the trust also aims to fund one major project each year.

Financial information

In 2016 the trust had assets of £5.3 million and an income of £645,000. During the year, it made 135 grants to organisations totalling £330,000. This included a major grant of almost £73,000 to Lincoln Cathedral Fabric Fund, for the sponsorship of a Cathedral Mason, Stonemason and a Junior Glazier. Grants were broken down in the accounts as follows:

Charitable organisations – local	£141,500
Local sport, social clubs, schools and charitable donations	£80,000
National charitable organisations	£66,000
Local donations	£43,000

Recent beneficiaries were not listed in the accounts.

Previous beneficiaries have included:
Lincolnshire Blind Society (£6,000); Canine Partners, Lincolnshire and Nottinghamshire Air Ambulance and the Order of St John (£4,000 each); Deaf Blind (£2,500); Action for Kids, Gurkha Welfare Trust and Marine Conservation Society (£1,000); Braille Chess Association, Children's Safety Education Foundation and Royal National Lifeboat Fund (£500 each); Mouth and Foot Painting Artists (£100).

Exclusions

The foundation does not provide grants to individuals.

Applications

Apply in writing to the correspondent. When contacting the charity provide your name, address, organisation, and contact details, with a brief outline of your activities and proposal. All decisions connected with grant awards are made by the trustees.

Sources of information

Accounts; annual report; Charity Commission record; funder's website.

The Worwin UK Foundation

 General charitable purposes

UK and Canada

£936,000 (2016/17)

CC number: 1037981

Trustees: Brian Moore; Anthony Graham; Oliver McGinley; Dan Hill.

Correspondent: David Ward, Secretary, 5 Fleet Place, London EC4M 7RD (tel: 020 7427 6400)

The foundation was established and registered with the Charity Commission in 1994 to provide grants for general charitable purposes in the UK and in Canada. In previous years, the foundation focused its grant-making on the advancement of education, the promotion of the arts (particularly among young people and people from low-income backgrounds), the prevention and relief of sickness and the advancement of health.

Financial information

In 2016/17 the foundation had assets of £1.26 million and an income of £740,000. Grants were made totalling £936,000.

Beneficiaries included: Alexandra Community Health Centre and Vibe Arts (£21,000 each); Holland Bloorview Kids Foundation, Operation Come Home and Spinal Cord Injury Alberta (£20,500 each); Sutton Trust (£20,000).

Applications

Apply in writing to the correspondent.

Sources of information

Accounts; annual report; Charity Commission record.

The Eric Wright Charitable Trust

 Young people, older people, education and training, health, carers' support

UK, with a preference for the north west of England

£401,000 (2016)

CC number: 1002966

Trustees: Michael Collier; Hugh Macdonald; Alan Sturrock; Alison Wright; Benard Whewell.

Correspondent: Michael Collier, Trustee, Sceptre House, Sceptre Way, Bamber Bridge, Preston PR5 6AW (email: rebeccam@ericwright.co.uk)

 www.ericwright.co.uk/charitable-trust

The Eric Wright Charitable Trust was established in 1990 by businessman Eric Wright. According to the trust's website, the trust was formed, 'based on the belief that the role of business in society is not to create wealth for the few but instead is fundamental to the building of a strong community'. Following a gift from Mr Wright, the trust today holds 100% of shares in The Eric Wright Group Ltd – provider of construction, civil engineering, property development and facilities management services.

The trust works with a broad range of charities, primarily in the north west of England, with particular emphasis on the well-being of young people, services for older people, education and training, health, and carers' support. According to the trust's website:

> The Trustees are willing to consider a range of applications, both capital and revenue, but with emphasis on applications that will either build capacity and therefore sustainability within the applicant organisation or which will broaden the range of its target beneficiaries. A high volunteer involvement in the applicant organisation is likely to be influential although not essential.

In addition to its grant-making activities, the trust is also directly involved in running two of its own charities, namely:

▶ **Water Park Lakeland Adventure Centre:** provides outdoor adventure facilities in Coniston, working particularly with socially and physically disadvantaged groups

▶ **Eric Wright Learning Foundation:** works collaboratively with Preston College to provide vocational learning as part of the college's overall curriculum and supports local schools through bursaries

Financial information

In 2016 the trust had assets of almost £67 million and an income of

£35 million. During the year, the trust awarded grants totalling £401,000.

Previous beneficiaries have included: Age Concern Central Lancashire; Blackburn Youth Zone; Derian House; Galloway's Society for the Blind.

Applications

Apply in writing to the correspondent.

Sources of information

Accounts; annual report; Charity Commission record; funder's website.

WWDP (World Day of Prayer National Committee for England, Wales and Northern Ireland)

 Christian causes

UK and worldwide

£281,500 (2017)

CC number: 233242

Trustees: Margaret Pickford; Elizabeth Burroughs; Kathleen Skinner.

Correspondent: Mary Judd, Commercial Road, Tunbridge Wells TN1 2RR (tel: 01892 541411; email: office@wwdp.org.uk)

www.wwdp.org.uk/grants

The charity's website states that Women's World Day of Prayer is a global, ecumenical movement of informed prayer and prayerful action, organised and led by Christian women who call the faithful together on the first Friday in March each year to observe a common day of prayer and who, in many countries, have a continuing relationship in prayer and service.

The trustees' report for 2017 states that the main object of the charity is to unite Christians in prayer, which it does in a number of ways including by distributing Christian literature and supporting women around the world through prayer and prayerful action. The report states that 'after meeting overhead expenses and maintaining reserves as stated, the National Committee allocates surplus income to assist projects run by Christian charities throughout the world'.

A number of grants are given each September on a one-off basis. Project grants are made to organisations supporting only one project and they should not re-apply within three years. Larger organisations involved with a number of projects or which operate internationally may apply for grants in consecutive years so long as each grant serves a different project and country.

Priority is given to charities based in the UK, which may operate around the globe, and projects in the country that has written the service for the current year (Suriname in 2018).

Financial information

In 2017 the trust held assets of £391,000 and an income of £530,500. During the year, the charity awarded almost £281,500 in grants to organisations.

Beneficiaries included: Bible Society Northern Ireland and Christian Aid East Africa Crisis Appeal (£10,000 each); Traidcraft Exchange (£7,000); Feed the Minds (£5,000); RNIB and The Leprosy Mission (£4,000 each); Morning Star Trust (£3,500); Methodist Church House (£1,000).

Exclusions

No grants are given to individuals.

Applications

Application forms can be obtained from the WWDP office. The closing date for grants each year is 1 August.

Sources of information

Accounts; annual report; Charity Commission record.

Wychdale Ltd

Orthodox Jewish religion, relief of poverty, education, general charitable purposes

England and Wales

£546,500 (2016/17)

CC number: 267447

Trustees: Chaskel Schlaff; Jacob Schlaff; Ziporah Schlaff.

Correspondent: The Trustees, c/o Sugarwhite Meyer Accountants Ltd, 5 Windus Road, London N16 6UT (tel: 020 8880 8910)

The charity was registered with the Charity Commission in 1974. The charity makes grants to organisations in support of the Orthodox Jewish faith, the relief of poverty, education and general charitable purposes.

Financial information

In 2016/17 the charity had assets of almost £1.2 million and an income of £588,500. During the year, the charity gave around £546,500 in grants to organisations. Grants were distributed as follows:

Education	£234,500
General charitable purposes	£212,500
Advancement of religion	£79,000
Relief of poverty	£20,500

Beneficiaries included: ABC Trust (£179,000); United Talmudical Association (£125,000); Yesamach Levav

(£31,000); Kahal Chassidim Bobov (£26,000).

Applications

The 2016/17 annual report states: 'In general the trustees select the institutions to be supported according to their personal knowledge of work of the institution. Whilst not actively inviting applications, they are always prepared to accept any application which will be carefully considered and help given according to circumstances and funds then available.'

Sources of information

Accounts; annual report; Charity Commission record.

The Wyfold Charitable Trust

General charitable purposes

England and Wales

£241,000 (2016/17)

CC number: 1157483

Trustees: Adam Fleming; Roderick Fleming; Nicholas Powell; Angus Fleming.

Correspondent: The Trustees, c/o RF Trustee Co. Ltd, 15 Suffolk Street, London SW1Y 4HG (tel: 020 3696 6721; email: charities@rftrustee.com)

This trust was registered with the Charity Commission in June 2014. It is administered by RF Trustee Co. Ltd, the office of the Fleming family, and three members of the Fleming family act as trustees. The Fleming family has associations with various charities, notably The Fleming-Wyfold Art Foundation (Charity Commission no. 1080197), which is responsible for The Fleming Art Collection, a gallery exhibiting a private collection of Scottish art.

The trust supports general charitable purposes in England and Wales. Grants are only made to registered charities.

Financial information

In 2016/17 the foundation held assets of £10.4 million and had an income of £302,500. Grants to 49 organisations totalled £241,000 and were broken down as follows:

Social welfare	13	£62,000
Health	12	£39,000
Education	5	£35,000
Arts, culture, heritage and science	6	£32,000
Community development	2	£21,000
The environment	3	£16,000
Relief of poverty	2	£10,000
Animal welfare	1	£6,000
Amateur sport	1	£5,000
Armed forces	1	£5,000
Human rights	1	£5,000
Religion	1	£5,000
Other	1	£40

Beneficiaries included: Garden Museum (£20,000); The Fleming-Wyfold Art Foundation (£12,500); Abberley Hall, Restore, Soldiers of Oxfordshire Trust, SOS Children's Villages and TaxPayers' Alliance (£10,000 each).

Grants of less than £10,000 totalled £158,500 during the year.

Applications

Applications should be made in writing on no more than two sides of A4 and sent to the correspondent along with any supporting documentation. The Wyfold Charitable Trust should be referenced in the application.

Only successful applications will be responded to and it may be several months before trustees are able to consider an application. Only one application may be made within a 12-month period.

Sources of information

Accounts; annual report; Charity Commission record.

The Yapp Charitable Trust

Social welfare, education, disability

England and Wales

£199,500 (2016/17)

CC number: 1076803

Trustees: Tim Brooke; Ron Lis; Alfred Hill; Jane Fergusson; Lisa Suchet; Liz Islam.

Correspondent: Joanne Anderson, Administrator and Trust Secretary, First Floor, Mile House, Bridge End, Chester Le Street, County Durham DH3 3RA (tel: 0191 389 3300; email: info@yappcharitabletrust.org.uk)

 www.yappcharitabletrust.org.uk

The Yapp Charitable Trust was formed in 1999 from the Yapp Welfare Trust (two-thirds share) and Yapp Education and Research Trust (one-third share). The trust makes donations to small registered charities in the UK to cover core costs.

Eligibility

To be eligible for funding, the applicant charity must have been registered for at least three years and have an annual expenditure of less than £40,000. The charity must also be undertaking work in one of the following priority areas:

- Older people
- Children and young people aged 5 to 25
- People with physical impairments, learning difficulties or mental health challenges

- Social welfare – people trying to overcome life-limiting problems of a social, rather than medical, origin (such as addiction, relationship difficulties, abuse, offending)
- Education and learning (with a particular interest in people who are educationally disadvantaged, whether adults or children)

Grant-making policy

Priority is given to:

- Work that is unattractive to the general public or unpopular with other funders
- Services that help to improve the lives of marginalised, disadvantaged or isolated people
- Applicants that can demonstrate an effective use of volunteers
- Charities that seek to be preventive and aim to change opinion and behaviour through raising awareness of issues, education and campaigning
- Applicants that can demonstrate (where feasible) an element of self-sustainability by charging subscriptions/fees to service users

Applications that don't address at least two of the above are unlikely to receive a grant.

Grants are only made for core funding, defined by the trust as costs associated with regular services and activities that have been ongoing for at least one year. New projects, extra services, delivery costs, and creating a paid post for volunteer work already underway will not be funded.

Financial information

In 2016/17 the trust had assets of £6.7 million and an income of £236,500. During the year, 189 completed applications were received, of which 143 were eligible. The trust awarded 37 grants totalling £199,500.

Disability	12	£72,500
Young people	7	£42,500
Social welfare	8	£42,500
Education	4	£25,500
Older people	6	£24,000

Beneficiaries included: Refugee and Migrant Network – Sutton and York Women's Counselling Service (£9,000 each); Dorset Reading Partners (£7,500); Muslim Women's Welfare Association (£6,600); Firebird Theatre (£6,000); Remembering the Past, Resourcing the Future (£4,500); House of Play and Education and Moss Allotment Garden Project (£3,000 each); Pregnancy Options Centre (£2,500); Wallsend Sea Cadets (£1,500).

Exclusions

The trust's website states that the trustees cannot fund:

- Charities with a total annual expenditure of more than £40,000

- Charities that are not registered with the Charity Commission; you must have your own charity number or be excepted from registration
- Industrial provident societies
- Community interest companies
- Work that is not based in England or Wales
- Charities with unrestricted reserves that equate to more than 12 months' expenditure
- Branches of national charities
- Newly established organisations (under three years)
- New work that has not been occurring for at least a year
- New paid posts – even if the work is now being done by volunteers
- Additional activities, expansion or development plans
- Special events, trips or outings
- Capital expenditure – including equipment, buildings, renovations, furnishings, minibuses
- Work with children under five
- Childcare
- Holidays and holiday centres
- Core funding of charities that benefit the wider community such as general advice services and community centres unless a significant element of their work focuses on one of our priority groups
- Bereavement support
- Debt advice
- Community safety initiatives
- Charities raising money to give to another organisation, such as schools, hospitals or other voluntary groups
- Individuals, including charities raising funds to purchase equipment for or make grants to individuals

Applications

An application form and further guidelines are available on the trust's website. The trust welcomes initial enquiries by telephone. Applicants should review the eligibility questions available on the website prior to making an application.

Sources of information

Accounts; annual report; Charity Commission record; funder's website.

Yorkshire and Clydesdale Bank Foundation

🔍 Health, education, relief of poverty, citizenship and community development, sport, environment, arts, heritage, culture and science, saving of lives, money advice

📍 Areas of England and Scotland where the bank operates

£ £723,000 (2016/17)

OSCR number: SC039747

Trustees: Douglas Campbell; Lorna Macmillan; Graeme Duncan; David Blair; Debbie Crosbie; Sandra Delamere.

Correspondent: The Trustees, Level 3, 30 St Vincent Place, Glasgow G1 2HL

 secure.cbonline.co.uk/about-clydesdale-bank/community/charitable-donations-about-us

The Yorkshire and Clydesdale Bank Foundation was established in 2008 and is registered with the Office of the Scottish Charity Regulator. It is the corporate charity of the Clydesdale Bank, a commercial bank formed in Glasgow in 1838. The bank itself has a long tradition of providing funds that help make life easier, healthier and better for the communities in which it works.

The foundation's 2016/17 annual report states that it looks to support registered charities, not-for-profit organisations and community and other voluntary organisations under the following categories:

- Prevention and relief of poverty
- Advancement of education
- Advancement of health
- Advancement of citizenship or community development
- Advancement of the arts, heritage, culture or science
- Advancement of public participation in sport
- Promotion of equality and diversity
- Advancement of environmental protection or improvement
- Relief of those in need by reason of age, ill health, disability, financial hardship or disadvantage
- Advancement of animal welfare
- Saving of lives

Spirit of the Community Awards

The foundation also offers grants of up to £5,000 through its Spirit of the Community Awards. In 2018 there were three award categories, details of which have been taken from the award guidelines:

Awards will be considered for projects in one of the following three categories:

Help people have a healthy relationship with money – This category will focus on initiatives that advance financial education including initiatives that promote accessibility to both financial education and financial services.

Help people into employment – This category will focus on initiatives that build on and develop skills in individuals to equip them for the workplace and help them become ready for work.

Help people improve their local environment – This category will focus on projects seeking to protect or improve the environment.

Financial information

In 2016/17 the foundation had assets of £21,000 and an income of £710,500.

Grants awarded to organisations totalled £723,000.

Health	£282,500
Education	£158,500
Relief of poverty	£79,000
Sports	£75,500
Citizenship and community development	£61,500
Environmental protection or improvement	£54,500
Arts, heritage, culture or science	£7,600
Saving of lives	£2,000
Animal welfare	£1,000

Beneficiaries of grants over £5,000 included: Hospice UK (£282,500); Money Advice Trust (£50,000); Business in the Community (£39,000); British Red Cross (£20,000); The Tutor Trust (£10,000); Charities Aid Foundation (£6,000).

Applications

Application forms and guidelines can be found on the foundation's website.

Sources of information

Accounts; annual report; OSCR record; funder's website.

Yorkshire Building Society Charitable Foundation

 General charitable purposes, education and training, health, animal welfare, people with disabilities, children and young people, older people

UK, with a preference for grant-making in the society's branch localities

£ £548,000 (2016)

CC number: 1069082

Trustees: Christopher Parrish; Richard Brown; Vanessa White; Tanya Jackson; Gordon Rogers.

Correspondent: Fiona May, Yorkshire Building Society, Yorkshire House, Yorkshire Drive, Bradford, West Yorkshire BD5 8LJ (tel: 0345 166 9271; email: corporateresponsibility@ybs.co.uk)

 www.ybs.co.uk/your-society/charity/charitable-foundation/apply.html

Registered with the Charity Commission in 1998, the Yorkshire Building Society Charitable Foundation is the channel of giving of Yorkshire Building Society. Its purpose is to support good causes where the society's members and staff live and work, helping to demonstrate the value and support that it provides to local communities throughout the UK.

The foundation's income is acquired from Yorkshire Building Society and Small Change Big Difference, a scheme promoted by Yorkshire Building Society under which members donate the annual pence of interest from their savings or mortgage accounts to the charitable foundation.

Following a full strategic review of the foundation's donations policy in 2016, the foundation redefined the focus of its charitable purposes, as follows:

- The prevention or relief of poverty
- The advancement of health or the saving of lives
- Any other purposes currently recognised as charitable

According to its website, 'the foundation considers applications to fund a specific project and/or items that will have a positive impact to the charity's beneficiaries. Examples of these could be: sensory toys for children with special needs, social activities for the vulnerable/isolated elderly or training of charity employees to deliver programmes to help their beneficiaries.'

Grants generally range in size from £250 up to a maximum of around £2,000.

Financial information

In 2016 the foundation has assets of £104,500 and an income of £455,500. During the year, grants totalling £548,000 were awarded.

Beneficiaries included: Bradford District Community Fund, Community Foundation for Calderdale, Leeds Community Foundation and Two Ridings Community Foundation (£5,000 each); MS Society Bournemouth (£2,500); Facial Palsy UK (£2,300); Hope into Action, Cherry Trees Paws and Claws and Pathways to Independence Ltd (£2,200 each); Ashgate Hospicecare, Cheltenham and Gloucester Hospitals Charity (£2,100 each).

Exclusions

The foundation's website states:

> Applications for general ongoing funding, running costs, contributions towards large funding, research, individual beneficiaries, sponsorship, payment of salaries or expenses are not eligible, nor are the requests for office items/IT equipment for the charity's own use. We are unable to consider requests from charities that only support a specific sector of society based on ethnicity, faith, sexual orientation or political beliefs.

Furthermore, the foundation will only consider donations to UK-registered charities.

Applications

Since the majority of funding available to the foundation is generated by the society's members through the Small Change Big Difference scheme, the foundation has stated that it will only accept recommendations of charities to support from members or employees of the society.

If you are a YBS, CBS or N&P member and would like the foundation to consider supporting a charity, applications can be submitted via the foundation's website.

All applications are reviewed on a quarterly basis by the trustees. Donations are sent directly to successful charities at the end of each quarter (April, July, October and January).

Sources of information

Accounts; annual report; Charity Commission record; funder's website.

Yorkshire Cancer Research

Cancer research

Yorkshire

£ £3 million (2016/17)

CC number: 516898

Trustees: Sandra Dodson; Dr Alan Suggett; Alan Sidebottom; Graham Berville; Catherine Rustomji; Margaret Kitching; Janet Myers; Dr Yvette Oade.

Correspondent: Research Team, 7 Grove Park Court, Harrogate HG1 4DP (tel: 01423 501269; email: research@ycr.org.uk)

 www.ycr.org.uk

Yorkshire Cancer Research is a charity which aims to 'improve cancer outcomes for people in Yorkshire by investing in research-led innovation that will help us all avoid, survive and cope with cancer'. The charity achieves its objectives by working with researchers, the NHS, public health bodies and charities – particularly universities and teaching hospitals.

According to the charity's website, it aims to:

- Become one of the leading authorities on regional cancer-related issues so that people living in Yorkshire are amongst the best-informed in England
- Educate and influence better lifestyle decisions that will improve health, reduce the risk of cancer or support successful recovery from cancer
- Encourage the earliest possible diagnosis and increase uptake rates into national screening programmes, improve services and develop more effective techniques and practices
- Invest in research-led innovation at every stage of the cancer patient journey from first diagnosis through to treatment, clinical trials, palliative and end-of-life care
- Act as a catalyst for change to facilitate the delivery of better cancer services and significant increases in national research funding specifically to improve cancer outcomes in the region

Research grants

Each year the charity opens a targeted funding round, the details of which are posted on the website. Applications are accepted only from organisations in Yorkshire.

Financial information

In 2016/17 the charity held assets of £42.2 million and had an income of £20.9 million. During the year, 68 grants were awarded to eight organisations and totalled £3 million.

Beneficiaries included: Leeds University (£1.5 million in 23 grants); Sheffield University (£296,500 in ten grants); York University (£187,500 in five grants); Leeds NHS (£60,000).

Applications

Refer to the website for information on current funding rounds, as well as deadlines, guidance and application forms.

Sources of information

Accounts; annual report; Charity Commission record; funder's website.

The Yorkshire Dales Millennium Trust

 Environment, conservation, heritage, rural communities

The Yorkshire Dales

£85,000 to organisations (2016/17)

CC number: 1061687

Trustees: Prof. Christine Leigh; Carl Lis; Jane Roberts; Peter Charlesworth; Stephen Macare; Thomas Wheelwright; Andrew Campbell; David Shaw; Karen Cowley; Eileen Spencer; Heather McQue; Tracy Walker; Eloise Brown; Mark Cunliffe-Lister.

Correspondent: Josephine Boulter, Secretary, Main Street, Clapham, Lancaster LA2 8DP (tel: 01524 251002; email: info@ydmt.org)

 www.ydmt.org

 facebook.com/ydmt.news

 @ydmt

The Yorkshire Dales Millennium Trust was established 'to support the environmental, social and economic well-being of the Yorkshire Dales'. It achieves this objective by raising and distributing funds to local projects, managing and distributing grants on behalf of external funder's such as the Heritage Lottery Fund and the Learning and Skills Council, and delivering projects directly.

Grants programmes

The trust manages a wide variety of grant programmes. Here is a small sample of the charity's current programmes:

- **Green Futures:** aims to empower and support young people to become more involved, aware and connected to the natural environment
- **Meadow Links:** aims to restore wildflower rich hay meadows along ecological networks, helping pollinators and other wildlife move across the Yorkshire Dales landscape
- **Stories in Stone:** aims to connect and co-ordinate the plans and actions of a range of public, private and community bodies to conserve, enhance and celebrate the unique historical and natural elements of the Ingleborough Dales' landscape
- **Roger Stott Community Grants:** supports community initiatives that benefit local people in the Yorkshire Dales and nearby areas
- **Woodland Grants:** offers advice and funding for new woodland creation
- **Yorkshire Dales LEADER:** supports innovative rural partnership projects

For a full list of all current programmes, see the trust's website.

Financial information

In 2016/17 the trust had assets of £1.5 million and an income of around £1.8 million. Grants totalled £221,000, with £85,000 given to organisations and £136,500 awarded to individuals.

No list of beneficiaries was available.

Exclusions

Eligibility criteria vary between programmes. See the trust's website for full details.

Applications

Application processes may vary depending on the specific programme applied to. Guidance and application forms for all current grant programmes can be downloaded from the trust's website.

Sources of information

Accounts; annual report; Charity Commission record; funder's website.

The William Allen Young Charitable Trust

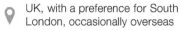 General charitable purposes, health, social welfare, education, human rights, animal welfare, arts and culture, community projects

UK, with a preference for South London, occasionally overseas

£629,000 (2016/17)

CC number: 283102

Trustees: Torquil Sligo-Young; James Young; Caroline Chelton.

Correspondent: Torquil Sligo-Young, Trustee, c/o Young & Co. Brewery plc, Riverside House, 26 Osiers Road, Wandsworth SW18 1NH (tel: 020 8875 7000; email: claire.cooper@youngs.co.uk)

The trust supports humanitarian causes, with a large number of health and social welfare organisations supported each year. Grants are made to local and national organisations throughout the UK, although there appears to be a preference for South London.

Financial information

In 2016/17 the trust had assets of £44.2 million and an income of £586,000. Grants totalling £629,000 were made to 185 organisations and were categorised as follows:

Community	£212,500
Medical	£210,000
Cultural	£70,000
Educational	£60,000
Social welfare	£51,500
Human rights	£20,000
Animal welfare	£5,500

Previous beneficiaries have included: The Greenwich Foundation (£50,000); British Benevolent Fund of Madrid (£42,000); Anti-Slavery International (£20,000); Crisis UK (£10,000); Fly Navy Heritage Trust (£5,000); London Harness Horse Parade (£4,500); Wimbledon BookFest (£3,000); Housing for Women (£2,000); Holy Trinity Church – Clapham (£1,000); Wandsworth Community Transport (£700); Russian Arctic Convoy Museum (£500); Juvenile Diabetes Research Fund (£250).

Applications

The 2016/17 annual report notes: 'The trustees aim to support those organisations they have supported in the past on an ongoing basis although one-off donations are considered.'

Sources of information

Accounts; annual report; Charity Commission record.

Youth Music

Music, children and young people

England

£9.3 million (2016/17)

CC number: 1075032

Trustees: Andy Parfitt; Richard Peel; David Poole; Nicholas Cleobury; Sean Gregory; Clive Grant; Constance Agyeman; Timothy Berg; Rafi Gokay; Rachel Lindley.

Correspondent: Angela Linton, Suites 3–5, Swan Court, 9 Tanner Street,

London SE1 3LE (tel: 020 7902 1060; email: angela.linton@youthmusic.org.uk)

 network.youthmusic.org.uk/i-need-funding

 facebook.com/youthmusicuk

 @youthmusic

Previously known as the National Foundation for Youth Music, the primary object of Youth Music is 'to advance the education of the public (especially young people) in the art and science of music'. Youth Music supports music-making activities, particularly for the country's most disadvantaged children and young people.

Youth Music is funded by Arts Council England with funds from the National Lottery. The charity also raises funds through gifts and donations. In March 2016 the charity launched a four-year strategy 'Towards a Musically Inclusive England' that will run until 2020. The aims are laid out in the 2016/17 annual report, which states that there are five priority groups/areas:

- Early years
- Special educational needs and/or disability
- Not in education, employment or training
- Youth justice
- Cold spots of access to diverse music-making opportunities

Funding schemes

The upper age limit for participants has been extended from 18 to 25. The funding programme is now made up of three separate funds:

- **Fund A:** offers small grants of £2,000 to £30,000 for high-quality music-making projects and involves a simple application process
- **Fund B:** offers medium-sized grants of £30,001 to £200,000 for larger programmes of work
- **Fund C:** offers grants of £50,000 to £180,000 for strategic programmes to help embed sustainable, inclusive music-making across a local area

Financial information

In 2016/17 the charity had assets of £1.3 million and an income of £10.25 million. Grants awarded totalled almost £9.3 million and were given to 179 organisations to support 183 projects. A total of 42% of these organisations had not been supported by the charity before and the annual report states that this is in line with the strategy to continue to diversify the range and type of organisations that the charity supports.

A list of beneficiaries was not available.

Exclusions

The charity does not support:

- Individuals and sole traders
- Profit-making projects
- Activities that promote party-political or religious beliefs
- Activities that have taken place before you have received confirmation of grant award
- Costs incurred in making your application
- Significant capital costs (over 10%)
- The purchase of land or buildings
- Reserves, loans or interest payments
- VAT costs that can be recovered
- Art forms not related to music
- Activities that other statutory bodies would be expected to fund
- Projects unable to evidence that they will achieve the minimum match funding requirement
- Projects using Arts Council or National Lottery funding as their minimum match funding requirement

Applications

The three funds from which grants are awarded each differ in their funding criteria and application process. Potential applicants are advised to refer to the Youth Music Network website for up-to-date criteria, priorities, guidelines and deadlines. Applications are made online, via the Youth Music Network website.

Sources of information

Accounts; annual report; Charity Commission record; funder's website.

Elizabeth and Prince Zaiger Trust

Older people, disability, the education of children and young people, the care and protection of animals, general charitable purposes

UK, with some preference for Somerset, Dorset and the South West

£699,000 to organisations (2016/17)

CC number: 282096

Trustees: John Davidge; Peter Harvey; Derek Long; Edward Parry; Dr Robin Keyte.

Correspondent: Peter Harvey, Trustee, Gatesmoor, Hawkridge, Spaxton, Bridgwater TA5 1AL (tel: 01278 671353)

As well as supporting general charitable causes, the trust has the following objects:

- The relief of older people
- The relief of people who have mental and physical disabilities
- The advancement of education of children and young people
- The provision of care and protection for animals

Grants are made to organisations in the UK, although our research suggests that there is some preference for those based in Somerset, Dorset and the South West.

Financial information

In 2016/17 the trust held assets of £19.2 million and had an income of £669,500. Grants awarded to organisations totalled £699,000 with a further £6,000 awarded to individuals.

Beneficiaries included: Salisbury District Hospital Charitable Fund (£50,000); Variety – the Children's Charity (£25,000); Teenage Cancer Trust (£14,000); Dorset and Somerset Air Ambulance Charity (£12,000); St Giles Trust (£11,000); Somerset Sight (£9,000); Go Kids Go (£8,000); Leeds Women's Aid (£4,000); Ferne Animal Sanctuary (£3,000); Yeovil Great Lyde Scout Group (£1,000).

Applications

The trust makes the following statement on its Charity Commission record: 'Please note – this trust does not respond to unsolicited applications for funds. Please don't apply – it wastes your time and money.'

Sources of information

Accounts; annual report; Charity Commission record.

The Marjorie and Arnold Ziff Charitable Foundation

General charitable purposes, education, Jewish causes, arts, young people, older people, medicine, social welfare

UK, with a preference for Yorkshire, especially Leeds and Harrogate

£559,500 (2016/17)

CC number: 249368

Trustees: Dr Marjorie Ziff; Michael Ziff; Edward Ziff; Ann Manning.

Correspondent: Debra Evans, Town Centre House, The Merrion Centre, Leeds LS2 8LY (tel: 0113 222 1234)

The trust was established in 1966 to support causes that will provide good value for the money donated by benefitting a large number of people, as well as encouraging others to make contributions to the work. This includes a wide variety of schemes that involve the community at many levels, including education, public places, the arts, and helping people who are disadvantaged.

Capital costs and building work are particularly favoured by the trustees, as they feel projects such as these are not given the support they deserve from statutory sources.

Financial information

In 2016/17 the foundation had both assets and an income of £10.7 million. During the year, the foundation gave a total of 78 grants to organisations totalling £559,500.

Beneficiaries included: Tropical World (£100,000); Leeds Jewish Welfare Board (£51,000); Maccabi GB (£45,500); Chabad Lubavitch Leeds (£30,000); Western Marble Arch Synagogue (£12,200); Shabbat UK (£10,000); Waldenström's Macroglobulinemia UK (£5,000); UK Association of Wellbeing of Israel's Soldiers (£500).

Exclusions

No grants are given to individuals.

Applications

Apply in writing to the correspondent. The trust has previously stated that funds available are limited and requests not previously supported are unlikely to be successful. Initial telephone calls are welcome but applicants should note the foregoing comments. Replies will only be given to a request accompanied by an sae.

Sources of information

Accounts; annual report; Charity Commission record.

The Zochonis Charitable Trust

General charitable purposes, education of young people, social welfare

UK, particularly Greater Manchester, and overseas, particularly Africa

£4.2 million (2016/17)

CC number: 274769

Trustees: Christopher Green; Archibald Calder; Paul Milner.

Correspondent: Marie Gallagher, Manchester Business Park, 3500 Aviator Way, Manchester M22 5TG (tel: 0161 435 1005; email: enquiries@ zochonischaritabletrust.com)

Registered in 1978, the trust was established by the late Sir John Zochonis, former head of P. Z. Cussons plc, the soap and toiletries manufacturer, with shares in the company. It has general charitable objectives but tends to favour local charities with a particular emphasis on education and the welfare of children.

Financial information

In 2016/17 the trust held assets of £181.7 million and had an income of over £4.9 million. Grants were made to 171 organisations totalling over £4.2 million and were broken down as follows:

Education	£1.36 million
Health	£744,500
Other	£500,000
Overseas	£444,000
Children and young people	£360,500
Social provision	£310,500
Homeless	£135,000
Community	£125,000
Emergency – East Africa famine and Nepal earthquake	£100,000
Armed forces	£46,500
Family	£45,500
Older people	£35,000
Rescue services	£30,000

A list of beneficiaries was not available.

Previous beneficiaries have included: British Red Cross; Cancer Research UK; Manchester High School for Girls; National Talking Newspapers and Magazines; University of Manchester.

Exclusions

There are no grants awarded to individuals.

Applications

Apply in writing to the correspondent.

Sources of information

Accounts; annual report; Charity Commission record.

Zurich Community Trust (UK) Ltd

Social welfare, community and economic development, helping disadvantaged people move from dependence to independence

UK and overseas, with priority given to locations where the company has offices

£1.8 million (2016)

CC number: 266983

Trustees: Tim Culling; Vinicio Cellerini; Jonathon Plumtree; Ian Lovett; Miranda Chalk; Dr Subo Shanmuganathan; Wayne Myslik; Georgina Farrell; Anne Torry; Andrew Jepp; Conor Brennan.

Correspondent: Pam Webb, Head of Zurich Community Trust (UK) Ltd, PO Box 1288, Swindon SN1 1FL (tel: 01793 502450; email: zct@zct.org.uk or pam.webb@zct.org.uk)

www.zct.org.uk

Registered with the Charity Commission in 1974, the Zurich Community Trust (UK) Ltd is the corporate charity of Zurich Financial Services (UKISA) Ltd, a holding company and part of the Zurich Financial Services Group, which comprises the group's operations in the UK, Ireland and South Africa and provides insurance services.

The charity's main purpose is helping disadvantaged people to move from dependence to independence by giving time, money and skills donated by Zurich and Openwork and its employees. It focuses on issues that are often overlooked and where the charity can have the biggest impact.

Grant programmes

According to the 2016 accounts, the trust fulfils its objectives through:

Long-term transformation programmes

Long-term transformation programmes focusing on particular areas of social need are delivered over a minimum of five years. During 2016 this included: making core funding grants to southern Indian NGOs to build their capacity; supporting isolated older people by providing core funding to Age UK and providing Zurich volunteers for a telephone befriending service; funding Addaction family workers who address parental substance misuse; developing The Children and Young People's Mental Health Coalition in partnership with the Mental Health Foundation; and providing young people who are not in education and training with employment opportunities through an apprenticeship scheme.

In 2016 grants were made totalling £416,000 under this programme.

Zurich cares programme

In 2016 charity partnerships through the Zurich Cares programme were with CLIC Sargent, Alzheimer's Society and Mind. Zurich employees are involved in the selection of these partnerships and also volunteer and donate. Donations are matched from the Zurich UK businesses. During 2016, around £1 million was committed through partnerships and an extensive grant programme.

The Openwork Foundation

The objective of the Openwork Foundation is to help disadvantaged children under a theme of Cares 4 Kids through charity partnerships and grant programmes. In 2016 the foundation focused on supporting the national charity partner, the Carers Trust, in supporting a project to identify hidden young carers, provide respite for existing young carers, and prevent bullying of young carers. Other children's charities are supported through a regional grant programme, through sponsored application.

The trust's accounts for 2016 state: 'There is also a small discretionary grant programme supporting disadvantage people, where advisors and employees of Openwork can recommend charities for support.'

In 2016, £353,000 was donated for this programme, 61% of which went on regional grants, 9% to national partners, and 1% on the discretionary grants programme.

ZURICH COMMUNITY TRUST (UK) LTD

Grant programme	Sub-category	Amount
Zurich cares		
	Local grants	£609,000
	Employee-nominated grants	£227,000
	National partners	£150,000
	Overseas grants	£74,000
	Local partners	-
Transformation and trust		
	Breaking the Cycle (Addaction)	£133,000
	India programme	£64,000
	Young People's Mental Health	£63,000
	Call in Time (Age UK)	£24,000
	Generation Gains Programme	£5,000
Openwork Foundation		
	Regional grants	£302,000
	National partnerships	£47,000
	Discretionary grants	£4,000

The trust's website has further information on the following grant programmes open to applications.

Local grant programmes

Zurich Community Trust (UK) Ltd gives to local community organisations that are located close to where the company operates. Local budgets are delegated to staff committees which award grants, usually in the range of £100 to £5,000, depending on location. The following locations are eligible:

- Birmingham (within a 25-mile radius of the Zurich office) – grants of £250 to £1,000 are available
- Farenham (within a 25-mile radius of the Zurich office) – grants of up to £3,000 are available
- Farnborough (within 25 miles of the Zurich office) – grants of up to £2,000 are available
- Gloucestershire (within a 25-mile radius of the office in Bishops Cleeve, near Cheltenham in Gloucestershire) – grants in the region of £1,500 to £3,000 are available
- Glasgow (within a 25-mile radius of Glasgow) – grants of up to £30,000 are available
- Leeds (within a 25-mile radius of Leeds) – grants of up to £1,000 are available
- Swindon (within a 25-mile radius of Swindon) – grants in the range of £1,000 to £4,000 are available

The trust's website states: 'We do have smaller local grant budgets around our office locations in Brighton, Bristol, Cardiff, Croydon, London and Manchester, and following a review of our grant programme in these locations, we will no longer have an open application process in the way that we have had before.'

On a national level, the trust has also committed funding to national partners Dementia UK and Place2Be.

Overseas grant programme

The trust considers applications for overseas projects provided there is a UK partner organisation to administer the grant. The trust's annual overseas budget is £75,000 and in 2016 it made grants to 16 charities. The social issues were wide ranging and included: safe water in Zambia; cataract operations in Bihar, India; training Bangladeshi women through a livelihood project; and delivering treatment and training on infant club foot in Delhi India.

Financial information

In 2016 the trust had assets of £5.2 million and an income of £4 million, of which £2.5 million was a donation from Zurich UK businesses. There were grants made totalling £1.8 million that were broken down into the categories shown in the table above.

Beneficiaries of major grants only included: Addacion (£133,000); Saints Foundation (£103,000); Mental Heath Foundation (£63,000); Mind (£57,000); Carer's Trust (£47,000); Purple Community Fund (£36,000).

Exclusions

No grants are made to/for:

- Individuals
- Medical research
- Statutory organisations, including mainstream schools and hospitals, unless exclusively for a special needs group
- Animal welfare
- Conservation or environmental projects, unless involving disadvantaged people
- Political or military organisations
- Religious organisations
- Sports clubs, village halls, playgroups and mother-and-toddler groups, unless for a special needs group
- Scouts, girl guides, cadets and other similar organisations, unless

specifically supporting disadvantaged children
- Fundraising events including appeals or events for national charities
- Advertising or sponsorship connected with charitable activities

For overseas projects the trust will not fund: disaster relief or emergency work; proposals which show any racial, political or religious bias; individuals; expeditions or study exchanges; medical research; or fundraising events or appeals.

Applications

Applicants must firstly visit the trust's website and follow the links to check eligibility and download the guidelines and application forms. The website provides detailed contact information and deadlines for each of the local communities programmes.

If applying for an overseas grant, note that the trustees hold a series of meetings from May to September each year. The deadline date for applications is usually in March; check the trust's website for further details.

Sources of information

Accounts; annual report; Charity Commission record; funder's website.

Community foundations

This section of the guide includes the details of the 46 UK community foundations, which distribute funding for a wide range of purposes.

Potential applicants are advised to visit their local community foundation's website or contact its grants team to find the most suitable funding stream.

Name	Website	Phone	Email
Bedfordshire and Luton Community Foundation	www.blcf.org.uk	01234 834930	Contact form on website
Berkshire Community Foundation	www.berkshirecf.org	0118 930 3021	info@berkshirecf.org
Buckinghamshire Community Foundation	www.heartofbucks.org	01296 330134	info@heartofbucks.org
Cambridgeshire Community Foundation	www.cambscf.org.uk/home.html	01223 410535	info@cambscf.org.uk
Cheshire Community Foundation	www.cheshirecommunityfoundation.org.uk	01606 330607	office@cheshirecommunity foundation.org.uk
Community Foundation for Calderdale	www.cffc.co.uk	01422 349700	grants@cffc.co.uk
Community Foundation for Northern Ireland	www.communityfoundationni.org	028 9024 5927	Contact form on website
Community Foundation for Staffordshire	www.staffsfoundation.org.uk	01785 339540	office@staffsfoundation.org.uk
Community Foundation for Surrey	www.cfsurrey.org.uk	01483 478092	info@cfsurrey.org.uk
Community Foundation for Wakefield District	www.wakefieldcf.org.uk	01924 239181	info@wakefieldcf.org.uk
Community Foundation for Wiltshire and Swindon	www.wiltshirecf.org.uk	01380 729284	Contact form on website
Community Foundation in Wales	www.cfiw.org.uk/eng/home	02920 379580	grants@cfiw.org.uk
Community Foundation Tyne & Wear and Northumberland	www.communityfoundation.org.uk	0191 222 0945	general@communityfoundation.org.uk

Name	Website	Phone	Email
Community Foundations for Lancashire and Merseyside	www.cfmerseyside.org.uk	0330 440 4900	info@cflm.email
Cornwall Community Foundation	www.cornwallcommunity foundation.com	01566 779333	office@cornwallfoundation.com
County Durham Community Foundation	www.cdcf.org.uk	0191 378 6340	info@cdcf.org.uk
Cumbria Community Foundation	www.cumbriafoundation.org	01900 825760	enquiries@cumbriafoundation.org
Devon Community Foundation	www.devoncf.com	01884 235887	grants@devoncf.com
Dorset Community Foundation	www.dorsetcommunityfoundation.org	01202 670815	admin@dorsetcf.org
East End Community Foundation	www.eastendcf.org	020 7345 4444	info@eastendcf.org
Essex Community Foundation	www.essexcommunity foundation.org.uk	01245 356018	grants@essexcf.org.uk
Foundation Derbyshire	www.foundationderbyshire.org	01773 525860	hello@foundationderbyshire.org
Foundation Scotland	www.foundation scotland.org.uk	0131 524 0300 (Edinburgh office) 0141 341 4960 (Glasgow office) 01557 814927 (South of Scotland office)	edinburgh@foundationscotland.org.uk (Edinburgh office) grants@foundationscotland.org.uk (Glasgow office) office@foundationscotland.org.uk (South of Scotland office)
Gloucestershire Community Foundation	www.gloucestershirecf.org.uk	01242 851357	info@gloucestershirecf.org.uk
Hampshire and the Isle of Wight Community Foundation	www.hiwcf.com	01256 776101	online@hiwcf.com
Heart of England Community Foundation (serves Coventry, Warwickshire, Solihull, Birmingham and the Black Country)	www.heartofenglandcf.co.uk	02476 883297	info@heartofenglandcf.co.uk
Herefordshire Community Foundation	www.herefordshirecf.org	01432 272550	administrator@herefordshirecf.org
Hertfordshire Community Foundation	www.hertscf.org.uk	01707 251351	office@hertscf.org.uk
Kent Community Foundation	www.kentcf.org.uk	01303 814500	admin@kentcf.org.uk
Leeds Community Foundation (also serves Bradford)	www.leedscf.org.uk	0113 242 2426	info@leedscf.org.uk
Leicestershire and Rutland Community Foundation	www.llrcommunityfoundation.org.uk	0116 262 4916	grants@llrcommunity foundation.org.uk
Lincolnshire Community Foundation	www.lincolnshirecf.co.uk	01529 305825	lincolnshirecf@btconnect.com
London Community Foundation	www.londoncf.org.uk	020 7582 5117	info@londoncf.org.uk
Milton Keynes Community Foundation	www.mkcommunityfoundation.co.uk	01908 690276	info@mkcommunityfoundation.co.uk
Norfolk Community Foundation	www.norfolkfoundation.com	01603 623958	grants@norfolkfoundation.com
Northamptonshire Community Foundation	www.ncf.uk.com	01604 230033	enquiries@ncf.uk.com

Name	Website	Phone	Email
Nottinghamshire Community Foundation	www.nottscf.org.uk	01623 620202	enquiries@nottscf.org.uk
One Community Foundation (serves Kirklees)	www.one-community.org.uk	01484 468397	info@one-community.org.uk
Oxfordshire Community Foundation	www.oxfordshire.org	01865 798666	ocf@oxfordshire.org
Quartet Community Foundation (serves Bristol, Bath and North East Somerset, North Somerset and South Gloucestershire)	www.quartetcf.org.uk	0117 989 7700	applications@quartetcf.org.uk
Somerset Community Foundation	www.somersetcf.org.uk	01749 344949	info@somersetcf.org.uk
South Yorkshire's Community Foundation	www.sycf.org.uk	0114 242 4294	grants@sycf.org.uk
Suffolk Community Foundation	www.suffolkcf.org.uk	01473 602602	info@suffolkcf.org.uk
Sussex Community Foundation	www.sussexgiving.org.uk	01273 409440	grants@sussexgiving.org.uk
Two Ridings Community Foundation (serves York, Hull, East Yorkshire and North Yorkshire)	www.trcf.org.uk	01904 435 277	grants@trcf.org.uk
Worcestershire Community Foundation	www.worcscf.org.uk	01684 312752	wcf@comfirst.org.uk

Glossary of terms

This glossary has been written to clarify some of the terms you may come across when using this guide.

Assets

Money, goods and property owned or controlled by an organisation, including any legal rights it may have to receive money, goods, services and property from others.

Capacity building

Grants, loans, pro bono services or in-kind support to increase an established organisation's ability to deliver services.

Capital costs

The costs of tangible items (such as building/refurbishment costs or the costs of purchasing equipment or vehicles).

Capital appeals

A capital appeal or campaign is a co-ordinated organisational fundraising initiative with a defined timetable and goals which has the aim of increasing an organisation's assets.

Charitable objects

Charitable objects describe and identify the legal purpose for which a charity has been set up.

Core costs

The costs of keeping an organisation going, not directly connected to any particular project (such as administration, management, research and development, audit, head office costs, IT and finance costs, or insurance). Sometimes called 'running' or 'central' costs.

Development funding

Grants, loans or in-kind support to extend or improve an established project or service.

Direct costs

Direct costs are costs directly related to an activity (such as the salaries of the staff who work on a specific project, their expenses, or the hire of the venue for a particular event).

Indirect costs

Indirect costs are costs not directly related to an activity but still incurred by the organisation, without which the activity would not happen (in other words, the costs of managing and administering an activity).

In-kind support

Also referred to as gifts in kind, this is the provision of goods or services given to an organisation (such as office equipment, computers, software, pro bono work or administrative support).

Match funding

Funding that depends on an organisation raising a proportion of the total funding it needs from other sources.

Permanent endowment

Assets to be held by a charity forever, which are often used to generate income for the charity (as in the case of permanently endowed investments).

Project funding

A project is an activity or a service which is separate from the organisation's primary work. Project funding covers the costs of specific projects but not the 'core costs' of the organisation.

Seed funding/start-up funding

Seed funding assists with the start-up costs of an organisation or an organisation's new project.

SORP (Statement of Recommended Practice)

Sets out standards for accounting by charities, including what information should be included in annual accounts. It applies to almost all charitable organisations in England and Wales, Scotland and Northern Ireland. The only exceptions are charities that have their own SORP (for example, the SORP for Registered Social Landlords).

Strategic funding

Grants or loans to deliver an established organisation's strategy.

Statutory funding

Funding for activities which are the legal responsibility of the government or local authority (such as teachers' salaries).

Support costs

Additional costs incurred in the process of making a grant. DSC does not include support costs in the grant totals quoted in its funding guides.

Unsolicited applications

These are applications that have not been invited by the funder.

Unrestricted funding

Funding that can be used for any purpose to advance the objects of a charity or to support its administration or management.

Subject index

The following subject index begins with a list of categories used. The categories are very wide-ranging, in order to keep the index as simple as possible. DSC's subscription website (www.trustfunding.org.uk) has a much more detailed search facility for the categories. There may be considerable overlap between the categories – for example, children and education, or older people and social welfare.

The list of categories is followed by the index itself. Before using the index, please note the following.

How the index was compiled

1) The index aims to reflect the most recent grant-making practice. It is therefore based on our interpretation of what each funder has given to, rather than what its policy statement says or what its charitable objects allow it to do in principle. For example, where a grant-maker states that it has general charitable purposes, but its grants list shows a strong preference for social welfare, we index it under social welfare.

2) The index has been compiled from the latest information available to us.

Limitations

1) Policies may change – some more frequently than others.

2) Sometimes there will be a geographical restriction on a funder's grant-giving which is not shown in this index, or the grant-maker may not give for the specific purposes you require under that heading. It is important to read each entry carefully.

You will need to check whether:

(a) The grant-maker gives in your geographical area of operation

(b) The funder gives for the specific purposes you require

(c) There is no other reason to prevent you from making an application to this grant-maker

Under no circumstances should the index be used as a simple mailing list. Remember – each funder is different. Often the policies or interests of a particular grant-maker do not fit easily into the given categories. Each entry must be read individually before you make an application. Indiscriminate applications are usually unsuccessful. They waste time and money, as well as greatly annoying the funders.

The categories are as follows.

Arts, culture, sport and recreation *page 490*

A very diverse category including: performing, written and visual arts; crafts; theatres; museums and galleries; heritage; architecture; archaeology; and sports and recreation. As this is such a varied category, we have also included sections with more specific sub-headings.

Arts and culture page 490

Heritage and the built environment page 492

Humanities page 493

Media and communications page 493

Recreation and sport page 493

Children and young people *page 493*

Mainly for welfare and welfare-related activities.

Development, housing and employment *page 496*

Disability *page 498*

Disadvantaged people *page 500*

This includes people who are:

- Socially excluded
- Socially and economically disadvantaged
- Unemployed
- Homeless
- Offenders
- Educationally disadvantaged
- Victims of social/natural occurrences (including refugees and asylum seekers)

Education and training *page 502*

Environment and animals *page 505*

This includes:

- Agriculture and fishing
- Conservation
- Animal care
- Environment and education
- Transport
- Sustainable environment

As this is such a broad category, we have also included separate sections with sub-headings for 'Animals' and 'Environment'.

Animals page 506

Environment page 506

General charitable purposes
page 507

This is a very broad category and includes grant-makers that often have numerous specific strands to their programmes, as well as those that will consider any application (subject to other eligibility criteria).

Health *page 510*

Medical research *page 512*

Older people *page 514*

Overseas aid *page 515*

Religion *page 516*

Christianity *page 516*

Inter-faith activities *page 517*

Islam *page 517*

Judaism *page 517*

Religious understanding *page 518*

Rights, law and conflict
page 518

This includes:

▷ Citizen participation
▷ Conflict resolution
▷ Legal and advice services
▷ Rights
▷ Equity and justice

Science and technology
page 519

Social sciences, policy and research *page 519*

Social welfare *page 519*

This is another very broad category, and includes:

▷ Community care and services
▷ Counselling and advice
▷ Social preventative schemes
▷ Community centres and activities

Voluntary sector management and development *page 523*

Women *page 523*

Arts, culture, sport and recreation

The 29th May 1961 Charitable Trust
Barnes Workhouse Fund
The Borrows Charitable Trust
The Brelms Trust CIO
Chapman Charitable Trust
Clark Foundation
The John Coates Charitable Trust
The Enkalon Foundation
Doris Field Charitable Trust
Donald Forrester Trust
The Golden Bottle Trust
GrantScape
The Kenneth and Susan Green Charitable Foundation
Greenham Trust Ltd
William Harding's Charity
Edward Harvist Trust (The Harvist Estate)
The Charlotte Heber-Percy Charitable Trust
The Hillingdon Community Trust
The Hobson Charity Ltd
P H Holt Foundation
The Isle of Anglesey Charitable Trust
Joseph Levy Foundation
The Kensington and Chelsea Foundation
The Sir James Knott Trust
The David Laing Foundation
Duchy of Lancaster Benevolent Fund
The Lennox Hannay Charitable Trust
John Lewis Partnership General Community Fund
The Lynn Foundation
The Mactaggart Third Fund
The W M Mann Foundation
The Manoukian Charitable Foundation
The Millichope Foundation
The Alexander Moncur Trust
Moondance Foundation
The George A. Moore Foundation
Near Neighbours
P F Charitable Trust
The Rothschild Foundation
The Roughley Charitable Trust
The Saintbury Trust
The M J Samuel Charitable Trust
The ScottishPower Foundation
Sutton Coldfield Charitable Trust
The Tompkins Foundation

The Constance Travis Charitable Trust
The Barbara Ward Children's Foundation
The Weir Charitable Trust
The Garfield Weston Foundation
The Maurice Wohl Charitable Foundation
Yorkshire and Clydesdale Bank Foundation

Arts and culture

AKO Foundation
The Aldama Foundation
D C R Allen Charitable Trust
The AMW Charitable Trust
The Anson Charitable Trust
The John Armitage Charitable Trust
Arts Council England
Arts Council of Northern Ireland
Arts Council of Wales (also known as Cyngor Celfyddydau Cymru)
The Ashden Trust
The Ashley Family Foundation
Backstage Trust
The Rachel Baker Memorial Charity
The Ballinger Charitable Trust
The Band Trust
The Barbour Foundation
The Baring Foundation
Barnwood Trust
BC Partners Foundation
The Beaverbrook Foundation
The John Beckwith Charitable Trust
The Big Lottery Fund
The Michael Bishop Foundation
The Sir Victor Blank Charitable Settlement
The Boltini Trust
The Bowland Charitable Trust
The Liz and Terry Bramall Foundation
The Bransford Trust
The Britford Bridge Trust
British Record Industry Trust (BRIT Trust)
The Rory and Elizabeth Brooks Foundation
The Edward Cadbury Charitable Trust
The William Adlington Cadbury Charitable Trust
David William Traill Cargill Fund
The Carpenters' Company Charitable Trust
The Castansa Trust
The Thomas Sivewright Catto Charitable Settlement
The Cayo Foundation
The Chalk Cliff Trust
CHK Charities Ltd

The Clore Duffield Foundation
Denise Coates Foundation
The John S Cohen Foundation
The R and S Cohen Foundation
Colwinston Charitable Trust
The Ernest Cook Trust
The Catherine Cookson Charitable
    Trust
The Sir Tom Cowie Charitable
    Trust
Creative Scotland
Cruden Foundation Ltd
The D'Oyly Carte Charitable Trust
The Daiwa Anglo-Japanese
    Foundation
The Davidson Family Charitable
    Trust
The Gwendoline and Margaret
    Davies Charity
The Davis Foundation
Peter De Haan Charitable Trust
The Roger De Haan Charitable
    Trust
The De Laszlo Foundation
The Djanogly Foundation
The Dorfman Foundation
Drapers' Charitable Fund
Dunard Fund 2016
The Charles Dunstone Charitable
    Trust
The Dyers' Company Charitable
    Trust
The Earley Charity
John Ellerman Foundation
The Emerald Foundation
The Englefield Charitable Trust
The Eranda Rothschild Foundation
Esmée Fairbairn Foundation
The Lord Faringdon Charitable
    Trust
The Thomas Farr Charity
The Fidelity UK Foundation
The Sir John Fisher Foundation
Fishmongers' Company's Charitable
    Trust
The Fort Foundation
The Foyle Foundation
The Elizabeth Frankland Moore and
    Star Foundation
The Hugh Fraser Foundation
The Gatsby Charitable Foundation
Gatwick Airport Community Trust
The Robert Gavron Charitable
    Trust
Sir Robert Geffery's Almshouse
    Trust
The GC Gibson Charitable Trust
The Simon Gibson Charitable Trust
The Glass-House Trust
Goldman Sachs Gives (UK)
The Goldsmiths' Company Charity
The Granada Foundation

The Great Britain Sasakawa
    Foundation
The Grimmitt Trust
The Grocers' Charity
Calouste Gulbenkian Foundation –
    UK Branch
The Hadfield Charitable Trust
The Hadrian Trust
Paul Hamlyn Foundation
The Helen Hamlyn Trust
Hampton Fuel Allotment
The W A Handley Charity Trust
The Harbour Foundation
The David and Claudia Harding
    Foundation
The Charles Hayward Foundation
The Headley Trust
The Heathside Charitable Trust
Heritage Lottery Fund
The Lady Hind Trust
The Hintze Family Charity
    Foundation
The Henry C. Hoare Charitable
    Trust
The Holywood Trust
Horne Foundation
Huntingdon Freemen's Trust
The Ireland Fund of Great Britain
The Jerwood Charitable Foundation
The Neil Kreitman Foundation
Christopher Laing Foundation
The Martin Laing Foundation
The Lake House Charity
The Allen Lane Foundation
The Lauffer Family Charitable
    Foundation
The Law Family Charitable
    Foundation
The Edgar E Lawley Foundation
The Raymond and Blanche Lawson
    Charitable Trust
The Leathersellers' Company
    Charitable Fund
The Leche Trust
The Leverhulme Trust
Lord Leverhulme's Charitable Trust
The Linbury Trust
The Enid Linder Foundation
The Charles Littlewood Hill Trust
The Andrew Lloyd Webber
    Foundation
The Lockwood Charitable
    Foundation
John Lyon's Charity
Sylvanus Lysons Charity
The Mackintosh Foundation
The Ian Mactaggart Trust (The
    Mactaggart Second Fund)
The Marsh Christian Trust
Sir George Martin Trust
The Nancie Massey Charitable
    Trust

The Master Charitable Trust
The Brian Mercer Charitable Trust
The Mercers' Charitable
    Foundation
The Merchants' House of Glasgow
Millennium Stadium Charitable
    Trust (Ymddiriedelaeth Elusennol
    Stadiwm Y Mileniwm)
The Laurence Misener Charitable
    Trust
The Brian Mitchell Charitable
    Settlement
The Monument Trust
The Henry Moore Foundation
The Miles Morland Foundation
The John R. Murray Charitable
    Trust
National Art Collections Fund
Nesta
Network for Social Change
    Charitable Trust
The Nisbet Trust
Normanby Charitable Trust
The Oakdale Trust
Odin Charitable Trust
The Ofenheim Charitable Trust
Oglesby Charitable Trust
Old Possum's Practical Trust
The Doris Pacey Charitable
    Foundation
The James Pantyfedwen Foundation
Parabola Foundation
The David Pearlman Charitable
    Foundation
The Pebble Trust
The Performing Right Society
    Foundation
The Pilgrim Trust
The Austin and Hope Pilkington
    Trust
The Polonsky Foundation
David and Elaine Potter
    Foundation
Mr and Mrs J A Pye's Charitable
    Settlement
The Radcliffe Trust
The Rayne Foundation
The Revere Charitable Trust
Rhondda Cynon Taff Welsh Church
    Acts Fund
The Clive and Sylvia Richards
    Charity Ltd
The Roddick Foundation
The Gerald Ronson Family
    Foundation
The David Ross Foundation
The Rothermere Foundation
Rothschild Foundation (Hanadiv)
    Europe
The Rowlands Trust
Royal Docks Trust (London)

The Ruddock Foundation for the Arts
The RVW Trust
The Sackler Trust
The Alan and Babette Sainsbury Charitable Fund
The Basil Samuel Charitable Trust
Schroder Charity Trust
The Frieda Scott Charitable Trust
The Finnis Scott Foundation
The Segelman Trust
The Shears Foundation
The Sheepdrove Trust
The Sylvia and Colin Shepherd Charitable Trust
The Archie Sherman Charitable Trust
The Shetland Charitable Trust
The Sino-British Fellowship Trust
The Martin Smith Foundation
Spielman Charitable Trust
The Steel Charitable Trust
Stevenson Family's Charitable Trust
Mark Stolkin Foundation
The Summerfield Charitable Trust
The John Swire 1989 Charitable Trust
C B And H H Taylor 1984 Trust
Humphrey Richardson Taylor Charitable Trust
The Taylor Family Foundation
Khoo Teck Puat UK Foundation
The Tedworth Charitable Trust
Theatres Trust
The Tolkien Trust
The Trusthouse Charitable Foundation
The Roger and Douglas Turner Charitable Trust
The Turtleton Charitable Trust
Ulster Garden Villages Ltd
The Underwood Trust
The Vandervell Foundation
The Vardy Foundation
Variety, the Children's Charity
Sylvia Waddilove Foundation UK
The Bruce Wake Charitable Trust
The William Wates Memorial Trust
The Geoffrey Watling Charity
The Weavers' Company Benevolent Fund
The Weinstock Fund
The Welton Foundation
Westway Trust
The Harold Hyam Wingate Foundation
The Wolfson Family Charitable Trust
The Wolfson Foundation
The Woodward Charitable Trust
The Worwin UK Foundation
The Yapp Charitable Trust

The William Allen Young Charitable Trust
Youth Music
The Marjorie and Arnold Ziff Charitable Foundation

Heritage and the built environment

Allchurches Trust Ltd
The Architectural Heritage Fund
The Baird Trust
The Barbour Foundation
The Barclay Foundation
The Beaverbrook Foundation
The Michael Bishop Foundation
G & K Boyes Charitable Trust
David William Traill Cargill Fund
The Clore Duffield Foundation
The John S Cohen Foundation
Community First
Congregational and General Charitable Trust
The Ernest Cook Trust
Country Houses Foundation
The Sir Tom Cowie Charitable Trust
Cruden Foundation Ltd
The D'Oyly Carte Charitable Trust
The Roger De Haan Charitable Trust
Drapers' Charitable Fund
The Dulverton Trust
Dunard Fund 2016
The Charles Dunstone Charitable Trust
The Gerald Palmer Eling Trust Company
The Englefield Charitable Trust
The February Foundation
The Fidelity UK Foundation
Fisherbeck Charitable Trust
Fishmongers' Company's Charitable Trust
The Simon Gibson Charitable Trust
The Glass-House Trust
The Goldsmiths' Company Charity
The Gosling Foundation Ltd
The Grocers' Charity
The Helen Hamlyn Trust
The W A Handley Charity Trust
The Charles Hayward Foundation
The Headley Trust
Heritage Lottery Fund
The Henry C. Hoare Charitable Trust
The Ireland Fund of Great Britain
The Ironmongers' Company
The Jerusalem Trust
The Jordan Charitable Foundation
The Kirby Laing Foundation
The Lake House Charity

The Raymond and Blanche Lawson Charitable Trust
The Leathersellers' Company Charitable Fund
The Leche Trust
The Linbury Trust
The Charles Littlewood Hill Trust
The Andrew Lloyd Webber Foundation
The Lockwood Charitable Foundation
The Marsh Christian Trust
Charity of John Marshall
Sir George Martin Trust
The Master Charitable Trust
The Mercers' Charitable Foundation
The Monument Trust
The Alexander Mosley Charitable Trust
The John R. Murray Charitable Trust
The National Gardens Scheme
Normanby Charitable Trust
Old Possum's Practical Trust
The James Pantyfedwen Foundation
The David Pearlman Charitable Foundation
The Pilgrim Trust
Postcode Local Trust
The Prince of Wales's Charitable Foundation
Mr and Mrs J A Pye's Charitable Settlement
The Radcliffe Trust
Rhondda Cynon Taff Welsh Church Acts Fund
The Clive and Sylvia Richards Charity Ltd
The Rose Foundation
The David Ross Foundation
Rothschild Foundation (Hanadiv) Europe
The Rowlands Trust
Royal Docks Trust (London)
Schroder Charity Trust
The Sylvia and Colin Shepherd Charitable Trust
SITA Cornwall Trust Ltd
The Steel Charitable Trust
Stevenson Family's Charitable Trust
Mark Stolkin Foundation
The Summerfield Charitable Trust
The Swire Charitable Trust
The Trusthouse Charitable Foundation
The Roger and Douglas Turner Charitable Trust
The Turtleton Charitable Trust
Ulster Garden Villages Ltd
The Michael Uren Foundation

Mrs Waterhouse Charitable Trust (formerly known as the Houghton Dunn Charitable Trust)
The Geoffrey Watling Charity
The David Webster Charitable Trust
The Wolfson Family Charitable Trust
The Wolfson Foundation
Worth Waynflete Foundation
The Yorkshire Dales Millennium Trust
The Marjorie and Arnold Ziff Charitable Foundation

Humanities

The British Academy for the Promotion of Historical Philosophical and Philological Studies (The British Academy)
The Daiwa Anglo-Japanese Foundation
The Great Britain Sasakawa Foundation
The Neil Kreitman Foundation
The Pears Family Charitable Foundation
Polden-Puckham Charitable Foundation
The Rayne Trust
Mrs L D Rope's Third Charitable Settlement
The Joseph Rowntree Charitable Trust
The Sino-British Fellowship Trust
The Tinsley Foundation
The Wolfson Family Charitable Trust

Media and communications

The Daiwa Anglo-Japanese Foundation
The Miles Morland Foundation

Recreation and sport

Access Sport CIO
The Aldama Foundation
The Anne Duchess of Westminster's Charity
The Arsenal Foundation Ltd
The Asda Foundation
Barnwood Trust
BBC Children in Need
The John Beckwith Charitable Trust
The Big Lottery Fund
The Booth Charities
The Bowland Charitable Trust
The Britford Bridge Trust
The Cadbury Foundation
Church Burgesses Trust
The Coalfields Regeneration Trust

Community First
England and Wales Cricket Trust
The Hamilton Davies Trust
The Roger De Haan Charitable Trust
The Emerald Foundation
The Englefield Charitable Trust
The Essex Youth Trust
The Lord Faringdon Charitable Trust
The Football Foundation
The Fort Foundation
The Joseph Strong Frazer Trust
Charles S French Charitable Trust
Gatwick Airport Community Trust
The Granada Foundation
The Great Britain Sasakawa Foundation
The Hadrian Trust
Hampton Fuel Allotment
The Harpur Trust
The Peter Harrison Foundation
Hedley Foundation Ltd
The Holywood Trust
Huntingdon Freemen's Trust
The Ireland Fund of Great Britain
The Kyte Charitable Trust
Lancashire Environmental Fund Ltd
The Leathersellers' Company Charitable Fund
The William Leech Charity
The London Marathon Charitable Trust Ltd
The Lord's Taverners
John Lyon's Charity
Sir George Martin Trust
The Master Charitable Trust
Millennium Stadium Charitable Trust (Ymddiriedolaeth Elusennol Stadiwm Y Mileniwm)
The Morton Charitable Trust (Dundee)
The National Gardens Scheme
The Nisbet Trust
The David Pearlman Charitable Foundation
Postcode Community Trust
Postcode Dream Trust
Postcode Local Trust
The Professional Footballers' Association Charity
The Racing Foundation
Rhondda Cynon Taff Welsh Church Acts Fund
Richmond Parish Lands Charity
The David Ross Foundation
The Rothermere Foundation
Royal Docks Trust (London)
Rugby Football Foundation
The Saddlers' Company Charitable Fund
The Frieda Scott Charitable Trust

SITA Cornwall Trust Ltd
The Martin Smith Foundation
Stadium Charitable Trust
The Summerfield Charitable Trust
The John Swire 1989 Charitable Trust
The Tennis Foundation
Variety, the Children's Charity
Viridor Credits Environmental Company
The Bruce Wake Charitable Trust
Wates Family Enterprise Trust
The William Wates Memorial Trust
The Geoffrey Watling Charity
Welcome To Our Future (Local Agenda 21)
The Wembley National Stadium Trust
Westway Trust
The Wimbledon Foundation
The Wixamtree Trust
Wooden Spoon Society

Children and young people

The 1989 Willan Charitable Trust
The 29th May 1961 Charitable Trust
Access Sport CIO
The ACT Foundation
Action Medical Research
The Sylvia Adams Charitable Trust
The Adint Charitable Trust
The AIM Foundation
Ajahma Charitable Trust
Al-Fayed Charitable Foundation
D C R Allen Charitable Trust
Viscount Amory's Charitable Trust
The AMW Charitable Trust
Anglo American Group Foundation
Anguish's Educational Foundation
The Armourers' and Brasiers' Gauntlet Trust
The Arsenal Foundation Ltd
Arts Council England
The Asfari Foundation
Autonomous Research Charitable Trust (ARCT)
The Avon and Somerset Police Community Trust
The Ballinger Charitable Trust
Banbury Charities
The Band Trust
The Barbour Foundation
The Barclay Foundation
Barnes Workhouse Fund
Misses Barrie Charitable Trust
The Louis Baylis (Maidenhead Advertiser) Charitable Trust

BBC Children in Need
The John Beckwith Charitable Trust
The Berkeley Charitable Foundation
Ruth Berkowitz Charitable Trust
Percy Bilton Charity
The Blagrave Trust
The Bluston Charitable Settlement
The Boltini Trust
The Booth Charities
The Bothwell Charitable Trust
The Bowland Charitable Trust
The Bransford Trust
The Breadsticks Foundation
The Britford Bridge Trust
The British and Foreign School Society
British Record Industry Trust (BRIT Trust)
The Bromley Trust
The Buffini Chao Foundation
The Clara E Burgess Charity
The William Adlington Cadbury Charitable Trust
David William Traill Cargill Fund
The W.A. Cargill Fund
The Carpenters' Company Charitable Trust
Sir John Cass's Foundation
The Castansa Trust
The Cattanach Charitable Trust
The Joseph and Annie Cattle Trust
The Cayo Foundation
The Chalk Cliff Trust
The Childhood Trust
Children With Cancer UK
CHK Charities Ltd
The Churchill Foundation
The CIBC World Markets Children's Foundation
J A Clark Charitable Trust
Clark Foundation
The Clore Duffield Foundation
The Clothworkers' Foundation
The Coalfields Regeneration Trust
The John Coates Charitable Trust
Colwinston Charitable Trust
Colyer-Fergusson Charitable Trust
Comic Relief
The Thomas Cook Children's Charity
The Ernest Cook Trust
The Catherine Cookson Charitable Trust
The Sir Tom Cowie Charitable Trust
Dudley and Geoffrey Cox Charitable Trust
Credit Suisse EMEA Foundation
The Crerar Trust
The Peter Cruddas Foundation

The Ronald Cruickshanks Foundation
Cullum Family Trust
The D'Oyly Carte Charitable Trust
Baron Davenport's Charity
The Hamilton Davies Trust
The Crispin Davis Family Trust
The Davis Foundation
The Roger De Haan Charitable Trust
Debenhams Foundation
The J N Derbyshire Trust
The Desmond Foundation
The Djanogly Foundation
Drapers' Charitable Fund
The Dromintee Trust
The Royal Foundation of the Duke and Duchess of Cambridge and Prince Harry
The Dulverton Trust
Dumbreck Charity
The Charles Dunstone Charitable Trust
The Dyers' Company Charitable Trust
The James Dyson Foundation
The Sir John Eastwood Foundation
The EBM Charitable Trust
Echoes of Service
The Gerald Palmer Eling Trust Company
The Marian Elizabeth Trust
The Maud Elkington Charitable Trust
The Ellerdale Trust
EMI Music Sound Foundation
The Englefield Charitable Trust
The Enkalon Foundation
The Eranda Rothschild Foundation
The Essex Youth Trust
The Eventhall Family Charitable Trust
The Eveson Charitable Trust
The Exilarch's Foundation
The Expat Foundation
Esmée Fairbairn Foundation
The Lord Faringdon Charitable Trust
The Thomas Farr Charity
Doris Field Charitable Trust
The Sir John Fisher Foundation
The Football Foundation
Donald Forrester Trust
The Fort Foundation
Four Acre Trust
The Foyle Foundation
The Hugh Fraser Foundation
The Joseph Strong Frazer Trust
Charles S French Charitable Trust
The Patrick and Helena Frost Foundation
The Fulmer Charitable Trust

The Gale Family Charity Trust
The Gannochy Trust
Gatwick Airport Community Trust
The Robert Gavron Charitable Trust
Sir Robert Geffery's Almshouse Trust
The Generations Foundation
The Simon Gibson Charitable Trust
The Glass-House Trust
The Gloag Foundation
Global Charities
The Goldsmiths' Company Charity
The Goodman Foundation
The Mike Gooley Trailfinders Charity
The Gosling Foundation Ltd
The Grace Trust
The Grant Foundation
The Green Hall Foundation
Greenham Trust Ltd
The Grimmitt Trust
The Grocers' Charity
Calouste Gulbenkian Foundation – UK Branch
Hackney Parochial Charities
The Hadfield Charitable Trust
The Hadley Trust
The Hadrian Trust
Paul Hamlyn Foundation
Hammersmith United Charities
Hampton Fuel Allotment
The W A Handley Charity Trust
The Haramead Trust
The Harbour Foundation
William Harding's Charity
The Edith Lilian Harrison 2000 Foundation
The Peter Harrison Foundation
The Heathcoat Trust
Heathrow Community Fund (LHR Airport Communities Trust)
The Charlotte Heber-Percy Charitable Trust
Hedley Foundation Ltd (The Hedley Foundation)
Henderson Firstfruits
The Christina Mary Hendrie Trust
The Hilden Charitable Fund
The Lady Hind Trust
The Hobson Charity Ltd
The Jane Hodge Foundation
The Holywood Trust
The Homelands Charitable Trust
Sir Harold Hood's Charitable Trust
Horne Foundation
The Thomas J Horne Memorial Trust
Hospice UK
Housing Pathways Trust
The Reta Lila Howard Foundation
The Albert Hunt Trust

The Hunter Foundation
Huntingdon Freemen's Trust
Hyde Charitable Trust (Youth Plus)
Ibrahim Foundation Ltd
Impetus – The Private Equity Foundation
Investream Charitable Trust
The Ireland Fund of Great Britain
The Ironmongers' Company
The J Isaacs Charitable Trust
The J J Charitable Trust
The Jabbs Foundation
The Frank Jackson Foundation
John James Bristol Foundation
Jewish Child's Day (JCD)
The Johnson Foundation
The Jones 1986 Charitable Trust
The Jordan Charitable Foundation
Joseph Levy Foundation
Anton Jurgens Charitable Trust
The Kensington and Chelsea Foundation
The Kentown Wizard Foundation
The Kiawah Charitable Trust
The Mary Kinross Charitable Trust
The Ernest Kleinwort Charitable Trust
The Sir James Knott Trust
The KPMG Foundation
Kusuma Trust UK
The Kyte Charitable Trust
Ladbrokes Coral Trust
John Laing Charitable Trust
Maurice and Hilda Laing Charitable Trust
Christopher Laing Foundation
The David Laing Foundation
The Kirby Laing Foundation
The Martin Laing Foundation
The Beatrice Laing Trust
The Lancashire Foundation
Duchy of Lancaster Benevolent Fund
Lancaster Foundation
LandAid Charitable Trust (Land Aid)
The Lauffer Family Charitable Foundation
The Kathleen Laurence Trust
The Law Family Charitable Foundation
The Edgar E Lawley Foundation
The Leathersellers' Company Charitable Fund
The William Leech Charity
The Lehman Brothers Foundation Europe
The Mark Leonard Trust
The Leverhulme Trade Charities Trust
Lord Leverhulme's Charitable Trust

Bernard Lewis Family Charitable Trust
David and Ruth Lewis Family Charitable Trust
John Lewis Partnership General Community Fund
Life Changes Trust
The Lind Trust
The Enid Linder Foundation
The Charles Littlewood Hill Trust
The Ian and Natalie Livingstone Charitable Trust
Lloyds Bank Foundation for the Channel Islands
Loftus Charitable Trust
London Catalyst
The Lord's Taverners
The Lyndal Tree Foundation
The Lynn Foundation
John Lyon's Charity
Sylvanus Lysons Charity
The MK Charitable Trust
The RS Macdonald Charitable Trust
The MacRobert Trust
Man Group plc Charitable Trust
The Manoukian Charitable Foundation
The Michael Marsh Charitable Trust
The Marsh Christian Trust
Sir George Martin Trust
John Martin's Charity
Masonic Charitable Foundation
The Nancie Massey Charitable Trust
The Matliwala Family Charitable Trust
MBNA General Foundation
The Robert McAlpine Foundation
D D McPhail Charitable Settlement
The Medlock Charitable Trust
Mercaz Torah Vechesed Ltd
The Mercers' Charitable Foundation
T. & J. Meyer Family Foundation Ltd
The Gerald Micklem Charitable Trust
Millennium Stadium Charitable Trust (Ymddiriedlaeth Elusennol Stadiwm Y Mileniwm)
The Millichope Foundation
The Monument Trust
Moondance Foundation
The George A. Moore Foundation
John Moores Foundation
The Steve Morgan Foundation
Morgan Stanley International Foundation
G M Morrison Charitable Trust
The Morrisons Foundation

The Edith Murphy Foundation
The NFU Mutual Charitable Trust
The Nisbet Trust
Educational Foundation of Alderman John Norman
The Norman Family Charitable Trust
Normanby Charitable Trust
The Northwick Trust
The Norton Rose Fulbright Charitable Foundation
Oizer Charitable Trust
The Oldfield Charitable Trust
Open Gate
The Doris Pacey Charitable Foundation
Peacock Charitable Trust
The David Pearlman Charitable Foundation
The Pears Family Charitable Foundation
The Persula Foundation
The Jack Petchey Foundation
The Prince of Wales's Charitable Foundation
The Professional Footballers' Association Charity
Mr and Mrs J A Pye's Charitable Settlement
Quintessentially Foundation
The Radcliffe Trust
The Rank Foundation Ltd
The Joseph Rank Trust
Rashbass Family Trust
The Rayne Foundation
The Rayne Trust
The Sir James Reckitt Charity
Richard Reeve's Foundation
Reuben Foundation
The Revere Charitable Trust
The Clive and Sylvia Richards Charity Ltd
Richmond Parish Lands Charity
The River Farm Foundation
The Robertson Trust
Mrs L D Rope's Third Charitable Settlement
The David Ross Foundation
The Rothermere Foundation
The Rothley Trust
The Roughley Charitable Trust
The Saddlers' Company Charitable Fund
The Alan and Babette Sainsbury Charitable Fund
The Saintbury Trust
The Basil Samuel Charitable Trust
The Samworth Foundation
Santander UK Foundation Ltd
The Save the Children Fund
Schroder Charity Trust

The Francis C. Scott Charitable Trust

The Frieda Scott Charitable Trust

Scottish Property Industry Festival of Christmas (Spifox)

Sam and Bella Sebba Charitable Trust

The Segelman Trust

The Shanly Foundation

The Shears Foundation

The Shetland Charitable Trust

SHINE (Support and Help in Education)

The Slaughter and May Charitable Trust

The Henry Smith Charity

The Sobell Foundation

Sofronie Foundation

Sparks Charity (Sport Aiding Medical Research For Kids)

Spielman Charitable Trust

The Spoore, Merry and Rixman Foundation

The Geoff and Fiona Squire Foundation

St James's Place Foundation

The Stafford Trust

The Sir Sigmund Sternberg Charitable Foundation

The Stoller Charitable Trust

Stratford-upon-Avon Town Trust

The WO Street Charitable Foundation

The Summerfield Charitable Trust

The Bernard Sunley Charitable Foundation

The Swire Charitable Trust

The Talbot Village Trust

Tallow Chandlers Benevolent Fund No. 2

C B And H H Taylor 1984 Trust

The Taylor Family Foundation

The Tedworth Charitable Trust

The Tennis Foundation

DM Thomas Foundation for Young People

The Tolkien Trust

Toras Chesed (London) Trust

The Tottenham Grammar School Foundation

The Toy Trust

The True Colours Trust

The Trusthouse Charitable Foundation

The Tudor Trust

The Tuixen Foundation

The Roger and Douglas Turner Charitable Trust

Ulster Garden Villages Ltd

The Union of The Sisters of Mercy of Great Britain

United Jewish Israel Appeal

United Purpose

The Vardy Foundation

Variety, the Children's Charity

The Vintners' Foundation

The Virgin Money Foundation

Volant Charitable Trust

Sylvia Waddilove Foundation UK

The Barbara Ward Children's Foundation

Mrs Waterhouse Charitable Trust (formerly known as the Houghton Dunn Charitable Trust)

The Waterloo Foundation

Wates Family Enterprise Trust

The Wates Foundation

The Weavers' Company Benevolent Fund

The Weinstock Fund

The Wembley National Stadium Trust

The Westminster Amalgamated Charity

The Garfield Weston Foundation

White Stuff Foundation

Charity of Sir Richard Whittington

The Williams Family Foundation

The Willmott Dixon Foundation

The Wimbledon Foundation

The Maurice Wohl Charitable Foundation

The Wolfson Family Charitable Trust

Wooden Spoon Society

Woodroffe Benton Foundation

The Woodstock Family Charitable Foundation

The Woodward Charitable Trust

Worth Waynflete Foundation

The Worwin UK Foundation

The Eric Wright Charitable Trust

The Yapp Charitable Trust

Yorkshire Building Society Charitable Foundation

Youth Music

Elizabeth and Prince Zaiger Trust

The Marjorie and Arnold Ziff Charitable Foundation

The Zochonis Charitable Trust

Zurich Community Trust (UK) Ltd

Development, housing and employment

Aberdeen Asset Management Charitable Foundation

The 1989 Willan Charitable Trust

ABF The Soldiers' Charity

The AIM Foundation

Ajahma Charitable Trust

D C R Allen Charitable Trust

Anglo American Group Foundation

The Anne Duchess of Westminster's Charity

The Apax Foundation

Ove Arup Partnership Charitable Trust

The Asda Foundation

The Ashden Trust

The Ashley Family Foundation

Aston-Mansfield Charitable Trust

Autonomous Research Charitable Trust (ARCT)

Awards for All

The Bank of Scotland Foundation

The Barbour Foundation

Barnes Workhouse Fund

Barnwood Trust

The Battersea Power Station Foundation

BC Partners Foundation

The Berkeley Charitable Foundation

Ruth Berkowitz Charitable Trust

The Big Lottery Fund

The Blagrave Trust

Boots Charitable Trust

The Borrows Charitable Trust

The Liz and Terry Bramall Foundation

The Bransford Trust

The Brelms Trust CIO

The Britford Bridge Trust

The Edward Cadbury Charitable Trust

The Cadbury Foundation

The Castansa Trust

The Chalk Cliff Trust

Chapman Charitable Trust

CHK Charities Ltd

The Churchill Foundation

The Coalfields Regeneration Trust

Denise Coates Foundation

Colyer-Fergusson Charitable Trust

Comic Relief

Community First

Co-operative Community Investment Foundation

Corra Foundation

CRASH

The Peter Cruddas Foundation

The D'Oyly Carte Charitable Trust

Baron Davenport's Charity

The Hamilton Davies Trust

The Roger De Haan Charitable Trust

Debenhams Foundation

Drapers' Charitable Fund

The Dulverton Trust

The Dyers' Company Charitable Trust
EDF Energy Trust
The Englefield Charitable Trust
The Enkalon Foundation
The Eveson Charitable Trust
The Expat Foundation
Esmée Fairbairn Foundation
The Thomas Farr Charity
Allan and Nesta Ferguson Charitable Settlement
The Fidelity UK Foundation
The Sir John Fisher Foundation
Fisherbeck Charitable Trust
The Football Foundation
Donald Forrester Trust
The Fort Foundation
The Elizabeth Frankland Moore and Star Foundation
Charles S French Charitable Trust
Friends Provident Charitable Foundation
The Gannochy Trust
Gatwick Airport Community Trust
The GC Gibson Charitable Trust
The Golden Bottle Trust
Goldman Sachs Gives (UK)
The Grace Trust
GrantScape
The Green Hall Foundation
Greenham Trust Ltd
The Greggs Foundation
The Grimmitt Trust
Groundwork UK
Calouste Gulbenkian Foundation – UK Branch
HCD Memorial Fund
The Hadfield Charitable Trust
The Hadrian Trust
Halifax Foundation for Northern Ireland (previously known as Lloyds Bank Foundation for Northern Ireland)
Hammersmith United Charities
Hampton Fuel Allotment
The W A Handley Charity Trust
The Haramead Trust
The Harborne Parish Lands Charity
The Harbour Foundation
The David and Claudia Harding Foundation
William Harding's Charity
The Charles Hayward Foundation
The Heathcoat Trust
Heathrow Community Fund (LHR Airport Communities Trust)
The Hilden Charitable Fund
The Hillingdon Community Trust
The Lady Hind Trust
The Henry C. Hoare Charitable Trust
The Hobson Charity Ltd

The Thomas J Horne Memorial Trust
Housing Pathways Trust
The Albert Hunt Trust
The Hunter Foundation
Hyde Charitable Trust (Youth Plus)
Impetus – The Private Equity Foundation
The Innocent Foundation
Investream Charitable Trust
The Ireland Fund of Great Britain
The Isle of Anglesey Charitable Trust
St John's Foundation (Bath)
The Johnson Foundation
The Kensington and Chelsea Foundation
The Mary Kinross Charitable Trust
The Sir James Knott Trust
The KPMG Foundation
Kusuma Trust UK
The Kyte Charitable Trust
Ladbrokes Coral Trust
John Laing Charitable Trust
The Beatrice Laing Trust
The Lake House Charity
Duchy of Lancaster Benevolent Fund
Lancaster Foundation
LandAid Charitable Trust (Land Aid)
The Allen Lane Foundation
The Leathersellers' Company Charitable Fund
The William Leech Charity
Lempriere Pringle 2015
The Lennox Hannay Charitable Trust
The Mark Leonard Trust
David and Ruth Lewis Family Charitable Trust
John Lewis Partnership General Community Fund
The Charles Littlewood Hill Trust
Lloyds Bank Foundation for the Channel Islands
Trust for London
London Housing Foundation Ltd (LHF)
John Lyon's Charity
The Mactaggart Third Fund
Man Group plc Charitable Trust
The W M Mann Foundation
The Master Charitable Trust
The Mathew Trust
The Matliwala Family Charitable Trust
The Medlock Charitable Trust
Merchant Navy Welfare Board
The Merchants' House of Glasgow
T. & J. Meyer Family Foundation Ltd

Millennium Stadium Charitable Trust (Ymddiriedolaeth Elusennol Stadiwm Y Mileniwm)
The Millfield House Foundation
The Monument Trust
The George A. Moore Foundation
John Moores Foundation
The Steve Morgan Foundation
The Nationwide Foundation
The NFU Mutual Charitable Trust
The Nisbet Trust
Norwich Town Close Estate Charity
The Oakdale Trust
Oxfam (GB)
Paradigm Foundation
The Pebble Trust
People's Health Trust
People's Postcode Trust
The Persula Foundation
The Pilgrim Trust
Power to Change Trust
The Prince of Wales's Charitable Foundation
The Prince's Countryside Fund
The Sigrid Rausing Trust
The Reece Foundation
Richmond Parish Lands Charity
The Robertson Trust
Mrs L D Rope's Third Charitable Settlement
The David Ross Foundation
The Rothley Trust
The Joseph Rowntree Charitable Trust
The Royal British Legion
Royal Docks Trust (London)
Royal Society of Wildlife Trusts
The Saddlers' Company Charitable Fund
The Alan and Babette Sainsbury Charitable Fund
Santander UK Foundation Ltd
The Save the Children Fund
The ScottishPower Foundation
The Shears Foundation
Sherburn House Charity
The Simmons and Simmons Charitable Foundation
SITA Cornwall Trust Ltd
The Mrs Smith and Mount Trust
The Henry Smith Charity
Social Business Trust
Social Investment Business Foundation
Peter Sowerby Foundation
The Stafford Trust
The Peter Stebbings Memorial Charity
Sir Halley Stewart Trust
Streetsmart – Action For The Homeless
The Summerfield Charitable Trust

The Bernard Sunley Charitable Foundation
Sutton Coldfield Charitable Trust
The Talbot Village Trust
C B And H H Taylor 1984 Trust
The Tolkien Trust
The Constance Travis Charitable Trust
The Trusthouse Charitable Foundation
The Tudor Trust
The Roger and Douglas Turner Charitable Trust
United Purpose
United St Saviour's Charity
UPP Foundation
The Vandervell Foundation
The Veolia Environmental Trust
The Virgin Money Foundation
Viridor Credits Environmental Company
The Vodafone Foundation
Volant Charitable Trust
Voluntary Action Fund (VAF)
Sylvia Waddilove Foundation UK
The Wakefield and Tetley Trust
Walton On Thames Charity
The Waterloo Foundation
Wates Family Enterprise Trust
The Wates Foundation
Welcome To Our Future (Local Agenda 21)
The Welton Foundation
Westhill Endowment
The Westminster Amalgamated Charity
The Westminster Foundation
Westway Trust
White Stuff Foundation
The Willmott Dixon Foundation
The Wixamtree Trust
Worth Waynflete Foundation
Yorkshire and Clydesdale Bank Foundation
The Yorkshire Dales Millennium Trust
The William Allen Young Charitable Trust
Zurich Community Trust (UK) Ltd

Disability

The ACT Foundation
Action on Hearing Loss (The Royal National Institute For Deaf People)
The Adint Charitable Trust
Ajahma Charitable Trust
The Alchemy Foundation
D C R Allen Charitable Trust

The AMW Charitable Trust
The Anne Duchess of Westminster's Charity
The Arsenal Foundation Ltd
Autonomous Research Charitable Trust (ARCT)
The Baily Thomas Charitable Fund
Banbury Charities
The Band Trust
The Barclay Foundation
Barnes Workhouse Fund
Barnwood Trust
Misses Barrie Charitable Trust
The Berkeley Charitable Foundation
Percy Bilton Charity
The Boshier-Hinton Foundation
The Bothwell Charitable Trust
The Liz and Terry Bramall Foundation
The Brelms Trust CIO
The Britford Bridge Trust
British Council for Prevention of Blindness (Save Eyes Everywhere)
British Eye Research Foundation (Fight for Sight)
Bill Brown 1989 Charitable Trust
The William Adlington Cadbury Charitable Trust
The Cadbury Foundation
The Joseph and Annie Cattle Trust
The Thomas Sivewright Catto Charitable Settlement
The Charities Advisory Trust
The Childwick Trust
CHK Charities Ltd
Church Burgesses Trust
The Clothworkers' Foundation
The John Coates Charitable Trust
The Catherine Cookson Charitable Trust
Corra Foundation
The Crerar Trust
Cruden Foundation Ltd
The Ronald Cruickshanks Foundation
Cullum Family Trust
The D'Oyly Carte Charitable Trust
The Davis Foundation
The Roger De Haan Charitable Trust
Debenhams Foundation
The J N Derbyshire Trust
Drapers' Charitable Fund
Dumbreck Charity
The Charles Dunstone Charitable Trust
The Sir John Eastwood Foundation
The EBM Charitable Trust
Echoes of Service
Edupoor Ltd
The Marian Elizabeth Trust

The Ellerdale Trust
The Englefield Charitable Trust
The Eranda Rothschild Foundation
The Eveson Charitable Trust
Esmée Fairbairn Foundation
The Lord Faringdon Charitable Trust
The Thomas Farr Charity
The February Foundation
Doris Field Charitable Trust
The Sir John Fisher Foundation
Fishmongers' Company's Charitable Trust
Donald Forrester Trust
The Foyle Foundation
The Elizabeth Frankland Moore and Star Foundation
The Hugh Fraser Foundation
The Joseph Strong Frazer Trust
Charles S French Charitable Trust
The Patrick and Helena Frost Foundation
The Fulmer Charitable Trust
The Gale Family Charity Trust
Gatwick Airport Community Trust
The Robert Gavron Charitable Trust
The Generations Foundation
The GC Gibson Charitable Trust
The Simon Gibson Charitable Trust
The Goldsmiths' Company Charity
The Goodman Foundation
The Gosling Foundation Ltd
The Grace Trust
The Green Hall Foundation
Greenham Trust Ltd
The Greggs Foundation
The Hadley Trust
The Hadrian Trust
The Hampstead Wells and Campden Trust
Hampton Fuel Allotment
The W A Handley Charity Trust
The Haramead Trust
The Harborne Parish Lands Charity
The Harbour Foundation
William Harding's Charity
The Edith Lilian Harrison 2000 Foundation
The Peter Harrison Foundation
The Heathcoat Trust
Hedley Foundation Ltd (The Hedley Foundation)
Henderson Firstfruits
The Hillingdon Community Trust
The Lady Hind Trust
The Hobson Charity Ltd
The Jane Hodge Foundation
The Thomas J Horne Memorial Trust
Hospice UK
The Hospital Saturday Fund

Housing Pathways Trust
The Albert Hunt Trust
Miss Agnes H Hunter's Trust
Huntingdon Freemen's Trust
The Inman Charity
Investream Charitable Trust
The Frank Jackson Foundation
Jewish Child's Day (JCD)
The Johnson Foundation
The Jones 1986 Charitable Trust
The Jordan Charitable Foundation
Joseph Levy Foundation
Anton Jurgens Charitable Trust
The Ian Karten Charitable Trust
The Kennedy Trust For
    Rheumatology Research
The Kensington and Chelsea
    Foundation
The Kentown Wizard Foundation
The Kirschel Foundation
The Ernest Kleinwort Charitable
    Trust
The Sir James Knott Trust
Ladbrokes Coral Trust
Maurice and Hilda Laing Charitable
    Trust
Christopher Laing Foundation
The David Laing Foundation
The Kirby Laing Foundation
The Beatrice Laing Trust
Duchy of Lancaster Benevolent
    Fund
The Lauffer Family Charitable
    Foundation
The Kathleen Laurence Trust
The Edgar E Lawley Foundation
The Leathersellers' Company
    Charitable Fund
The William Leech Charity
Lord Leverhulme's Charitable Trust
David and Ruth Lewis Family
    Charitable Trust
John Lewis Partnership General
    Community Fund
Life Changes Trust
The Linbury Trust
The Enid Linder Foundation
The Charles Littlewood Hill Trust
Lloyds Bank Foundation for
    England and Wales
Lloyds Bank Foundation for the
    Channel Islands
Lloyd's Patriotic Fund
London Catalyst
The Lord's Taverners
The Lyndal Tree Foundation
The Lynn Foundation
M and C Trust
The MK Charitable Trust
The RS Macdonald Charitable
    Trust

The Michael Marsh Charitable
    Trust
The Marsh Christian Trust
Sir George Martin Trust
John Martin's Charity
Masonic Charitable Foundation
MBNA General Foundation
The Robert McAlpine Foundation
D D McPhail Charitable Settlement
Merchant Taylors' Consolidated
    Charities for the Infirm
The Merchants' House of Glasgow
T. & J. Meyer Family Foundation
    Ltd
The Gerald Micklem Charitable
    Trust
The Millichope Foundation
The Clare Milne Trust
The Laurence Misener Charitable
    Trust
The George A. Moore Foundation
The Steve Morgan Foundation
G M Morrison Charitable Trust
The Ken and Lynne Morrison
    Charitable Trust
The Morrisons Foundation
The Edith Murphy Foundation
Newby Trust Ltd
The Norman Family Charitable
    Trust
Normanby Charitable Trust
The Northwick Trust
Odin Charitable Trust
Oizer Charitable Trust
OneFamily Foundation
Open Gate
The Doris Pacey Charitable
    Foundation
Peacock Charitable Trust
The David Pearlman Charitable
    Foundation
The Pears Family Charitable
    Foundation
The Dowager Countess Eleanor
    Peel Trust
The Persula Foundation
Mr and Mrs J A Pye's Charitable
    Settlement
The Radcliffe Trust
Rashbass Family Trust
The Rayne Foundation
Reuben Foundation
Rhondda Cynon Taff Welsh Church
    Acts Fund
The Clive and Sylvia Richards
    Charity Ltd
The Robertson Trust
Mrs L D Rope's Third Charitable
    Settlement
The Cecil Rosen Foundation
The Rothley Trust
The Roughley Charitable Trust

The Rowlands Trust
The Saddlers' Company Charitable
    Fund
The Basil Samuel Charitable Trust
Scott (Eredine) Charitable Trust
The Frieda Scott Charitable Trust
Sam and Bella Sebba Charitable
    Trust
The Shanly Foundation
The Shears Foundation
The Mrs Smith and Mount Trust
The Henry Smith Charity
The Sobell Foundation
R H Southern Trust
Spielman Charitable Trust
The Geoff and Fiona Squire
    Foundation
St James's Place Foundation
The Peter Stebbings Memorial
    Charity
The Sir Sigmund Sternberg
    Charitable Foundation
The Stewarts Law Foundation
The WO Street Charitable
    Foundation
The Street Foundation
The Summerfield Charitable Trust
The Bernard Sunley Charitable
    Foundation
The Swire Charitable Trust
The Charles and Elsie Sykes Trust
The Talbot Village Trust
Tallow Chandlers Benevolent Fund
    No. 2
C B And H H Taylor 1984 Trust
The Tennis Foundation
DM Thomas Foundation for Young
    People
The Sir Jules Thorn Charitable
    Trust
The Three Guineas Trust
The Toy Trust
The Constance Travis Charitable
    Trust
The True Colours Trust
The Trusthouse Charitable
    Foundation
The James Tudor Foundation
The Tudor Trust
The Tuixen Foundation
The Roger and Douglas Turner
    Charitable Trust
The Van Neste Foundation
Variety, the Children's Charity
Sylvia Waddilove Foundation UK
The Bruce Wake Charitable Trust
The Walker Trust
The Barbara Ward Children's
    Foundation
Mrs Waterhouse Charitable Trust
    (formerly known as the

Houghton Dunn Charitable
Trust)
Wates Family Enterprise Trust
The Wates Foundation
The Geoffrey Watling Charity
The Weinstock Fund
The Welton Foundation
The Wembley National Stadium
Trust
The Westfield Health Charitable
Trust
The Westminster Amalgamated
Charity
The Garfield Weston Foundation
White Stuff Foundation
The Will Charitable Trust
The Williams Family Foundation
The Maurice Wohl Charitable
Foundation
The Wolfson Family Charitable
Trust
The Wolfson Foundation
Wooden Spoon Society
The Woodward Charitable Trust
Worth Waynflete Foundation
The Yapp Charitable Trust
Yorkshire Building Society
Charitable Foundation
Youth Music
Elizabeth and Prince Zaiger Trust
Zurich Community Trust (UK) Ltd

Disadvantaged people

Aberdeen Asset Management
Charitable Foundation
The 29th May 1961 Charitable
Trust
The A B Charitable Trust
The Aberdeen Foundation
Access Sport CIO
Achisomoch Aid Company Ltd
The Alchemy Foundation
The Allen and Overy Foundation
D C R Allen Charitable Trust
The AMW Charitable Trust
The Anchor Foundation
Anglo American Group Foundation
Anguish's Educational Foundation
The Anne Duchess of Westminster's
Charity
The John Apthorp Charity
The Arsenal Foundation Ltd
Arts Council England
The Ashden Trust
Aston-Mansfield Charitable Trust
Autonomous Research Charitable
Trust (ARCT)

The Avon and Somerset Police
Community Trust
The Balcombe Charitable Trust
Barnwood Trust
Bay Charitable Trust
BBC Children in Need
The Berkeley Charitable
Foundation
Percy Bilton Charity
The Booth Charities
Boots Charitable Trust
The Bowland Charitable Trust
The Liz and Terry Bramall
Foundation
The Brelms Trust CIO
The British and Foreign School
Society
British Gas (Scottish Gas) Energy
Trust
The Bromley Trust
Bill Brown 1989 Charitable Trust
Brushmill Ltd
The E F Bulmer Benevolent Fund
The William Adlington Cadbury
Charitable Trust
The Cadbury Foundation
The Barrow Cadbury Trust
Sir John Cass's Foundation
The Thomas Sivewright Catto
Charitable Settlement
The Charities Advisory Trust
Charitworth Ltd
The Childhood Trust
CHK Charities Ltd
The City Bridge Trust (Bridge
House Estates)
The Clore Duffield Foundation
The Clothworkers' Foundation
Richard Cloudesley's Charity
The R and S Cohen Foundation
Colyer-Fergusson Charitable Trust
Co-operative Community
Investment Foundation
The Evan Cornish Foundation
General Charity of Coventry
The Sir Tom Cowie Charitable
Trust
CRASH
The Crerar Trust
The Cross Trust
The Ronald Cruickshanks
Foundation
The Crispin Davis Family Trust
Debenhams Foundation
The J N Derbyshire Trust
The Double 'O' Charity Ltd
Drapers' Charitable Fund
The Dulverton Trust
The Charles Dunstone Charitable
Trust
The Dyers' Company Charitable
Trust

The Earley Charity
The EBM Charitable Trust
EDF Energy Trust
Edupoor Ltd
The Gerald Palmer Eling Trust
Company
The Enkalon Foundation
Entindale Ltd
The Eventhall Family Charitable
Trust
The Eveson Charitable Trust
Fisherbeck Charitable Trust
The Foyle Foundation
The Hugh Fraser Foundation
The Freshfield Foundation
Friends of Wiznitz Ltd
Friends Provident Charitable
Foundation
The Gannochy Trust
The Robert Gavron Charitable
Trust
The GC Gibson Charitable Trust
The Goldsmiths' Company Charity
The Goodman Foundation
The Gosling Foundation Ltd
Grace Charitable Trust
The Grant Foundation
The Green Hall Foundation
HCD Memorial Fund
Hackney Parochial Charities
The Hadley Trust
The Hadrian Trust
Paul Hamlyn Foundation
Hammersmith United Charities
Hampton Fuel Allotment
The W A Handley Charity Trust
The Harborne Parish Lands Charity
The Harbour Foundation
William Harding's Charity
The Harpur Trust
The Edith Lilian Harrison 2000
Foundation
Edward Harvist Trust (The Harvist
Estate)
The Charles Hayward Foundation
Hedley Foundation Ltd (The
Hedley Foundation)
The Helping Foundation
The Hilden Charitable Fund
The Hillingdon Community Trust
The Holden Charitable Trust
P H Holt Foundation
Horne Foundation
The Thomas J Horne Memorial
Trust
Housing Pathways Trust
The Hunter Foundation
Huntingdon Freemen's Trust
Hyde Charitable Trust (Youth Plus)
The Innocent Foundation
The Ireland Fund of Great Britain
The J J Charitable Trust

The Jabbs Foundation
The Frank Jackson Foundation
The Elton John AIDS Foundation (EJAF)
The Johnson Foundation
The Jones 1986 Charitable Trust
The Kirschel Foundation
The Sir James Knott Trust
The KPMG Foundation
The Kreitman Foundation
Kusuma Trust UK
Ladbrokes Coral Trust
John Laing Charitable Trust
Maurice and Hilda Laing Charitable Trust
The Kirby Laing Foundation
The Martin Laing Foundation
The Beatrice Laing Trust
The Lancashire Foundation
LandAid Charitable Trust (Land Aid)
The Allen Lane Foundation
The LankellyChase Foundation
Largsmount Ltd
The Edgar E Lawley Foundation
The Leathersellers' Company Charitable Fund
The Mark Leonard Trust
Bernard Lewis Family Charitable Trust
John Lewis Partnership General Community Fund
The Linbury Trust
The Enid Linder Foundation
The Charles Littlewood Hill Trust
Lloyds Bank Foundation for England and Wales
Lloyds Bank Foundation for the Channel Islands
Lloyd's Patriotic Fund
Loftus Charitable Trust
London Catalyst
London Housing Foundation Ltd (LHF)
The Lord's Taverners
The Lyndal Tree Foundation
The Lynn Foundation
The MK Charitable Trust
Man Group plc Charitable Trust
The Manoukian Charitable Foundation
The Michael Marsh Charitable Trust
Sir George Martin Trust
The Mathew Trust
Mayfair Charities Ltd
The Melow Charitable Trust
Mercaz Torah Vechesed Ltd
The Brian Mercer Charitable Trust
The Mercers' Charitable Foundation

Merchant Taylors' Consolidated Charities for the Infirm
The Merchants' House of Glasgow
T. & J. Meyer Family Foundation Ltd
The Millfield House Foundation
Money Advice Trust
The Monument Trust
John Moores Foundation
The Steve Morgan Foundation
The Edith Murphy Foundation
Near Neighbours
Network for Social Change Charitable Trust
Newby Trust Ltd
Newpier Charity Ltd
The Nisbet Trust
The Norman Family Charitable Trust
The Norton Rose Fulbright Charitable Foundation
Norwich Town Close Estate Charity
The Oakdale Trust
Odin Charitable Trust
The Ogle Christian Trust
Oglesby Charitable Trust
The Oldfield Charitable Trust
Open Gate
Oxfam (GB)
The Doris Pacey Charitable Foundation
The Panacea Charitable Trust
Parabola Foundation
Paradigm Foundation
The Park House Charitable Trust
People's Health Trust
People's Postcode Trust
The Persula Foundation
The Pilgrim Trust
The Austin and Hope Pilkington Trust
Postcode Dream Trust
Pret Foundation Trust
Sir John Priestman Charity Trust
The Prince's Countryside Fund
The Professional Footballers' Association Charity
The Queen Anne's Gate Foundation
Rachel Charitable Trust
The Eleanor Rathbone Charitable Trust
The Sigrid Rausing Trust
The Rayne Foundation
The Rayne Trust
Reuben Foundation
Rhodi Charitable Trust
Rhondda Cynon Taff Welsh Church Acts Fund
The River Farm Foundation
Mrs L D Rope's Third Charitable Settlement
The David Ross Foundation

The Rowlands Trust
The Joseph Rowntree Charitable Trust
SF Foundation
The Alan and Babette Sainsbury Charitable Fund
The Samworth Foundation
Santander UK Foundation Ltd
The Save the Children Fund
The Francis C. Scott Charitable Trust
The Frieda Scott Charitable Trust
Sam and Bella Sebba Charitable Trust
The Segelman Trust
The Shanly Foundation
The Shears Foundation
SHINE (Support and Help in Education)
The Simmons and Simmons Charitable Foundation
The Mrs Smith and Mount Trust
The Sobell Foundation
Sofronie Foundation
The Souter Charitable Trust
The W F Southall Trust
R H Southern Trust
Standard Life Foundation
The Peter Stebbings Memorial Charity
The Sir Sigmund Sternberg Charitable Foundation
Stratford-upon-Avon Town Trust
Streetsmart – Action For The Homeless
The Summerfield Charitable Trust
The Bernard Sunley Charitable Foundation
The Sutton Trust
The Swire Charitable Trust
The Charles and Elsie Sykes Trust
The Talbot Village Trust
Tallow Chandlers Benevolent Fund No. 2
C B And H H Taylor 1984 Trust
Khoo Teck Puat UK Foundation
DM Thomas Foundation for Young People
The Tinsley Foundation
The Tolkien Trust
The Constance Travis Charitable Trust
The Triangle Trust (1949) Fund
The Tuixen Foundation
The Turtleton Charitable Trust
Tzedakah
The Union of The Sisters of Mercy of Great Britain
United Purpose
United Utilities Trust Fund
The Vandervell Foundation
The Vintners' Foundation

The Virgin Money Foundation
Voluntary Action Fund (VAF)
Sylvia Waddilove Foundation UK
The Walcot Foundation
The Walker Trust
Walton On Thames Charity
Mrs Waterhouse Charitable Trust
(formerly known as the
Houghton Dunn Charitable
Trust)
Wates Family Enterprise Trust
The Wates Foundation
The Geoffrey Watling Charity
The Weavers' Company Benevolent
Fund
Westway Trust
White Stuff Foundation
The Willmott Dixon Foundation
The Harold Hyam Wingate
Foundation
The Maurice Wohl Charitable
Foundation
Wooden Spoon Society
Woodroffe Benton Foundation
The Woodstock Family Charitable
Foundation
The Woodward Charitable Trust
The Worwin UK Foundation
The Yapp Charitable Trust
Youth Music
The Zochonis Charitable Trust
Zurich Community Trust (UK) Ltd

Education and training

4 Charity Foundation
The 1989 Willan Charitable Trust
The 29th May 1961 Charitable
Trust
The A. H. Trust
The Aaronson Foundation
Aberdeen Asset Management
Charitable Foundation
The Aberdeen Foundation
ABF The Soldiers' Charity
AKO Foundation
The Alborada Trust
The Aldama Foundation
Al-Fayed Charitable Foundation
The All Saints Educational Trust
Allchurches Trust Ltd
The Allen and Overy Foundation
D C R Allen Charitable Trust
Viscount Amory's Charitable Trust
Anglo American Group Foundation
Anguish's Educational Foundation
The Anne Duchess of Westminster's
Charity
The Apax Foundation

The John Apthorp Charity
The John Armitage Charitable
Trust
The Armourers' and Brasiers'
Gauntlet Trust
The Arsenal Foundation Ltd
Arts Council of Wales (also known
as Cyngor Celfyddydau Cymru)
Ove Arup Partnership Charitable
Trust
The Asfari Foundation
Atkin Charitable Foundation
Autonomous Research Charitable
Trust (ARCT)
The Baily Thomas Charitable Fund
The Balcombe Charitable Trust
Banbury Charities
The Band Trust
The Barbers' Company General
Charities
The Barbour Foundation
Barnes Workhouse Fund
BBC Children in Need
BC Partners Foundation
The Beaverbrooks Charitable Trust
The John Beckwith Charitable Trust
Bellview Charitable Trust
Benesco Charity Ltd
The Berkeley Charitable
Foundation
Ruth Berkowitz Charitable Trust
The Big Lottery Fund
The Michael Bishop Foundation
Asser Bishvil Foundation
The Blagrave Trust
Bloodwise
The Booth Charities
Boots Charitable Trust
The Bowland Charitable Trust
G & K Boyes Charitable Trust
The Bransford Trust
The Breadsticks Foundation
The Brelms Trust CIO
The Brenley Trust
The Britford Bridge Trust
The British Academy for the
Promotion of Historical
Philosophical and Philological
Studies (The British Academy)
The British and Foreign School
Society
British Record Industry Trust
(BRIT Trust)
The Rory and Elizabeth Brooks
Foundation
Brushmill Ltd
The Buffini Chao Foundation
The Clara E Burgess Charity
The Edward Cadbury Charitable
Trust
The William Adlington Cadbury
Charitable Trust

The Cadbury Foundation
The Cadogan Charity
Calleva Foundation
Cannon Charitable Trust
The Carnegie Trust for the
Universities of Scotland
The Carpenters' Company
Charitable Trust
Sir John Cass's Foundation
The Castansa Trust
The Cayo Foundation
Charitworth Ltd
The Childhood Trust
The Childwick Trust
CHK Charities Ltd
Christie Foundation
Church Burgesses Trust
The City Bridge Trust (Bridge
House Estates)
J A Clark Charitable Trust
The Roger and Sarah Bancroft
Clark Charitable Trust
Clark Foundation
The Clore Duffield Foundation
The Clothworkers' Foundation
CMZ Ltd
The Coalfields Regeneration Trust
The John Coates Charitable Trust
Denise Coates Foundation
The John S Cohen Foundation
The R and S Cohen Foundation
Colyer-Fergusson Charitable Trust
Comic Relief
The Thomas Cook Children's
Charity
The Ernest Cook Trust
The Catherine Cookson Charitable
Trust
Co-operative Community
Investment Foundation
The Evan Cornish Foundation
General Charity of Coventry
Dudley and Geoffrey Cox
Charitable Trust
The Elizabeth Creak Charitable
Trust
Credit Suisse EMEA Foundation
The Cross Trust
The Peter Cruddas Foundation
Cruden Foundation Ltd
The Ronald Cruickshanks
Foundation
Cullum Family Trust
The Davidson Family Charitable
Trust
The Gwendoline and Margaret
Davies Charity
The Hamilton Davies Trust
The Crispin Davis Family Trust
Dawat-E-Hadiyah Trust (United
Kingdom)

The Roger De Haan Charitable Trust
The De Laszlo Foundation
The J N Derbyshire Trust
The Laduma Dhamecha Charitable Trust
Dina Perelman Trust Ltd
The Djanogly Foundation
The Double 'O' Charity Ltd
Drapers' Charitable Fund
The Royal Foundation of the Duke and Duchess of Cambridge and Prince Harry
The Dyers' Company Charitable Trust
The James Dyson Foundation
The Edge Foundation
D.M.H. Educational Trust Ltd
Edupoor Ltd
The Eighty Eight Foundation
EMI Music Sound Foundation
The Englefield Charitable Trust
Entindale Ltd
The Eranda Rothschild Foundation
The Essex Youth Trust
The Exilarch's Foundation
The Expat Foundation
Esmée Fairbairn Foundation
The Lord Faringdon Charitable Trust
The Thomas Farr Charity
The February Foundation
Allan and Nesta Ferguson Charitable Settlement
Doris Field Charitable Trust
The Sir John Fisher Foundation
Fisherbeck Charitable Trust
Fishmongers' Company's Charitable Trust
The Football Foundation
Donald Forrester Trust
The Fort Foundation
Four Acre Trust
The Foyle Foundation
The Hugh Fraser Foundation
The Joseph Strong Frazer Trust
Charles S French Charitable Trust
The Freshfield Foundation
Friends of Wiznitz Ltd
The Fulmer Charitable Trust
The Gannochy Trust
The Robert Gavron Charitable Trust
Sir Robert Geffery's Almshouse Trust
The GC Gibson Charitable Trust
The Gloag Foundation
Global Charities
Goldman Sachs Gives (UK)
The Goldsmiths' Company Charity
The Gosling Foundation Ltd
Grace Charitable Trust

The Grace Trust
The Granada Foundation
The Grant Foundation
The Great Britain Sasakawa Foundation
The Kenneth and Susan Green Charitable Foundation
Greenham Trust Ltd
The Grimmitt Trust
The Grocers' Charity
M and R Gross Charities Ltd
Groundwork UK
Calouste Gulbenkian Foundation – UK Branch
HCD Memorial Fund
Hackney Parochial Charities
Hadras Kodesh Trust
The Hadrian Trust
Halifax Foundation for Northern Ireland (previously known as Lloyds Bank Foundation for Northern Ireland)
Paul Hamlyn Foundation
The Helen Hamlyn Trust
Hampton Fuel Allotment
The W A Handley Charity Trust
The Haramead Trust
The Harbour Foundation
William Harding's Charity
Edward Harvist Trust (The Harvist Estate)
The Maurice Hatter Foundation
The Headley Trust
The Heathcoat Trust
Heathrow Community Fund (LHR Airport Communities Trust)
The Heathside Charitable Trust
The Charlotte Heber-Percy Charitable Trust
Hedley Foundation Ltd (The Hedley Foundation)
The Michael Heller Charitable Foundation
The Helping Foundation
The Hilden Charitable Fund
The Hillingdon Community Trust
The Lady Hind Trust
The Hintze Family Charity Foundation
The Henry C. Hoare Charitable Trust
The Hobson Charity Ltd
Hockerill Educational Foundation
The Jane Hodge Foundation
The Holden Charitable Trust
P H Holt Foundation
Horne Foundation
The Horse Trust
Hospice UK
Housing Pathways Trust
The Reta Lila Howard Foundation
The Hunter Foundation

Miss Agnes H Hunter's Trust
Huntingdon Freemen's Trust
Hurdale Charity Ltd
Hyde Park Place Estate Charity
IBM United Kingdom Trust
Ibrahim Foundation Ltd
Impetus – The Private Equity Foundation
The Worshipful Company of Information Technologists
Integrated Education Fund
Investream Charitable Trust
The Ireland Fund of Great Britain
The Ironmongers' Company
The J Isaacs Charitable Trust
The Isle of Anglesey Charitable Trust
The J J Charitable Trust
The Jabbs Foundation
The Frank Jackson Foundation
John James Bristol Foundation
The Jerusalem Trust
St John's Foundation (Bath)
The Johnson Foundation
The Jones 1986 Charitable Trust
Joseph Levy Foundation
Anton Jurgens Charitable Trust
The Ian Karten Charitable Trust
The Kensington and Chelsea Foundation
Keren Association Ltd
E And E Kernkraut Charities Limited
The Kiawah Charitable Trust
The Mary Kinross Charitable Trust
The Kirschel Foundation
The Sir James Knott Trust
Kollel and Co Ltd
Kolyom Trust Ltd
The KPMG Foundation
The Kreitman Foundation
The Neil Kreitman Foundation
Kusuma Trust UK
The Kyte Charitable Trust
Ladbrokes Coral Trust
John Laing Charitable Trust
The Kirby Laing Foundation
The Beatrice Laing Trust
The Lake House Charity
The Lancashire Foundation
Duchy of Lancaster Benevolent Fund
The Lancaster-Taylor Charitable Trust
The Allen Lane Foundation
Largsmount Ltd
The Lauffer Family Charitable Foundation
The Law Family Charitable Foundation
The Edgar E Lawley Foundation

The Raymond and Blanche Lawson
Charitable Trust
The Leathersellers' Company
Charitable Fund
The Leche Trust
The Legal Education Foundation
The Lehman Brothers Foundation
Europe
The Lennox Hannay Charitable
Trust
The Mark Leonard Trust
The Leverhulme Trade Charities
Trust
The Leverhulme Trust
Lord Leverhulme's Charitable Trust
Bernard Lewis Family Charitable
Trust
David and Ruth Lewis Family
Charitable Trust
John Lewis Partnership General
Community Fund
The Linbury Trust
The Charles Littlewood Hill Trust
The Second Joseph Aaron Littman
Foundation
Lloyds Bank Foundation for the
Channel Islands
Lloyd's Patriotic Fund
Lloyd's Register Foundation
The Lockwood Charitable
Foundation
Loftus Charitable Trust
Trust for London
The Lord's Taverners
The Lynn Foundation
John Lyon's Charity
M and C Trust
M B Foundation
The MK Charitable Trust
The Mackintosh Foundation
The MacRobert Trust
Man Group plc Charitable Trust
The W M Mann Foundation
The Manoukian Charitable
Foundation
The Michael Marsh Charitable
Trust
The Marsh Christian Trust
Sir George Martin Trust
John Martin's Charity
Masonic Charitable Foundation
The Nancie Massey Charitable
Trust
The Master Charitable Trust
The Mathew Trust
The Matliwala Family Charitable
Trust
The Robert McAlpine Foundation
The Medlock Charitable Trust
The Melow Charitable Trust
The Mercers' Charitable
Foundation

The Merchants' House of Glasgow
T. & J. Meyer Family Foundation
Ltd
The Millichope Foundation
The Brian Mitchell Charitable
Settlement
The Alexander Moncur Trust
Moondance Foundation
The George A. Moore Foundation
The Henry Moore Foundation
John Moores Foundation
The Steve Morgan Foundation
Morgan Stanley International
Foundation
G M Morrison Charitable Trust
The Ken and Lynne Morrison
Charitable Trust
The Morton Charitable Trust
(Dundee)
Moto in the Community
J P Moulton Charitable Foundation
The Edith Murphy Foundation
MW (RH) Foundation
The National Gardens Scheme
Nesta
Newby Trust Ltd
The NFU Mutual Charitable Trust
The Nisbet Trust
Educational Foundation of
Alderman John Norman
Normanby Charitable Trust
The Norton Rose Fulbright
Charitable Foundation
Norwich Town Close Estate Charity
The Nuffield Foundation
Oglesby Charitable Trust
Oizer Charitable Trust
Old Possum's Practical Trust
The John Oldacre Foundation
OneFamily Foundation
Open Gate
The Doris Pacey Charitable
Foundation
The Panacea Charitable Trust
The James Pantyfedwen Foundation
Parabola Foundation
Paradigm Foundation
The Park House Charitable Trust
Peacock Charitable Trust
The David Pearlman Charitable
Foundation
The Pears Family Charitable
Foundation
The Pebble Trust
The Dowager Countess Eleanor
Peel Trust
People's Postcode Trust
The Performing Right Society
Foundation
The Jack Petchey Foundation
The Austin and Hope Pilkington
Trust

The Polonsky Foundation
Postcode Dream Trust
David and Elaine Potter
Foundation
Sir John Priestman Charity Trust
The Prince of Wales's Charitable
Foundation
The Professional Footballers'
Association Charity
The PwC Foundation
Mr and Mrs J A Pye's Charitable
Settlement
The Queen Anne's Gate Foundation
The Racing Foundation
The Radcliffe Trust
The Rank Foundation Ltd
Rashbass Family Trust
The Rayne Foundation
The Reece Foundation
Richard Reeve's Foundation
Responsible Gambling Trust
(GambleAware)
Reuben Foundation
Rhondda Cynon Taff Welsh Church
Acts Fund
Edmund Rice Bicentennial Trust
Ltd
The Clive and Sylvia Richards
Charity Ltd
Richmond Parish Lands Charity
The River Farm Foundation
The Roan Charitable Trust
Mrs L D Rope's Third Charitable
Settlement
The David Ross Foundation
The Rothermere Foundation
The Rothley Trust
The Rothschild Foundation
Rothschild Foundation (Hanadiv)
Europe
The Roughley Charitable Trust
Rowanville Ltd
The Rowlands Trust
The Royal British Legion
Royal Docks Trust (London)
The Sackler Trust
The Saddlers' Company Charitable
Fund
The Alan and Babette Sainsbury
Charitable Fund
The Saintbury Trust
The Basil Samuel Charitable Trust
The M J Samuel Charitable Trust
The Samworth Foundation
Santander UK Foundation Ltd
The Savoy Educational Trust
Schroder Charity Trust
The ScottishPower Foundation
Seafarers UK (King George's Fund
for Sailors)
Sam and Bella Sebba Charitable
Trust

The Segelman Trust
The Shears Foundation
The Sheepdrove Trust
The Archie Sherman Charitable
    Trust
SHINE (Support and Help in
    Education)
The Simmons and Simmons
    Charitable Foundation
The Sino-British Fellowship Trust
The Slaughter and May Charitable
    Trust
Sloane Robinson Foundation
The DS Smith Charitable
    Foundation
The Martin Smith Foundation
Sodexo Stop Hunger Foundation
Sofronie Foundation
R H Southern Trust
Peter Sowerby Foundation
Spielman Charitable Trust
The Spoore, Merry and Rixman
    Foundation
The Geoff and Fiona Squire
    Foundation
Standard Life Foundation
Starlow Charities Ltd
The Steel Charitable Trust
The Steinberg Family Charitable
    Trust
Stevenson Family's Charitable Trust
The Stewarts Law Foundation
Mark Stolkin Foundation
The Stoneygate Trust
Stratford-upon-Avon Town Trust
The WO Street Charitable
    Foundation
The Street Foundation
The Summerfield Charitable Trust
The Bernard Sunley Charitable
    Foundation
Sutton Coldfield Charitable Trust
The Sutton Trust
The John Swire 1989 Charitable
    Trust
The Swire Charitable Trust
Tallow Chandlers Benevolent Fund
    No. 2
The David Tannen Charitable Trust
C B And H H Taylor 1984 Trust
Humphrey Richardson Taylor
    Charitable Trust
The Taylor Family Foundation
Khoo Teck Puat UK Foundation
The Tolkien Trust
The Tompkins Foundation
Toras Chesed (London) Trust
The Tottenham Grammar School
    Foundation
Ufi Charitable Trust

The Underwood Trust
The Union of The Sisters of Mercy
    of Great Britain
United Jewish Israel Appeal
United Purpose
UPP Foundation
The Michael Uren Foundation
The Utley Family Charitable Trust
The Vandervell Foundation
The Vardy Foundation
Variety, the Children's Charity
The Vintners' Foundation
The Vodafone Foundation
Sylvia Waddilove Foundation UK
The Walcot Foundation
The Walker Trust
The Barbara Ward Children's
    Foundation
The Waterloo Foundation
Wates Family Enterprise Trust
The Wates Foundation
The William Wates Memorial Trust
The Geoffrey Watling Charity
The Weavers' Company Benevolent
    Fund
The Weinstock Fund
The Welton Foundation
The Garfield Weston Foundation
Westway Trust
The Wheeler Family Charitable
    Trust
The Harold Hyam Wingate
    Foundation
Winton Philanthropies
The Wixamtree Trust
The Maurice Wohl Charitable
    Foundation
The Charles Wolfson Charitable
    Trust
The Wolfson Family Charitable
    Trust
The Wolfson Foundation
The Foster Wood Foundation
Woodroffe Benton Foundation
The Worwin UK Foundation
The Eric Wright Charitable Trust
The Yapp Charitable Trust
Yorkshire and Clydesdale Bank
    Foundation
Yorkshire Building Society
    Charitable Foundation
The William Allen Young
    Charitable Trust
Youth Music
Elizabeth and Prince Zaiger Trust
The Marjorie and Arnold Ziff
    Charitable Foundation
The Zochonis Charitable Trust

Environment and animals

The Anne Duchess of Westminster's
    Charity
The Balcombe Charitable Trust
The Barbour Foundation
The Barclay Foundation
Lord Barnby's Foundation
G & K Boyes Charitable Trust
The Bromley Trust
The Edward Cadbury Charitable
    Trust
The William Adlington Cadbury
    Charitable Trust
The Cadogan Charity
Sandra Charitable Trust
The John Coates Charitable Trust
The Sir Tom Cowie Charitable
    Trust
Peter De Haan Charitable Trust
The Royal Foundation of the Duke
    and Duchess of Cambridge and
    Prince Harry
The Gerald Palmer Eling Trust
    Company
John Ellerman Foundation
The Emerald Foundation
The Enkalon Foundation
The Lord Faringdon Charitable
    Trust
Gatwick Airport Community Trust
The Simon Gibson Charitable Trust
The Golden Bottle Trust
The Kenneth and Susan Green
    Charitable Foundation
Greenham Trust Ltd
Groundwork UK
The Hadfield Charitable Trust
The W A Handley Charity Trust
The Charlotte Heber-Percy
    Charitable Trust
The Lady Hind Trust
The Henry C. Hoare Charitable
    Trust
The Hobson Charity Ltd
The Frank Jackson Foundation
The Ernest Kleinwort Charitable
    Trust
The Sir James Knott Trust
The Martin Laing Foundation
Lancashire Environmental Fund Ltd
The Lennox Hannay Charitable
    Trust
Lord Leverhulme's Charitable Trust
John Lewis Partnership General
    Community Fund
The Lynn Foundation
The Mackintosh Foundation
The Mactaggart Third Fund

505

The Marsh Christian Trust
The Master Charitable Trust
The Millichope Foundation
The Monument Trust
The George A. Moore Foundation
Moto in the Community
The Ofenheim Charitable Trust
Oxfam (GB)
Peacock Charitable Trust
Mr and Mrs J A Pye's Charitable
    Settlement
The Revere Charitable Trust
The Roddick Foundation
The Rothschild Foundation
The Rowlands Trust
Royal Docks Trust (London)
Royal Society of Wildlife Trusts
The Basil Samuel Charitable Trust
The M J Samuel Charitable Trust
The Samworth Foundation
Scott (Eredine) Charitable Trust
The ScottishPower Foundation
The Sheepdrove Trust
The SMB Trust
The DS Smith Charitable
    Foundation
The W F Southall Trust
R H Southern Trust
The Spear Charitable Trust
The Steel Charitable Trust
The Tolkien Trust
The Constance Travis Charitable
    Trust
The Underwood Trust
The Michael Uren Foundation
The Van Neste Foundation
The Veolia Environmental Trust
Viridor Credits Environmental
    Company
Sylvia Waddilove Foundation UK
Mrs Waterhouse Charitable Trust
    (formerly known as the
    Houghton Dunn Charitable
    Trust)
The Geoffrey Watling Charity
Welcome To Our Future (Local
    Agenda 21)
The HDH Wills 1965 Charitable
    Trust
The Wixamtree Trust
Yorkshire and Clydesdale Bank
    Foundation
The Yorkshire Dales Millennium
    Trust

Animals

The Alborada Trust
The Ashden Trust
The Charities Advisory Trust
The Childwick Trust
The Catherine Cookson Charitable
    Trust

Dumbreck Charity
The EBM Charitable Trust
Doris Field Charitable Trust
Donald Forrester Trust
The Joseph Strong Frazer Trust
The Maurice Hatter Foundation
The Horse Trust
The Jordan Charitable Foundation
The Kennel Club Charitable Trust
The RS Macdonald Charitable
    Trust
The Marchig Animal Welfare Trust
The Kristina Martin Charitable
    Trust
The Alexander Mosley Charitable
    Trust
The Edith Murphy Foundation
The Nineveh Charitable Trust
The Sir Peter O'Sullevan Charitable
    Trust
The Oakdale Trust
Open Gate
The Persula Foundation
Petplan Charitable Trust
Postcode Local Trust
The Racing Foundation
The Jean Sainsbury Animal Welfare
    Trust
SITA Cornwall Trust Ltd
The Stafford Trust
Support Adoption For Pets
The Thompson Family Charitable
    Trust
The David Webster Charitable
    Trust
The Weir Charitable Trust
The Garfield Weston Foundation
Whitley Animal Protection Trust
Yorkshire Building Society
    Charitable Foundation
The William Allen Young
    Charitable Trust
Elizabeth and Prince Zaiger Trust

Environment

The 29th May 1961 Charitable
    Trust
The A Team Foundation Ltd
The Aldama Foundation
Anglo American Group Foundation
Ove Arup Partnership Charitable
    Trust
The Ashden Trust
The Banister Charitable Trust
BC Partners Foundation
The Big Lottery Fund
The Bothwell Charitable Trust
The Bowland Charitable Trust
The Britford Bridge Trust
The Cadbury Foundation
The Castansa Trust
The Chalk Cliff Trust

Chapman Charitable Trust
The Charities Advisory Trust
CHK Charities Ltd
The City Bridge Trust (Bridge
    House Estates)
Clark Foundation
Community First
The Ernest Cook Trust
The Elizabeth Creak Charitable
    Trust
The D'Oyly Carte Charitable Trust
The Davis Foundation
The Dulverton Trust
Dunard Fund 2016
The Englefield Charitable Trust
Esmée Fairbairn Foundation
The Fidelity UK Foundation
Doris Field Charitable Trust
Fisherbeck Charitable Trust
Fishmongers' Company's Charitable
    Trust
The Fort Foundation
The Hugh Fraser Foundation
The Joseph Strong Frazer Trust
The Freshfield Foundation
The Generations Foundation
The Gosling Foundation Ltd
GrantScape
The Great Britain Sasakawa
    Foundation
The Greggs Foundation
Calouste Gulbenkian Foundation –
    UK Branch
HCD Memorial Fund
The Hadrian Trust
Heathrow Community Fund (LHR
    Airport Communities Trust)
Heritage Lottery Fund
The Hillingdon Community Trust
The Innocent Foundation
The Ireland Fund of Great Britain
The Isle of Anglesey Charitable
    Trust
The J J Charitable Trust
The Jabbs Foundation
The Jordan Charitable Foundation
Christopher Laing Foundation
The Kirby Laing Foundation
The Lauffer Family Charitable
    Foundation
The Raymond and Blanche Lawson
    Charitable Trust
The Leche Trust
The Mark Leonard Trust
The Charles Littlewood Hill Trust
Trust for London
The MacRobert Trust
The Kristina Martin Charitable
    Trust
Sir George Martin Trust

General charitable purposes

The Medlock Charitable Trust

T. & J. Meyer Family Foundation Ltd

The Gerald Micklem Charitable Trust

Millennium Stadium Charitable Trust (Ymddiriedolaeth Elusennol Stadiwm Y Mileniwm)

The Frederick Mulder Foundation

The National Gardens Scheme

Network for Social Change Charitable Trust

The NFU Mutual Charitable Trust

The Nineveh Charitable Trust

The Northwick Trust

The Oakdale Trust

Oglesby Charitable Trust

The John Oldacre Foundation

Open Gate

The Pilgrim Trust

Cecil Pilkington Charitable Trust

Polden-Puckham Charitable Foundation

Postcode Dream Trust

Postcode Local Trust

The Prince of Wales's Charitable Foundation

The Prince's Countryside Fund

The Sigrid Rausing Trust

The Rothley Trust

The Roughley Charitable Trust

The Saintbury Trust

Schroder Charity Trust

The Finnis Scott Foundation

Seafarers UK (King George's Fund for Sailors)

The Shears Foundation

SITA Cornwall Trust Ltd

The Martin Smith Foundation

The Sobell Foundation

Peter Sowerby Foundation

The Stone Family Foundation

C B And H H Taylor 1984 Trust

The Tedworth Charitable Trust

The Roger and Douglas Turner Charitable Trust

Ulster Garden Villages Ltd

United Purpose

The Valentine Charitable Trust

The Vandervell Foundation

The Waterloo Foundation

Wates Family Enterprise Trust

The David Webster Charitable Trust

The Garfield Weston Foundation

Westway Trust

Woodroffe Benton Foundation

Worth Waynflete Foundation

The 1989 Willan Charitable Trust

The 29th May 1961 Charitable Trust

The 3Ts Charitable Trust

4 Charity Foundation

The Aaronson Foundation

The Aberdeen Foundation

ABF The Soldiers' Charity

Allchurches Trust Ltd

D C R Allen Charitable Trust

The AMW Charitable Trust

The Annandale Charitable Trust

The Anne Duchess of Westminster's Charity

The Anson Charitable Trust

The Ardeola Charitable Trust

The John Armitage Charitable Trust

The Armourers' and Brasiers' Gauntlet Trust

The Arsenal Foundation Ltd

Ove Arup Partnership Charitable Trust

The Asda Foundation

Atkin Charitable Foundation

Autonomous Research Charitable Trust (ARCT)

Awards for All

The Bacit Foundation

The Bamford Charitable Foundation

Banbury Charities

The Band Trust

The Barbers' Company General Charities

The Barbour Foundation

The Barclay Foundation

The Barker-Mill Foundation

Lord Barnby's Foundation

Misses Barrie Charitable Trust

Robert Barr's Charitable Trust

The Paul Bassham Charitable Trust

The Batchworth Trust

The Battersea Power Station Foundation

The Louis Baylis (Maidenhead Advertiser) Charitable Trust

BBC Children in Need

The Beaverbrook Foundation

The Beaverbrooks Charitable Trust

Bideford Bridge Trust

The Big Lottery Fund

Binks Trust

The Sir Victor Blank Charitable Settlement

The Bloom Foundation

The Bluston Charitable Settlement

The Booth Charities

Boots Charitable Trust

The Bothwell Charitable Trust

The Bowland Charitable Trust

The Bradley Family Charitable Foundation

The William Brake Charitable Trust

The Liz and Terry Bramall Foundation

The Britford Bridge Trust

The Broomton Foundation

The Buffini Chao Foundation

The Bulldog Trust

The Cadbury Foundation

Calleva Foundation

The W.A. Cargill Fund

The Carpenters' Company Charitable Trust

Catkin Pussywillow Charitable Trust

The Joseph and Annie Cattle Trust

The Thomas Sivewright Catto Charitable Settlement

The Cayo Foundation

The Charities Advisory Trust

Charitworth Ltd

CHK Charities Ltd

Christie Foundation

The Roger and Sarah Bancroft Clark Charitable Trust

Clark Foundation

The Coalfields Regeneration Trust

The John Coates Charitable Trust

The John S Cohen Foundation

Martin Connell Charitable Trust

The Catherine Cookson Charitable Trust

The Alice Ellen Cooper Dean Charitable Foundation

Co-operative Community Investment Foundation

The Gershon Coren Charitable Foundation (also known as The Muriel and Gus Coren Charitable Foundation)

General Charity of Coventry

The Sir Tom Cowie Charitable Trust

Cripplegate Foundation

The Ronald Cruickshanks Foundation

The Gwendoline and Margaret Davies Charity

The Crispin Davis Family Trust

The J N Derbyshire Trust

The Desmond Foundation

The Laduma Dhamecha Charitable Trust

Dina Perelman Trust Ltd

The Dorfman Foundation

The Double 'O' Charity Ltd
Drapers' Charitable Fund
The Dromintee Trust
The Dulverton Trust
Dumbreck Charity
The Charles Dunstone Charitable
  Trust
The Dyers' Company Charitable
  Trust
The James Dyson Foundation
The Earley Charity
The Sir John Eastwood Foundation
D.M.H. Educational Trust Ltd
Edupoor Ltd
The Eighty Eight Foundation
The Maud Elkington Charitable
  Trust
The Ellerdale Trust
The Englefield Charitable Trust
The Eventhall Family Charitable
  Trust
The Exilarch's Foundation
The Lord Faringdon Charitable
  Trust
The Thomas Farr Charity
Fayre Share Foundation
The February Foundation
Doris Field Charitable Trust
The Sir John Fisher Foundation
Fisherbeck Charitable Trust
Forever Manchester
Donald Forrester Trust
Gwyneth Forrester Trust
The Fort Foundation
The Elizabeth Frankland Moore and
  Star Foundation
The Hugh Fraser Foundation
The Joseph Strong Frazer Trust
Charles S French Charitable Trust
The Patrick and Helena Frost
  Foundation
The Fulmer Charitable Trust
The Funding Network
The Gale Family Charity Trust
Gatwick Airport Community Trust
The Robert Gavron Charitable
  Trust
Sir Robert Geffery's Almshouse
  Trust
The GC Gibson Charitable Trust
The Simon Gibson Charitable Trust
Global Charities
The Golden Bottle Trust
Goldman Sachs Gives (UK)
The Goldsmiths' Company Charity
The Goodman Foundation
The Mike Gooley Trailfinders
  Charity
The Gosling Foundation Ltd
Grace Charitable Trust
The Grace Trust
The Grant Foundation

GrantScape
The Kenneth and Susan Green
  Charitable Foundation
The Green Hall Foundation
Greenham Trust Ltd
The Greggs Foundation
M and R Gross Charities Ltd
Groundwork UK
H & T Clients Charitable Trust
HCD Memorial Fund
Hampton Fuel Allotment
The W A Handley Charity Trust
The Robert Fleming Hannay
  Memorial Charity
The Haramead Trust
The Harborne Parish Lands Charity
The Harbour Foundation
William Harding's Charity
The Edith Lilian Harrison 2000
  Foundation
Edward Harvist Trust (The Harvist
  Estate)
The Maurice Hatter Foundation
The Charles Hayward Foundation
The Heathcoat Trust
The Heathside Charitable Trust
The Charlotte Heber-Percy
  Charitable Trust
The Michael Heller Charitable
  Foundation
The Helping Foundation
Henderson Firstfruits
The Hilden Charitable Fund
The Lady Hind Trust
The Hintze Family Charity
  Foundation
The Hobson Charity Ltd
The Jane Hodge Foundation
P H Holt Foundation
The Thomas J Horne Memorial
  Trust
Housing Pathways Trust
The Reta Lila Howard Foundation
James T Howat Charitable Trust
The Hull and East Riding
  Charitable Trust
The Albert Hunt Trust
Huntingdon Freemen's Trust
Ibrahim Foundation Ltd
The Indigo Trust
The Ingram Trust
The Inman Charity
Investream Charitable Trust
The J Isaacs Charitable Trust
The Isle of Anglesey Charitable
  Trust
The Jabbs Foundation
John James Bristol Foundation
The Johnson Foundation
The Joicey Trust
The Jones 1986 Charitable Trust
The Muriel Jones Foundation

The Jordan Charitable Foundation
Joseph Levy Foundation
Anton Jurgens Charitable Trust
Keren Association Ltd
E And E Kernkraut Charities
  Limited
The King Henry VIII Endowed
  Trust – Warwick
King/Cullimore Charitable Trust
The Ernest Kleinwort Charitable
  Trust
The Sir James Knott Trust
Kollel and Co Ltd
The Kreitman Foundation
The Neil Kreitman Foundation
Ladbrokes Coral Trust
John Laing Charitable Trust
Christopher Laing Foundation
The David Laing Foundation
The Martin Laing Foundation
The Lake House Charity
The Lancashire Foundation
Duchy of Lancaster Benevolent
  Fund
The LankellyChase Foundation
The Basil Larsen 1999 Charitable
  Trust
The Lauffer Family Charitable
  Foundation
The Kathleen Laurence Trust
The Law Family Charitable
  Foundation
The Betty Lawes Foundation
The Edgar E Lawley Foundation
The Leathersellers' Company
  Charitable Fund
The William Leech Charity
The Lehman Brothers Foundation
  Europe
Lempriere Pringle 2015
The Lennox Hannay Charitable
  Trust
The Mark Leonard Trust
Leri Charitable Trust
The Leverhulme Trade Charities
  Trust
Lord Leverhulme's Charitable Trust
Bernard Lewis Family Charitable
  Trust
David and Ruth Lewis Family
  Charitable Trust
John Lewis Partnership General
  Community Fund
The Lind Trust
The Enid Linder Foundation
The Charles Littlewood Hill Trust
The George John and Sheilah
  Livanos Charitable Trust
Lloyds Bank Foundation for
  England and Wales
Lloyd's Patriotic Fund
The Locker Foundation

The Lockwood Charitable
Foundation
The William and Katherine
Longman Trust
LPW Ltd
The Lynn Foundation
M and C Trust
The Mackintosh Foundation
The Mactaggart Third Fund
The Ian Mactaggart Trust (The
Mactaggart Second Fund)
The W M Mann Foundation
The Michael Marsh Charitable
Trust
The Kristina Martin Charitable
Trust
John Martin's Charity
Mayheights Ltd
Mazars Charitable Trust
MBNA General Foundation
The Robert McAlpine Foundation
The Medlock Charitable Trust
The Melow Charitable Trust
The Brian Mercer Charitable Trust
The Mercers' Charitable
Foundation
Merchant Navy Welfare Board
The Merchants' House of Glasgow
The Millichope Foundation
The Clare Milne Trust
The Laurence Misener Charitable
Trust
The Brian Mitchell Charitable
Settlement
The Alexander Moncur Trust
The Monument Trust
The George A. Moore Foundation
The Steve Morgan Foundation
G M Morrison Charitable Trust
The Ken and Lynne Morrison
Charitable Trust
The Morrisons Foundation
The Morton Charitable Trust
(Dundee)
The Alexander Mosley Charitable
Trust
Moto in the Community
The John R. Murray Charitable
Trust
Network for Social Change
Charitable Trust
The Norman Family Charitable
Trust
Normanby Charitable Trust
The Northwick Trust
Northwood Charitable Trust
Odin Charitable Trust
The Ofenheim Charitable Trust
Oglesby Charitable Trust
Oizer Charitable Trust
OneFamily Foundation
P F Charitable Trust

The Doris Pacey Charitable
Foundation
The James Pantyfedwen Foundation
Parabola Foundation
Paradigm Foundation
Payne-Gallwey 1989 Charitable
Trust
Peacock Charitable Trust
The David Pearlman Charitable
Foundation
The Pebble Trust
The Dowager Countess Eleanor
Peel Trust
People's Health Trust
The Persula Foundation
Cecil Pilkington Charitable Trust
Sir John Priestman Charity Trust
Mr and Mrs J A Pye's Charitable
Settlement
Quintessentially Foundation
Rachel Charitable Trust
The Rank Foundation Ltd
The Joseph Rank Trust
Rashbass Family Trust
The Ratcliff Foundation
The Sir James Reckitt Charity
The Reece Foundation
Reuben Foundation
Rhondda Cynon Taff Welsh Church
Acts Fund
Richmond Parish Lands Charity
The River Farm Foundation
The Roan Charitable Trust
The Romeera Foundation
The Gerald Ronson Family
Foundation
The Rose Foundation
The Rothermere Foundation
The Rothley Trust
The Rowlands Trust
Royal Artillery Charitable Fund
The Rugby Group Benevolent Fund
Ltd
The Saddlers' Company Charitable
Fund
The Saintbury Trust
The Samworth Foundation
Schroder Charity Trust
The Schroder Foundation
Scott (Eredine) Charitable Trust
The Frieda Scott Charitable Trust
The ScottishPower Foundation
Scottish Property Industry Festival
of Christmas (Spifox)
Sam and Bella Sebba Charitable
Trust
The Shanly Foundation
ShareGift (The Orr Mackintosh
Foundation)
The Sheepdrove Trust
The Sheffield Town Trust

The Sylvia and Colin Shepherd
Charitable Trust
The Archie Sherman Charitable
Trust
The Charles Skey Charitable Trust
The Slaughter and May Charitable
Trust
The SMB Trust
Social Business Trust
Social Investment Business
Foundation
Social Tech Trust
The W F Southall Trust
The Spear Charitable Trust
Spielman Charitable Trust
The Geoff and Fiona Squire
Foundation
Stadium Charitable Trust
The Peter Stebbings Memorial
Charity
Stevenson Family's Charitable Trust
The Stoller Charitable Trust
The Stoneygate Trust
Stratford-upon-Avon Town Trust
Strathnairn Community Benefit
Fund Ltd
Sutton Coldfield Charitable Trust
Swansea and Brecon Diocesan
Board of Finance Ltd
The John Swire 1989 Charitable
Trust
The Adrian Swire Charitable Trust
The Syder Foundation
The Charles and Elsie Sykes Trust
The Talbot Village Trust
Tallow Chandlers Benevolent Fund
No. 2
Tay Charitable Trust
C B And H H Taylor 1984 Trust
The Tedworth Charitable Trust
The Thompson Family Charitable
Trust
The Trusthouse Charitable
Foundation
The Tudor Trust
The Tuixen Foundation
G J W Turner Trust
Tzedakah
UnLtd (Foundation for Social
Entrepreneurs)
The Michael Uren Foundation
The Utley Family Charitable Trust
The Vail Foundation
The Valentine Charitable Trust
The Vandervell Foundation
The Vardy Foundation
VHLT Ltd
The Vintners' Foundation
The Vodafone Foundation
The Geoffrey Watling Charity
The Weavers' Company Benevolent
Fund

The Weinstock Fund
The James Weir Foundation
Welcome To Our Future (Local
    Agenda 21)
The Welton Foundation
The Garfield Weston Foundation
The Melanie White Foundation Ltd
White Stuff Foundation
The Wigoder Family Foundation
The HDH Wills 1965 Charitable
    Trust
Brian Wilson Charitable Trust
Sumner Wilson Charitable Trust
The Wimbledon Foundation
The Harold Hyam Wingate
    Foundation
Winton Philanthropies
The Wixamtree Trust
The Maurice Wohl Charitable
    Foundation
The Charles Wolfson Charitable
    Trust
The F Glenister Woodger Trust
Woodroffe Benton Foundation
The Woodstock Family Charitable
    Foundation
The Woodward Charitable Trust
Worth Waynflete Foundation
The Worwin UK Foundation
Wychdale Ltd
The Wyfold Charitable Trust
Yorkshire Building Society
    Charitable Foundation
The Yorkshire Dales Millennium
    Trust
The William Allen Young
    Charitable Trust
Elizabeth and Prince Zaiger Trust
The Marjorie and Arnold Ziff
    Charitable Foundation
The Zochonis Charitable Trust
Zurich Community Trust (UK) Ltd

Health

The 1989 Willan Charitable Trust
The 29th May 1961 Charitable
    Trust
4 Charity Foundation
The Aaronson Foundation
The Aberdeen Foundation
ABF The Soldiers' Charity
The ACT Foundation
Action on Hearing Loss (The Royal
    National Institute For Deaf
    People)
The Sylvia Adams Charitable Trust
The Adint Charitable Trust
The AIM Foundation
Ajahma Charitable Trust

The Alchemy Foundation
The Aldama Foundation
Al-Fayed Charitable Foundation
D C R Allen Charitable Trust
The AMW Charitable Trust
The Andrew Anderson Trust
Anglo American Group Foundation
The Anne Duchess of Westminster's
    Charity
Ardbarron Trust Ltd
The John Armitage Charitable
    Trust
Arts Council England
Ove Arup Partnership Charitable
    Trust
Atkin Charitable Foundation
Autonomous Research Charitable
    Trust (ARCT)
The Balcombe Charitable Trust
The Ballinger Charitable Trust
The Barbers' Company General
    Charities
The Barbour Foundation
The Barclay Foundation
Barnes Workhouse Fund
Barnwood Trust
The Batchworth Trust
BBC Children in Need
The Beaverbrook Foundation
The Beaverbrooks Charitable Trust
Benesco Charity Ltd
The Berkeley Charitable
    Foundation
The Big Lottery Fund
The Michael Bishop Foundation
The Sir Victor Blank Charitable
    Settlement
The Bloom Foundation
The Bluston Charitable Settlement
The Booth Charities
Boots Charitable Trust
The Borrows Charitable Trust
The Boshier-Hinton Foundation
The Tony Bramall Charitable Trust
The Liz and Terry Bramall
    Foundation
The Bransford Trust
The Breadsticks Foundation
The Brelms Trust CIO
The Britford Bridge Trust
The Burdett Trust for Nursing
The Clara E Burgess Charity
The William Adlington Cadbury
    Charitable Trust
David William Traill Cargill Fund
Chapman Charitable Trust
Sandra Charitable Trust
Chest Heart and Stroke Scotland
The Childwick Trust
Church Burgesses Trust
The Churchill Foundation

The CIBC World Markets
    Children's Foundation
The City Bridge Trust (Bridge
    House Estates)
Clark Foundation
The Clothworkers' Foundation
Richard Cloudesley's Charity
The Coalfields Regeneration Trust
The John Coates Charitable Trust
Denise Coates Foundation
The Colchester Catalyst Charity
The Colt Foundation
Comic Relief
The Thomas Cook Children's
    Charity
The Catherine Cookson Charitable
    Trust
The Gershon Coren Charitable
    Foundation (also known as The
    Muriel and Gus Coren Charitable
    Foundation)
The Evan Cornish Foundation
Corra Foundation
General Charity of Coventry
Dudley and Geoffrey Cox
    Charitable Trust
CRASH
The Crerar Trust
Cruden Foundation Ltd
CSIS Charity Fund
Itzchok Meyer Cymerman Trust
    Ltd
The D'Oyly Carte Charitable Trust
Baron Davenport's Charity
The Davidson Family Charitable
    Trust
The Gwendoline and Margaret
    Davies Charity
The Crispin Davis Family Trust
The Roger De Haan Charitable
    Trust
Debenhams Foundation
The J N Derbyshire Trust
The Desmond Foundation
The Laduma Dhamecha Charitable
    Trust
Dinwoodie Charitable Company
The Djanogly Foundation
Dollond Charitable Trust
The Double 'O' Charity Ltd
The Royal Foundation of the Duke
    and Duchess of Cambridge and
    Prince Harry
Dumbreck Charity
The Charles Dunstone Charitable
    Trust
The Dyers' Company Charitable
    Trust
Echoes of Service
Edupoor Ltd
The Gerald Palmer Eling Trust
    Company

The Marian Elizabeth Trust
The Eranda Rothschild Foundation
The Evelyn Trust
The Eveson Charitable Trust
The Exilarch's Foundation
The Lord Faringdon Charitable
    Trust
The Thomas Farr Charity
The February Foundation
The Fidelity UK Foundation
Doris Field Charitable Trust
The Sir John Fisher Foundation
Donald Forrester Trust
The Fort Foundation
The Elizabeth Frankland Moore and
    Star Foundation
The Hugh Fraser Foundation
The Joseph Strong Frazer Trust
Charles S French Charitable Trust
The Freshfield Foundation
Friends of Wiznitz Ltd
The Robert Gavron Charitable
    Trust
The Generations Foundation
The GC Gibson Charitable Trust
The Simon Gibson Charitable Trust
The Gloag Foundation
Global Charities
The Golden Bottle Trust
Goldman Sachs Gives (UK)
The Goldsmiths' Company Charity
The Goodman Foundation
Grace Charitable Trust
The Grace Trust
The Kenneth and Susan Green
    Charitable Foundation
The Green Hall Foundation
Greenham Trust Ltd
The Grimmitt Trust
HCD Memorial Fund
The Hadley Trust
Paul Hamlyn Foundation
The Helen Hamlyn Trust
The Hampstead Wells and
    Campden Trust
Hampton Fuel Allotment
The W A Handley Charity Trust
The Haramead Trust
The Harborne Parish Lands Charity
The Harbour Foundation
The Harpur Trust
The Edith Lilian Harrison 2000
    Foundation
Edward Harvist Trust (The Harvist
    Estate)
The Maurice Hatter Foundation
The Charles Hayward Foundation
The Headley Trust
The Health Foundation
Heart Research UK
The Heathcoat Trust
The Heathside Charitable Trust

The Charlotte Heber-Percy
    Charitable Trust
Hedley Foundation Ltd (The
    Hedley Foundation)
The Christina Mary Hendrie Trust
The Hilden Charitable Fund
The Lady Hind Trust
The Hintze Family Charity
    Foundation
The Henry C. Hoare Charitable
    Trust
The Hobson Charity Ltd
The Homelands Charitable Trust
The Thomas J Horne Memorial
    Trust
Hospice UK
The Hospital Saturday Fund
Housing Pathways Trust
The Albert Hunt Trust
Miss Agnes H Hunter's Trust
Huntingdon Freemen's Trust
Hurdale Charity Ltd
The Inman Charity
The Innocent Foundation
Investream Charitable Trust
The J Isaacs Charitable Trust
John James Bristol Foundation
Jewish Child's Day (JCD)
St John's Foundation (Bath)
The Johnson Foundation
The Jones 1986 Charitable Trust
The Jordan Charitable Foundation
Joseph Levy Foundation
Anton Jurgens Charitable Trust
The Ian Karten Charitable Trust
The Kentown Wizard Foundation
Kidney Research UK
The Kirschel Foundation
The Ernest Kleinwort Charitable
    Trust
The Sir James Knott Trust
The Kreitman Foundation
The Neil Kreitman Foundation
The Kyte Charitable Trust
Ladbrokes Coral Trust
Christopher Laing Foundation
The David Laing Foundation
The Beatrice Laing Trust
The Lake House Charity
The Lancashire Foundation
Lancaster Foundation
The Allen Lane Foundation
The Lauffer Family Charitable
    Foundation
The Kathleen Laurence Trust
The Law Family Charitable
    Foundation
The Edgar E Lawley Foundation
The Raymond and Blanche Lawson
    Charitable Trust
The Leathersellers' Company
    Charitable Fund

The Lehman Brothers Foundation
    Europe
Leng Charitable Trust
The Lennox Hannay Charitable
    Trust
Lord Leverhulme's Charitable Trust
Bernard Lewis Family Charitable
    Trust
David and Ruth Lewis Family
    Charitable Trust
John Lewis Partnership General
    Community Fund
The Linbury Trust
The Enid Linder Foundation
The Charles Littlewood Hill Trust
The Second Joseph Aaron Littman
    Foundation
The George John and Sheilah
    Livanos Charitable Trust
Lloyds Bank Foundation for
    England and Wales
Lloyd's Patriotic Fund
The Locker Foundation
The Lolev Charitable Trust
Trust for London
London Catalyst
London Housing Foundation Ltd
    (LHF)
The Lyndal Tree Foundation
The Lynn Foundation
M and C Trust
The MK Charitable Trust
The Mactaggart Third Fund
The Ian Mactaggart Trust (The
    Mactaggart Second Fund)
The Michael Marsh Charitable
    Trust
The Marsh Christian Trust
The Kristina Martin Charitable
    Trust
John Martin's Charity
Masonic Charitable Foundation
The Master Charitable Trust
The Matliwala Family Charitable
    Trust
Maudsley Charity
Mayheights Ltd
The Robert McAlpine Foundation
The Medlock Charitable Trust
Meningitis Research Foundation
Merchant Navy Welfare Board
Merchant Taylors' Consolidated
    Charities for the Infirm
T. & J. Meyer Family Foundation
    Ltd
The Gerald Micklem Charitable
    Trust
The Millichope Foundation
The Laurence Misener Charitable
    Trust
The Alexander Moncur Trust
The Monument Trust

Moondance Foundation
The George A. Moore Foundation
John Moores Foundation
The Steve Morgan Foundation
Morgan Stanley International
  Foundation
G M Morrison Charitable Trust
The Morton Charitable Trust
  (Dundee)
The Edith Murphy Foundation
The National Gardens Scheme
Nesta
Network for Social Change
  Charitable Trust
Newby Trust Ltd
The Frances and Augustus Newman
  Foundation
Normanby Charitable Trust
The Norton Rose Fulbright
  Charitable Foundation
The Nuffield Foundation
Odin Charitable Trust
The Ofenheim Charitable Trust
Oizer Charitable Trust
OneFamily Foundation
The Doris Pacey Charitable
  Foundation
The JGW Patterson Foundation
Peacock Charitable Trust
The David Pearlman Charitable
  Foundation
People's Health Trust
The Persula Foundation
Pilkington Charities Fund
The Austin and Hope Pilkington
  Trust
Postcode Community Trust
Postcode Dream Trust
Prostate Cancer UK
The PwC Foundation
Mr and Mrs J A Pye's Charitable
  Settlement
The Queen Anne's Gate Foundation
Rashbass Family Trust
The Rayne Foundation
Responsible Gambling Trust
  (GambleAware)
Reuben Foundation
The Revere Charitable Trust
The Clive and Sylvia Richards
  Charity Ltd
The River Farm Foundation
The Robertson Trust
The Roddick Foundation
The Gerald Ronson Family
  Foundation
The Cecil Rosen Foundation
The Rothley Trust
The Roughley Charitable Trust
The Saintbury Trust
The Basil Samuel Charitable Trust
The M J Samuel Charitable Trust

The Save the Children Fund
Schroder Charity Trust
Scott (Eredine) Charitable Trust
Sam and Bella Sebba Charitable
  Trust
The Shears Foundation
The Sheepdrove Trust
The Sylvia and Colin Shepherd
  Charitable Trust
Sherburn House Charity
The Shetland Charitable Trust
The Mrs Smith and Mount Trust
The Henry Smith Charity
The Sobell Foundation
Sodexo Stop Hunger Foundation
R H Southern Trust
Peter Sowerby Foundation
St James's Place Foundation
Stadium Charitable Trust
The Peter Stebbings Memorial
  Charity
The Steel Charitable Trust
Stevenson Family's Charitable Trust
Mark Stolkin Foundation
The Stoneygate Trust
The WO Street Charitable
  Foundation
The Bernard Sunley Charitable
  Foundation
Sutton Coldfield Charitable Trust
The John Swire 1989 Charitable
  Trust
The Swire Charitable Trust
C B And H H Taylor 1984 Trust
Khoo Teck Puat UK Foundation
Tenovus Cancer Care
DM Thomas Foundation for Young
  People
The Sir Jules Thorn Charitable
  Trust
The Three Guineas Trust
The Tinsley Foundation
The Tolkien Trust
Jane Tomlinson Appeal
The Tompkins Foundation
The Constance Travis Charitable
  Trust
The True Colours Trust
The Trusthouse Charitable
  Foundation
The Tuixen Foundation
Ulster Garden Villages Ltd
The Underwood Trust
United Purpose
The Utley Family Charitable Trust
The Valentine Charitable Trust
The Vandervell Foundation
Variety, the Children's Charity
Volant Charitable Trust
Voluntary Action Fund (VAF)
Sylvia Waddilove Foundation UK
The Walker Trust

The Barbara Ward Children's
  Foundation
Mrs Waterhouse Charitable Trust
  (formerly known as the
  Houghton Dunn Charitable
  Trust)
Wates Family Enterprise Trust
The Wates Foundation
The Geoffrey Watling Charity
The Weinstock Fund
The Weir Charitable Trust
The Wellcome Trust
The Welton Foundation
The Westfield Health Charitable
  Trust
The Westminster Amalgamated
  Charity
The Garfield Weston Foundation
Westway Trust
The Melanie White Foundation Ltd
The Will Charitable Trust
The Williams Family Foundation
The Wixamtree Trust
The Maurice Wohl Charitable
  Foundation
The Charles Wolfson Charitable
  Trust
The Wolfson Family Charitable
  Trust
The Wolfson Foundation
The Lord Leonard and Lady Estelle
  Wolfson Foundation
The Woodward Charitable Trust
The Worwin UK Foundation
The Eric Wright Charitable Trust
The Yapp Charitable Trust
Yorkshire and Clydesdale Bank
  Foundation
Yorkshire Building Society
  Charitable Foundation
Yorkshire Cancer Research
The William Allen Young
  Charitable Trust
The Marjorie and Arnold Ziff
  Charitable Foundation
The Zochonis Charitable Trust
Zurich Community Trust (UK) Ltd

Medical research

The Abbeyfield Research
  Foundation
Action Medical Research
The Alborada Trust
The Alchemy Foundation
D C R Allen Charitable Trust
Alzheimer's Research UK
Alzheimer's Society
The John Armitage Charitable
  Trust

The Armourers' and Brasiers' Gauntlet Trust
Arthritis Research UK
Asthma UK
The Bacit Foundation
The Baily Thomas Charitable Fund
The Barbers' Company General Charities
The Barclay Foundation
The John Beckwith Charitable Trust
Ruth Berkowitz Charitable Trust
The John Black Charitable Foundation
Bloodwise
The Boltini Trust
The Bothwell Charitable Trust
G & K Boyes Charitable Trust
Breast Cancer Now
British Council for Prevention of Blindness (Save Eyes Everywhere)
British Eye Research Foundation (Fight for Sight)
British Heart Foundation (BHF)
British Lung Foundation
Bill Brown 1989 Charitable Trust
The Edward Cadbury Charitable Trust
The Cadogan Charity
David William Traill Cargill Fund
The Thomas Sivewright Catto Charitable Settlement
The Cayo Foundation
The Charities Advisory Trust
Chest Heart and Stroke Scotland
Children With Cancer UK
CHK Charities Ltd
Clark Foundation
The Colt Foundation
Dudley and Geoffrey Cox Charitable Trust
Cruden Foundation Ltd
The Cunningham Trust
The De Laszlo Foundation
Diabetes UK
Dinwoodie Charitable Company
The Dromintee Trust
The Dunhill Medical Trust
The James Dyson Foundation
The EBM Charitable Trust
The Eighty Eight Foundation
The Englefield Charitable Trust
Epilepsy Research UK
The Eranda Rothschild Foundation
The Evelyn Trust
The Eveson Charitable Trust
The Sir John Fisher Foundation
Fishmongers' Company's Charitable Trust
Donald Forrester Trust
The Elizabeth Frankland Moore and Star Foundation
The Hugh Fraser Foundation

The Joseph Strong Frazer Trust
The Mike Gooley Trailfinders Charity
The Great Britain Sasakawa Foundation
The Grocers' Charity
Heart Research UK
The Michael Heller Charitable Foundation
The Jane Hodge Foundation
The Homelands Charitable Trust
The Thomas J Horne Memorial Trust
The Hospital Saturday Fund
The Jabbs Foundation
The Elton John AIDS Foundation (EJAF)
The Jones 1986 Charitable Trust
The Ian Karten Charitable Trust
The Caron Keating Foundation
The Kay Kendall Leukaemia Fund
The Kennedy Trust For Rheumatology Research
Kidney Research UK
The Mary Kinross Charitable Trust
The Kirschel Foundation
The Ernest Kleinwort Charitable Trust
Kollel and Co Ltd
The Kirby Laing Foundation
The LankellyChase Foundation
The Edgar E Lawley Foundation
The William Leech Charity
Life Changes Trust
The Enid Linder Foundation
The Charles Littlewood Hill Trust
Lloyds Bank Foundation for the Channel Islands
The Lockwood Charitable Foundation
Robert Luff Foundation Ltd
The RS Macdonald Charitable Trust
The Mackintosh Foundation
The W M Mann Foundation
The Manoukian Charitable Foundation
The Kristina Martin Charitable Trust
The Nancie Massey Charitable Trust
Maudsley Charity
The Robert McAlpine Foundation
D D McPhail Charitable Settlement
Medical Research Foundation
Medical Research Scotland
Meningitis Research Foundation
The Brian Mercer Charitable Trust
The Alexander Mosley Charitable Trust
Motor Neurone Disease Association
J P Moulton Charitable Foundation

Multiple Sclerosis Society
The Frances and Augustus Newman Foundation
North West Cancer Research
The Oakdale Trust
Odin Charitable Trust
Oglesby Charitable Trust
Orthopaedic Research UK
Parkinson's UK
The JGW Patterson Foundation
The Dowager Countess Eleanor Peel Trust
Cecil Pilkington Charitable Trust
Pink Ribbon Foundation
Thomas Pocklington Trust
Prostate Cancer UK
Mr and Mrs J A Pye's Charitable Settlement
Queen Mary's Roehampton Trust
Responsible Gambling Trust (GambleAware)
Reuben Foundation
The Revere Charitable Trust
Rhondda Cynon Taff Welsh Church Acts Fund
The Roan Charitable Trust
Rosetrees Trust
The Rothermere Foundation
The Rowlands Trust
The Sackler Trust
The Alan and Babette Sainsbury Charitable Fund
The Jean Shanks Foundation
The Sheepdrove Trust
The SMB Trust
Sparks Charity (Sport Aiding Medical Research For Kids)
The Spear Charitable Trust
Spielman Charitable Trust
The Geoff and Fiona Squire Foundation
St James's Place Foundation
The Stafford Trust
Sir Halley Stewart Trust
The Stoller Charitable Trust
The Stone Family Foundation
The Charles and Elsie Sykes Trust
Tallow Chandlers Benevolent Fund No. 2
Tenovus Cancer Care
Tenovus Scotland
The Tolkien Trust
The James Tudor Foundation
The Roger and Douglas Turner Charitable Trust
The Michael Uren Foundation
The Vandervell Foundation
The Vintners' Foundation
Volant Charitable Trust
The Waterloo Foundation
The Wellcome Trust
The Will Charitable Trust

The Harold Hyam Wingate Foundation
Winton Philanthropies
The Charles Wolfson Charitable Trust
The Lord Leonard and Lady Estelle Wolfson Foundation
Yorkshire Cancer Research

Older people

The 1989 Willan Charitable Trust
The Abbeyfield Research Foundation
The ACT Foundation
The Adint Charitable Trust
Ajahma Charitable Trust
Viscount Amory's Charitable Trust
The AMW Charitable Trust
Autonomous Research Charitable Trust (ARCT)
The Avon and Somerset Police Community Trust
The Ballinger Charitable Trust
Banbury Charities
The Band Trust
The Barclay Foundation
The Baring Foundation
Barnes Workhouse Fund
Misses Barrie Charitable Trust
The Louis Baylis (Maidenhead Advertiser) Charitable Trust
The Beaverbrook Foundation
Percy Bilton Charity
The Bothwell Charitable Trust
The Britford Bridge Trust
Bill Brown 1989 Charitable Trust
The William Adlington Cadbury Charitable Trust
David William Traill Cargill Fund
The W.A. Cargill Fund
The Castansa Trust
The Joseph and Annie Cattle Trust
The Chalk Cliff Trust
The Childwick Trust
CHK Charities Ltd
Church Burgesses Trust
The Churchill Foundation
The City Bridge Trust (Bridge House Estates)
Clark Foundation
The Clore Duffield Foundation
The John Coates Charitable Trust
The Catherine Cookson Charitable Trust
The Evan Cornish Foundation
General Charity of Coventry
The Crerar Trust
The Ronald Cruickshanks Foundation

The D'Oyly Carte Charitable Trust
Baron Davenport's Charity
The Davis Foundation
Debenhams Foundation
The J N Derbyshire Trust
The Djanogly Foundation
Drapers' Charitable Fund
The Dulverton Trust
Dumbreck Charity
The Dunhill Medical Trust
The Earley Charity
The Sir John Eastwood Foundation
Echoes of Service
Edupoor Ltd
The Maud Elkington Charitable Trust
The Englefield Charitable Trust
The Enkalon Foundation
The Eveson Charitable Trust
The Expat Foundation
Esmée Fairbairn Foundation
The Lord Faringdon Charitable Trust
The Thomas Farr Charity
Doris Field Charitable Trust
Donald Forrester Trust
Gwyneth Forrester Trust
The Hugh Fraser Foundation
The Joseph Strong Frazer Trust
Charles S French Charitable Trust
The Patrick and Helena Frost Foundation
The Gale Family Charity Trust
Gatwick Airport Community Trust
The GC Gibson Charitable Trust
The Simon Gibson Charitable Trust
The Gloag Foundation
The Goldsmiths' Company Charity
The Goodman Foundation
The Green Hall Foundation
Greenham Trust Ltd
The Grimmitt Trust
The Grocers' Charity
Calouste Gulbenkian Foundation – UK Branch
The Hadfield Charitable Trust
The Hadrian Trust
The Helen Hamlyn Trust
Hampton Fuel Allotment
The W A Handley Charity Trust
The Haramead Trust
The Harbour Foundation
William Harding's Charity
The Edith Lilian Harrison 2000 Foundation
Edward Harvist Trust (The Harvist Estate)
The Charles Hayward Foundation
The Heathcoat Trust
The Charlotte Heber-Percy Charitable Trust
The Helping Foundation

Henderson Firstfruits
The Christina Mary Hendrie Trust
The Hillingdon Community Trust
The Lady Hind Trust
The Hobson Charity Ltd
The Jane Hodge Foundation
The Thomas J Horne Memorial Trust
Hospice UK
Housing Pathways Trust
The Albert Hunt Trust
Huntingdon Freemen's Trust
Hyde Charitable Trust (Youth Plus)
The Inman Charity
Investream Charitable Trust
The Ireland Fund of Great Britain
The J Isaacs Charitable Trust
John James Bristol Foundation
The Jones 1986 Charitable Trust
The Jordan Charitable Foundation
Joseph Levy Foundation
The Kensington and Chelsea Foundation
The Ernest Kleinwort Charitable Trust
The Sir James Knott Trust
Ladbrokes Coral Trust
John Laing Charitable Trust
Maurice and Hilda Laing Charitable Trust
Christopher Laing Foundation
The David Laing Foundation
The Kirby Laing Foundation
The Martin Laing Foundation
The Beatrice Laing Trust
Duchy of Lancaster Benevolent Fund
The Allen Lane Foundation
The Kathleen Laurence Trust
The Edgar E Lawley Foundation
The Leathersellers' Company Charitable Fund
The William Leech Charity
The Leverhulme Trade Charities Trust
Bernard Lewis Family Charitable Trust
David and Ruth Lewis Family Charitable Trust
John Lewis Partnership General Community Fund
Lloyds Bank Foundation for the Channel Islands
Loftus Charitable Trust
London Catalyst
The Lyndal Tree Foundation
The Lynn Foundation
The Michael Marsh Charitable Trust
The Marsh Christian Trust
Sir George Martin Trust
John Martin's Charity

Masonic Charitable Foundation
The Nancie Massey Charitable Trust
The Matliwala Family Charitable Trust
MBNA General Foundation
The Robert McAlpine Foundation
D D McPhail Charitable Settlement
The Medlock Charitable Trust
Mercaz Torah Vechesed Ltd
The Mercers' Charitable Foundation
Merchant Taylors' Consolidated Charities for the Infirm
The Merchants' House of Glasgow
T. & J. Meyer Family Foundation Ltd
The Gerald Micklem Charitable Trust
The George A. Moore Foundation
The Steve Morgan Foundation
G M Morrison Charitable Trust
The Morrisons Foundation
The Edith Murphy Foundation
The Norman Family Charitable Trust
Normanby Charitable Trust
Oizer Charitable Trust
The David Pearlman Charitable Foundation
The Dowager Countess Eleanor Peel Trust
The Persula Foundation
Pilkington Charities Fund
Sir John Priestman Charity Trust
The Radcliffe Trust
The Rank Foundation Ltd
Rashbass Family Trust
The Rayne Foundation
The Rayne Trust
The Sir James Reckitt Charity
Reuben Foundation
The Revere Charitable Trust
Rhondda Cynon Taff Welsh Church Acts Fund
Richmond Parish Lands Charity
The Cecil Rosen Foundation
The Rothley Trust
The Roughley Charitable Trust
The Rowlands Trust
The Saintbury Trust
Santander UK Foundation Ltd
Schroder Charity Trust
The Frieda Scott Charitable Trust
The Shanly Foundation
The Shears Foundation
The Shetland Charitable Trust
The Slaughter and May Charitable Trust
The Henry Smith Charity
The Sobell Foundation
Spielman Charitable Trust

The Stafford Trust
The Sir Sigmund Sternberg Charitable Foundation
Stratford-upon-Avon Town Trust
The WO Street Charitable Foundation
The Summerfield Charitable Trust
The Bernard Sunley Charitable Foundation
Sutton Coldfield Charitable Trust
The Talbot Village Trust
C B And H H Taylor 1984 Trust
The Tolkien Trust
Toras Chesed (London) Trust
The Trusthouse Charitable Foundation
The Tudor Trust
The Roger and Douglas Turner Charitable Trust
The Union of The Sisters of Mercy of Great Britain
The Van Neste Foundation
Voluntary Action Fund (VAF)
Sylvia Waddilove Foundation UK
Walton On Thames Charity
Wates Family Enterprise Trust
The Wates Foundation
The Weinstock Fund
The Westminster Amalgamated Charity
The Garfield Weston Foundation
Charity of Sir Richard Whittington
The Williams Family Foundation
The Francis Winham Foundation
The Maurice Wohl Charitable Foundation
Woodroffe Benton Foundation
Worth Waynflete Foundation
The Eric Wright Charitable Trust
The Yapp Charitable Trust
Yorkshire Building Society Charitable Foundation
Elizabeth and Prince Zaiger Trust
The Marjorie and Arnold Ziff Charitable Foundation
The Zochonis Charitable Trust
Zurich Community Trust (UK) Ltd

Overseas aid

Aberdeen Asset Management Charitable Foundation
Ajahma Charitable Trust
The Alborada Trust
The Alchemy Foundation
Al-Fayed Charitable Foundation
The Allen and Overy Foundation
The Allen Trust
The Andrew Anderson Trust
Anglo American Group Foundation

The Apax Foundation
Ove Arup Partnership Charitable Trust
The Asfari Foundation
The Baring Foundation
The John Beckwith Charitable Trust
The Big Lottery Fund
The Bloom Foundation
The Boltini Trust
The Breadsticks Foundation
The British and Foreign School Society
British Council for Prevention of Blindness (Save Eyes Everywhere)
The Rory and Elizabeth Brooks Foundation
The William Adlington Cadbury Charitable Trust
The Thomas Sivewright Catto Charitable Settlement
The Chalk Cliff Trust
The Childwick Trust
J A Clark Charitable Trust
Denise Coates Foundation
The Cole-Medlock Foundation
Comic Relief
The Thomas Cook Children's Charity
The Gershon Coren Charitable Foundation (also known as The Muriel and Gus Coren Charitable Foundation)
Corra Foundation
Credit Suisse EMEA Foundation
Dawat-E-Hadiyah Trust (United Kingdom)
The Roger De Haan Charitable Trust
Debenhams Foundation
The Dulverton Trust
Echoes of Service
The Englefield Charitable Trust
The Expat Foundation
Allan and Nesta Ferguson Charitable Settlement
Donald Forrester Trust
Four Acre Trust
The Freshfield Foundation
The Fulmer Charitable Trust
The Gatsby Charitable Foundation
The Generations Foundation
Goldman Sachs Gives (UK)
The Goodman Foundation
The Grace Trust
The Green Hall Foundation
The Grimmitt Trust
HCD Memorial Fund
The Haramead Trust
The Harbour Foundation
The Charles Hayward Foundation
The Headley Trust

The Charlotte Heber-Percy Charitable Trust
The Michael Heller Charitable Foundation
Henderson Firstfruits
The Hilden Charitable Fund
Hockerill Educational Foundation
The Thomas J Horne Memorial Trust
The Hunter Foundation
Ibrahim Foundation Ltd
The Indigo Trust
The Innocent Foundation
Investream Charitable Trust
The J J Charitable Trust
The Jerusalem Trust
The Elton John AIDS Foundation (EJAF)
The Kiawah Charitable Trust
The Kyte Charitable Trust
Maurice and Hilda Laing Charitable Trust
The David Laing Foundation
The Kirby Laing Foundation
The Martin Laing Foundation
The Beatrice Laing Trust
The Lancashire Foundation
Lancaster Foundation
The William Leech Charity
David and Ruth Lewis Family Charitable Trust
The Linbury Trust
Lloyd's Charities Trust
The Mackintosh Foundation
The Mactaggart Third Fund
The Manoukian Charitable Foundation
The Kristina Martin Charitable Trust
Masonic Charitable Foundation
The Matliwala Family Charitable Trust
T. & J. Meyer Family Foundation Ltd
The Millichope Foundation
The Brian Mitchell Charitable Settlement
Moondance Foundation
The Alexander Mosley Charitable Trust
The Frederick Mulder Foundation
Network for Social Change Charitable Trust
The Northwick Trust
The Norton Rose Fulbright Charitable Foundation
The Oakdale Trust
Odin Charitable Trust
The Ogle Christian Trust
Oizer Charitable Trust
Open Gate
Oxfam (GB)

The Park House Charitable Trust
David and Elaine Potter Foundation
The Bishop Radford Trust
The Eleanor Rathbone Charitable Trust
The Revere Charitable Trust
The Clive and Sylvia Richards Charity Ltd
The Roan Charitable Trust
The Roddick Foundation
The Romeera Foundation
Mrs L D Rope's Third Charitable Settlement
The Alan and Babette Sainsbury Charitable Fund
The Basil Samuel Charitable Trust
The M J Samuel Charitable Trust
The Samworth Foundation
The Save the Children Fund
Schroder Charity Trust
Scott (Eredine) Charitable Trust
The Shears Foundation
The Archie Sherman Charitable Trust
The SMB Trust
The Souter Charitable Trust
The W F Southall Trust
The Stafford Trust
The Peter Stebbings Memorial Charity
Stevenson Family's Charitable Trust
Sir Halley Stewart Trust
The Stobart Newlands Charitable Trust
The Stone Family Foundation
C B And H H Taylor 1984 Trust
The Tinsley Foundation
The Tolkien Trust
The Toy Trust
The Constance Travis Charitable Trust
The True Colours Trust
The James Tudor Foundation
The Roger and Douglas Turner Charitable Trust
The Union of The Sisters of Mercy of Great Britain
United Jewish Israel Appeal
United Purpose
The Utley Family Charitable Trust
The Valentine Charitable Trust
The Van Neste Foundation
The Vandervell Foundation
The Vardy Foundation
The Vodafone Foundation
Volant Charitable Trust
The Waterloo Foundation
The Westminster Foundation
The Harold Hyam Wingate Foundation
The Wixamtree Trust

WWDP (World Day of Prayer National Committee for England, Wales and Northern Ireland)
The Zochonis Charitable Trust
Zurich Community Trust (UK) Ltd

Religion

Christianity

Allchurches Trust Ltd
Andrews Charitable Trust
Viscount Amory's Charitable Trust
The Anchor Foundation
The Andrew Anderson Trust
The John Apthorp Charity
Ardbarron Trust Ltd
The Armourers' and Brasiers' Gauntlet Trust
The Baird Trust
The Bowland Charitable Trust
The Bradley Family Charitable Foundation
The Liz and Terry Bramall Foundation
The British and Foreign Bible Society
Buckingham Trust
The William Adlington Cadbury Charitable Trust
The Catholic Trust for England and Wales
The Roger and Sarah Bancroft Clark Charitable Trust
Richard Cloudesley's Charity
Congregational and General Charitable Trust
The Dromintee Trust
The Dyers' Company Charitable Trust
The Englefield Charitable Trust
Fisherbeck Charitable Trust
Fishmongers' Company's Charitable Trust
The Fulmer Charitable Trust
The Gale Family Charity Trust
The Simon Gibson Charitable Trust
The Gloag Foundation
The Goshen Trust
Grace Charitable Trust
The Grace Trust
The Grant Foundation
The W A Handley Charity Trust
The Headley Trust
Henderson Firstfruits
The Hintze Family Charity Foundation
Hockerill Educational Foundation
The Homelands Charitable Trust
Sir Harold Hood's Charitable Trust
Housing Pathways Trust

Hyde Park Place Estate Charity
International Bible Students
    Association
The Jerusalem Trust
The King Henry VIII Endowed
    Trust – Warwick
Maurice and Hilda Laing Charitable
    Trust
The Kirby Laing Foundation
The Beatrice Laing Trust
Lancaster Foundation
The William Leech Charity
The Lind Trust
The Charles Littlewood Hill Trust
The Lockwood Charitable
    Foundation
Sylvanus Lysons Charity
The Manoukian Charitable
    Foundation
The Marsh Christian Trust
Charity of John Marshall
The Kristina Martin Charitable
    Trust
John Martin's Charity
The Mercers' Charitable
    Foundation
The National Churches Trust
The Ogle Christian Trust
The Panacea Charitable Trust
The James Pantyfedwen Foundation
The Park House Charitable Trust
Sir John Priestman Charity Trust
The Bishop Radford Trust
The Joseph Rank Trust
The Sir James Reckitt Charity
Rhondda Cynon Taff Welsh Church
    Acts Fund
Edmund Rice Bicentennial Trust
    Ltd
Mrs L D Rope's Third Charitable
    Settlement
The SMB Trust
The Sola Trust
The Souter Charitable Trust
The W F Southall Trust
Stewards' Company Ltd
Sir Halley Stewart Trust
The Stobart Newlands Charitable
    Trust
Swansea and Brecon Diocesan
    Board of Finance Ltd
C B And H H Taylor 1984 Trust
The Union of The Sisters of Mercy
    of Great Britain
The Van Neste Foundation
The Vardy Foundation
Mrs Waterhouse Charitable Trust
    (formerly known as the
    Houghton Dunn Charitable
    Trust)
The Foster Wood Foundation

WWDP (World Day of Prayer
    National Committee for England,
    Wales and Northern Ireland)

Inter-faith activities

The All Saints Educational Trust
The Edward Cadbury Charitable
    Trust
The Exilarch's Foundation
Fayre Share Foundation
The Ireland Fund of Great Britain
Near Neighbours
The Rayne Trust
The Alan and Babette Sainsbury
    Charitable Fund
The Sir Sigmund Sternberg
    Charitable Foundation
Sir Halley Stewart Trust

Islam

Dawat-E-Hadiyah Trust (United
    Kingdom)
The Matliwala Family Charitable
    Trust

Judaism

4 Charity Foundation
A W Charitable Trust
The A. H. Trust
The Aaronson Foundation
The Aberdeen Foundation
Achisomoch Aid Company Ltd
Amabrill Ltd
Bay Charitable Trust
Bellview Charitable Trust
Ruth Berkowitz Charitable Trust
Asser Bishvil Foundation
The Sir Victor Blank Charitable
    Settlement
The Bloom Foundation
The Bluston Charitable Settlement
Bourneheights Ltd
Friends of Boyan Trust
Brushmill Ltd
Cannon Charitable Trust
Charitworth Ltd
The Childwick Trust
The Clore Duffield Foundation
The Gershon Coren Charitable
    Foundation (also known as The
    Muriel and Gus Coren Charitable
    Foundation)
Itzchok Meyer Cymerman Trust
    Ltd
The Davidson Family Charitable
    Trust
The Davis Foundation
The Desmond Foundation
The Djanogly Foundation
Dollond Charitable Trust
The Dorfman Foundation
Entindale Ltd

The Esfandi Charitable Foundation
The Eventhall Family Charitable
    Trust
The Exilarch's Foundation
Friends of Wiznitz Ltd
M and R Gross Charities Ltd
Hadras Kodesh Trust
The Maurice Hatter Foundation
The Heathside Charitable Trust
The Helping Foundation
The Holden Charitable Trust
Hurdale Charity Ltd
Investream Charitable Trust
Jewish Child's Day (JCD)
Keren Association Ltd
E And E Kernkraut Charities
    Limited
The Kirschel Foundation
Kollel and Co Ltd
Kolyom Trust Ltd
Largsmount Ltd
The Lauffer Family Charitable
    Foundation
Bernard Lewis Family Charitable
    Trust
David and Ruth Lewis Family
    Charitable Trust
The Second Joseph Aaron Littman
    Foundation
The Locker Foundation
Loftus Charitable Trust
The Lolev Charitable Trust
LPW Ltd
M and C Trust
M B Foundation
The MK Charitable Trust
Mayfair Charities Ltd
Mayheights Ltd
The Melow Charitable Trust
Menuchar Ltd
Mercaz Torah Vechesed Ltd
The Laurence Misener Charitable
    Trust
MW (RH) Foundation
Newpier Charity Ltd
Oizer Charitable Trust
The Doris Pacey Charitable
    Foundation
The David Pearlman Charitable
    Foundation
The Pears Family Charitable
    Foundation
Rachel Charitable Trust
The Rayne Trust
Reuben Foundation
The Gerald Ronson Family
    Foundation
The Cecil Rosen Foundation
Rothschild Foundation (Hanadiv)
    Europe
Rowanville Ltd
SF Foundation

Samjo Ltd
Sam and Bella Sebba Charitable
  Trust
The Archie Sherman Charitable
  Trust
The Sobell Foundation
Starlow Charities Ltd
The Steinberg Family Charitable
  Trust
The Sir Sigmund Sternberg
  Charitable Foundation
The Tajtelbaum Charitable Trust
The Talmud Torah Machzikei
  Hadass Trust
The David Tannen Charitable Trust
Toras Chesed (London) Trust
Truedene Co. Ltd
Tzedakah
The Union of Orthodox Hebrew
  Congregations
United Jewish Israel Appeal
The Vail Foundation
VHLT Ltd
The Wigoder Family Foundation
The Harold Hyam Wingate
  Foundation
The Maurice Wohl Charitable
  Foundation
The Charles Wolfson Charitable
  Trust
The Wolfson Family Charitable
  Trust
Wychdale Ltd
The Marjorie and Arnold Ziff
  Charitable Foundation

Religious understanding

Ardbarron Trust Ltd
The Edward Cadbury Charitable
  Trust
Itzchok Meyer Cymerman Trust
  Ltd
The Davis Foundation
Fayre Share Foundation
Ibrahim Foundation Ltd
The Ireland Fund of Great Britain
Near Neighbours
The Rayne Trust
The Alan and Babette Sainsbury
  Charitable Fund
Sir Halley Stewart Trust
The Tolkien Trust

Rights, law and conflict

The A B Charitable Trust
ABF The Soldiers' Charity
Ajahma Charitable Trust
The Alchemy Foundation

The Allen and Overy Foundation
The Bank of Scotland Foundation
The Baring Foundation
Barnwood Trust
The Big Lottery Fund
The Michael Bishop Foundation
The Britford Bridge Trust
British Gas (Scottish Gas) Energy
  Trust
The Bromley Trust
The Rory and Elizabeth Brooks
  Foundation
The William Adlington Cadbury
  Charitable Trust
The Barrow Cadbury Trust
The Charities Advisory Trust
J A Clark Charitable Trust
The Evan Cornish Foundation
The Daiwa Anglo-Japanese
  Foundation
The Davis Foundation
The Dulverton Trust
Dunard Fund 2016
EDF Energy Trust
The Enkalon Foundation
Esmée Fairbairn Foundation
Fayre Share Foundation
Allan and Nesta Ferguson
  Charitable Settlement
The Fort Foundation
The Elizabeth Frankland Moore and
  Star Foundation
Friends Provident Charitable
  Foundation
The Robert Gavron Charitable
  Trust
The Grace Trust
Greenham Trust Ltd
Calouste Gulbenkian Foundation –
  UK Branch
HCD Memorial Fund
The Hadrian Trust
Paul Hamlyn Foundation
The Helen Hamlyn Trust
The Charles Hayward Foundation
The Hilden Charitable Fund
The Hunter Foundation
The Indigo Trust
The Ireland Fund of Great Britain
The J Isaacs Charitable Trust
The Allen Lane Foundation
The LankellyChase Foundation
The Legal Education Foundation
The Lennox Hannay Charitable
  Trust
The Mark Leonard Trust
Trust for London
London Legal Support Trust
  (LLST)
John Lyon's Charity
The Mactaggart Third Fund
The Master Charitable Trust

Money Advice Trust
John Moores Foundation
The Miles Morland Foundation
The Nationwide Foundation
Near Neighbours
Network for Social Change
  Charitable Trust
The Nuffield Foundation
The Oakdale Trust
Open Gate
Oxfam (GB)
The Pears Family Charitable
  Foundation
People's Postcode Trust
The Persula Foundation
Polden-Puckham Charitable
  Foundation
The Polonsky Foundation
David and Elaine Potter
  Foundation
The Eleanor Rathbone Charitable
  Trust
The Sigrid Rausing Trust
The Rayne Trust
The Roddick Foundation
Rosa Fund
The Joseph Rowntree Charitable
  Trust
Joseph Rowntree Reform Trust Ltd
The Alan and Babette Sainsbury
  Charitable Fund
Santander UK Foundation Ltd
The Save the Children Fund
The ScottishPower Foundation
Sam and Bella Sebba Charitable
  Trust
Sherburn House Charity
The Simmons and Simmons
  Charitable Foundation
The Slaughter and May Charitable
  Trust
The Henry Smith Charity
The W F Southall Trust
The Stewarts Law Foundation
The Street Foundation
C B And H H Taylor 1984 Trust
The Tinsley Foundation
The Tolkien Trust
The Tudor Trust
United Purpose
United St Saviour's Charity
United Utilities Trust Fund
UPP Foundation
Variety, the Children's Charity
Voluntary Action Fund (VAF)
The Wakefield and Tetley Trust
Yorkshire and Clydesdale Bank
  Foundation
The William Allen Young
  Charitable Trust

Science and technology

Action on Hearing Loss (The Royal National Institute For Deaf People)
The Aldama Foundation
The Armourers' and Brasiers' Gauntlet Trust
Ove Arup Partnership Charitable Trust
The Borrows Charitable Trust
The Britford Bridge Trust
Calleva Foundation
The John Coates Charitable Trust
The De Laszlo Foundation
The James Dyson Foundation
The Lord Faringdon Charitable Trust
The Gatsby Charitable Foundation
The Granada Foundation
The Great Britain Sasakawa Foundation
The Kenneth and Susan Green Charitable Foundation
The Harbour Foundation
The David and Claudia Harding Foundation
The Michael Heller Charitable Foundation
The Henry C. Hoare Charitable Trust
IBM United Kingdom Trust
The Indigo Trust
The Worshipful Company of Information Technologists
The Frank Jackson Foundation
The Lennox Hannay Charitable Trust
The Leverhulme Trust
Lloyd's Register Foundation
The MacRobert Trust
Man Group plc Charitable Trust
The W M Mann Foundation
The NFU Mutual Charitable Trust
The Nuffield Foundation
Open Gate
Petplan Charitable Trust
Mrs L D Rope's Third Charitable Settlement
The Sackler Trust
Social Tech Trust
Khoo Teck Puat UK Foundation
The Vodafone Foundation
The Waterloo Foundation
The Wellcome Trust
Winton Philanthropies
The Wolfson Family Charitable Trust
The Wolfson Foundation

Yorkshire and Clydesdale Bank Foundation

Social sciences, policy and research

The Abbeyfield Research Foundation
Action on Hearing Loss (The Royal National Institute For Deaf People)
The All Saints Educational Trust
The British Academy for the Promotion of Historical Philosophical and Philological Studies (The British Academy)
The Edward Cadbury Charitable Trust
The Daiwa Anglo-Japanese Foundation
The De Laszlo Foundation
The Lord Faringdon Charitable Trust
The Joseph Strong Frazer Trust
Friends Provident Charitable Foundation
The Gatsby Charitable Foundation
The Robert Gavron Charitable Trust
The Glass-House Trust
The Great Britain Sasakawa Foundation
The Kenneth and Susan Green Charitable Foundation
The Hadley Trust
The Harbour Foundation
The Maurice Hatter Foundation
The Health Foundation
The Allen Lane Foundation
The LankellyChase Foundation
The Legal Education Foundation
The Leverhulme Trust
Trust for London
London Housing Foundation Ltd (LHF)
The Millfield House Foundation
The Nuffield Foundation
Polden-Puckham Charitable Foundation
The Institute for Policy Research
The Polonsky Foundation
David and Elaine Potter Foundation
The Sigrid Rausing Trust
The Resolution Trust
The Joseph Rowntree Charitable Trust
The Joseph Rowntree Foundation

Standard Life Foundation
Sir Halley Stewart Trust
UPP Foundation
Wates Family Enterprise Trust
The Wellcome Trust

Social welfare

The 1989 Willan Charitable Trust
The 29th May 1961 Charitable Trust
4 Charity Foundation
The A B Charitable Trust
The A. H. Trust
The Aaronson Foundation
The Aberdeen Foundation
ABF The Soldiers' Charity
The ACT Foundation
The Adint Charitable Trust
The AIM Foundation
Ajahma Charitable Trust
The Alchemy Foundation
Al-Fayed Charitable Foundation
Allchurches Trust Ltd
D C R Allen Charitable Trust
The Allen Trust
Amabrill Ltd
Viscount Amory's Charitable Trust
The Anchor Foundation
The Andrew Anderson Trust
Andrews Charitable Trust
The Anne Duchess of Westminster's Charity
The Apax Foundation
The John Apthorp Charity
Ardbarron Trust Ltd
The John Armitage Charitable Trust
The Armourers' and Brasiers' Gauntlet Trust
The Arsenal Foundation Ltd
Ove Arup Partnership Charitable Trust
The Asfari Foundation
Aston-Mansfield Charitable Trust
Atkin Charitable Foundation
The Avon and Somerset Police Community Trust
Awards for All
The Balcombe Charitable Trust
The Ballinger Charitable Trust
Banbury Charities
The Bank of Scotland Foundation
The Barbour Foundation
The Barclay Foundation
Lord Barnby's Foundation
Barnes Workhouse Fund
Barnwood Trust
The Batchworth Trust
Bay Charitable Trust

BBC Children in Need
The Beaverbrook Foundation
The Beaverbrooks Charitable Trust
The John Beckwith Charitable Trust
Bellview Charitable Trust
The Berkeley Charitable Foundation
The Big Lottery Fund
Percy Bilton Charity
Asser Bishvil Foundation
The Blagrave Trust
The Sir Victor Blank Charitable Settlement
The Bloom Foundation
The Bluston Charitable Settlement
The Boltini Trust
The Booth Charities
Boots Charitable Trust
The Borrows Charitable Trust
The Bothwell Charitable Trust
Friends of Boyan Trust
The Liz and Terry Bramall Foundation
The Brelms Trust CIO
The Brenley Trust
The Britford Bridge Trust
The Bromley Trust
Bill Brown 1989 Charitable Trust
Brushmill Ltd
The E F Bulmer Benevolent Fund
The Clara E Burgess Charity
The Edward Cadbury Charitable Trust
The William Adlington Cadbury Charitable Trust
The Cadbury Foundation
The Cadogan Charity
Cannon Charitable Trust
David William Traill Cargill Fund
Sir John Cass's Foundation
The Cattanach Charitable Trust
The Joseph and Annie Cattle Trust
The Cayo Foundation
The Chalk Cliff Trust
Sandra Charitable Trust
Charitworth Ltd
The Childhood Trust
The Childwick Trust
CHK Charities Ltd
Christie Foundation
Church Burgesses Trust
The Churchill Foundation
The CIBC World Markets Children's Foundation
The City Bridge Trust (Bridge House Estates)
The Clothworkers' Foundation
Richard Cloudesley's Charity
CMZ Ltd
The Coalfields Regeneration Trust
The John Coates Charitable Trust
Denise Coates Foundation

The R and S Cohen Foundation
The Cole-Medlock Foundation
Comic Relief
Community First
The Thomas Cook Children's Charity
Co-operative Community Investment Foundation
The Evan Cornish Foundation
The Corporation of Trinity House of Deptford Strond
Corra Foundation
The Sir Tom Cowie Charitable Trust
Dudley and Geoffrey Cox Charitable Trust
CRASH
Credit Suisse EMEA Foundation
The Crerar Trust
Cripplegate Foundation
The Cross Trust
Cruden Foundation Ltd
The Ronald Cruickshanks Foundation
CSIS Charity Fund
Itzchok Meyer Cymerman Trust Ltd
Baron Davenport's Charity
The Davidson Family Charitable Trust
The Gwendoline and Margaret Davies Charity
The Hamilton Davies Trust
The Davis Foundation
Dawat-E-Hadiyah Trust (United Kingdom)
Peter De Haan Charitable Trust
The Roger De Haan Charitable Trust
Debenhams Foundation
The J N Derbyshire Trust
The Desmond Foundation
The Djanogly Foundation
Dollond Charitable Trust
The Double 'O' Charity Ltd
Drapers' Charitable Fund
The Dromintee Trust
The Royal Foundation of the Duke and Duchess of Cambridge and Prince Harry
The Dulverton Trust
Dumbreck Charity
The Dunhill Medical Trust
The Charles Dunstone Charitable Trust
The James Dyson Foundation
The Earley Charity
The EBM Charitable Trust
EDF Energy Trust
D.M.H. Educational Trust Ltd
Edupoor Ltd
The Eighty Eight Foundation

The Gerald Palmer Eling Trust Company
The Maud Elkington Charitable Trust
The Ellerdale Trust
John Ellerman Foundation
The Englefield Charitable Trust
The Enkalon Foundation
Entindale Ltd
The Eranda Rothschild Foundation
The Essex Youth Trust
The Eveson Charitable Trust
The Exilarch's Foundation
The Expat Foundation
Esmée Fairbairn Foundation
The Lord Faringdon Charitable Trust
The Thomas Farr Charity
The February Foundation
Doris Field Charitable Trust
The Sir John Fisher Foundation
Fisherbeck Charitable Trust
Fishmongers' Company's Charitable Trust
Donald Forrester Trust
The Fort Foundation
Four Acre Trust
The Elizabeth Frankland Moore and Star Foundation
The Hugh Fraser Foundation
The Joseph Strong Frazer Trust
Charles S French Charitable Trust
The Freshfield Foundation
Friends of Wiznitz Ltd
The Gannochy Trust
The Robert Gavron Charitable Trust
The Generations Foundation
The GC Gibson Charitable Trust
The Simon Gibson Charitable Trust
The Glass-House Trust
The Gloag Foundation
Global Charities
Goldman Sachs Gives (UK)
The Goldsmiths' Company Charity
The Goodman Foundation
The Mike Gooley Trailfinders Charity
The Gosling Foundation Ltd
Grace Charitable Trust
The Grace Trust
The Grant Foundation
The Kenneth and Susan Green Charitable Foundation
The Green Hall Foundation
Greenham Trust Ltd
The Greggs Foundation
The Grimmitt Trust
The Grocers' Charity
M and R Gross Charities Ltd
Groundwork UK
HCD Memorial Fund

Hackney Parochial Charities
The Hadfield Charitable Trust
The Hadley Trust
The Hadrian Trust
Halifax Foundation for Northern Ireland (previously known as Lloyds Bank Foundation for Northern Ireland)
Paul Hamlyn Foundation
The Helen Hamlyn Trust
Hammersmith United Charities
The Hampstead Wells and Campden Trust
Hampton Fuel Allotment
The W A Handley Charity Trust
The Haramead Trust
The Harborne Parish Lands Charity
The Harbour Foundation
William Harding's Charity
The Harpur Trust
The Edith Lilian Harrison 2000 Foundation
The Peter Harrison Foundation
Edward Harvist Trust (The Harvist Estate)
The Maurice Hatter Foundation
The Charles Hayward Foundation
The Headley Trust
The Heathcoat Trust
Heathrow Community Fund (LHR Airport Communities Trust)
The Charlotte Heber-Percy Charitable Trust
Hedley Foundation Ltd (The Hedley Foundation)
The Helping Foundation
Henderson Firstfruits
The Christina Mary Hendrie Trust
The Hilden Charitable Fund
The Hillingdon Community Trust
The Lady Hind Trust
The Henry C. Hoare Charitable Trust
The Hobson Charity Ltd
The Holden Charitable Trust
P H Holt Foundation
The Holywood Trust
The Homelands Charitable Trust
Horne Foundation
The Thomas J Horne Memorial Trust
Housing Pathways Trust
The Reta Lila Howard Foundation
The Albert Hunt Trust
The Hunter Foundation
Miss Agnes H Hunter's Trust
Huntingdon Freemen's Trust
Hyde Charitable Trust (Youth Plus)
Hyde Park Place Estate Charity
Ibrahim Foundation Ltd
The Inman Charity
The Innocent Foundation

Investream Charitable Trust
The Ireland Fund of Great Britain
The Ironmongers' Company
The J Isaacs Charitable Trust
The Isle of Anglesey Charitable Trust
The ITF Seafarers' Trust
The Jabbs Foundation
John James Bristol Foundation
Jewish Child's Day (JCD)
St John's Foundation (Bath)
The Johnson Foundation
The Jones 1986 Charitable Trust
The Jordan Charitable Foundation
Joseph Levy Foundation
Anton Jurgens Charitable Trust
The Kensington and Chelsea Foundation
The Kentown Wizard Foundation
The Kiawah Charitable Trust
The Mary Kinross Charitable Trust
The Kirschel Foundation
The Ernest Kleinwort Charitable Trust
The Sir James Knott Trust
Kollel and Co Ltd
Kolyom Trust Ltd
The KPMG Foundation
The Kreitman Foundation
The Neil Kreitman Foundation
Ladbrokes Coral Trust
John Laing Charitable Trust
Maurice and Hilda Laing Charitable Trust
Christopher Laing Foundation
The David Laing Foundation
The Kirby Laing Foundation
The Beatrice Laing Trust
The Lake House Charity
Lancashire Environmental Fund Ltd
The Lancashire Foundation
Duchy of Lancaster Benevolent Fund
Lancaster Foundation
LandAid Charitable Trust (Land Aid)
The Allen Lane Foundation
The LankellyChase Foundation
Largsmount Ltd
The Lauffer Family Charitable Foundation
The Kathleen Laurence Trust
The Edgar E Lawley Foundation
The Raymond and Blanche Lawson Charitable Trust
The William Leech Charity
Leng Charitable Trust
The Lennox Hannay Charitable Trust
The Mark Leonard Trust
The Leverhulme Trade Charities Trust

Lord Leverhulme's Charitable Trust
Bernard Lewis Family Charitable Trust
David and Ruth Lewis Family Charitable Trust
John Lewis Partnership General Community Fund
Life Changes Trust
The Linbury Trust
The Enid Linder Foundation
The Charles Littlewood Hill Trust
The Second Joseph Aaron Littman Foundation
The George John and Sheilah Livanos Charitable Trust
The Ian and Natalie Livingstone Charitable Trust
Lloyd's Charities Trust
Lloyds Bank Foundation for England and Wales
Lloyds Bank Foundation for the Channel Islands
Lloyd's Patriotic Fund
Loftus Charitable Trust
The Lolev Charitable Trust
Trust for London
London Catalyst
London Housing Foundation Ltd (LHF)
The London Marathon Charitable Trust Ltd
The Lord's Taverners
LPW Ltd
The Lyndal Tree Foundation
The Lynn Foundation
John Lyon's Charity
Sylvanus Lysons Charity
M and C Trust
M B Foundation
The RS Macdonald Charitable Trust
The Mackintosh Foundation
The MacRobert Trust
The Mactaggart Third Fund
The Ian Mactaggart Trust (The Mactaggart Second Fund)
The Manoukian Charitable Foundation
The Michael Marsh Charitable Trust
The Marsh Christian Trust
Sir George Martin Trust
John Martin's Charity
Masonic Charitable Foundation
The Nancie Massey Charitable Trust
The Master Charitable Trust
The Matliwala Family Charitable Trust
Mayfair Charities Ltd
Mayheights Ltd
The Robert McAlpine Foundation

The Medlock Charitable Trust
The Melow Charitable Trust
The Brian Mercer Charitable Trust
The Mercers' Charitable Foundation
Merchant Navy Welfare Board
Merchant Taylors' Consolidated Charities for the Infirm
The Merchants' House of Glasgow
The Gerald Micklem Charitable Trust
Millennium Stadium Charitable Trust (Ymddiriedlaeth Elusennol Stadiwm Y Mileniwm)
The Millichope Foundation
The Laurence Misener Charitable Trust
The Alexander Moncur Trust
Money Advice Trust
The Monument Trust
Moondance Foundation
The George A. Moore Foundation
John Moores Foundation
The Steve Morgan Foundation
Morgan Stanley International Foundation
The Miles Morland Foundation
G M Morrison Charitable Trust
The Ken and Lynne Morrison Charitable Trust
The Morton Charitable Trust (Dundee)
The Alexander Mosley Charitable Trust
J P Moulton Charitable Foundation
The Edith Murphy Foundation
MW (RH) Foundation
The National Gardens Scheme
The Nationwide Foundation
Newby Trust Ltd
The NFU Mutual Charitable Trust
The Nisbet Trust
Normanby Charitable Trust
The Northwick Trust
The Norton Rose Fulbright Charitable Foundation
Norwich Town Close Estate Charity
The Nuffield Foundation
The Oakdale Trust
Odin Charitable Trust
The Ofenheim Charitable Trust
The Ogle Christian Trust
Oglesby Charitable Trust
The Oldfield Charitable Trust
OneFamily Foundation
Oxfam (GB)
The Doris Pacey Charitable Foundation
The Panacea Charitable Trust
Parabola Foundation
Paradigm Foundation
The Park House Charitable Trust

Peacock Charitable Trust
The David Pearlman Charitable Foundation
The Pears Family Charitable Foundation
The Pebble Trust
People's Health Trust
People's Postcode Trust
The Jack Petchey Foundation
The Pilgrim Trust
Pilkington Charities Fund
The Austin and Hope Pilkington Trust
Postcode Community Trust
Pret Foundation Trust
Sir John Priestman Charity Trust
Mr and Mrs J A Pye's Charitable Settlement
Queen Mary's Roehampton Trust
Quintessentially Foundation
The Racing Foundation
The Rank Foundation Ltd
Rashbass Family Trust
The Eleanor Rathbone Charitable Trust
The Sigrid Rausing Trust
The Rayne Foundation
The Rayne Trust
The Sir James Reckitt Charity
The Revere Charitable Trust
Rhodi Charitable Trust
Rhondda Cynon Taff Welsh Church Acts Fund
The River Farm Foundation
The Roan Charitable Trust
The Robertson Trust
The Roddick Foundation
The Gerald Ronson Family Foundation
Mrs L D Rope's Third Charitable Settlement
The Cecil Rosen Foundation
The David Ross Foundation
The Rothley Trust
The Rothschild Foundation
The Roughley Charitable Trust
The Rowlands Trust
The Joseph Rowntree Foundation
Royal Artillery Charitable Fund
The Royal British Legion
Royal Docks Trust (London)
The Royal Navy And Royal Marines Charity
The Saintbury Trust
The Basil Samuel Charitable Trust
The M J Samuel Charitable Trust
Santander UK Foundation Ltd
The Save the Children Fund
Schroder Charity Trust
Scott (Eredine) Charitable Trust
The Francis C. Scott Charitable Trust

The Frieda Scott Charitable Trust
The ScottishPower Foundation
Scottish Property Industry Festival of Christmas (Spifox)
Seafarers UK (King George's Fund for Sailors)
Sam and Bella Sebba Charitable Trust
The Segelman Trust
The Shears Foundation
The Sylvia and Colin Shepherd Charitable Trust
Sherburn House Charity
The Archie Sherman Charitable Trust
The Shetland Charitable Trust
The Simmons and Simmons Charitable Foundation
SITA Cornwall Trust Ltd
The Slaughter and May Charitable Trust
The SMB Trust
The Mrs Smith and Mount Trust
The Henry Smith Charity
The Martin Smith Foundation
The Sobell Foundation
Social Tech Trust
Sodexo Stop Hunger Foundation
The Souter Charitable Trust
The W F Southall Trust
R H Southern Trust
Spielman Charitable Trust
The Spoore, Merry and Rixman Foundation
The Geoff and Fiona Squire Foundation
St James's Place Foundation
The Stafford Trust
Starlow Charities Ltd
The Peter Stebbings Memorial Charity
The Steel Charitable Trust
The Steinberg Family Charitable Trust
Sir Halley Stewart Trust
The Stewarts Law Foundation
Mark Stolkin Foundation
The Stoller Charitable Trust
The Stoneygate Trust
Stratford-upon-Avon Town Trust
The WO Street Charitable Foundation
The Street Foundation
Streetsmart – Action For The Homeless
The Summerfield Charitable Trust
The Bernard Sunley Charitable Foundation
Sutton Coldfield Charitable Trust
The John Swire 1989 Charitable Trust
The Swire Charitable Trust

The Charles and Elsie Sykes Trust
The Tajtelbaum Charitable Trust
The Talbot Village Trust
Tallow Chandlers Benevolent Fund
    No. 2
The David Tannen Charitable Trust
C B And H H Taylor 1984 Trust
The Taylor Family Foundation
Khoo Teck Puat UK Foundation
The Tedworth Charitable Trust
DM Thomas Foundation for Young
    People
The Sir Jules Thorn Charitable
    Trust
The Three Guineas Trust
The Tinsley Foundation
Jane Tomlinson Appeal
The Tompkins Foundation
Toras Chesed (London) Trust
The Toy Trust
The Constance Travis Charitable
    Trust
The Triangle Trust (1949) Fund
The True Colours Trust
The Trusthouse Charitable
    Foundation
The James Tudor Foundation
The Tudor Trust
The Tuixen Foundation
The Roger and Douglas Turner
    Charitable Trust
The Turtleton Charitable Trust
Tzedakah
Ulster Garden Villages Ltd
The Underwood Trust
The Union of The Sisters of Mercy
    of Great Britain
United Purpose
United St Saviour's Charity
The Utley Family Charitable Trust
The Valentine Charitable Trust
The Van Neste Foundation
The Vandervell Foundation
The Vardy Foundation
Variety, the Children's Charity
VHLT Ltd
The Vintners' Foundation
Viridor Credits Environmental
    Company
The Vodafone Foundation
Volant Charitable Trust
Voluntary Action Fund (VAF)
The Bruce Wake Charitable Trust
The Wakefield and Tetley Trust
The Walcot Foundation
The Walker Trust
Walton On Thames Charity
The Barbara Ward Children's
    Foundation
Mrs Waterhouse Charitable Trust
    (formerly known as the Houghton
    Dunn Charitable Trust)

The Waterloo Foundation
Wates Family Enterprise Trust
The Wates Foundation
The Weavers' Company Benevolent
    Fund
The Weinstock Fund
The Westfield Health Charitable
    Trust
Westhill Endowment
The Westminster Amalgamated
    Charity
The Westminster Foundation
The Garfield Weston Foundation
Westway Trust
The Melanie White Foundation Ltd
White Stuff Foundation
Charity of Sir Richard Whittington
The Will Charitable Trust
The Williams Family Foundation
The Willmott Dixon Foundation
The Francis Winham Foundation
The Wixamtree Trust
The Maurice Wohl Charitable
    Foundation
The Charles Wolfson Charitable
    Trust
The Wolfson Foundation
The Foster Wood Foundation
Wooden Spoon Society
Woodroffe Benton Foundation
The Woodstock Family Charitable
    Foundation
The Woodward Charitable Trust
The Eric Wright Charitable Trust
The Yapp Charitable Trust
Yorkshire and Clydesdale Bank
    Foundation
Yorkshire Building Society
    Charitable Foundation
The Yorkshire Dales Millennium
    Trust
The William Allen Young
    Charitable Trust
Youth Music
Elizabeth and Prince Zaiger Trust
The Marjorie and Arnold Ziff
    Charitable Foundation
The Zochonis Charitable Trust
Zurich Community Trust (UK) Ltd

Voluntary sector management and development

The Alchemy Foundation
The Asfari Foundation
The Baring Foundation
The Big Lottery Fund
The Bulldog Trust

The Barrow Cadbury Trust
The Charities Advisory Trust
The City Bridge Trust (Bridge
    House Estates)
Esmée Fairbairn Foundation
Fayre Share Foundation
The Joseph Strong Frazer Trust
Gatwick Airport Community Trust
The Grace Trust
Calouste Gulbenkian Foundation –
    UK Branch
The W A Handley Charity Trust
The Ireland Fund of Great Britain
The Allen Lane Foundation
The William Leech Charity
The Legal Education Foundation
The Lehman Brothers Foundation
    Europe
The Mark Leonard Trust
Lloyds Bank Foundation for
    England and Wales
Lloyds Bank Foundation for the
    Channel Islands
Trust for London
London Housing Foundation Ltd
    (LHF)
The Millfield House Foundation
John Moores Foundation
The Frederick Mulder Foundation
Nesta
The Pears Family Charitable
    Foundation
The Jack Petchey Foundation
The Joseph Rowntree Charitable
    Trust
The Slaughter and May Charitable
    Trust
The Triangle Trust (1949) Fund
The Tudor Trust
United Purpose
UnLtd (Foundation for Social
    Entrepreneurs)
Voluntary Action Fund (VAF)
Walton On Thames Charity
The Wates Foundation
The Westminster Foundation
Worth Waynflete Foundation
The Yapp Charitable Trust

Women

Ove Arup Partnership Charitable
    Trust
The Baring Foundation
The Bromley Trust
J A Clark Charitable Trust
Comic Relief
Baron Davenport's Charity
The J N Derbyshire Trust
Esmée Fairbairn Foundation

The Gloag Foundation
The Goldsmiths' Company Charity
The Hadrian Trust
Paul Hamlyn Foundation
The Harborne Parish Lands Charity
The Hilden Charitable Fund
The Albert Hunt Trust
The Jabbs Foundation
The Elton John AIDS Foundation
   (EJAF)
The Mary Kinross Charitable Trust
The Beatrice Laing Trust
The Allen Lane Foundation
The LankellyChase Foundation
London Catalyst
John Lyon's Charity
The Monument Trust
John Moores Foundation
Oxfam (GB)
The Pilgrim Trust
The Eleanor Rathbone Charitable
   Trust
The Sigrid Rausing Trust
Rosa Fund
The Alan and Babette Sainsbury
   Charitable Fund
The Henry Smith Charity
The Peter Stebbings Memorial
   Charity
C B And H H Taylor 1984 Trust
The Union of The Sisters of Mercy
   of Great Britain
United Purpose
The Vodafone Foundation
Volant Charitable Trust
Voluntary Action Fund (VAF)
The Wembley National Stadium
   Trust
The Woodward Charitable Trust
WWDP (World Day of Prayer
   National Committee for England,
   Wales and Northern Ireland)

Geographical index

The following index aims to highlight when a grant-maker gives preference for, or has a special interest in, a particular geographical area. Before using the index, please note the following.

1) Before using this index please read the following information, as well as the introduction to the subject index on page 491. We must emphasise that this index:

   (a) should not be used as a simple mailing list, and;

   (b) is not a substitute for detailed research.

2) When you have used this index to identify relevant grant-makers, please read each entry carefully before making an application. Simply because a funder gives grants in your geographical area, it does not mean that they give to your type of work.

3) Most funders in this list are not restricted to one area – usually the geographical index indicates that the grant-maker gives some priority for the area(s) in question.

Each section is ordered alphabetically according to the name of the funder. The categories for indexes are as follows.

United Kingdom *page 526*

England *page 530*

We have divided England into the following ten categories:

North East *page 531*

North West *page 531*

Yorkshire and the Humber *page 531*

East Midlands *page 531*

West Midlands *page 531*

Eastern England *page 532*

South West *page 532*

South East *page 532*

Greater London *page 533*

Channel Islands *page 533*

Some grant-makers may be found in more than one category due to them providing grants in more than one area (for example, those with a preference for the north of England will appear under both North East and North West).

Wales *page 533*

Scotland *page 534*

Northern Ireland *page 535*

Republic of Ireland *page 535*

Europe *page 535*
Overseas categories

Individual continents *page 535*

Worldwide *page 536*
The Middle East has been listed separately. Please note that most of the funders listed are primarily for the benefit of Jewish people and the advancement of the Jewish religion.

United Kingdom

The 3Ts Charitable Trust
The 29th May 1961 Charitable Trust
4 Charity Foundation
The A B Charitable Trust
Aberdeen Asset Management Charitable Foundation
The Aberdeen Foundation
ABF The Soldiers' Charity
Achisomoch Aid Company Ltd
The ACT Foundation
Action Medical Research
Action on Hearing Loss (The Royal National Institute For Deaf People)
The Adint Charitable Trust
The AIM Foundation
Ajahma Charitable Trust
The Alborada Trust
The Alchemy Foundation
The Aldama Foundation
Al-Fayed Charitable Foundation
The All Saints Educational Trust
Allchurches Trust Ltd
D C R Allen Charitable Trust
The Allen Trust
Alzheimer's Research UK
Alzheimer's Society
Amabrill Ltd
The Anchor Foundation
The Andrew Anderson Trust
Andrews Charitable Trust
The Annandale Charitable Trust
The Anson Charitable Trust
The Apax Foundation
The Architectural Heritage Fund
Ardbarron Trust Ltd
The Ardeola Charitable Trust
The Armourers' and Brasiers' Gauntlet Trust
Arthritis Research UK
Ove Arup Partnership Charitable Trust
The Asfari Foundation
The Ashden Trust
Asthma UK
Autonomous Research Charitable Trust (ARCT)
Awards for All
The Bacit Foundation
Backstage Trust
The Baily Thomas Charitable Fund
The Balcombe Charitable Trust
The Bamford Charitable Foundation
The Band Trust
The Banister Charitable Trust

The Barbers' Company General Charities
The Barclay Foundation
The Baring Foundation
Lord Barnby's Foundation
Misses Barrie Charitable Trust
The Paul Bassham Charitable Trust
The Batchworth Trust
Bay Charitable Trust
BBC Children in Need
The Beaverbrooks Charitable Trust
The John Beckwith Charitable Trust
Bellview Charitable Trust
Benesco Charity Ltd
Ruth Berkowitz Charitable Trust
The Big Lottery Fund
Percy Bilton Charity
The Michael Bishop Foundation
The John Black Charitable Foundation
The Sir Victor Blank Charitable Settlement
Bloodwise
The Bloom Foundation
The Bluston Charitable Settlement
The Boltini Trust
The Bothwell Charitable Trust
Bourneheights Ltd
Friends of Boyan Trust
G & K Boyes Charitable Trust
The William Brake Charitable Trust
The Tony Bramall Charitable Trust
The Liz and Terry Bramall Foundation
The Breadsticks Foundation
Breast Cancer Now
The Brenley Trust
The Britford Bridge Trust
The British Academy for the Promotion of Historical Philosophical and Philological Studies (The British Academy)
The British and Foreign Bible Society
The British and Foreign School Society
British Council for Prevention of Blindness (Save Eyes Everywhere)
British Eye Research Foundation (Fight for Sight)
British Heart Foundation (BHF)
British Lung Foundation
British Record Industry Trust (BRIT Trust)
The Bromley Trust
The Rory and Elizabeth Brooks Foundation
Bill Brown 1989 Charitable Trust
Brushmill Ltd
Buckingham Trust
The Buffini Chao Foundation
The Bulldog Trust

The Burdett Trust for Nursing
The Clara E Burgess Charity
The Cadbury Foundation
The Barrow Cadbury Trust
The Cadogan Charity
Cannon Charitable Trust
The Carpenters' Company Charitable Trust
Catkin Pussywillow Charitable Trust
The Thomas Sivewright Catto Charitable Settlement
The Cayo Foundation
Chapman Charitable Trust
Sandra Charitable Trust
The Charities Advisory Trust
Charitworth Ltd
Children With Cancer UK
CHK Charities Ltd
Christie Foundation
The Churchill Foundation
The CIBC World Markets Children's Foundation
J A Clark Charitable Trust
The Roger and Sarah Bancroft Clark Charitable Trust
Clark Foundation
The Clore Duffield Foundation
The Clothworkers' Foundation
CMZ Ltd
The John Coates Charitable Trust
Denise Coates Foundation
The John S Cohen Foundation
The R and S Cohen Foundation
The Cole-Medlock Foundation
The Colt Foundation
Colwinston Charitable Trust
Comic Relief
Congregational and General Charitable Trust
The Thomas Cook Children's Charity
The Ernest Cook Trust
The Catherine Cookson Charitable Trust
The Alice Ellen Cooper Dean Charitable Foundation
Co-operative Community Investment Foundation
The Gershon Coren Charitable Foundation (also known as The Muriel and Gus Coren Charitable Foundation)
The Evan Cornish Foundation
The Corporation of Trinity House of Deptford Strond
Dudley and Geoffrey Cox Charitable Trust
CRASH
The Elizabeth Creak Charitable Trust
The Cross Trust

The Ronald Cruickshanks
  Foundation
CSIS Charity Fund
Cullum Family Trust
Itzchok Meyer Cymerman Trust
  Ltd
The D'Oyly Carte Charitable Trust
The Daiwa Anglo-Japanese
  Foundation
The Davidson Family Charitable
  Trust
The Crispin Davis Family Trust
Dawat-E-Hadiyah Trust (United
  Kingdom)
Peter De Haan Charitable Trust
The De Laszlo Foundation
Debenhams Foundation
The J N Derbyshire Trust
The Desmond Foundation
The Laduma Dhamecha Charitable
  Trust
Diabetes UK
Dina Perelman Trust Ltd
Dinwoodie Charitable Company
The Djanogly Foundation
Dollond Charitable Trust
The Dorfman Foundation
The Double 'O' Charity Ltd
The Dromintee Trust
The Royal Foundation of the Duke
  and Duchess of Cambridge and
  Prince Harry
Dunard Fund 2016
The Dunhill Medical Trust
The Charles Dunstone Charitable
  Trust
The Dyers' Company Charitable
  Trust
The James Dyson Foundation
The Sir John Eastwood Foundation
The EBM Charitable Trust
Echoes of Service
EDF Energy Trust
The Edge Foundation
Edupoor Ltd
The Eighty Eight Foundation
The Marian Elizabeth Trust
John Ellerman Foundation
EMI Music Sound Foundation
Entindale Ltd
Epilepsy Research UK
The Eranda Rothschild Foundation
The Esfandi Charitable Foundation
The Essex Youth Trust
The Exilarch's Foundation
The Expat Foundation
Esmée Fairbairn Foundation
The Lord Faringdon Charitable
  Trust
Fayre Share Foundation
The February Foundation

Allan and Nesta Ferguson
  Charitable Settlement
The Fidelity UK Foundation
Doris Field Charitable Trust
The Sir John Fisher Foundation
Fisherbeck Charitable Trust
Donald Forrester Trust
Four Acre Trust
The Foyle Foundation
The Elizabeth Frankland Moore and
  Star Foundation
The Hugh Fraser Foundation
The Freshfield Foundation
Friends Provident Charitable
  Foundation
The Patrick and Helena Frost
  Foundation
The Fulmer Charitable Trust
The Funding Network
The Gale Family Charity Trust
The Gatsby Charitable Foundation
The Robert Gavron Charitable
  Trust
Sir Robert Geffery's Almshouse
  Trust
The Generations Foundation
The GC Gibson Charitable Trust
The Simon Gibson Charitable Trust
The Glass-House Trust
The Gloag Foundation
Global Charities
The Golden Bottle Trust
Goldman Sachs Gives (UK)
The Goldsmiths' Company Charity
The Goodman Foundation
The Mike Gooley Trailfinders
  Charity
The Gosling Foundation Ltd
Grace Charitable Trust
The Grace Trust
The Grant Foundation
GrantScape
The Great Britain Sasakawa
  Foundation
The Kenneth and Susan Green
  Charitable Foundation
The Green Hall Foundation
The Grocers' Charity
Groundwork UK
Calouste Gulbenkian Foundation –
  UK Branch
HCD Memorial Fund
The Hadley Trust
Hadras Kodesh Trust
Paul Hamlyn Foundation
The Haramead Trust
The Harbour Foundation
The David and Claudia Harding
  Foundation
The Peter Harrison Foundation
The Edith Lilian Harrison 2000
  Foundation

The Maurice Hatter Foundation
The Charles Hayward Foundation
The Headley Trust
Heart Research UK
The Heathside Charitable Trust
The Charlotte Heber-Percy
  Charitable Trust
Hedley Foundation Ltd (The
  Hedley Foundation)
The Michael Heller Charitable
  Foundation
Henderson Firstfruits
Heritage Lottery Fund
The Hilden Charitable Fund
The Lady Hind Trust
The Henry C. Hoare Charitable
  Trust
The Hobson Charity Ltd
Hockerill Educational Foundation
The Jane Hodge Foundation
The Holden Charitable Trust
P H Holt Foundation
The Homelands Charitable Trust
Sir Harold Hood's Charitable Trust
Horne Foundation
The Thomas J Horne Memorial
  Trust
The Horse Trust
Hospice UK
The Hospital Saturday Fund
The Reta Lila Howard Foundation
James T Howat Charitable Trust
The Albert Hunt Trust
The Hunter Foundation
IBM United Kingdom Trust
Ibrahim Foundation Ltd
Impetus – The Private Equity
  Foundation
The Indigo Trust
The Worshipful Company of
  Information Technologists
The Ingram Trust
The Inman Charity
The Innocent Foundation
International Bible Students
  Association
Investream Charitable Trust
The Ireland Fund of Great Britain
The Ironmongers' Company
The Jabbs Foundation
The Frank Jackson Foundation
The Jerusalem Trust
The Jerwood Charitable Foundation
Jewish Child's Day (JCD)
The Elton John AIDS Foundation
  (EJAF)
The Joicey Trust
The Muriel Jones Foundation
The Jordan Charitable Foundation
Joseph Levy Foundation
Anton Jurgens Charitable Trust
The Caron Keating Foundation

The Kay Kendall Leukaemia Fund
The Kennel Club Charitable Trust
The Kentown Wizard Foundation
Keren Association Ltd
E And E Kernkraut Charities Limited
The Kiawah Charitable Trust
Kidney Research UK
King/Cullimore Charitable Trust
The Mary Kinross Charitable Trust
The Kirschel Foundation
The Ernest Kleinwort Charitable Trust
Kollel and Co Ltd
Kolyom Trust Ltd
The Kreitman Foundation
The Neil Kreitman Foundation
Kusuma Trust UK
The Kyte Charitable Trust
Ladbrokes Coral Trust
Maurice and Hilda Laing Charitable Trust
John Laing Charitable Trust
The Martin Laing Foundation
The Kirby Laing Foundation
Christopher Laing Foundation
The Beatrice Laing Trust
The Lake House Charity
The Lancashire Foundation
Lancaster Foundation
The Lancaster-Taylor Charitable Trust
LandAid Charitable Trust (Land Aid)
The Allen Lane Foundation
The LankellyChase Foundation
Largsmount Ltd
The Basil Larsen 1999 Charitable Trust
The Lauffer Family Charitable Foundation
The Kathleen Laurence Trust
The Law Family Charitable Foundation
The Betty Lawes Foundation
The Edgar E Lawley Foundation
The Leathersellers' Company Charitable Fund
The Leche Trust
The Legal Education Foundation
The Lehman Brothers Foundation Europe
The Mark Leonard Trust
Leri Charitable Trust
The Leverhulme Trade Charities Trust
The Leverhulme Trust
Lord Leverhulme's Charitable Trust
Bernard Lewis Family Charitable Trust
David and Ruth Lewis Family Charitable Trust

John Lewis Partnership General Community Fund
The Linbury Trust
The Lind Trust
The Enid Linder Foundation
The Charles Littlewood Hill Trust
The Second Joseph Aaron Littman Foundation
The George John and Sheilah Livanos Charitable Trust
The Ian and Natalie Livingstone Charitable Trust
The Andrew Lloyd Webber Foundation
Lloyd's Charities Trust
Lloyd's Register Foundation
Loftus Charitable Trust
The Lolev Charitable Trust
The William and Katherine Longman Trust
The Lord's Taverners
LPW Ltd
Robert Luff Foundation Ltd
The Lyndal Tree Foundation
The Lynn Foundation
M and C Trust
M B Foundation
The MK Charitable Trust
The Mackintosh Foundation
The MacRobert Trust
The Mactaggart Third Fund
The Ian Mactaggart Trust (The Mactaggart Second Fund)
Man Group plc Charitable Trust
The W M Mann Foundation
The Manoukian Charitable Foundation
The Marchig Animal Welfare Trust
The Marsh Christian Trust
The Kristina Martin Charitable Trust
The Master Charitable Trust
The Matliwala Family Charitable Trust
Mayfair Charities Ltd
Mazars Charitable Trust
The Robert McAlpine Foundation
D D McPhail Charitable Settlement
The Medlock Charitable Trust
The Melow Charitable Trust
Meningitis Research Foundation
Menuchar Ltd
The Brian Mercer Charitable Trust
The Mercers' Charitable Foundation
Merchant Navy Welfare Board
T. & J. Meyer Family Foundation Ltd
The Millichope Foundation
The Laurence Misener Charitable Trust

The Brian Mitchell Charitable Settlement
Money Advice Trust
The Monument Trust
Moondance Foundation
The Henry Moore Foundation
The Miles Morland Foundation
G M Morrison Charitable Trust
The Morrisons Foundation
The Alexander Mosley Charitable Trust
Motor Neurone Disease Association
J P Moulton Charitable Foundation
The Frederick Mulder Foundation
Multiple Sclerosis Society
The Edith Murphy Foundation
The John R. Murray Charitable Trust
MW (RH) Foundation
National Art Collections Fund
The National Churches Trust
The National Gardens Scheme
The Nationwide Foundation
Nesta
Network for Social Change Charitable Trust
Newby Trust Ltd
The Frances and Augustus Newman Foundation
Newpier Charity Ltd
The NFU Mutual Charitable Trust
The Nineveh Charitable Trust
Normanby Charitable Trust
The Northwick Trust
The Norton Rose Fulbright Charitable Foundation
The Nuffield Foundation
The Sir Peter O'Sullevan Charitable Trust
The Oakdale Trust
Odin Charitable Trust
The Ofenheim Charitable Trust
The Ogle Christian Trust
Oizer Charitable Trust
Old Possum's Practical Trust
The John Oldacre Foundation
OneFamily Foundation
Open Gate
Orthopaedic Research UK
Oxfam (GB)
P F Charitable Trust
The Doris Pacey Charitable Foundation
The Panacea Charitable Trust
The Park House Charitable Trust
Parkinson's UK
Peacock Charitable Trust
The David Pearlman Charitable Foundation
The Pears Family Charitable Foundation

The Dowager Countess Eleanor Peel Trust
The Performing Right Society Foundation
The Persula Foundation
Petplan Charitable Trust
The Pilgrim Trust
The Austin and Hope Pilkington Trust
Cecil Pilkington Charitable Trust
Pink Ribbon Foundation
Thomas Pocklington Trust
Polden-Puckham Charitable Foundation
The Institute for Policy Research
The Polonsky Foundation
David and Elaine Potter Foundation
Pret Foundation Trust
The Prince of Wales's Charitable Foundation
The Prince's Countryside Fund
The Professional Footballers' Association Charity
Prostate Cancer UK
The PwC Foundation
Mr and Mrs J A Pye's Charitable Settlement
The Queen Anne's Gate Foundation
Queen Mary's Roehampton Trust
Quintessentially Foundation
Rachel Charitable Trust
The Racing Foundation
The Radcliffe Trust
The Bishop Radford Trust
The Rank Foundation Ltd
The Joseph Rank Trust
Rashbass Family Trust
The Ratcliff Foundation
The Eleanor Rathbone Charitable Trust
The Sigrid Rausing Trust
The Rayne Foundation
The Rayne Trust
The Sir James Reckitt Charity
The Reece Foundation
The Resolution Trust
Responsible Gambling Trust (GambleAware)
Reuben Foundation
The Revere Charitable Trust
Rhodi Charitable Trust
Edmund Rice Bicentennial Trust Ltd
The Clive and Sylvia Richards Charity Ltd
The River Farm Foundation
The Roan Charitable Trust
The Roddick Foundation
The Romeera Foundation
The Gerald Ronson Family Foundation

Mrs L D Rope's Third Charitable Settlement
Rosa Fund
The Cecil Rosen Foundation
The David Ross Foundation
The Rothermere Foundation
The Rothschild Foundation
Rothschild Foundation (Hanadiv) Europe
Rowanville Ltd
The Rowlands Trust
The Joseph Rowntree Charitable Trust
The Joseph Rowntree Foundation
Joseph Rowntree Reform Trust Ltd
Royal Artillery Charitable Fund
The Royal Navy And Royal Marines Charity
Royal Society of Wildlife Trusts
The Ruddock Foundation for the Arts
The RVW Trust
SF Foundation
The Saddlers' Company Charitable Fund
The Jean Sainsbury Animal Welfare Trust
The Alan and Babette Sainsbury Charitable Fund
The Saintbury Trust
The M J Samuel Charitable Trust
Santander UK Foundation Ltd
The Save the Children Fund
Schroder Charity Trust
The Schroder Foundation
Scott (Eredine) Charitable Trust
The Finnis Scott Foundation
The ScottishPower Foundation
Seafarers Hospital Society
Seafarers UK (King George's Fund for Sailors)
Sam and Bella Sebba Charitable Trust
The Jean Shanks Foundation
ShareGift (The Orr Mackintosh Foundation)
The Shears Foundation
The Sheepdrove Trust
The Sylvia and Colin Shepherd Charitable Trust
The Archie Sherman Charitable Trust
The Sino-British Fellowship Trust
The Charles Skey Charitable Trust
Sloane Robinson Foundation
The SMB Trust
The Henry Smith Charity
The Martin Smith Foundation
Social Business Trust
Social Investment Business Foundation
Social Tech Trust

Sodexo Stop Hunger Foundation
Sofronie Foundation
The Sola Trust
The Souter Charitable Trust
The W F Southall Trust
Peter Sowerby Foundation
Sparks Charity (Sport Aiding Medical Research For Kids)
The Spear Charitable Trust
Spielman Charitable Trust
The Geoff and Fiona Squire Foundation
St James's Place Foundation
Stadium Charitable Trust
The Stafford Trust
Standard Life Foundation
The Peter Stebbings Memorial Charity
The Steel Charitable Trust
The Steinberg Family Charitable Trust
The Sir Sigmund Sternberg Charitable Foundation
Stevenson Family's Charitable Trust
Stewards' Company Ltd
Sir Halley Stewart Trust
The Stewarts Law Foundation
The Stobart Newlands Charitable Trust
The Stone Family Foundation
The Stoneygate Trust
The WO Street Charitable Foundation
Streetsmart – Action For The Homeless
Support Adoption For Pets
The Sutton Trust
The John Swire 1989 Charitable Trust
The Adrian Swire Charitable Trust
The Swire Charitable Trust
The Syder Foundation
The Charles and Elsie Sykes Trust
The Tajtelbaum Charitable Trust
The Talmud Torah Machzikei Hadass Trust
The David Tannen Charitable Trust
Tay Charitable Trust
C B And H H Taylor 1984 Trust
The Taylor Family Foundation
Khoo Teck Puat UK Foundation
The Tedworth Charitable Trust
The Tennis Foundation
Tenovus Cancer Care
Theatres Trust
DM Thomas Foundation for Young People
The Thompson Family Charitable Trust
The Sir Jules Thorn Charitable Trust
The Three Guineas Trust

The Tinsley Foundation
The Tolkien Trust
The Tompkins Foundation
Toras Chesed (London) Trust
The Toy Trust
The Constance Travis Charitable
	Trust
The Triangle Trust (1949) Fund
The True Colours Trust
Truedene Co. Ltd
The Trusthouse Charitable
	Foundation
The James Tudor Foundation
The Tudor Trust
The Tuixen Foundation
The Turtleton Charitable Trust
Tzedakah
Ufi Charitable Trust
The Underwood Trust
The Union of Orthodox Hebrew
	Congregations
The Union of The Sisters of Mercy
	of Great Britain
United Jewish Israel Appeal
United Purpose
UnLtd (Foundation for Social
	Entrepreneurs)
UPP Foundation
The Michael Uren Foundation
The Utley Family Charitable Trust
The Vail Foundation
The Valentine Charitable Trust
The Van Neste Foundation
The Vandervell Foundation
The Vardy Foundation
Variety, the Children's Charity
The Veolia Environmental Trust
The Virgin Money Foundation
The Vodafone Foundation
Sylvia Waddilove Foundation UK
The Bruce Wake Charitable Trust
The Barbara Ward Children's
	Foundation
Mrs Waterhouse Charitable Trust
	(formerly known as the
	Houghton Dunn Charitable
	Trust)
The Waterloo Foundation
Wates Family Enterprise Trust
The Wates Foundation
The William Wates Memorial Trust
The Weavers' Company Benevolent
	Fund
The David Webster Charitable
	Trust
The Weinstock Fund
The Wellcome Trust
The Welton Foundation
The Westfield Health Charitable
	Trust
Westhill Endowment
The Garfield Weston Foundation

The Melanie White Foundation Ltd
White Stuff Foundation
Whitley Animal Protection Trust
The Will Charitable Trust
The Willmott Dixon Foundation
The HDH Wills 1965 Charitable
	Trust
Sumner Wilson Charitable Trust
The Wimbledon Foundation
The Harold Hyam Wingate
	Foundation
Winton Philanthropies
The Wixamtree Trust
The Maurice Wohl Charitable
	Foundation
The Charles Wolfson Charitable
	Trust
The Wolfson Family Charitable
	Trust
The Lord Leonard and Lady Estelle
	Wolfson Foundation
The Wolfson Foundation
Wooden Spoon Society
Woodroffe Benton Foundation
The Woodward Charitable Trust
Worth Waynflete Foundation
The Worwin UK Foundation
The Eric Wright Charitable Trust
WWDP (World Day of Prayer
	National Committee for England,
	Wales and Northern Ireland)
Wychdale Ltd
Yorkshire Building Society
	Charitable Foundation
The William Allen Young
	Charitable Trust
Elizabeth and Prince Zaiger Trust
The Marjorie and Arnold Ziff
	Charitable Foundation
The Zochonis Charitable Trust

England

The A Team Foundation Ltd
The A. H. Trust
The Aaronson Foundation
The Abbeyfield Research
	Foundation
Access Sport CIO
The Sylvia Adams Charitable Trust
AKO Foundation
The John Armitage Charitable
	Trust
Arts Council England
The Asda Foundation
The Ashley Family Foundation
The Rachel Baker Memorial Charity
The Beaverbrook Foundation
The Borrows Charitable Trust
The Boshier-Hinton Foundation

The Bradley Family Charitable
	Foundation
British Gas (Scottish Gas) Energy
	Trust
The Catholic Trust for England and
	Wales
Country Houses Foundation
England and Wales Cricket Trust
The Peter Cruddas Foundation
The Davis Foundation
Drapers' Charitable Fund
D.M.H. Educational Trust Ltd
The Football Foundation
Gwyneth Forrester Trust
The Fort Foundation
The Joseph Strong Frazer Trust
The Greggs Foundation
H & T Clients Charitable Trust
The Hintze Family Charity
	Foundation
The J Isaacs Charitable Trust
The Ian Karten Charitable Trust
The Kennedy Trust For
	Rheumatology Research
The KPMG Foundation
The Lennox Hannay Charitable
	Trust
Lloyds Bank Foundation for
	England and Wales
Lloyd's Patriotic Fund
The Lockwood Charitable
	Foundation
Charity of John Marshall
Masonic Charitable Foundation
Moto in the Community
Newby Trust Ltd
Parabola Foundation
People's Health Trust
People's Postcode Trust
Postcode Community Trust
Postcode Dream Trust
Postcode Local Trust
Power to Change Trust
Rosetrees Trust
The Royal British Legion
Rugby Football Foundation
The Sackler Trust
The Savoy Educational Trust
The Segelman Trust
SHINE (Support and Help in
	Education)
The DS Smith Charitable
	Foundation
The Sobell Foundation
R H Southern Trust
Starlow Charities Ltd
Mark Stolkin Foundation
The Street Foundation
The Bernard Sunley Charitable
	Foundation
Viridor Credits Environmental
	Company

The Wembley National Stadium Trust
The Wheeler Family Charitable Trust
The Wigoder Family Foundation
The Francis Winham Foundation
The Foster Wood Foundation
The Woodstock Family Charitable Foundation
The Wyfold Charitable Trust
The Yapp Charitable Trust
Yorkshire and Clydesdale Bank Foundation
Youth Music

North East

The 1989 Willan Charitable Trust
The Ballinger Charitable Trust
The Barbour Foundation
The Coalfields Regeneration Trust
The Catherine Cookson Charitable Trust
The Sir Tom Cowie Charitable Trust
The Dulverton Trust
The Greggs Foundation
The Hadrian Trust
The W A Handley Charity Trust
The Sir James Knott Trust
The William Leech Charity
Lempriere Pringle 2015
The Mercers' Charitable Foundation
The Millfield House Foundation
The JGW Patterson Foundation
Sir John Priestman Charity Trust
The Reece Foundation
The Rothley Trust
The Shears Foundation
Sherburn House Charity
The Henry Smith Charity
Jane Tomlinson Appeal
The Vardy Foundation
The Virgin Money Foundation

North West

A W Charitable Trust
Access Sport CIO
The Anne Duchess of Westminster's Charity
Asser Bishvil Foundation
The Booth Charities
The Bowland Charitable Trust
The Coalfields Regeneration Trust
The Hamilton Davies Trust
The Dulverton Trust
The Eventhall Family Charitable Trust
The Sir John Fisher Foundation
The Fort Foundation
Forever Manchester

The Granada Foundation
The Hadfield Charitable Trust
The W A Handley Charity Trust
The Helping Foundation
The Holden Charitable Trust
The Johnson Foundation
Lancashire Environmental Fund Ltd
Lancaster Foundation
Duchy of Lancaster Benevolent Fund
Leri Charitable Trust
Lord Leverhulme's Charitable Trust
MBNA General Foundation
John Moores Foundation
The Steve Morgan Foundation
Near Neighbours
North West Cancer Research
Oglesby Charitable Trust
Oizer Charitable Trust
The Dowager Countess Eleanor Peel Trust
Cecil Pilkington Charitable Trust
Pilkington Charities Fund
The Eleanor Rathbone Charitable Trust
Rhodi Charitable Trust
Samjo Ltd
The Francis C. Scott Charitable Trust
The Frieda Scott Charitable Trust
SHINE (Support and Help in Education)
The Stoller Charitable Trust
The WO Street Charitable Foundation
Jane Tomlinson Appeal
United Utilities Trust Fund
The Vardy Foundation
Mrs Waterhouse Charitable Trust (formerly known as the Houghton Dunn Charitable Trust)
The Westminster Foundation
The Williams Family Foundation
Brian Wilson Charitable Trust
The Eric Wright Charitable Trust
The Yorkshire Dales Millennium Trust
The Zochonis Charitable Trust

Yorkshire and the Humber

The Tony Bramall Charitable Trust
The Liz and Terry Bramall Foundation
The Brelms Trust CIO
The Joseph and Annie Cattle Trust
Church Burgesses Trust
The Coalfields Regeneration Trust
The Dulverton Trust
The Emerald Foundation

The Hull and East Riding Charitable Trust
Duchy of Lancaster Benevolent Fund
The Lyndal Tree Foundation
Sir George Martin Trust
The George A. Moore Foundation
The Ken and Lynne Morrison Charitable Trust
Near Neighbours
Sir John Priestman Charity Trust
The Sir James Reckitt Charity
The Sheffield Town Trust
The Charles and Elsie Sykes Trust
Worth Waynflete Foundation
Yorkshire Cancer Research
The Yorkshire Dales Millennium Trust
The Marjorie and Arnold Ziff Charitable Foundation

East Midlands

The Michael Bishop Foundation
Boots Charitable Trust
The Childwick Trust
The Coalfields Regeneration Trust
The Dulverton Trust
The Maud Elkington Charitable Trust
The Thomas Farr Charity
The Haramead Trust
Horne Foundation
The Jones 1986 Charitable Trust
The David Laing Foundation
The Charles Littlewood Hill Trust
The London Marathon Charitable Trust Ltd
Charity of John Marshall
The Edith Murphy Foundation
Near Neighbours
Open Gate
The Ratcliff Foundation
The Rugby Group Benevolent Fund Ltd
The Samworth Foundation
The Henry Smith Charity
Jane Tomlinson Appeal
The Constance Travis Charitable Trust
G J W Turner Trust
Worth Waynflete Foundation

West Midlands

The 29th May 1961 Charitable Trust
The John Apthorp Charity
Misses Barrie Charitable Trust
The Berkeley Charitable Foundation
The Michael Bishop Foundation

The Bransford Trust
The E F Bulmer Benevolent Fund
The Barrow Cadbury Trust
The Edward Cadbury Charitable
    Trust
The William Adlington Cadbury
    Charitable Trust
CHK Charities Ltd
The Coalfields Regeneration Trust
General Charity of Coventry
The Elizabeth Creak Charitable
    Trust
Baron Davenport's Charity
The Dulverton Trust
Dumbreck Charity
The Eveson Charitable Trust
The Grimmitt Trust
The Harborne Parish Lands Charity
The Jabbs Foundation
The Jordan Charitable Foundation
The King Henry VIII Endowed
    Trust – Warwick
The Edgar E Lawley Foundation
The Michael Marsh Charitable
    Trust
John Martin's Charity
MBNA General Foundation
The Millichope Foundation
Near Neighbours
The Park House Charitable Trust
The Ratcliff Foundation
The Clive and Sylvia Richards
    Charity Ltd
The Roughley Charitable Trust
The Rugby Group Benevolent Fund
    Ltd
Stratford-upon-Avon Town Trust
Sutton Coldfield Charitable Trust
C B And H H Taylor 1984 Trust
Jane Tomlinson Appeal
The Roger and Douglas Turner
    Charitable Trust
G J W Turner Trust
The Walker Trust
Welcome To Our Future (Local
    Agenda 21)

Eastern England
AIM Foundation
Anguish's Educational Foundation
The John Apthorp Charity
The Arsenal Foundation Ltd
The Paul Bassham Charitable Trust
The Broomton Foundation
The Childwick Trust
The Colchester Catalyst Charity
The Dulverton Trust
The Ellerdale Trust
The Evelyn Trust
Charles S French Charitable Trust
The Gale Family Charity Trust
The Simon Gibson Charitable Trust

The Harpur Trust
Hockerill Educational Foundation
Horne Foundation
Huntingdon Freemen's Trust
The Frank Jackson Foundation
Christopher Laing Foundation
The David Laing Foundation
The Martin Laing Foundation
The Lind Trust
The Charles Littlewood Hill Trust
London Legal Support Trust
    (LLST)
The Kristina Martin Charitable
    Trust
The Mercers' Charitable
    Foundation
Near Neighbours
Educational Foundation of
    Alderman John Norman
Norwich Town Close Estate Charity
The Panacea Charitable Trust
The Jack Petchey Foundation
Mrs L D Rope's Third Charitable
    Settlement
The Rugby Group Benevolent Fund
    Ltd
The Shanly Foundation
The Henry Smith Charity
The Steel Charitable Trust
The Virgin Money Foundation
The Geoffrey Watling Charity

South West
Access Sport CIO
Viscount Amory's Charitable Trust
The Avon and Somerset Police
    Community Trust
Barnwood Trust
The Berkeley Charitable
    Foundation
Bideford Bridge Trust
The Blagrave Trust
The Childwick Trust
The Roger and Sarah Bancroft
    Clark Charitable Trust
The John Coates Charitable Trust
Community First
The Dulverton Trust
The Fulmer Charitable Trust
The Heathcoat Trust
John James Bristol Foundation
St John's Foundation (Bath)
Sylvanus Lysons Charity
The Clare Milne Trust
The Nisbet Trust
The Norman Family Charitable
    Trust
Payne-Gallwey 1989 Charitable
    Trust
Peacock Charitable Trust
SITA Cornwall Trust Ltd
The Henry Smith Charity

The Summerfield Charitable Trust
The Talbot Village Trust
The Valentine Charitable Trust
The Van Neste Foundation
Elizabeth and Prince Zaiger Trust

South East
Access Sport CIO
The Anson Charitable Trust
The John Apthorp Charity
The Bamford Charitable
    Foundation
Banbury Charities
The Barker-Mill Foundation
Misses Barrie Charitable Trust
The Louis Baylis (Maidenhead
    Advertiser) Charitable Trust
The Berkeley Charitable
    Foundation
The Blagrave Trust
The Bloom Foundation
The Boltini Trust
The William Brake Charitable Trust
Bill Brown 1989 Charitable Trust
Calleva Foundation
The Chalk Cliff Trust
Chapman Charitable Trust
Sandra Charitable Trust
The Childwick Trust
The Coalfields Regeneration Trust
The John Coates Charitable Trust
Colyer-Fergusson Charitable Trust
The Ronald Cruickshanks
    Foundation
The Roger De Haan Charitable
    Trust
The Dulverton Trust
The Earley Charity
The Gerald Palmer Eling Trust
    Company
The Englefield Charitable Trust
The Lord Faringdon Charitable
    Trust
The Fidelity UK Foundation
Doris Field Charitable Trust
The Foyle Foundation
Gatwick Airport Community Trust
Greenham Trust Ltd
William Harding's Charity
The Peter Harrison Foundation
Heathrow Community Fund (LHR
    Airport Communities Trust)
Horne Foundation
Hyde Charitable Trust (Youth Plus)
The Ingram Trust
Anton Jurgens Charitable Trust
The Ian Karten Charitable Trust
The Ernest Kleinwort Charitable
    Trust
Christopher Laing Foundation
The David Laing Foundation

The Raymond and Blanche Lawson Charitable Trust
London Legal Support Trust (LLST)
The London Marathon Charitable Trust Ltd
Charity of John Marshall
The Gerald Micklem Charitable Trust
The Ofenheim Charitable Trust
The Oldfield Charitable Trust
P F Charitable Trust
Paradigm Foundation
Peacock Charitable Trust
The Pebble Trust
Cecil Pilkington Charitable Trust
The Rothschild Foundation
The Rugby Group Benevolent Fund Ltd
The Shanly Foundation
The Henry Smith Charity
The Mrs Smith and Mount Trust
The Spoore, Merry and Rixman Foundation
Humphrey Richardson Taylor Charitable Trust
The Tolkien Trust
Walton On Thames Charity
The F Glenister Woodger Trust
Zurich Community Trust (UK) Ltd

Greater London

A W Charitable Trust
Access Sport CIO
The Allen and Overy Foundation
Amabrill Ltd
Anglo American Group Foundation
The Armourers' and Brasiers' Gauntlet Trust
The Arsenal Foundation Ltd
Aston-Mansfield Charitable Trust
The Barbers' Company General Charities
Barnes Workhouse Fund
The Battersea Power Station Foundation
The Berkeley Charitable Foundation
Asser Bishvil Foundation
The Cadogan Charity
Calleva Foundation
Sir John Cass's Foundation
Chapman Charitable Trust
The Childhood Trust
The Childwick Trust
The City Bridge Trust (Bridge House Estates)
Richard Cloudesley's Charity
Cripplegate Foundation
The Englefield Charitable Trust
The Fidelity UK Foundation

Fishmongers' Company's Charitable Trust
Charles S French Charitable Trust
Friends of Wiznitz Ltd
The Generations Foundation
The Goldsmiths' Company Charity
The Grocers' Charity
M and R Gross Charities Ltd
Hackney Parochial Charities
Hadley Trust
Hammersmith United Charities
The Hampstead Wells and Campden Trust
Hampton Fuel Allotment
The Harbour Foundation
Edward Harvist Trust (The Harvist Estate)
The Health Foundation
Heathrow Community Fund (LHR Airport Communities Trust)
The Helping Foundation
The Hillingdon Community Trust
Housing Pathways Trust
Hurdale Charity Ltd
Hyde Charitable Trust (Youth Plus)
Hyde Park Place Estate Charity
The ITF Seafarers' Trust
The J J Charitable Trust
The Ian Karten Charitable Trust
The Kensington and Chelsea Foundation
The Allen Lane Foundation
The Leathersellers' Company Charitable Fund
Leri Charitable Trust
Lloyd's Charities Trust
The Lolev Charitable Trust
Trust for London
London Catalyst
London Housing Foundation Ltd (LHF)
London Legal Support Trust (LLST)
The London Marathon Charitable Trust Ltd
John Lyon's Charity
Maudsley Charity
Mayheights Ltd
Mercaz Torah Vechesed Ltd
The Mercers' Charitable Foundation
Merchant Taylors' Consolidated Charities for the Infirm
Morgan Stanley International Foundation
Near Neighbours
Peacock Charitable Trust
The Jack Petchey Foundation
Rashbass Family Trust
Richard Reeve's Foundation
Richmond Parish Lands Charity
The Rose Foundation

Royal Docks Trust (London)
The Alan and Babette Sainsbury Charitable Fund
The Basil Samuel Charitable Trust
The Shanly Foundation
SHINE (Support and Help in Education)
The Simmons and Simmons Charitable Foundation
The Sheepdrove Trust
The Slaughter and May Charitable Trust
The Mrs Smith and Mount Trust
Tallow Chandlers Benevolent Fund No. 2
The Talmud Torah Machzikei Hadass Trust
Humphrey Richardson Taylor Charitable Trust
The Taylor Family Foundation
The Tottenham Grammar School Foundation
United St Saviour's Charity
VHLT Ltd
The Vintners' Foundation
The Wakefield and Tetley Trust
The Walcot Foundation
The Westminster Amalgamated Charity
The Westminster Foundation
Westway Trust
Charity of Sir Richard Whittington
Winton Philanthropies
The William Allen Young Charitable Trust

Channel Islands

Lloyds Bank Foundation for the Channel Islands

Wales

The A. H. Trust
The Aaronson Foundation
The Abbeyfield Research Foundation
Access Sport CIO
The Sylvia Adams Charitable Trust
The Anne Duchess of Westminster's Charity
The John Armitage Charitable Trust
Arts Council of Wales (also known as Cyngor Celfyddydau Cymru)
The Asda Foundation
The Ashley Family Foundation
The Rachel Baker Memorial Charity
The Borrows Charitable Trust
The Boshier-Hinton Foundation
The Bradley Family Charitable Foundation

British Gas (Scottish Gas) Energy Trust
The Catholic Trust for England and Wales
Chapman Charitable Trust
The Coalfields Regeneration Trust
Colwinston Charitable Trust
Country Houses Foundation
England and Wales Cricket Trust
The Peter Cruddas Foundation
The Gwendoline and Margaret Davies Charity
Drapers' Charitable Fund
The Dulverton Trust
D.M.H. Educational Trust Ltd
Gwyneth Forrester Trust
The Fort Foundation
The Joseph Strong Frazer Trust
The Simon Gibson Charitable Trust
The Granada Foundation
The Greggs Foundation
H & T Clients Charitable Trust
The Hintze Family Charity Foundation
The Jane Hodge Foundation
The J Isaacs Charitable Trust
The Isle of Anglesey Charitable Trust
The Ian Karten Charitable Trust
The KPMG Foundation
The Lennox Hannay Charitable Trust
Lloyds Bank Foundation for England and Wales
Lloyd's Patriotic Fund
The Lockwood Charitable Foundation
Charity of John Marshall
Masonic Charitable Foundation
MBNA General Foundation
Millennium Stadium Charitable Trust (Ymddiriedlaeth Elusennol Stadiwm Y Mileniwm)
Moondance Foundation
The Steve Morgan Foundation
Moto in the Community
North West Cancer Research
The James Pantyfedwen Foundation
People's Health Trust
People's Postcode Trust
Postcode Community Trust
Postcode Dream Trust
Postcode Local Trust
The Ratcliff Foundation
Rhondda Cynon Taff Welsh Church Acts Fund
Rosetrees Trust
The Royal British Legion
The Sackler Trust
The Savoy Educational Trust
The Segelman Trust

The DS Smith Charitable Foundation
The Sobell Foundation
R H Southern Trust
Starlow Charities Ltd
Mark Stolkin Foundation
The Street Foundation
The Bernard Sunley Charitable Foundation
Swansea and Brecon Diocesan Board of Finance Ltd
Tenovus Cancer Care
Viridor Credits Environmental Company
The Wheeler Family Charitable Trust
The Wigoder Family Foundation
The Williams Family Foundation
The Foster Wood Foundation
The Woodstock Family Charitable Foundation
The Wyfold Charitable Trust
The Yapp Charitable Trust

Scotland

The AMW Charitable Trust
The Anne Duchess of Westminster's Charity
The Baird Trust
The Bank of Scotland Foundation
Misses Barrie Charitable Trust
Binks Trust
British Gas (Scottish Gas) Energy Trust
The Cadogan Charity
David William Traill Cargill Fund
The W.A. Cargill Fund
The Carnegie Trust for the Universities of Scotland
The Castansa Trust
The Cattanach Charitable Trust
Chest Heart and Stroke Scotland
The Coalfields Regeneration Trust
Martin Connell Charitable Trust
Corra Foundation
Creative Scotland
The Crerar Trust
Cruden Foundation Ltd
The Cunningham Trust
The Dulverton Trust
The Englefield Charitable Trust
The Hugh Fraser Foundation
The Gannochy Trust
The Greggs Foundation
The Robert Fleming Hannay Memorial Charity
Heathrow Community Fund (LHR Airport Communities Trust)

The Christina Mary Hendrie Trust
The Holywood Trust
James T Howat Charitable Trust
Miss Agnes H Hunter's Trust
The Jordan Charitable Foundation
The Ian Karten Charitable Trust
The KPMG Foundation
Leng Charitable Trust
Life Changes Trust
The Lyndal Tree Foundation
The RS Macdonald Charitable Trust
The MacRobert Trust
The Ian Mactaggart Trust (The Mactaggart Second Fund)
The W M Mann Foundation
The Nancie Massey Charitable Trust
The Mathew Trust
Medical Research Scotland
The Merchants' House of Glasgow
The Alexander Moncur Trust
Morgan Stanley International Foundation
The Morton Charitable Trust (Dundee)
Northwood Charitable Trust
P F Charitable Trust
People's Health Trust
People's Postcode Trust
Postcode Community Trust
Postcode Dream Trust
Postcode Local Trust
The Robertson Trust
Rosetrees Trust
The Royal British Legion
The Sackler Trust
Scottish Property Industry Festival of Christmas (Spifox)
The Shetland Charitable Trust
The Souter Charitable Trust
R H Southern Trust
The Stafford Trust
Strathnairn Community Benefit Fund Ltd
Tay Charitable Trust
Tenovus Scotland
The Turtleton Charitable Trust
The Virgin Money Foundation
Viridor Credits Environmental Company
Volant Charitable Trust
Voluntary Action Fund (VAF)
The Weir Charitable Trust
The James Weir Foundation
The Westminster Foundation
Yorkshire and Clydesdale Bank Foundation

Northern Ireland

The Allen and Overy Foundation
Church of Ireland Priorities Fund
The Enkalon Foundation
Halifax Foundation for Northern
 Ireland (previously known as
 Lloyds Bank Foundation for
 Northern Ireland)
Integrated Education Fund
The Ian Karten Charitable Trust
John Moores Foundation
The Royal British Legion
The Sackler Trust
R H Southern Trust
Ulster Garden Villages Ltd
Viridor Credits Environmental
 Company

Republic of Ireland

Allchurches Trust Ltd
Arts Council of Northern Ireland
Breast Cancer Now
The William Adlington Cadbury
 Charitable Trust
Church of Ireland Priorities Fund
EMI Music Sound Foundation
Calouste Gulbenkian Foundation –
 UK Branch
The Charles Hayward Foundation
The Hospital Saturday Fund
The Reta Lila Howard Foundation
Ladbrokes Coral Trust
Mazars Charitable Trust
The Joseph Rank Trust
Sodexo Stop Hunger Foundation
DM Thomas Foundation for Young
 People

Europe

The Aaronson Foundation
AKO Foundation
The Apax Foundation
Credit Suisse EMEA Foundation
The Headley Trust
IBM United Kingdom Trust
Jewish Child's Day (JCD)
The Elton John AIDS Foundation
 (EJAF)
Kusuma Trust UK
The Martin Laing Foundation
Merchant Navy Welfare Board
Morgan Stanley International
 Foundation

The Nuffield Foundation
Oxfam (GB)
Rachel Charitable Trust
Rothschild Foundation (Hanadiv)
 Europe
Sofronie Foundation
R H Southern Trust
DM Thomas Foundation for Young
 People
The Tolkien Trust

Africa

The Aaronson Foundation
The Allen and Overy Foundation
Anglo American Group Foundation
The Apax Foundation
The Baring Foundation
The Breadsticks Foundation
The Brenley Trust
The William Adlington Cadbury
 Charitable Trust
The Childwick Trust
J A Clark Charitable Trust
Corra Foundation
Credit Suisse EMEA Foundation
The Dulverton Trust
The Expat Foundation
The Gatsby Charitable Foundation
The Maurice Hatter Foundation
The Charles Hayward Foundation
The Headley Trust
The Hunter Foundation
IBM United Kingdom Trust
The Indigo Trust
The Frank Jackson Foundation
The Elton John AIDS Foundation
 (EJAF)
Lancaster Foundation
The Lauffer Family Charitable
 Foundation
Morgan Stanley International
 Foundation
The Miles Morland Foundation
The Nuffield Foundation
Oxfam (GB)
David and Elaine Potter
 Foundation
The Eleanor Rathbone Charitable
 Trust
The Alan and Babette Sainsbury
 Charitable Fund
The Samworth Foundation
Mark Stolkin Foundation
The Tolkien Trust
The True Colours Trust
The Tudor Trust
United Purpose
The Zochonis Charitable Trust

Americas and the West Indies

The Aaronson Foundation
AKO Foundation
Anglo American Group Foundation
The Apax Foundation
The William Adlington Cadbury
 Charitable Trust
CMZ Ltd
The Christina Mary Hendrie Trust
Jewish Child's Day (JCD)
John Laing Charitable Trust
The Lauffer Family Charitable
 Foundation
Oxfam (GB)
The Polonsky Foundation
Reuben Foundation
United Purpose
The Worwin UK Foundation

Asia

The Allen and Overy Foundation
Anglo American Group Foundation
The Apax Foundation
The Breadsticks Foundation
The William Adlington Cadbury
 Charitable Trust
J A Clark Charitable Trust
The Cross Trust
The Daiwa Anglo-Japanese
 Foundation
The Great Britain Sasakawa
 Foundation
Paul Hamlyn Foundation
The Helen Hamlyn Trust
The Elton John AIDS Foundation
 (EJAF)
The Kiawah Charitable Trust
Kusuma Trust UK
The Martin Laing Foundation
The Lauffer Family Charitable
 Foundation
Oxfam (GB)
The Queen Anne's Gate Foundation
The Eleanor Rathbone Charitable
 Trust
Rhodi Charitable Trust
The Sino-British Fellowship Trust
R H Southern Trust
United Purpose

Australasia

The Cross Trust
John Laing Charitable Trust

The Lauffer Family Charitable
Foundation

Middle East

4 Charity Foundation
A W Charitable Trust
The Aaronson Foundation
The Allen and Overy Foundation
The Asfari Foundation
Atkin Charitable Foundation
The Beaverbrooks Charitable Trust
The John Black Charitable
Foundation
The Bluston Charitable Settlement
Charitworth Ltd
CMZ Ltd
Credit Suisse EMEA Foundation
Itzchok Meyer Cymerman Trust
Ltd
The Davis Foundation
The Djanogly Foundation
Dollond Charitable Trust
Entindale Ltd
The Exilarch's Foundation
The Maurice Hatter Foundation
The Heathside Charitable Trust
IBM United Kingdom Trust
Investream Charitable Trust
Jewish Child's Day (JCD)
Joseph Levy Foundation
The Ian Karten Charitable Trust
Keren Association Ltd
Largsmount Ltd
The Lauffer Family Charitable
Foundation
David and Ruth Lewis Family
Charitable Trust
The Locker Foundation
Mayfair Charities Ltd
Mayheights Ltd
The Melow Charitable Trust
Mercaz Torah Vechesed Ltd
Morgan Stanley International
Foundation
Newpier Charity Ltd
The Polonsky Foundation
The Eleanor Rathbone Charitable
Trust
The Rayne Trust
Reuben Foundation
Rowanville Ltd
Sam and Bella Sebba Charitable
Trust
The Archie Sherman Charitable
Trust
The Sobell Foundation
The Steinberg Family Charitable
Trust

The Sir Sigmund Sternberg
Charitable Foundation
The Tajtelbaum Charitable Trust
The David Tannen Charitable Trust
Tzedakah
The Vail Foundation
VHLT Ltd
The Maurice Wohl Charitable
Foundation
The Wolfson Family Charitable
Trust
The Wolfson Foundation

Worldwide

The 3Ts Charitable Trust
Aberdeen Asset Management
Charitable Foundation
The Aberdeen Foundation
ABF The Soldiers' Charity
Achisomoch Aid Company Ltd
The ACT Foundation
Action on Hearing Loss (The Royal
National Institute For Deaf
People)
Ajahma Charitable Trust
The Alborada Trust
The Alchemy Foundation
The Aldama Foundation
Al-Fayed Charitable Foundation
The Allen Trust
The Anchor Foundation
The Andrew Anderson Trust
Ardbarron Trust Ltd
The Ashden Trust
The Batchworth Trust
Bay Charitable Trust
The John Beckwith Charitable Trust
Bellview Charitable Trust
Ruth Berkowitz Charitable Trust
The Michael Bishop Foundation
The Sir Victor Blank Charitable
Settlement
The Bloom Foundation
The Boltini Trust
Friends of Boyan Trust
The Britford Bridge Trust
The British Academy for the
Promotion of Historical
Philosophical and Philological
Studies (The British Academy)
The British and Foreign Bible
Society
The British and Foreign School
Society
British Council for Prevention of
Blindness (Save Eyes Everywhere)
The Rory and Elizabeth Brooks
Foundation
Brushmill Ltd

The Buffini Chao Foundation
The Clara E Burgess Charity
Cannon Charitable Trust
The Thomas Sivewright Catto
Charitable Settlement
Christie Foundation
Denise Coates Foundation
The John S Cohen Foundation
The R and S Cohen Foundation
The Cole-Medlock Foundation
Comic Relief
The Gershon Coren Charitable
Foundation (also known as The
Muriel and Gus Coren Charitable
Foundation)
The Evan Cornish Foundation
The Cross Trust
The Crispin Davis Family Trust
Dawat-E-Hadiyah Trust (United
Kingdom)
The Desmond Foundation
The Laduma Dhamecha Charitable
Trust
Dina Perelman Trust Ltd
The Dorfman Foundation
The Double 'O' Charity Ltd
The Royal Foundation of the Duke
and Duchess of Cambridge and
Prince Harry
Echoes of Service
Edupoor Ltd
The Eranda Rothschild Foundation
The Esfandi Charitable Foundation
Fayre Share Foundation
Allan and Nesta Ferguson
Charitable Settlement
Fisherbeck Charitable Trust
Donald Forrester Trust
Four Acre Trust
The Freshfield Foundation
The Fulmer Charitable Trust
The Generations Foundation
The GC Gibson Charitable Trust
The Gloag Foundation
The Golden Bottle Trust
Goldman Sachs Gives (UK)
The Goodman Foundation
Grace Charitable Trust
The Grace Trust
The Grant Foundation
The Green Hall Foundation
Hadras Kodesh Trust
The Haramead Trust
The Charlotte Heber-Percy
Charitable Trust
The Michael Heller Charitable
Foundation
Henderson Firstfruits
Sir Harold Hood's Charitable Trust
Hospice UK
The Innocent Foundation

International Bible Students Association
The Muriel Jones Foundation
The Kentown Wizard Foundation
E And E Kernkraut Charities Limited
The Ernest Kleinwort Charitable Trust
Kollel and Co Ltd
Kolyom Trust Ltd
Maurice and Hilda Laing Charitable Trust
The Martin Laing Foundation
The Kirby Laing Foundation
The Beatrice Laing Trust
The Lake House Charity
The Lancashire Foundation
The Lancaster-Taylor Charitable Trust
The Law Family Charitable Foundation
The Betty Lawes Foundation
The Lehman Brothers Foundation Europe
The Linbury Trust
Lloyd's Charities Trust
Lloyd's Register Foundation
The Mackintosh Foundation
The Mactaggart Third Fund
The Manoukian Charitable Foundation
The Marchig Animal Welfare Trust
The Kristina Martin Charitable Trust
The Master Charitable Trust
The Brian Mercer Charitable Trust
T. & J. Meyer Family Foundation Ltd
The Henry Moore Foundation
The Alexander Mosley Charitable Trust
The Frederick Mulder Foundation
MW (RH) Foundation
Network for Social Change Charitable Trust
The Northwick Trust
The Norton Rose Fulbright Charitable Foundation
The Sir Peter O'Sullevan Charitable Trust
The Oakdale Trust
The Ogle Christian Trust
Open Gate
The Doris Pacey Charitable Foundation
The Park House Charitable Trust
The Pears Family Charitable Foundation
Quintessentially Foundation
The Bishop Radford Trust
The Eleanor Rathbone Charitable Trust

The Sigrid Rausing Trust
Reuben Foundation
The Revere Charitable Trust
Edmund Rice Bicentennial Trust Ltd
The Clive and Sylvia Richards Charity Ltd
The River Farm Foundation
The Roddick Foundation
The Romeera Foundation
The Gerald Ronson Family Foundation
Mrs L D Rope's Third Charitable Settlement
SF Foundation
The M J Samuel Charitable Trust
The Save the Children Fund
Schroder Charity Trust
Seafarers UK (King George's Fund for Sailors)
The SMB Trust
Social Tech Trust
The Sola Trust
The Souter Charitable Trust
St James's Place Foundation
Standard Life Foundation
Stewards' Company Ltd
Sir Halley Stewart Trust
The Stone Family Foundation
C B And H H Taylor 1984 Trust
The Tinsley Foundation
The Tolkien Trust
The Toy Trust
The Union of The Sisters of Mercy of Great Britain
The Utley Family Charitable Trust
The Barbara Ward Children's Foundation
The Waterloo Foundation
The Wellcome Trust
Westhill Endowment
Whitley Animal Protection Trust
WWDP (World Day of Prayer National Committee for England, Wales and Northern Ireland)
Wychdale Ltd
The Zochonis Charitable Trust

What else can DSC do for you?

Let us help you to be the best you possibly can be. DSC equips individuals and organisations with expert skills and information to help them provide better services and outcomes for their beneficiaries. With the latest techniques, best practice and funding resources all brought to you by our team of experts, you will not only boost your income but also exceed your expectations.

Publications

We produce fundraising directories and research reports, as well as accessible 'how to' guides and best practice handbooks, all to help you help others.

Training

The voluntary sector's best-selling training, with courses covering every type of voluntary sector training.

In-house training

All DSC courses are available on your premises, delivered by expert trainers and facilitators. We also offer coaching, consultancy, mentoring and support.

Conferences and fairs

DSC conferences are a fantastic way to network with voluntary sector professionals while taking part in intensive, practical training workshops.

Funding websites

DSC's funding websites provide access to thousands of charities, grants, statutory funds and corporate donations. You won't get more funders, commentary and analysis anywhere else. Demo our sites free today.

www.dsc.org.uk/**fundingwebsites**

 **@DSC_Charity**
For top tips and special offers

Visit our website today and see what we can do for you:

www.dsc.org.uk

Or contact us directly:
publications@dsc.org.uk